MR. W. FRED. VERNON,

Resident Dental Surgeon,

114 ROXBURGH STREET, KELSO.

MONTHLY PROFESSIONAL VISITS TO
Melrose, Jedburgh, Hawick, and Coldstream.

MELROSE
On the first Monday in each month.
Attendance at
ANDERSON'S TEMPERANCE HOTEL.

HAWICK
On the 2nd Monday in each month.
Attendance at
MURRAY'S TEMPERANCE HOTEL.

JEDBURGH
On the first Tuesday in each month.
Attendance at
MRS. COWAN'S, 8 MARKET PLACE.

COLDSTREAM
On the second Tuesday in each month.
Attendance at
THE NEWCASTLE ARMS INN.

Select Dental Preparations, Tooth Powders, Lotions,
&c., prepared by Mr. Vernon.

CARBONATED OTTO DENTIFRICE.
A very agreeable and excellent preparation for cleansing the Teeth & Gums.

CAMPHORATED, ALKALINE, & ASTRINGENT DENTIFRICE.
This preparation neutralizes the effects of acids on the Teeth,
and imparts firmness and strength to the Gums.

**ASTRINGENT POWDER AND ASTRINGENT WASH
FOR THE MOUTH.**
Highly useful in cases of Inflammation of the Gums.

AROMATIC TINCTURE OF MYRRH AND BORAX.
PREPARED WITH EAU DE COLOGNE.
A very refreshing and elegant preparation for Strengthening the Gums.

With the above exceptions, he may be consulted Daily, from 10 to 5 (or by appointment), at his Residence,

114 ROXBURGH STREET, KELSO.

THE SCOTTISH PROVIDENT INSTITUTION.

ESTABLISHED 1837.

THE TERMS of this Society secure a larger original Assurance for the same Premium, and eventually, to good lives, as large Additions as where the ordinary high rates are charged.

A Policy for £1200 to £1250 (with right to Whole Profits) may generally be had for the Premium elsewhere charged to assure £1000 only.

Policies originally for £1000 have already, under the peculiar system of the Society, been increased to £1300, £1500, and even to £1700.

Examples of Annual Premium for Assurance of £100 at Death, with right to Whole Profits.

Age.	Premium.	Age.	Premium.	Age.	Premium.	Age.	Premium.
21	£1 16 3	29	£2 0 8	37	£2 9 8	44	£3 3 3
22	1 16 9	30*	2 1 6	38	2 11 3	45	3 5 9
23	1 17 2	31	2 2 6	39	2 12 11	46	3 8 5
24	1 17 7	32	2 3 5	40	2 14 9	47	3 11 5
25	1 18 0	33	2 4 6	41	2 16 8	48	3 14 8
26	1 18 6	34	2 5 7	42	2 18 8	49	3 18 1
27	1 19 2	35	2 6 10	43	3 0 11	50	4 1 7
28	1 19 11	36	2 8 2				

* Thus a person of 30 may secure £1000 at death (with profits) for a yearly premium of £20, 16s., which in the other Mutual Offices would assure £800 only.

Or, if unwilling to burden himself with payments during the whole of his life, he may secure a Policy for £1000 for a Premium of £27, 13s. 4d., limited to twenty-one payments, being thus relieved of payment before he has passed the prime of life, for a Premium nearly the same as most Offices require during the whole term of life.

☞ *Tables of Premiums payable for 21 years, or other fixed period, may be had on application.*

Above 15,000 Policies issued. Subsisting Assurances upwards of 4¾ Millions. Accumulated Fund, arising entirely from Premiums, considerably above a Million.

Reports and every information may be had on application.

EDINBURGH, *April* 1866.   JAMES WATSON, *Manager.*

Agents:—DUNSE—William K. Hunter, Royal Bank; EARLSTON — James Smail, Commercial Bank; GALASHIELS—John Pringle, Writer; HAWICK—Walter Haddon, Writer; JEDBURGH—George Hilson. jun., City of Glasgow Bank; KELSO —Roberton & Broomfield, British Linen Company's Bank; PEEBLES—Robert Stevenson, Writer.

RUTHERFURD'S

THE SOUTHERN COUNTIES' REGISTER
& DIRECTORY

Borders Regional Council
Borders Regional Library

First published 1866

This edition specially produced by Cedric Chivers Ltd, Bristol

for

Borders Regional Library, Selkirk

ISBN 0 9516756 0 5

Printed in Great Britain by Redwood Press Ltd, Melksham, Wilts.
Bound by Cedric Chivers Ltd, Bristol, Avon

THE

SOUTHERN COUNTIES' REGISTER AND DIRECTORY:

CONTAINING

MUCH USEFUL AND INTERESTING INFORMATION, AND VERY COMPLETE LISTS

CONNECTED WITH THE

COUNTIES OF ROXBURGH, BERWICK, AND SELKIRK.

KELSO: J. AND J. H. RUTHERFURD, No. 17 SQUARE.

LONDON: LONGMAN & CO.   EDINBURGH: JOHN MENZIES.

MDCCCLXVI.

NOTES AND ERRATA.

At page 82 we state the Kelso Assessment for poor rate to be 1s. 8d. per £—this is the total rate, 10d. being paid by the proprietor and 10d. by the occupier. In all the other parishes we give the half-rate, or that payable by the individual, except in the case of Jedburgh (p. 254), which has a peculiar method of rating.

These rate entries have been objected to as an instance of over much attention to minutiæ in the *Register*. They are so, perhaps, to numerous individuals ; but take the case of a farmer wishing to settle in a parish, for *him* to know that a poor rate of 10d. (or nothing *see* p. 587) will be exacted for each pound of his rent becomes an important matter, and will enter accordingly into his calculations when he offers for a lease. What we have said of the poor rates, we think, will hold good with the other minutiæ—they will be important or not according to the light in which they are viewed.

At page 547 we should have made the date of Mr. Broughton's purchase of Rowchester, 1858—it should have been 1856.

PRIOR BANK, MELROSE (*see* p. 152.)

THIS mansion is now the summer residence of Adam Black, Esq., publisher (late M.P.), Edinburgh, he having succeeded to his brother-in-law, William Tait, Esq., deceased.

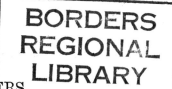
TO OUR SUBSCRIBERS.

TEN years ago we published our first issue of the " SOUTHERN COUNTIES' REGISTER—a Supplement to the Almanacs," in a shape suitable for binding up with Oliver & Boyd's Edinburgh Almanac. But although of use for official purposes, and of interest to country gentlemen, we found, after its second issue, that it was of little value for commercial purposes; and our object ever since has been to compile a publication which might interest, and be of use to, all classes of the community. This object we expected to have carried out in 1863, and had accumulated, and to some extent arranged, materials for that purpose, when circumstances compelled us, for the time being, to relinquish the publication—a delay which rendered our materials of too old a date to be of much use, and caused us a heavy expense in renewing and re-arranging type, which, from the same circumstances, had become necessary. These disadvantages, however, had the good effect of bringing some unknown matters to the surface, and causing our thorough investigation of others, which might otherwise have been superficially passed over.

Although the work has been in hand for four years, the matter which we now issue has been all investigated and got up since the spring of 1864 ;* and by far the greatest part of it has been printed within the last twelve months. When we began in earnest the compilation of the work for publication, we had little idea of the labour it would entail before it could be carried out, and when we quoted 600 columns in our circulars as the probable number, we thought we were over-stating the matter. Instead of 600, it will be observed they foot-up to 798, and this despite of close packing and exclusive of advertisements.† This extension, with the fact of the compiler's health having given way for three months, explains our delay in publishing so long beyond the time anticipated.

While we take credit to ourselves for much labour bestowed on the compilation, we have to acknowledge

---

* Except the Calendars, which are suitable for any year.

† This has necessarily caused a rise in the quoted probable price of the volume—a rise in strict proportion to the increase of text.

the assistance received by us with the returns, without which our own labour would have been purposless. We have especially to specify the returns connected with the Hawick and Melrose lists, the introductory matter of Galashiels, Castleton, and Ettrick; and generally of Whitsome, Ashkirk, Cockburnspath, and Coldingham parishes, as having been supplied to us with more than ordinary completeness, in each case through the interest of one individual. From the Ordnance Survey officials, both at Edinburgh and Southampton, we received very important and prompt assistance. By their aid the parochial areas in land, water, roads, &c., are inserted, and the parochial geography of Selkirkshire (next to Cromarty the most scattered county in Scotland) has been accurately described. We are indebted to the friendship of the Rev. R. O. Bromfield, Sprouston, to the Editor of "Younger's River Angling" [Mr. James Smail, banker, Earlston] and to T. T. Stoddart, Esq., Kelso, for the Calendars and Tweed Fishery Information. At page 697 we have acknowledged our obligations to the Fishery Board for Scotland.

While acknowledging the assistance received with the parochial and county lists, we beg also to tender thanks for the kindly courtesy of our county family subscribers in sending us returns.

In compiling the REGISTER, we found that the publication would be incomplete without a handy-sized and accurate Map of the District. This led us to correspond with Mr. Bartholomew, F.R.G.S., Edinburgh, and arranging with him for the preparation (from the Ordnance plans), and the engraving of a suitable map. This map, in different stages of completion, has now been in use by the public for six months, and its accuracy is every where admitted. It does not contain *every* name or place ; but the omissions are of little importance. To ensure its accuracy we transmitted copies for revisal to nearly every parish in the district. It will be observed we have also inserted a Map shewing the position of the District with its Railway System, etc.

Our printed edition is 1300 copies. Of these there have been already subscribed, in anticipation of pub-lication, nearly 1000.* If an extra issue be required, we may state that except the bringing up of some directory and list matters, and the correction of errors (mostly clerical errors, we hope, which were, under the circumstances, scarcely avoidable), and an improvement in the arrangement, little or no alteration can be made in the present issue.† After the publication of the census for 1871 (which will not be till

---

* For a classification of our Subscribers, *see* note after the Index to Advertisements.

† Add to these a more careful *reading :* the pressure under which many of the sheets were compiled and hurried through the press, made crudities and apparent slovenliness unavoidable.

1873) an edition thoroughly revised will be published, in which the introductory accounts of the different towns and parishes will have to be conformed to the new data; but even then the fresh edition will be founded on the present one.

To facilitate reference we have printed the Indexes on tinted paper; and connected therewith we beg to draw the attention of the reader to the following matter, which may be of importance :—When searching for information, on *any* subject, do not be satisfied with its details in its own parish, or under its own heading, but turn to the Index, where different references to the subject may be found, as we frequently, in our investigations of one parish, discovered matter connected with the information in another, already printed off.

J. & J. H. RUTHERFURD.

KELSO, *May* 1866.

NOTE.—We beg to draw the attention of Subscribers to our Prospectus (*see* following page) of " THE BORDER ALMANAC." We think that such a publication might be made both useful and interesting; but to be so to its fullest extent, the interest in it of the community must be secured—of those individuals especially who are bookishly or archæologically inclined, and willing to supply suitable materials, or able to suggest ideas. Communications are respectfully invited.

In the Press, and speedily will be published,

In 1 volume, foolscap 8vo, pp. 340.

#

INCLUDING

TALES, BALLADS, AND SONGS.

BY

ROBERT WHITE,

Author of

"The History of the Battle of Otterburn."

and Editor of

"Poems and Ballads, by Dr. John Leyden."

KELSO: J. & J. H. RUTHERFURD.

PROSPECTUS

OF

THE BORDER ALMANAC.

FOR four years—1862-65—we published what we called our *Household Almanac*, a compilation, the Calendar sheet of which was printed in London, and supplied to any bookseller or printer who might require it for use in a local publication, or for issuing separately under his own name. This Calendar sheet, useful as it was in many ways, and full of instruction and moral sentiment, was purposely somewhat inane ; and any local interest possessed by our Almanac was secured by extra sheets tagged on before and behind. We had thus a very heterogeneous affair, and, while admitted, as a whole, to be amusing, not representing the district sufficiently.

Owing to the necessity of our having to push through the *Register*, we were unable to produce an Almanac of any kind for the current year ; but with 1867 we hope to renew the Annual under the title of *The Border Almanac*—to contain the usual Calendar Information (compiled and printed by ourselves), and, as formerly, some sheets of information and amusement, but all to have a District or domestic interest —whether a proverb, such as " Worse and worse like the elders of Maxton," with an account of its origin, another extract from our Journal or that of " any other man," the publication of an unedited or nearly forgotten ballad, a reminiscence of an old event, or the true account of a matter now traditionary.

For these, and such as these, the pages of our Almanac will be a receptacle ; and we hope it will be the means of saving something of value from oblivion. In our investigations for the *Register* we came on many suitable materials for such a publication, but which, in the *Register* itself, would have been out of place. These we intend to use up ; and we shall also be glad to receive contributions.* Anything of *real* interest connected with the Scotch Border or Northumberland cannot come amiss.

At or before Christmas of this year we hope to send out our first of the new issue.

KELSO, *May* 1866.

J. & J. H. RUTHERFURD.

* Here is a Ballad—unpublished so far as we know—of which we would like to get the remainder ; or parts of it would be useful, which might be compared and a whole patched up.

" Jenny, gang an' fetch some water,
Nocht's the thing ye ever du ; "
Jenny hears her mother's clatter,
Sits and ties her shauchelt shue.

" Jean may gang," says Jenny moongin';
" She can gang as weel as me ;
She sits up the corner groongin',
Ne'er dis nocht withoot a plea."—

" Jock may gang,—he's aye sae lazy,—
A' fetched in the last yestreen ;
See ! a'm shooin up my crazzy"—
Doon the tears fell frae her een.

" Bless my heart ! the pitcher's broken ; "
" It wasna me," cries ane and a',
Kate sits by the creddle rockin',
Telt that Jenny let it fa'.

" Jenny broke the jug in flinders,
Afore my very lookin' een ; "
Sic a set o' uiseless members,
Never on this yirth was seen."

" Baith the jug an' pitcher broken !
Was the like o't ever kenned ?
Naething else I need ha' ettled,
But I'll shank ye tae the fremd."

We believe the Ballad proceeds with an amusing description of the adventures of the " useless members " at the fremd —*i.e.*, at service.

SCOTTISH NATIONAL INSURANCE COMPANY.

ESTABLISHED 1841.

EDINBURGH—22 ST. ANDREW SQUARE.

DIRECTORS.

CHARLES LAWSON, Esq., of Borthwick Hall, *Chairman.*

JOHN A. MACRAE, Esq. of Wellbank, W.S., *Deputy Chairman.*
BENJAMIN H. BLYTH, Esq., C.E.
JAMES DUNCAN, Esq., W.S.
CHARLES COWAN, Esq. of Logan House.

E. S. GORDON, Esq., Sheriff of Perthshire.
JAMES CUNNINGHAM, Esq., 50 Queen Street.
JAS. TAYLOR, Esq., of Starley Hall.
PATRICK ARKLEY, Esq. of Duninald.

WILLIAM DICKSON, Esq., Wholesale Stationer.

LONDON, 69 Lombard Street.
*Resident Secretary—*ALEX. H. WHYTT.

GLASGOW, 42 West George Street.
*Resident Secretary—*J. T. MACLAGAN.

DUBLIN, 28 Westmoreland Street.
*Resident Secretary—*H. D. DICKIE.

MANCHESTER, 70 Cross Street.
*Resident Secretary—*SAMUEL HEYWOOD.

THE Directors invite special attention to three most vital considerations :—

First.—By publishing the details of their **Balance Sheet,** and of the principles adopted in their periodic Investigations, they enable every one interested to judge of the **Soundness** and **Stability** of the Company, and give the best guarantee for continued prudence in all their operations.

Secondly—Whilst making the ample provision for future liabilities, of which the evidence has just been referred to, they have made **Bonus Additions** to their policies in their Life Assurance Branch at the rates successively of **One Pound, One Pound Five Shillings,** and **One Pound Twelve Shillings and Sixpence per cent per annum.** These Bonuses will stand a favourable comparison with those declared by the oldest and most successful Life Offices in Scotland, whether mutual or proprietory, when the relative rates of premium are taken into account.

Thirdly.—Whilst thus providing for safety on the one hand and for liberal Bonuses to the assured on the other, the Directors have had the satisfaction of accumulating such large additions to the **Paid up Capital** and **Reserve** as have greatly increased the security of the persons insured, and at the same time improved the value of the stock to the shareholders in a degree which far exceeds the experience of the great majority of Scottish as well as English Offices, notwithstanding the greater age, and in some cases the more extensive transactions of these Offices.

Every description of Life Assurance, Fire Assurance, and Annuity business transacted on the most favourable terms.

JOHN M. M'CANDLISH, *Manager.*
WALTER BROWN, *Secretary.*

Prospectus, Forms of Proposal, &c., may be had on application at the Head Office, Branches, or Agencies.

CONTENTS.

———◆———

NOTE.—As it is scarcely possible to give every particular in the following Indexes, a knowledge that the Parishes are compiled in the following order will be of further use in facilitating reference.

I. INTRODUCTORY LETTERPRESS—
1. Descriptive of the boundaries and natural features ; the towns, villages, and hamlets ; with importance, peculiarities, objects of interest and associations, climate and sanitary conditions, angling and other amenities, &c.
2. Holidays, Anniversaries, Market Days, Hirings, Fairs, and Cattle Sales—dates of, and full particulars.
3. Census particulars—1st April 1861.
4. Principal Landed-Proprietors, and Superiors.

II. LISTS—
1. Magistrates and Council, Justices of the Peace, Courts, and Public Offices.
2. Post Office—arrivals, despatches, &c.
3. Clergy, &c., Churches, Officials, Patrons, and Fasts.
4. Church Societies—Missionary, Bible, Colportage &c.
5. Educational Institutions.
6. Parochial Board and Union Poorhouse, Rates, &c.
7. Benevolent Institutions, Societies, and Charitable Bequests.

8. Mutual Assistance—Sick, Burial, and Benefit.
9. Mutual Benefit—Masons', Oddfellows', Forresters', &c.
10. Mutual Improvement—Literary and Scientific, Libraries, Lectures, &c.
11. Rural—Horticultural and Agricultural Societies, &c.
12. Mutual Profit—Gas and Water Companies, &c.
13. Sports and Amusements, and Volunteer Corps
14. Bank Branches, and Insurance and other Agents.
15. Professions—Law and Medicine.
16. Newspapers.
17. Mills, Manufacturers, Auctioneers, Curing-Establishments, Skinneries, &c.
18. Conveyance—Carriers and Railways.
19. Statute Labour Roads.

III. DIRECTORY—
1. Towns—streets arranged alphabetically.
2. Villages.
3. County Families, Seats, and Smaller Residences.
4. Registered Voters—Non-Resident.

GENERAL INDEX.

INDEX TO THE COUNTY FAMILIES, SEATS, AND SMALLER RESIDENCES IN THE DISTRICT.

FAIRS.

The figures within parenthesis—thus (78)—occurring after the fairs, markets, and anniversaries, denote the page where the event is fully described; the letter *n* denotes that the fair preceding it has become nominal or defunct; where no figure or letter occurs, the event is not in the district, and the entry is made from other almanacs for convenience of reference; but for its existence or the accuracy of its date we do not vouch.

MARCH.

Alnwick, hiring, 1 Saturday
Berwick-on-Tweed, hiring, 1 Sat.
Cornhill, hinds' hiring, 1 Monday (484)
Dunse, hinds' hiring, 1 Tues. (549)
Ettrick, hiring shepherds, & sale of ewes, last Wed. (*n*, 417)
Galashiels, seed-corn, &c., 3 Wednesday (*n*, 430)
Gifford Tryst, last Tuesday
Hexham, stock, 25
Jedburgh, hinds' hiring, 1 Tuesday (248)
Kelso, hinds' and herds' hiring, 1 Friday (73)
Kelso Horse Fair, 2 Friday (73)
Lauder, hinds and herds, 1 Tuesday (519)
Melrose, hinds' hiring, 1 Mon.; ewes and other stock, Saturday before last Tuesday (129)
Morpeth, horses and cattle, 28
Peebles, hiring, 1 Tuesday
Selkirk, shepherds' and hinds' hiring, 1 Wed. (375)
Stow, ewes, seeds, corn, hiring, 2 Tuesday

APRIL.

Belford, last Wednesday
Carlisle, cat., Saturday nearest 20
Castleton, hiring, 2 Friday (236)
Ladykirk, linen cloth, plants, &c., 5 (*n*, 504)
Lauder, servants, 6 Tuesdays after 1 Tuesday of March (519)
Selkirk, hiring servants, 5 (375)

MAY.

Alnwick, 12
Berwick-on-Tweed, hiring, and horses, 1 Sat.
Castleton, hir., Frid. bef. 17 (236)
Dunse, hir. young men & women, 2 Tues. before 26 (549)
Falkirk, catt'e and horse show, 3d Thursday
Greenlaw, cows, &c., 22 (*n*, 541)
Heriot House, sheep, cattle, and turnip-seed, Friday after 26
Hawick, hir. servants, 17 (305)
Jedburgh, cat and horses, 1 Tues. aft. 26; hir. serv., 1 Tues. (248)
Kelso, hinds' hiring, 1 Friday (73)
Langholm, cat., last Tuesday, *o.s*
Melrose, hiring young men and women, 1 Monday (129)

Norham, 3 Thursday
Peebles, 2 Wednesday

JUNE.

Dumfries, hor., Wed. after 17, *o.s.*
Dunse, cat., shp. & hor., 1 Thurs. (549)
Earlston, cat. and horses, 29 (507)
Gifford Fair, 3 Tuesday
Linton (Peeblesshire), sheep, 28
Melrose, cattle, 1 Wednes. (129)
Norham, 3 Thursday
Swinton, 3 Thursday (*n*, 608)
Yetholm (Kirk), sheep, 27 (157)

JULY.

Alnwick, last Mon.; wool, Saturday after 5
Coldingham, 2 Tuesday, *o. s.* (*n*)
Cornhill, lambs and wool, 3 (484)
Dunse, cat., sheep & wool, 2 Tues. (549)
Ettrick, lambs and wool 30, (*n* 417)
Galashiels, wool, 8 (430)
Hawick, wool, 1 Thursday after St. Boswell's; shearers, 1 Thursday after 26 (305)
Hexham, wool, 2
Jedburgh (Rink), 20, or two days after St. Boswell's (249)
Kelso, wool, 2 Friday (74)
Langholm, lambs and wool, 26
Linton (Peeblesshire), wool, Wed. after 18
Morpeth, Wednesday before 22
Peebles, wool, Tuesday after 18
Pennymuir, lambs and wool, 31 (229)
St. Boswell's, 18 (121)
Selkirk, shearers, 15
Stagshawbank, 5

Thirlestane, lambs, 30
Yetholm (Town), lambs, wool, &c. 2 Wednesday (*n*, 158)

AUGUST.

Berwick, hiring, 1 Saturday
Carlisle, cattle, 26
Dunse, cattle, sheep, and horse, 26 or Tuesday after (549)
Hexham, stock, 6
James', St. (Kelso), 5 (74)
Jedburgh, cattle, horses, shearers, 20, if Tuesday; if not, Tuesday before
Kelso, shearers' port every Monday morning during harvest
Lauder, lambs, Friday bef. 12 (*n*, 519)
Melrose, shearers, 1 Mon.; Lammas, 12; but if Saturday, Sunday, or Monday, Tuesday after (129, 130)
Newcastle, horses, cattle, and general business, 2 Wednesday
Peebles, Tuesday before 24
Stagshawbank, lambs, 5

SEPTEMBER.

Belford, ewes, 26
Carlisle, cattle, 20
Castleton, ewes and lambs, Friday before 2 Wednesday (237)
Cornhill, draft ewes (26)
Dunse, ewe tryst, 3 Tuesday (550)
Ettrick, tups and fat sheep 24 (*n*)
Hawick, tups, 20 and 21 (305)
Jedburgh (Rood Day), cattle and horses, 25 (249)
Kelso Union Agricultural Society's Exhibition of sheep, and sale and hire of Leicester and

Cheviot Tups, 2 Thursday and Friday (47 and 89)—*see* note (613); Leicester and half-bred draft ewes and cattle market, 24 (74)
Langholm, sheep, 18
Moffat, 2 Friday aft. Falkirk Tryst
Peebles, Tuesday before 12
St Ninian's, 27

OCTOBER.

Alnwick, 1 Tuesday
Belford, hiring, 1 Wednesday
Castleton, draft ewes and lambs, Thursday bef. 2 Tuesday (237)
Earlston, cat. and horses, 3 Thursday (507)
Galashiels, general business, 11 (*n*)
Greenlaw, cows, last Thurs. (541)
Hawick (Tryst), horses and cattle. 3 Tuesday (305)
Jedburgh (Rink), 14 (*obs.*, 249)
Lauder, servants, 4 Friday (519)
Melrose, ewes and other stock, Saturday after 1 Tuesday (130)
Morpeth, horses and cattle, 25
Norham, 2 Thursday
Peebles, 2 Tuesday
Penicuick, 1 Friday
Pennymuir, sheep and cat, 15 (229)
Rothbury, stock, 3
Selkirk, servants' hiring, 31 (375)

Swinton, 4 Tuesday (*n*, 608)
Stagshawbank, lambs, 24
Wooler, cattle, sheep, 17
Yetholm (Kirk), sheep, 24 (158)

NOVEMBER.

Alnwick, hiring, 1 Saturday
Berwick, hiring, 1 Saturday
Castleton, hiring, Friday before 8 (236); cattle and small lambs, 3 Friday (237)
Chirnside, last Thursday (*n*)
Dumfries, horse, Wed.before 22
Dunse, servants' hiring, 1 Tues. ; cattle and sheep, 17, or Tuesday after (550)
Edinburgh (Hallow Fair), 2d Mon.
Ettrick (Little Fair), 3 Friday (*n*)
Hawick, cat., & hiring servants, (305)
Hexham, stock, 9 ; hiring, 11
Haltwhistle, cattle, 22.
Jedburgh, hiring, 1 Tuesday (248); cat. and horses, 1 Tues. (249)
Kelso, servants' hir., 1 Friday (73)
Langholm, cattle, 5
Melrose, servants, 1 Monday ; cat. 22 (130)
Newcastle, cattle, last Wednesday ; hiring, 1 Tuesday
Rothbury, stock, 1

WEEKLY MARKETS.

Dunse—Grain in bulk, Tues. (549)
Earlston—Grain (508)
Galashiels—Grain in bulk, Tuesday (429)
Hawick—Corn, Meal, &c., Thursday (304)

Jedburgh—Corn, &c., Tuesday (248)
Kelso—General (73); Corn, &c. (73, 117)
Melrose—Corn, &c., Mond. (129)
Selkirk—Wednesday (375)

CATTLE MARKETS AND SALES.

Note —The Berwick and Kelso Fat Cattle Markets fall on alternate Mondays during the season, viz.—November to July. The Melrose and Coldstream Cattle Markets (both Monday) are both regulated so as not to fall on the Kelso days. The Coldstream dates are fixed annually by the Bailie (*see* p. 484).

Berwick-on-Tweed—Fortnightly Monday
Coldstream—Monthly, an unfixed Monday (484)
Dunse—Monthly, 1st Friday (549)
Earlston—Sales, Saturday (508)

Galashiels—Sales, Fortnightly, Saturday (430)
Hawick—Sales (304)
Jedburgh—Monthly, 3 Thu. (248)
Kelso—Fortnightly, Monday (73)
Melrose—Fortnightly, Mon. (129)

ANNIVERSARIES AND FASTS.

[In the following list G. H. means General Holiday ; F., Fast Day ; S., Sunday.—*New Year's Day is a Gen. Holiday in the district.*

Ayton—F., Thursdays bef. last S. of Feb. and July (598)
Castleton—F., Fridays before second S. of June and Nov. (238)
Chirnside—F., last Thursdays of April and October (*627)
Coldstream—G. H. in July, unfixed (484) F., Wed. before first S. of May, and in Oct., unfixed (487)
Coldingham—F., Thursday bef. last S. of June, and in December, unfixed
Denholm—F., first Wed. in May and last in Oct. (292)
Dunse—G. H. in June, unfixed (549) ; F., Thursday bef. second S. of July—winter unfixed (553)
Earlston—F. in Feb. and July—unfixed (509)
Eyemouth—F., varies in the different churches
Galashiels—G. H., Michaelmas Day (429), F., Thursdays before first S. of May and second S. of Nov. (433)
Greenlaw—F., Wed. bef. first S. in May and Nov. (543)
Hawick—Common Riding, Friday on or before 20th May ; G. H., days following the May and

Nov. hirings (304, 305) ; F., Wed. before last S. in June and second S. of Dec. (311)
Jedburgh—Handball match, Fastren's E'en ;* G. H., Wed. after hiring in May (248); F., Thursdays before first S. of July, and in Dec. unfixed (253)
Kelso—G. H., 1 Wed. July (73) ; F., Wed. before first S. of May and Nov. (79)
Lauder—F., Wed. bef. last S. in June, and in Dec. unfixed (521)
Melrose—Foot - ball, Fastren's E'en ;* G. H. 18th July (129) ; F. Thursdays before second S. of April and Nov. (133)
Selkirk—Common Riding, regulated by that of Hawick—generally early in June (375) ; F., Thursdays bef. last S. of April and second S. of Nov. (378)
St. Boswell's—Handball match, 12th March (121) ; F., Thursdays before last S. of Feb. and first S. of July (122)
Yetholm — Football and Games, Fastren's E'en* (157) ; F., early Wed. in Jan. and July—unfixed (159)

* *See* note, p. 157.

(For the F. D. of country parishes, *see* their individual lists, under Clergy).

ENGLISH AND SCOTCH TERMS.

English.		Scotch.	*New*	*Old*
Lady Day	Mar. 25	Candlemas	Feb. 2	Feb. 13
Midsummer	June 24	Whitsunday	May 15	May 26
Michaelmas	Sept. 29	Lammas	Aug 1	Aug. 12
Christmas	Dec. 25	Martinmas	Nov. 11	Nov. 22

In the district the old Scotch Whitsunday term (May 26) is that when houses are changed, leases of farms are entered upon, and hinds and shepherds change their service ; unmarried ploughmen, and domestic servants change places at both the Whitsunday and Martinmas old Scotch terms. The new Scotch terms of Whitsunday and Martinmas prevail in some of the gentlemen's houses, and are the rule on the English Border. The quarterly terms of Candlemas and Lammas are seldom used ; the rule in hiring servants being by the year and half-year, and of houses and farms by the year or a longer period. The English terms are practically unknown in the district.

GARDENERS' CALENDAR FOR THE DISTRICT.

GARDENING MEMORANDA.

Good cultivation is essential in a garden kept either for pleasure or profit. The soil should be well and deeply dug ; if it be naturally shallow let a little fresh sub-soil be brought up to the surface every year, and in the course of time a shallow soil will become a deep one. Where the soil is naturally deep and good, trenching it occasionally will be of great service.

Weeds should never be allowed to go to seed, for "one year's seeding is seven years' weeding." If persevering efforts are made to ·keep them down, a garden may be got almost entirely rid of them. Hand-picking is far more effective than hoeing, and cheaper in the long run.

All edgings of walks and borders should be tidily kept ; nothing is more unsightly than tall straggling box ; it should not be higher than from two to four inches in the common run of gardens.

Fruit trees and bushes should be kept within limits. Large standards are not suited to small gardens : dwarfs are more manageable, can be cultivated in greater variety, produce the finest fruit, and are not easily shaken by high winds. These remarks are specially true of the apple, which may be abundantly produced in this climate, and is one of the most healthful and serviceable fruits which we possess.

In gardening all overcrowding should be carefully avoided. Trees, Bushes, Vegetables, and almost all Plants, require light and air, and the more they get of these the better ; they must have room also for their roots to grow and feed in. With sufficient room there will be the greater produce.

EXAMPLES :

Peas should be thinly sown in the drill : planting the seed is preferable to sowing it : and two drills should never be placed alongside of each other. It is best to keep each drill entirely by itself, occupying the intervals with other crops. In this way peas yield a great deal more than when crowded ; and room, trouble, staking, and expense are saved. The same treatment should also be given to beans.

Onions, Carrots, and Turnips, should be thinned very early to a proper distance ; the Onions grown in rows one foot apart, and from four to six inches asunder, if it be wished to have them large : the Carrots, early sorts, in rows nine inches apart, and plants from four to six inches ; the larger kinds in rows of 15 or 18 inches apart, and plants six or eight inches : early Turnips, in rows two feet apart, and plants thinned from six to nine inches according to sorts.

For growing Carrots and Onions the ground should be dug and manured in autumn. These crops are liable to be attacked by maggot ; where this is the case a good topdressing of soot laid on in the autumn, to lie on the surface during winter, and pointed in at spring time, has been found to be beneficial ; also a good watering of soft soap and water, the mixture being made at the rate of about one pound of soap to a tub of water, and applied as soon as the plants are fairly above ground. The liquid from a cow byre or dung heap, diluted with its own bulk of water, is excellent manure for young carrots, and will often secure a large crop ; it may be applied frequently at intervals of a few days.

To make sure of a good plant of Onions, the seed may be sown in the end of February or early in March, in a pot or box placed either in a hot-bed or window ; the young plants should be gradually exposed to the open air, and planted out as soon in April as possible, in rows one foot apart, and four or six inches asunder ; in this way fine large bulbs are got, the young plants are not so liable to be attacked by maggot, and this plan is at least as easy as sowing and thinning.

All vegetables like good manure, and should have it. Potatoes may be excepted, for though the produce of potatoes is less without manure than with it, the quality is better, and there is less liability to disease. The truth, however, is all but universal, that vegetables can only be produced in perfection on rich soil. Autumn planted Cabbages benefit from manure water or guano water applied to their roots once or twice in the spring.

The same ground should not be planted twice in immediate succession with the same crop if it can be avoided : a variety should be studied.

The planting and pruning of Fruit Trees and Bushes should be gone about in fresh weather and not in frost, and be all over by the end of November, if possible : it should be remembered that a cut is a wound, and that when it is exposed to frost, the plant is thereby liable to injury. The object of pruning is to remove superfluous wood, to force the branch to make fruit spurs, and thereby secure greater fertility, and to give air and light to every part of the tree or bush. Gooseberry and Currant Bushes are benefited by having the ends of the young shoots taken off during the growing period, as this disposes the bush to form and mature fruit buds. Vegetables should not be grown too close to fruit trees or bushes. Trees on walls are often choked in this way, and their roots robbed of moisture and food : good fruit, and a good crop of it, cannot be expected with such treatment.

To keep away caterpillars, soot may be laid pretty thickly around the roots of bushes in the autumn. Some people have tried, with apparent success, tobacco liquor diluted with water to the colour of port wine, and sprinkled with a brush on the bushes, *when in bloom.* Some recommend tanner's bark to be laid under the bushes in the autumn, to remain on the ground ; and others pour liquid from the cow byre over the bushes and roots during the winter.

When bushes are seized with caterpillar, they should either be carefully hand-picked, without loss of time, or have dusted over them, when wet with dew, or rain, or by a watering pan, powder of hellebore, which will kill the caterpillars ; after this the fruit should not be eaten till the bushes are washed clean, as the powder is poisonous.

As Potatoes grown in gardens are now so liable to disease, it will be prudent to plant there only FIRST Early kinds ; such sorts have the advantage of being ripe usually before the disease becomes prevalent. Some of the ROUND FIRST EARLIES are as productive as the later sorts, and nearly as soon usable as the Ash-leaf, and much better.

Proper attention should be given to have a constant succession of vegetables, and a good variety : potatoes have largely usurped the place of all other vegetables.

JANUARY.*

DIGGING, planting, and pruning, not done in autumn, should be completed without delay.

Up to the end of the month, if not done before, take cuttings of Pears and Apples for grafting in April, and insert them two-thirds of their length in the ground, out of the sun, until they are required.

BEANS.—In favourable weather Early Mazagan Beans may be planted three or four inches apart in the rows, and rows at least 2½ feet asunder. Single rows are however most prolific.

CABBAGE.—In warm situations Cabbage may be planted in open weather in the end of this month, and blanks in the autumn planted, filled up.

PEAS.—Plant one or more early sorts about the third week of this month: Dillingstone's Early, Sangster's No. 1 (Syn. Daniel O'Rourke), Early Emperor, may all be sown at the same time and will form a good succession. The above directions can only be carried out when the season is open and the ground sufficiently dry to allow the operations.

In this month, if the Calendar be followed, there ought to be found in gardens a supply of Savoys, Brussels Sprouts, Coleworts, Curled Greens, Delaware Greens, Asparagus Kale, Cottager's Kale, and Fearnought Cabbage, which may be cut the whole winter. Asparagus Kale is a tender and delicious green, and after the head is cut, will afford many successive growths of young shoots, which may either be cooked as greens, or stripped and treated as Asparagus. Cottager's Kale is a new vegetable, which sends out tufts of growth from the base of its leaves; the tufts are stripped off and used as greens.

If early Rhubarb or Seakale be desired, place pots or boxes over the plants, and cover with leaves or stable litter.

Though little can, or should, be done in a garden during this month, it ought to be kept clean and orderly, for a garden well kept is pleasant at every season; many gardens lie in ruins all the winter.

FEBRUARY.

BEANS.—Plant for a main crop such as Early Longpod, Mackie's Monarch (called also Sangster's Wonderful Longpod), Marshall's Dwarf Prolific, a dwarf sort of about one foot in height, a great bearer, and suitable for small gardens. In gardens much shaded, or moist and growthy, beans, when they have flowered enough, should have their tops nipped off to force them to fill their pods.

CABBAGE.—Plant out Cabbage to succeed the more advanced.

CARROTS.—In the end of the month sow on soil prepared in the autumn, FRENCH Early Horn Carrots: this sort is smaller than the common Early Horn, and considerably earlier: it is a distinct, handsome, and most useful and excellent variety.

CHIVES.—Plant Chives in any out of the way place: they are used in spring in various ways in the place of onions when the latter are scarce or done.

PEAS.—Sow early sorts, same as for last month, with the addition

* As the Calendar is adapted to the neighbourhood of Kelso, its directions for the spring months should be followed a little later in colder and later districts, and in the autumn months a little earlier.

of the Ringwood, a good sized melting pea of better quality than the first earlies.

Planting and pruning of fruit trees and shrubs are often done at this season and even later; but it is much better to have the work all over before Christmas, or in November, where it is practicable; excepting, however, the Peach, Nectarine, and Apricot, which may now be pruned and nailed.

ROSE BUSHES may be pruned to one or two eyes: Climbing and China Roses should be little cut.

Where the soil is dry and fine, and the weather open, box and other edgings may be made, which will so far further the work of the garden; but on wet or stiff cold soils it is better to delay this till the ground work quite freely.

A garden established at this period supply Savoys, Fearnought Cabbage, Brussels Sprouts, Coleworts, Kale of sorts, Asparagus Kale, Cottager's Kale, and sometimes Brocoli, according to the season and situation, at least towards the latter end of the month.

MARCH.

This month, when weather permits, ought to be a busy time in the garden, as many principal crops must now be sown or planted.

ASPARAGUS.—This is one of the best of Vegetables, and indeed esteemed by many as the very best. On the dry, light, gravelly soil of the valley of the Tweed, it grows with great luxuriance, and almost without trouble after the beds are in working order. A small space of ground will afford a constant succession of heads and as much as a moderate family will require, from early in April, in the average of seasons, to the middle of June or later. Light soil needs no previous preparation for Asparagus, but stiff and retentive soil should be made porous by having fine gravel and sand dug into it. There has been a great deal of the "much-a-do about nothing" said and written on the growing of Asparagus, and this may be one reason why the cultivation of this plant is almost restricted to what are called gentlemen's gardens.

Any person who has a patch of ground, of five or six yards each way, to devote to this vegetable, may enjoy a fair supply of it. The beds may be laid off four feet wide, with one foot alleys; each bed should contain two rows of plants, the rows being respectivly one foot from the edge, and two feet apart in the bed. Sowing the seed is the most certain way to obtain a proper corner of plants. Sow in rows, already described: when the young plants are about two inches high, thin them out to one foot apart in the rows, water now and then with guano water not too strong, or with water in which a little salt has been dissolved, every week or fortnight. Treated in this way the young plants will make great progress during the first summer. In February following, give a top-dressing of guano, and rake it in: and when the ground is dry the beds may be watered in spring and summer. In the spring of the third year, or two years from the time of sowing, the beds will begin to yield their produce: they should be moderately cut at first. When the beds come to be cut it is best to apply guano or liquid manure *after* cutting is over, and not before, as otherwise a bad flavour might be communicated. Covering the beds with litter in the winter, and forking in the spring, is objectionable for the same reason, and besides may rot the plants or destroy the crowns. Asparagus beds require no protection at all from frost in this district, and should just be let alone. Salt is an excellent top-dressing for Asparagus: it may be laid on in spring without harm and beneficially, or it may be applied after cutting and when the plants are making their summer growth. This is the most suitable period for the application of any manure.

BEANS.—Plant further crops as desired.

BROCOLI.—Sow early sorts for autumn use ; such as Purple Sprouting, &c.

CABBAGE.—A good time for planting main crops of all sorts of Cabbage, Early, Red, and Late, or Drumhead, from the autumn sown beds. Sow about third week seed of early and second early sorts : of the latter the Pomeranian is a handsome, distinct, and excellent sort, and will be in use about September and later. Indeed, it is advisable always to have a few Cabbage plants ready, as there may be at times spots of ground capable of receiving them, which otherwise might lie waste. Cabbages not required for family use may be given to a pig or cow. Cabbages after being cut are often allowed to sprout, with a view of forming young heads : this, it is said, saves the trouble of making fresh plantations. It is certain, however, that such heads cannot be so tender as those first cut, for the plant will most likely have taken up, for the first growth, the best and the greatest part of its food : it is preferable to dig, dung, and plant afresh, and the garden looks better.

CARROTS.—Sow Early Horn as soon as possible, to come into use after the first crop of French Horn is over. Though the Early Horn is commonly used in summer, yet when thinned, as previously directed, it grows to a good size, and may be stored for winter use. In the end of the month the intermediate and larger sorts may be sown if the ground and weather be suitable.

CAULIFLOWER.—In the end of the month plant out the autumn sown, and sow seed in choice situations.

CELERY.—Sow in a pot or box, under protection, for early planting.

LEEKS.—Sow early and thinly, in a warm situation, and rich soil.

LETTUCE.—Sow seed, and plant out such plants as may have been under cover.

ONIONS.—Sow about the middle of the month, on ground prepared in the autumn. Where large bulbs are desired, sow in rows one foot apart, and thin quickly, to four or six inches. If smaller bulbs be preferred, sow broadcast, and cover the beds with a little soil out of the alleys. Previous to sowing, the beds are all the better of being well beaten and firmed with the back of the spade, or even trampled fairly over : this should not be done if the ground be wet : the less working of ground, of any sort, and in any way, in such condition, the better. Or sow seed in a box or pot : gradually expose the plants to the air, and in the first week in April, if the weather and ground will allow, plant out in wide rows, as already directed. The young plants though not larger than stout darning needles will be found quite hardy and prove a safe crop, and ripen earlier and better than if sown in open ground : the practice of sowing in boxes will be found further to be a great saving of seed. Danver's Early bulbs quickly, and is much sooner fit for use than the common sorts. The main crop, whether sown or planted, may consist of White Globe, Deptford, and James' Keeping. For pickling, sow broadcast Small Silver Skin and White Small Nocera.

PARSLEY.—Sow either as edging in the quarters, or in rows, 18 inches apart, and thin afterwards.

PARSNIPS.—Sow early in the month, in drills at least one foot wide, and thin to six or eight inches.

PEAS.—Make sowings of Second Earlies : Harrison's Glory, Harri-

son's Perfection, Napoleon or Climax, are good peas, with plenty of pods though not well filled : MacLean's Advancer is earlier than the above and a good bearer ; Hair's Mammoth, Lord Raglan, Veitch's Perfection are large melting peas, the last perhaps the largest grown : the three last mentioned are much of the same kind, and all the above have the merit of being only from two to three feet in height. Where there is but little room for peas, and where stakes are scarce, Burbidge's Eclipse will be found the most useful pea which can be grown : it is in height from one-and-a-half to two feet ; may be sown in drills two feet apart, requires a few short stakes ; may be sown on from the beginning of this month up to the tenth of June, and will fruit till checked by frost ; for Scotch broth it may be used all the winter, and if sowings are made for this object the peas should be taken up in September early, dried and kept in the haulms, which may be tied up in bundles and hung over a rope in any outhouse, and brought in as required.

POTATOES.—Plant early sorts in the end of the month. Cuttings of large potatoes answer better for sets than those taken from smaller sizes. For it may be held to be a rule, that well-developed seed, of whatever sort, is always to be preferred either for sowing or planting. Kidneys are most safe when planted whole. When the young shoots first appear above ground, they may be earthed over, and this may be done two or three times, to secure them from late spring frosts.

RADISH.—Sow in the beginning of the month.

SHALOTS.—Plant as soon as the ground will permit working, in rows about eight inches wide, and the bulbs six inches apart in the rows. The Shalot is a small mild onion, which grows like the potato onion, and may be used in June, and before either the autumn or spring sown ones.

SPINACH.—Sow once or twice in succession.

TURNIPS.—At the end of the month a sowing may be made in warm, sheltered ground. Crops sown at this time sometimes succeed, and are always worthy of a trial.

A garden should at this season still supply some Brussels Sprouts, Fearnought Cabbage, Savoys, Coleworts, Kale of sorts, Delawares, Asparagus Kale, Cottager's Kale ; and Brocoli, in forward seasons, will be more plentiful. Leeks are to be found in every garden in this district, and are usable throughout the winter and spring : they are particularly useful now, as in many gardens other vegetables will be scarce.

APRIL

BEANS.—Continue to plant if required.

BROCOLI AND BRUSSELS SPROUTS.—Sow in the beginning of the month.

CABBAGE.—Sow a little seed : plant out autumn plants if not done earlier.

CARROTS.—Sow in the beginning of the month the main crop of large sorts, such as Altringham, Long Red Surrey, Intermediate, James's Scarlet : the last is very fine and beautiful. Sow in drills 15 or 18 inches wide, and thin to six inches.

CAULIFLOWER.—Sow seed and plant out protected plants if not done last month.

CELERY.—Sow under a hand-glass, or in a hot-bed or pot, for the main crop.

KALE.—Common Curled and German, Cottager's Kale, Chou de Milan, to be used like the last.

CRESS AND MUSTARD.—Sow for Salad.

KIDNEY BEANS.—Plant towards the end of the month : the Newington Wonder is an excellent cropper.

LETTUCE.—Sow for a succession.

PEAS.—Plant for a succession.

POTATOES.—Plant Second Earlies and common varieties in the beginning of this month : it is advisable to plant the sets before the eyes have sprung much, as the first shoots are the best. Cuttings from large potatoes are always to be preferred when cuttings are made. Kidneys, of almost all sorts, do not bear cutting well, and medium-sized tubers may be planted whole. Perhaps it may be worth while to try *large* whole Kidneys as sets, planted well off each other, say fifteen or eighteen inches in the drill. Potatoes, according to their kinds, have their proper season of use. After the First Earlies there come in a succession, the Lapstone Kidney about the middle of August ; this is a particularly fine sort, but very tender and liable to disease : and about the same time, Rilott's Flour Ball, a small cropper, but of first-rate quality, and a very desirable variety. American Earlies may succeed the Flour Ball, and be used till the end of the year : Harold's American is of the very highest quality : York Regents follow on through the winter and spring, and Reds may be used till young potatoes make their appearance. The Fluke, where it can be grown, is a most useful potatoe, as it can be used for a long time, and is a late potatoe.

COUVE TRONCHUDA.—Sow seed for planting out when ready: it may be used just like Cabbage, and is excellent in November. If seed of the curled variety can be sown at the same time, it will be in use till February.

GRAFTING.—This is a good time for the grafting of fruit trees : it is easily done, and it is quite as well to have good sorts of fruit as bad.

HARDY ANNUALS.—Sow in the beginning of the month.

RADISHES.—Sow for succession.

SAVOYS AND SCOTCH GREENS.—Sow for planting for succession.

SCARLET RUNNERS.—Plant seed.

SEA-KALE.—Sow seed and plant out year-old plants.

SPINACH.—Sow if desired.

TURNIPS.—Sow about third week, sorts.

VEGETABLE MARROW.—Sow in a pot for turning out in the end of May. The New Custard Marrow is the best, but appears to require more heat than the common sorts.

Gardens should now give a fair supply of Brocoli, some Asparagus, Lettuce, and Early Cabbage towards the latter part of the month ; also, Radishes, Rhubarb, and Sea-Kale from the open ground.

MAY.

BEANS.—Plant if desired : late crops come handily in when peas are becoming scarce.

BEET.—Sow seed about the 8th or 10th of the month : it is usual enough to do this in April, but when early sown the plants are apt to run : the early part of May will be found to be a safe season.

CABBAGE.—Sow in the middle of the month for autumn cutting.

CAULIFLOWER.—Sow in the middle of the month for autumn use, and plant out the spring sown when ready.

CELERY.—Prick out plants from pots or boxes, to harden and prepare for the trench.

KALE—Sow Asparagus Kale.

KIDNEY BEANS.—Plant for a main crop in drills two feet wide : the

seeds may be put in every two inches to secure a full plant, and thinned to six inches apart. It will be found that plenty of room affords the largest crops.

LETTUCE.—Sow for succession.

MANGOLD WURZEL.—Though this be properly a plant for field culture, yet where there is room in a garden, and a cow is kept, it may be sown, as it is invaluable for cow-feeding. Sow the Long Red or Globe Orange about the eighth or tenth of the month : the latter is very rich, and a good cropper : the former keeps a long time. Should any plants run, cut out the shoot and they will still form bulbs. Mangold should be taken up and stored out of the reach of frost before the middle of October. The leaves should be cut at about an inch from the crown of the bulb, and the roots be left on uncut and unbroken : it will keep in store for a long time : the leaves are excellent for milch cows, and should be given fresh. It is advisable to lift the plants just as the leaves can be consumed. The bulbs should be stored in pits like turnips, only they should be completely protected from frost.

PEAS.—Sow for succession ; also, about the middle of the month sow Knight's Dwarf Green Marrow : it is the latest pea grown, and will be useful when other sorts are done.

RADISHES.—Sow if desired.

SCARLET RUNNERS.—Sow as before.

TURNIPS.—Sow in the middle of the month.

SALSAFY AND SCORZONERA.—Sow in rows fifteen inches wide, and thin to six inches : the long tap root of Scorzonera is scraped, washed, and boiled, and served with butter or white sauce : it comes in in September, and is usable two or three months. Salsafy is sometimes called Vegetable Oyster : it is used with boiled fowl or turkey, and may be taken up and stored like beet, and kept during the winter.

Gardens should now supply Asparagus, Brocoli, Early Cabbage, Lettuce, Radishes and Salad Herbs, and Sea-Kale : Leeks will still be usable.

JUNE.

BROCOLI.—Plant out when ready.

BRUSSELS SPROUTS.—Plant out in the latter part of the month.

CABBAGE.—Sow a pinch of seed.

CELERY.—Plant in the first week the young plants previously pricked out and prepared : plant also at intervals during the month, and give plenty of water.

FRENCH HORN CARROTS may be sown in the beginning and middle of the month, and also throughout next month ; in this way what are called young carrots may be had all the summer, and the latest sown may be left for use in spring.

KALE.—Plant Asparagus Kale, Cottager's, Curled, Chou de Milan, and Couve Tronchuda, if not done before.

KIDNEY BEANS.—Plant for the latest crop in the beginning of the month.

LEEKS.—Leeks should be got in without delay, and whenever they are fit to remove from the seed-bed, plant a good breadth, as they are very useful : the rows should be eighteen inches wide, and plants nine inches apart.

PEAS.—Sow a good breadth, about the 10th, of Burbidge's Eclipse, or some middle sort : crops seldom do much good when planted later, but may be tried on to the end of the month.

SAVOYS AND SCOTCH GREENS.—Plant a few about the end of the month.

STRAWBERRIES.—Where young plants are required for fresh plantations, the runners should be encouraged to root: this may be done by laying a stone on them before a joint, and pinching off all after growths.

TURNIPS.—Sow for succession at intervals during the month, and always thin well and soon.

Gardens should supply in this month late Brocoli in the early part of it, and Asparagus, Cabbage, Lettuce, Radishes, and Salad Herbs throughout; also the French Horn Carrot, and in a fair season Peas and Early Cauliflower about the 20th.

JULY.

ASPARAGUS KALE AND DELAWARE GREENS, &c.—Plant out if not previously done, or if done make new plantations.

BROCOLI.—Plant the main crop early in the month.

BRUSSELS SPROUTS.—Plant the main crop early.

CABBAGE.—The first sowings of early cabbage for the next spring may be sown about the 20th of the month. There are many names of sorts of early cabbage; but according to a comparative experiment made at the Royal Horticultural Society's Garden at Chiswick, in the year 1862, it is shown that there are very few distinct varieties. In the report of the experiment, Dr. Hogg says, "Of the 61 varieties of cabbages examined, the following were the only distinct sorts:—Fulham, or Early Battersea, Aitken's Matchless, Sugar Loaf, Early Plaw, and Early York." The following are given in the report as being the same as the Fulham, viz.: Blenheim, Carter's Matchless, Cox's Early London, Cattell's Reliance, Early Champion, Early Emperor, Early Monarch, Early Paradise, Early Paragon, Early Lancashire, East Ham, Heale's Imperial, Jacob's Early, King of the Cabbages, May's Paragon, Mitchell's Prince Albert, Myatt's Eclipse, Paragon, Pearson's Early Conqueror, Prince of Wales, Sealey's Victoria, Shilling's Queen, Superfine Early Dwarf, Sutton's Imperial, Wheeler's Imperial, Wellington, West Ham; all the above are held to be "more or less pure stocks" of the Fulham. The Enfield Market is very like the Fulham but has more leaves and is a little later. The Nonpareil is believed to have been obtained from the Fulham, but comes in more early and is smaller. Aitken's Matchless is held to be a small form of the Fulham. Wheeler's Imperial, Improved Nonpareil, Enfield Market, and Aitken's Matchless will give an abundant variety of the large early cabbages; and the smaller sorts, Macewen's, Vanack, and Little Pixie will be enough for first cutting; and for Winter cabbage sow Drumhead and Glen Dwarf Drumhead.

Plant out in this month on the potatoe ground the June sowing for autumn use.

CELERY.—Plant for late spring use.

CAULIFLOWER.—Plant beginning of the month.

COLEWORTS.—Sow seed in the beginning of the month.

RADISHES.—Sow Turnip Radish: the new Chinese, a scarlet sort, is very good: it will be in use from the autumn, through the winter, till February.

SAVOYS AND SCOTCH KALE.—Plant in the beginning of the month.

SPINACH.—Sow winter Spinach.

TURNIPS.—Make a last sowing second week.

As vegetables will now be abundant, the Asparagus should be allowed to grow: it might still be cut, and often is cut, a part of this month, but when Peas come in the Asparagus should be let alone.

Budding of Fruit Trees and Roses may be begun about the middle of the month if the bark rise freely, and may be continued for some time.

AUGUST.

CABBAGE.—Sow seed first week for a second plantation in the autumn.

CAULIFLOWER.—Sow about the 20th, to be protected during winter for planting in April.

COLEWORTS.—Plant out if ready on any vacant ground—plant about nine inches apart each way: they will be serviceable in winter as greens.

LETTUCE.—Sow Brown Dutch Cabbage and Hammersmith Hardy Green for standing over the winter.

ONIONS.—Sow first week to transplant in spring or autumn.

RADISHES.—Sow some Turnip Radishes first week.

SPINACH.—Sow main crop of winter Spinach first week.

STRAWBERRIES.—If the runners have been properly attended to, and the young plants are strong and well rooted, they may be planted beginning of this month; unless, however, they be in a condition to get properly established in the spring.

SEPTEMBER.

CABBAGE.—Plant out for spring use; also plantations may be made in rows one foot apart, and plants about eight inches in the row to be cut during the winter for use, as Coleworts or Greens.

CARROTS.—Store as they ripen: when left too long in the ground they form fresh roots, and when the ground becomes wet are liable to be worm-eaten.

CELERY.—Earth up very gradually,

ONIONS.—Gather and dry as they ripen; where the tops would remain standing they should be bent down at the neck.

POTATOES.—Potatoes should be early lifted, especially when the haulm begins to decay, as the disease appears first in the haulm, and quickly finds its way to the tuber: when early taken up they should be speedily covered, as the light is apt to spoil their colour.

FRUIT.—Gather and store as varieties ripen. Apples may be packed in layers, in jars and boxes, in pure dry sand, sufficient to keep the layers separate; or they may be packed in boxes, in layers, amongst clean fresh moss, its *external* moisture being dried, and will keep remarkably fresh, as the natural moisture of the apple is by this means retained. Before being used they should be washed and dried and exposed to the air for a little. Keep in a dark and cool place out of the reach of frost. Pears do not appear to agree with cold treatment, as they are apt, in consequence, to lose in quality: they may be kept in a moderate temperature, covered say with cotton cloth, or wadding, which is better, and light and air carefully excluded. When sufficiently ripe they should be brought into a warm place for a day or two before using, which will much improve them: when fruit is cold the flavour cannot be properly discerned by the palate.

OCTOBER.

BEET.—Beet may now be stored: in open seasons this will do next month.

CABBAGE.—Plant still for spring use; also prick out plants in vacant ground three or four inches apart, to stand over the winter for spring planting.

CARROTS.—Store the large sorts: they should not be left in the ground to make a second root growth.

CELERY.—Attend to the earthing up.

FRUIT.—Continue to store as directed last month : fruit is not improved by being allowed to hang in frost.

PARSNIPS.—Store.

Vacant ground may now be dug rough, or thrown up in ridges. Where the soil is stiff dung may be dug in with the winter furrow, but in all light or gravelly soils dung laid on in autumn is almost lost, as its particles are carried down by the rains to a depth where plants cannot find them.

EDGINGS OF BOX, &c., may now be laid. About the end of the month Gooseberry bushes may be pruned, and cuttings prepared for young plants. Where the wood is ripe, Apple and Pear trees may be pruned : this may always be done when the leaf is fading and drops, or is ready to fall. Prune Currants of all sorts.

Gardens should at this season afford some Cauliflower, Cabbage, Sprouting, Brocoli, Salsafy and Scorzonera, Lettuce, Radishes, and Salad Herbs ; also Kidney Beans and Scarlet Runners if frost be absent.

NOVEMBER.

BEANS AND PEAS.—A planting of Early Mazagan Bean, and of some sort of Early Pea, or Second Early, such as Dickson's Early Favourite, may be made : when planted at this season they are only a chance crop, but they may be risked.

BEET.—Take up and store : cut off the leaves about an inch from the crown, and don't damage or break the skin, nor cut the roots : they may be stored away in dry sand.

SALSAFY AND SCORZONERA.—Take up and store like Beet : they may be kept and used all the winter.

EDGINGS may still be made of Box, &c.

Remove fallen leaves, dead leaves of winter stock, and whatever might render the garden unsightly.

PRUNING AND PLANTING should be finished, if possible, this month. In the pruning of gooseberry bushes it is essential that the bearing stems should not cross nor interfere with one another, and that they should be at such distances respectively as will allow air and light to reach them properly, as well as afford room for the hand to pass freely all round to gather the fruit : the forms of bushes are of less importance. Some varieties make fruit spurs quite readily on their leading branches, and such may have the young wood closely cut : others are less manageable in this respect, having the habit of making their blossom buds principally on the young wood : these should have the young side shoots shortened back to one or two eyes from the main stem. From inattention to the different habits of different varieties, it often happens that the bearing wood is almost all cut off, and that is one reason why gooseberry bushes are frequently seen with great lengths of their branches bare and unproductive. The points of the main stems should also be shortened back to three or four eyes. If the points of the shoots have been taken off in summer there will be a greater likelihood of the formation of fruit buds on the leading stems, and also at the *base* of the shoots, which will allow closer pruning, and make the bush more sightly.

Young bushes grow the largest fruit, and older ones fruit of the best quality. Where large fruit is desired it should be early thinned, single fruit for show should be grown about four inches apart, and from bushes not more than six years old.

Cuttings for planting should have all the buds rubbed or cut carefully off, except two or three at the top.

Red and White Currants should be close pruned, care being taken to leave a sufficiency of fruit buds.

Black Currants should have the young wood thinned out, and what young shoots are required to remain may be left uncut.

Standard pear and apple trees should, as far as possible, be pruned as carefully as espaliers or wall trees : the saw is often required to thin and clear out cross branches.

Large standards are totally unfitted to small gardens, and it is very questionable whether they ever should be grown in large ones. Gardens are sometimes so cumbered with them that nothing can be grown well. Dwarf apple trees are most convenient, when properly pruned, can scarcely be shaken, and usually afford better and riper fruit than large standards. They should be made to spring as nearly as possible from the ground ; if they can be obtained with stems not more than six inches high, or under, so much the better. Dwarf apple trees are often planted in the form of half standards, as they are called ; that is, the heads spring from stems two or four feet in height. This is no advantage at all, but the contrary ; for the nearer the ground they can be got to bear, there will just be the greater certainty of fruit, and that, too, of superior quality.

Dwarf standards may be trained either as bushes or pyramids : in the latter case one main central stem is preserved, from which side branches are allowed or encouraged to proceed at regular intervals, and clear spaces. When trained as bushes, several stems are allowed to spring from near the ground. In either case the leading stems and branches should have all the young side shoots closely cut off them at pruning time, and the leaders cut back to from two to six eyes, according to the age, growth, vigour, and habits of the tree or variety : if the leaders be cut too long some of the eyes remain dormant ; if too close cut the eyes become young shoots : if cut at a suitable length the eyes will become fruit spurs, and that is what is wanted, and what the cultivator must aim to effect. The undermost branches should come furthest out, and the trees and bushes (for many dwarf trees are mere bushes) should be more or less of a conical form : this allows all the parts of the tree to get out to the light and air ; they are often allowed to grow in an entirely opposite form, in which case the lower branches are overshadowed and rendered useless : if treated as directed, however, they will bear throughout, from the main stem, if they have but one, to the extremities, and from their tops down to the very ground, where perfect fruit may be expected. Every branch should be quite clear of its neighbour, and light and air be allowed to pass freely all through a fruit tree, and all around its branches. With such a mode of cultivation the fruit is properly exposed, and ripens and colours, and the fruit buds become healthily developed for another season, and are in better condition for resisting winter's frost, and doing their work properly in spring.

Dwarf trees ought to be properly manured in the autumn : or if they set their fruit well and promise a large crop, the surface of the soil over their roots may be scraped off, to the depth of two inches, and some good cow dung or rich manure laid on, and the soil replaced on the dung : this will assist the tree to carry a large crop fully out. Nothing should ever be allowed to grow over the roots of dwarf trees, nor any tall crops be planted near or amongst them.

Trees on walls are often seriously hurt by the heavy cropping of the borders : the trees being thereby cheated out of food and moisture, and the ground is kept colder than it would be if the direct rays of the sun were allowed to penetrate it. It ought to be studied only to grow on fruit borders such vegetables as are required early, and which may be soon cleared away, which will allow a portion of the summer's heat to warm the ground, and by benefiting the roots of the trees assist the proper ripening both of the fruit and wood.

Dwarf trees may be forced into bearing either by root-pruning, or, what is better, by taking them out of the ground, cutting a little off the ends of the roots, and replanting; this must be very carefully done, especially on light dry gravelly soil. Large trees are often benefited by having their roots cut at a proportionable distance from their boles: a trench should be dug all round, and the roots cut, and when the trench is refilled it should be manured: this will encourage the tree to make fresh roots, and add to its vitality and productiveness.

When young trees are planted the ground ought to be dry, not wet, and the roots should be spread well out on *all sides*: where roots are growing on one side the tree is apt to become one-sided, and thus become deformed. Whether a tree be planted for the first time, or re-planted after lifting, it ought not then to be cut or pruned: allow it to get itself established (which it probably will do the first year, which will be shewn by the growth it makes), and then cut it into the shape desired. It is desirable that the cuts should get healed over, which can only be done where there is a healthy root action: for a cut or wound, when large, especially if not covered by new wood, may, through exposure to rain and drought, become crooked and carry death down the branch; this must be kept in mind with dwarf trees, where the root action is less vigorous than in trees grown on crab or free stocks. Therefore where a dwarf tree has become too large, and it is determined to cut it back say into wood of two or three years old, it will be safest to cut it a year before lifting and re-planting, or root-pruning. If trees be properly managed, however, they will not require such severe discipline. It is customary to advertise young trees as well set with blossom buds, and capable of giving fruit the first year after planting. This is no advantage at all, though it pleases inexperienced persons. It would be much better to begin with a young tree which had no blossom buds; train it into proper shape from the beginning, and wait two or three years for fruit, which by that time is sure to be produced by a dwarf tree. Large trees are sometimes cut over to be grafted with better sorts: in small gardens it would be better to take them out and re-plant the ground with young dwarfs. Where a good number of trees can be grown, it is an advantage to plant a considerable variety; for as trees have different seasons of blooming, there is a better chance of at least some of those grown being favoured with suitable weather for blooming and setting fruit even in unfavourable springs.

If Seakale or Rhubarb be desired very early, they should be covered in the beginning of the month, or even sooner, with leaves or stable litter, or a mixture of both: if pots or boxes cannot be got to cover the plants, take willow or hazel sticks, or even short pea stakes: stake them all round the plant, bringing them to a point at the top: cover all over with protecting material, and in ordinary seasons Seakale and Rhubarb may be had at Christmas.

A garden should at this season supply Brussels Sprouts, Couve Tronchuda, Scotch Greens after frost, Drumhead Cabbage, Lettuce, and Savoys.

DECEMBER.

Work suitable for last month, and not overtaken, should be done: dead plants removed and all rubbish: digging, ridging, and trenching

effected in favourable weather, and the garden kept trim: it should afford such vegetables as are mentioned for last month, which will constitute an agreeable and healthful variety at such a season, with the addition of Rhubarb at Christmas, if the forcing of it has been attended to.

If the work of the garden be now properly done, it will not look the dead, cheerless, desolate waste which so many gardens are at this season; but ready, waiting, and hopeful for the joyous spring, when the earth, rested and refreshed, shall put forth new life, the flowers once more appear, the blossoms burst on the tree, and nature shall have risen again out of the death of winter.

LIST OF DWARF STANDARD DESSERT APPLE TREES, ON PARADISE STOCKS,

Suited to small Gardens, arranged in the order of their use and time: to be grown as Bushes.

1 Joanetting, called also Jennetting; or White Juneating, &c.— early in August; in favourable summers in end of July.
2. Margaret, or Early Red Margaret, or Early Red Juneating, &c.— Middle of August.
3. Irish Peach; very excellent—August and beginning of Sept.
4. Thorle Pippin, beautiful and excellent—September.
5. Oslin or Arbroath Pippin, frequently in this district called the Aromatic; highly flavoured—September.
6. Devonshire Quarrenden—September to October.
7. Yellow Ingestrie, a beautiful little apple raised from th Golden Pippin—September and beginning of October.
8. Kerry Pippin, one of the best and most beautiful—September and October.
9. White Paradise, or Paradise Pippin; Lady's Finger, &c.—Oct.
10. Lady of the Wemyss—October to Christmas.
11. Cambusnethan Pippin, or Watch Apple, or Winter Redstreak— November.
12. Golden Winter Pearmain, commonly called in this district King of the Pippins—November to January.
13. Blenheim Pippin, or Blenheim Orange, &c.—December to Feb.
14. Court of Wick—December to February.
15. Ribston Pippin—December to March—tree subject to canker.
16. Golden Russet—December to March.
17. Margill, a small rich dessert apple, with Ribston flavour—December to March.
18. Dutch Mignonne—January to April.
19. Sam Young, a small russety apple, very excellent—Christmas to April.
20. Cockle Pippin—January to April.

Selections of six from the above, Nos. 3, 4, 8, 12, 13, 20. Selections of twelve; to the above add Nos. 1, 5, 14, 16, 18, 19. All the above list are suited to this district, and most of them will succeed up to an elevation of 400 or 500 feet above the sea level.

KITCHEN APPLES.

1. White or Dutch Codlin—may be used when half-grown in July. In use on to Oct.
2. Mank's Codlin—October to December.

3. Hawthornden—October to December.
4. Emperor Alexander—October to December.
5. Stirling Castle—November and December.
6. Mere de Menage—November and December.
7. Nonesuch—November and December.
8. Cellini—November to February.
9. Aitken's Seedling—November to February.
10. Cockpit—December to February or March.
11. Golden Noble—November to March.
12. Bedfordshire Foundling—December to April.
13. Baxter's Pearmain—December to April.
14 Fearn's Pippin—December to April.
15. Winter Ruby—December to April.
16. Reinnette du Canada—January to April.

Selection of six from the above, Nos. 1, 8, 10, 11, 15, 16

SHORT LIST OF PEARS ON THE QUINCE.

Stock to be grown as Bushes or Pyramids.

1. Doyenne d'ete—end of July.
2. Citron des Carmes—beginning of Aug.—sometimes end of July.
3. Jargonelle—August and September.
4. William's Bon Chretien—September; to be pulled before ripe.
5. Beurre d'Amanlis—October.
6. Louise Boune of Jersey—October.
7. Comte de Lamy—October.
8. Gratioli of Jersey—October and November.
9. Broom Park—January.
10. Beurre Rance—December to February.
11. Orpheline, or Soldat Laboureur—January and February.

For a Wall any way between West and South East

1. Urbaniste—October—very excellent.
2. Comte de Lamy—October to the end—a first-rate Pear.
3. Marie Louise—October and November—one of the best.
4. Beurre d'Aremberg—November and December.
5. Passe Colmar Doré—December.
6. Beurre Rance—December to February.
7. Glou Morceau—January and February.
8. Easter Beurre—March.

Pears grown upon the Quince Stock come much earlier into bearing than when grafted on the Pear Stock, and bear fruit of excellent quality.

STRAWBERRIES.—May Queen (earliest), Black Prince, Keen's Seedling, Carolina Superba, British Queen, Elton, Frogmore Late Pine.

RASPBERRIES.—Fastolf, Northumberland Fillbasket, Yellow Antwerp.

CURRANTS.—White, White Dutch; Red, Raby Castle, Long Bunched Red; Black, Naples Black.

GOOSEBERRIES.—White Champagne, Red Champagne (always called Ironmonger in Scotland), Turkey Red (a smooth red very fine), Sulphur, Glenton Green, Ironmonger, Tree Upright, Hedgehog, Bampton's

Golden Turse, Warrington, Whitesmith, Jolly Printer: the above are common and well flavoured sorts. For show gooseberries of the Lancashire and Cheshire sorts, the heaviest weights as shown in 1860 were—

	Red.	
London	Clayton.	Lion's Provider
Dan's Mistake	Napoleon le Grand	Magnet
	Yellow	
Catherina	Drill	Lord Rancliffe
Leveller	Peru	Leader
	Green	
Rough Green	Stockwell	Turnout
Thumper	Telegraph	Queen Victoria
	White	
Antagonist	Snowdrop	Careless
Queen of Trumps	Freedom	Hero of the Nile

Heaviest Red Berry, London, 33 dwts.
,,　　Yellow, Drill, 27 dwts. 22 grs.
,,　　Green, Thumper, 27 dwts. 8 grs
,,　　White, Antagonist, 30 dwts. 8 grs.

CALENDAR OF THE WOODS AND FIELDS.

JANUARY.

JANUARY sometimes presents a mild, spring-like season, sometimes it is rough and blustering, and it sometimes also gives us a glimpse of what we understand the Arctic regions present. When it presents the first or the last of these phases, any one in health may enjoy an outdoor ramble: but when rough blustering sleet and rain dash over the streets and fields, every one tries as much as possible to make it an in-door January. When mild and open, old meadow lands and the grass-fringes along our river margins, spotted here and there with the daisy that "never dies," look fresh and pretty under the noon-day sun; and life begins to move early weeds and flowers under sheltered hedgerows; for whenever the winter is mild in January, the first leaves of the creeping cinquefoil (a common hedge creeper throughout most of the country) may always be seen. The red deadnettle too shews its pretty little flowers; and the lover of black currants may in such a season, by pressing the leaves of the ground-ivy, have the scent at least of this fruit; for the scent of the leaves of ground-ivy strongly reminds almost every one of the pleasant odour that comes from the black currant fruit when pressed in the hand. Chickweed and groundsel also show their tiny flowers; and in the woods, hanging gracefully on brush-wood and trees, stately and small, the wild honeysuckle shews its tender spring petals, which almost every spring are repeat-edly nipt and killed by frost ; for whenever a few weeks of mild weather come, even in midwinter, this climber is sure to put forth leaves. In the fields the most lieful sight is the ploughmen and their teams, followed often by large numbers of rooks, and occasionally a number of black-headed and a few brown-backed gulls. House sparrows also begin to chatter and gossip, and the dainty wren will occasionally lift up her voice, and a pretty voice and a merry song she has. Chaffinches begin to *fink*, and sometimes they get half way through their short song and abruptly stop. If mild, by the end of February we sometimes hear the whole song—" see see see, a wee wee wee wee drunken sooie !" But when winter rules with icy hand, the coming or partly come greenness is unseen, birds are mute, and the plough-boy's whistle can be heard only in the farm-yard, or by the side of his noisy cart. The bracing air and the clear grey sky, however, make it a pleasure to tramp over either field or road ; and the fact that frost and snow are the natural accompaniments of the month, makes their presence seasonable and agreeable withal.

> What though his locks with icicles be hung ;
> What though his breath go up to heaven like smoke,
> Shall there no joyous song for him be sung?
> Shall not for him the bardic strain be woke?
> Ay, for a fresh career before us lies,
> And hope's sunlighted wings are glittering in the skies.

FEBRUARY.

During this month the year begins to open, and spring-feelings begin to stir in the breast of every lover of nature. The early leafing trees begin to open, and the buds of the general forest begin visibly to swell : while underneath, the young leaves of the coming primroses point skyward, and the anemone, a com-mon flower in our sheltered and loamy woods, is now spreading its gracefully shaped leaves over the young thin grass or moss, where it generally blooms. In one of the woods on the Jed we have seen the anemone grow so luxuriantly that the ground seemed white when it was in blossom. The snowdrop now lights up the woodlands in many of our Border districts; and the sunny dandelion begins to blink here and there along our as yet prosy highways; and where the grass is prevalent and the mould fine, by lanes and waysides, the early leaves of the speed-well may be seen. This very pretty flower is often, but errone-ously, called the forget-me-not, in the Borders. The leaves of the speedwell are somewhat round in shape, and they grow in twos, one on each side of the stem; whereas the leaves of the forget-me-not are comparatively long and narrow, and they grow singly—each leaf by itself—on the stem. By noting this, any one may know the one plant from the other. Like a huge rosebloom-bud, looking through the sand on the edges of our rivers, the coltsfoot may be seen by the end of the month ; and in sheltered corners, neck-deep in water, the bright marsh mari-gold may now be seen; and ragweed and hemlocks begin to top the soil. The bird family are now in a state of excitement ; and from this to the time when their nest-eggs require a sitter, they sing, and fight, and love in a somewhat Hibernian style. In the old pea sticks in a quiet corner in a garden, the thrush will now even build and lay, if the weather be mild. By the end of the month, in open weather, thrushes, blackbirds, finches, hedge-sparrows, and wrens sing: and the bat may now be seen on a mild evening on its wavering rounds, darting and wheeling as if for amusement, but in reality trying to satisfy its newly awakened digestive organs on any early gnats it can pick up. We have often noticed that in frosty weather in this month, and with snow covering the soil, if a blink of sunshine come, finches, robins, and titmice chatter and sing. The raven nests by the end of the month; and skylarks and linnets con-gregate. Badgers leave their holes, and begin to wander about at nightfall; and as the spring advances, they extend their wanderings sometimes a few miles from home. These quad-rupeds have been on the increase of late years. They breed in early summer. By the end of the month some hares get paired; and some very early rabbits bring forth young, which sit at hole-mouths, about the size of rats. Early spawned fish leave the rivers for the sea.

MARCH.

Lambs now add beauty to the grass lands, and if the month has shewn a predominance of the peacock's tail, the white sheeted sower will now be seen stalking over the red land with a will. The deep green of the autumn sown wheat also adds variety to the shades that as yet but slightly diversify the landscape. In the woods the poplar now fairly shews its leafage, and from the yellow tinge of the leaves, a clump of poplars at this season brings autumn into remembrance. The resinous buds of the horse chestnut open, and push out a thick and beautiful mass of leaves. Violets, anemones, and primroses now deck the wood-lands, and daffodils and daisies the lawns and meadows. The black thorn also shews its snowy blossom, and drooping catkins hang on the hazels,

> And downy palm-buds glisten in the sun.

Gnats come out by old sheltering hedge-sides and decayed walls; and honey bees now begin, often on languid wing, to seek the flowering gooseberry bushes, and other early flowers; and the large humble-bee gloats during the sunny noon on the swelling flower of the coltsfoot. The primrose or sulphur-butterfly also comes out. Crows begin to repair their old nests, and jackdaws and rooks also become busy, and are constantly on the move, carrying the lath and flooring of their nests. Tremendous battles the rooks have over disputed nests, but no sooner does a matron rook drop an egg in her disputed abode, than all clamour ceases, and she is left to repose. Partridges and red grouse now pair, and blackcocks (the male birds) on the upper fells and table-land of Upper Coquetdale, Redesdale, and in the high lands in the vicinity of Keilder, may be seen early in the month in very large flocks—soon to be broken up, for the pairing season is at hand. The voices of the feathered tribes may now be heard at all hours in fine weather. The ring-dove coos this month; but from this bird's destructiveness to the green crops of the farmer, a deadly war is now waging against it in Border districts. It is a beautiful bird, and has a sweet, and to many a romantic cry; but poetry aside, no alderman has a more insatiable stomach. The black-headed gull comes to our marshes to breed, and the curlew or whaup may now be heard giving forth the prolonged "wheefle." The yellow bunting sings, and also the golden crested wren. The latter is yearly becoming more plentiful. The song of the gold-crest is low and abrupt, but pleasing: it is, however, much inferior to the merry and clear song of the dainty dipping kitty. Wagtails —pied, yellow, and grey, arrive. We have seen the pied wagtail sometimes in February, in Berwickshire. The otter now breeds, and it continues to breed till near the end of the year. This animal has increased in the Borders within the last twenty years. Pike and perch spawn.

APRIL.

Hearts again are stirred to pleasure
By the coming of the spring;
Stirred to meet and greet the sweetness
April showers and sunshine bring.

This is perhaps the most stirring and lifeful month in the year. In field and garden there is full work this month, if there ever is full work. And among our fellow bipeds of the feathered tribes there is work from dawn to twilight; for younglings must be fed, and food at this season is sometimes scarce; for when coldness prevails, earth worms and slugs keep snugly in their houses, and live at home at ease. In the fields and woods rosy-faced merry younglings of the human family may be seen on pleasant days, lifefully moving from spot to spot where primroses and daisies abound. Lambs too, madly run and frisk on the leas. And over this scene of toil and pleasure, the fine, though fitful, streaming sunshine falls, while bright and fleecy clouds keep ever sailing athwart the sky: these combined making

The earth enjoyable,
For beautiful it is, and harmony
Unites the sunshine and the laughing sky
With earth's sweet greenery.

Here and there, early leafing trees spot the woodlands; and larches are arrayed in garments of delicate green, some of them graced with tasseled lilac-coloured flowers. The speedwell family now show their bright blue eyes almost everywhere, but ever most numerously by green lanes and on sunny grassy banks, —and the wild hyacinth begins to raise its head on rich and sometimes damp meadows. This plant flowers with us in May and June. In the woods the pretty delicate woodsorrel, Scotland's sensitive plant, begins to show its pencilled cup, streaked and faintly marked like the eggs of some of our song-birds. The summer visitors of the bird family have by the end of the month mostly all arrived. To our Border counties we have the arrival this month of the whitethroat, garden warbler, whinchat, redstart, and some of the larger wrens; also the swallow and the cuckoo. The redstart is a rare bird, but it frequents some of the sheltered wood-banks in Roxburghshire. The cuckoo is seldom heard about Kelso, but in the higher and wilder portions of the county, especially where young fir plantations exist, it is often heard. In wild moorlands a solitary plantation of this kind is the favourite resort of this bird. The insect world has yet little show in the upper element, for the alternating sunshine and shower of April scarcely suit the winged portion of this numberless family. Bees are abroad however, and the copper, wall, and cabbage butterflies may be occasionally seen sporting in the noon-day sunshine. Of the creeping things now to be seen, the small common garden snail is one, newly aroused, for the sweet tender plants on which it feeds are in leaf. Its very pretty, though loathed brother, the banded or snake snail, generally remains torpid to the end of the month. The most amorous of the frogs begin thus early to strike up their love songs in the marshes. Eels begin to appear, some of them coming from the sand and mud-banks, and some from the mouth of the Tweed; and by the end of May, they are clinging in large numbers to the rocks at the bottom of our rivers. They may now be taken, for they are in season for the table.

MAY.

Away into the woodland paths
And yield this heart of thine.

May is generally looked on as the first month of summer, although in late seasons the scarcely opened buds on oaks and ashes, and the half-grown leaves of the other common trees, give it more the look of a spring month. In ordinary seasons, however, the general forest presents a pretty full leafage in May; and in the woods and fields of our district the flush of wild flowers is immense. By the end of the month, if the season is early, tangled glens and old half-deserted roadsides are rendered bright by the bloom of wild roses; and although we have fewer mazy patches of the wild rose now than hitherto, owing to the spread of soil-culture, the wanderer never requires to look long for these beautiful flowers. By the time the wild-briar begins to blossom, a spot of snowy or creamy hawthorn may generally be seen here and there along our field or roadsides, often in close proximity to the "roses, white and red." Both hawthorn and briar, however, attain their full bloom in the succeeding month. On the walls of old abbeys and keeps, the yellow wallflower may now be seen, adding beauty to the grey ruins on which it lives. This is also a most stirring and lifeful month. At daylight—if a very fresh morning, before daybreak—the feathered tribes, from the wren to the heron, lift up their united voices, and their utterances only cease with the down-going of the sun. And for the sake of enjoying such music, and the green earth and pleasant sunshine, wanderers leave their houses and roam by wood and field, to their heart's delight. Anglers too, tempted by the pleasant waters and the rising trout, hunt up their favourite casts; and naturalists and lovers of nature begin to look for their favourite insects, plants, and birds and their nests:

> And all the earth is gay;
>   Land and sea
> Give themselves up to jollity,
> And with the heart of May
> Doth every beast keep holiday.

The simple enumerating of the flowers of this month would alone take up our space. It is common to note the woodland strawberry flower as belonging to May; but over the most of Roxburghshire and Berwickshire, we have found this wild plant in flower in February and March: and we have seen it in January. Forget-me-not is this month in its glory; and we know of no finer wild-flower sight than this flower yields in the woods of Springwood Park. There we have found forget-me-not in distinct shades of pink, white, and blue; and it fringes the woodland walks by the river side so luxuriantly, that, in place of thinking it wild, which it is, many would think it had been planted and trained. For both anglers and the general public river sides are now very pleasant. The last of the salmon family that on the previous autumn or winter ascended to breed, now drop seawards; and during April and May immense numbers

of their young also drop seawards with every flood. Few clean fish are in the river this month; but the common fresh water trout are now a treat on the table; and are captured with fly and creeper.

JUNE.

> Briskly rins the caller stream,
> Blithe the siller troots are loupin;
> Saft the dew wi' diamond gleam,
> Frae the infant harebell's coupin.

There is more flower blossom this month than even in May. Woods and fields shew a deeper green, and leafage is quite full and matured as to growth. It is now full summer; for May can seldom swell the forest leaves to completion, and in this light may pass as a spring month. There is no month like June for the enjoyment of delightful mornings and evenings. Either by wood or field at such times there is a richness, a freshness so palpable, that every one may feel its power. In the woods the honeysuckle now sheds its fragrance, roadsides are rendered sweet by the blooming hedgerows, half-neglected waysides and tangled banks are rich with the flush of wild roses, and the moorlands and uplands are a-blaze with whin-blossom. The tall and stately foxglove too, decks the rocky shallow-soiled hillside, as well as the woodland. The surface of the stream now shews the pretty white crowfoot and the pondweed; and the yellow iris shews its bright head by the quiet waters. In the corn fields the pretty convolvulus now shews its head, supported on the corn stalk on which it climbs, and poppies begin to flower. Little music is now heard during the day from the feathered tribes, but at evening and morning the thrush keeps fluting, and the blackbird whistles; but the solitary stonechat ceases to sing. Most birds have young to rear now; and young rooks are on the wing by the end of the month, but they still require feeding. Hawks, magpies, and jackdaws have very tender families on hand, being a little later than the rook in breeding. Ravens with us are now scarce, the only place we know where they now nest being Henhole in the great Cheviot. Rooks and daws however are yearly increasing, especially the latter. Wild bees are busy this month with nesting operations. The drone yellow wasp may be found beginning her nest; and she is often so found when the nest is not larger than a large gooseberry. There are, it is stated, forty distinct species of humble bees in Britain, but as these insects change often in outward appearance from age and otherwise, individuals of the same species may have been wrongly classed. We have anyhow not a tithe of the number in the Border counties. The large and beautiful lamprey leaves the sea this month and spawns in the Tweed. The spawn bed is made deeper than that of the salmon, and in places similar to where the salmon deposit their ova. Minnows also begin to spawn this month; and the heron, when he happens to alight among a body of spawning minnows—"streamers" as boys call them—gobbles large quantities of them. Herons, by the way, are on the increase all over the Borders. The fox breeds.

JULY.

Balmy freshness fills the woods,
In the ear the corn is swelling.

This is a month of full leafage, and a number of fruit trees flower or blossom. The lime, with its creamy, scented flowers is now in its glory; and all over it there is a perpetual humming from dawn to sunset of garden and humble-bees. By the end of the month the moorland and heathlands begin to assume a purple shade; and on cliffs and dry hillsides the wild thyme is in flower; and this pretty sweetly-scented plant is common over all the Border counties. "The Scottish blue bells" also reach their full blossom, and they grow numerously both by hedgerows and on dry bare banks and ridges. Thistles also blossom, and the ragweed opens its broad yellow heading to the sun. But the grandest display of wild blossom that this month brings forth, is that of the broom. Cultivation has cleared many of our hillsides and glens of the "bonnie bonnie broom," but we know many such places where it is still allowed to remain, and where it may now be seen in its greatest beauty. Most of the June flowers are still in blossom; but the sunshine is so strong now that we instinctively wander from the fields to the cool river-sides. Here we find in the shaded wood-banks the raggedrobin; and we have both kinds, white and red. The white, or rather the cream-coloured specimen of this flower has a scent scarcely differing from the primrose. The water-cress, in half-hidden springs of running water, is also in bloom, its cross-shaped flowers standing a few inches above the water. The pheasant, partridge, and grouse now have young; and keepers employ their time in looking after the young game, and in traversing the woods for the purpose of shooting down the young of carrion crows, magpies, and hawks. A number of our song-birds have now a second brood on hand; and unless at daybreak the songsters of the grove are mute, and some of the finches now cease to sing for the season. The lizard lies in the sun; and by river-sides and over marsh lands the gaudy dragonfly, erroneously pronounced by the youth of the Border the "fleein stangin-ether," sports on wavering wing. Beetles now become numerous; and the catterpillars of some of the early butterflies now begin to shelter themselves against their approaching change to a crysalis or pupa state. In shallow river pools the toad now breeds We

have seen toad-spawn in May in the Borders, but much more of it in June and July. The spawn consists of a long chain of transparent gluten, four or five feet in length, and the ova is encased in this, in a double row, like black beads thinly strung. Frog spawn consists of the same material, but it is in a compact body, like a dish of boiled sago. Corn fields now stand filled to the hedges; and soft winds play over the land, and gently surge and sway the lusty grain, making it look not unlike a rippling sea.

AUGUST.

The scarlet pimpernell creeps here and there,
Amid the corn the crimson poppies blush;
Still on the brooks gleam water-lilies rare,
And purple loosestrife and the flowering rush.

August with its ripening fruit and grain, has a plenteous aspect; and with the yellowing corn-fields, the fine dark-green of the spreading turnip plants; the purple heath-lands and the green uplands, the country is beautiful. And the air is filled with the ceaseless hum of countless insects. Moths dance and waver over tall grass tufts on meadows, and round oaks and limes. Cattle stand in the rivers and switch their pliant tails, glad of the cool water to stand in, and of its effect, from the coldness of the temperature over its surface, in keeping off the flies by which they are at this season so much annoyed. Farmers secure their hay, and prepare for the harvest, which by the end of the month is common in the low lands. About the beginning of the month sportsmen begin to exercise their dogs and their own limbs against the coming Twelfth. By the end of the month, about nightfall, the wild sad winds, the precursors of autumn, rise and sweep along upland woods and ridges. In the woods blaeberries may be gathered; and some of the creeping pea-plants now flower, and depend from the branches of hazel and hawthorn. The yellow-fringed ladies'-bed-straw, and ladies' mantle, with a similar blossom, deck dry sandy road and river-sides. The latter flower gets its name from the peculiarity of the shape of its leaves, which much resemble the cloaks or mantles which were in fashion a few years ago, and which must of course have been in fashion centuries ago. The white campanula is common in the Border counties, but to see it in perfection the valley of the Jed must be visited. The rich soil in the lower portion of this valley, and the fine sheltered nooks and spots which it here and there contains, are the means of producing a large and varied crop of wild flowers. We have here seen the campanula fully six feet in length. Ferns are now to be gathered in great variety; and the satin-threaded flowers of the bramble are open. And the grain fields in some low districts are now purple with the flowers of the wild poppy. The bird family is comparatively quiet: rooks caw, but no song is heard, unless from a few dawn-singers: and autumn is advancing. The curlew has left our inland heights and moors; the yellow wagtail departs, and swallows begin to congregate, and to hold converse, perhaps about the "dangers of the seas." Great numbers of wild-ducks now nightly feed in the barley fields, on the grain. A large number of butterflies now haunt the moorlands, most of them very small, but decked in every variety of colour; and glow-worms may be seen about their haunts in the early part of the month. They appear about mid-June and disappear in August. This light-giving insect is the wingless female of a beetle. It is not so common now as it was some twenty or thirty years ago. A few summers ago we saw a number on the roadside by the Tweed, between Ashiesteel and Ettrick foot. Mossy banks are the places where these insects are generally found.

SEPTEMBER.

Under the pointed knives of the reaping machine, and the scythe of the mower the ripe grain is falling; and the face of the field is gradually becoming changed. The wind no longer passes softly, as if whispering through the tree leaves, for their fibre is hardened, and a rustling is now heard in place of a whispering or hushing sound. On the inner or small trunk-branches of the elm may now also be seen leaves faded into a pretty bright yellow: and young limes in parks and by waysides are yellow all over. Flowers, though still pretty numerous, are perceptibly lessening in number. The summer blossoms are mostly decayed, though a few of the prettiest still remain, the foremost and finest being the harebell. The gaudy golden ragweed or ragwort is still bright and pretty, and with good weather will keep up its head till the close of the month. Autumn has mastered summer however, for

> The orchard fruits hang mellow,
> Mute are the tuneful throng,
> Save Robin, happy fellow,
> Who sings the whole day long
> In bowers of elm leaves yellow.

Hazel nuts may be gathered, and haws and hips hang in ruddy clusters by the waysides. The fleabane is now common on dampish lands; and by the sea a number of autumn flowers may be gathered. The fields are again recovering their greenness, for the after-grass is growing where the hay was cut down; and clover foggage is fresh and green in the barley stubbles. The goatsucker, the first of the swallows, and the whitethroat depart; and large numbers of lapwings occasionally assemble about night-fall on newly-broken land. The first fresh water trout

begin to spawn: and a second supply of trout flies come to the surface of the running streams. These flies, it is believed, are from the eggs dropped by some of the insects that appeared in the spring. The insect world is still busy. Ants swarm at this season: and there is scarcely a dry grassy meadow or hillside in our district but there colonies of these busy insects may be found. It has occurred to us several times that ant hillocks are old mole hillocks, grass-covered. They are the same in shape as mole hillocks, and are of the same lightness as to density. But we have occasionally seen ant hillocks much larger than any mole hillocks we ever saw. Wasps also swarm this month; and this is the reason why our grocers' shops are so infested with them at this season, the scent of the sugar, etc., being the cause of bringing them thence. On the moorlands gay vested butterflies yet flit about in the sunshine. We may here note that a number of our butterflies present us with two broods during the summer, the first in May or June and the second in August or September. The evenings during this month, under the softened light of the moon, are the finest of the year; and mostly all lovers of out-door nature who have health love in such nights to

> Linger mid the chequered light,
> The dreamy light and shadow.

OCTOBER.

> The wind is sadly sighing,
> The passage birds are fled,
> The forest leaves are dying,
> The summer flowers are dead.

This is the month that crowns the woods with their fullest beauty; and but for the somewhat pensive reflections it calls up, would be welcomed with as much delight as May. The colouring along the woodland slopes, if the trees are of various kinds, is generally very beautiful, especially when brightened up by the mellow sunlight. In the mornings now the dew lies heavy; and it is a very fine sight to see the numberless dew-covered webs of the gossamer spider at such a time. Before the sun breaks the dew, these beautiful fabrics may be seen covering almost every inch of land in grass and stubble fields; and hedge-rows and whin clumps are literally covered by them. We once saw in Berwickshire a row of tall spruces so covered that they looked like ship masts clad in _outre_ sails; for the slender network was so heavily laden with dew that the trees in place of appearing green were of cloud-like grey. Flowers are now few. Solitary harebells may still be seen under some shady hedge or bush, and a sprinkling of daisies now dot the old pastures, which still look pretty and green, as also do the hills. Mosses are at their prettiest; and in the Borders we have a fine variety. At this season the colouring in some of the mosses is rich and fine; and under the shelter of these interwoven plants millions of insects cosily nestle both at this season and during most of the year. In the insect world there is now considerable agitation. Caterpillars are creeping everywhere in search of proper shelter against the coming winter. Some fasten to old posts, some creep under the bark of trees, some seek shelter under the eaves of our houses, and many inside our country houses; and millions die. They get into the pupa state very soon after they get into proper quarters. The beetle tribe is also fast disappearing: some seek protection beneath stones and beds of moss, some bore into soft and some into hard wood, and some under the bark; others delve into the earth or mud, and some live under water. All our birds that come as summer visitors are now departed; and redwings arrive, and snipes increase in number, for they come southward. Salmon and sea-trout leave the sea in great numbers to spawn in our rivers. Rats now leave their summer residences in the corn-fields and ditches, and take up their winter quarters in our homesteads and houses.

NOVEMBER.

A dull brown shade is creeping
Over mead and mound and hill;
The drooping fern is weeping
Above the murmuring rill;
And red the brook is sweeping
Where it erst was clear and still.

The beauty of October is now gone, and dreary dark November reigns; but if the month is mild we would recommend the lover of "trees and buds and flowers" to wander away into the cosy woodland nooks in which he plucked the early spring flowers, and there push aside the protecting covering of dead leaves, and he will find—what? He will find that even in winter the flowers that deck the woodland are not asleep, but green and fresh and growing. There he may at this season see the tips of the spring leaves of the lovely primrose, and the strawberry flower; and a number of small delicate stems of humble spring creepers; and overhanging these he will find the woodbine putting forth rich green spring leaves; and he will also see the green buds shining at the old leaf roots of early opening trees: these combined bringing him strongly in mind of spring. We have many a time derived much pleasure from excursions of this sort, which often carried our thoughts from November to

Whispering leaves, and freshening dewdrops lying
On infant flowers.

Several of our resident birds now move about in flocks; and

The merry robin,
How he frisks about!
Sporting round the dog-house,
Hopping in and out.
How his dark eyes twinkle
In the sunny light
As with joy he warbles,
Giving us delight.

Even late though it is, a few moths may still be seen on the wing in the noonday sun; but we sometimes witness the month pass without getting a single glimpse of the orb of day. And when the wild wind comes it sweeps through the leafless trees with a dreary *sough*. There is no soft music now in the voice of brook or river; and after nightfall, as the wind sweeps over them, it bears aloft and over the plains the now wild or mournful sound of their rushing waters. The landscape is gloomy; but if the weather be mild the sportsman enjoys the month greatly. He may either give chase to the fox or hare, or bring out his fowling-piece against grouse, black-game, or partridge.

DECEMBER.

The time of frost is the time for me!
When the gay blood spins through the heart with glee,
When the voice leaps out with a chiming sound,
And the footstep rings on the musical ground.

Should frost and snow come this month (and when could they be more seasonable?), and cover up our flush of late daisies, our opening chickweed, and groundsel, and ivy-blossom, and the green meadows and hills, and the fresh green fields of Autumn-sown wheat, it is a comfort to know that much enjoyment comes with them—enjoyment all the more welcomed, because of a kind that comes seldom. Either by day or in moonlight, there is much that is beautiful to be noted when snow covers the soil and frost prevails.

Morning! each pane is a garden of frost,
Full of delicate flowers, soon raised, soon lost.

Before the wind dismantles the snow-covered trees each individual tree appears as if from fairy land, so beautiful and often grotesque are they; and many pleasant mornings have we had in tracing the plants, forests, lakes, and castles on the frozen window glass. In the moonlight when the frost is very keen the snow shines and twinkles with countless crystals, beautiful as diamonds; and the very *crunch* it makes below the feet at such a time rings with music. Watch the radiant faces of the youths as they slide: what enjoyment!

Here the hobnailed brog is the aristocrat,
The weak soled boot must give way to that.

Now is the time when our gentlemen and tradesmen leave their homes and join heartily in the "roaring game." Then the skaters—

Away! hurrah! the lake is like glass!
Buckle and strap on the iron grass!
Off we shoot and poise and wheel,
And swiftly turn on the scoring heel;
And our flying sandals chirp and sing,
Like a flock of swallows upon the wing.

This is a time when our poor birds suffer considerably from a want of food. Snipe and wild duck may now be easily reached at the fresh springs, where they find their food; and wood-pigeons seek turnip leaves and seakale; rooks, the stackyard; and finches live on forest and garden buds. The soft billed birds suffer most; for blackbirds, robins, titmice, and hedge-sparrows are often found dead in severe frosts. Let us then spread our window-sills with food daily. We shall have music for our outlay in spring. The thrush will now sing sometimes, the robin often. We have one true winter songster, a bird that sings in the severest frosts. We have heard it many a time at the dawn, when snow was deep and our blood almost freezing. It sings chiefly at morn and eve; and its song is very low and particularly sweet and charming. This bird is the dipper, commonly called in the Borders, the "water craw." Many people have never heard it sing; but its song is so low that unless when the surroundings are in a state of quiet, it almost requires one to listen in order to hear it. Perched on the top of an ice-bound stone in the river, it will in the gloaming sing for a quarter of an hour sometimes, with very few breaks. In midwinter it dives as briskly as in summer; and when under water it picks up its food from the stones, which consists in the winter season almost entirely of water insects. The last lingering leaves have fallen, the year is closed, and we end our notes.

Man cannot stand beneath a loftier dome
Than the cerulean canopy of light—
The ETERNAL'S vast, immeasurable home,
Lovely by day, and wonderful by night!
Than the enamelled earth, so greenly bright,
A richer pavement man hath never trod.
He cannot gaze upon a lovelier sight,
Than fleeting cloud, fresh wave, and fruitful sod—
Leaves of the boundless Book, writ by the hand of God!

ANGLERS' CALENDAR.

JANUARY.

IN this month the true angler never thinks of casting a line. The trouts are thin and watery in the flesh; and they can only be taken with worm—roe-angling being now prohibited —and in flooded or "falling-in" waters, — a sort of fishing that requires no skill in casting, and by which a novice could capture almost as many trouts as a practised angler, provided he were properly placed on the water. He may purchase his gut this month, however, as tackle-makers generally have their new stock supplied by mid-winter; and by purchasing early, finer gut may be had.

FEBRUARY.

Though this is a month of something more than promise to the salmon angler, it is of little value to the trout angler. Unless in a very mild and sunny season (and February seldom witnesses such), no trout flies come into existence; so that angling with the fly would yield no sport. The trouts are however beginning to get into better condition; because the grubs on which they feed—which they get below the pebbles, and from which the water or trout flies emerge — are many of them well advanced in growth by the end of the month, and thereby yield more feeding substance. In this month it is generally very cold work to fish for salmon, but on the same days it is doubly cold to fish for trout.

MARCH.

The angler may now have his March Browns, the largest size, ready for the Tweed or Teviot; and for the smaller streams (few of which yield much sport in March), he may bring out smaller March Browns, or spiders. In early spring, on the Leader and Gala, for instance, spiders dressed from the inner small feathers of the shoulder of the woodcock-wing are killing hooks; and they are often used along with black spiders. On mostly all small streams spiders are deadly. During this month the angler should ply his art at the necks of pools, and where the streams are easy, for trouts cannot as yet keep ground in rough water. When the day is mild and sunny a fair basket may be made in March. The best time of the day for the angler is from about eleven to one o'clock. Bull-trouts are often taken with trout flies in this and the succeeding month in Tweed and Teviot.

D

APRIL.

The Tweed angler, at least on the lower portions of the river, generally looks on this as the prince of fly-fishing months; and on the smaller waters it is also a good month for fly-fishing, especially from about the middle, at least if the season be mild. The same flies are used in this as in last month, but the angler should have two sizes on his line, large and small. Trouts are now creeping more and more into the streams, so that these, when they are not very rapid or heavy, should have the angler's attention. When the stream continues to ripple the pool down its centre for some distance, the angler should cast over the ripple, as trouts are generally plentiful in such places, especially in the opening of the year. The best time to angle is from ten to four o'clock.

MAY.

The Hare's-lug-and-Woodcock-wing fly is a general favourite during this month—indeed it is a good hook for almost any "fly" month : the Pale Yellow Dun is another good fly for the same season. The trouts are now still more spread in the streams, and are strong enough many of them to lie in pretty rough water. This the learner should note. The best time for fly-fishing in this month is from about eight to four or five o'clock. Earlier in the morning the Creeper is a deadly bait about the beginning of this month ; and by the end of it, it is deadly in the forenoons. It is only successfully angled with in roughish and clear water. Should the river swell an inch or two, and even remain clear, it is an unsuccessful lure. Worm is also deadly this month in the early morning, but principally in and about the edges of mild streams. In a rising or falling river the minnow also becomes a good bait in May. We may note here concerning minnow fishing, that in June and July it is a deadly bait both in rising and falling waters, but especially the latter. It is also a good bait in clear water during these two months, to the angler who can throw a long line and work it skilfully. Par-tail is also a good bait after a flood, and on gloomy days, or at nightfall. Very large trouts are taken by both of these lures, and they are deadliest in streams. The angler should also know that worm is often very deadly after summer floods, and before the water loses its muddiness ; and fly also is generally a successful lure after early summer floods.

JUNE.

Creeper fishing gets to its height in this month ; and all through the day, especially if very sunny, it is an excessively deadly bait, till about the middle of the month, when it becomes scarce, and Stone-flies become plentiful. The Stone-fly is a very sure lure after a flood, both in stream and pool, but most so in the former. It is not so good a bait in clear water. Worm fishing is now pleasant work ; and on sunny days the angler may, with either creeper or worm, or both, have little difficulty in making a good basket on any stream where trouts are plentiful ; and trouts are now in their prime, and are scattered over all the streams, as well as all parts of the streams, be they deep or shallow ; and wherever the water is running, and is of sufficient depth to cover their backs, they may be captured. Creepers are bred at the edges of the river, and as hungry trouts are often prowling near them, the angler should often cast to the very edge of the water. Fly-fishers have not such good sport in June as in May, and the flies used in this month should be made up in a lighter manner than in May, and should also be dressed on smaller wires. On the small waters a blae midge-fly, of smallish size, is often a good killer in June, and in Tweed both in June and July, a good basket is occasionally made with the blae midge-fly dressed on the very smallest wires made. Some good sport is had by fishing with fly during this season in the gloaming, and even after nightfall. In this month the angler may fish early or late, and all through the day if he choose.

JULY.

This is chiefly a month for worm fishing. The waters are generally very low, rendering fly-fishing almost useless ; but worm is so sure a lure during this month, especially in the smaller waters, that the angler need not regret having to use the same bait for a succession of weeks. It is a month when worms seem to be the main food of the trouts, most of the water grubs on which they feed having become flies. The worms are plentiful however, and by watching from a bank the angler may notice a trout now and then nosing round and round some of the flatish pebbles near the shore : this is to obtain worms—for the black-headed water-worms are very plentiful in midsummer below the pebbles in all rivers. The angler should therefore cast his bait into all sorts of river corners and shallows, as well as the main stream, and he may be repaid for doing so. By throwing a very long line, trouts may be often got with worm in the pools in July. They take it as it falls, as they take fly. It requires fine light casting, of course, but almost any angler may soon learn to throw both a long and soft line. Trouts take best during this month from about eight to four o'clock, or so.

AUGUST.

This is generally a sort of angle-with-everything-and-get-little month, a month for which there is no particular or sure lure, especially on large waters like Tweed and Teviot. It is a better month for the upland streams, or burns, and among these the worm is generally a very good bait at this season. From the larger rivers, by dint of perseverance, we can generally produce a dish of respectable appearance, but at same time we can hardly say we ever had the trouts " taking" freely during August, and we have often tried them with fly, minnow, and worm. Those in the large rivers are now falling back in condition, and are consequently leaving the strongest parts of the streams. If the weather be sunny, the middle of the day is the best time to fish in August.

SEPTEMBER.

The first of the trouts now begin to spawn in the large rivers; but those not so far advanced are still palatable, though not by any means like what they were in June. Fly and worm are both about equal as lures at this season, the former perhaps best in larger waters, but the latter the preferable in the upland streams. By the end of this month trout angling may be looked upon as resembling the season—approaching the " sere and yellow leaf." The day may be delightful, the river side charming, but the lifey ".bir and whir" no longer stirs the soul of the angler. The time to fish now should be from about ten till four or five o'clock. Summer and spring flies may both be used with tolerable success.

OCTOBER.

Fly-fishing is better, in general, during the early part of this month than in September, in small waters at least; and the flies used should be those made use of in spring. Trouts numerously ascend the small waters for spawning purposes, and in October, with spring flies, we have, in our earlier years, had many a successful day's sport in these small streams, and generally got pretty large trouts too; and the time when they seized the flies most readily was generally a short time before nightfall, when the waters were clearing from a flood ; the place—a mild stream falling into a feeding pool.

NOVEMBER.

Now that roe-fishing is prohibited, this may be looked upon as a dead month for the trout angler, and few of those anglers we daresay who love to wield a deft wand and a light line over the clear sunny waters in summer will regret that roe-angling is among the things that were. It afforded sport, however, to a pretty large number of people who, during the summer months, generally found it difficult to secure trouts even in small numbers ; but these anglers may, if they will only exercise a little patience and practice, have the higher pleasure of running down their game when it is in season, for any one may learn to angle so as to be able to ensure moderate success. Many years ago

we had the curiosity to try worm-fishing in clear water and in frosty weather in November, and we captured eleven large trouts in one pool. We might have got more, but from numbness we could not bait the hook. This was in Leader Water.

DECEMBER.

Fishing *nil.*, we shall add a few *memoranda.*

In the foregoing notes we do not attempt to give a complete set of hints on angling ; we have simply, in the space allotted to us, given a few notes that we hope may prove useful to novices and some who can scarcely be called beginners, who angle with little success from year to year, without paying attention to the little odds and ends that all successful anglers have to put into practice.

A well-balanced rod should be used, and a pirn line and casting line that each taper toward the hooks, and fine stained gut; and in order to cast well, the learner should throw out the arm with vigour, but give the line plenty time to play round the head before casting.

Fish up stream with everything but minnow. If this cannot be done in large rivers, throw straight across.

Keep well back from the place you cast into. No trout that sees you will take your lure. Never make more than a cast or two over the same water; by moving on, new trouts are constantly getting tempted with the fly or bait.

Fish mostly in streams. The pools yield most sport immediately after floods.

All our remarks in the foregoing notes refer to fishing in *clear water*, unless where the reverse is stated.

RIVER TWEED FISHERIES.

COMMISSIONERS.

Every person who is the owner of a fishing of the annual value of £30, or which extends half a-mile in length where such Fishing is only on one side of the River, or a quarter of a mile where such Fishing comprehends both sides of it,—the Husband of every Proprietrix or Liferentrix, one guardian of each minor, one trustee of every estate, one member of each corporation or associated body holding, enjoying, or possessing such a Salmon Fishing of the annual value or extent aforesaid.

OFFICIALS.

General Clerk and Collector in the Upper District—Alexander Curle, Esq., Melrose.

Treasurer—J. M. Meggison, Esq., Berwick.

Superintendent—Charles Smurthwaite, Peebles.

The special general meeting of Commissioners is held at Cornhill on the first Monday of September.

ANALYSIS OF THE TWEED FISHERY ACT.

THE TWEED SALMON FISHINGS ARE REGULATED BY THE ACT OF PARLIA-
MENT, 20° & 21° VICTORIÆ, CAP. cxlviii, AND THE AMENDMENT
ACT, 22° & 23° VICTORIÆ, CAP. lxx.

THESE measures are the result of enquiries made in 1857 and 1859, before Committees of the Lower and Upper Houses, into the existing state of the Fishings. In the course of this investigation the fact of a gradual decrease in the produce of the river was established, beyond dispute, by the Tables of the Berwick Shipping Company, who, as proprietors and tacksmen, for a number of years back, have occupied the largest proportion of the netting stations. Of the causes assigned for this decrease, one of the most prominent was the employment of stell and other fixed nets at the entrance of the river. In the Acts of Parliament above recited, these, as well as cairn-nets, which, on the occasion of a flood or spate, were numerously made use of along the entire course of Tweed, are declared illegal. The stake or bag-nets also, placed beyond the limits of the river's mouth have been made subject to a weekly close-time, and other salutary regulations. In regard to the wear shot net, it is held unlawful in future to use meshes of less than seven inches round, or extending an inch and three-quarters from knot to knot.

The Acts in question are also armed with provisions which greatly alter the terms of the Annual and Weekly Close-times, as these were formerly observed. According to Section vi., in the Amendment Act of 1859, "It shall not be lawful for any Person to fish for, or take, or aid, or assist in fishing for, or taking, any Salmon in or from the River at any time between the fourteenth day of September in any Year, and the fifteenth day of February in the Year following, except by means of the Rod and Line, with the Artificial Fly only, nor with the Rod and Line at any time between the thirtieth day of November in any year, and the first day of February in the Year following, and which respective Periods above defined shall be, and be held to be the 'Annual Close-times,' within the meaning of the Recited Act, and this Act; provided that the Commissioners, or any five of their number may, by writing under their hands, or under the hand of their Clerk, authorize any Persons appointed by them to fish for and take Salmon in and from the River, with the consent of the Owner of the Fishery from which Salmon are taken, during the Annual Close-times, for the purpose of Artificial Propagation."

By the clause which regulates the Weekly Close-time, it is made unlawful for any person, between the fifteenth of February, and the fourteenth of September, to fish for, or assist in fishing for Salmon in or from the river, at any time, or in any way whatsoever, except by means of the Rod and Line, or by means of Stake-nets and Bag-nets as after-provided, betwixt 6 p.m. on Saturday, and 6 a.m. on the Monday following. The Weekly Close-time for the Stake and Bag-nets falls to be regulated under the same Section, by the state of the tide on the Monday morning. The penalties incurred by infringement of these provisions in the Amendment Act, are properly severe.

Under the Statutes above recited, the slaying of Salmon by means of the leister is made illegal. A clause also, in the Act of 1859, renders obligatory the restoration of all kelts and foul fish to the river, whether taken by the Net or by the Rod and Line. To this obligation, so far as the angler is concerned, an exception has been made in the recent Amendment Act, permitting the retention of Sea-trout, although foul or unseasonable; it being supposed that the presence of these fish in the river imperils the security of the fry and ova of the true salmon, and otherwise interferes with their increase.

In landing salmon the angler is restricted betwixt the 15th of September and the 1st of May in the year following, to the use of the Landing Net; the Cleek or Gaff-Hook, which was formerly employed for that purpose, being prohibited during the period specified.

To the trout fishers on Tweed and its tributaries, clause lxxv. has a peculiar interest.'

It is worded as follows :—

"Every person who wilfully kills any smolt, fry, or young brood of salmon by the rod and line, between the first day of April and the first day of June in each year, or has in his possession any smolt, fry, or young brood of salmon taken by means of the rod and line during the said period, shall, for every such first offence, be liable to a penalty of sixpence, and shall for every second or subsequent offence be liable to a penalty not exceeding two pounds, and an additional penalty of two shillings, for each of the smolts, fry, or young brood of salmon so killed, or found in his possession ; and the rod and line whereby the same have been killed, and the baskets or packages in which the same may be found, may in the case of every such second or subsequent offence, be seized or forfeited."

The interests of the angling community have plainly been consulted in this provision of the statute. A modified penalty, compared with what was formerly imposed, has been affixed in the case of a first offence ; and the leniency shewn to trout-fishers is further exemplified by the limitation of the period, during which it is held unlawful to kill salmon-fry, to TWO months.

It is not to be inferred, however, that salmon-fry are not in the river, or in taking humour, throughout the remainder of the angling season. As pars or finger-lings they abound ; and it rests with every conscientious angler, not to make abuse of the forbearance which refrains from making their capture, while in this state, the subject of a penalty.

(Printed from Report of Committee on Tweed Fishings.)

Estimated Produce of all the Salmon Fishings in the River Tweed, calculated from the produce of those Fisheries occupied by the Berwick Shipping Company, by comparing one year with the preceding, and reckoning the other Fishings in the Tweed to be in the same proportion :—

	Salmon	Grilse	Trout
In 1829 the Company's Fishings produced .	2350	15,273	28,389
The other Fishings in the Tweed, calculated at	3000	19,500	36,241
Total estimated produce of the Tweed in 1829,	5350	34,773	64,630

From the data, the calculations were carried backwards to 1808, and have been continued yearly since 1829 on the principle above stated, as in the following table :—

Year.	Salmon.	Grilse.	Trout.
1808	37,333	25,324	21,033
1809	30,949	32,679	21,402
1810	40,782	49,332	23,963
1811	38,566	24,852	12,439
1812	27,711	82,538	33,604
1813	35,273	61,643	36,319
1814	58,890	73,521	34,161
1815	41,044	97,734	39,653
1816	54,041	120,594	62,074
1817	36,199	66,694	37,131
1818	39,267	59,848	37,346
1819	31,895	71,813	47,386
1820	38,288	116,495	61,454
1821	34,657	55,291	61,339
1822	25,250	47,266	70,413
1823	12,122	50,794	49,934
1824	23,664	73,381	71,161
1825	18,957	61,506	59,531
1826	12,040	85,378	59,203
1827	10,725	54,034	43,441
1828	13,511	39,248	39,563
1829	5,350	34,773	64,630
1830	7,415	66,520	37,486
1831	13,197	43,244	77,037
1832	9,709	41,411	77,308
1833	10,428	93,939	60,178
1834	10,106	59,262	48,852
1835	22,642	87,707	82,229
1836	16,957	34,846	63,616
1837	14,577	60,429	57,426
1838	12,785	78,577	40,876
1839	15,608	35,449	56,124
1840	10,920	52,117	56,342
1841	10,464	71,254	64,672
1842	19,198	109,935	76,071
1843	17,777	66,293	54,209
1844	21,830	88,003	99,256
1845	18,962	69,750	54,355
1846	17,878	37,506	38,679
1847	9,032	53,076	67,796
1848	9,478	97,102	52,541
1849	11,484	59,405	39,435
1850	9,522	33,864	49,701
1851	8,789	16,855	45,326
1852	5,808	28,902	24,773
1853	9,199	43,075	37,341
1854	15,299	16,739	32,645
1855	6,329	13,952	23,736
1856	4,885	33,992	30,597

These Tables show that, whereas 37,333 adult salmon were taken in the River Tweed in the year 1808, a number exceeded in some subsequent years, the take had dwindled down by irregular, though certain steps, to 4885 adult salmon in 1856. Again, in turning to the rentals, there will be found a gradual decline from £12,061 in 1811 to £4859 in 1856, and this notwithstanding an increase in the value of what may be called Sporting Fisheries, and the greater facilities afforded by railways for the transmission of the produce of the Commercial Fisheries to more numerous markets.

In 1807 the rents of the Salmon Fishings on Tweed amounted to £15,766, and the number of boxes of salmon sent to London, each box containing 8 stone weight, was no less than 8445. The present rents of the river do not greatly exceed £4000 [this statement was published in December 1858].

PRODUCE of the Salmon Fishings of the River Tweed from 1857 to 1862, being continuation of the preceding table ; extracted from the "Quarterly Review" of April 1863 :—

Year.	Salmon.	Grilse.	Trout.
1857	11,475	46,553	31,846
1858	14,614	23,590	41,059
1859	12,273	13,952	35,081
1860	8,940	20,323	26,052
1861	5,379	15,036	28,607
1862	8,467	25,042	20,988

The following is a return of the Fish caught [mostly by the Rod] in the Chief Upper Fisheries in the years 1856-57-58 :—

	1856.	1857.	1858.
Netherbarns,	318	281	82
Westhouses,	405	623	68
Maxton,	56	4	8
Craigover,	200	188	42
Mertoun-under-Water,	110	90	48
Rutherford,	108	160	24
Makerstoun,	354	312	60
Ormiston and Mounteviot,	237	248	4
Floors,	512	298	90
Sprouston,	450	410	79
	2750	2614	505*

[Taken from the evidence of Richard Hodgson, Esq., in the course of Parliamentary inquiry, 1859.]

* Owing to a misapprehension by the House of Lords, in the passing of the Tweed Fisheries' Bill in August 1857, the Annual Close-time for Rod Angling extended from the 14th of October to the 1st

COMPARATIVE SKETCH

OF THE

AGRICULTURE OF BERWICKSHIRE AND ROXBURGHSHIRE*.

SOILS.

Both counties have a great diversity of soils. These consist of clay, loam, sand, peat, and I add, as distinguished from all these, friable mould. In general, each description of soil is in considerable patches, and less broken than in many counties. There are, doubtless, farms which consist of every variety of soil named, but these are exceptional, and one kind of soil generally extends over large tracts of land.

Clay prevails in the Merse, where it is very retentive. It is, however, of a fertile character, which is at once apparent from its black colour. It has here also a considerable surface-depth, and is much more productive than the Roxburgh clays.

Loam in its best character prevails on the banks of the Leader, to the north of Lauder, of Whitadder, and Blackadder, in Lower Teviotdale, and all along the banks of the Tweed, from Dryburgh to Berwick. It forms, indeed, all the peninsula between Tweed and Teviot, extending from Nisbet on the one side to Rutherford on the other, to the junction of these rivers, and which peninsula constitutes the most fertile soil in Roxburgh.

---

of March. This misapprehension was rectified by the Tweed Amendment Act of 1859, by which the Annual Close-time for Rod Angling was restricted, commencing on the 1st of December and ending on the 1st February. This will sufficiently account for the comparative small number of Salmon taken by the rod in 1858. Rod fishing has since greatly improved, both as regards the quantity and the size of the fish caught.

We here add a quotation from the "Quarterly Review" of April 1863, in reference to the new Act:—"The experience of the Tweed, we venture to maintain, though still imperfect, shews that the decay of the river has been arrested, and that large Salmon of some age—the best and surest breeders—now abound in its waters, and the result is, in the main, to be attributable to improved legislation."

The Rental of the River from a sum not greatly exceeding £4000 in 1858 had increased to £7052, 7s. at 7th September 1863.

* Compiled, by permission, from a very interesting Essay on the subject, by James Sanderson. Originally published in the Transactions of the Highland Society, and subsequently published in a separate form. Edinburgh : W. Blackwood & Sons. Price, 1s. 6d

---

Peat, like the mountain-ranges, is most abundant in the outskirts of the counties, and is rarely met with in the interior, with the exception of some patches in the parishes of Gordon and Greenlaw. This soil is chiefly confined to the pastoral districts. It partially extends along the southern base of the Lammermuirs, slightly intersperses the Hawick range, and is singularly interstratified with clay in Liddesdale. *Deep peat moss* is not prevalent.

Sand covers a comparatively small area, In the valley of Upper Teviot the soil is partly sand and partly gravel. In the parish of Westruther there is a considerable portion of black sand, which has the appearance of peat. In the Merse, sand of a similar character is to be met with, but the area it covers is not large.

Friable Earth.—This description of soil covers a large area, and is what is generally designated a barley soil. The upland slopes of Leader, of Ellem, and Rule are of this character of soil.

SIMILARITY OF THE TWO COUNTIES.

Although Roxburgh and Berwick in some respects differ, yet, on the whole, no two counties could be named which have such a similarity of soil and farming. With respect to minor matters there is doubtless some variance. Roxburgh is more highly favoured than Berwick for markets; has, on the whole, a better turnip soil; its fields are larger, its fences better trimmed, and its land generally requires less labour, and is better adapted for fattening flocks. Berwick, on the other hand, has the best wheat soil, produces the bulkiest crops of beans and the best mangold, has the advantage of being bounded on the east by a maritime coast, and the flocks which depasture its mountains are less liable to disease than the mountain flocks of Roxburgh. The hills in Roxburgh are green and grassy; those in Berwick are black and heathy. Both counties are alike in having various modes of sheep-farming, in having the same system of rotation, in producing the same varieties of crops, in invariably associating tillage and pasture, in adopting the same principles and using the same forces in husbandry. They agree, too, in each having mountainous tracts and undulating plains, diversified woodlands, and verdant slopes,—in fact, in having the same description of farms and the same style of farming.

SYSTEM OF ROTATION AND HUSBANDRY.

The general system of farming embraces stock and crop husbandry, and the farmers' attention to, and profits derived from each, are somewhat equally divided. It is the union of these two branches of farming that is the mainspring of the Border farmers' success, and which, indeed, forms the basis of all advanced and successful farming. In this respect either of the counties is not equalled by any other county in Scotland; for they excel not only on account of uniting the two branches, but in the efficient manner in which both departments are carried out.

The rental of arable land varies from £1, 5s. to £3, 10s. per acre; 35s. being about the average rental. During the last twenty-five years rents have risen 35 per cent, but in most of cases farmers have got in return improved homestead accommodation, and an increased number of farm cottages. *The average rental of pastoral land* is 6s. 6d. per acre. This description of land has recently risen, and is rising very rapidly, doubtless attributable to the fact that the store-producing area is being rapidly diminished, and that while the British farmer suffers from foreign competition in grain, yet in the production of stock—more especially sheep—he has no competitor. Hence it is that the Border farmer evinces sound judgment in his management; for while he devotes much attention to the cultivation of white crops, and regards this department as an essential adjunct, yet he makes it a subordinate or rather an auxiliary branch of stock-farming.

The *Steadings* are generally conveniently placed near to the centre of the farms. Modern steadings are very compact, yet commodious, and contain fixed steam-powers, with barn and granaries attached, well-ventilated single-stalled stables, with every feeding convenience for hay, boiled and dried food; stalls, boxes, and courts for fattening cattle; boiling and turnip houses, cart-sheds, piggeries, etc. On large farms there are generally a smithy and occasionally a saw-mill, the latter driven by steam-power. For the sake of lessening the cartage of grain and manure, there are occasionally two steadings on one farm.

CROP HUSBANDRY.

Wheat is the most valuable cereal crop, and in both counties occupies a prominent place.—Adapted to the strong clays of the Merse, and to the land more especially north of the Tweed in Roxburghshire, the wheat crops raised, both as regards yield and quality, are not much inferior to those of the best wheat-growing districts in Scotland.

According to the agricultural statistics drawn up under the auspices of the Highland Society in 1857, Berwick takes the sixth rank amongst the counties of Scotland in respect to the proportional area under wheat, while Roxburgh occupies an average place.

Barley.—With respect to acreage under this crop, Berwick is the fourth and Roxburgh the sixth county in Scotland. The quality is generally very superior.

Oats.—The oat crop, as might be supposed, occupies a larger area than any of the other cereals. Both counties have a greater acreage of oats than that of wheat and barley combined. The quality is generally superior; the potato oat especially, which is extensively grown in Kelso district and in the west of Berwickshire, is not surpassed, if equalled, for quality, in any district.

Beans do not occupy a prominent place in either county. The Merse clays are well adapted for beans, and produce very bulky crops.

Peas—Though less than 1000 acres, for both counties, are under this crop, yet either of them has a much larger area under it than any other county in Scotland. This may be partly ascribed to the demand for grey pease to make peasemeal and barley bannocks—so much used on the eastern Borders—and partly because some of the dry soils and sunny slopes of the Border counties are singularly well adapted for the growth of peas.

Rape.—Next to Dumfries, Berwick grows the largest area of rape, and Roxburgh follows as the third rape-producing county.

Turnips.—Roxburgh has the largest proportional acreage, and Berwick next, under this crop, both counties having under turnips about one-fifth part of their total acreage under a rotation of crops. This fact of itself is perhaps the highest eulogium that can be paid to the agriculture of these counties; for, as a general rule, turnip culture and its usual attendant, sheep husbandry, form the basis of the highest farming. Nor is it only with respect to acreage that they excel in turnips; it may safely be affirmed, that for efficient turnip culture and yield of roots per acre the county of Roxburgh is not surpassed by any county in the United Kingdom: the same is applicable to several districts of Berwick; but, on the whole, the latter county, from having a larger area of retentive clays, is not so well adapted for the culture of turnips as Roxburgh.

Mangold.—The small acreage Roxburgh produces is not worth noticing. Berwick ranks along with Haddington, as next to Ayr and Wigton, though far short of the area of these mangold-producing counties. This reveals a singular anomaly, as the two eastern counties have nothing in common with those of the west. In fact, the nature of the respective soils is quite different, while the much greater quantity of rain which falls on the west coast renders the respective climates dissimilar. Depth of soil is probably an explanation of the seeming anomaly. Crops, however, are not grown solely for adaptability to soils, but their extent is influenced by other circumstances. Mangolds, for example, are an essential adjunct to dairy farming or the soiling of cattle; and generally where these are most carried out, there are mangolds most grown. Berwick, on the whole, produces excellent mangold, and several fields of this root, which the writer witnessed in the Merse this season [1862], could not be far short of forty tons per acre.

Potatoes, as might be anticipated, from the extensive area that is allotted to the turnip crop, do not take a prominent place in the husbandry of Roxburgh and Berwick. On the contrary, Roxburgh has the least proportionate acreage of any of the Scottish counties under this crop, and Berwick next.

Of *Carrots, Cabbage, Bere, Rye, Flax, etc.*, the area under each and all is so small in both counties, that they belong more to the garden than the field.

Implements of Husbandry.—In this 'department there have not been many new introductions, but chiefly improvements effected on old inventions. The farmers of either county have not been carried away by a mania for possessing new, and often comparatively worthless, implements.

STOCK HUSBANDRY

embraces several important branches of Border agriculture. The solely pastoral farming is confined to the Cheviot and Lammermuir ranges, the lofty-peaked fells of Upper Teviot, and the Liddesdale hills. This kind of farming has undergone little change for a long period, save that the area under it has greatly diminished, and is rapidly diminishing. The breeds of *sheep* in the pastoral districts are *blackfaced* and *Cheviot*. Though there are a few flocks of the former in Liddesdale, yet this breed is now almost solely confined to the Lammermuirs. The Cheviot breed still prevails on its native mountains, the Cheviot Hills— and is also the chief breed in Liddesdale, Teviotdale, and on the Lammermuirs. With the exception of Dumfries, Roxburgh is not equalled for a superior breed of Cheviots by any county. In the absence of statistics it is difficult to form a close estimate of the comparative numbers of blackfaced and Cheviot sheep in the counties, but these may be roughly estimated as six Cheviots for one blackfaced. Occupying the highest hills, the blackfaced breed, as improvements advance, is diminishing; indeed, all upland improvements tend to make the Cheviot breed supplant the blackfaced; and, again, the half Leicesters supplant the Cheviot, and the full-bred Leicester goes on extending its range. The last and best variety of breeding sheep are pure-bred *Leicesters*. These are kept as regular stock by a great many farmers in the Kelso district, as well as in the low lands of Berwickshire, for breeding rams. This system has sprung up within the last twenty years; and so rapid has been its progress and so marked its success, that at the annual tup show and auction sales held at Kelso in September, the show of Leicester rams is not equalled for numbers and quality at any fair or auction sales in Scotland (*see* notice of the Kelso Ram Sale in the lists for that parish). Considerable discussion has recently taken place concerning the true Leicester or Dishley breed, some contending that the sheep of Kelso district are pure Leicesters, while others contend that the smaller-boned sheep south of the Tweed are the true descendants of the Dishley breed. Both parties are probably correct; and the difference of form now manifested by the so-called different breeds is not greater than might be supposed, between two off shoots of the same breed having been differently treated in different climates. As it is, the Kelso farmers ought to stick to the breed of sheep they have adopted, as they yield more wool, and have larger frames, than the other off shoot from Dishley; and their aptitude to fatten is borne out by the unequalled rapidity with which they are matured for the market. And this brings under notice a most important branch of farming lately sprung up also—viz., the fattening of hoggs (one-year-old sheep); and here also, in this branch of farming, Berwick and Roxburgh take the foremost position. In concluding these cursory statements regarding the breeds of sheep in the counties, the writer has pleasure in recording that 'the Leicester breed of sheep in the counties of Roxburgh and Berwick [known as the *Border Leicester*] is not equalled in any county in Scotland; that the Cheviot breed in Roxburgh is not surpassed in any other county; and that both counties, maintain a greater number of sheep, in proportion to their total acreage, than any two other counties in Scotland.

Cattle.—Concurrent with sheep husbandry in lowland districts is that of cattle. This department, too, occupies a prominent place in both counties, and they both stand high, especially in the department of fattening cattle: of the cattle thus fattened, half are bred in the district and half bought in from other counties. *Dairy farming* there is none, save that only which is necessary to supply domestic wants. Nor does the Border farmer boast of owning a long-pedigreed breed of cattle, such as are only kept to swell the successful lists of the National Show. The breed of cattle however, as shorthorns, are equal to, if they do not surpass, those of any other county, but they are generally more for profit than fancy.

Horses—The few that are bred are chiefly for agricultural work, not for sale. They are partly of Clydesdale, and partly of English breed, and partly a cross between these breeds (*see* Kelso horse fair).

Swine—In neither of the counties takes a prominent place. Nearly all of them are kept for home use—[Kelso being the only place in the district where pork curing is carried on to any extent—which *see*; *see* also Kelso fortnightly cattle market.]

PEASANTRY.

The wages of a hind, or married ploughman, average in the district about £35 a year, paid mostly in kind—the proportions varying in different localities.

Unmarried ploughmen, boarded in the farmers kitchen, receive about £20 a year. Servant girls for house or out work receive on the average £6, 10s. for the summer, and £3 for the winter half-year, including board.

Steward's wages average about £50, and shepherd's about £45 a year.

Mr. Sanderson concludes his Essay with well merited paragraphs on the Border farmers and peasantry. Than the latter, there is perhaps not such a respectable and intelligent class of labourers existing anywhere: as for the farmers, their farms vouch for *them*.

[If further information be required on the subject of the Agriculture of Berwick and Roxburgh shires, the reader cannot do better then consult Mr. Sanderson's Essay.]

Of the *Bondage* system, which is universal in the district, Mr. Sanderson possesses a rose-coloured opinion, and passes it with a pat on the shoulder; but as the system is evidently destined, sooner or later, to be the means of trouble, and affect the present relations of farmer and hind; and as many living in the district know only of the system by the name; and the name to many, living where the system does not exist implying a sort of serfdom, we may state that the following are its principles:—

The *Bondager* (*i.e.* stout lass, employed by the farmer in his fields, at so much per day [10d. to 1s.], *when required;* and whom the hind, by use and wont, is *bound*—and hence, we presume, the name of *Bondager*—to provide) is by law the servant of the hind (*i.e.*, married ploughman, living in his own cottage, and having a wife and family); she is hired by him, and although she is employed by the farmer, the hind is responsible for her wages; in many instances, however, the hind finds a bondager in his own daughter.

The present wages of a bondager, or *out-worker* as she is sometimes called, [she has generally better wages than a house servant] average about seven pounds ten shillings for the summer half-year, and four pounds in winter—these wages at all events are common—and these the hind is bound to pay whatever work may be done by her; but as she is generally well employed, there are comparatively few cases when her annual earnings do not amount to about fourteen pounds, so that the hind actually receives about two pounds ten shillings more than he pays; and if by any possibility she could be boarded on fifty shillings for the year, the hind could have no reason to complain in a money point of view. The field has its charms for these women; their general strength enables them to do all that is expected of them; the demand for their services gives them full independence; the high wages furnish a dress agreeable to their taste; and there is a lightsomeness in the half-yearly tenure and the coming market, which, inducing a change of place and company, fills up an existence of agreeable excitement.

There are three stages in the life of every hind who keeps to his calling, of very unequal circumstances: first—when a young man, boarded in the farmer's kitchen, and having his bed in the stable loft, he receives £20 a year, and having neither house, wife, nor bondager to give him trouble or expense, he lives an easy thoughtless life: at this stage he is known in the district as a *ploughman,* as distinguished from a hind or married ploughman; the second, when he marries and has a young family; the third, when his family are able to work. The bondage system is felt only when he enters the second stage; in the other two he finds himself rid of it, or practically so, and his wages are then fair and adequate; but the second stage compels many to abandon the plough for the spade and pick; others emigrate rather than submit to the ordeal it entails; whilst others drag through the stage in poverty and wretchedness, the effects of which never leave them: and this must be apparent to any who will take the trouble to look into his circumstances during this period of his hindship. Allowing his wages to be £35, or rather £37:10, including the fifty shillings gained by his bondager, and from that deduct the board of the bondager, which cannot be estimated under fifteen or sixteen pounds, which include lodgings and washing; leaving but a little over twenty pounds for himself, his wife, and generally a large family—a family often of four or five unfit for work. From these circumstances his whole wage cannot be estimated above eight shillings a-week on an average; in fact the money received by a young man when boarded, and having no responsibility, is just about the same as that he has for himself and family when married; and has incurred the responsibility of providing a field hand for the farmer, and of being liable for her wages. Add to this the discomfort of having the continual presence of a strange woman in the cottage—limited in many cases to a single apartment, divided by the beds into a but and a ben: with the addition of a loft, which may happen to be habitable or not, but which is seldom or never used for bedroom accommodation; and the effect which such a circumstance must have in deteriorating the moral feeling both of the hind's family and the hired girl. It may be suggested, and occasionally with truth, that these circumstances do not, or seldom, affect the feeling of comfort or privacy in the hind's family—that they are accustomed to the system, and do not mind the stranger's intrusion. Taking this for granted it tells the worse for the system, as shewing in many instances the deadening of genuine home feeling.

The third stage—when the hind's family has grown up, and one of his daughters can take the bondage work—may be thus described in Mr. Sanderson's words:—

"In such cases bondage is a blessing, as it not only secures employment for the families of the hinds, but, along with this, they are kept under the influence of parental example and reproof, *instead of being sent abroad on the world, away from the parental eye, and at a time when they are most susceptible of good or evil.*"

These few words, while they proclaim the blessing of the system when it assumes the limited parental form, imply also its danger when it assumes the aggregate form of service. Even in its second and best stage the hind's welfare must depend on the *gratuitous* labour of his daughter; for had he to pay her the wages he would to a hired bondager, he would remain at the second stage level.

The *Bothy* system, such as exists in some of the northern counties, is unknown in the district.

In the introductory notice of Selkirkshire a few remarks will be made on the agriculture of that county.

REMARKS

UPON THE

POPULATION OF THE COUNTIES OF BER-WICK, ROXBURGH, AND SELKIRK.

WE here give a few comparative statements extracted from the Population Returns of 1861 (published 1862).

On the 8th of April 1861, the number of persons in Scotland, including the Military, and Royal Navy and Merchant Seamen, as were in Scotch waters on that day, was 3,062,294. From this it appears that the population of Scotland, between the years 1851 and 1861, increased only at the rate of 6 per cent; while during the previous 10 years it had increased at the rate of $10\frac{1}{4}$ per cent.

This population of over Three Millions was divided into 678,584 families, who inhabited 393,220 houses, containing are 46 persons in every 10 families (or rather over $4\frac{1}{2}$), 17 1,708,405 rooms with windows, thus indicating that there families in every 10 houses, 77 persons in every 10 houses, 43 rooms in every 10 houses, 25 rooms for every 10 families, 17 persons to every 10 rooms. Of these 678,584 families, the males were 1,449,848, and the females 1,612,446 (including the navy and merchant shipping, which seems to have had 120 women aboard); being a population of 111 females to 100 males.* The several counties exhibit the greatest possible

---

* These numbers, however, do not take into account the large number of

difference in the proportion of the sexes. Thus in Roxburgh there were only 102 females to each 100 males, and it is quoted as being (after Peebles, whose proportion was over $101\frac{1}{2}$ to 100) the county where the nearest equality of the sexes exist [this is accounted for by the influx of railway labourers at the time]; while in Shetland the females were in such excess that they were slightly over 142 to each 100 males. This excess is difficult to account for, except by the supposition of the greater proportion of males who enter the mercantile navy and the high male mortality from drowning. In three years (1855 '6 and '7) no fewer then 1263 males in Shetland were drowned; while only 238 females died from the same cause.

The proportions of Roxburgh are already stated. Berwick is near the average, being 110 females to 100 males; while Selkirk is under it, being 105 to 100. The exact numbers were as follows :—

County.	Separate families.	Males.	Females.	Both Sexes.	Children at School, 5 to 15.
Roxburgh .	11,626	26,782	27,337	54,119	8,471
Selkirk . .	2,237	5,026	5,352	10,449	1,632
Berwick . .	7,912	17,423	19,190	36,613	6,062

The returns of population for 1861 embrace some new features not given in former censuses, which, from their important bearing on some of our most interesting social enquiries, merit special notice. The first of these is the number of families in each county and parish ; the second is the number of inhabited rooms having no windows, and one or more windows ;—this, when compared with the number of inhabited houses, affords a means of judging of the housing accommodation of the population, as they shew the average number of families and the average number of rooms to each family. Thus in Roxburgh 223 families lived in rooms with no windows [*see* Castleton, Bowden, and Cavers lists]. In Berwick 24 thus lived, and in

---

Scotsmen who are serving in the army, navy, and mercantile shipping, and who in the census returns are only represented by the number of military, or of seamen actually in Scotland or on its coasts when the census was taken. As compared with England, however, where the proportion is 105 females to 100 males, the proportion of females in Scotland is disproportionally great, and must be accounted for by the fact that a much larger proportion of men leave the country than in England, either as emigrants to the colonies, foreign countries, and England, or to engage themselves in the army, navy, and merchant shipping. The common belief is that England is the great nursery for our seamen ; and so in one sense she is, if mere numbers be considered. But in proportion to her population, Scotland furnishes 62 persons for every 25 furnished by England, while the emigration returns furnish a proof that Scotland sends out in proportion to its population nearly twice as many emigrants as England.

Selkirk 2. The importance of this information in a sanatory point of view cannot be over-estimated. The third feature is the introduction of the number of children, between the ages of 5 and 15, in actual attendance at school during the first week of April. The particulars of these for each parish will be found in the parochial lists—*see* also comparative sketches of the housing accommodation of the towns in the district at the end of the Selkirkshire and Berwickshire lists.

Scotland exceeds all other countries in the proportion of her female population.

BORDER DISTRICT INFORMATION.

REGISTERS OF SASINES, &c.,

FOR THE COUNTIES OF ROXBURGH, SELKIRK, PEEBLES.

Keeper—John Murray, Esq. of Wooplaw, W.S. (Office, Melrose).

FOR THE COUNTY OF BERWICK.

Keeper—Robert Romanes (Office, Lauder).

DISTRICT LUNACY BOARD FOR THE COUNTIES OF ROXBURGH, SELKIRK, AND BERWICK.

20 and 21 Victoria, cap. 71.

MEMBERS FOR ROXBURGHSHIRE.

W. O. Rutherfurd of Edgerston, Sher.-Dep. of the County, Chairman.

Sir Wm. Scott of Ancrum, Bart.	John Paton of Crailing.
John Ord of Muirhouselaw.	The Provost of Jedburgh for the
Right Hon. the Earl of Minto.	time being.

MEMBER FOR SELKIRKSHIRE.

Charles Plummer, Esq., of Sunderland Hall.

MEMBERS FOR BERWICKSHIRE.

Sir Geo. Houston Boswall, Bart. of Blackadder.	George C. T. Cranstoun, Esq. of Dewar.
Major Wm. H. Smith of Cruicks-field.	Lieut.-Col. Geo. Logan Home of Broomhouse.
John Hood, Esq. of Stoneridge.	

Clerk—James Erskine, writer, Melrose.

ROXBURGHSHIRE AND SELKIRKSHIRE TEMPERANCE AGENCY.

President—Peter Hunter, Darnick. Vice-President—W. Waterston.

Treasurer—A. Anderson. Secretary—D. D. Deans.

Committee—Rev. W. Crombie, Melrose, James Hart, Charles Smith, A. Milne, W. Tait, W. Macbean.

EVANGELICAL ALLIANCE.

SOUTH-EASTERN SUB-DIVISION,

Comprehending the Counties of Roxburgh, Berwick, and Selkirk.

President—The Hon. Robert Baillie, Eildon Hall.

Vice-Presidents—Mr Nixon, Lynwood ; Mr Dudgeon, Spylaw ; David. Pringle, Esq. of Wilton Lodge ; Mr Paton, and Mr Rodger, Selkirk. Thomas J. Dunn, Melrose, Secretary and Treasurer.

Annual General Meeting at Melrose, with District Meetings occasionally.

ROXBURGHSHIRE AND SELKIRKSHIRE ADMINISTRATIVE BATTALION OF RIFLE VOLUNTEERS.

(Head-Quarters, Melrose.)

Colonel—Right Hon. Lord Polwarth, of Mertoun.

Major—Sir George H. S. Douglas, Bart., of Springwood Park.

Captain and Adjutant—J. F. Macpherson, Melrose.

The Battalion is composed of the following corps (the particulars of which are extracted from the Adjutant's Report, made up to 30th November 1863) :—

Corps.	Stgth.	Mksm.	Best Shot.	Points in 1st Class
1st Roxburgh (Jedburgh)	85	11	Sergt. W. S. Davidson	13
2d Do. (Kelso)	89	36	Private George Kerr ..	18
3d Do. (Melrose)..	69	4	Sergt. R. Somerville ..	11
4th Do. (Hawick)..	115	12	Sergt. F. Deans	16
1st Selkirk (Galashiels)..	97	11	Private George Hall...	11
2d Do. (Selkirk)	77	12	Sergt. Thos. Mitchell..	12

Best Shot of Battalion—Private G. Kerr, 2d Roxburgh, 18 points.

Total enrolled strength of the Battalion .... 532.

(For particulars of the corps, *see* the lists of their respective towns. For Berwickshire Battalion, *see* Berwickshire lists.)

BORDER RIFLE ASSOCIATION.

Annual Subscription—Effective Members of Battalion and Associated Companies, 2s. 6d. ; all others, 5s. ; Life Membership, £5, 5s.

Patron—His Grace the Duke of Buccleuch and Queensberry.

President—His Grace the Duke of Roxburghe, K.T.

Convener—Major Sir G. H. S. Douglas, Bart., of Springwood Park.

Hon. Secretary—Colin A. Hutchinson, solicitor, Kelso.

The object of the Association is to give permanence to Volunteer Corps, and to promote Rifle Shooting generally, but more particularly among the Volunteers in the Counties of Roxburgh and Selkirk.

The annual contest is held in the autumn at Melrose, when prizes are awarded. Their value in 1863 was £193, 15s. 4d. Total number of winners, 43.

BORDER COURSING CLUB.

Entry-Money which constitutes a life-membership, £2.

Hon. Secretary—Mr John Usher, Stodrig.

The meeting takes place annually about the beginning of October on the Sprouston Barony. The Spring Meeting has been discontinued. The contests are entirely for sweepstakes.

ROAD TRUSTS.

ROXBURGHSHIRE AND BERWICKSHIRE

Road from Carter Bar to Bridgehaugh, near Nether Blainslie.
Road from near Eildon to the confines of the county, near Cartha.
Road from Carter to Hawick ; from Hawick to Kelso.
Road from Jedwater line, by Swinnie, to the Hawick line.
Road from Ancrum Toll, by Belses, to Midlem Bridge.
Road from Jedburgh, over the Dunion, to Spittal guide-post.
Road from near Langhaugh to the Bridge at Galashiels, and thence along Bridge Street, to junction with county of Selkirk, near Post-Office, and thence by Wilderhaugh to the Damhead, to where it joins the county of Selkirk on the Peebles road.

James Erskine and Alexander Curle, solicitors, Melrose, Clerks.
J. M'Connell, Penrith, General Surveyor.
J. Nelson, Jedburgh, Assistant-Surveyor.

Special General Meeting held at Jedburgh first Tuesday in June, and Statutory Meeting held at Jedburgh second Wed. of September.

DRYGRANGE PONTAGE.

Act under Statute 46 Geo. 3, cap. 4.

Jas. Erskine and Alex. Curle, solicitors, Melrose, Clerks.
John M'Connell, Penrith, General Surveyor.
John Nelson, Jedburgh, Assistant-Surveyor.

The letting of Tolls, on above roads, takes place annually at Jedburgh on the second Tuesday of March, at One o'clock.

GREAT ROAD AND OTHER TURNPIKE TRUSTS, PARTLY SITUATED IN THE COUNTY OF ROXBURGH.

Roads from Kelso to Fireburn Mill, and from Kelso to Orange Lane—J. Cunningham, Coldstream, Surveyor.
Road from Kelso to Cornhill, by south side of the Tweed—William Brown, Surveyor.
Road from Kelso to St Boswells—William Brown, Kelso, and Thomas Mitchell, Melrose, Surveyors.
Road from Jedburgh Road, near Eckford, through Morebattle and Yetholm, to the English Border—Wm. Brown, Surveyor.
Kelso Bridge—William Brown, Surveyor.
Wm. Smith and Chas. Robson, Kelso, Clerks and Treasurers.
Road from Lauder, through Kelso, by Haddon Rigg, to the English Border—William Brown, Kelso, Surveyor.

William Smith and Charles Robson, solicitors, Kelso, Clerks.
Robert Curry, Treasurer.
Meetings not fixed.

The letting of Tolls on above Roads takes place annually at Kelso, generally on the last Friday of March.

SELKIRK AND ST. BOSWELLS TURNPIKE TRUST.

James Curle, solicitor, Melrose, Clerk and Treasurer.
Thomas Mitchell, Surveyor.

MERTOUN BRIDGE TRUST.

Alexander Curle, Melrose, Clerk and Treasurer.
Thomas Mitchell, Surveyor.
Tolls let annually, on last Saturday of March.

HAREMOSS AND SCOTSDIKE TURNPIKE TRUST, (Eastern Division.)

Qualification of Trustees, £200 Scots in County Valuation Books.
Geo. and Jas. Oliver, Hawick, Clerks. Wm. Sime, Surveyor.

LIDDESDALE TURNPIKE TRUST.

Qualification of Trustees, £100 Scots in County Valuation Books.
Geo. and Jas. Oliver, Hawick, Clerks. A. Wilson, Surveyor.

BERWICKSHIRE ROAD TRUSTS.

MIDDLE DISTRICT, AND UPSETTLINGTON BRANCH (now called Middle District).

Quarterly Meetings are held on the first Wednesdays of January, July, and October, and second Wednesday of March. Half-yearly Meetings are held on the first Wednesdays in April and November. Roup of Tolls, at Dunse, on first Wednesday of April.
G. Peat, Dunse, Clerk and Treasurer.
John Waite, Dunse, Surveyor.

EASTERN DISTRICT.

James Bowhill, Ayton, Clerk and Treasurer.
John Waite, Dunse, Surveyor.

GREENLAW TURNPIKE.

9 Vic., Session 1846.

James C. Robson, Dunse, General Clerk and Treasurer.
James Cunningham, Coldstream, Surveyor.
Jonathan Melrose, Coldstream, Clerk to the Southern Division.

WHITEBURN AND KELSO TURNPIKE.

R. Romanes, Lauder, Clerk and Collector.
Thomas Mitchell, Melrose, Surveyor.

COLDSTREAM BRIDGE.

Two fixed General Meetings are held each year at Greenlaw, upon the first Monday of April, and upon the Monday before the last Tuesday of October. Other Meetings are held when required.
James C. Robson, Dunse, Clerk.

LAUDER DISTRICT.

Robert Romanes, Lauder, Clerk.

DUNSE AND WESTRUTHER.

William Stevenson, accountant, Dunse, Clerk.

LADYKIRK AND NORHAM BRIDGE.

Let of Tolls takes place at Dunse, on first Wednesday of April.
Jonathan Melrose, Coldstream, Clerk.
James Cunningham, Coldstream, Surveyor.

ROXBURGHSHIRE.

◆

THIS county lies on the south-eastern border of Scotland, and is bounded by Berwickshire on the north, by Northumberland on the east, by Northumberland and part of Cumberland on the south, by Dumfriesshire on the south-west, and by the county of Selkirk on the west. The figure of the county is very irregular, and measures from its apex in the south, to that part which is inserted between the counties of Berwick and Edinburgh, upwards of forty miles; and from east to west about thirty miles. The area of the shire was formerly estimated to contain 720 square miles (*see* par. next column), one half being in cultivation. The county is divided, by its rivers, into several districts, the chief of which is Teviotdale, being that division drained by the Teviot and its tributary streams. Liddesdale, which forms the south-west corner of the county, is drained by the Liddle and its tributaries. The third division lies between the rivers Gala and Leader; and the fourth, which is situated north of the Tweed, is included in "the Merse."

The southern parts of Roxburghshire are very mountainous, the hills frequently rising in beautiful swells from the rich valleys at their base. The aspect of the county is thus finely diversified, and its beauty greatly enhanced by many clear rivers which pour through the different vales. The soil of the county is various, but much of it exceedingly fertile; and everywhere the finest farming prevails, extraordinary improvements having been made upon the capabilities of the land, and in the rearing of stock (*see* notice of the Agriculture of Berwickshire and Roxburghshire, p. 43). There are many antiquities in the county worthy of inspection,—viz., the abbeys of Melrose, Dryburgh, Jedburgh, and Kelso; the castles of Hermitage, in Liddesdale, and Roxburgh, near Kelso; and many other structures of modern celebrity. The railway connected with the county is the North British from Edinburgh to Carlisle, by Hawick. A branch line to Kelso strikes off at Newtown St. Boswells, and at Riccarton, 13 miles beyond Hawick, a junction is formed with the Border Counties' Railway, by which this district is brought into immediate connection with Newcastle. At Kelso the North British and North-Eastern Railways meet. A branch to Jedburgh was opened on the 16th of July 1856; it commences at Roxburgh Station, 3 miles above Kelso, and runs up the vale of the Teviot, through a fertile and beautiful country, terminating close upon the town, whose manufacturing and other resources it has been the means of developing.

The county of Roxburgh comprises thirty parishes, and five parts of parishes; it contains many villages, the important market towns of Kelso, Hawick, and Melrose, with one Royal Burgh—Jedburgh, which, in connection with Haddington, Dunbar, North Berwick, and Lauder, returns one Member to Parliament, and the county sends another.

The area of the county, according to the Ordnance Survey, just completed, is 670 square miles, or 428,494 statute acres, which is as near as possible 8 statute acres to each of the present population.

The population of the county was, in 1801, 33,721; in 1811, 37,230; in 1821, 40892; in 1831, 43,663; in 1841, 46,225; in 1851, 51,642; and in 1861, 54,119. The number of inhabited houses was 7255; uninhabited, 224; building, 50. Total annual value of real property, as assessed in April 1815, was £254,180; in 1849, £306,315; in 1855, £316,131:4:8½; in 1856, £324,844, 13s. 9½d.; in 1857, £295,328:2:8; in 1858, £334,971:5:5; in 1859, £345,431:1:10; in 1863-4, £381,597:7:4.

VALUATION AND AREA OF THE SEVERAL PARISHES
IN THE COUNTY OF ROXBURGH,

FOR THE YEAR TO WHITSUNDAY 1863-64.

Acres.	Parishes.	Amount.		
	DISTRICT OF JEDBURGH.			
10,388.921	Amount of parish of Ancrum	£12,498	17	0
3952.375	.. Bedrule	3674	0	0
6043.351	.. Crailing	7994	17	0
6084.903	.. Edgerston*			
16,242.117	.. Hobkirk	9008	14	9
16,585.863	{ parish of Jedburgh	22,108	15	10
	{ burgh of Jedburgh	9303	1	8
5620.482	parish of Minto	4667	13	8
21,223.319	.. Oxnam	10,526	0	8
27,983.658	.. Southdean	8922	3	3
	DISTRICT OF KELSO.			
10,097.309	Amount of parish of Eckford	10,751	4	11
3919.724	.. Ednam	8136	19	5
15,107.271	.. Hounam	6907	12	9
5542.053	.. Kelso	32,848	14	4
6427.823	.. Linton	7717	12	3
2912.959	.. Makerstoun	5001	1	0
22,518.072	.. Morebattle	13,013	18	11
7924.785	.. Roxburgh	10,441	3	8
4202.171	.. Smailholm .	5492	3	11

* Edgerston has been parochially separated from the parish of Jedburgh since 1851.

Acres.	Parishes.	Amount.
	DISTRICT OF KELSO—*continued*.	
8731.643	. Sprouston	£13,064 1 5
2803.898	.. Stitchel	4196 5 6
6036.220	.. Yetholm	8080 12 3
	DISTRICT OF MELROSE.	
26,058.286 {	Amount of parish of Melrose	40,091 2 2
	.. Galashiels	2253 6 0
7682.818	.. Bowden	7543 17 0
3198.541	.. St Boswells	6403 12 8
4494.732	.. Maxton	5431 4 0
6707.429	.. Lilliesleaf	6923 16 3
	DISTRICT OF HAWICK.	25,115 18 0
6203.282	Amount of parish of Hawick	8271 0 10
3,1559.618	.. Teviothead	8805 10 6
18,352.870	.. Cavers	11,428 2 2
6222.861	.. Kirkton	3065 13 3
8417.142	.. Ashkirk	3788 4 0
8820.112	.. Wilton	13,199 8 5
1358.115	.. Selkirk (detached)	1384 10 0
18,038 223	.. Roberton do.	6318 7 11
	DISTRICT OF CASTLETON.	
68,152.437	Amount of Parish of Castleton	17,218 0 0
425,615.383	Exclusive of Railways.	£381,597 7 4

LIEUTENANCY.

Lord-Lieutenant—His Grace the Duke of Buccleuch and Queens
berry, 1841.

Vice-Lieutenant—Sir John Pringle, Bart. 1812.

DEPUTY-LIEUTENANTS.

Elliot, R. K., of Harwood and Clifton, created 1848.	Polwarth, Lord, 1826.
Eliott, Sir W. F., of Stobs and Wells, Bart., 1817.	Rutherfurd, W. O., of Edgerston, 1848.
Kerr, William S., of Chatto, 1848.	Scott, Sir Wm., of Ancrum, Bart., M.P.
Lockhart, A. E., of Borthwickbrae, 1848.	Sprot, Mark, of Riddell, 1848.
Ogilvie, Wm., of Chesters, 1827.	Tod, T., of Drygrange, 1848.
	Waldie, John, of Hendersyde, 1831

Clerk of Lieutenancy—William Millar, solicitor, Jedburgh.

PARLIAMENTARY REPRESENTATION.

Member for the County—Sir William Scott of Ancrum, Bart., 1859.
Constituency for the County, 1578.

Member for the Burgh of Jedburgh, (forming part of the Haddington
District of Burghs)—Sir Henry Robert Ferguson Davie of Creedy,
Bart., 1857.

Constituency for the Burgh, 178.

Auditor of Election Expenses for Roxburghshire—George Rutherford,
Sheriff-Clerk, Jedburgh.

SHERIFF AND COMMISSARY COURT.

Sheriff-Principal — His Grace the Duke of Buccleuch, the Lord-
Lieutenant of the County.

Sheriff-Depute and Commissary—William Oliver Rutherfurd.

Sheriff-Substitutes and Commissary-Deputes—Francis Russell, and
William Deans.

Sheriff-Clerk—George Rutherford.

Sheriff-Clerk-Depute—James Oliver.

Commissary-Clerk—William Elliot.

Procurators-Fiscal—James Stevenson and James C. Stevenson.

The Sheriff-Court for the County, and the Commissary Court are
held at Jedburgh on Monday and Thursday of each week, during
Sessions.

PLACES AND DAYS OF MEETING OF THE COURTS UNDER THE SMALL DEBT ACT.

The Small Debt Courts are held at Jedburgh on Thursday (weekly),
during sessions, and in vacation, on days fixed by the Sheriff;
George Rutherford, Sheriff-clerk, and James Oliver, Depute-clerk.
Kelso, second Tuesdays of February, April, June, August, October,
and December; Adam Woodman Main, Depute-clerk. Hawick,
first Tuesdays of February, April, June, August, October, and
December; Charles Kirk, Depute-clerk. Melrose, first Fridays of
February, May, August, and November; Allan Freer and Thomas
J. Dunn, Depute-clerks. The Clerks above named are the only
issuers of summonses.

COMMISSIONERS OF SUPPLY.

Convener of the County—William O. Rutherfurd of Edgerston.

Aitchison, William, Brieryhill	Boyd, John, of Maxpoffle.
Antrobus, Sir E., of Rutherford.	Brewster, Sir David, of Allerly.
Antrobus, J., yr. of Rutherford.	Brunton, James, of Hiltonshill.
Bailie, the Eldest, of Hawick, for the time being.	Brunton, W., of Ladhope.
Bailies, the Three, of Jedburgh, for the time being.	Buccleuch and Queensberry, His Grace the Duke of.
Balfour, Charles, of Newton Don.	Buchan, Earl of.
Binning, Lord.	Cardross, Lord.
Black, William, Netherwells.	Carre, Walter R., of Caverse Carre.
Borthwick, John, of Crookston.	Clark, William, Langhaugh.
Boston, Thomas, Gattonside	Clark, William, the younger.
Boyd, John B., of Cherrytrees.	Cleghorn, Geo., of Weens.
	Chisholme, John S., of Stirches.

Cochrane, Alex., of Ashkirk.
Cotesworth, R., of Cowden-knowes.
Cotesworth, Robt., yr. of Cowden-knowes.
Currie, William, of Linthill.
Curle, Alex., of East Morriston.
Dalkeith, Earl of.
Dalrymple, James, of Wester-Langlee.
Dalrymple, General John.
Darling, Robert, Broomlands, factor for the Duke of Roxburghe.
Darling, James S., Kelso, factor for Mr Baird of Stitchell.
Dickson, Wm. R., of Alton.
Dickson, Jas., of Chatto.
Dickson, A., yr. of Chatto.
Dickson, Sir W., Bart., of Sydenham.
Douglas, C., of Chesterhouse.
Douglas, Sir G. H. S., of Springwood Park.
Douglas, James, of Cavers.
Eliott, Sir William Francis, Bart. of Stobs and Wells.
Eliott, W. F. A., the younger.
Elliot, Robert Kerr, of Clifton.
Elliot, William C., younger of Clifton.
Elliot, Robert, of Redheugh.
Elliot, Robert, yr. of Redheugh
Elliot, Wm., manufacturer, Hawick.
Elliot, Walter, of Wolflee.
Elliot, John, of Binks.
Elliot, William of Benrig.
Erskine, James of Shielfield.
Factor, The, for the Earl of Minto.
Factor, The, for the Hon. Walter Elliot of Wolflee.
Factor, The, for the Earl and Countess of Home.
Factor, The, for the Marquis of Lothian.
Fair, J. S. E., of Langlee.
Fair, R. S. E., the younger.
Fairholme, Wm., of Chapel.
Freer, Allan, solicitor, Melrose.
Gibson, John, jun., Edinburgh.
Gifford, Earl of.
Grieve, Robert.
Grieve, Wm., Branxholmpark.
Haddington, The Earl of.
Hamilton, Sir H. D., Bart., of North Berwick.
Hay, George W., of Whiterig.

Henderson, David, of Abbotrule.
Hilson, Geo., sen., manufacturer, Jedburgh.
Home, G. H. M. B., of Softlaw.
Hopkins, John C.
Horne, Donald, W.S.
Humble, George, of Old Graden.
James, James, of East Samieston.
Jardine, James, of Larriston.
Jardine, John, of Thorlieshope.
Karr, Rev. J. S., of Kippielaw.
Karr, George, yr., Kippielaw.
Keir, William, of Whithaugh.
Ker, William, of Gateshaw.
Ker, Gilbert, the younger.
Kerr, Lord Henry.
Kerr, Robert D., Edinburgh.
Kerr, Thomas, of Craighouse.
Kerr, William Scott, of Chatto.
Laidlaw, Thomas, manufacturer, Hawick.
Lang, John, of Overwells.
Lauderdale, Lord.
Lees, Robert, of Fens.
Lockhart, Allan Eliott, of Borthwickbrae.
Lockhart, Allan Eliott, younger.
Lothian, Most Noble the Marquis of.
Maconochie, R. B. of Gattonside.
Macdonald, William, of Ormiston.
Mein, Andrew W., of Hunthill.
Mercer, Adam, of Blainslie.
Milne, Nichol, of Whitehill.
Milne, Nicol, of Faldonside.
Minto, The Right Hon. the Earl of.
Mitchell, Alexander, of Stow.
Murray, John N., of Philiphaugh.
Nixon, William, manufacturer, Hawick.
Ogilvie, William, of Chesters.
Ogilvie, Thomas E., younger, of Chesters.
Oliver, George, writer, Hawick.
Oliver, John, of Bush.
Oliver, Robert, of Lochside.
Oliver, William, of Langraw.
Ord, John, of Muirhouselaw.
Ormiston, Wm. T., of Glenburnhall
Panton, William, of Edenbank.
Paton, John, of Crailing.
Paton, James, the younger.
Paterson, Adam, Whitelee.
Pennycook, Peter, of Bewlie.
Plummer, C. S., of Sunderlandhall.

Polwarth, Lord.
Pott, George, of Todrig.
Pott, Gideon, of Knowsouth.
Pringle, David, of Wilton Lodge.
Pringle, William, Edinburgh.
Provost, the, of Jedburgh, for the time being.
Pringle, James, of Torwoodlee.
Purves, John, of Whitehouse.
Rea, Charles, of Halterburn.
Richardson, John, of Kirklands.
Riddell, George H., of Muselee.
Robison, Ebenezer, thongmaker, Hawick.
Robson, Charles, Kelso, factor for John Waldie of Hendersyde.
Roxburghe, His Grace the Duke of.
Roxburghshire, Sheriff of, for the time being.
Roxburghshire, Sheriff-substitute of, for the time being.
Rutherford, G., of Sunnyside.
Rutherford, G., writer, Jedburgh, factor for Lord Somerville and Lord Stratheden.
Rutherfurd, Henry, Fairnington
Rutherfurd, Robert, Honeyfield.
Rutherfurd, W. O., of Edgerston.
Rutherfurd, W. A. O., yr. of Edgerston.
Rutherford, W., Crailing Tofts.
Sanderson, H., manufacturer, Galashiels.
Sanderson, William, Galashiels.
Scott, Archibald, of Howcleuch.
Scott, Admiral Geo., of Wooden.
Scott, Andrew, of Ettrickbank.
Scott, Charles, Sinlatie, factor for the Trustees of Mr. Scott of Wauchhope.
Scott, J. S. E. of Riccalton.
Scott, James R. Hope, Abbotsford.
Scott, James R., of Ashtrees.
Scott, John, of Upper Samieston.
Scott, John C., of Sinton.
Scott, Robert, of Raeburn.
Scott, Thomas R., of Newton
Scott, Thomas, of Graden.
Scott, Sir Wm., Bart., of Ancrum.
Scott, W. E. of Peel.
Scott, William, yr. of Ancrum.
Sime, James, manufacturer, Galashiels.
Simson, Charles, of Threepwood.

Simson, Charles.
St Clair, Hon. J., of Stonedge.
St Clair, Chas., younger of Stonedge.
Smith, James, Edinburgh.
Smail, W., Catshawhill.
Somerville, Lord.
Somerville, James, of Charlesfield.
Sprot, Mark, of Riddell.
Sprot, John, the younger.
Stratheden and Campbell, Lord, of Hartrigge.
Swan, Robert, Kelso, factor for the Earl of Haddington; And. Wauchope of Niddrie; and G. H. Munro Binning Home.
Tait, William, of Priorbank.
Tod, Thomas, of Drygrange.
Thomson, John, Edinburgh.
Thomson, James, of Merrick.
Thomson, Rev. John, Hawick.
Thomson, William, of Kaimflat.
Treasurer, the, of Jedburgh, for the time being.
Tulloh, John, of Arthurshiel.
Tulloh, Capt. Thomas, of Elliston.
Turnbull, A. O., Writer, Jedburgh, Factor for J. G. Henderson of Abbotrule.
Turnbull, William, of Merrylaw.
Turnbull, Robert, yr., Merrylaw.
Turnbull, Thomas, of Fenwick.
Turnbull, Robert, Galalaw.
Tweeddale, Marquis of.
Waldie, John, of Hendersyde.
Walker, James, of Fodderlie.
Ward, Lord.
Warrender, Sir John, Bart., of Lochend.
Watson, William, of Burnhead.
Watson, Wm. S., yr. of Burnhead.
Wauchope, Andrew, of Niddrie.
Wilson, Adam, Farmer, Midshiels.
Wilson, George, manufacturer, Hawick.
Wilson, John, of Otterburn.
Wilson, John, manufacturer, Hawick.
Wilson, Walter, manufacturer, Hawick.
Williamson, Wm., of Larretburn.
Williamson, Robert, of Kerfield.
Wilson, John, Buccleuch Street, Hawick.

Head Court of Commission of Supply held first Tuesday of Oct., at Jedburgh.

Clerk of Supply—James Stevenson, solicitor, Jedburgh
Collector of County Rates—Gideon Pott of Knowsouth.

JUSTICES IN THE COMMISSION OF THE PEACE FOR THE COUNTY OF ROXBURGH.

Walter Francis, Duke of Buccleuch and Queensberry.
James H., Duke of Roxburghe.
George, Marquis of Tweeddale.
Wm. S. R., Marquis of Lothian.
Henry W., Earl of Dalkeith.
Jas. H. R., Marquis of Bowmont.
William, Earl of Minto.
George, Earl of Haddington.
Anthony, Earl of Lauderdale.
George, Earl of Gifford.
Henry Francis, Lord Polwarth.
William Fred., Lord Campbell.
Walter H., Master of Polwarth.
Lord Henry John M. D. Scott.
Lord Walter C. M. D. Scott.
George, Lord Binning.
Lord Schomberg Henry Kerr.
Kenelin, Lord Somerville.
Charles, Lord Sinclair.
James, Master of Sinclair.
The Hon. Francis Scott.
Sir W. F. Eliott of Stobbs, Bart.
Sir W. Scott of Ancrum, Bart.
Sir John Pringle, Bart.
Sir John Warrender of Whitton, Bart.
Sir George Henry Scott Douglas of Springwood Park, Bart.
Sir Wm. Dickson, Bart. of Sydenham.
Sir E. Antrobus of Rutherford.
Sir William G. H. T., Fairfax, Bart.
Sir David Brewster of Allerly.
Thomas Eliott, yr. of Redheugh.
James S. E. Fair of Langlee.
Robert S. E. Fair, yr. of Langlee.
William Fairholme of Chapel.
George Fairholme of Old Melrose.
David Henderson of Abbotrule.
George W. Hay of Whiterig.
George H. M. B. Home of Softlaw.
James James of Samieston.
James Jardine of Larriston.
James Johnstone of Alva.

William Ker of Gateshaw.
William Keir of Whithaugh.
William Scott Kerr of Chatto.
A. E. Lockhart of Borthwickbrae.
William E. Lockhart, yr. of Borthwickbrae.
William Macdonald of Ormiston.
Ed. H. Maxwell of Teviotbank.
Nicol Milne of Faldonside.
Alexander Mitchell of Stow.
Andrew W. Mein of Huntill.
John Meiklam of Gladswood.
John Murray, Kersknowe.
John Murray of Uplaw.
John N. Murray of Whitmuir.
Robert B. Maconochie of Gattonside House.
William Ogilvie of Chesters.
Thomas Ogilvie, yr. of Chesters.
Robert Oliver of Blakelaw.
John Ord of Muirhouselaw.
William T. Ormiston of Glenburnhall.
William Paterson of Glendearg.
Adam Paterson of Whitelee.
John Paton of Crailing.
Thomas Paton, yr. of Crailing.
George Pott of Todrig.
Gideon Pott of Knowsouth
Chas. S. Plummer of Sunderland Hall.
James Pringle of Torwoodlee.
James Pringle, yr. of Newhall.
David Pringle of Carrubber.
George Pringle of Buckholm.
David Pringle of Wilton Lodge.
John Richardson of Kirklands.
Major Rowland Richardson, yr. of Kirklands.
Charles Balfour of Newton-Don.
George Baird of Stitchell.
John B. Boyd of Cherrytrees.
Major-General William Carre Riddell of Camieston.
Walter Robert Carre of Caverse Carre.

Thos. Riddell Carre, yr. of Caverse Carre.
Captain Clark, Commander, R.N.
Jas. A. Clark, yr. of Langhaugh.
John S. Chisholme of Stirches.
William Currie of Linthill.
Robert Cotesworth of Sorrowlessfield.
Robert Cotesworth, yr. of Sorrowlessfield.
George Cleghorn of Weens.
Alexander Cochrane of Ashkirk.
James Connell of Conheath.
James Dalrymple of Langlee.
James Dickson, of Nether Chatto.
Archibald Dickson, yr. of Nether Chatto.
James Douglas of Cavers.
Christopher Douglas of Chesterhouse.
Robert K. Elliot of Harwood and Clifton.
William C. Elliot. yr. of Clifton.
Walter Elliot of Wolflee.
John Elliot of Binks, Burnmouth.
William F. Elliot, yr. of Stobs.
Robert Elliot of Redheugh.
Geogre W. H. Riddell of Muselee.
W. O. Rutherford of Edgerston.
William Alex. Oliver Rutherfurd, yr. of Edgerston.
Henry Rutherfurd of Fairnington.
Archibald Scott of Howcleuch.
William Scott, yr. of Ancrum.
John Corse Scott of Sinton.
Rear-Admiral George Scott of Wooden.
James R. H. Scott of Abbotsford.
Hugh Scott of Gala.

Robert Scott of Raeburn.
Thomas Scott of Graden.
Thomas Robson Scott of Newton.
James Robson Scott of Ashtrees.
Charles Simson of Threepwood.
Mark Sprot of Riddell.
John Sprot, yr. of Riddell.
Thomas Tod of Drygrange.
John Tulloh of Arthurshiel.
Thomas Tulloh of Elliston.
John Waldie of Hendersyde.
William Watson of Burnhead.
Wm. S. Watson, yr. of Burnhead.
John Wilson of Otterburn.
Walter Wilson, Hawick.
George Warrender, yr. of Whitton.
Andrew Wauchope of Yetholm.
William J. Wauchope, yr. of Yetholm.
The Sheriff-Depute for the County of Roxburgh, for the time being.
The Sheriff-Sub. for the County of Roxburgh, for the time being.
The Provost of Jedburgh, for the time being.
The Provost of Hawick, for the time being.
The Senior Bailie of Hawick, for the time being.
The Junior Bailie of Hawick, for the time being.
The Chief Magistrate of Kelso, for the time being.
The Chief Magistrate of Galashiels, for the time being.
The Senior Bailie of Jedburgh, for the time being.
William Tait of Priorbank.

Clerk to the Justices—James Stedman, solicitor, Jedburgh.

DEPUTES.

HAWICK—C. M. Wilson, solicitor.   KELSO—Wm. Robson, solicitor.
MELROSE—Thomas J. Dunn, solicitor.

PROCURATOR-FISCALS.

HAWICK—J. Carmichael, solicitor. | KELSO—Chas. Robson, solicitor.
JEDBURGH—Jas. Stevenson, solicitor. | MELROSE—Alexander Rutherford, writer, Galashiels.

Quarter Sessions of the Justices are held at Jedburgh first Tuesdays of March, May, and August, and last Tuesday of October. The Justice of Peace Court for the District of Jedburgh, is held there on the first Tuesday of every month; for the District of Kelso, at that burgh, on the first Friday of every month; for the District of Hawick, at that burgh, on the first Thursday of every month; for the District of Melrose, at that town, on the first Saturday of every month.

PROPERTY AND INCOME TAX COMMISSIONERS.

GENERAL COMMISSIONERS.

The Sheriff-Depute of the County.
The Sheriff-Substitute.
John Ord of Muirhouselaw.
Gideon Pott of Knowsouth.
Wm. A. Oliver Rutherfurd, yr. of Edgerston.
James S. E. Fair of Langlee.
John Paton of Crailing.
Hon. Walter Elliot of Wolflee.
R. K. Elliot of Clifton.
John B. Boyd, of Cherrytrees.
Archd. Dickson, yr. of Chatto.
Robert Darling, Kelso.
Bobert Swan, Kelso.
Robt. Oliver of Lochside.

Wm. Clark of Langhaugh.
James Dalrymple of Langlee.
James Pringle of Torwoodlee
Charles Simson of Threepwood.
Thomas Tod of Drygrange.
Alex. Curle of East Morriston.
W. Currie of Linthill.
Wm. Ogilvie of Chesters.
George Pott of Todrig.
Allan E. Lockhart of Borthwick-brae.
Wm. Scott Watson, yr. of Burn-grove.
W. J. Macdonald of Powderhall.
J. S. Chisholme of Stirches.

COMMISSIONER FOR SUPPLYING VACANCIES.

John Wilson, Esq. of Otterburn.

ADDITIONAL COMMISSIONERS.

James Stevenson, Jedburgh.
A. W. Mein of Hunthill.
Alex. F. Douglass, Jerdonfield.
Andw. Scott, Glendouglas.
John Dudgeon, Spylaw.
James Roberton, Kelso.
Js. Tait of Langrigg, W.S., Kelso.

George Rutherford of Sunnyside.
William Tait of Priorbank.
William Park, Abbotsmeadow.
W. Grieve, Branxholm Park.
Ephraim Selby, Hassendeanbank.
T. Usher, Courthill.

Clerk—James Erskine, solicitor, Melrose.
Assistant-Clerk—Alex. Curle, solicitor, Melrose.
Inspector—Alex. Paterson, Edinburgh.
Surveyor—Edward Henderson, Melrose.

ASSESSORS.

JEDBURGH—Walter Clark.
HAWICK—T. Purdom, solicitor.

KELSO—A. Elliot, Stamp Office.
MELROSE—T. J. Dunn, solicitor.

The Commissioners of Supply are Commissioners under the Assessed Tax Act in all the Counties.

POLICE COMMITTEE OF ROXBURGHSHIRE,

Under 20 and 21 Vict. cap. 72.

Chairman—William Oliver Rutherfurd, Esq. of Edgerston.

The Lord Lieutenant of the County.
The Sheriff-Depute of the County, or in his absence, the Sheriff-substitute.
Sir Wm. Scott, of Ancrum, Bart.
John Paton, Esq. of Crailing.
James James, Esq. of Samieston.
John Ord, Esq. of Muirhouselaw.
William Ogilvie, Esq. of Chesters.
J. S. Chisholme, Esq. of Stirches.
The Provost of Jedburgh.

William Watson of Burnhead.
W. A. O. Rutherfurd, yr. of Edger-ston.
The Right Hon. Lord Polwarth.
Robt. Oliver, Esq. of Lochside.
William Clark, Esq. of Lang-haugh.
Thomas Tod, Esq. of Drygrange.
Sir George H. S. Douglas, Bart. of Springwood Park.
R. K. Elliot, Esq. of Clifton.

Clerk—James Stevenson, solicitor, Jedburgh.
Chief Constable—James M'Master, Jedburgh.
Superintendent—Alexander Porter, Hawick.

SERGEANTS OF CONSTABLES.

Jedburgh—Arch. Hogarth
Kelso—Robert Ainslie.

Hawick—John Ainslie.
Melrose—M. Oliver.

PRISON BOARD.

CHAIRMAN.

William Oliver Rutherfurd of Edgerston.

Robert Kerr Elliot of Clifton.
Sir Wm. Scott, Bart., M.P.
John Ord of Muirhouselaw.
Jas. S. E. Fair of Langlee.
The Right Hon. Lord Polwarth.
John Paton of Crailing.

The Right Hon. the Earl of Minto.
Andrew Scott, Glendouglas.
The Provost of Jedburgh.
The Provost of Hawick.
The Senior Magistrate of Kelso
David Pringle of Wilton Lodge.

The Sheriff-Depute of the County, and in his absence the Sheriff-Substitute being ex-officio members of the Board, in terms of the Prisons' Administration Act.

Clerk and Treasurer—Archibald Oliver Turnbull, writer, Jedburgh.

Governor of Jedburgh Castle—Charles Sprunt.
    ,,   Hawick Prison—Michael Anderson.
    ,,   Kelso Prison—George Lamb.
Sheriff Officer at Hawick—John Guild.
    ,,   Jedburgh—Geo. Robertson
    ,,   Kelso—Alexander Brown.
    ,,   Melrose—Angus Sutherland.

INLAND REVENUE.

Stamp and Tax Department, Distributor of, and Collector—Archibald Jerdon, Jedburgh.

SUB-DISTRIBUTORS AND COLLECTORS OF TAXES.

Hawick—Charles Kirk, solicitor.
Kelso—Alex. Elliot, Stamp and Tax Office.
Melrose—Thomas Murray.

Surveyor of Taxes, and Land Valuation Assessor for the County, and for the Burgh of Jedburgh—Edward Henderson, Melrose.

EXCISE DEPARTMENT.

Collector—J. Luckie, Haddington.   Supervisor—B. F. Dunn, Kelso
Officer at Jedburgh—W. E. Cheese.
    ,,   Hawick—John Brett.
    ,,   Kelso—Wm. Wight.
    ,,   Melrose—James Deans.

F

The following explanations are necessary for the accurate understanding of the statements connected with the Census in the following lists :—

CENSUS DEFINITION OF A FAMILY.

" Without entering into the question of what constitutes a Family, it may be mentioned that at the taking of the Census it was directed that all who *boarded* together in the same house should be considered as one family ; but that *lodgers*, who are *not boarders*, should be considered as separate families."

DEFINITION OF A HOUSE.

" A ' House' is defined by Johnson, and by all pure English writers and scholars, as 'a place of human abode,' 'a place where a man lives.' And in conformity with this, a ' HOUSE-HOLD ' is invariably defined as a ' Family living together ;' and a ' HOUSEHOLDER' as ' the master of a family.' Conform to this definition all our Acts of Parliament are drawn up."

" Not a little strange is it, therefore, to find that in taking the Census of the population, where for social, for sanitary, for political, and other purposes, it was deemed necessary that exact information of the number of Houses should be procured, the above definition has been departed from."

" The definition of a ' HOUSE' adopted for the Census of England, was ' *a distinct building* separated from others by party walls.' This definition was quite unintelligible in Scotland, where the whole houses of a street or square are built continuously, on an uniform plan, and in *flats*, so that from the outside it would be difficult to say where one house begins and another ends."

" If, therefore, the Returns for Scotland on this subject are utterly worthless, it must be understood that the blame lies not with the Scottish officials, for they were, against their better convictions, forced to accept the erroneous definition of a ' HOUSE ' which had been adopted for England in 1851, and re-imposed in 1861."

NUMBER OF ROOMS WITH WINDOWS.

" Perhaps one of the most important facts ascertained at the taking of the Census in 1861, was the Number of Rooms with Windows ; to the facts brought out by this inquiry, Social Reformers will look with the greatest eagerness and profit. The mere number of Houses, or even the number of Families or of Persons inhabiting them, gives no idea whatever of the house accommodation of the people."

" This Return was specially ordered for Scotland."

In the lists it will be found we make no mention of the number of *Houses* the parishes contain (the Return in this particular being valueless), but we have of the *window* privileges of its Families—a Return of much greater importance, and allowed in the main to be correct.

KELSO.

THE Parish of Kelso, situated in the north-eastern division of the county, is bounded on the north by Nenthorn in Berwickshire ; on the north-east by Ednam ; on the east by Sprouston, which intervenes between it and the English Border ; on the south-east by Eckford ; on the south-west by Roxburgh ; and on the west by Makerstoun and Smailholm ; and is beautifully placed on both sides of the river Tweed, which divides it into nearly two equal parts. The shape of the parish is nearly triangular ; its greatest length is about 5 miles, and its greatest breadth about 3 miles. Its area, according to the Ordnance Survey, is 5542 acres, sub-divided as follows :—5227¾ acres, land ; 158½ acres, water ; 102¼ acres, nearly, in public, and 19 acres, nearly, in private roads ; 34½ acres are occupied by railway.

" Seen from the eminences at a short distance, the parish appears to be part of an extensive and picturesque strath, but when viewed from the vicinity of the river, it presents the appearance of an amphitheatre, diversified in its outlines, intersected by two broad and noble rivers, and circled in the distance by a boundary of wooded heights." " The picturesque scenery about Kelso is too well known to require any description. It belongs, indeed, to the class of the beautiful rather than the romantic ; and its pleasing effect is due, not so much to the commanding character of any single object, as to the blending, combination, and harmony of the whole." In the country part of the parish cultivation is carried on on the most approved principles, and the surface is ornamented with beautiful plantations.

The Town of Kelso occupies a beautiful and extensive plain on the north bank of the Tweed, opposite the confluence of the Teviot with that river, and is surrounded on all sides by a delightful amphitheatre of wood-clad hills. The town is of great antiquity, and has been the scene of many memorable events,— its border situation having subjected it to continued warfare, attacks, and conflagrations. Kelso now consists of a spacious square or market place,* from which four handsome streets diverge in different directions ; there are also several minor streets and two other squares, smaller than the former, but containing a number of excellent houses. Being situated in the centre of a rich and fertile district, and itself the residence of a number of

* In Mitchell's " Newspaper Press Directory for 1864," Kelso market place is stated to be the finest in Scotland.

families in easy circumstances, who live in a style of considerable elegance, Kelso is a sort of provincial capital,* possessing numerous handsome shops, several of which would not be unworthy of the metropolis. There is a daily market for vegetables; a weekly (Friday) general and corn market (*see* Corn Exchange for further particulars), and during the winter and spring months a fortnightly (Monday) market for fat cattle and sheep (*see* Fairs), where a very extensive business is transacted. There are also very extensive fairs for the sale of ewes and cattle, and the hire and sale of tups in September (*see* Fair List for that month, and notices of the Kelso Fairs, pp. 73-74).

Kelso was one of the first provincial towns in Scotland to adopt the printing press, and the revival of the art of printing in Scotland was commenced in Kelso under James Ballantyne, where he printed the first edition of Sir Walter Scott's "Minstrelsy of the Scottish Border."

There are two newspapers published in the town—viz., the "Kelso Mail," twice a-week, and the "Kelso Chronicle," once a-week. There are two subscription libraries, the oldest and most extensive of which, the "Kelso Library," was established in 1750, and now contains a very valuable collection of about 8000 volumes; it occupies a handsome building on the Terrace, overlooking the river, and commands a most beautiful and extensive prospect. The other library, though inferior in extent, possesses a considerable collection of valuable works, in the various branches of literature. Attached to Kelso Library, fronting towards Roxburgh Street, is the "Tweedside Physical and Antiquarian Society's Museum," (*see* lists), an edifice of two storeys, of tasteful design and convenient arrangement. This society dates its origin in 1834, its object being "to promote the study of the natural history and antiquities of the district traversed by the Tweed and its tributaries, and to cause to be preserved, in a museum set apart for the purpose, whatever objects may be acquired, illustrative of these branches of science." The collection is now a large and valuable one, and is shown gratuitously on Mondays, Wednesdays, and Fridays.

The most striking object in Kelso is the venerable Abbey, founded by David I. in 1128; it is a noble specimen of the solid and majestic style of architecture called the Saxon or Early Norman. Admission within the burying-ground rails, the better to view the interior of the Abbey, can be had by applying to the sexton. A broken dangerous stair leads to the Abbey top, a

height of 91 feet. Near to the Abbey, and its fit companion for magnificence and beauty, is Kelso Bridge, built in 1803; it consists of five noble elliptical arches, each 72 feet span. The singular elegance of this bridge is the more fortunate, as its situation, when viewed from different directions, renders it the most prominent object in some of the finest landscapes on the Tweed. Connecting two banks, each remarkable for beauty, it forms the centre of a vast variety of pictures; and it affords a striking contrast and relief to the dark colour of the wooded scenery on either side. Rennie was the architect, and he is said to have made it his model for Waterloo Bridge (of which he was also the architect), across the Thames at London. The prospect from the Bridge is exceedingly beautiful, but perhaps a view still more admired is that from the Terrace, where the view comprehends the junction of the rivers Tweed and Teviot, with the river islet, around which their waters flow. Tradition, in its goblin legend, says, that the long mill cauld stretching above and below the islet, was built by Michael Scott the wizard, when "he bridled the Tweed with a curb of stone." The islet belongs to the town of Kelso, and in the summer it is used as a public bleaching and drying ground. But a scene unique in the district, is the walk, on a dark night, from Kelso Bridge along the river side to Maxwellheugh Mill, when the hoarse roar from Michael's *curb*, the splash from the neighbouring mills, and the "dark and deathlike flow" of the broad and rapid river, have a startling effect—greatly heightened if the river be in flood, and its darkness made visible, at intervals, by the faint lights from the Bridge and the town.

The outskirts of the town are dotted over with beautiful residences, of which foremost among them comes Floors Castle,* the seat of the Duke of Roxburghe, on the north bank of the Tweed, about a mile from the town. The grounds surrounding the house are finely laid out; and the gardens, lately finished, are unrivalled in the south of Scotland. They are open to the public every Wednesday, by card, procurable from Mr. Darling of the Bank of Scotland. Springwood Park, the mansion of Sir George H. Scott Douglas, Bart., is pleasantly situated on the south bank of the Teviot, where that river sweeps past the ruins of the ancient castle of Roxburgh; the gardens and woods here are beautifully laid out, the latter abounding with wild flowers to a more than ordinary extent. The gateway forming the main entrance into Springwood Park is very generally ad-

---

* It may give some idea of the central position of Kelso when we state that its radia of eight miles include two kingdoms, three counties, and twenty parishes. All these parishes are in the highest state of cultivation; and of eighteen of them, Kelso may be considered the market town and natural outlet.

* Floors Castle, a stately building but severely plain, was erected in 1718; the architect was Sir John Vanbrugh, the dramatist. Its grandeur was greatly enhanced and its plainness relieved by alterations under the direction of Mr. Playfair of Edinburgh, commenced in 1849 and carried on for some years. The name *Floors* is a common one in various parts of Scotland, and is applied to the flat parts of valleys.

mired. EDNAM HOUSE, the residence of Mrs. Robertson, stands conspicuously a little above Kelso Bridge on the north side. WOODEN HOUSE, the residence of Admiral Scott, occupies a conspicuous position on the south side of the Tweed, below the town. Near Wooden House is a romantic glen, in which, when there is water sufficient, a very pretty waterfall is produced. PINNACLEHILL is prettily situated on the summit of a rock, overhanging the Tweed (south side), a little below the Bridge. Through openings in the woods, which here fringe the banks of the river, some of the finest views of Kelso and the Bridge are to be had. ROSEBANK, a little beyond the town to the east, is celebrated as having been for some time the property and residence of Sir Walter Scott; and the tree which he here fitted up as an agreeable retreat for reading, still exists in a flourishing condition; it is an aged elm overhanging the Tweed.

For Hendersyde Park House—another place of note, within two miles of Kelso—*see* Ednam parish; for Newton-Don and the Falls of the Eden—within three miles—*see* Nenthorn parish; and for Stitchill and Stitchill House, *see* Stitchill parish.

At a short distance from the town, but in the neighbouring parish of Roxburgh, are the remains of Roxburgh Castle, already mentioned. A few shapeless pieces of wall, some of them of enormous thickness, bear witness to the former strength of the castle, and are all that remain of its magnificence and regal grandeur. From the old walls beautiful views of the vales of the Tweed and the Teviot are to be had; and from the high part of the road leading to the ruins from Teviot bridge is the best view of Floors Castle.

A great addition has lately been made to the beauty and amenity of Kelso, by Shedden Park, a gift presented by Mrs. Robertson of Ednam House, to the inhabitants, for their recreation and enjoyment; it is situated close upon the town to the east. The inhabitants, as a mark of their gratitude to the liberal and kind-hearted donor of the Park, have erected a handsome entrance gateway, with suitable inscription.

Besides the town of Kelso there is also in the parish the hamlet or suburb of Maxwellheugh, on the south side of the river and on the road to the Kelso station of the North British Railway, which is a very short distance beyond. The station, considering the amount of business done at it, is a very shabby building, and its distance from Kelso is a great inconvenience. A mile below Kelso the North British line from Edinburgh and the west joins that of the North-Eastern from Berwick and the south. The opposition between these two lines is the cause of considerable delay and inconvenience to passengers passing Kelso, but their competition has had a favourable effect, so far as Kelso and its neighbourhood are concerned, in lessening the price of coal, lime, etc.

Though, upon the whole, mild and genial, the climate of Kelso is scarcely so salubrious as might be expected. Hoar frost is prevalent during the winter months; and at almost all seasons the atmosphere is generally in an unfavourable condition with regard to extent of humidity; under ordinary states of the atmosphere, the free circulation of air is intercepted by the hills and woods encircling the town, while the gales from the west often sweep with great violence down the vale of the Tweed, hurting vegetation and damaging house property; and easterly winds are also common, especially in the spring when the blighting *haur* is by no means unfrequent. Still the comparatively humid atmosphere of the immediate vicinity agrees with many invalids: thus there are a number of persons living in Kelso, and enjoying a fair amount of good health throughout the year, who would have been much less comfortable and well in a drier, harder atmosphere. It is expected that the thorough system of sewerage, and water supply, at present being carried into execution, will have an ameliorating effect on the climate of the town.

Having said so much against and for the salubrity of Kelso, we now go out of our way a little to repel some splenetic accusations against the moral character of its inhabitants, which appeared in Fullerton's "Gazetteer of Scotland," a work, published in 1844, and ever since widely circulated by means of hawkers; and as it is the only Gazetteer of the country of any account, it has been, and is, largely employed as a book of reference.

The writer's remarks, which are written in an ill-natured spirit throughout, are especially objectionable when he refers to the Kelso Theatre (*see* No. 10 Horse Market), and to the residence of the French prisoners in the town during the French war. He asserts that the "Kelsonians" had with "great facility imbibed the spirit of French levity and dissipation," and that they had "become innoculated with French laxity of morals and fashionable follies." As a proof that the writer in the Gazetteer was both ignorant (wilfully or otherwise) and ill-natured when he penned his remarks about Kelso, we have only to draw attention to the panegyric of Dr. M'Culloch (now of Greenock), on the town and its inhabitants, in the "Statistical Account of Scotland," published four years before the Gazetteer appeared; and to state that at the date these remarks were published the Kelso Theatre had been converted to other uses for more than ten years, and from that time up till now even a strolling player has been almost unknown in the town; and of all the towns in the district Kelso is probably one in which *dissipated* amusements succeed as little as in any, and where the means of intellectual improvement, and recreation, and manly out-door sports, have been in most request and most steadily carried out.

Without doubt, the town, like all other towns, had and has

its vices and follies, but it should not on that account be gibbeted as a little Paris and have its worth ignored; but probably the best disproof of the aspersions, at least so far as the present standing of the town is concerned, is to be found in the number of its charitable, humane, and provident societies in the lists following.

The Tweed and Teviot abound in trout; and salmon, grilse, bull-trout, etc., ascend in immense numbers to spawn. The finest rod-fishings for salmon, on the Tweed, are in this parish. They belong to the Duke of Roxburghe, by whom they are preserved; but free grants to fish for salmon in the Teviot can be had by application to Mr. Darling, Broomlands, chamberlain to His Grace, or to Mr. Darling, banker, Kelso.

The trout fishing in the Teviot is all that could be desired by the angler, and it is open to everybody—streams plentiful and good—trouts ditto. For some miles above Kelso the Tweed is strictly preserved for trout, but below Kelso it is open as far as Carham: trouts plentiful and large.

Besides the Tweed and the Teviot, there are within easy distances from Kelso, the Eden and the Kale, first-rate trouting streams—*see* descriptive accounts of the parishes of Ednam, Yetholm and Morebattle.

During the season the Duke of Buccleuch's fox hounds regularly hunt the neighbourhood; and foxes are occasionally drawn in Springwood Park policy, in close proximity to Kelso, but there are no regular fox covers in the parish. Accommodation can readily be had by sportsmen either in the inns or private houses of Kelso.

Kelso General Holidays—First Wednesday of July, and New Year's Day.

Market Days—Friday, weekly (general and corn); Mondays, fortnightly (fat cattle, sheep, and cows). Buyers attend regularly from as far south as Manchester and Leeds, and from Edinburgh, and occasionally from Glasgow: the market, which takes place in the Square for cattle, the Knowes for sheep, and the Wood Market for cows, begins about 9 a.m., and is generally over by 11. The following is a statement of the quantity of fat stock despatched from the Kelso Railway Station, north and south, for the three months ending March 1864, which may give some idea of the quantity raised and sold in the locality:—

2719 cattle.   11,966 sheep.   224 pigs.

Great Hiring Days—Hinds, first Friday of March; Young Men and Women, first Fridays of May and November.

Kelso Horse Fair—second Friday of March; still the principal horse fair in the district, although greatly fallen off in importance, and at which a good show of valuable work horses are exposed, some hacks and a very few hunters, besides a large quantity of inferior animals. The animals sold are mostly draft—few or none being reared in the locality specially for sale; buyers attend from Edinburgh, Newcastle, and Aberdeen. A preliminary fair takes place on the first Friday of March, and a supplementary one on the third Friday, but the show of horses on both these occasions is comparatively small.

Kelso Wool Fair—second Friday of July. This fair, which makes so little stir in the town that to ordinary observers it would pass unnoticed, is one of great importance; at it the greater part of the Leicester wool grown in the district is sold, principally to buyers from the Yorkshire and other Midland manufacturing districts. Business generally begins in front of the Cross Keys about 2 p.m. and terminates about 4 (*see* St. Boswells' Fair).

St. James's Fair (on the Friars' Haugh on the Tweed, opposite Floors Castle, and situated in the parish of Roxburgh)—August 5th, or the Monday following if the 5th be a Sunday. St. James's is now almost entirely a pleasure fair, where a crowd of people assemble to eat gingerbread and drink ale and whisky. A little real business is done in hiring shearers, and settling wool and manure accounts: a few old cows and secondary horses are also sold. The burgh of Jedburgh shares the right of superiority over the fair; the provost of Jedburgh and senior bailie of Kelso conjointly hold a court during its continuance, and take cognizance of offences. Of the dues drawn, one-third goes to the burgh of Jedburgh and two-thirds to the Duke of Roxburghe. The origin of St. James's Fair is lost in obscurity; and although now of very little real importance, it, till the beginning of the present century, had for an indefinite period held the most important place as a *general* fair in the south of Scotland; and it is still recollected as a great place for the sale of linen, cheese, wool, ready-made clothes, and shoes, and, to a smaller extent, of hats, and of books by auction; while for the sale of sheep, cattle, and horses, it ranked next to St. Boswells. The only branch of its general trade which seems to have kept its place is the sale of crockery by the gipsies, who, by use and wont, occupy their portion of the fair ground for some days both before and after the event. (*See* St. Boswells Fair.)

The *September Sale of Leicester and Half-Bred Tups* is the largest of its kind in the kingdom, and at it animals are purchased for the improvement of stock, not only in the other parts of Great Britain, but in Ireland, Australia, New Zealand, and the Continent. (For particulars of this sale, *see* notice of the "Union Agricultural Society" in the lists.)

Lean Cattle and Draft Ewe Market (held on a field near the railway station, generally on Spylaw farm)—24th September, or the Saturday preceding if the date be a Sunday [the object of this being to keep off the Jedburgh Rood Day Fair, which falls on the 25th]; established by the Kelso Farmers' Club (Mr. R. Swan, Kelso, secretary) so lately as 1854. At the market of 1863 the following stock was exposed for sale:—

990 Cattle.   157 *score* Sheep.   170 Calves.

This fair is found to be of great convenience to the locality and its importance is increasing.

According to the census of 1861, the population of the town of Kelso (within the burgh boundaries, which include Maxwellheugh), was 4309; of the parish (including the town), 5192. According to the same census the parish contained 1264 families, one of whom lived in a house without windows; 369 in houses of one window, and the same number in houses of two windows; leaving 525, or rather more than two-fifths (a very high average compared with the other parishes in the district or Scotland generally) living in houses of three or more windows.

Assessed property in the parish in 1863-4, £32,848 : 14 : 4.

The largest landed-proprietor in the parish is His Grace the Duke of Roxburghe, who is generally resident at Floors. The other resident landed-proprietors are Sir George H. S. Douglas, Bart., of Springwood Park, and Rear-Admiral Scott of Wooden. The principal non-resident proprietors are:—Walter Macmillan Scott of Wauchope (minor—*see* Hobkirk parish); Admiral Sir William Dickson of Sydenham; John Waldie, Esq., of Hendersyde Park (*see* Ednam parish); George Home Binning Home, of Softlaw (Argaty, Doune, Perthshire); Governors of George Wattson's Hospital [Merchant Company Edinburgh], of Spylaw; Governors of Merchant Maiden Hospital [Merchant Company, Edinburgh] of Ladyrig.

Superior of Kelso—Duke of Roxburghe.

MAGISTRATES AND COUNCIL.

The Government of the Town is under the New Police Act of 25 and 26 Victoria, cap. 101.

Jas. Stormonth Darling, Esq., Chief Magistrate.
George Craig, Esq., and James Johnston, Esq., Junior Magistrates.

COMMISSIONERS OF POLICE.

Bridge Street Ward:—
James Tait (Edenside).
Richard Porteous.
James Johnston.

Horse Market Ward:—
George Craig.
John Kennedy.
Robert Rutherfurd (Paradise.)

Wood Market Ward:—
James S. Darling.
Wm. Mein.
John Bulman.

Roxburgh Street Ward:—
A. W. Robson.
Archibald Hervey.
Charles Robson.

Robert Curry, Clerk; John Guthrie, Treasurer and Collector; Wm. Robson, Procurator-Fiscal; John Moscrip, Superintendent of Police. George Lamb, Jailor   George Boag and James Kerr, Policemen.

Police rates, which include charges for laying down an extensive system of sewerage, 1s. 3d. per £.

An extensive system of water supply is at present being laid down.

JUSTICES OF THE PEACE.

Those marked thus (*) are Resident in the Parish: the others are non-resident but attend the Courts regularly.

*His Grace the Duke of Roxburghe	R. K. Elliot, Esq. of Clifton.
John B. Boyd, Esq. of Cherrytrees.	W. S. Kerr, Esq. of Chatto.
	Dr John Murray, Kersknowe.
*Sir George Henry Scott Douglas, Bart. of Springwood Park.	R. Oliver, Esq., of Lochside.
	*Admiral Scott of Wooden.
Jas. Robson Scott, Esq., Belford.	James S. Darling, Esq., Kelso.

COURTS.

POLICE COURTS are held as occasion may require.
JUSTICE OF PEACE COURTS are held on first Wednesday of each month.
SHERIFF SMALL DEBT COURTS are held on the second Tuesdays of February, April, June, August, October, and December.

PUBLIC OFFICES, &c.

Billet Master—John Moscrip, 28 Roxburgh Street.
Burial Grounds, Custodier of—Thomas Aitchison, Bowmont Street.
Heritors' Clerk—Thomas Aitchison, Bowmont Street.
Inland Revenue (Excise) Office, *Cross Keys*, Market Place—W. Wight, Roxburgh Street, Officer; Barclay F. Dunn, Kelso, Supervisor.
Inland Revenue, Collector of—Alex. Elliot; Office, Wood Market.
Justice of the Peace Clerk Depute—William Robson; Office, Square.
Medical Officer and Public Vaccinator—Dr. Hamilton, Roxburgh St.
Nuisances, Inspector of—Robert Rutherford, Bridge Street.
Police Assessment, Collector of,—John Guthrie, Roxburgh Street.
Poor, Inspector of—Alexander Morrison; Office, Horse Market.
Poor, Sub-Inspector—Thomas Aitchison, Bowmont Street.
Poor's Rates, Collector and Treasurer—Charles Robson, Bridge St.
Procurator-Fiscal for Kelso District—Charles Robson, Bridge Street.
Property and Income Tax, Assessor of—Alex. Elliot, Wood Market.
Road Trustees' Office, Bridge Street—Smiths & Robson, Clerks.
Registrar of Births, Marriages, and Deaths—Walter Hilson; Office, Maxwellheugh.
Sub-Registrar of   do.   do.   Thomas Aitchison, Kelso.
Session Clerk and Kirk Treasurer—Walter Hilson, Maxwellheugh.
Sexton, Town-Crier, and Customs' Collector—James Allan, Ragged School Close, Roxburgh Street.
Sheriff-Clerk Depute—Adam Woodman Main, Maxwell Place.
Sheriff-Officer—Alexander Brown, 25 Bridge Street.
Stamps and Taxes, Distributor and Collector of—Alexander Elliot, Wood Market.
Stamps and Taxes, Surveyor of—Edward Henderson, Melrose.
Statute Labour, Collector of—Charles Robson, Bridge Street.
Town Treasurer—John Guthrie, Roxburgh Street.
Union Agricultural Society, Bridge Street—Robert Curry, Sec.
Works, Master of—William Clazy, Knowes.

POST OFFICE (Wood Market).

Postmaster—James Lorimer Romanes, who attests this List.
Town Deliverers—James Allan, James Tait.

ARRIVALS AND DESPATCHES OF MAILS, &c., 1864

POSTS.	Box Closes for Despatch.	Arrival.	Delivery Commences.	SUNDAY.	
				Box Closes for Despatch	Arrival.
Edinburgh and North . {	9.40a 2.55p 6.50p	9.37a 6.5 p	about 10.45a 6.30p	} 4.55p	10.26a
London, England, Berwick .	2.30p	10.10a	10.45a	} 6.30p	6.0 p
Do. Do. Do. .	6.30p	*8.25p	8.40p		
Coldstream . . . {	9.20a 6.30p	10.10a 8 25p	10.45a 8.40p	} 6.30p	6.0 p
Galashiels, Melrose, & Hawick {	7.15a 2.55p	9.37a 6.5 p	10.45a 6.30p	} 6.55p	10.26a
Jedburgh . . . {	7.15a 2.55p	9.37a 6.5 p	10.45a 6.30p	} 6.55p	10.26a
St. Boswells	2.55p	6.5 p	6.30p	4.55p	10.26a
Heiton, Kirkbank, & Crailing	5.45a	4.30p	6.30p	5.45a	12 n
Makerstoun, Smailholm, Ednam	5.45a	4.0 p	6.30p		
Holefield, Stitchel, Sprouston, } Hume, and Hadden . .	10.0a	4.0 p	6.30p	No Despatch.	No Arrival.
Yetholm, Morebattle, Hownam	10.0a	9.0 a	10.45a		
Nenthorn and Gordon .	10.0a	9.0 a	10.45a	12.30p	10.30a

Birgham Letters are sent to Coldstream.

Letters may be posted in the late letter box ten minues after box closing by attaching an extra stamp.

RECEIVING PILLAR BOXES.

Roxburgh Street—Collected at 7 and 8.50 a.m , 2, 3.50, and 5.50 p.m.
Kelso Ry. Station .. 8 a.m., 3 and 5.30 p.m.

On Sunday the office is open from 12.30 till 1.30 p.m. A delivery takes place over the town between half-past 12 and 2 o'clock p.m. Money Order Office open every day from 9 a.m. till 6 p.m.

* When the mail arrives at the Post Office at 8.25 p.m., the delivery takes place the same evening.

POST RUNNERS.

Heiton, Kirkbank, and Crailing—James Tait, jun.
Smailholm and Makerstoun—John Mather.
Sprouston and Hadden—Ralph Wright.
Stitchel and Hume—George Fairbairn.
Holefield and Lurdenlaw—Philip M'Leod.
Ednam and Harpertoun—Alexander Henderson.
Nenthorn and Gordon—William Allan.

Morebattle and Hounam—Thomas Edmondstone, carrier.
Yetholm—William Watson, carrier.

The Post Runners are allowed to carry small parcels on their own account, but no letters or newspapers. The Carriers can take goods of any weight.

CLERGY.

Kelso is the seat of a Presbytery, in the Synod of Merse and Teviotdale.

Patron—The Duke of Roxburghe.

ESTABLISHED CHURCH—Rev. James Smith (Inducted 1844). Sittings, 1314. Sabbath School attendance : Boys, under the superintendence of Mr John Kennedy, 85 ; Girls, under the superintendence of Mr William Smith, 95. MAXWELLHEUGH (Boys and Girls), under the superintendence of Mr John Tait, teacher, Kelso, 50. Precentor—Robert Inglis, 13 Coal Market ; Church Officer—Edward Ballantyne, 31 Butts. Treasurer of Sabbath Schools—Mr W. Smith, Kirk Style. Session Clerk and Kirk Treasurer—Mr. Walter Hilson, Maxwellheugh.

NORTH FREE CHURCH*—Rev. Horatius Bonar, D.D. (Inducted 1837). Sittings, 750. Sabbath School attendance : Boys, under the superintendence of Mr. Kirkland, 40 ; Girls, under the superintendence of Mr. Logan, 50. Precentor—James Cook, 14 Horse Market ; Church Treasurer—Mr. J. B. Ker ; Home Missionaries —William Stoddart, 29 Horse Market, and Alexander Murray, 54 Roxburgh Street.

FREE EAST CHURCH (Sprouston)—Rev. George Craig (Inducted 1835). Sittings, 700. Sabbath School attendance (at the Church, Sprouston, and Wooden Mills), under the superintendence of Mr. James Henderson, Square, 134. Precentor—John Aimers, 31 Bowmont Street ; Church Treasurer—Mr. James Henderson.

* The North Parish Church is at present occupied as the North Free Church, but it has been claimed by the Established Presbytery of Kelso, and is to be opened by the Presbytery in connection with the Established Church on the first Sabbath of October. A new North Free Church is about to be built in place of this, on a fine commanding situation in Roxburgh Street, and near to the present edifice ; it is intended to accommodate 700 sitters.

Dr. M'Culloch, in the " Statistical Account of Scotland," describes the present Free Church and the Town Hall as the only buildings in Kelso possessing any architectural merit (this was before the Corn Exchange was built—which see). The Parish Church is only remarkable for its outside ugliness, the economical arrangement of its walls, and its awkward area passages.

UNITED PRESBYTERIAN (First)—Rev. Henry Renton, A.M. (Inducted 1830); assistant and successor Rev. Robert Whyte, A.M. (Inducted 1864). Sittings, 950. Sabbath School attendance, under the superintendence of Mr. William Mein, 60; attendance at the minister's private class, 30. Precentor—Thomas Slight, 14 Wood Market; Church Treasurer—Mr John Scott, 21 Wood Market; Treasurer for Missionary Purposes—Mr J. Forrest, Square.

UNITED PRESBYTERIAN (East)—Rev. James Jarvie (Inducted 1837). Sittings, 740. Sabbath School attendance, 50. Precentor—Robert Purves, 34 Shedden Park Road; Church Treasurer—Mr Thomas Mitchell; Treasurer for Missionary Purposes—Mr William Rae; Treasurer for Sabbath School—Mr Arch. Milne.

REFORMED PRESBYTERIAN CHURCH—Rev. John Guy (Inducted 1853). Sittings, 300. Precentor—Alexander Hall, Ednam; Treasurer—Mr Joseph Middlemas, grocer.

CONGREGATIONAL CHURCH,* no regular pastor. Sittings, 150. Treasurer—Mr. Robert Rutherford, 25 Bridge Street.

ST. ANDREW'S EPISCOPAL CHURCH,†—Rev. J. H. Scott (Inducted 1862). Sittings, 214. Sabbath School attendance, 30. Managers—Mr. Vost, Kelso, and Mr. Smith, Windywalls; Treasurer—Mr. James Douglas, banker; Church Officer and Clerk—Alex. Robson, 4 Shedden Park Road.

ROMAN CATHOLIC CHAPEL—Rev. F. M'Kerrell (non-resident).

FAST DAYS—Wednesdays before first Sundays of May and November.

PAROCHIAL MISSIONARY ASSOCIATION,

For collecting subscriptions in aid of the Schemes of the Established Church. Average annual income about £50. (This sum does not include the quarterly collections in behalf of the Schemes.)
President—Rev. Jas. Smith.   Vice-President—Jas. S. Darling, Esq.
Treasurer—Mr John Kennedy.   Secretary—Mr J. Tunna.

ASSOCIATION FOR FEMALE EDUCATION IN INDIA

(Estab. in connection with the Established Church of Scotland, 1838).
President—Rev. James Smith.
Treas.—Miss Scott, Wooden.   Secy.—Mrs. Wm. Smith, Kirk Style.

COLLECTORS.

Mrs. Thomson, Maxwell Cottage | Miss Broomfield, Square
Miss Roberton, Harpertoun | Mrs. William Smith
Amount collected 1863-4, £25, 5d.

* This was formerly the Quaker Meeting-house.
† The Episcopal Church is a pretty little building, nestled in ivy, finely situated on the high bank of the river, and adjoining the grounds of Ednam House.

FIRST UNITED PRESBYTERIAN CHURCH MISSIONARY SOCIETY.

President—Rev. H. Renton.   Treasurer—Mr John Forrest.
Average annual income about £100.
Treasurer of Tract Society—Mr G. Gilray.
Average annual income of Tract Society about £12.

SABBATH SCHOOL TEACHERS' UNION.

President—Mr P. Logan.   Vice-President—Mr James Kinghorn.
Secretary and Treasurer—Mr James Smith, Oven Wynd.

BIBLE SOCIETY.

The object of this Society is to collect funds to aid in the work of Bible distribution both at home and abroad. Most of the sum collected annually is sent to the National Bible Society of Scotland. Average annual income, £45.

President—Duke of Roxburghe.
Vice-President—J. S. Darling, Esq.
Treasurer—Mr John Henderson.   Secretary—Mr Peter Logan.

COLPORTAGE SCHEME (established 1859).

Chairman and Treasurer—Robert Oliver of Lochside.
Convener and Secretary—Rev. John Guy, Kelso.

COMMITTEE.

Rev. H. Renton, Kelso.	William Dunn, Redden.
Dr. Bonar ..	William Broad, Cliftonhill.
G. Craig ..	Thomas Scott, Whitton.
J. Smith ..	Walter Arras, Ormiston.
J. Guy ..	George Simson, Courthill.
W. Lee, Roxburgh.	John Brough, New Smailholm.
J. S. Darling, Kelso.	James Tait, Roxburgh St., Kelso.
Robert Oliver, Lochside.	James Roberton, Ladyrig.
Convener—Rev. John Guy.	Treasurer—Robert Oliver, Esq.

DISTRICT COLLECTORS.

For Linton—Mr Oliver.	For Sprouston—Mr Dunn.
Roxburgh—Mr Roberton.	Nenthorn—Mr Simson.
Ednam—Mr Broad	Smailholm—Mr Brough.
Morebattle—Mr Scott.	Yetholm—Mr Calder.
Eckford—Mr Arras.	

The following have been the Colporteur's monthly averages of sales of books and periodicals for the five years the scheme has existed:—for the first year, £10 : 8 : 4; for the second, £11 : 16 : 2¾; for the third, £13 : 9 : 5½; for the fourth, £14 : 9 : 7½; and for the fifth, just closed, £17 : 6 : 6¾—the total for the five years being £207 : 18 : 9.

The books and periodicals sold are supplied at a reduced rate by the Tract Society, Edinburgh. The subscriptions for the year just closed (February 1864), amount to £28 : 14 : 6.

Since the Colporteur began his work five years ago, he has sold 73,478 periodicals, and of bibles and testaments he has sold 1302 copies; which, with a great variety of books, represent a money value of about £802: he has also distributed gratuitously about 200 tracts monthly, supplied by the Edinburgh Society.

The district of the Colporteur includes, with the exception of the town of Kelso, nearly all the country that lies between Haddon and Eckford, Gateshaw and Mellerstain.

EDUCATIONAL INSTITUTIONS.*

Bowmont House Boarding Seminary for Young Ladies—Misses Paterson.

Maitland House Boarding Seminary for Young Ladies—Misses Watt and Williams.

Grammar School (Parochial), and Boarding Establishment for Young Gentlemen—George Duncan Hunter, Rector; Assistant—James Henderson.

English School (Parochial), under the superintendence of the Rector of the Grammar School; Master—James Henderson, first-class certificated teacher; William H. Cook, assistant. Average attendance at Grammar and English Schools, 150.

Maxwellheugh English School (endowed to a small extent out of Frater's Trust)—Walter Hilson, Master; average attendance, 140. The school and house accommodation, and garden are granted by Sir George H. S. Douglas, the proprietor of the hamlet.

Educational Establishment for Young Gentlemen—Rev. John Guy, R. P. Manse.

New Academy, West Bowmont Street—Master—John Kirkland, late of the Shedden Park Academy (now closed), and formerly assistant to the late Dr. Fergusson of the Kelso Grammar School.

Girls' School, 25 Horse Market—Miss Woodrow.

Do. 58 Wood Market—Miss Knox.

Roman Catholic School—Mary Macman, Teacher. Average attendance, 30.

ROXBURGHE SUBSCRIPTION SCHOOLS (estab. 1817).
(With which was combined the Friendly School in 1838.)

Patroness—Her Grace the Duchess of Roxburghe.
Mr J. Henderson, Secretary. Mr J. Kennedy, Treasurer.
Wm. Smith, Teacher. Average attendance, 110.
Girls' Sewing Class—Miss Hambly, Teacher.

The school accommodation is granted by His Grace the Duke of Roxburghe; and Her Grace the Duchess of Roxburghe is the principal subscriber to the funds. The house accommodation was built partly by His Grace and partly by a grant from the Fergusson

* During the first week of April 1861, the number of children in the parish, from 5 to 14, attending school, was 796; of all ages 855.

Fund. The fees are at the nominal rate of one penny per week. The ordinary branches of a useful English education are taught; besides sewing, knitting, &c., to the girls.

INDUSTRIAL RAGGED SCHOOL.

Supported by voluntary subscriptions—the property, consisting of ample school, house, and garden accommodation, was purchased in 1858, partly by subscription and partly by a donation of £100 from the Fergusson Fund.

Chairman and Treasurer—James Roberton, Esq., Ladyrig.
Secretary—Rev. John Guy. Teacher—John Tait.
Average attendance, 30.

The children are partly fed in the school, and a man is regularly employed to teach shoemaking to the older boys, and superintend net-making, etc. The girls are taught sewing by Mrs. Tait.

PAROCHIAL BOARD.

Chairman—James Tait, Esq. W.S.

ACTING COMMITTEE.

Messrs. James Tait (Convener), Robert Darling, Robert Curry, Rev. James Smith, Rev. Henry Renton, George Craig, Charles Robson, Rev. James Jarvie.

ELECTED MEMBERS, AND MEMBERS OF KIRK SESSION.

Messrs. Thomas Crosbie, Robert Woodrow, James S. Darling, John Scott, Jas. Hogg, Dr. Hamilton, John Kennedy, William Smith, Robert Rutherford, Walter Hilson, Peter Lugton, Robert Gray, John Rule.

Medical Officer—Thomas Hamilton, M.D.
Charles Robson, Collector and Treasurer of Poor Rates.
Alexander Morrison, Inspector. T. Aitchison, Sub-Inspector.
Average No. of Poor on Roll, 100. Assessment for the year, 1s. 8d. per £—less one-fourth on house property for repairs.
Total Collection 1863-4 from all sources, £1987 : 4 : 10.
Office—Horse Market.

UNION POORHOUSE.

The Parishes forming the Combination or Union, are—Kelso, Earlston, Eccles, Eckford, Ednam, Gordon, Hounam, Linton, Morebattle, Nenthorn, Smailholm, Sprouston, Stitchel and Hume, Roxburgh, and Yetholm.

COMMITTEE OF MANAGEMENT.

Chairman—Robert Swan, Esq., Kelso.

Rev. James Smith, Kelso.	James S. Darling, W.S., Kelso.
Robert Curry, solicitor, Kelso.	Jas. Roberton, Tenant of Lady-
Robert Darling, Broomlands.	rig.
Charles Robson, solicitor, Kelso.	John B. Boyd of Cherrytrees.
Rev. Henry Renton, Kelso.	F. Calder, Tenant of Yetholm
Rev. James Jarvie, Kelso.	Mains.
John Hood of Stoneridge.	Robert Kerr Elliot of Clifton.

G

Secretary and Treasurer—James Tait, W.S., Kelso.
Governor and Matron—Mr and Mrs Miller.
Average number of Inmates, 45.

DISPENSARY (Roxburgh Street).

Founded 1777, for the benefit of the sick poor of the town and district, principally through the exertions of the late Hon. Mrs. Baillie of Mellerstain and Dr. C. Douglas of Kelso. Supported by voluntary subscription.

Amount of Accumulated Funds, October 1863, over £5600.

President—His Grace the Duke of Roxburghe.

VICE-PRESIDENTS.
The Right Hon. the Earl of Haddington.
The Right Hon. Lord Polwarth.
John Waldie, Esq. of Hendersyde.
Andrew Wauchope, Esq. of Niddrie Marischall.

Physician—Dr John Robertson.
Surgeons—Dr T. Hamilton ; Dr William M. Mackenzie.
Apothecary—Mr H. Vost.   Treasurer and Secretary—Mr R. Swan.
Housekeeper—Mrs Janet Stewart.

BATHS.

There is one Bath kept exclusively for the Patients of the Dispensary ; another, handsomely fitted up with marble, for the accommodation of the Public, and may be had at an hour's notice, on application to the Housekeeper, for payment of 1s. Hot Bath, and 6d. Cold and Shower Bath, which sums go towards the support of the charity.
(For Public Baths and Wash-Houses, *see* Directory, Roxburgh St.)

LADIES' CLOTHING SOCIETY (established 1819.)

For supplying clothing at a reduced rate to the poorer and more necessitous inhabitants. No membership subscription is required ; the society works by the sale of tickets.

Patroness—Her Grace the Duchess of Roxburghe.
Secretary and Treasurer—Miss Catherine Stuart, Roxburgh Place.

MERCHANT COMPANY (Date of present Charter, 1757).

Master—Thomas Mitchell.
Box-Masters—William Brotherston and Peter Hooper.
Auditors—William Torrie and John Johnston.

Annual subscription, 1s.

The privileges of the Merchant Company previous to the passing of the Reform Bill were extensive, and its duties of considerable importance. Its proceedings are now limited to assisting the widows, in needful circumstances, of deceased merchants, late members of the Company, and subscribing occasionally to useful objects connected with the town. The Company, which has some accumulated funds, is nearly defunct.

CHARITABLE BEQUESTS.

James Jamieson of Herdrig, late Surgeon in Kelso, by his will, dated 7th July, 1760, bequeathed to the Heritors and Kirk Session £200 Sterling, the Interest to be annually applied for behoof of poor householders in the town of Kelso who are not on the pension roll of the parish.

John Slone, Kelso, by his will, dated 15th June, 1775, bequeathed £50 Sterling to the Minister and Heritors, for the use and behoof of the poor of the town of Kelso, as they should see best to apply it : and £50 Sterling, for the use and behoof of the poor, as the Minister thinks fit.

Alexander Douglas, Kelso, by his will, dated 15th August, 1782, bequeathed to the Minister and Kirk Session of Kelso £240 Sterling, the Interest to be applied to the educating of poor children belonging to the parish.

John Samson, Maxwellheugh, by will, dated 10th April, 1788, bequeathed £100 Sterling to the Minister and Kirk-Session of Kelso, the Interest to be applied yearly towards maintaining, clothing, and educating poor orphans in the said parish.

Mrs Barbara Scott or Curll, Kelso (widow of William Curll, farmer, Yetbyre, in the county of Dumfries ; and aunt of Sir Walter Scott), who died in 1826, bequeathed to the Minister and Kirk Session of Kelso £50, the Interest to be applied for the relief of poor old inhabitants of the parish, chiefly to assist them in paying their house rents.

Miss Charlotte Ann Waldie (afterwards Mrs Eaton), by deed of gift and mortification, dated 15th August, 1822, paid over and mortified £200 to, and in favour of, the Minister and Kirk Session of Kelso, the Interest to be applied in paying school wages, and for relief of poor aged or infirm inhabitants of the parish who are not paupers on the ordinary poors' roll.

John Robertson, Esq. of Ednam House, who died in 1842, bequeathed £200 to the Kirk Session, for behoof of the poor of the parish of Kelso, the Interest to be distributed annually as the Session thinks fit.

Miss Alicia Dickson of Paisley, who died 1845, bequeathed £150 to the Kirk Session of Kelso, for behoof of the poor and needy of the parish, whether on the ordinary poors' roll or not, to be distributed in such manner as the Kirk Session may think proper, so as not to come in place of, or lessen the allowance of the Heritors and Kirk Session to the regular poor.

Mr John Frater, sometime residing at Wooden, by deed of settlement, dated 2d January, 1832, bequeathed to the Minister and Kirk Session of Kelso £100 Sterling, the Interest to be applied for the support or clothing of old deserving men in the parish—the name of Frater or Downie to be preferred ; also £100 Sterling, the Interest to be applied for educating poor children at the parish school, in the town of Kelso—the name of Frater or Downie to be preferred ; Mr John Frater also, by his deed of settlement, bequeathed the residue of his estate, which consists of lands in the parish of Kelso, to certain Trustees, under burden of certain legacies, to be disposed of by them for such charitable purposes as they should think fit.—[*See* Maxwellheugh School.]

James Leadbetter, writer in Kelso, by his settlement and codicil executed in 1832, bequeathed in Trust to the Minister of Kelso, the Ministers of the United Associate Congregation, the Relief Congregation, the Original Seceding Congregation, and the Reformed Presbyterian Congregation, the sum of £300, the Interest thereof to be applied annually, in the month of January, for behoof of the poor persons in the town of Kelso.

The late George Bruce, Esq. of Slogarie, tenant in Greenknowe, who died in 1861, directed his trustees to invest in name of the Clergymen of the different religious persuasions in Kelso and their successors, a tenth part of his estates, the amount to be ascertained at Whitsunday 1862 [over £1000]; the interest of said tenth to be accumulated until the price of oatmeal in Kelso is 2s. 8d. per stone, and the 4 ℔s loaf 11d.; when the accumulated Interest is to be divided amongst poor persons, members of the different congregations in the parishes of Kelso, Gordon, Stow, and Balmaghie. The lists to be reduced so that each person shall receive 5s. weekly for six weeks. In the event of the interest, or any part of it, not being required for that purpose, it is to be septennially applied to the promotion of education in India.

[Some difficulties having arisen as to the constitution and administration of this charity, the matter is at present before the Court of Session.]

Miss Janetta Dods, lately residing in Kelso, who died in 1862, by a codicil to her settlement, bequeathed to the Session and Minister of the Kelso Parish Church, in connection with the Established Church of Scotland, the sum of £100, for behoof of the Kelso Parish Sabbath School.

SHEDDEN PARK.

Presented by Mrs Robertson of Ednam House to the inhabitants of Kelso, 1851. (*See* p. 71 and *Seats*—Ednam House.)

Mrs Robertson also at a later date presented to the trustees of the Park a large number of dwelling houses and gardens, the rents of which are applicable to the proper maintenence of the Park or other benevolent purposes.

The size of the Park is a trifle over 8 acres.

Charles Robson, Secretary and Treasurer. G. Welsh, Park-Keeper.

SICK AND BURIAL YEARLY SOCIETIES,

Which are all nearly alike in principle.

Each member pays 1s. 2d. per week, and is entitled to receive, while sick, 4s. per week for the first three months, 2s. per week for the next three months, and 1s. per week afterwards to the end of the financial year of the Society, when it breaks up, and the funds are divided, no deduction being made from the shares of members on account of sick money.

In addition to sick money, when a member dies, funeral money to the amount of 6d. from each member is paid from the funds to his widow or heirs ; at the death of a member's wife he receives 3d. from each member ; and, in at least two of the societies, a payment is made at the death of a child under fifteen years of age.

These payments for sick and funeral money, and the payments for expenses of management, are expected never to exceed the odd 2d. per week paid by each member.

All these societies also advance small sums of money out of the funds to members, on security, and at legal interest.

BRISBANE PLACE YEARLY BENEVOLENT SOCIETY.

Preses—Wm. Wilson. Clerk—W. Watson. Treas.—Wm. Townley.

Average number of Members, 320.

BRISBANE PLACE WHITSUN YEARLY SOCIETY.

Preses—W. Wilson. Clerk—W. Watson. Treasurer—W. Townley.

Average number of Members, 150.

BRIDGE STREET YEARLY BENEFIT SOCIETY.

Preses—T. Aitchison. Clerk—D. Cook. Treasurer—J. Young.

Average number of Members, 220.

ROXBURGH STREET YEARLY BENEFIT SOCIETY.

Preses—Jas. Allan. Secretary—W. Currie. Treasurer—J. Aimers.

Average number of Members, 144.

BOWMONT STREET WHITSUN BENEFIT SOCIETY.

Preses—Geo. M'Call. Treasurer—T. Brown. Secretary—D. Cook.

Average number of Members, 150.

TWEED LODGE OF FREEMASONS (founded 1815).

R.W. Master—William Crease, druggist.

Past Master—George Weddell. Secretary—Robert Scoon.

Treasurer—John Gow.

INDEPENDENT ORDER OF ODD FELLOWS (founded 1841).

(MANCHESTER UNITY.)

Tweedside Lodge, No. 2619, registered under the Friendly Society's Act, meets every other Monday in the Cross Keys Hotel.

Permanent Secretary—James Cook.

Medical Officer—W. M. Mackenzie, M.D.

Accumulated Funds in January 1864, £1640.

ANCIENT ORDER OF FORESTERS (founded 1845).

Court Thistle of the Forest Friendly Society, No 1709, registered under the Friendly Society's Act, 13 and 14 Victoria, cap. 115, meets every other Tuesday in the Queen's Head Hotel.

William Mole, Secretary. John Ledgerwood, Treasurer.

Medical Officer—John Bookless, surgeon.

Accumulated Funds, over £920.

TOTAL ABSTINENCE SOCIETY (estab. 1862).

President—James Tait, Esq., Editor of " Kelso Chronicle."
Vice-Presidents—Alexander Mollison and Robert Rutherford.
Secretary—W. Robertson.   Treasurer—G. Grieve,

TWEEDSIDE PHYSICAL AND ANTIQUARIAN SOCIETY'S MUSEUM (estab. 1834).

Acknowledged to contain one of the best and most varied and inte-
teresting collections in Scotland.

Open gratuitously on Mondays, Wednesdays, and Fridays, from
12 to 3 p.m. ; and during the summer months, on Saturday evenings,
when an Instrumental Band attends and performs.

Annual Subscription, 10s. 6d.   Life Membership, £5, 5s.
Patron—His Grace the Duke of Roxburghe.
President—Sir George H. S. Douglas, Bart.

VICE-PRESIDENTS.

P. J. Selby, Esq. of Twizel House. | Mr Stuart of Roxburgh House,
The Right Hon. the Earl of Home. | Kelso.

CURATORS.

Dr. Hamilton, Mr. Tait of Langrigg (Edenside), Mr. Robertson of
Neworth, Dr. Mackenzie, and Mr. James Douglas.

Secretary—Mr. J. F. S. Darling.   Treasurer—Mr J. H. Rutherfurd.

Artist—Mr Frain.

Conservator—   Custodier—Mr Scott.

LIBRARIES.

KELSO LIBRARY * (Terrace—estab. 1750).
Open on Mondays, Wednesdays, and Fridays.
Annual Subscription, £1, 1s.   Nearly 8000 volumes.
Preses—Thomas Fair Robertson, Esq. of St Foin (Hermitage).
Curators—Dr Stuart, Mr Peter Robertson, Mr James Roberton,
Rev. D. Swan, and Rev. Wm. Lamb.
Librarian and Treasurer—James Scott.

UNITED LIBRARY (Oven Wynd).

(An Amalgamation [1859] of the " Kelso New Library," instituted
in 1778, and the " Modern Library," founded in 1794.)

Open on Tuesdays and Fridays from 12 to 2 o'Clock.
Annual Subscription, 10s.   Nearly 3500 volumes.
Preses—Thomas Mitchell.   Treasurer—Thomas Train.
Secretary—John Henderson, plumber.
Librarian—James Purves.

There are also Congregational Libraries in connection with the
Parish, North Free, First United Presbyterian, and East United
Presbyterian Churches.   (For BOOK CLUB, see 17 Square.)

* The copy of " Percy's Reliques " which entranced the boyhood of Sir
Walter Scott, and which is said to have made him a poet, still exists in
this library.

BILLIARD AND READING ROOM CLUB (Abbey-Row).

Date of present building and funding of the stock 1855.   The date
of its origin is lost ; but it is known to have existed for over fifty
years.

James Tait, W.S., Secretary and Treasurer.

Annual Subscription for Town Members, £1, 5s. ; Reading Room
only, £1 ; for Country Members, 10s.

Amount of Stock, £775.   Pays 5 per cent.

NEW READING ROOM (16 Square.—Estab. 1852).

President—Thomas Crosbie.
William Milne, Secretary.   William Clazy, Treasurer.
Annual Subscription, 10s.   Stock, £40.

YOUNG MEN'S MUTUAL IMPROVEMENT SOCIETY.

Meets in the First U. P. Church on the Monday evenings (those of
May, June, July, August, and early part of September excepted), for
the purpose of reading original essays, and discussing subjects of
religious, moral, and intellectual importance.

President—Rev. H. Renton.
Vice-Presidents—Thomas Craig and George M'Call.
Secretary and Treasurer—John Bower, printer.
Subscription, 1s. per annum.

FERGUSSON CLUB.

(Instituted 1855, by the Scholars of the late Dr. Fergusson,
Rector of Kelso).

President—John Munro, Fairnington
Secretary and Treasurer—A. W. Main, Kelso.
Honorary Chaplain—The Rev. Robert S. Darling.

HORTICULTURAL SOCIETY.

Patron—His Grace the Duke of Roxburghe.
President (elected annually) for 1864—The Hon. George Dalrymple
of Elliston.
Convener—Fred. L. Roy, Esq., jun. of Nenthorn.
Secretary—Mr John Allan.   Treasurer—Mr Andrew Roberton.

The principal Exhibition is held annually on a Wednesday in
September ; the prizes awarded in 1863 amounted to over £70.

POULTRY EXHIBITION (estab. 1861).

President—F. L. Roy, yr. of Nenthorn.
Secretary—James Steel, Bridge Street.
Treasurer—John Gow, Roxburgh Street.

Annual Exhibition in February.
Amount given in prizes at the Exhibition of 1864, £71 : 10 : 6.

UNION AGRICULTURAL SOCIETY.

(Formerly Border Society. Established 1812 ; amalgamated with the
Tweedside Society in 1820.)

President—Duke of Roxburghe.
Vice-Presidents—Lord Binning ; Sir H. P. H. Campbell, Bart. ;
Sir G. H. S. Douglas, Bart. ; J. Scott Dudgeon, Esq.
Chaplain—Rev. James Smith.
Joint Treasurers—F. L. Roy and F. L. Roy, jun.
Secretary—Robert Curry.
Hon. Seedsmen—Stuart & Mein.

The Ploughing Competition takes place in February. General
Exhibition of Stock in March, which is held at Kelso and Coldstream
alternately. At the Show of this year (1864) at Kelso, £198 was given
in premiums. Sheep Show and Tup Sale in September, second
Thursday and Friday.

The prizes given at the show are for the Border breed of Leicester,
and Cheviot sheep, and amount to £35.

The sale consists of pure bred Border Leicesters principally, and
of Half-Breds and Cheviots.

The number of Tups put up to auction, September 1863, was 2300,
the market being topped as usual by Lord Polwarth, four of whose
animals brought the following prices—£60, £51, £50, and £41. His
average for 35 animals was £21 : 6 : 3. The next highest average—
that of Mr. Simson, Courthill (whose Tup took the head prize at the
Highland Society's Show at Kelso in August 1863, and where Lord
Polwarth also competed) [we mention this circumstance to show
that although Lord Polwarth generally tops the market, others in
the neighbourhood may have equally good animals]—was, for 30 animals, £11 : 16 : 6. The next highest was that of Mr. William Purves,
Burnfoot, 100 animals, £10 : 12 : 3.

This sale, admitted to be now the largest of its kind in the world
[see introductory notes on the Agriculture of Berwickshire and Roxburghshire, page 47], has sprung into existence within the last
twenty years : the first sale of any consequence having occurred so
lately as 1850 ; previously the animals had been principally brought
for hiring out and competition. The competition still exists, but it is
of limited interest in the proceedings ; and the hiring has gone out
of practice.

In 1845 the number of Tups put up to auction was only 224, which
brought in prices averaging £4, 10s.—over £9 being the highest
price. 230 other sheep were also sold, and in the Kelso papers of
the date these numbers and prices are quoted as remarkably large.
In 1851 the Tups sold had more than doubled in number, but still
they only summed up to 652, and other descriptions of sheep had
fallen off to about 50.

Up to, and including the sale, etc. of 1863, the proceedings were
limited to one day ; but for some years this having been found to
work inconveniently—the auctioneers being often unable to get
through the lots entrusted to their charge—a new system is to begin
with the sale of this year [1864], of which the following minute, extracted from the report of the meeting of the members held at Kelso,
11th March 1864, intimates the most important change—viz., "that
taking into consideration the increasing importance and extent of
the business connected with the annual show of sheep, it is expedient
that it should be extended over the space of two days. . . . The
Show and allotment of premiums should take place on the first day,
with the sale of all sheep other than the high-bred Leicesters ; while
the Friday should be devoted exclusively to the sale of Leicester
sheep." It was also agreed that the entry-money for each sheep be
raised from 6d. to 9d., and that the auctioneers begin the first day's
sale at noon, after the awarding of the premiums, etc., for the animals
brought for show ; and that the sale of the second day begin at 10
a.m.

In previous years the sale had begun at 9 a.m. At that of 1863,
four auction rinks had been required, but so many rinks having been
found to work badly for both buyer and seller, that these might be
limited to two or three was one of the principal reasons for the extension of time.

The Show and sale ground are adjoining the Inch Road. Admission
to the public, 6d. each day.

As a rule the animals shewn are very fine, and splendid specimens
have in many instances been brought forward. Berwickshire, Roxburghshire, and Northumberland are, with few exceptions, the
localities where they are raised.

FARMERS' CLUB (founded 1850).

Meets on the first Friday of every month in the Cross Keys Hotel,
for the discussion of questions relating to the improvement of agriculture, breeding and management of stock, etc.

Entry-Money, 10s.   Annual Subscription, 25s.

Chairmen and Vice-Presidents elected in January 1864, for the year
ensuing :—Mr Purves, Burnfoot ; Mr Broad, Cliftonhill ; Mr Usher,
Stodrig ; Mr Stuart, Runningburn ; Mr Ross, Newtonlees ; Mr Henderson, East Gordon.

Secretary and Treasurer—Mr Swan, Kelso.
Keeper of Register for Farm Servants—Daniel Cook, Forrest Field.

ASSOCIATION FOR ANALYSING AND TESTING MANURES, &c.

This Association was formed in 1859 by several of the farmers in
the neighbourhood of Kelso, for the purpose of preventing the adulteration of articles used by them, such as manures, food for cattle,
and seeds, by getting the same analysed and tested by competent
persons. From the large number of members, and the almost certain detection of adulterated or inferior articles, the Association has
hitherto been very successful. The subscription payable at present
is at the rate of 2s. 6d. for each 100 acres of arable land occupied by
each member. The ordinary business of the Association is managed

by a Committee of not less than five members, and there is an additional Committee of twelve members to whom all disputes and questions of difficulty are referred.

ORDINARY COMMITTEE FOR 1864.

John Munro, Fairnington, Convener; James Ross, Newtonlees: John Ord, of Muirhouselaw ; James Elliot, Galalaw ; Andrew Scott, Frogden ; the Treasurer *ex officio.*

Treasurer—James Roberton, British Linen Co.'s Bank, Kelso. Secretaries—Roberton & Broomfield, solicitors, Kelso.

The Analyses are made by Dr. Stevenson Macadam, Edinburgh; and the seeds are tested by Mr. Wemyss, gardener, Springwood Park.

ASSOCIATION FOR REDUCING THE NUMBER OF WOOD-PIGEONS.

Committee (who are appointed by the Farmers' Club):— Convener—John S. Johnston, Crailing Hall. Members—Wm. Purves, John Usher, Wm. Broad, James Ross. Treasurer—Robert Swan.   Secretary—Thomas Hunter.

Subscription, 2s. 6d. per 100 acres.

CORN EXCHANGE (opened 1856).

Jas. Stormonth Darling, W.S., Secretary and Treasurer. Edward Ballantyne, Butts, Officer.

Contains 71 Stalls. Net Rental, £158. Rate for Exhibitions, including gas—first day, £3 ; second day, £1 ; for Sales, £2, 2s.

Amount of Stock, £1980, which pays 5 per cent. There is some debt on the building which is gradually being cleared off.

It has been stated that more grain is sold by the *grower*, in Kelso Corn Exchange, than in any other building in Great Britain. The grain is all sold by sample ; business begins at 12 and is over by 2 p.m.

The building, situate in the Wood Market, is a striking edifice in the Tudor style. Its interior arrangements are very appropriate for the business of the Exchange ; when fitted up as a ball-room it is magnificent, but its size makes it a trying concert or lecture room.

As a rule, the stall holders, or their representatives, will be found every Friday in the Exchange during business hours. A list of them will be found after the Kelso non-resident Registered Voters.

GAS COMPANY (established 1831).

Treasurer—Robt. Rutherfurd (Paradise).   Secretary—Robt Curry. Manager—William Clazy.

6s. 8d. per 1000 feet.

Amount of Stock, £3000. Annual Dividend, 10 per cent.

Kelso has always been noted for the excellent quality of its Gas.

MUTUAL PLATE GLASS SOCIETY (established 1856).

Originated by the late Mr George M'Dougal (father of the present president), " to effect Insurance against Loss by Accidental Breakage of Plate Glass, in the most economical manner, by the following method :—In the event of a breakage occurring to the property of any member, it shall be replaced by an assessment laid on in proportion to the amount of feet of glass possessed by each member, he paying his own proportion of the sum necessary to replace the same."

This method of insurance has been found to effect an enormous saving over the ordinary method of insuring in proprietary societies —many years the members having had no call on them whatever, and in other years 1s. or 1s. 6d. paying the entire risk of an ordinary shop front.

Stock, none.   Entry-Money, 6d.

President—Mr. James M'Dougall.   Secretary—Mr. Arch. Milne.

ANGLING ASSOCIATION.

Established in 1859 for the Suppression of Poaching and the encouragement of Fair Angling. Prizes are given for Trout Angling in June.

President—Sir George H. S. Douglas, Bart. Vice-President—James Stormonth Darling, Esq. Secretary and Treasurer—John F. S. Darling.

Annual Subscription, 1s.

RACES.

Stewards (Elected Annually). Judge—Mr R. Johnson, of York. Clerk of Course—Mr. John Usher, Stodrig. Resident Keeper of Grand Stand—William Dick.

The ordinary Meetings take place about the 20th October, and continue for two days. Admission to the Course 2s. each day ; to the Grand Stand, 5s.

The Caledonian Meeting is held every fifth year about the beginning of October, and continues for three days. The last Caledonian Meeting was held in 1862 ; the next will be held in 1867.

The present race course, about a mile from the town to the northeast, was opened in 1822 ; previously it was an extensive morass, known as the Berrymoss, and was a great breeding place for seagulls and a resort for wild ducks. It is considered to be the best race course in the kingdom.

THE BORDER RACING CLUB (established 1854).

President—His Grace the Duke of Roxburghe. Vice-Presidents—The Earl of Dalkeith and the Earl of Haddington. Honorary Secretary and Treasurer—Jas Tait, W.S., Kelso.

Annual Subscription, £3 3s.

BOWLING CLUB (established 1818).

Mr. Kennedy, President.   Mr. J. F. S. Darling, Vice-President.
Mr. C. A. Hutchinson, Secretary and Treasurer.
Committee—Messrs. Allan, Train, and Robertson.
Annual Subscription, 10s.

CURLING CLUB (established 1790).

Admitted into the Royal Caledonian Curling Club, 1853.

Entry-Money, 20s.   Annual Subscription, 5s.

Patron—Charles Balfour, Esq., of Newton Don.
President—Thomas Fair Robertson, Esq., of Saint Foin.
Vice-President—Charles Robson, Esq., of Grove Hill.
Treasurer and Secretary—Mr George Craig, Kelso.
Chaplain—Rev. M. H. Graham, Nenthorn.

The Pond is situated about 2 miles from Kelso on the Stitchill road, and on the property of Mr. Balfour, the patron.

CRICKET CLUB (established 1850).

Patron and President—The Marquis of Bowmont.
Captain—Lord Charles Innes Ker.

Hon. Secretary—Mr Wm. Laing.   Treasurer—Mr J. Aitken.
The Club is supported by voluntary subscriptions amongst the members.

BORDER CRICKET CLUB (established 1854).

President—H. F. Beverley.   Captain—James Rodgers.
Secretary and Treasurer—John Wood.
Entry-Money, 2s. 6d.   Annual Subscription, 4s 4d.

QUOITING CLUB (instituted 1851,

For quoiting practice and competition amongst the Members).

Meets weekly for practice during the season, and for competitions on the annual opening day in April, when small prizes are awarded ; and on the annual field day in September, when the medal is played for, the following prizes are awarded : four, each of 10s., 5s., and 2s. 6d.—amounting to £3, 10s.

Entry-Money, 1s.   Annual Subscription, 2s.
President—(Vacant).   Vice-President—George Walker.
Secretary and Treasurer—Thomas Jeffrey.

KELSO BRASS BAND.

Head-Quarters—15 Bowmont Street.
Bandmaster—James Cook.

2ND ROXBURGHSHIRE RIFLE VOLUNTEERS—(KELSO).

Barracks and Armoury at Mayfield.

Major Sir George H. S. Douglas, Captain.
James Johnston, Lieutenant.   John Munro (Fairnington), Ensign.
Hon. Surgeon—W. M. Mackenzie.   Hon. Chaplain—Rev. Jas. Smith.
Secretary—A. Roberton.
Drill Sergeant—William Horsburgh.   Bandmaster—James Fraser.
Annual Subscription for Hon. Members, 10s. 6d.

Hon. Members—70.   Effective Force—123 (119 is the official limit.)

BANK BRANCHES.

BANK OF SCOTLAND (estab. 1774)—James S. Darling and John F. S. Darling, Agents ; James Rutherford, Teller ; Richard Davidson, First Clerk.
     This branch was one of the first provincial bank branches permanently established in Scotland.*

BRITISH LINEN COMPANY (opened 1833)—James & Andrew Roberton, Agents.

COMMERCIAL BANK OF SCOTLAND (opened 1820)—Jas. Douglas, Agent ; James B. Ker, Accountant.

CITY OF GLASGOW BANK (opened 1857)—C. & W. Robson, Agents ; Robert Knox, Accountant.

---

* "In the present month (September 1774) the Bank of Scotland established a branch at Dumfries, and another at Kelso, where credits are given on cash-accounts, bills of exchange are purchased, and bills payable at those places and at Edinburgh are discounted."—*Scots Magazine.*
For a long period of years this branch at Kelso was the only bank between Edinburgh and Newcastle. "In 1731 branches had been attempted at Glasgow, Aberdeen, Dundee (at each of these places for the second time), and at Berwick ; but it was found that after two years' trial, the effort was as yet premature, and these branches were all recalled."—*Robert Chambers.*
The *Scots Magazine*, of date April 1776, when noticing the establishment of another branch of the Bank of Scotland at Stirling, states—"So now the bank has *six* branches: at Dumfries, Kelso, Inverness, Kilmarnock, Ayr, and Stirling. [If this list gives them in their order of date, *Kelso*, contemporary with Dumfries, was the first branch of a joint-stock bank established in Scotland]. . . . Little specie is needed at these branches, for the Company's notes are only payable at Edinburgh." How many of those who daily handle notes know that they are still only payable at the head offices of the different banks, and that *legally*, except at the head offices, they are no better than waste paper ; although, *in fact*, the refusal of payment for these notes at any of the branches is, with rare exceptions, unknown.
Although of so old a date, a still earlier branch of a bank existed in Kelso—a branch of the private bank of Douglas, Heron & Co. ; having been established under the agency of a Mr. Scott, and that bank failing, he left Kelso, and returned some years afterwards (1774) as the first agent of the Bank of Scotland. Mr. Scott's successor was Mr. James Potts, who was succeeded (in 1809) by Mr. Darling, father of the present senior agent. The Bank of Scotland agency in Kelso is thus one of the oldest banking establishments in the country, and it is generally understood to have been one of the most successful.

NATIONAL BANK OF SCOTLAND (opened 1833)—Jas. Tait, W.S., Agent; Thomas E. Watson, Accountant.

SAVINGS' BANK (estab. 1849)—Jas. B. Ker, Actuary; Jas. Douglas, Treasurer. Deposits (20th Nov. 1863), £20,518. 10s. 5d. ; Depositors, 1038. Interest allowed, £2 : 18 : 6 per cent. per annum.

INSURANCE AGENTS.

ACCIDENTAL DEATH ....John F. S. Darling.
BRITISH GUARANTEE.........C. A. Hutchinson.
CALEDONIAN................ { William Archbald, writer.
                        { Thomas Hunter, writer.
EDINBURGH LIFE.............Robert Swan, writer.
ENGLISH AND SCOTTISH LAW...Robert Curry, writer.
INSURANCE CO. OF SCOTLAND. James Tait, banker.
LIFE ASSOCIATION .... { James Tait, banker.
                      { J. B. Ker, accountant.
MINERVA LIFE...............Stuart & Mein, seedsmen.
NATIONAL GUARANTEE AND } Roberton & Broomfield.
SURETYSHIP .... }
NORTH BRITISH & MERCANTILE. J. Stormonth Darling, banker.
NORWICH UNION..............A. W. Main, writer.
PHŒNIX FIRE...............C, A. Hutchinson, writer.
PROVINCIAL.................William Robson, banker.
ROCK (LIFE)................Alexander Elliot, Stamp Office.
ROYAL FIRE AND LIFE.......James Tait, " Kelso Chronicle."
SCOTTISH AMICABLE.........John Kennedy, draper.
SCOTTISH EQUITABLE.........Francis Somner, seed-merchant.
SCOTTISH INDUSTRIAL ...... Ebenezer Hardie, cabinet-maker.
SCOTTISH NATIONAL......... { Roberton & Broomfield, writers.
                     { James Aitken.
SCOTTISH PROVIDENT INST.... Roberton & Broomfield, writers.
SCOTTISH PROVINCIAL (LIFE)..John Henderson.
                   { Charles Robson, writer.
SCOTTISH UNION. .... { James Douglas, banker.
                   { John Pringle.
SCOTTISH WIDOWS' FUND.... { James Douglas, banker.
                   { C. A. Hutchinson, writer.
STANDARD ....A. W. Main, writer.
SUN........................Robert Curry, writer.
UNITED KINGDOM LIFE........J. L. Romanes, postmaster.
WEST OF ENGLAND...........John Pringle.

ASSOCIATION FOR THE PROMOTION OF THE FINE ARTS IN SCOTLAND.

Alexander Elliot, Hon. Secretary.

EMIGRATION AGENTS.

Alexander Elliot, Stamp Office.
Andrew Murray, " Chronicle " Office.

PROCURATORS, NOTARIES PUBLIC, &c.

Curry, Robert, Bridge Street.
Broomfield David (firm of Roberton & B., Square).
Darling, James Stormonth, W.S., N.P., Wood Market.
Hunter, James, Bowmont Street.
Hunter, Thomas, N.P., Wood Market.
Hutchinson, Colin A., Square.
Main, Adam Woodman, N.P., Maxwell Place.
Roberton, Andrew, (firm of R. & Broomfield, Square).
Robson, Chas., N.P., (firm of Smiths & R., Bridge Street).
Smith, William, (firm of S. & Robson, Bridge Street).
Swan, Robert, N.P., Wood Market.
Tait, James, W.S., N.P., Square.

MEDICAL PRACTITIONERS.

John Bookless, Bowmont Street ; John Robertson, M.D., Belmount Place ; Thos. Hamilton, M.D., Roxburgh Street ; W. M. Mackenzie M.D., Square ; John Stuart, Roxburgh House ; Henry Vost, Square

DENTISTS—Vernon & Son, 114 Roxburgh Street.

VETERINARY SURGEON—William Robertson, Shedden Park Road.

NEWSPAPERS, &c.

The " Kelso Mail,"* price 3d., stamped, 4d. (established 1797, in opposition to the then *Kelso Chronicle—see* note), published every Monday and Thursday. Principles, Conservative, and proceeding on the maxim, "let well alone." Office, Bridge Street. Proprietor—William Jerdan, Abbey Gardens ; Editor—John Muir, 28 Roxburgh Street.

The " Kelso Chronicle,"† price 3d., stamped, 4d. (established 1832), published every Friday. Principles, Liberal ; completely identified with the popular cause, and advocates the opinions of the Voluntary church party in politics. Office, 27 Bowmont Street. Proprietress, —Mrs. Dawson of Duncan House ; Lessee—Andrew Murray, Goshen House ; Editor—James Tait, 86 Roxburgh Street.

The " Southern Counties' Register " (established 1856), published annually. Office, 17 Square. Proprietor, Jas. H. Rutherfurd.

" Rutherfurd's Household Almanac " (established 1862), published annually. Office, 17 Square. Proprietor, Jas. H. Rutherfurd.

---

* Except the " Aberdeen Journal" (estab. 1748), the " Kelso Mail" is the oldest provincial newspaper in Scotland. It was established by the celebrated James Ballantyne, who, after his removal to Edinburgh, to become publisher for Sir Walter Scott, transferred it to the late George Jerdan, Esq., father of the present proprietor. The next oldest provincial newspaper in Scotland is the " Greenock Advertiser " (estab. 1799).

† Another Kelso " Chronicle" existed from 1783 to 1803, when (under the name of the " British Chronicle") it expired. Its principles, like those of the present one, were Liberal—too liberal for the age in which it existed. Mr. James Palmer was the proprietor, and his publication was nicknamed the " Palmer-woom." A set of this newspaper (the only one known) is in the possession of J. & J. H. Rutherfurd.

MILLS.

KELSO—Corn and Flour—Thomas Crosbie & Co.
Do. —Steam Saw—Mollison & M'Vitie.
MAXWELLHEUGH—Corn and Flour—Robert Hogarth.
WOODEN—Woollen—Alexander Boyd.

Medical Inspector of Mills—John Bookless, surgeon, Kelso.

AUCTIONEERS.

David Broomfield, 32 Roxburgh Street.
John Chambers ; house, Maxwellheugh.
Fairbairn & Penny ; office, 52 Square.
William Ross ; house. 8 Roxburgh Street.

PORK-CURING ESTABLISHMENTS. *

William Broomfield, Square.
Smith and Son, Oven Wynd.
James Plummer, 111 Roxburgh Street.

SKINNERIES, &c.—*see* Terrace and 112 Roxburgh Street.

STATUTE LABOUR ROADS.

DISTRICT OF KELSO,

Embracing the Parishes of Eckford, Ednam, Hounam, Kelso, Makerstoun, Morebattle, Roxburgh, Smailholm, Sprouston, Stichill, Linton, and Yetholm.

One Meeting annually, on the first Thursday of May.
William Brown, Surveyor.
Wm. Smith and Chas. Robson, Clerks and Treasurers.

---

* Kelso does the only very extensive pork-curing business in the district (*see* p. 48). The carcases are collected over a radius of above 30 miles (taking in Selkirk, Stowe, and Eyemouth). The accounts at the different establishments not having been kept with a view to such a return, we have been unable to procure the definite number of the carcases received for the season just ended ; but 4000 is supposed to be near, and *under*, the mark, weighing 48,000 stones, and representing a value of at least £16,000.
The following statement will shew the position of Kelso as a pork-curing locality in the south of Scotland :—

	Carcases.	Imp. stones.	Value.
Dumfries	7307	102,298	£34,949
Kelso	4000	48,000	16,000
Annan	3200	44,800	15,306
Castle-Douglas, &c.	3200	44,800	14,933
Lockerbie	2092	32,343	11,050

(*See* Hawick, Jedburgh, and Yetholm.)

CARRIERS.

BERWICK—Railway Station, daily ; Andrew Mack, Spread Eagle, Tuesday and Friday.
COLDSTREAM, CORNHILL, AND DUNSE—Railway Station, daily ; Andrew Mack, Spread Eagle, Tuesday and Friday.
DUNSE—John Dick, Commercial Inn, Friday.
EARLSTOUN—Alex. Simpson, and Thos. Kerr, Square, Friday.
ECCLES—John Grant, Square, Friday.
EDINBURGH AND THE NORTH—Railway Station, daily ; Alex. Simpson, Square, Friday.
GALASHIELS—Railway Station, daily.
GLASGOW AND THE WEST—Railway Station, daily.
GORDON—W. Murray, daily, Coal Market ; John Frisken, Friday ; R. Robinson, Tuesday and Friday—both Square.
GREENLAW—John Dick, Commercial Inn, Friday.
HAWICK AND CARLISLE—Railway Station, daily.
HAWICK—Thomas Robson, Weigh-House, Tuesday and Friday.
HASSINGTON—Robt. Stark, Square, Friday.
HOSELAW-HILL—Wm. Davidson, Square, Friday.
HOWTEL—James Wallace, Square, Friday.
HOUNAM—T. Edmonstone, daily ; A. Riddell, Friday—both Weigh-House.
HUME—Charles Lauder, Square, Friday.
JEDBURGH—Thomas Robson, Weigh-House, Tuesday and Friday.
LEITHOLM—Thomas Brown, Square ; John Gibb, Salmon Inn ; Wm Fair ; J. Riddell—both Square—all Friday.
MERTOUN—Railway, daily, to Maxton Station.
MOREBATTLE—Wood, Square, Tuesday and Friday ; Thomas Edmonstone, Weigh-House, daily.
NEWCASTLE AND THE SOUTH, Railway Station, daily.
OXNAM—James Bruce, Weigh-House, Friday.
PLOUGHLANDS—John Grierson, Square, Friday.
ROXBURGH—John Fair, Square, Friday.
ROXBURGH-NEWTOWN—Robert Inglis, Square, Friday.
ST BOSWELL'S AND BOWDEN—Robert Clark, Commercial Inn, Friday.
SMAILHOLM—Thos. Kinghorn, and A. Scott, Square, Friday.
SPROUSTON—William Jamieson, Weigh-House, Friday.
STICHILL—James Wood, Square, Friday.
WARK—James Brown, Weigh-House, Friday.
WOOLER—Andrew Mack. Spread Eagle, Tuesday and Friday.
YETHOLM—W. Watson, Weigh-House, daily ; J. Cockburn, Weigh-House, Tuesday and Friday ; Robt. Walker, and James Steel—both Square—both Friday.

CONVEYANCE BY RAILWAY.

To Edinburgh, Jedburgh, Hawick, and all parts of the North-East and West, by Kelso Branch of North British line.
To Berwick, Newcastle, and all parts of the South, by Kelso Branch of North-Eastern line.
(For arrivals and departures, *see* Monthly Time Tables.)
Omnibuses from the Cross Keys and Queen's Head Hotels attend all the trains—Fares, 6d.

H

DIRECTORY.

————

TRADES, RESIDENTS, AND PUBLIC OFFICES.

Those marked thus (*) are Registered Voters.

Abbey Court

6 Aitken, James, cattle dealer
9 Brown, William, Belmount Cottage, road surveyor
24 Haldane, Mrs.
20 Kydd, John
1 Paxton, Mrs., dressmaker
St. Andrew's Episcopal Chapel (Rev. Hill Scott's)—*see* page 79
14*Wright, George (clerk to Smiths & Robson)
(See *Belmount Place*)

Abbey Row

Abbey Parish Church (Rev. James Smith's)—*see* p. 78
*Darling, Jas S., W.S., *senior magistrate* (agent, Bank of S.)
Henderson, Misses, Abbey View Cottage
Kelso Grammar and Parish Schools.
Kelso Reading Room, Mary Tennant, housekeeper.
*Robson, Alexander W. (of Robson & Son, Bowmont Street)

Belmount Place (Abbey Court)

30 Pilkington, Thomas
28 Robertson, John, M.D.
26 Roberton, Mrs. (late of Harpertoun)
26 Walker, Major (late E.I.C.S.)

Bowmont Street.

39 Aimers, John, cooper (house, No. 38)
*Allan, Richard, of Allanbank
34 Aitchison, Gilbert (of Henderson & Co., Roxburgh Street)
21 Aitchison, Thomas, *sub-inspector of poor,* of Bowmont Cottage
52*Archbald, William, Orchard Field
14*Bookless, John, surgeon

32 Broomfield, Misses
4 Bryce, John, shoemaker
*Bulman, John, of Pringle Bank (west)
10 *Commercial Inn,* *John Rodgers
30 Dawson, Mrs., sen.
33 Dodds, David, builder
26 Fearby, John, potatoe merchant
First U. P. Church (Rev. H. Renton's)—*see* page 79
Greenlaw, Miss, Allanbank
37 Hume, John, joiner
2 Hunter, Mrs. James
*Hunter, James, writer, of Pringle Bank (east)
40 Hutchison, Colin, writer (office, 52 Square)
16 Jarvie, Rev. James (*East U. P. Manse*)
Johnston, James, (late of Rumbleton Law)
27 *Kelso Chronicle,* Andrew Murray, publisher (house, Edenside Road)
   Assistant—Thomas Craig
Kelso Jail, George Lamb, keeper
Kirkland, John, of *Bowmont Street Academy*
13 M'Kerron, Rev. Peter (of North Church; appointed 1864)
50*Mein, William (of Stuart & M., 2 Square) of Croft House
37 Mollison & M'Vitie, millwrights, engineers, and machine makers.
37 Mollison, Alexander (of M. & M'Vitie)
22 Paterson's, Misses, *Boarding Establishment*
40 Pound, Miss, Inch Cottage
42 Pringle, Mrs. (late of Gordon Mid-Mill)
40 Pyle, Mrs., Inch Cottage
12 Rathie, Robert, livery stables
Robertson & Son, builders and joiners
20 Robertson, Mrs. Dr.
Robson & Son, wool merchants and tanners (*see* Abbey Row)
Roman Catholic Chapel
30 Ross, Mrs. and Misses
7 Rutherford, Miss
11 Smith, Mrs. C., rope and net maker
41 Stoddart, Thomas Tod, advocate, Bellevue House
36 Symington, John, slater
17 Tunna, John (of Henderson & Co.)
5 Weatherston & Co., fleshers
33 White, Rev. Robert (of *First U.P. Church*)

Bowmont Street (East)

*Chirnside, Benjamin
Reformed Presbyterian Church (Rev. John Guy's), John Bennet, 56 Horse Market, custodier

Hogarth, Mrs. John
5 Kennedy, Thomas, coach-builder
    Foreman—Thomas Brown
 *Robson, Charles (of Smiths & R., Bridge Street) of Grove Hill
 *Renton, Rev. Henry, M.A., *First U.P. Manse*
4 Wilson, William, joiner

Butts

1 Ballantyne, Edward
    County Police Station—Sergeant Robert Ainslie.
    Hambly, Misses
    Independent Chapel (*see* page 79)
3 *Roxburghe School-house*
    Rutherford, Thomas, gardener

Bridge Street

    Abbey of Kelso, Ruins of
6 Broomfield, Misses, bakers
10*Brotherston, William (late grocer)
    Croall, P., & Sons, coachmakers (of Edinburgh), Bridge-end
26 Crosbie, James (of Kelso Mills)
    Dickson, Miss, dressmaker
29*Fleming, David
31 Glaister, William, jobbing smith and bell-hanger
    Hardie, Alexander, shoemaker, Kelso Bridge House
38 Hogarth, Andrew, painter and paper-hanger
8*Jeffrey, James
8 Jeffrey, John, shoemaker
 *Jerdan, William (of *Kelso Mail*), Abbey Gardens
1 Johnston, J. & J., saddlers, iron merchants, and rope manufacturers (*see* Oven Wynd)
10 *Kelso Mail Office*, William Jerdan, printer
    Foreman—John Maclean
18 Lauder, Charles, grocer
5, 7 Lugton & Porteous, general drapers, silk mercers, and clothiers
    Millinery Department—Miss Mitchell
    Cutter—Benjamin Robertson
 7*Lugton, Peter (of L. & Porteous)
27 Mackintosh, James, carver and gilder
34 Mitchell, Misses, milliners
 *Porteous, Richard R. (of Lugton & P.) 5 Havannah Close
22 *Queen's Head Hotel*, *Thomas Hownam
46 Reid, Mrs., nurse
    Agent for Littlejohn's Confectionery
    Servants' Register

25*Rutherford, Robert, grocer
19 Scott, George, bootmaker
15 Scott, John, grocer and spirit dealer
12 Seton, Misses, milliners.
    Smiths & Robson's writing chambers, Abbey House (*see* Grove Hill, East Bowmont Street)
    Managing Clerk—George Wright.
 *Smith, Rev. James, *Manse of Kelso*
 *Smith, William (of S. & Robson), of Abbey House
30 *Spread Eagle Inn*, Thomas Hall
11 Steel, James, licensed dealer in game, fishmonger, and poulterer, &c.
23 Strathearn & Cornwall, china merchants
50 Taylor, Andrew, shoemaker
3 Turnbull, John, flesher
28 Walker, James, baker
40 Watson, George, tobacconist
13 *Weigh House Inn*, James Milne
    Wilson, Miss Margaret, Abbey Gardens

Coal Market

4 Boyd, William, (of C. W. & W. B., 11 Wood Market)
13 Bulman's, John, joiner works (house, Pringle Bank, east)
    Clerk—John Gray
    Foreman—James Henderson
15 Crosbie, Thomas, baker
2 Hume, James, cow-keeper
3 Johnston, James, baker
11 Kerr, George, grocer
4 Laing, George, watchmaker
9*Michie, John, architect and slater
10*Riddell, John, innkeeper
4 Rutherford, Mrs. Thomas (late of Jedburgh)
16 Slight, John, meal-dealer
1 Stuart, George, gardener
(See *Simon Square*)

Crawford Street

    Maxwell, D., & Son, coach-builders
    Red Lion Inn, Alexander Buddo
    Rickets, James, cabinet-maker

Dunn's Wynd

6 Middlemas, Andrew, soda water manufacturer
    Cork manufacturer, and ale and porter merchant
3 Young, John, innkeeper

Edenside Road

Broomfield, David (of Roberton & B., writers, Square), Goshen Cottage
Dunn, Andrew, corn dealer and manure agent
Hogg, William, market gardener
*Logan, Peter (of Redpath and Sons), Goshen Bank
Milne, William (of M. Brothers, 8 Wood Market)
*Murray, Andrew, (of *Kelso Chronicle*), Goshen House
*Rathie, John, farmer
*Redpath, James (of R. & Sons), of Goshen Bank
*Robertson, Peter, of Neworth
*Rutherfurd, Robert, of Paradise
Rutherfurd, Mrs., sen., Paradise
*Williamson, Robert, of Kerrfield
Wilson, Robert, colporteur

Forest Field

 4 Allan, James, letter-carrier
15 Balmer, Robert, joiner at Floors
 1*Bonar, Rev. H., D.D., *North Free Church Manse*
 2 Brown, Mrs.
11 Brown, Thomas, foreman coachmaker
 9 Cockburn, James, saddler
 7 Cook, Daniel
 8 Cook, James, tinsmith
10 Henderson, John, coachmaker
 6 Hume, Thomas, joiner
10 Keith, John, hairdresser (shop, 18 Wood Market)
17 Ledgerwood, John
14 M'Call, George, printer
18 Mills, Miss
13 Mitchell, Mrs.
    North Parish (quoad sacra) Church and Schools (Rev. P. M'Kerron's; appointed September 1864), William Dickson, 11 Coal Market, custodier
16 Park, Miss
 7 Ridge, Richard
 5 Tyce, William, joiner
    Union Poor House, John Millar, governor
 3 Williamson, James, coachsmith
12 Winchester, John

Forest Field Villas

Aitchison, Alexander
Aitchison, William

Douglas, Mrs. G. A.
Hogarth, Mrs. and Miss
*Somner, Francis
Williams, Miss, *Maitland House Boarding Academy*
Wilson, Misses Margaret and Jane

Horse Market

52 Allan, Robert, shoemaker
23 Awburn, Mrs., confectioner and refreshment room keeper
 5 *Black Swan Inn*, Thomas Irvine
40 Bell, Peter, grocer and meal dealer
 7 Bruce, George, shoemaker
14 Cook, James, teacher of music
12 Dods, Mrs. E., grocer
    Managing Assistant—John Cooper
    East U. P. Church (Rev. James Jarvie's), John Currie, 23 Forest Field, custodier
10*Ellis, James, tailor
 1 Gilray, George, ironmonger
    Kelso Agent for Smith & Wellstood's Cooking Stoves and Portable Boilers
    Girls' School, Miss Woodrow, teacher
70 Henderson & Son, plumbers
70 Henderson, Mrs. (of H. & Son)
    Hogg, William, joiner
57 Hope, *James & *John, smiths
    Infant School, Miss Knox, teacher
10*Johnston, Andrew (late of the *K. Chronicle*)
 8 Kennedy, John, draper
64 Kerr, George, shoemaker
56 Liddell, Robert, fishmonger
 3*M'Dougall, James (late shoemaker)
62 Middlemas, Joseph (late grocer)
 3 Milne Brothers, drapers. (See 8 *Wood Market*)
34*Mitchell, Thomas, draper
48 Nelson, Thomas, grocer and spirit dealer
10 Nichol, William, cabinet-maker †
 6 Nicholson & Son, clothiers
 4*Nicholson, Alexander (of N. & Son)
27 *Office of Parochial Board*, Alexander Morrison, inspector
67 Oliver, Frederick, professor of music
38 Ormston, Jonathan, shoemaker
20*Pittillo, Archibald, horse dealer, *Elliot's Close*
29*Pringle, John, agricultural implement depôt

---

† Mr. Nichol's premises were formerly the Kelso Theatre, erected by the French prisoners, who, to the number of about 200, resided in Kelso, on parole, from 1810 to the end of the war (see introductory notice, p. 72).

36*Romanes, Simon, iron-founder (house, 3 Simon Square)
17*Rule, John, watchmaker
36*Smith, Alexander, currier
60 Stewart, Alexander, grocer
 2 Watson, William, tailor
16 Watt, Margaret, dealer in small wares
18 Weatherston, John, cattle dealer, *Elliot's Close*
15 Welsh, William, baker (late Mrs. Scott's)
25 Woodrow, Robert, basket maker
61*Young, John, wright

Horse Market Foot

1 Gray, John, grocer
6*Middlemas, Robert, grocer
 *Rutherford, William, dairy farmer
2 Rutherfurd's, J. & J. H., printing and bookbinding establishment †
         David Cottam, foreman, printing office
         William Adams, foreman, bindery

Knowes

7 Clazy, William, *manager of Gas Works*
 *Darling, William, of Abbey Bank
   Darling, Misses, of Abbey Bank
 *Humble, John, of Waverley Cottage ‡
 *Hunter, George Duncan, *Rector*, *Grammar School*
6 *Kelso Gas Works*
 *Kerr, James B., of Walton Cottage
8 Lawson, Mrs.
   Miller, John, corn dealer

Maxwell Lane

   Douglas, Miss Arabella, of St. Leonards
1 Jack, Ralph, gardener and contractor
   Lillie, Andrew, market gardener
5 Fair, Miss   ⎫
   Dunlop, Mrs.   ⎪ *Maxwell*
4 Main, Mrs.   ⎬ *Place*
   Main, A. W., writer ⎭

---

† These premises were formerly the Church of the Original Seceders, who have long ceased to exist as a separate community in Kelso.
‡ Sir Walter Scott, when a boy, and attending the Kelso Grammar School, resided in this house (then known as *The Cottage*) with his aunts. The present proprietor has greatly enlarged the premises.

Mill Wynd

 *Crosbie, Thomas (of C. & Co., Kelso Mills)
11 Hume, Martha, grocer
24 Jeffrey, Peter, shoemaker
 Kelso Flour Mills, Thomas Crosbie & Co.
12 Munro, Mrs., china merchant
 7 Nisbet, William, grocer
 4*Robson, George, grocer
11 Sadler, Miss, dressmaker
 3 *Salmon Inn*, David Robertson
20 Scott, Walter, broker
   Scottish Legal Burial Society, George Geddes, agent
22 Walker, George, grocer
14 Wilson, James, tinsmith

Mayfield (suburb of)

(*See* p. 113.)

(*See* p. 113.)

Oven Wynd

 *Brown, John, (late baker)
 *Elliot, Alexander, of Ramsay Lodge
 *Johnston, John (of J. & J. J.)
 *Johnston, James, *jun. magistrate* (of J. & J. J.)
   Kelso United Library
   Smith & Son, pork curers, &c.
   Smith, Mrs., (of S. & Son)
 *Smith, James (of S. & Son)

Peat Wynd

   Jack, Andrew, carter
 *Liddell, James, carter

Pointfield Lane (Shedden Park Road)

   Gillie, J. F., of Pointfield (late of Jedburgh)
   Guy, Rev. John (*R. P. Manse*)
 *Robertson, Thomas Fair (of St. Foin), Hermitage.
   Rutherfurd, Mrs. John, Prior Bank

Rose Lane

 *Clark, John J., of Victoria Cottage, horse trainer
   Dodds, Thomas, street contractor
   Nichol, Robert, Park Cottage, cattle dealer
   Whitelaw, George, cow-keeper

Roxburgh Street

75 Allan, Mrs., grocer
41 Archibald, Miss B.
 Arneil, Mrs., nurse
 *Baird, Alexander (late of Parkend), *Gray's Close*
 Baird, William, carter,   *do.*
30 *Baths and Steam Wash-Houses*, A. M'Kenzie, Anna Cottage, proprietor
153 *Bowhill, James, shoemaker
155 Brooks, James, grocer
151 *Brooks, John, farmer, carter, and contractor
32 Broomfield, David, cabinet maker (house, No. 81)
153 Brunlees, Robert, rope, twine, and sheep net-manufacturer
5 Bunyan, James, haircutter
80 *Calvert, James, hatter
80 Calvert, Miss, dressmaker
12 *Clark, John, grocer
13 *Crown Inn*, John Speirs
19 Dickinson, Mrs.
68 Dodds, Alexander, gardener
175 Duncan, Mrs., Elms
30 Dunn, William, supervisor of Excise
116 *Elliot, Thomas
 Floors Castle—Principal Entrance
50 Frain, Mr., artist, Studio of (house, 15 Square)
145 Gardiner, Walter, groom of the chambers, Floors Castle
62 Gibb, William, grocer
119 *Gow, John, grocer, tea, wine, and spirit merchant
133 *Guthrie, John, *Town Treasurer*
24 Hall, James, poulterer and fishmonger
91 Hamilton, Thomas, M.D., Tweed View House
2 Henderson & Co., drapers and clothiers
 Millinery Department—Miss Reynolds
 Cutter—James Hastie
 (See 17 & 34 *Bowmont Street*)
81 Henderson, George, cooper
4 *Henderson, John (late draper)
53 Hervey, Archibald, currier and exporter
 Manager—James Kinghorn
48 *Hill, Thomas, smith and bell-hanger
25 Honeyman, John, baker
120 Hood, Miss, of Walton Hall
31 Hooper & Miller, ironmongers
 Working Foreman—William Laidlaw
33 *Hooper, Peter (of H. & Miller)
35 Hunter, John, plumber and gas-fitter
55 Jack, John, baker
52 Jack, Mrs., meal dealer

11 Johnston, Thomas, grocer
91 *Johnston, James, plasterer, dealer in cements, plaster of Paris, etc.
84 *Kelso Dispensary*, Mrs. Janet Stewart, housekeeper
50 *Kelso Library*, James Scott, resident custodier
112 Kyle, Peter, tanner and skinner
16 Laidlaw, William, grocer, tea, wine, and spirit merchant
126 *Lamb, James shoemaker
81 Lamb, Mrs. Alexander
14 Lockie, George, flesher
18 Millar, J. & Co., watchmakers and photographers
 Mills, Thomas, gardener, *Gray's Close*
38 Mitchell, John (of M. & Balmer, 16 Square)
54 Murray, Alexander, missionary, North Free Church
27 Murray, Andrew, clogger
82 Murray, John, clogger
82 Murray, Mrs., grocer
28 Moscrip, John, *police superintendent*
28 Muir, John, editor of *Kelso Mail*
 North Free Church (Rev. Dr. Bonar's), in course of erection
125 *Ormiston, John, farmer
101 Plummer, James, grocer, pork curer, and rabbit dealer
66 Porteous, Misses, china merchants
6 *Purves, George, R. baker
15 Rae, William, baker
26 Redpath & Sons, jewellers, hardware merchants, and general warehousemen. (See *Goshen House, Edenside Road*)
 Manager of Retail Department— William Brown
 Foreman of Wholesale Department—Henry Dick
 Commercial Traveller—John Thomson
19 Renwick, P. A., china merchant
128 Reynolds, Henry, Floors' head groom
79 *Robertson, Andrew, builder and contractor
45 Robertson, James, & Son, builders and joiners
47 *Robertson, James (of J. R. & Son)
99 *Robertson, Ninian, cattle dealer
8 Ross, William, nail manufacturer
105 Rutherford, Mrs., baker
47 Sadler, Gavan, grocer
21 Sadler, William, clothier
1 Scoon, Robert, flesher
16 Scott, Mrs. and Miss
23 Scott, Robert, pavier
39 Sinclair, Joseph, baker
143 Skeete, H. A., commission agent
 *Stuart, John (late surgeon) of Roxburgh Place
 Stuart, Misses Ellen and Catharine, *do.*
86 Tait, James, editor of *Kelso Chronicle*, Falcon Hall

103 Tait, Thomas, pavier and thatcher
 75 Trotter, Robert, grocer
    Town Water Works
147 Turton, Mrs. and Miss
 50 *Tweedside Physical and Antiquarian Society's Museum*, Jas.
    Scott, resident custodier
114 Vernon, William Frederick, dentist (of V. & Son)
139 Wakefield, William, hatter and clothes' cleaner
149 Waldie, Mrs. and Miss
 43 Whitlock, Misses (late of Maisondieu)
    Wight, William, excise officer
  7 Wood, George, bootmaker

Sydenham Road (Roxburgh Street).

Lamb, William, & Son, gardeners
Tait, H., nurseryman and seedsman (shop, 22 Wood Market)

Shedden Park Road

 45 Aitken, James (of 14 Square), Lime House
 38*Davidson, Adam, smith
 31 Dickison, Benjamin, builder
  5 Elliot, William, stocking-weaver
 33 Eskdale, John, cattle salesman
 29*Henderson, Francis, gardener
 16 Hogarth, Andrew, millwright and engineer
 12 Huggan, Robert, grocer
 25 Miller, James, gardener
 46 Pirie, Mrs., of Lime Cottage
 43 Purves, Robert, slater
 35 Robertson, William, v.-surgeon
  1 Romanes, Miss, dressmaker
    Shedden Park Academy, Miss Allan, teacher
 21 Smith, George, cabinetmaker
    Sprouston Free Church (Rev. George Craig's), Walter Mat-
    thewson, 35 Roxburgh Street, custodier
    Stewart, Archibald, Tweedbank (late of Calcutta)
  6 Watson, Mrs., grocer
 12 Wight, James, cow-keeper
(See *Pointfield Lane*)

Square

 14*Aitken, James, jeweller and watchmaker
    Hardware and fancy goods, fishing tackle, etc. (house, 45
    Shedden Park Road)
 48 Allan, James, saddler
 28 Ballantyne, George, wine merchant and grocer
  3 Balmer, Mrs. S., ironmonger.
 10 *British Linen Co.'s Bank*, Andrew Roberton, resident agent
 29*Broomfield, William, provision dealer

 51 Broomfield, Miss, confectioner
    Servants' Register
 46 *City of Glasgow Bank*, William Robson, resident agent
  8 *Commercial Bank*, *James Douglas, resident agent
 54*Craig, George, *junior magistrate*, shoemaker
 39 *Cross Keys Hotel*, *George Oliver, jun.
    Robert Forsyth, head waiter
  7 Douglas, Charles, M.D. (late H.M. Bengal Army)
  7 Douglas, Mrs. and Misses
 52 Fairbairn & Penny's office
 36 Forrest & Sons, fishing tackle makers
 35*Forrest, John (of F. & Sons)
 15 Frain, Robert, artist
  6*Gray, Robert, coppersmith
 18*Hardie, Ebenezer, cabinet-maker and upholsterer
 23*Henderson, James, draper and clothier
    Cutter—John Cairns
 13 Hogg, John (successor to the late George Watt), grocer
    James Wood, clerk
 52 Hutchinson, Colin A., writing chambers (house Inch cottage)
  1 Mackenzie, William M., M.D.
 33 M'Gregor, William, house painter
 19 Macpherson, John S., china merchant
 49 Matthew, Mrs., dressmaker
 15 Mein, Mrs. and Miss
 16 Mitchell & Balmer, drapers and clothiers (*see* 38 *Roxburgh St.*)
    Millinery Department—Miss Hardie
 12 *National Bank*, Thomas E. Watson, resident accountant
  8 *N. S. Savings Bank*, J. B. Kerr of Walton Cottage, actuary
 15 *New Reading and Billiard Rooms*
 39 Oliver, George, sen., farmer
 34*Pattison, Joseph, bookseller
 15 Purves, Mrs. and Miss
 14 *Receiving Office for the North British Railway Company*
 48 *Receiving Office for the North-Eastern Railway Company*
  9 Roberton & Broomfield, writing chambers
 15*Rutherfurd, James H. (of J. & J. H. R.)
 17 Rutherfurd, J. & J. H., booksellers, stationers, printers, and
    bookbinders (printing office, etc., 2 Horse Market Foot)
 21*Shiels, James, wine merchant and grocer
  5 Smith, William (of Roxburghe School)
  2 Stuart & Mein, seedsmen. *Nurseries*—Rosebank and Croft
    House. Nursery Manager—George Greig (*see* Croft
    House, *Bowmont Street*)
 12 Tait, James, W.S. (of Edenside), writing chambers
    Head Clerk—Robert Faulds
 51 *Temperance Hotel and Refreshment Rooms*, Miss Broomfield
 31 Torrie, William, grocer

Town Hall—James Ker, policeman, Elliot's Close, custodier
27*Train, Thomas, hatter
26 Train, Miss B.
45*Vost, Henry, chemist and druggist
12 Watson, Mr., sen. (late of Dumfries)
41*Weddell, George, plumber, glazier, and gas-fitter
50 Wight, Mrs. and Misses
43 Wilson, Mrs. Christopher, stationer, news-agent, bookseller
    and bookbinder

Simon Square

1 Middlemiss, James, smith
3*Romanes, James L., postmaster
2*Young, John, livery stables

Susie's Lane

*Dunn, Thomas, of Hempseed Cottage
Melrose, Mrs., of Rose Cottage
Robson, James, Maxwell Cottage
Thomson, Mrs.,   Do.

The Terrace

5 Allan, Misses, dressmaker
1 Craig, Rev. George (of *Sprouston Free Church*), Hilton Mye
2 Dawson Mrs., of Duncan House
6 Fairbairn, Misses
*Mackenzie, A., of Anna Cottage, Terrace Foot
1 Morrison, Miss, of Hilton Mye.
Robson, W., & Son, wool merchants and tanners
4*Scott, James, *librarian of Kelso Library*

Union Street

2 Adams, David, draper
8 Hall, Mrs.
6 Laing, William (late china merchant)
1*Martin, Peter, painter
4 *Ragged School*, E. Naismith, resident teacher (*see* p. 119)
9 Thomson, Miss
9 Thomson, Robert (late of Sucleridge)
8 Wilson, Miss Elizabeth (late of Abbey Gardens)

Wood Market

19 Aitken, John, flesher
27 *Bank of Scotland*, J. S. & J. Darling, resident agents
22 Borgh, Baroness de
9*Boyd, Charles W. (of C. W. & W. B.)
11 Boyd, C. W. & W., grocers
68 Bruce, Robert, grocer
4 Brunlees, Miss

22 Christison, John, foreman tailor
44 Cleland, William, shoemaker
3 Curry, Miss Phebe
29 Darling's J. S., writing chambers and house
    Bookkeeper—John Robertson
28*Davidson, Thomas, shoemaker
40 Dippie, Misses, milliners
26 Dodds & Co., druggists
62 Ferguson, W. K., grocer
62 Gillies, Miss, tea merchant
34 Guthrie, John, watchmaker
3 Hastie, David (of H. & Co.)
5 Hastie, D. & Co., grocers
2 Henderson, James, tobacconist
64 Hunter, Mrs.
42 Johnson, Miss Ellison (late of Greenlaw)
18 Keith, John, hairdresser
31 *Kelso Corn Exchange*, Edward Ballantyne, 1 Butts, custodier
22 Ker, Miss, dressmaker
37 Knox, Mrs., dressmaker
48*Mabon, Robert, cutler
22 Mein, Misses
7 *Medical Hall*, George F. Dodds
42 Melrose, Miss, grocer
4 Melrose, Mrs., dressmaker
10 Milne, Archibald (of M. Brothers. See *Edenside Road*)
8 Milne Brothers, drapers. (See 3 *Horse Market*)
    Millinery Department—Miss Paxton
41 *Post Office*, J. L. Romanes, postmaster
16 Rutherford, George baker
21 Scott, John, shoemaker
62 Simpson, Mrs.
30 Somner, Francis, seedsman
24 *Stamp and Tax Office*, Alexander Elliot, collector and dis-
    tributor (house, Ramsay Lodge, Oven Wynd)
33*Swan, Robert, writer
35 Swan's, Robert writing chambers
    Thomas Hunter, N.P.
20*Tait, Henry, seedsman. *Nursery*—Sydenham
6 Tait, Peter, tinsmith
14 *Temperance Hotel*, Thomas Slight
9 *White Swan Inn*, H. F. Beverley

Winchester Row

*Davidson, Peter, mason
5 Meikle, Mrs.
3*Stevenson, Walter, Floors' fisherman
    Warren, Mrs.

Suburb of Mayfield

Armoury, Kelso Volunteer Rifle Company
Hospital of the Kelso Parochial Board
Mill, Mrs. and Misses
Public Bleaching and Drying Ground *

Village of Maxwellheugh

Armstrong, William, mason.
Bozman, Hodgson T., cattle dealer.
Briggs, Hugh, meal dealer.
Chambers, John, auctioneer.
Glendinning, Misses.
Hogarth, Robert (of Heiton and Maxwellheugh Mills).
Lillie, Mrs.
Maxwellheugh School, Misses Hilson.
Murray, John, smith.
Scott, Mrs., baker.

Kelso Railway Station

(Beyond Maxwellheugh, ⅛ of a mile distant from Kelso—a good 15 minutes' walk, by a sloping and generally muddy road.)
Resident Station Master, Manager of Goods Department, and N. B. Railway Company's Coal Agent—David Trotter.

OFFICES AND DEPOTS

Armstrong, Adam, corn merchant.
Dunn, Andrew,   do.
Dunn, Thomas,   do.
Fearby, John, potatoe and commission merchant.
Gordon, David, weigher
Johnson & Co. (Berwick-on-Tweed), of Scremerston and Shoreswood Collieries, and Lime and Manure Agents—John Hills, manager.
Miller, J., corn merchant.
Pringle, John, coal, lime, and manure agent.
Refreshment Rooms—John Chambers.
Skeete, Henry, Plashett's coal agent ; Robt. Low, manager
Stawart, Robert, coal and lime agent.

Railway Receiving Offices

North British Railway Company—James Aitken, 14 Square.
North Eastern—James Allan, 48 Square.

---

* At page 70 we state that the Anna, or islet in the Tweed at Kelso, belongs to the town ; we find it really belongs to the Duke of Roxburghe, but that the town has a *right* to it as a bleaching and drying ground.

COUNTRY RESIDENTS IN THE PARISH.

Aitchison, George, manager, Pylestead farm.
*Bell, Alexander, farmer, Oakfield.
Black, Alexander, butler, Floors Castle.
Blaickie, Walter, master of works, Floors estate
*Boyd, Alexander, manufacturer, Wooden Mills.
*Brodie, Thomas, farmer, Easter Muirdean.
Cairns, John, manager, Spylaw farm.
*Cockburn, William, superintendent, Hendersyde Park estate, Westwood Cottage.
Dance, Mrs., Moss Cottage.
Dryden, William, manager, home farm, Springwood Park.
*Dunn, David, farmer, Berryhill.
*Elliot, James (of Hermitage, Kelso), farmer, Galalaw.
Grogan, Charles, *chef de cuisine*, Floors Castle.
*Kay, John, farmer. Middle Softlaw.
Lamb, Mrs., housekeeper, Floors Castle.
*Murray, James, farmer, Wallace Nick.
Rose, Hector, head gardener, Floors Gardens.
*Scott, James, farmer, Softlaw Hill-head.
Scott, Andrew, farmer and cattle salesman, Maisondieu.
Scott, Rev. Hill (of *St. Andrew's Chapel*), Bamff Mill Cottage.
Swanston, James, manager, home farm, Wooden.
Trotter, John, agricultural implement maker, Shepherd's Bush.
Turnbull, Thomas, Muserig (formerly of Charleston U. S.)
Turnbull, John, manager, Floors home farm, Muserig.
Turnbull, Thomas, blacksmith, Muserig.
Waldie, Mrs., Pinnaclehill farm.
Wood, James, head game-keeper, Floors kennels
Wemyss, George, head gardener, Springwood Park.

SEATS OF COUNTY FAMILIES, SMALLER RESIDENCES, &c.

FLOORS CASTLE (*see* p. 70).

The principal residence of his Grace the Duke of Roxburghe (James Henry Robert Innes Ker, K.T.), Marquis of Bowmont and Cessford, Earl of Roxburghe, Earl of Kelso, Viscount Broxmouth, Baron Ker of Cessford and Caverton, in the peerage of Scotland ; Earl Innes, in that of the United Kingdom ; and a Baronet of Nova Scotia ; born 12th July 1816 ; succeeded to the Scottish honours, as 6th Duke, at the decease of his father, 19th July 1823 ; and created a Peer of the United Kingdom, as Earl Innes, in 1838 ; married 29th December 1836, Susanna Stephenia, only child of the late Lieut.-General Sir Charles Dalbiac, K.C. H., and has issue—
James Henry Robert, Marquis of Bowmont and Cessford, born 5th September 1839.

Charles John, Lieutenant, Scots Fusilier Guards, born 31st December 1842; married, 15th January 1866, Blanche-Mary, fourth daughter of Lieutenant-Col. Thomas Peers Williams, of Temple House, Great Marlow, M.P.

Susan Harriet, married 5th August 1857, to James Grant Suttie, Esq., yr. of Balgone, now residing at Maines, Chirnside parish, Berwickshire (which *see*).

Charlotte Isabella, married 28th October 1862, to George Russell, Esq., of Curzon Street, London, and has issue—a son, born 28th October 1864.

Other Seats of the Roxburghe family—Broxmouth Park, Haddingtonshire; Greenhill, in Hounam parish; Byrecleugh, in Longformacus, Berwickshire. London Residence—Clarendon Hotel, Albemarle Street.

SPRINGWOOD PARK (*see* p. 70).

The residence of Sir George Henry Scott Douglas, bart., born 19th June 1826; succeeded his father, as 4th baronet, 23d January 1836; married 1st November 1851, Maria Juna Petronilla, eldest daughter of Senor Don Francisco Sanchez de Pina, of Gibraltar, and has issue—

> James Henry, born 27th May 1853.
> George Brisbane, born 22d December 1856.
> Francis John, born 27th November 1858.
> Mary Helena Henrietta.

Sir George was formerly a Captain in the 34th Regiment, and is now Major of the Roxburgh and Selkirkshire Battalion of Volunteers.

BROOMLANDS.

In the immediate neighbourhood of Kelso—the property of the Duke of Roxburghe. Occupied by James Brunton, Esq., Chamberlain to His Grace.

EDENSIDE.

At Edenside Road—the property and residence of *James Tait, Esq., W.S. (of Langrigg, Berwickshire).

EDNAM HOUSE (*see* pp. 71, 85).

Originally the *Havanna House*—the residence of Mrs. Robertson (Margaretta Jane Miller, daughter of the late Commander William Miller, R.N.), widow of the late John Robertson, Esq., who purchased the property in 1819.

Mrs. Robertson was maternal aunt of the late Robert Shedden, Esq., who died at Mazatlan in 1849, from exposure and fatigue endured in Behring's Straits, while generously searching for the missing expedition under Sir John Franklin. Mr. Shedden had previously, in his pleasure yacht (the celebrated Royal Thames schooner *Nancy Dawson*, of only 164 tons), been the first to circumnavigate the globe in a vessel of so small a size; and in the same vessel, in his search for the Franklin Expedition, he reached Elson's Bay, in long. 154° W.—about two degrees farther to the N.E. than any sailing vessel had hitherto gone. As Mr. Shedden died unmarried, and was the last of his family, Mrs. Robertson, to perpetuate the name of her nephew, presented the town of Kelso with the Park, described at p. 85.

EDENBANK.

A newly erected house, situated about 2 miles from Kelso by the race course road—the property and summer residence of Patrick Panton, Esq., M.D. (of London and Rodmersham, Kent).

PINNACLEHILL (*see* p. 71).

The property of Walter Macmillan Scott, Esq., of Wauchope. (*see* Hobkirk parish) Henry Kelsall, Esq., occupier.

ROSEBANK (*see* p. 71).

The property of J. J. E. Brown, Esq., Penang, who purchased it in 1863. William Younger, Esq. (of 15 Moray Place, Edinburgh), occupier.

SYDENHAM HOUSE.

Situated two miles from Kelso on the Ednam Road—the property of Sir William Dickson, Bart.† J. B. Parker, Esq. (of Manor House, Little Cawthorpe, Lincolnshire), occupier.

TWEEDBANK.

In the immediate neighbourhood of Kelso—the property and residence of *Edward Johnson, Esq. (late of Calcutta), of Adderstone Mains, Northumberland.

WALTON HALL.

Situated at the head of Roxburgh Street, on a pinnacle overhanging the Tweed—the residence and property of Miss Hood, daughter of the late Thomas Hood, Esq., of Hardacres.

Walton Hall was originally erected in 1820 by John Ballantyne, of "Ballantyne Press" celebrity. In the Life of Sir Walter Scott, Lockhart describes the view from Walton Hall [over-looking the Tweed] as "extensive," and "perhaps the most beautiful in Scotland."

WOODEN (*see* p. 71).

The residence of *Admiral George Scott (who succeeded his brother, the late Robert Haldane Scott, Esq., in 1836), and of his sisters, the Misses Barbara and Jessie Scott.

---

† Sir William Dickson, Bart., of Hardingham, near Norfolk. eldest son of the late Admiral Sir Archibald Collingwood Dickson; born 1798; succeeded as third baronet 1827; married, 1850, Lauretta Emmeline, daughter of Colonel L. A. Northey, of Llangwathan, Pembrokeshire. Has no family. Heir-presumptive, his brother Colpoys, Major H.E.I.C.S.; born 1807; married, 1831, Emma, daughter of William Knyvett, Esq.; and has issue.

Sir William Dickson is a magistrate for Roxburghshire, and a Rear-Admiral reserved; was present at the storming of Algiers. London Address—United Service Club, S.W.

WOODSIDE.

In the immediate neighbourhood of Kelso—the property of Lord Polwarth (*see* Mertoun parish, Berwickshire).   Misses Paton, occupiers.

REGISTERED VOTERS (Non-Resident).

Aitchison, Jasper, Dunse
Angus, James, Newcastle
Balfour, Chas., of Newton Don
Brodie, Francis, Chrichtondean
Brown, Rev. William, Perth
Bruce, Rev. Jas., Manchester
Davidson, Thomas, Sprouston
Dove, John, Eccles Newtown
Elliot, William, London
Falconer, William D., Glasgow
Grainger, John Mair, Yorkshire
Gray, George, Middle Heppel, Rothbury, Northumberland
Hall, George, Glendarvie, Lanark
Heckford, Robert
Home, Geo. H. M. B., of Argaty, Perthshire
Hood, John, of Stoneridge
Hume, William, farmer, Baillieknowe, Stitchel
Innes, James, Cairnmount
Jack, J. R., manufacturer, 37 Virginia Street, Glasgow
Ker, Rob. D., St Leonard's House, Edinburgh
Macdonald, John, gamekeeper, Mellerstain
M'Dougall, William, Bigby Street, Brigg, Lincolnshire
Main, Adam, mason, Newcastleon-Tyne
Mason, Rev. Peter (abroad)

Mein, Robert, joiner, Newcastle
Mitchell, Thos., Kirk-Yetholm
Morrison, Alexander, Pengelly, Cheshunt, Herts
Morrison, Joseph R., 11 Rutland Villas, Hampstead
Nimmo, James, Gourock
Ormiston, Samuel, farmer, Glendearg, Melrose
Ormiston, Wm., farmer, Hardie's Mill Place, Greenlaw
Pearson, Adam, Arniston Place, Edinburgh
Primrose, James, farmer, Turniedykes, Dalkeith
Riddell, James, Mertoun
Robson, Charles, London
Robson, William, London
Rose, James, 96 George Street, Edinburgh
Scott, Thomas, Edinburgh
Scott, Archibald, architect, 10 Teviot Row, Edinburgh
Spottiswoode, John, of Spottiswoode
Stevenson, A., writer, Edinburgh
Stewart, B., Orchard Dell, Lanark
Taylor, Thomas, 21 Berners St., London (of J. Nisbet & Co.)
Wight, James
Wilson, Charles, Earlston
Young, George, writer. Glasgow,

CORN EXCHANGE—LIST OF STALL HOLDERS;

Who, as a general rule, will be found at their stalls every Friday from 12 to 2 p.m.—*see* p. 91.

[Since the paragraph at p. 69 was printed the following modifications of rates have been adopted ;—Exhibitions held in the Exchange reduced to £2 2s. Stall Holders not required to take out the ordinary admission ticket (4s. a year)—the stall rent to include that charge.]

No.
1 John Usher, farmer, Stodrig by Kelso.
2 Jas. Johnston, commission-agent, Kelso.
3 Robert Stawart, commission agent, Kelso.
4 John Burn, farmer, Ednam, by Kelso.
5 Walter Rutherford, farmer, Crailing Tofts, do.
6 John Munro,   do.,   Fairnington, do.
7 John Ord of Muirhouselaw, farmer, Upper Nisbet, do.
8 A. Cunningham, farmer, Morebattle Tofts,   do.
9 Henry A. Skeete, commission agent, Kelso.
10 William Hume, farmer, Baillieknowe, by Kelso.
11 Alexander Stuart, Linseed Oil Mills, Leith.
12 Hogg & Wood, nurserymen and seedsmen, Coldstream.
13 George Watson, farmer, Easter Softlaw, by Kelso.
14 Adam Arras   do.,   Ormiston,   do.
15 M'Lean & Hope, merchants, Edinburgh.
16 T. & J. Hubback, farmers, Sunlawshill, by Kelso.
17 Geoge Ogilvie, farmer, Holefield,   do.
18 J. & J. Cunningham, merchants. Edinburgh
19 Roughead & Park, merchants, Haddington
20 William Purves, farmer, Linton Burnfoot, by Kelso.
21 William Broad,   do.,   Clifton Hill,   do.
22 George Dove, farmer, Wark, by Coldstream.
23 John Dove,   do.,   Eccles Newtown, do.
25 William Turnbull, farmer, Graden, do.
26 Francis Calder,   do.,   Yetholm Mains, by Kelso
27 John Kay,   do.,   Softlaw,   do.
29 Patrick Johnston, farmer, Kennetsideheads.
30 Robert Tait, Lees Flour Mill, Coldstream.
31 William Scott, farmer, Spylaw, &c.
32 John B. Boyd, do., of Cherrytrees, by Kelso.
33 Thomas Penny, do., Bartlehill
34 Charles Robson, do., Lurdenlaw, by Kelso.
35 John Murray,   do., Kersknowe, do.
36 Robert Hardie, do., Harrietfield, do.
37 A. Logan, Caverton Mill.
38 George Sholto Douglas, farmer, Riddletonhill
39 James Elliot, farmer, Galalaw, by Kelso.
40 R. G. Thomson, do., Rutherford, do.
41 Andrew Dunn, corn and manure dealer, Kelso.
42 Adam Paterson & Co., timber and manure merchants, Galashiels.
43 James Turnbull, farmer, Lempitlaw Eastfield, by Kelso.
45 John Nisbet,   do.,   Rumbleton,   do.
46 John Roberton, do.,   Harpertown,   do.
47 James Roberton, do.,   Ladyrig,   do.
48 John Clay & Son, corn and manure merchants, and Gainslaw Flour Mills, Berwick.
49 Thomas Allan, farmer, Fogorig, Dunse.*
50 George Logan,   do.,   Humehall, by Kelso.
51 James, Ross,   do.,   Newtonlees, do.

* Present address—East Seymour, Canada W.

52 William Dunn, farmer, Redden, by Kelso.
53 George Simson,   do.,   Courthill,   do.
54 George Turnbull, do.,   Homebyres (Trustees).
55 George & John Henderson, farmers, East Gordon and Middlethird.
56 M. Young, linseed cake manufacturer, Berwick.
57 George Thomson, agent for grain, manures, &c., 12 London Street, Edinburgh.
58 Crossman & Paulin, corn, guano, and manure merchants, Berwick.
59 Adam Darling (of Johnson & Co.), Berwick and Shidlaw Tileworks.
    Agent for Scremerston lime, coal, &c., &c.
60 David Logan, corn merchant, Berwick.
a1 John Pringle, Kelso.
a2 Henderson & Son, corn merchants, and manure manufacturers, Berwick.
a3 Thomas Ovens, guano, cake, and seed merchant, Galashiels.
a4 Stuart & Mein, nurserymen and seedsmen, Kelso.
a5 Walter Anderson, grain merchant, Edinburgh.
a6 Robert Hogarth, Heiton and Maxwellheugh Flour Mills, Kelso.
a7 J. & G. Pendreigh, Catcune Flour Mills, Fushie Bridge, and 135 Constitution Street, Leith.

Other School Changes.

Mr. and Mrs. Tait have resigned the Ragged School, Kelso, and succeeded to the Clarilaw Side School, Wilton parish, resigned by Mr. Stewart.
Mr. and Mrs. Naismith have succeeded Mr. and Mrs. Tait, Kelso Ragged School.

ST. BOSWELL'S.

THIS is a small parish lying to the south of the river Tweed, which forms its northern boundary. It is bounded on the east by Maxton and Ancrum, on the south by Ancrum and Bowden, and on the west by Bowden and Melrose. The general outline is oblong. It is about 3 miles in length, and $1\frac{1}{2}$ in breadth; and according to the Ordnance Survey its area is $3198\frac{1}{2}$ acres —$43\frac{3}{4}$ being occupied by railway, over $60\frac{1}{4}$ by roads, public and private, and about $43\frac{1}{4}$ by water.

"The surface of the upper portion of the parish is undulating, rising into ridges, or small eminences, with hollows or flats intervening. The lower grounds, however, approaching the Tweed are more free from inequalities. The banks of the river, with the exception of the north-east boundary, are bold, precipitous, and well wooded." The climate is dry, being sheltered by hills both on the north and south.

The Tweed is the only river connected with the parish. In it are some good salmon casts and trout fishing. Some of the water is free for trout fishing, but salmon fishing is preserved.

The head-quarters of the Duke of Buccleuch's fox-hounds are near the village; and foxes are drawn occasionally during the season at the neighbouring fox-cover on the Eildon Hills. Very good hotel accommodation can be had in St. Boswell's and its neigbourhood, and private houses, during the season. There are several mansion houses in the parish, among which, near to the village, is LESSUDDEN HOUSE, "the small but still venerable and stately abode of the lairds of Raeburn" (represented by the present proprietor, Robert Scott, Esq., whose grandfather and Sir Walter Scott were near akin), is the only one possessing more than ordinary interest. The Duke of Buccleuch's fox-hound kennels, situated at the end of the green, possess an interest of a peculiar kind; but except these two places and the Fair green itself, there is nothing in the parish worthy of special notice.

In the northern part of the parish, and close to the river Tweed, is the village of LESSUDDEN, better known out of the district as St. Boswell's, consisting of a single street, containing a number of good houses. It was anciently a place of considerable importance, for, when burned by the English in 1544, it contained "sixteen strong bastile houses." From the "Braeheads," behind the village, a beautiful view is obtained of the ruins of Dryburgh Abbey, with the Tweed below winding round the peninsula of Dryburgh, and the Eildon Hills for a background to the scene. This view may vie with any in the south of Scotland.

The village of St. Boswell's, from which the parish derives its name, stood near the church, and extended from the high bank to the east of it overlooking the Tweed, to a considerable distance west of the Kelso turnpike road beyond the farm onstead of " The Temple." In many gazetteers, etc., it is said that the few houses near St. Boswell's Green are all that remain of the village of St. Boswell's; but this is a mistake. The last house of this village stood where now stands Maxton Cottage.

Anniversaries.—On the 12th March, or Monday after, a hand-ball match is played on the green, the sides being composed of the inhabitants of the district lying to the east or west of that locality. Shooting for prizes also takes place.

The *Annual Holidays* are the Fair day and the day following.

St. Boswell's Fair takes place on the 18th of July (or the Monday following if the date be a Sunday). As a general fair this has long been, and still continues to be, the most important in the south of Scotland, and till within the last twenty years (till Melrose Lammas Fair overshadowed it in this particular—which *see*) was the most important also for the sale of sheep and lambs, and it is still the second in the district for the sale of that kind of stock. Soon after daylight (by which time the special trains have commenced to arrive) the fair begins with the sale of sheep and lambs, many of which had arrived on the ground the previous night, consisting principally of full bred Leicesters, three-parts bred, and half-breds ; a large number of once-clipped sheep are also sold. About 10 the sale of cattle begins, and that of horses about 12, the sale of both being large, particularly the horses, in which St. Boswell's ranks next to the Kelso March market in the district. About 1 p.m. the sale of wool commences, when nearly all the different kinds of Leicester wool left over from Kelso are disposed of, also a few clips of Cheviot, but this sort is principally sold at Jedburgh and Hawick—which *see*. St. Boswell's is also the great settling place for lime and manure accounts. To facilitate business the agents of the different branches of the banks established in Melrose attend the fair. The afternoon of St. Boswell's is pretty much like that of St. James's—devoted to pleasure, with this exception, that at the former articles of household use are still sold to some extent, especially ready-made shoes. Both fairs are alike in reference to crockery selling by the gipsies—*see* p. 74.

There are no means of knowing the numbers of the stock exposed for sale, as the dues belonging to the Duke of Buccleuch are leased, and the collector keeps no statement of his

drawings ; the rent, however, to be paid for the St. Boswell's dues for 1864 will be £32 ; while that of Melrose, for sheep and lambs only, will be £36, 10s.

The nearest market town is Melrose, about 4 miles distant. Population of the parish in 1861, 865 ; of the village about 600. The families in the parish at the same date numbered 189, one of whom was returned as living in a house of no windows, and 107 as living in houses of one and two windows.

Assessed property in 1863-4, £6403 : 12 : 8.

The principal landed-proprietors in the parish are—His Grace the Duke of Buccleuch, who is Superior of the village ; Lord Polwarth ; Sir William Fairfax of St. Boswell's Bank ; Major-General Riddell, C.B., of Camieston (the Anchorage, Melrose) ; Robert Lees, Esq., of Fens (Lee Brae, Galashiels) ; Hon. Mrs. John B. Bibor Erskine of Dryburgh ; Mrs. Mary Ann Mills of Weirgate—all non-resident ; and the following, who are resident :—John Boyd, Esq., of Maxpoffle ; Hon. George Dalrymple of Elliston ; William Elliot, Esq. of Benrig ; Robert Scott, Esq. of Lessudden House ; Miss Williamson Ramsay of Maxton Cottage.

Those marked thus (*) are Voters registered in the parish

RESIDENT JUSTICE OF THE PEACE—Robert Scott, Esq., of Raeburn.

POLICE OFFICER—James Burnet.

POST OFFICE—under Newtown (which *see*)—a Money Order Office. Miss M. Paton, postmistress. Delivery at 9-30 a.m., and 5-50 p.m. Box closes for Despatch at 7-15 a.m., and 3-15 p.m.

PUBLIC OFFICES—Inspector of Poor, Kirk Treasurer, Session and Heritors' Clerk, and Registrar of Births, Marriages, and Deaths —James Dickson.
Medical Officers and Public Vaccinators—Drs. Brown and Smith Melrose.

CLERGY, &c.—Presbytery of Selkirk, Synod of Merse and Teviotdale Patron—Duke of Buccleuch.
Established Church—*Rev. Robt. Sommerville (Inducted 1844) Sittings, 400.
Free Church—*Rev. John Duncan (Inducted   ) ; Rev. Alexander Terras, assistant and successor (Inducted 1861). Sittings, Average attendance at Sabbath School,   .

FAST DAYS—Thursday before the last Sunday of February and the first Sunday of July.

SCHOOL†—Parochial—*James Dickson, master ; average attend., 80.

---

† Children in the parish between 5 and 15, attending school during the first week of April 1861, 123 ; of all ages, 127.

PAROCHIAL BOARD—Chairman—John Brown, Esq., of Boswall Cottage. Average No. of Poor on Roll, 20. Rate of Assessment, 4d. per £. Total Assessment, 1863-4, £200. Inspector—J. Dickson.

CONVEYANCE—Hawick and Kelso, Jedburgh, &c., by N. B. line of Railway, Station at Newtown, about a mile from St. Boswell's.

CARRIERS—Galashiels and Melrose—Robert Clark, Tuesday; Kelso—Robert Clark, Friday.

TRADES, &c.

*Adamson, Walter, mason
Ballantyne, Walter, general dealer
Buccleuch Arms Inn, St. Boswell's Green, John Cochrane
Clark, Robert, general dealer
*Cochrane, James, tailor
*Common, Robert, plumber
Fairbairn, James, baker
*Hamilton, George, weaver
Hogarth, John, spirit-dealer, St. Boswell's Green
*Hume, George, spirit-dealer
Kerr, George, tailor
*Lamb, Charles, slater
Lawrie, Robert & *James H., blacksmith
*Martinson, John N.
Millar, George L., watchmaker
*Paton, John, farmer and carter
Paton, Margaret, seed merchant
*Quarry, William, shoemaker
Rae, Elizabeth, general dealer
Rankin, Robert, shoemaker
Rankin, William, general dealer
*Scott, Robert, flesher
Scott, William, tailor.
Scott, William, cutler
Shiel, George, general dealer
Smith, James, flesher
Stirling, Stuart E., general dealer
Thomson, William, joiner and house agent
Trotter, Jessie, grocer
*Turnbull, Robert, saddler
*Waugh, Richard, builder
Wood & Dodds, joiners

RESIDENTS, FARMERS, &c.

*Bain, Alexander, farmer, Bankhead
*Blaikie, William L., farmer, Camieston
*Brown, John, of Boswall Cottage
*Davidson, John, farmer, Weirgate Mains
*Graham, Thomas, farmer, Whinfield
*Jeffrey, John, of Greycrook Villa
*Jeffrey, James, Lessudden
Kyle, Mark, head-gardener, Elliston
*Marshall, Adam, farmer, Fens
*Murray, John, farmer, Holmes
*Rae, Robert, of Temple, farmer
Shore, William, huntsman to His Grace the Duke of Buccleuch, Kennels
*Somervaille, James of Charlesfield, farmer
Stoddart, William, farm steward, Benrig
Thomson, Andrew of Mainhill, farmer (occasional)
*Thomson, James of Merrick, farmer
*Thomson, James, farmer, Thornielaw and Whitelee
Young, Matthew, gardener, Maxpoffle
*Williamson, James, farmer, Laretburn
*Williamson, William, (late huntsman to His Grace the Duke of Buccleuch) of Laretburn

SEATS OF COUNTY FAMILIES IN THE PARISH.

BENRIG

On the Tweed, near the old village of St. Boswells and the church—the residence of William Brownrigg Elliot, Esq. son of the late Hon. John Edmund Elliot, late M.P. for Roxburghshire; who purchased the property in 1862; born 8th October 1820; married, 2d January 1858, Mary Geraldine, 5th daughter of Justin MacCarthy, Esq of Carrignavar, and widow of T. C. Morton, Esq., and has issue:—

William Gerald, born 9th November 1858.
Cyril Herbert John, born 6th October 1861.

ELLISTON.

In the west of the parish—the residence of the *Hon. George Grey Dalrymple, second son of the present Earl of Stair; who purchased the property in 1863; born 22d May 1832; married, 10th Nov. 1853, Ellinor Alice, 5th daughter of the late Lord Napier, and has issue:—

George North, born 14th February 1856.
Walter Francis, born 27th July 1857.
Hew Norman, born 27th April 1864.
Mary Adelaide Wilhemina Elizabeth

Mr. Dalrymple was an officer in the Scots Fusilier Guards.

LESSUDDEN HOUSE.

The residence of Robert Scott, Esq. of Raeburn (county of Dumfries) and Lessudden, the eldest surviving son of the late William Scott, Esq.; born 1817; succeeded his father 1856; married, 1861, Louisa, eldest daughter of William Campbell, Esq. of Ederline, Argyleshire, and has issue, two daughters:—

Matilda Wishart, born 13th January 1863.
Susan Horsburgh, born 18th December 1863.

MAXPOFFLE.

Near to Bowden—the property and summer residence of John Boyd, Esq., 34 Albany Street, Edinburgh; who succeeded to the estate on the death of his father (the late John Boyd, Esq.) in 1861; is married, and has a family.

Mr. Boyd is a Justice of the Peace for the city of Edinburgh, and is Major of the City of Edinburgh Artillery Volunteers.

MAXTON COTTAGE.

At the Maxton boundary of the parish—the property and residence of Miss Williamson Ramsay.

ST. BOSWELL'S BANK,

On the Kelso road—the property of Sir William G. H. T. Fairfax, Bart.†; occupied by T. F. Bolton, Esq.

REGISTERED VOTERS (Non-Resident).

Ballantyne, John, Mumbie Hirst, Canonbie
Crammond, Andrew, Chatto
Edgecumbe, James, 20 Orange Grove, Bath
Erskine, George E. B., Esq., London
Henry, William, Nottingham Place, Edinburgh
Jardine, Sir W., Bart. of Applegarth
Lees, Robert, of Lee Brae, Galashiels
Menzies, Rev. George, Glenshee, Blairgowrie
Milne, Nichol, Esq., Dryhope, Yarrow
Paton, Adam, gardener, New Berriet, St. Albans

---

† Sir William George Herbert Taylor Fairfax, Bart., born 1831; succeeded his father as second baronet, 3d February 1860; entered the army in 1851; is Captain 15th foot, and Aide-de-Camp to the governor and commander-in-chief at Malta; served in the Crimea 1855-6, and obtained a medal and clasp at the siege of Sebastopol; he also received a Turkish medal. London Address—Army and Navy Club.

MELROSE.

—◆—

THIS extensive parish forms the north-western extremity of the county of Roxburgh. Bowden, St. Boswells, and part of Galashiels bound it on the south; Berwickshire on the north and east; and the counties of Edinburgh and Selkirk, on the west. It stands out from the rest of the county like a promontory, whose base may be roughly estimated at six miles, and its outlines at over 30; and it is the only instance in the county of a boundary not naturally defined.

In extent it is the fourth in the county, being about 9 miles in length, and 6 broad. The area, according to the Ordnance Survey, is 26,058¼ acres—114 1-5th being occupied by railways, 324 2-3ds by roads, and 264½ by water.*

The vale of the Tweed which flows through the southern part of the parish and cuts off about a fourth of it, consists of fine rich level lands, except in one part where the the ground ascends to the Eildon Hills. Along the banks of the Leader, which bounds the parish for a considerable distance on the east, the lands are level and fertile, and are finely cultivated. The rest of the parish is for the most part hilly, a large portion of it being pasture land.

The whole of the parish is well watered, the Tweed and its tributaries, the Gala, Alwyn, and Leader waters bound or intersect it. They are all, except the Alwyn, excellent trouting streams, and are much frequented by anglers. The Alwyn is poorish fishing. There are some excellent salmon fishings on the Tweed in this parish. The salmon fishings belong to the respective proprietors, and are strictly preserved, but permission to fish is occasionally given. Trout anglers, within the bounds of the parish, are little interfered with. A large fox cover exists on the south side of the eastern Eildon Hill; and during the hunting season foxes are frequently drawn there. His Grace the Duke of Buccleuch's fox-hounds have their kennels at St. Boswell's, within three miles of Melrose.

A large number of mansion houses are in this parish—especially in the neighbourhood of the town—the most famous, and the only one which can be accounted a show place, is ABBOTSFORD (open to the public daily), famous as the residence of Sir Walter Scott, now the residence of J. R. Hope Scott, Esq.

---

* Castleton first, Teviothead second, and Southdean third—being the three that precede Melrose.

Not far from, and on the Abbotsford estate, lies the small mansion of CHIEFSWOOD, which was occupied during Sir Walter Scott's lifetime by his son-in-law and daughter, Mr. and Mrs. Lockhart. In the same neighbourhood is HUNTLY BURN HOUSE, the seat of Lord Henry Kerr. The Huntly Burn, a mountain brook, from which the house is named, finds its way from Cauldshiels Loch, through the Rhymers' Glen, one of Scott's famous retreats, and worthy a visit for its wild scenery and its associations with Thomas of Ercildoun, and Sir Walter Scott.

In the south of the parish, conspicuously situated on a ledge of the Eildon Hill, is EILDON HALL, the intended seat of the Earl of Dalkeith. It is a building of considerable architectural pretensions, in the Elizabethan style, and is a very marked feature in the landscape.

Lining the Tweed, and giving beauty to the scenery, other mansions and their grounds follow in close succession the entire extent of the parish. (*See* seats of county families for the parish following the town lists.)

In the southern part of the parish is the town of Melrose, a burgh of barony, delightfully situated on the south bank of the Tweed, at the base of the Eildon Hills. Of late years it has been much improved and enlarged, many strangers having been attracted to it by the salubrity of its neighbourhood, readiness of access, and interesting associations. In the centre of the Market Place stands the Cross, the shaft of which bears marks of great antiquity. It is about 20 feet high, with a carving on its apex of a unicorn sustaining the Royal arms of Scotland; but the great attraction and ornament of Melrose is the magnificent Abbey, which, from the beauty of its architecture, the harmony of its parts, and the extent of its remains, must be regarded as one of the greatest objects of interest of which this country can boast. Viewing the exterior of this noble building from the south, it has a most imposing effect; but on entering the interior, the lofty Gothic columns, in a double row, supporting the arched majestic roof, the elegance and variety of its sculptures and statues, the beauty of its carving, and the symmetry of the whole, must strike every observer with feelings of profound admiration. The custodier lives at the Abbey gate, and admission can be had any day except Sunday. Several modern erections also deserve notice, from the fine appearance they present, especially the Railway Station and the Corn Exchange, both of which are very spacious and handsome; the new Free Church, with its tapering spire of elegant proportions, forming a beautiful object in the landscape; while further to the west of the town, on the high road to Darnick, stands the neat Episcopal Church and its handsome parsonge. Abbotsford is within easy distance of the town, and conveyances can always be had to visit this picturesque spot. The walks about Melrose are re-

markably varied and interesting; one of the finest is to the top of the Eildon Hills—a task somewhat trying to the limbs, but which is well repaid by the magnificent prospects obtained in all directions. One, the Eastern Hill, and close above the fox cover, is the site of a Roman camp, the remains of which can still be distinctly traced.

Besides the town of Melrose there are several villages in the parish. The largest is GATTONSIDE, situated on the north side of the Tweed, and immediately opposite Melrose. Access from Melrose to this village is obtained by a chain bridge for foot passengers, and there is a ford about 200 yards below it. It occupies a very pretty site near the river, and is surrounded by a large number of villas and mansion-houses. Gattonside, which is famous for the extent of its orchards and fruit, is a delightful village from spring to autumn; but in winter, with its twisted impracticable roads, it is rather the reverse of this. The village has about 300 inhabitants.

DARNICK, about a mile to the west of Melrose, and on the same side of the river. Here is Darnick Tower, the ancient stronghold of the lairds of Darnick. This exquisite bit of Border antiquity was the chief object of Sir Walter Scott's passion for acquisition, and so well known was this foible of his, that he soon obtained the name of the "Duke of Darnick." Mr. Heiton, the proprietor, though inclined to dispose of a portion of the lands, was unwilling to part with the old tower, which had been for hundreds of years in his family. It is well worthy a visit from the tourist, in consequence of the present proprietor having converted it into a repository of many remarkable relics of Border antiquities. The tower is at all times open to visitors. Another ancient strong-hold in the village is Fisher's Tower, now modernized into a dwelling house. A third, designated as the Little Peel, occupied the site of Darnick Cottage. The number of the inhabitants of Darnick is also nearly 300.

NEWSTEAD is the next village in order, about a mile to the east of Melrose. It consists of one long street, and contains about 240 inhabitants. It is believed by some antiquaries that this is the site of the Roman town of *Trimontium*. At Leaderfoot Bridge, a short distance below Newstead, a splendid railway bridge is now in course of erection. This, when finished, will be a most imposing structure, and will be the highest bridge on the river Tweed—height 133 feet above water level.

NEWTOWN ST BOSWELL'S, the junction station of the Kelso branch of the N. B. Railway with the Hawick and Carlisle branch of the same Company, is in the south-east extremity of the parish, about 3 miles from the town of Melrose. Newtown St Boswell's is also to be the junction for the Berwickshire railway, now fast progressing. There are some commodious houses in this village, and a hotel.

A large portion of the town of Galashiels, being all that part of it on the north side of the Gala water, is in the parish of Melrose. The *Directory* for this has been included in that of Galashiels, as it is included within the police bounds for that town.

Between Melrose and Galashiels, and opposite Lowood, the Alwyn, Elwand, or Allan Water falls into the Tweed. About 3 miles up the Elwand lies Colmslie, Hillslop, and Langshaw Towers, a leading scene in the "Monastery."

Annual Holidays—New Year's Day and St. Boswell's Fair Day (*see* p. 121).

Anniversary.—Fastreen's E'en, when a foot-ball match is played between the married and unmarried, in the streets of the town, for which occasion there is a half holiday. (*See* Yetholm parish).

Market Days—Monday (weekly, general and corn). The corn is sold both by bulk and sample. A moderate business is done. Mondays, fortnightly (fat cattle and sheep), at half-past 9 o'clock. Originated by the late Mr. Walter Lillico, and now conducted by Mr. Alexander Davidson, auctioneer and appraiser. Largely attended.

Great Hiring Days—First Mondays of March, for Hinds : May and November for Young Men and Women ; first Monday of August, for Shearers.

FAIRS.—*Ewes and other stock* (held in the Green Yards' Park), Saturday before the last Tuesday of March.

Cattle (held on the Green Yards' Park), first Wednesday of June.

Lammas, Lamb (held on the slopes of the Eildon Hills, on the grounds of Dingleton Mains, and close above Melrose), on the 12th August, or the Tuesday after, if the date fall on a Saturday, Sunday, or Monday. The greatest lamb fair in the Border counties. The lambs brought to this fair are composed generally of three-parts and half-bred Leicesters and Cheviots, which come from the rich lowland pastures, and the celebrated sheep walks of the Tweed, Teviot, Ettrick, Yarrow, and Gala; and every year attracts flock-masters from all parts of the united kingdom. A few aged sheep are also sold. The full bred lambs are so few as to be exceptional—only one lot of them is quoted as being sold at the fair of 1863 ; and of the few cows and kyloes exposed, most of them were driven away unsold. As many of the lambs arrive on the fair ground the previous evening—and the hill side is then an attractive and pretty sight—the business commences at daylight, and is over by noon. In the afternoon, after the lambs are off the ground, a pleasure fair is held—largely attended by the inhabitants of Melrose, Galashiels, and Selkirk. Of the definite number of lambs sold at this fair, no note has ever been taken, but the supposed number is about 70,000, which must be near the mark. The average annual let of the dues of this fair, by the Duke of Buccleuch, is £40, and lambs pay 4d. per score (last year the let was over £40, this year it is under—*see* St. Boswell's Fair, p. 121). The Melrose bankers attend at the fair ground. Although this fair is of old standing it is only within the last 20 years it has arrived at anything like its present importance ; previously it was held on the Green Yards where the other Melrose fairs are still held.

Draft Ewes, Shotts, and other stock (held on the slopes of the Eildon Hills), first Tuesday of October. This fair is supplementary to that of Lammas.

Cattle, 22d November (held on the Green Yards' Park). This fair follows the rule of the Lammas Lamb Fair as to the day of holding it, and they are the only ones in the district which follow this rule, although it is common with the fairs in other parts of Scotland.

The population of the whole of Melrose parish, including part of the town of Galashiels, was 7711 in 1861 ; being an increase, since the previous census, of 346, which occurred mostly in Galashiels. The following are the census particulars of the parish at 1st April 1861 :—

	Males.	Females.
Galashiels (part of)	1766	1865
Landward	1417	1522
Melrose burgh	502	639

These figures shew the very large proportion of the female population of Melrose burgh over the males to be more than 27 per cent—by much the highest of *all* the towns in the district (*see* note on the population, p. 51). The census of 1861 returns 906 as the number of families in the Galashiels district, one of whom lived in a house having no windows, 382 in houses of one window, and 330 in houses of two windows, and the small proportion of 193 living in houses having three or more windows. The Melrose district (town and landward) had 783 families, 7 of whom were returned as living in houses with no windows, 169 in houses of one window, and 210 in houses of two windows, and the large proportion of 397 (or more than one-half) in houses of three or more windows (*see* note on the housing accommodation of the population, p. 67).

Assessed property in the parish (including part of the town of Galashiels), £42,344 : 8 : 2—larger by nearly £10,000 than any other parish in the three counties.*

Melrose is distant from Edinburgh, by rail, 37 miles ; from Kelso, 15 miles ; and 16 from Hawick. The North British line

---

* The comparatively small parish of Kelso (of only 5542 acres) is the next in order, at £32,848 : 14 : 4.

K

of Railway passes so close to the town that it cuts off some of the outskirts. The Melrose Station is most conveniently situated, and is one of the finest on the line.

Among the largest landed-proprietors in the parish are—His Grace the Duke of Buccleuch ; Robert Cotesworth of Cowdenknowes ; *A. Paterson of Whitelee ; the Earl of Lauderdale ; *Nicol Milne of Faldonside ; the Earl of Haddington, Alexander Mitchell of Stow, Lord Somerville of the Pavilion, James Pringle of Torwoodlee, *James Dalrymple of Langlee, *R. B. Maconochie of Gattonside, *George K. E. Fairholme of Ravensworth and Old Melrose, William Paterson of Glendearg, *J. R. Hope Scott, of Abbotsford ; *Thomas Tod of Drygrange.

Superior of Melrose—The Duke of Buccleuch.

MAGISTRATE.

James Erskine, Esq., Baron Bailie (appointed by the Duke of Buccleuch).

ACTING JUSTICES OF THE PEACE.

The Right Hon. Lord Polwarth	*Adam Paterson of Whitelee
*Thomas Tod of Drygrange	The Chief Magistrate of Galashiels
*R. B. Maconochie of Gattonside	
*Sir David Brewster of Allerly	*G. K. E. Fairholme of Ravenswood and Old Melrose
John Meiklam of Gladswood	
*General William Riddell, C.B. of Camieston [The Anchorage]	William Paterson of Ettrickhall
R. Cotesworth of Sorrowlessfield	*William Clark of Langhaugh
*John Murray of Wooplaw	Mark Sprot of Riddell
Robert Scott of Raeburn	Charles Plummer of Sunderlandhall
*James Dalrymple of Langlee	The Right Hon. the Earl of Minto

Thomas John Dunn, Depute-Clerk of the Peace.
Alexander Rutherford, Galashiels, Procurator-Fiscal.

COURTS.

JUSTICE OF PEACE COURTS are held on the first Wednesday of each month.

SHERIFF SMALL DEBT COURTS are held on the first Fridays of February, May, August, and November.   Freer & Dunn, clerks.

William Miller, baron-officer.   Michael Oliver, police-sergeant.

PUBLIC OFFICES.

Billet Master—James Erskine.
Government Inspector of Drainage—T. Mitchell.

* * Those marked thus (*) are resident in the parish.*

Inland Revenue—James Deans, Officer ; Office, Dingleton.
Inspector of Poor—Thomas Murray ; Office, Corn Exchange.
Melrose Abbey—Mrs Tait, Keeper, Abbey Gate.
Registrar of Births, Marriages, and Deaths—Thomas Murray, District of Melrose.
Register of Sasines—John Murray, Esq. of Wooplaw, Keeper ; Office, Market Place.
Rifle Volunteer Battalion's Office, Corn Exchange—Captain Macpherson, adjutant.
Session Clerk and Kirk Treasurer—Thomas Murray.
Sheriff-Clerk Deputes—Allan Freer and Thomas J. Dunn.
Sheriff-Officer—Angus Sutherland, High Street.
Stamps and Taxes—Thomas Murray, Sub-Distributor and Sub-Collector. Edward Henderson, Surveyor. J. Miller, Clerk ; Office, Corn Exchange.
Town-Bellman—Simon Paterson,
Valuation Act—Edward Henderson, Assessor for the County of Roxburgh and Burgh of Jedburgh ; Office, Corn Exchange.

INCOME TAX.

James Erskine, Clerk to the Commissioners.
James Curle, Assistant-Clerk to the Commissioners.
Thomas J. Dunn, Assessor.   Edward Henderson, Surveyor.

POST OFFICE.

MISS ELLIOT, Postmistress.
William Grant, Town-Deliverer.

MAILS ARRIVE FROM.

Edinburgh and Galashiels	8-25 a.m.
London, Carlisle, Hawick, London and North-Western Railway P.O., Kelso, and Jedburgh . . .	8-33 a.m.
Berwick and Midland Railway P.O. . . .	11-8 a.m.
Kelso, Hawick, Newtown, and Jedburgh	4-19 p.m.
Edinburgh, Galashiels, and Selkirk . . .	5-10 p.m.
London and North-Western Railway P.O., and London and Carlisle	8-27 p.m.

English Letters are also received by both the Edinburgh Mails.

Town Deliveries begin at 9-10 a.m., 5-30 and 8-50 p.m.

A window delivery (for English Letters) at 11-15 a.m.

DESPATCHES.	Box closes.
Hawick, Newtown, Jedburgh, and Kelso . . .	8 a.m.
Galashiels and Selkirk . .	8 a.m.
Edinburgh . . .	10-30 a.m.
Edinburgh and Galashiels	3-45 p.m.
London, Carlisle, London and North-Western Railway P.O., Hawick, Kelso, Jedburgh, Berwick, and Midland Railway P.O.	4-30 p.m.
Edinburgh . . . . , . .	8 p.m.

Sundays.

Edinburgh and the North, arrive at 8-10 a.m.; Box closes 6-30 p.m.
Galashiels, arrive at 8-10 a.m.; Box closes 7-40 a.m.
London, England generally, Berwick, and Carlisle, arrive at 9-40 a.m.; Box closes at 5-50 p m.
Kelso, Hawick, Newtown, Jedburgh, &c., arrive at 9-40 a.m.; Box closes at 7-30 a.m.

A Window Delivery from 9 till 11-30 a.m.
Letter Box at Weirhill. Letters collected at 7 10 a.m.

SUB-OFFICES.

Despatches for Darnick and Earlston at 9-10 a.m., and 5-30 p.m.
Arrivals from　　do.　　　do.　at 8 a.m. and 4-15 p.m.
Despatch for Gattonside at 9.10a.m.　Arrival from do. at 4-15 p.m.

RUNNERS—Darnick, Thomas Emmond; Earlston, David Swanston; Gattonside, Andrew Johnston.

CLERGY, &c.

Melrose is in the Presbytery of Selkirk, and Synod of Merse and Teviotdale.

Patron—Duke of Buccleuch.

The Established and Free Church Presbyteries meet at Selkirk. The U. P. Presbytery at Melrose, the first Tuesday of every other month, beginning with February.

PARISH CHURCH—Rev.　　　　(Inducted 1865). Sittings, 1000. Attendance at Sabbath School, 120. Superintendent and Treasurer of Sabbath School—Mr. James Fairbairn; Session Clerk and Kirk Treasurer—Mr. Thomas Murray; Precentor—Thomas Emmond; Church Officer—William Millar.
FREE CHURCH—Rev. William Cousin (Inducted 1859). Sittings, 550. Average attendance at Sabbath School, 50, exclusive of those attending the various district Sabbath Schools, taught by members of the congregation. Precentor—Pringle Murray, Newstead; Church Treasurer—Wm. M'Bean; Church Officer—Wm. Cranstoun, Church Place.
UNITED PRESBYTERIAN CHURCH—Rev. Hugh Stevenson (Inducted 1860). Sittings, 450. Av. attend. at Sab. School, 74. Session Clerk—Thomas J. Dunn; Treasurer—Allan Freer: Precentor—John Wood; Church Officer—Andrew Newton, Dingleton.
U. P. CHURCH (Newtown)—Rev. David Lumgair (Inducted 1844). Sittings, 500. Average attendance at Sabbath School, 80.
CONGREGATIONAL CHURCH—Rev. William Crombie (Inducted 1851.) Sittings, 250. Average attendance at Sabbath School, Melrose, 20; at other schools, 45.
EPISCOPALIAN CHURCH—Rev. John G. Ryde, M.A. (Inducted 1855). Sittings, 200.　——

FAST DAYS—Thursdays before second Sunday of May and November.

BIBLE SOCIETY.

President—Hon. R. Baillie.　Vice-Pres.—The Master of Polwarth. Treasurer—Allan Freer.　Secretaries—John Broad and T. J. Dunn.

SABBATH SCHOOL TEACHERS' UNION.

President—T. J. Dunn.　Vice-President—John Broad
Secretary—Wm. Sinclair.　Treasurer—Adam Milne.

Meets first Friday of January, April, July, and October. The office-bearers are chosen annually.

SCOTTISH PROTESTANT ASSOCIATION (BRANCH).

Rev. William Crombie, President.　|　Francis Tocher, Secretary.
Agent for the Association's Publications—William Macbean.

LONDON CITY MISSION (BRANCH—estab. 1860).

An annual meeting is held in the Corn Exchange, in August, at which an interesting address regarding the work of the Mission. is delivered by the Rev. Francis Tyrrell, B.A. (of London).

President—Hon. Major Baillie, Dryburgh.
Chairman—John Meiklam, Esq., of Gladswood.
Local Secy. and Treas.—T. J. Dunn.
Committee—Clergymen of the district.

LADY COLLECTORS.

Mrs. Cousin (F. C. Manse), Mrs. Murray (Established do.), Mrs. M'Bean, High Street, Mrs. Thomson (Eildon), Miss Dunn, Miss Nichol (Laurel Bank), Miss Nicol (Buccleuch St.), Miss Smith (Darnick).

Average collection, remitted to London, £20.

LONDON TRACT SOCIETY (BRANCH).

Thomas J. Dunn, Treasurer.

COLPORTAGE ASSOCIATION (estab. 1857).

President—The Hon. Robert Baillie, Dryburgh Abbey.
Secretary—John Smith, Leaderfoot.　Treasurer—T. J. Dunn.
With an acting Committee of Eleven Members.

The district of the Association is at present undefined. The total amount of value of religious books sold during the past year, chiefly among the rural population of the district, amounted to £194. The number of religious periodicals sold monthly amounted to 1300, while the amount of tracts furnished by the Edinburgh Religious Tract and Book Society and other friends, and distributed gratuitously by the colporteur, amounted to 19,000. The annual income of the Society averages £35.

ASSOCIATION FOR CONDUCTING POPULAR LECTURES, 1865-6.

(Held in the Corn Exchange in Winter.)
Patron—The Honourable Major Baillie.
President—Rev. Wm. Stevenson.　Vice-President—John Broad.
Secretary—W. M'Bean.　Treasurer—Thos. Stevenson.

COMMITTEE 1865-66.

Revs. William Cousin and J. G. Ryde; Messrs John Smith (Tower Cottage), T. J. Dunn, Allan Freer, Jas. Curle, Dr. Brown, Gen. Riddell, J. Pattison, Wm. Sinclair, Walter Hogg, Thomas Laurie, J. M'Symon, John Freer, and Ralph Dunn.

Average attendance, 200.

EDUCATIONAL INSTITUTIONS.*

Parochial School—Francis Tocher, master.
Free Church School—Angus Stewart, master; Miss Thorburn, female teacher; average attendance, 60.
Darnick School—Robert Robertson, master.
Episcopal School—John Barham, master.
Gattonside School—Alex. Hopkirk, master.
Newstead School—   , master.
Newtown Subscription School—Peter Jack, master.
Female School—Mrs Houston, Melrose.
Girls' School, Newtown—Miss Hardie.

BOARDING SEMINARIES FOR YOUNG LADIES.

Misses Burn, Rose Bank. | Misses Liston, Laurel Bank.

PAROCHIAL BOARD.

182 Members.

Chairman—Rev. J. G. Ryde.
Thomas Murray, Inspector and Collector of Poor Rates.
Thomas H. Paterson, Sub-Inspector for Galashiels district.

COMMITTEE.

Revs. William Cousin and Hugh Stevenson; Messrs. Alex. Curle, James Erskine, Allan Freer, Thos. J. Dunn, Dr. W. N. Brown, James Curle, William M'Bean, Mark Turnbull, Geo. Rutherford of Sunnyside, John Smith, Kittyfield, Captain Clark, ot Langhaugh; Thomas S. Hall, and W. Sanderson, Galashiels.

ELECTED MEMBERS AND MEMBERS OF KIRK SESSION.

Rev. H. Stevenson, Messrs. M. Turnbull, William M'Bean, Robert Tait, William Sinclair, Gilbert Amos; J. Knox, John Broad, and J. Fairbairn.

Medical Officers and Public Vaccinators—J. B. Clarkson for Melrose District; James Brisbane, M.D., for Galashiels.

Average No. of Poor on Roll, 200; Assessment for the year, 10d. per £, less ¼ on house property for repairs, and ⅛ on land. Total collection, 1863-4, £1432 : 6 : 8.

Poor House, Galashiels Combination.

Parochial Representatives—Jas. Erskine and Thomas J. Dunn.

---

* Children in the parish between 5 and 15 attending school during the first week of April 1861—Galashiels district, 583; Melrose district, 668—total, 1251; total of all ages in both districts, 1316.

VAGRANT RELIEF SOCIETY.

The Hon. Robert Baillie, President.
James Erskine, Chairman.   Thomas J. Dunn, Treasurer.
Mrs. Newton, Relieving Agent.

Supported by private subscriptions. The same vagrant not relieved above once a month, and a register kept.

YEARLY FRIENDLY SOCIETY.

Preses—William Hart.   Secretary and Treasurer—John Young.
Number of Members, 140.

This Society is the same in principle as those of Kelso (*see* p. 86); but the scale of payment to sick members is more liberal—viz., 5s. a-week for the first three months, 3s. a-week for the second three months, and 2s. a-week till the close of the financial year.

ST JOHN'S LODGE OF FREE MASONS.

The Institution of this lodge is said to be as far back as the building of Melrose Abbey, "John Morow, who had in keeping all mason work" at the building of that celebrated ruin, having been the first Grand Master of the Lodge. It does not hold of the Grand Lodge of Scotland, having declined when that scheme was organised to fall in with the over-ruling and centralizing system which was then passed, and more fully carried out afterwards.

John Brown, Halidean Mill, R.W.G.M.
M. Berry, Earlston, S. Warden.   Wm. Miles, Newstead, J. Warden.
Jas. Fairbairn, Secretary.   Wm. Scott, Drygrange, Treasurer.
Robert Tacket, Tyler.

TOTAL ABSTINENCE SOCIETY.

Peter Hunter, President.   John Howden, Vice-President.

COMMITTEE.

Rev. W. Crombie, Melrose. | James Hart, Gattonside.
Barney Harkness, do. | George Brockie, Darnick.

MUTUAL IMPROVEMENT SOCIETY (Instituted 1858).

OFFICE-BEARERS.

President—Robert Tait.   Vice-President—Thomas Laurie.
Secretary—J. L. Muir.   Treasurer—Andrew Smith.
Journalist—A. B. Rodgers.   Assistant Journalist—J. G. Taylor.

COMMITTEE.

Messrs. William Corson, William Hart, and David D. Deans.
The office-bearers, etc., are subject to election quarterly.

An interesting Annual Meeting of this Society is held, attended by the different clergymen and other friends.

PUBLIC LIBRARY.

Parish Library—W. Macbean, Librarian. 1300 vols. Annual Subscription, 1s.

Libraries are also attached to the Free and Melrose U. P. churches, but their use is limited to the members. For Book Clubs, see Miss Elliot's and Miss Cameron's.

AGRICULTURAL SOCIETY (estab. 1840).

President—The Right Hon. Lord Polwarth.
Vice-Presidents—The Right Hon. Lord Binning, and T. Tod, Esq.
Secretary and Treasurer—John Freer.

The Judges and Committee are elected annually.

An Annual Show for hunting stock, cattle, sheep, and horses, is held in the Greenyards about the end of March or beginning of April.

HORTICULTURAL AND FLORAL SOCIETY.

COMMITTEE OF MANAGEMENT.

George Hills, Weirhill Villa.
George Thorburn, St Cuthberts.
John Richardson, Dryburgh.
David Hunter, Gladswood.
George Irvine, Linthill.
George Baxter, Fordell Villa.
William Stenhouse, Friarshall.
Mark Kyle, Elliston.
James Wilsher, Caverse Carre

Treasurer—Wm. Milton, Parsonage.   Secretary—Wm. Macbean.
Exhibitions in July and September.

FARMERS' CLUB (estab. 1832).

Consists at present of 34 Members.   Annual Subscription, £1.
John Broad, Secretary and Treasurer.

Meetings first Monday of each month, with exception of April, August, and September ; the day of meeting in the first-mentioned month being the second Monday, and the last two months blank.

CORN EXCHANGE AND NEW TOWN HALL.

This beautiful public building was added to the advantages of the town in 1863, and opened in the autumn of that year. The architect was Mr David Cousin, and the cost about £3000.

DIRECTORS.

George Mills, Greenend
James Simson, Melrose
T. J. Dunn   do.
General Riddell, do.
James Erskine, do.
William L. Blaikie, Camieston
Mark Turnbull, Melrose
Alexander Curle, do.
William Lockie, West Morriston

Secretary—James Curle.   Treasurer—Allan Freer.

RATES.

Concert, or similar purpose	£2 2	Public Meeting or Lecture..	£1 1
Ladies' Bazaar	2 2	Promenade Assembly or	
Evening Dress Assembly ..	3 3	Soiree	1 1
Public Dinner	1 1		

GAS COMPANY (estab. 1836).

DIRECTORS.

James Erskine, Alex. Curle, Thomas Murray, J. B. Clarkson, Thomas Paterson, Thomas J. Dunn, James Curle, James Simson, Thomas Scott, and Allan Freer.

Sec. and Treas.—Thomas Murray.   Manager—Walter Hogg.

10s. per 1000 feet, including Town Lighting and Service.
Pays 4½ per cent.

WATER COMPANY (estab. 1838).

DIRECTORS.

James Erskine.
Thomas J. Dunn.
Dr Brown.
Alexander Curle.
Thomas Scott.
Thomas Paterson.
James Curle.
James B. Clarkson.

Thomas Murray, Secretary and Treasurer.
Rate 6d. per £1 on Rental.
Amount of Stock, £476.   Pays 4 per cent.

SUSPENSION CHAIN BRIDGE BETWEEN MELROSE AND GATTONSIDE—(Erected in 1826).

DIRECTORS.

Thomas John Dunn, Melrose.
R. Marr, Gattonside.
Thomas Paterson, Melrose.
John Smith, Kittyfield.

James Curle, Clerk, Melrose.
Amount of Stock, £726.   Pays 6 per cent.

CURLING CLUB (estab. 1847).

T. Riddell Carre yr. of Cavers Carre, President.
C S. Plummer of Sunderland Hall, Vice-President.
John Freer, Fordell Villa, Secretary and Treasurer.
Committee—George Rutherford, Thomas Stevenson, Robert Easton, Richard Stirling, and Gilbert Amos.
Representative Member—George Rutherford.

Entry-Money, 5s.   Annual Subscription, 2s. 6d.

Curling Pond—Base of the Eildon Hills, on the property of the Duke of Buccleuch.

CRICKET CLUB (estab. 1862).

President—Thomas Tod of Drygrange.
Vice-President—James Erskine of Shielfield.
A. B. Rodgers, Captain.
Ralph Dunn, Secretary.   P. H. Patterson, Treasurer.
Committee—J. Barham, J. Lees, Ralph Dunn, A. B. Rodgers.
Quarterly Subscription, 1s. 6d.
Cricket Field—The Greenyards.

3RD ROXBURGHSHIRE RIFLE CORPS—(MELROSE).

Thos. Tod of Drygrange, Captain.   T. Riddell Carre, yr., Lieutenant.
John Broad, Ensign.   Allan Freer, Treasurer.
Dr. W. N. Brown, Honorary Surgeon.
Edmond Walsh, Drill Sergeant.   Effective Force, 71.

Annual Subscription for Honorary Members, £1, 1s.

Head-quarters—Corn Exchange.

BANK BRANCHES.

BRITISH LINEN COMPANY'S BANK —Curle, Erskine, & Curle, Agents ;
Henry Rae, Accountant

ROYAL BANK—Freer & Dunn, Agents ; John G. Taylor, Accountant.

INSURANCE AGENTS.

ALLIANCE (FIRE) ....Thomas Laurie, seedsman
BRITISH GUARANTEE.............Curle & Erskine, writers.
BRITON (Fire and Life) ....Angus Sutherland, auctioneer.
CITY OF GLASGOW LIFE ....Wm. Sinclair, merchant.
EDINBURGH LIFE.................Curle & Erskine, writers.
HOME AND COLONIAL ....R. Yule, merchant.
INSURANCE COY. OF SCOTLAND.....Thomas Mitchell, C.E.
LIFE ASSOCIATION OF SCOTLAND..David Manuel.
LONDON AND LANCASHIRE ....Angus Sutherland, auctioneer.
MUTUAL LIFE ....W. Macbean, bookseller.
NATIONAL GUARANTEE ....Freer & Dunn, writers.
NORTHERN.....................Mrs Walker, druggist.
NORTH BRITISH & MERCANTILE....A. Paterson, merchant.
PLATE GLASS INSURANCE COY.....Nichol Dodds, joiner and builder.
SCOTTISH AMICABLE LIFE.........W. Macbean, bookseller.
SCOTTISH UNION (FIRE)..........Alexander Curle, writer.
     ,,   (FIRE & LIFE)....Allan Freer, writer.
STANDARD ....Thomas John Dunn, writer.
UNITED KINGDOM PROVIDENT .....George Douglas, seedsman.
UNITED KINGDOM TEMPERANCE }
     AND GENERAL PROVIDENT.. } Mrs Walker, druggist.

ASSOCIATION FOR THE PROMOTION OF THE FINE ARTS. IN SCOTLAND.

Archibald Paterson, Hon. Secretary.

PROCURATORS, NOTARIES PUBLIC, &c.

Curle, Alexander (firm of C. & Erskine, Market Place).
Curle, James, N.P.,   do.   do.
Dunn, Thomas John, N.P. (firm of Freer & D., High Street).
Erskine, James, N.P. (firm of Curle & E., Market Place).
Freer, Allan (firm of F. & Dunn, High Street).

MEDICAL PRACTITIONERS.

William N. Brown, M.D. ; James B. Clarkson, surgeon ; Alexander
Dewar, M.D. ; and J. G. Smith, surgeon, M.D.

MILLS.

MELROSE—Corn—Mark Turnbull.
GATTONSIDE—Saw—George Scott & Sons, bobbin makers, wood tur-
ners, and wood merchants.
NEWSTEAD—Corn—John Knox, baker, Melrose.
NEWTOWN—Corn—Thomas Moffat.
LEADERFOOT—Corn—John Wintrup.

AUCTIONEERS.

Alexander Davidson, St. Dunstan's Villa.
Angus Sutherland, High Street.

STATUTE LABOUR ROADS.

DISTRICT OF MELROSE,

Comprising the parishes of Melrose, Bowden, St Boswell's, Maxton,
Lilliesleaf, and all parts of the Parishes of Galashiels and Selkirk in
the county of Roxburgh.

Alexander Curle, Clerk and Collector.   Thomas Mitchell, Surveyor.

Meets at Melrose on or about 28th March.

CARRIERS.

ANCRUM—J. Davidson, Ship Inn, Thursday.
EARLSTON—Robert Simson, Station, daily.
EDINBURGH AND GLASGOW, and all parts of the North and West—
Railway Station, daily.
GALASHIELS—Robert Clark, Mr Paterson's Shop, Tuesday.
GALASHIELS, HAWICK, JEDBURGH, KELSO, BERWICK, and all parts of
the South—Railway Station, daily.
ST BOSWELL'S—Robert Clark, Mr Paterson's, Tuesday.
SELKIRK—D. Chisholm, Ship Inn, Thursday.

CONVEYANCE BY RAILWAY.

To Galashiels, Edinburgh, and all parts of the North and West.
To Hawick, Kelso, Berwick, and all parts of the South. (For Arrival
and Departure of the Trains, see Monthly Time Tables.)

Omnibuses from the George and Commercial Hotels attend all the
Trains—fares, 6d.

GENERAL DIRECTORY.

Those marked thus (*) are Registered Voters.

Abbey Street

Abbey Hotel, *Hamilton, Archibald
Bell, Archibald, watchmaker
*Bell, John, stocking-maker
Boston, Mrs., Abbey Place
*Collier, Gideon, carter
Curle, James (of Evelaw), St. Cuthbert's
Davidson, Miss
Dodds, Alexander, Abbey Gate
Easton & Mather, Misses, dress makers
Edington, Mrs.
Gibson Misses
Hamilton, Archibald, wood merchant
Hamilton, Isabella, grocer
Henderson, Miss, Abbey Cottage
Manse, Murray, Rev. William
M'Bean, William, bookseller, stationer, and printer
Mercer, Robert, gardener
Mercer, George, painter and glazier
Musgrove, Miss
Ormiston, Walter
Paterson, James, tinsmith
*Simson, James, brewer, View Field
Tait, Mrs., Abbey Gate
Tocher, Francis, schoolmaster
Waterson, William, colporteur

Buccleuch Street

*Clarkson, J. B., surgeon
*Dodds, Nichol, joiner and builder
Jardine, John, plumber
*M'Donald, David, cabinet-maker and upholsterer
    Carver and gilder
*Mitchell Thomas, civil engineer, surveyor, etc.
Nicol, Misses, milliners
Patterson, Misses and Mr. P. H.
Young, John, grocer and wine merchant

East Port

Baptie, Robert, tailor
Brown, Thomas, joiner

Brydone, Misses
Riddell, John, flesher
Riddell, Robert, farmer
Scoon, William, flesher
Scott, George, labourer
*Scott, James, blacksmith.
Scott, Mrs., grocer

Market Place and High Street

Aikman, John, warehouseman, West Port
Amos, Gilbert, draper
Anderson, Alexander
*Anderson, Alexander mason,
Anderson, Mrs.
Bird, Robert, grocer
Cameron, Misses, stationers, small ware dealers, &c.
    Branch of Edmonstone & Douglas' Book Club (Edinburgh)
Cavers, Mrs.
Clark, Miss, confectioner
Corn Exchange Buildings—
    Inland Revenue Office
    Inspector of Poor's Office— Thomas Murray
    Battalion of the Roxburgh and Selkirk Rifle Volunteers'
        Office—Captain Macpherson, adjutant (*see* p. 54)
Curle & Erskine's writing chambers
    Managing Clerk—John C. Munro
Dawson, Michael, china merchant, The Wilderness
Don, Munro, coachbuilder,   do.
Douglas, George, ironmonger, seed and guano merchant
    Manager—Thomas Laurie
*Drysdale, Alexander, draper
Dunn, Mrs., sen.
*Easton, George, joiner
Elliot, Miss, stationer and small ware dealer
    Branch of J. & J. H. Rutherfurd's Book Club (Kelso)
Fiddes, G. & W., blacksmiths
*Fiddes, George (of G. & W. F.)
*Fiddes, William (of G. & W. F.)
George Hotel, *Menzies, James
Greig, William, bootmaker
Freer & Dunn's writing chambers
    Managing Clerk, John Macrae
Hogg, Walter, cabinet-maker and upholsterer
Hunter, Miss
Hunter, Robert, shoemaker
King's Arms Inn, *Cleaver, William
Knox, John, baker and miller
Lees, Alexander, upholsterer, West Port

Lillico, Mrs.
*Manuel, David
*Ormiston, Archibald, nurseryman and seedsman
*Paterson, Thomas, grocer and wine merchant
*Pattison, John, of Victoria Cottage
Post Office, Elliot, Miss, postmistress.
Railway Hotel, Easton, Robert
Registrar of Sasines' Office—John Murray
Robertson, Mrs., St. Dunstan's
Sanderson, Thomas, flesher
Scott, Misses, of Raeburn (Number 6)
Scott, Walter, tailor and clothier
Scott, Thomas, baker
Ship Inn, Muckersie, Michael
Simpson, Walter, saddler
*Sinclair, William, draper
Slater, Walter, grocer and wine merchant
Stewart, Misses, dress makers, St Cuthbert's Cot
Sutherland, Angus, Furniture Salerooms
Tait, Robert, boot and shoemaker
Telfer, George, slater
Walker, James, druggist
Walker, Mrs.
Wield & Corson, druggists
*Wishart, John, v. surgeon
Wood, Mrs.
*Wilson, Philip, painter
Yule, Robert, clothier

Melrose Railway Station

Resident Station Master, General Manager, and N. B. R. Company's Coal Agent—Henry O'Hagan.

OFFICES

George Mann, coal agent.
Robert Cairns,   do.
Refreshment Rooms—John Hogarth

Residences between Melrose and the Weirhill

Barham, John, teacher, Booklaws Cottages
Butler, Mrs., Madras Cottage
Dewar, Alexander, M.D., Douglas Cottage
Gasworks—Walter Hogg, manager
Gray, Adam, accountant, Bishopflat
Hepburn, Miss, Merchiston
Murray, Thomas, Inspector of Poor, of Abbotsknowe
M'Millan, Mrs., Douglas Cottage

Police Station, Oliver, sergeant
Stewart, James, gardener, Church Place
Stewart, A., teacher,   do.
Stewart, John, tailor,   do.
Turnbull, John, builder,   do.

SUBURBS AND VILLAGES.

Dingleton.

[Lying on a slope of the Eildons, close above Melrose, and reached by a road passing the Railway Station].

Burn, Misses, Boarding School, Rosebank House
Cowan, Mrs.
*Crombie, Rev. William, View Bank
Falla, Mrs.
Gibson, Adam
Grant, John, forester
Harkness, Barney
Henderson, Edward, surveyor of taxes, Mavis Bank
Phin, Miss, of St Mary's
Shiel, John
Whitehead, Mrs.

The Weirhill, &c.

[The Weirhill, lying in the direction of Darnick, is a new western suburb of villas, rather than a street, of Melrose. It is here the newly erected Free and Episcopal Churches are situated. High Cross is a continuation of Weirhill, beyond the Episcopal Church. Between Weirhill Place and Melrose, and surrounded by the public green of the Weirhill, is the Parish Church.]

Arras, Mrs., Trinity Villa
*Brown, William N., M.D., of St John's
Campbell, Misses, Torwood Lodge
Carmichael, Mrs., Meadowbank House
Free Church Manse, *Cousin, Rev. William
Douglas, Misses, The Elms
*Dunn, Thomas J. (of Freer & D.) of Weirhill Villa
Fairbairn Brothers, joiners, Weirhill Place
*Freer, Allan (of F. & Dunn) of Fordell Villa
*Freer, John, Fordell Villa
Fyall, Captain, of The Elms
*Glen, Andrew, Elmbank
Hastie, Mrs., Weirhill Place
Hay, Miss,   do.
Isaac, Mrs.,   do.
Liston, Misses, Boarding School, Laurel Bank

Mein, Miss, Weirhill Place
Millar, John, clerk, do.
Milton, William   do.
Murray, Misses, High Cross
M'Innes, Archibald, warehouseman, Trinity Cottage
*M'Lachlan, William E., cabinet-maker, of Waverley Cottage
M'Symon, John, of Avenel, High Cross
Nisbet, Mrs., Tweed Cottage
Ogilvie, Miss, High Cross
Pott, Miss, of Weirbank
Reid, Peter, M.D., Weirhill Place
Rodger, Miss, Eildon Bank
*Ryde, Rev. J. G., *The Parsonage*
*Riddell, Archibald, High Cross
Riddell, Mrs.,   do.
*Shiell, John (late of 3 East Newington Place, Edinburgh), Retreat Cottage
Sloan, Mrs., of Piccadilly House
Smith, John G., M.D., St. John's
*Stevenson, Rev. Hugh, *U. P. Manse*
*Stevenson, Thomas, Bleachfield
Stuart, Darnley, warehouseman
Sutherland, Angus, Bleachfield
Thomson, Mrs., Weirhill Place
Thomson, Mrs., Weirhlll
Turnbull, Miss, of The Knowe, High Cross

Gattonside (see p. 128)

MORTIFICATION—SIBBALD'S BEQUEST.—This Bequest, the net proceeds of which amounted to £360, was bequeathed by the late William Sibbald, Esq., architect in Edinburgh, and a native of Gattonside, to the poor of Melrose parish, after the decease of certain heirs, and which came into operation in January 1862, and is dispensed by a committee of the Parochial Board. The yearly interest amounts to £14, 8s., which is distributed among upwards of sixty poor persons, and proves a great boon to the poor of the parish.

*Allan, James
Boston, Thomas, farmer
Burnet, James, joiner
Clapperton, Mrs., Springbank
Clapperton, Robert, gardener
Dance, Mrs., and Miss Elizabeth Trotter (late of Hendersyde Park), Castle Cottage
Dodds, John, blacksmith
Dickenson, Robert
Hewat, John
*Hopkirk, Alexander, teacher
*Hopkirk, Robert, shoemaker

Knox, Andrew, farmer
*Johnston, John, plasterer
*Maconochie, R. B. of Gattonside House
*Marr, Robert, portioner
Post Office, Eliza Halliburton—(*see* Melrose, p. 133)
*Pringle, John, farmer
Pringle, Robert
Renwick, Mrs.
*Scott, George (of S. & Sons), Saw Mills
*Spottiswood, Joseph
*Stewart, George
*Tait, Walter, farmer
Turnbull, Joseph

Villas at Gattonside

GATTONSIDE VILLA, the property and residence of Richard Parnell, Esq., M.D.
ABBOTSMEADOW, occupied by *William Park, Esq., of Blegbie
FRIARS HALL, occupied by W. O. Dickinson, Esq.

Darnick (see p. 128)

Brodie & Wayness
*Brodie, George, joiner
Chisholm, James, shoemaker
*Currie, Andrew (of Fisher's Tower), sculptor
Elliot, David, manure manufacturer
*Gardiner, Robert, farmer.
Hunter, Peter, blacksmith
Kitchen, Miss, grocer
Mann, Charles, coal-agent, Darnick Vale
Mann, George, Darnick Vale
Manuel, William, blacksmith
Matthewson, William, grocer
Nichol, Rev. W. M.
*Nichol, Thomas, farmer, Broomilees
Post Office, William Matthewson (*see* Melrose, p. 133)
Rutherford, Mrs., innkeeper
Robertson, Robert, teacher
*Smith, John, sen., architect
Smith, Mrs. Thomas
Tait, Mrs. W.
*Waugh, John, farmer
Wight, Thomas
*Young, Adam

Villas at Darnick.

BRIDGE-END HOUSE, occupied by the Misses Clephane.

DARNICK COTTAGE, occupied by Mrs. Elliot.

DARNICK TOWER, the property of John Heiton, Esq. (*see* p. 128); occupied by *Adam Murray, Esq.

DARNLEE, the property of John Alexander Smith, Esq., M.D., Edinburgh; occupied by Mrs. J. Lawton.

TOWER COTTAGE, the property of John Heiton, Esq., Accountant, Edinburgh; occupied by John Smith, Esq., jun., late of Australia.

Newstead (see p. 128)

POST OFFICE BOX—Letters collected at 7-30 a.m. and 3-55 p.m., by the Earlston runner.

Blake, Archibald, thatcher
*Bunzie, Andrew
*Burnet, Francis, joiner
Cairns & Blyth, coal-agents
Davidson, Joseph
*Hart, George, mason
Kerr, Mrs. George
Miles, Mrs., innkeeper
*Pringle, Andrew, builder
*Pringle, Thomas, builder
Redpath, William, farmer
Scott, James, artist
Simson, James, miller
*Smith, Charles, carter
*Vair, James, farmer
Williamson, Miss

Villas at Newstead

OAKENDEAN, the property and residence of Alexander Mitchell, Esq., of the Exchequer, Edinburgh.

OAKENDEAN COTTAGE, the property and residence of Captain Smith, R.N.

Newtown (see p. 128)

POST OFFICE—Walter Paton, Postmaster. The Post Office of Newtown is now the District Post Office. Sub-Offices—St. Boswell's, Bowden, and Mertoun.

Newtown—Delivery at 8-50 a.m., and 5-30 p.m. Box closes for the North at 8-20 a.m., and 4 p.m.; for the South at 5-10 p.m.

St. Boswell's and Mertoun—Despatch, 9 a.m.; Arrival, 2-50 p.m. Messengers—James Thomson and William Younger.

Bowden—Despatch, 9 a.m. and 5-30 p.m.; Arrival, 8 a.m. and 3-50 p.m. Messenger—William Rutherford.

Aldcorn, James, blacksmith
Balmer, Samuel, grocer
Borthwick, Walter, cattle-agent and innkeeper
Bowman, James
Brodie, Robert, grain and manure dealer
Clark, Peter, tailor
Cochrane, John and Nichol, masons
Douglas, James, coal agent
*Galbraith, Thomas, road contractor
Grant, Robert, joiner
Grieve, Mrs.
Hardie, Miss, girls' school
Jack, Peter, schoolmaster
*Jeffrey, Thomas, farmer
Johnston, George, mason
*Kerr, Andrew, grocer
Laing, John, flesher
Lillico, John, cattle dealer
*Lockie, William, mason
M'Gregor, Allan, railway superintendant.
Moffat, Thomas, farmer and miller
Newtown U. P. Manse, *Lumgair, Rev. D. (*see* p. 128)
Park, Thomas, shoemaker
Railway Hotel, Rodger, Mrs.
Stenhouse, Miss
Stirling, Archibald
Walker, Alexander, coal agent

Newtown Railway Station

Resident Station-master, General Manager, and N. B. R. Coal Agent—Walter Riddell.
Goods' Clerk—David Fairbairn
Refreshment Rooms—Miss Steel

Villa at Newtown.

TWEEDBANK HOUSE, the property and residence of Thomas Waters.

Hamlet of Langshaw

Situated near Glendearg, in the Galashiels or Ladhope district.

POST OFFICE by Galashiels—which *see.*
SCHOOL—Francis Kerr, master. Average attendance, 34.
MORTIFICATION—Langshaw Side School, adopted in November 1862 as a Parochial Side School by the heritors of Melrose parish, with a salary of £15 per annum, for the benefit of the northern part of the parish. This School besides enjoys the annual interest of a mortification of £62, bequeathed by William Moffat, a former proprietor of Threepwood, and George Ailley, in 1785.
SAW MILL—William Turnbull, joiner.
BLACKSMITH—David Hope.

COUNTRY RESIDENTS IN THE PARISH.

*Anderson, J., farmer, Friars Haugh
Arnott, James, manager of home farm, Drygrange
*Brown, David, farmer, Easter Housebyres
*Bruce, J., farmer, Easter Langlee
*Cossar, Thos., do., Mosshouses
*Currie, G., shepherd, Threepwood
*Dalgleish, Js., do., So. Blainslie
*Davidson, W., farmer, Colmslie
Dickson, Alex., head-gardener, Old Melrose
*Dodds, Jas., farmer. Hawksnest
*Fortune, George, Eildon
*Fleming, John, farmer, Craigsford Mains
Ford,   farmer, Hawkslee
*Gladstone, John, farmer, Old Town Langlee
*Halliday, F., Bridgehaugh Mill
Hately, Arch., superintendant, Eildon Hall
*Hewat, J., farmer, Langlee Hill
*Hogg, W., do., Clackmae
*Hunter, A., farmer, Allanshaws
*Hume, Nath., do., Bluecairn
*Jamieson, J., do., Whitelee
*Leitch, J., farmer, New Blainslie
Lidster, George, Eildon
*Lun, Walter, farmer, Roan
*Macdougal, Geo., farmer, Sorrowlessfield Mains
*Macdougal, W., farmer, Sorrowlessfield Mains

*Mack, John, Eildon
Mackay, Murdoch, head-gardener, Ravenswood.
*Murray, John, farmer, Westerhousebyres
*Mercer, George, Coatgreen
*Oliver, John, farmer, Bridge End Mains
Ormston, S., farmer, Glendearg.
*Ovens, Thomas of Lynwood
Purves, John, Kittyfield
*Renwick, R., farmer, of Hawkburn
*Richardson, Thomas, sen., farmer, Gattonside Mains
*Riddell, Turnbull, farmer, Berryhall
*Robertson, J. of Nether Blainslie
*Robertson, T., mason, Blainslie
*Scott, J. S. E., farmer, Buckholm
*Shiels, Jas., farmer Colmsliehill
*Sibbald, Wm., do., Eildon Mains
*Simson, Thos., farmer, Blainslie
Smith, John, farmer, Leaderfoot
*Taylor, J., farmer, Newhouses
*Tod, Walter, Cleuchfoot
*Turnbull, Mark, farmer and miller, Danielton Mains
Walker, Thos., Appletreeleaves House
Watson, Richd., farmer, Plumbtree Hall
*Wilson, James, farmer, Carolside Mains
Waugh, Jn., farmer, Langshaw
*Wintrup, John, Leaderfoot Mills

SEATS, &c., OF COUNTY FAMIILES AND SMALLER RESIDENCES IN THE PARISH.

ABBEY PARK.

Villa at Weirhill Road, Melrose—the property of Mrs. Stedman of Kame, and the residence of Alexander Curle, Esq. (of Curle & Erskine, Melrose), of West Morriston, Berwickshire, eldest son of the late James Curle, Esq., of Evelaw; married, 1860, Christian, daughter of the late Sir James Anderson of Blairvadoch, Dumbartonshire, M.P.

ABBOTSFORD (see p. 126). (see p. 126)

The seat and occasional residence of *James Robert Hope Scott, Esq , third son of the late General Sir Alexander Hope (who was a son of the second Earl of Hopetoun); born 1812; married (first) 1847, Charlotte Harriet Jane, only child of the late J. G. Lockhart, Esq., and grand-daughter of Sir Walter Scott, Bart., whose name he assumed in 1853, and by whom he has a daughter—Mary Monica Scott. Married (second), 1861, Lady Victoria Fitzallan Howard, eldest daughter of Henry Granville, 7th Duke of Norfolk, and has issue.

Mr. Hope Scott became a Queen's Counsel in 1850; he is a Justice of Peace and Deputy-Lieutenant for the county of Inverness, and Lord of the Barony of Abbotsford.

Custodier of Abbotsford—Edward Geffney.

ALLERLY.

Near Gattonside—the seat of *Sir David Brewster, K.H., F.R.S., etc., second son of the late Mr. James Brewster, Rector of the Grammar School of Jedburgh; born 1781; married (first), Juliet second daughter of the late James Macpherson, Esq. (the translator of Ossian), of Bellville, M.P., and has issue:—

David Edward, Lieut.-Col. in the Indian Army; born 1815; married, 1849 Lydia Julia, eldest daughter of the late Henry James Blunt, Esq., of the Bengal Army.

Sir David married (second), 1857, Jane Kirk, second daughter of the late Thomas Purnell, Esq., of Scarborough, by whom he has issue, one daughter

Sir David was appointed Principal of the United Colleges of St. Salvator, St. Leonard, and St. Andrews, in 1837; Principal and Vice-Chancellor of Edinburgh University, in 1859; is a Magistrate for the county of Roxburgh; Vice-President of the Royal Society of Edinburgh; Hon. D.C.L. of Oxford and Durham; Hon. M.A. of Cambridge and Edinburgh; L.L.D. of King's College, Aberdeen; an Officer of the Legion of Honour; Chevalier of the Prussian order of Merit; one of the eight Foreign Associates of the Imperial Institute of France; and a Member of various foreign learned societies; is well known as the inventor of the Kaleidoscope, Lenticular Stereoscope, the Bude and Dioptric Lights; author of " More Worlds than One," " Martyrs of Science," " Memoirs of Sir Isaac Newton," Treatises on Optics, Natural Magic, the Kaleidoscope and Stereoscope, and other works; was editor of the " Edinburgh Philosophical Journal," " Edinburgh Journal of Science," and the " Edinburgh Encyclopædia;" received the honour of Knighthood in 1831, and also the Guelphic order of Knighthood, and several prizes for his scientific discoveries from the Royal Societies of Edinburgh and London, and the Imperial Institute of France.

Edinburgh address—the College. London address—Athenæum Club, S.W.

THE ANCHORAGE.

Villa at Weirhill, Melrose—the property and residence of Major-

General William Riddell of Camieston, C.B., eldest son of the late Thomas Riddell, younger of Camieston.

Major-General Riddell entered the Bengal Army in 1823, and retired on full pay in 1862.

CHIEFSWOOD.

A part of the Abbotsford property—*John Broad, Esq., occupier.

DRYGRANGE.

At the junction of the Tweed and Leader—the property and residence of *Thomas Tod, Esq.; born 1810; succeeded his father, the late Archibald Tod, Esq., 1817; married, 1837, Eliza, only daughter of the late Charles Smallwood Featherstonhaugh, Esq., of College, Kirkoswald, and has issue:—

Eliza Caroline, who was married in 1861 to Captain Sir George H. Leith, Bart., of Burgh St. Peters, Norfolk; and has issue a daughter.

Mr. Tod is a Justice of Peace and Deputy-Lieutenant for the county of Roxburgh, and a Magistrate for the county of Berwick; was formerly in the 1st Dragoon Guards. Edinburgh address—New Club.

EILDON HALL (see p. 127).

The property of the Duke of Buccleuch, and preparing for the residence of William Henry Walter, Earl of Dalkeith, the eldest son of His Grace, born 9th September 1831; married, 22d November 1859, Louisa, third daughter of the Marquis of Abercorn, and has a son, Walter Francis, Lord Eskdale, born 17th June 1861.

The Earl of Dalkeith is M.P. for the county of Edinburgh and Lord-Lieut. for the county of Dumfries. London Residence—Hamilton Place.

GATTONSIDE HOUSE.

The property and residence of *Robert Blair Maconochie, Esq. (son of the late Lord Meadowbank, one of the Lords of Session); born 1814; married, 1846, Charlotte Joanna, daughter of John Tod, Esq. of Kirkhill, and has issue three sons and one daughter.

HUNTLY BURN HOUSE (see p. 127).

The residence of Lord Henry Schomberg Kerr (brother of the present Marquis, and second son of the late Marquis of Lothian), born 2d December 1833.

LADHOPE HOUSE.

Near Galashiels—the property and residence of Wm. Brunton, Esq., eldest son of the late James Brunton, Esq. of Hilton's Hill.

LANGHAUGH.

Near Galashiels—the property and residence of *Capt. William Clark, R.N.; married, 17th February 1829, Janet Alston, second daughter of Major James Alston of Urrard, Perthshire; and has issue:—

James Alston, born March 1832, Captain 15th King's Hussars.
Bouverie Francis, born 19th March 1842, Lieutenant R.N.
Charlotte Jane Christina Janet Charles.

Captain Clark is a Justice of Peace for Roxburgh and Selkirk shires, and is Captain of the 1st Selkirkshire Rifle Volunteers.

LOWOOD.

On the south side of the Tweed, midway between Melrose and Abbotsford — the property and residence of Robert Charles Kidd, Esq.

Mr. Kidd, who was formerly in the 9th Lancers, married, in 1856, Mary Jane, the younger daughter of the late Rev. George Mason, M.A. of Norton-Cuckney, Notts, and has issue—two sons and two daughters.

London residence—Hyde Park Gate, W.

PAVILION.

On the north side of the Tweed, near the junction of the Allan —the property of Lord Somerville, and the summer occasional residence of *Henry Fowler Broadwood, Esq.; born 1811; married, 1840, Juliana Maria, daughter of Wyrley Birch, Esq. of Wreatham Hall, Norfolk; and has, with other issue, a son, James Henry Tschudi, born 1854.

Other seats—Lyne, in Surrey. London residence, 46 Bryanston Square, W.

PRIOR BANK.

In the immediate neighbourhood of Melrose—the property and residence of *William Tait, Esq. (late publisher, Edinburgh), brother-in-law of Adam Black, Esq., M.P. for Edinburgh.

THE PRIORY.

Near the Abbey—the property of the Duke of Buccleuch, and the residence of *James Erskine, Esq. (of Curle & E., Melrose), of Shielfield, Berwickshire; married, 1841, Barbara, second daughter of George Pott, Esq., of Todrig and Borthwickshiels, and has issue one son, Charles.

RAVENSWOOD.

On the south side of the Tweed, opposite its junction with the Leader—the property and residence of *George K. E. Fairholme,

Esq. of Old Melrose and Ludgate, Galashiels. Ravenswood was built in 1827; in 1859-60 an addition was made to it on the east end, and another addition is now in course of erection on the west end.

ST. CUTHBERTS.

Villa near the Abbey—the residence of Mrs. Curle, widow of the late James Curle, Esq., of Evelaw.

ST. HELENS.

Villa near Melrose—(lately the property of Francis Blaikie Esq., long factor to and coadjutor with the Earl of Leicester, the celebrated agricultural improver)—at present vacant.

SUNNYSIDE.

Near Darnick—the residence and property of *George Rutherford, Esq., of Sunnyside and Lochend.

THREEPWOOD.

In the upper district of the parish, near the sources of the Alwyn —the property and residence of *Charles Simson, Esq.

WESTER LANGLEE.

Near Galashiels—the property and residence of *Jas. Dalrymple, Esq., (of the Indian House of R. Watson, & Co., Indigo and Silk Merchants) of Wester Langlee and Greenknowe [Berwickshire]. Issue, two daughters.

WHITELEE.

At the south-west corner of the parish, near the Gala, 3 miles from Galashiels — the property and occasional residence of *Adam Paterson, Esq., W.S., Edinburgh.

WOOPLAW.

In the upper district of the parish, 6 miles from Melrose, and near the sources of the Alwyn, or Allan Water—the property and residence of John Murray, Esq.

Mr. Murray is Registrar of Sasines for the counties of Roxburgh, Selkirk, and Peebles. Appointed in 1857. Office, Melrose.

VOTERS REGISTERED IN MELROSE PARISH

RESIDENT IN GALASHIELS.

Anderson, Thomas, millwright, Channel Street
Brodie, Walter, 3 Wilderhaugh
Brown, Adam, roadman, Buckholmside
Brown, Ad., manufacturer, Buckholm Mill
Brown, George, manufacturer, Comely Bank
Brown, George, do., 8 King St.
Brown, Henry, do., Buckholm Mill
Brown, William, do. do.
Brown, William, 45 Island St.

Cairns, R., High Buckholmside
Carruthers, W., grocer, Bridge St.
Clapperton, Geo., manufacturer 4 Bridge St.
Clapperton, W., Darling's haugh
Cochrane, John, manufacturer
Coldwell, Peter
Darling, Adam, Buckholmside
Dickson, T., weaver, Island St.
Dickson, T., do., Wilderhaugh
Dixon, Rt., draper, 16 High St.
Drummond, Robert, weaver
Dun, J., seed mercht., Island St.
Fettes, Rev. Js., of Ladhope F.C.
Galbraith, J., roadmaker, Buckholmside
Gibb, William, slater
Graham William, 18 King St.
Gray, Ed., painter, 51 High St.
Grieve, Adam, Roxburgh St.
Haldane, Richd., writer, Bank St
Haldane, Wm., writer, Bank St.
Haldane, William, farmer, Buckholm Crofts
Haldane, W., Galashiels Brewery
Hall, James, 14 Slitrig St.
Hall, Thomas S., builder
Herbertson, And., builder, Abbotsford Road
Hill, Andrew, Buckholmside
Hislop, Andrew, hosiery manufacturer, 14 Bridge St.
Hood, John, plasterer
Hood, John, jun., plasterer
Hunter, W., grocer, Island St.
Jamieson, James, grocer, High Buckholmside
Kemp, William, Bridge St.
Laidlaw, T., sawyer, Island St.
Lees, George, Wilderburn
Lees, Thos., weaver, Channel St.
Leithead, James, farmer, Buckholm Crofts
Melrose, Robert, flesher
Mercer, G., mason, Wilderhaugh
Mercer, John, slubber
Mackay, J., chemist, High St.
M'Dougall, Henry, joiner, Buckholmside

Maxwell, Robert
Maxwell, Sam., Commercial Inn, Bridge St.
Melville, Alexander, 86 High St.
Murray, John, wool merchant, Longhaugh
Paisley, Peter, baker, 67 High St.
Paterson, Thos. H., teacher, Ladhope Bank
Patterson, William, tanner, Channel St.
Quin, E., china mercht., High St.
Rankine, William
Richardson, Robert, carrier
Roberts, Henry, manufacturer, Victoria Mill
Roberts, Hugh, do. do.
Roberts, Wm., jun. do. do.
Roberts, John, manufacturer
Ronald, John, painter, Roxburgh St.
Sanderson, D., joiner, High St.
Sanderson, Henry, Bridge St.
Sanderson, Thomas, shoemaker
Sanderson, Thos., mason, Buckholmside
Sanderson, Thomas
Sanderson, W., timber merchant
Sanderson, William, Channel St.
Scott, Hugh, Esq., of Gala
Scott, John, joiner, Buckholmside
Sime, James, manufacturer, Sime Place
Stewart, Robert (of Lees & Stewart), 88 High Street
Stirling Adam, builder, Green St.
Symington, Robert, joiner
Tait, James, baker
Thomson, Adam, grocer
Tinline William, mason
Toward, John, Abbotsford Arms Hotel
Walker, Alexander, weaver
Walker, Thomas, tailor
Watson, William, 21 Channel St.
Wilson, George, shoemaker
Wilson, Joseph, Buckholmside
Young, William

RESIDENT AT A DISTANCE.

Ainslie, John, farmer, Bemersyde West End
Binning, Lord, Mellerstain
Birch, Wyrley, of Wreatham Hall, Norfolk
Brown, H., Ormiston, Tranent
Blaikie, John, 4 West Princes St., Glasgow
Blythe, David, gardener, Telling, Newcastle-on-Tyne
Bogue, Thomas, merchant, Berwick-on-Tweed

Brydone, James M., Petworth
Carmichael, Jas., banker, Hawick
Cleaver, Fred. S., wholesale perfumer, 32 Red Lion Sq., London
Cochrane, James, late 11 Canning Place, Edinburgh
Coldwell, Andw., mason, Lauder
Coldwell, Wm., mason, Lauder
Cotesworth, R. of Cowdenknowes
Dods, William, cabinet-maker, Edinburgh
Dennell, James, Edinburgh
Dickinson, W., Longcroft, Lauder
Drummond, George, Woolwich
Dun, George, Laidlawsteel
Elliot, James, Torwoodlee, Selkirk
Erskine, George Pott
Fairholme, William, of Chapel
Geddes, Robert, Boldside Ferry
Gibson, J., jun., W.S., Edinburgh
Goodfellow, James, H.M. Dockyard, Devonport
Gladstone, Thomas, Canada
Heiton, John of Darnick Tower, Edinburgh
Hewitson, Robert, Auchenbinzie, Thornhill
Hogg, Walter, 30 Dundas Street, Edinburgh
Jamieson, Peter, 6 Nicholson Sq., Edinburgh
Johnston, J., Cattleshiel, Dunse
Kennedy, John of Kirklands
Leslie, John, 514 Gallowgate St., Glasgow
Matthewson, John, Williamhope
Miller, Hew, land-steward, Ochtertyre estate, Crieff
Miller, John, merchant, 13 York Place, Edinburgh
Mitchell, Alexander, of Stow
Mitchell, Alex., of Oakendean, Edinburgh
Moffat, John, Maxton
Morton, Bobert, engineer, 240 Wapping, London
Oliver, James, surgeon, 10 Roxburgh Place, Edinburgh
Oliver, Jas., late of Grove House, Roehampton, Surrey
Ormand, William, London
Paton, Robert, writer, Selkirk

Pearce, Robt. F., 21 Westminster Terrace, Glasgow
Pringle, G., Torwoodlee, Selkirk
Pringle, J. T., of Torwoodlee
Purdie, Adam, Ettrick Bank
Purdie, John, Craigover
Ramsay, R. B. W., of Whitehill
Robson, Rev. George, Lauder
Scott, George, baker, Warriston Place, Edinburgh
Scott, John, blacksmith, Clarilaw Burn
Scott, John, cooper, Hawick
Scott, Rev. W. of Abbotsmeadow, Glasgow
Shiels, William, wine merchant, Leith
Sibbald, Alex., Pathhead, Edinburgh
Sibbald, William, Fairneyside, Edinburgh
Simson, John, farmer, Bassendean, Gordon
Sives, John, late Arnotdale, Falkirk
Smith, Adam, Ballarat, Australia
Smith, James, Ballarat, Australia
Smith, John Alex., M.D., 7 West Maitland Street, Edinburgh
Somerville, James, S.S.C., Edinburgh
Spence, George, Stoneyford Toll, Lauder
Stevenson, Alex., writer, Langholm
Stewart, Thos., Bowhill, Selkirk
Tait, J. D , Badminton, Wilts
Taylor, A., merchant, Edinburgh
Thomson, Rev. John, Hawick
Turnbull, Robert, Midlem
Turnbull, Robt., builder, Nisbet
Turnbull, T., Spadeslee, Mertoun
Turnbull, Wm., Major, 69 Cornhill, London
Usher, Thomas, Byrecleuch
Weatherston, Hugh, Howe Street, Edinburgh
Welsh, Aitken, shepherd, Netherbarns
Woodger, John, coachman, Riddell
Wood, George, gas manufacturer, Earlston

YETHOLM.

The parish of Yetholm is situated on the east side of the county, bordering on Northumberland for nearly six miles. Linton and Morebattle bound it on the north-west, west, and south. It is about 4 miles long and 2 miles broad ; and the area, according to the Ordnance Survey, is 6036 acres, 38 of which are in roads and 76½ under water.

"The general aspect and outline of the parish is hilly, and some of the hills attain a great elevation: Starough, or Sturoich, has an elevation of 1629 feet, Latchley Hill, 1322 feet, Whitelaw, 1263 feet, and Wild Goose Hill, 1097 feet. The lower hills are cultivated, and the higher, which are a portion of the Cheviot range, are clothed with a rich green sward to their summits, affording excellent pasture to many thousands of sheep. Several peaceful and romantic little valleys lie embosomed amid these hills ; and the vale of the Bowmont itself, in which nine-tenths of the inhabitants of the parish reside, is only a larger vale of the same description."[*]

The climate is clear, healthy, and milder than, from its elevation, might be supposed, and has become noted in the district as a rural sanatarium ; and considering the size of the

---

[*] Although the Cheviot hills present, as a whole, a somewhat smooth surface, they shew to the pedestrian a number of rugged glens, of which the wildest is Henhole, situated on the northern side of the Great Cheviot. On the top of the Great Cheviot there is a waste table-land of some five or six square miles, from the mossy surface of which a pretty large quantity of water flows into Henhole ; and the glen from this circumstance shews deep rocky banks to within a mile or so of the highest point of the mountain. Within a space of about three-quarters of a mile the water—in a succession of cascades|of from six or eight to thirty feet in height—falls three hundred feet. It is called Colledge Water, and falls into the Bowmont. The cliffs at one part near the head of the glen stand like walls on each side to the height of nearly three hundred feet ; and on ledges and crevices about their summits the hunting falcon and the raven breed. This is the only place among the eastern division of the hills on the Borders in which the raven, so far as we know, still resides. There is a small cavern in the face of the highest cliff on the right bank —still accessible, though dangerously so, to the venturous—into which it is said one of the early hunting Percys, along with some of his hounds went, and never returned ; and that he and the hounds lie spell-bound, and can only be released by the blast of a hunting horn within the cavern. The Great Cheviot, which is 2676 feet above the level of the sea, lies in Northumberland, but is within pleasant excursion distance from Yetholm, and during the summer is occasionally the scene of pic-nics. By one of the routes carriages can be driven to within an easy walk of the summit.

village a considerable amount of accommodation can be had in it by visitors.

The Bowmont water, which intersects the parish from south-west to north-east, abounds with trout of very fine quality—fishing unrestricted. Yetholm Loch, a sheet of water about a mile and a half in circumference—half of it being in this parish—abounds with pike and perch (see Morebattle parish), and is the resort of water-fowl in great variety and numbers.

There are remains of several British and Roman camps on the various hills; and there were formerly two towers—Thirlestane and Lochtower—both of which are demolished.

The principal landed-proprietors in the parish are—Andrew Wauchope, Esq., of Niddrie Marischall [Niddrie, Edinburgh]; the Marquis of Tweeddale; John B. Boyd, Esq., of Cherrytrees; John Waldie, Esq., of Hendersyde; and Charles Rea, Esq., of Halterburnhead [Doddington, Wooler]. J. B. Boyd, Esq., is the only resident proprietor.

A little to the south-west from the centre of the parish are the villages of Town- and Kirk-Yetholm. They are separated from each other by the Bowmont merely, so that perhaps they may be considered as one village. Town-Yetholm stands on the west and Kirk-Yetholm on the east side of the stream. The latter has long been the head-quarters of a tribe of gipsies—a singular race, formerly remarkable for their disorderly lives and dangerous characters, and still distinguished to some extent by peculiarity of habit from the general body of the community.

Anniversaries—Fastren's E'en* foot-ball match and athletic games (held on the haugh at Town-Yetholm), once of some celebrity, and attracting visitors from a distance; but the interest of the event is now confined to the inhabitants of the village and the shepherds from the hills. In the evening balls take place in the villages, and a general feasting on currant dumplings, to cook which, most of the kail pots have been in requisition during the day. Drinking tents are now prohibited on the match ground.

Kirk-Yetholm Sheep Fair (held on the hill side above the church)—June 27, or the Monday after if the date be a Sunday. The class of sheep exposed for sale are Cheviot and half-bred hogs; while, on the occasion, a few grazing cattle are shewn in the village of Kirk-Yetholm.

---

* Fastrens E'en—Shrove Tuesday—a moveable date, which occurs between the 2d February and 8th March, and is thus fixed according to a Border rhyme—

> "First comes Candlemas,
> Then the new moon,
> The first Tuesday after
> Is Fastren's e'en."

(*See* Melrose, p. 129).

The sheep shewn at the fair of 1864 were 64 *score*, a larger number than had been shewn for some years previously. This fair (as are also the others connected with Yetholm) is only of local importance.

Sheep Fair (held as above) 24th October; on this occasion the business is confined to the sale of a few shotts.

Town-Yetholm Fair for Lambs, etc. (on the haugh)—2d Wednesday of July—may now be considered as defunct; those of Cornhill on the 6th, and St. Boswell's on the 18th (which *see*) having swamped it.

Yetholm is distant from Kelso 7½ miles, where is also the nearest railway station.

Population of the parish in 1861, 1207; of Town-Yetholm, 544; of Kirk-Yetholm, 358. Total number of families in the parish, 293; 97 of whom were returned as living in houses of one window, and 84 in houses of two windows. Assessed property in 1863-4, £8,080:12:3.

Superior of Town-Yetholm—Andrew Wauchope, Esq. of Niddrie Marischall; Kirk-Yetholm—Marquis of Tweeddale.

Those marked thus (*) are Registered Voters in the parish.

MAGISTRATES.

Baron Bailie of Town-Yetholm—Robert Swan, Esq., Kelso.
Do.   of Kirk-Yetholm—

Resident Justice of the Peace—J. B. Boyd, Esq. of Cherrytrees.
Police Officer—James Jackson, Yetholm.

POST OFFICE.

Money Order Office and Savings Bank.
Postmaster—James Shiell Laidlaw.   Messenger—William Watson.
Daily post to and from Kelso—Arrives at 1.30 p m.; departs at 7 a.m.
Town delivery on arrival.

PUBLIC OFFICES.

Heritors' Clerk—William Henderson.
Inspector of Poor—Robert M'Morran.
Kirk-Treasurer—Rev. Adam Davidson.
Registrar of Births, Marriages, and Deaths, and Session Clerk—Thomas H. Tait.
Medical Officer and Public Vaccinator—Vacant.

CLERGY.

Presbytery of Kelso, Synod of Merse and Teviotdale.
Patron—Andrew Wauchope of Niddrie.

Established Church†(Kirk-Yetholm)—*Rev. Adam Davidson, M.A. (Inducted 1862). Sittings, 700. Sabbath School attendance, 140.
Free Church (Town-Yetholm)—Rev. John Coventry (Inducted 1862). Sittings, 400. Sabbath School attendance, 90.
United Presbyterian Church (Town-Yetholm)—Vacant. Sittings, 450. Sabbath School attendance, 80.

Fast Days—Generally an early Wednesday in January and July— unfixed.

SCHOOLS.‡

Parochial (Town-Yetholm)—Robert M'Morran, master. Average attendance, 75.
General Assembly (Kirk-Yetholm)—Thomas H. Tait, teacher. Average attendance, 52.
Private School (Town-Yetholm)—Adam Hunter, teacher.
Girls' School (Town-Yetholm)—Miss Gardiner, teacher. Average attendance, 55.

PAROCHIAL BOARD.

Chairman—John B. Boyd, Esq., of Cherrytrees.
Rate of Assessment, 7d. per £. Total collection 1863-4, £518 : 4 : 6½. No. of Poor on Roll—40, of whom 29 live in the parish.
Poor House—Kelso Union.

SOCIETIES, &c.

Curling Club—Secretary—Adam Calder, Esq. Yetholm Mains. Pond at Thirlestane on Mr. Boyd's property.
Horticultural Society—Secretary—Mr. W. Henderson, Yetholm.

CARRIERS.

Edinburgh—John Fairbairn, Tuesday.
Kelso—W. Watson, daily ; G. Cockburn, Tuesday and Friday ; Robert Walker, Friday ; John Steel, Friday.

† The parish church situated in Kirk-Yetholm, a turreted structure built of squared blue whinstone pricked out with white cement, is in a style of excellent taste and keeping with its surrounding scenery.
‡ Children in the parish between 5 and 15, attending school during the first week of April 1861, 204 ; of all ages, 219.

MILLS.

Blunties—Woollen—*Peter Govenlock, manufacturer, proprietor.
Duncanhaugh—Corn and Flour—*Jn. Govenlock, miller and farmer.
Yetholm—Corn—George Whitelaw, farmer.
Yetholm—Co-operative Saw Mill—George Hogg & Co.

TRADES.

Town-Yetholm

Ainslie, Adam, flesher
Allan, John, saddler
Black, George, joiner
*Christie, William, joiner
*Cockburn, William, blacksmith
Davidson, Henry T., grocer
Davidson, Mary, dressmaker
Dixon, Archibald, grocer
*Dodds, George, farmer
Dodds, James, mason
Fairbairn, John, egg dealer and carrier
Fleming, Mary, straw-hat maker
Fox, Mrs., dressmaker
*Gladstone, George, blacksmith
Grahamslaw, William, farmer
Herbert, Andrew, mason
Hindmarsh, Helen, straw-hat maker
Hogg, Andrew, tailor
*Hogg, George, joiner
*Kennedy, John, millwright
*Kerr, George, farmer
Kerr, Helen, dressmaker
*Kerr, John, saddler
*Ker, Thomas, joiner
Kerr, Thomas, skinner
*Kerr, Walter, farmer
Kirkwood, George, baker
*Laidlaw, J. S., grocer, general merchant, and pork-curer†
Lees, George, cooper
*Leitch, Andrew, blacksmith
Leitch, Margaret, dressmaker
Lyon, Thomas, shoemaker
Lyon, John, tailor
Nag's Head (Temperance) Inn, John Scott, baker
Oliver, Adam, shoemaker

† The business done in the pork-curing trade at Yetholm is small—the collection of carcases being confined to the locality.

Outerstone, John, grocer
Plough Inn, James M'Callum
Rutherford, William, shoemaker
Smith, John, farmer
Swan Inn, Thomas Inglis
Turnbull, Andrew, shoemaker
Turnbull, Thomas, shoemaker
Watson, Andrew, clothier
Waddell, John B., watchmaker
*White, Andrew, grocer and farmer
*White, John, farmer
Wood, James, tailor
Young, George, flesher
*Young, Thomas, mason
*Young, William, mason
Yule, Mary, dressmaker

Kirk-Yetholm

Chalmers, Andrew, grocer
Cross Keys Inn, Alexander Purves
Fleming, William, grocer
Gladstone, James, tailor
Gray Horse Inn, Helen Govenlock, innkeeper and grocer
Hindmarsh, Walter, flesher
Plough Inn, Janet Richardson
Shepherd's Arms, Patrick Milligan, grocer
Strachan, John, thatcher
Telfer, Robert, wool merchant and skinner, Bowmont Crescent
Thomson, Helen, grocer
Walker, Robert, grocer and carrier
Wilson, Alexander, baker

Country

Bennett, John, blacksmith, Thirlstane
Cockburn, Adam, blacksmith, Primside Mill

RESIDENTS, FARMERS, &c.

*Calder, Francis, farmer, Yetholm Mains
*Clark, John,   do.   Lochtower
*Glass, Thomas, do.   Hayhope
*Glass, William, do.   Hayhope
 Grieve, George, do.   Kirk-Yetholm
 Henderson, William, Yetholm (late schoolmaster)
*Tait, William, farmer, Venchen
*Turner, Robert, do.   Town-Yetholm

SEATS OF COUNTY FAMILIES IN THE PARISH.

CHERRYTREES.

The residence of John Brack Boyd, Esq.; born 1818; succeeded his father, the late Adam Brack Boyd, Esq., 1862.

YETHOLM HALL.

In the outskirts of Town-Yetholm—the property of Andrew Wauchope, Esq.† of Niddrie and Yetholm—at present occupied by the Rev. John Coventry, of Yetholm Free Church.

REGISTERED VOTERS (Non-Resident).

Dodds, John, schoolmaster, Roseneath
Elliot, James, Garrah Wells
Gibb, George S., of Cults House, Aberdeen
Lynn, Francis P., farmer, Mindrum Mill
Oliver, Andrew, carter, Howtel
Rea, Charles, of Halterburnhead
Wauchope, Andrew, of Niddrie Marischall
Weir, William, of Langlands, Govan

---

† Andrew Wauchope, Esq., of Niddrie-Marischall, eldest son of the late Colonel Wauchope; born 1818; succeeded 1825; married, 1840, Frances Mary, daughter of Henry Lloyd, Esq. of Farinrory, county of Tipperary; and has, with other issue, William John, born 1841.
    Mr. Wauchope is a Justice of Peace and Deputy-Lieutenant for the county of Edinburgh, and is Lord of the Barony of Yetholm.
    Principal residence—Niddrie-Marischall, near Libberton.

M

MOREBATTLE.

—◆—

THE parish of Morebattle is situated in the north-eastern part of the county, bordering on Northumberland, which bounds it on the east and south. Its other boundaries are Yetholm and Linton on the north, and Eckford and Hounam on the west. Its extreme length is about 9 miles, and its greatest breadth about 6½ miles. The area, according to the Ordnance Survey, is 22,518 acres; nearly 70 of which are public roads, and 183¼ are under water.

"The parish extends to the summit of the Cheviot ranges and, with the exception of a small portion of the north and west sides, consists almost entirely of hills, and the intervening valleys. The hills are verdant and beautiful; the low grounds are under cultivation, as also the sides of several of the hills to a considerable height, and some of them to the summits. The principal vales are those of the Kale and Bowmont, neither of them of great breadth, but extending in length, the former about four, and the latter about six miles." The principal hills in the parish are—the Curr, the Schell, Cocklaw, White-law, Percy Hill, Woodside Hill, and Clifton Hill; the last, a beautiful hill, rising from the east side of the Bowmont in the form of a dome. Between the Bowmont and Kale, are Swindon, Belford, and Grubit Hills; and on the west of the Kale Gateshaw and Morebattle hills. These vary in height from 500 to 2000 feet.

"The climate is dry and healthy. In the lower part of the parish it is mild and temperate, but in the higher districts the winters are severe and stormy."

Yetholm loch is partly in this parish, and contains perch of excellent quality and a few pike—fishing free, or may be had by application. There are two small rivers in the parish, both of which take their rise in the Cheviot hills, and are fed by numerous burns—the Kale and the Bowmont—both of them excellent trouting streams; and in the Kale fish of the salmon kind are occasionally caught. The former joins the Teviot in the adjoining parish a short way to the west; and its whole course is through a district of great beauty: take it all in all, perhaps there does not exist a *sweeter* stream in the south of Scotland. The Bowmont enters the Till in Northumberland.

Throughout the parish are many remains of ancient camps. There are also the remains of two towers—Corbet House, on

Gateshaw estate, and Whitton Tower, the property of Sir John Warrender.

The village of Morebattle is prettily situated in the north-western part of the parish, on an eminence overlooking the Kale. It is entirely agricultural. Morebattle is 4 miles from Yetholm, and 7½ from Kelso, which is its market town. The nearest railway station is at Old Ormiston, on the Jedburgh line, 5½ miles, but that of Kelso (7 miles) is more convenient. Population of the village in 1861, 341 ; of the parish, 1031. Total number of families, 213 ; one of whom was returned as residing in a house with no windows, and 135 in houses of one and two windows.

Besides Morebattle, there is the very small hamlet, or rather farm-steading of GATESHAW BRAE, situated on the side of the Kale, near to the boundary of Hounam parish, and memorable as having been the site of the first Secession church in the south of Scotland. Mr. Hunter, their first minister, was ordained in 1739. The church was many years ago removed to the village. Situated in the upper or hilly part of the parish was the separate parish of Mow. The village of Mow has long been extinct. A farm-steading and a lately erected side school now occupy the site, and the name has been transformed into Mowhaugh.

Assessed property in 1863-4, £13,013 : 18 : 11.

The principal landed-proprietors in the parish are—the Duke of Roxburghe; the Marquis of Tweeddale ; William Ker, Esq., of Gateshaw ; Robert Oliver, Esq., of Lochside ; John Wilson, Esq., of Otterburn ; R. K. Elliot, Esq., of Clifton ; and Sir John Warrender of Lochend, Bart.

Superior of the village—Marquis of Tweeddale.

Those marked thus (*) are Registered Voters.

RESIDENT JUSTICES OF THE PEACE.

Robert Oliver, Esq. of Lochside.   Dr. Robson Scott, Belford.

POLICE OFFICER—Alexander Douglas, Morebattle.

PUBLIC OFFICES.

Heritors' Clerk, Inspector of Poor, Registrar of Births, Marriages, and Deaths, Kirk-Treasurer, and Session Clerk—John Swanston. Medical Officer and Public Vaccinator—Henry Vost, surgeon, Kelso.

POST OFFICE.

Violet Thomson, postmistress.   Thomas Edmondstone, messenger.

Daily post to and from Kelso.   Despatch, 6-30 a.m.   Arrival 1-40 p.m.

CLERGY, &c.

Presbytery of Kelso, Synod of Merse and Teviotdale.

Patron—Duke of Roxburghe.

ESTABLISHED CHURCH—*Rev. John Glen (Inducted 1856). Sittings, 450. Average attendance at Sabbath School, 25.

FREE CHURCH—Rev. Peter Charles Purves (Inducted 1855). Sittings, . Average attendance at Sabbath School, 60.

U. P. CHURCH—Rev. Robert Cranston (Inducted 1815); assistant and successor, Rev. Mungo Giffen (Inducted 1864). Sittings, Average attendance at Sabbath School, 30.

FAST DAYS—Thursday before the last Sundays of February and July.

SCHOOLS.†

Parochial (Morebattle)—*John Swanston, master. Average attendance, 100.
Auxiliary (Mowhaugh)—Robert Carter, master. Average attendance, .

PAROCHIAL BOARD.

Chairman—Robert Darling, Esq., factor to the Duke of Roxburghe.
No. of Poor on Roll, .
Rate of Assessment, 3d. per £. Total Assessment for 1863-4, £319.
Poor-House—Kelso Combination.

HOUNAM AND MOREBATTLE ANGLING CLUB (estab. 1857).

Having for its object a refinement in the mode of fishing, the suppression of poaching, and the encouragement of fair angling. Prizes are given to be competed for by members of the club annually.

President—Mr Gray, Sharplaw.
Vice-President—Mr Borthwick, Cowbog.
Secretary and Treasurer—Mr George Aitken.
Entry-Money, 1s. 6d. Annual Subscription, 1s.

SUNDRIES.

MORTIFICATION—A Mr. Moir of Otterburn, by his will, bequeathed to the Heritors the sum of £1500, the interest of which to be applied to the Education of Poor and Indigent Orphans.
LIBRARY—R. Fox, librarian. 800 vols. Annual Subscription, 3s. 9d.
CONVEYANCE—Post runner to Kelso, daily ; Kelso Carriers (see p. 98).

CORN MILLS.

DEAN—*Robert Govenlock. GRUBBIT—*John Short, miller.
PRIMSIDE—William Young.

† Children in the parish between 5 and 15, attending school during the first week of April 1861, 193 ; of all ages, 201.

TRADES.

*Aitken, George, baker
Craig, George, shoemaker
Currie, J. & G., fleshers
Davidson, Henry, spirit dealer
Entwistle, Jacob, tailor
*Fox, Robert, joiner
Hall, Ralph, tailor
Jack, Thomas, shoemaker
Laidlaw & Son, William, shoemakers
*Mills, Thomas, general dealer
Moscript, Grace, dressmaker
Moscript, Richard, mason
Ovens, William, shoemaker
Purves, John, blacksmith
Renwick, Francis, joiner
Rodger, James, mason
Scott, George, tailor
Smail, Walter, labourer
Thomson, Mary, dressmaker
Thomson, Violet, *postmistress*
Whelans, Andrew, shoemaker
Young, Andrew, builder

RESIDENTS, FARMERS, &c., IN THE PARISH.

*Borthwick, Gilbert, farmer, Cowbog
*Cunningham, Alexander, farmer, Morebattle Tofts
*Elliot, Thomas, farmer, Clifton Cote
*Johnston, Alexander, farmer, Primside
*Lillie, John, farmer, Clifton
*Rutherford, George, farmer, Heughhead
*Scott, James Robson (of Ashtrees), farmer, Belford
*Scott, Thomas, farmer, Whitton
*Shiell, Robert, farmer, Sourhope
*Shiell, Thomas, farmer, Sourhope
*Shortreed, Mrs., Attonburn
*Shortreed, Robert, farmer, Attonburn
*Young, William, farmer, Woodside

SEATS &c., OF COUNTY FAMILIES IN THE PARISH.

LOCHSIDE.

The residence of *Robert Oliver, Esq. of Lochside ; born 1818 ; succeeded his uncle in 1831 ; married, 1858, Margaret, daughter of William James Strickland, Esq., Dublin ; and has issue—Robert, born in 1859 ; and other sons.

GATESHAW.

The property and occasional residence of *William Ker, Esq., Torquay, Devonshire; born 1775; married his cousin-german, Jane, daughter of the late Ellis Martin, Esq. ; and has issue—

Gilbert, in Liverpool
Ellis Martin, resident at Gateshaw

and several daughters, one of whom, Georgina, married, 1849, William Scoresby, D.D., F.R.S., L. and E. (the celebrated navigator), who died at Torquay, 1859.

OTTERBURN.

The property of *John Wilson, Esq. of Otterburn and Yet, and the residence of himself and his aunt, Miss Milne.

REGISTERED VOTERS (Non-Resident).

Burnet, James, Leith
Crosbie, Peter, late steward, Morebattle Tofts
Davidson, Henry, weaver, Sprouston
Gorham, Robert, writer, Edinburgh
Hogg, Thomas, Roxburgh Boathouse
Hogg, John, joiner, Roxburgh
Miller, Andrew, Roxburgh
Macknight, Alexander E., advocate, Edinburgh
Scott, John, W.S., Edinburgh
Warrender, Sir John, Bart. of Lochend
Wilson, George, mason, Sprouston

ECKFORD.

———◆———

THIS is an entirely agricultural parish, intersected by the Kale water. It is about 6 miles long and from 4 to 5 miles broad. It is bounded on the north by Roxburgh and Kelso, on the east by Linton and Morebattle, on the south by Jedburgh, and on the west by Crailing. The total area of the parish, according to the Ordnance Survey, is 10,097¼ acres, divided as follows:—9897 acres are lands under cultivation or wood, 100 are water, 92 are public roads, and the railway occupies the remaining 8¼ acres.

The general appearance of the parish is undulating, gradually rising towards the south, and occasionally into considerable elevations, which command extensive views of the surrounding country. The climate is mild and healthy, and the prevailing winds are westerly.

There is the small village of Eckford in the parish, and the hamlets of CESSFORD and CAVERTON—all of them consisting almost entirely of the houses of the farm-labourers. The church* and manse are situated on the Kelso and Jedburgh road, which crosses the western extremity of the parish, a short distance from the village of Eckford. At Kale mouth a handsome chain bridge crosses the Teviot.

In the southern part of the parish are the remains of the once famous Cessford Castle, the ancient manorial residence of Sir Robert Ker (better known as Habbie Ker), warden of the Scottish midland marches—of whom the Dukes of Roxburghe are lineal descendants.

The only mansion in the parish is KIRKBANK, a small house prettily situated on the banks of the Teviot; for many years the hunting residence of the late Lord John Scott.

---

* " Close to the eastern door of the church is appended an iron collar, which is in a state of great preservation, and which is commonly known by the name of the *jugs* (or jougs). In former times, church offenders were sometimes sentenced by kirk sessions to stand with it fastened round their neck, and clothed in sackcloth, for several sabbaths, in presence of the congregation, in token of their repentance and humiliation." This is the only instance in the district of the preservation of this old instrument of torture in its original state and position: that hung up at Abbotsford was merely one of the curiosities collected by Sir Walter Scott, and was brought from Threeve Castle in Galloway, the ancient seat of the Douglasses.

"The Kale runs through the parish in a north-easterly direction, and divides it into nearly two equal parts. In some places its banks are bold and romantic in a high degree, and beautifully overhung with wood." The Teviot also crosses the parish, cutting off a small portion of it to the west, and receives the waters of the Kale somewhat to the north of the church. In both rivers the trout fishing is excellent, but restricted. In the Teviot salmon are occasionally caught, bull-trout are common, and whitelings frequent the Kale (see Morebattle and Hounam parishes). Near the village of Eckford is a small loch of about 7 acres, which was plentifully stocked with tench, perch, and trout, by the late Lord John Scott. It also contains splendid eels. Otters numerously frequent the mouth of the Kale.

The village of Eckford is about 5 miles from both Jedburgh and Kelso, the latter being the post town. Old Ormiston Station on the Jedburgh Railway is about 1½ miles distant.

The population of the parish in 1861 was 957, who comprised 194 families, one of whom was returned as living in a house having no windows, 106 in houses of one window, 52 in houses of two windows, and 35 in houses of three and more windows.

Assessed property 1863-4, £10,751 : 4 : 11.

The Duke of Buccleuch and the Duke of Roxburghe are the principal landed-proprietors in the parish—about four-fifths of the whole parish belonging to them.

Those marked thus (*) are Registered Voters.

RESIDENT JUSTICE OF THE PEACE—*John Murray, M.D., Kersknowe.

POLICE OFFICER—Allan Mitchell, Crailing.

PUBLIC OFFICES—Registrar of Births, Marriages, and Deaths, Inspector of Poor, and Session Clerk—H. R. Lawrie.
Kirk Treasurer—William Turnbull.

POST OFFICE (Kirkbank)—William Turnbull, postmaster. Daily Post to Kelso. Arrival, 7-40 a.m. ; Departure, 2-45 p.m. John Waldie, rural messenger, leaves Kirkbank daily at 8 a.m., and goes as far as Nisbet Mill, returning again in time for the Kelso post.

CLERGY, &c.—Eckford is in the Presbytery of Jedburgh, and Synod of Merse and Teviotdale. Patron—the Crown.
Established Church—Rev. Joseph Yair, A.M. (Inducted 1829). Sittings, 300. Average attendance at Sabbath School, 20.

FAST DAYS—Thursday before the second Sabbaths of May and November.

SCHOOLS†—Parochial (Eckford)—Henry R. Lawrie, master; average attendance, 70.

---

† Children in the parish from 4 to 15, attending school during the first week of April 1861, 174 ; of all ages, 183.

Parochial Side School (Caverton)—John Murray, teacher ; average attendance, 50.

PAROCHIAL BOARD—Robert Darling, Esq., Broomlands, Chairman. No. of Poor on Roll, 23. Poor House—Kelso Union. Assessment, 2½d. per £. Total Assessment 1863-4, £216 : 12 : 4½.

MILLS : Eckford—Corn—William Hart. Ormiston—Corn — Thomas Geggie, Bowmont Forest—Saw Mills—George Hall. Teviot Foot —Saw Mills—*George Charters.

TRADES IN ECKFORD VILLAGE.

Dalgleish, Fanny, grocer
M'Laren, Christian, dressmaker
Potts, Andrew, farmer
Rutherford, Thomas, tailor
Tait, Peter, joiner.
Tait, Thomas, tailor
Tait, William, hook dresser
Wood, Mary, grocer
Wood, John, blacksmith
Wood, William, tailor

RESIDENTS, FARMERS, &c., IN THE PARISH.

Arras, Adam, farmer, Ormiston.
*Bell, John,   do.,   Marchcleuch
*Bell, Robert, do.,   Cessford
Clinkscales, Jas , forester to the Duke of Buccleuch, Eckford
Craike, Mrs., Upper Wooden Villa
*Cunningham, Charles, farmer, Grahamslaw
Handyside, Alexander, Eckford Moss
*Johnston, George,   do.,   Marlfield.
Johnston, Miss, Marlfield
Johnston, Walter, baron officer to the Duke of Buccleuch
*Logan, A., farmer, Caverton
Macnish, Richard, station-master, Ormiston
Moffat, John, gamekeeper, Ormiston
Moffat, Mrs., Marlfield
*Park, Alexander B., farmer, Wester Wooden
*Purdom, Walter,   do.,   Easter Wooden
Rutherford, James, do.,   Eckford Moss
Telfer, Alexander, gamekeeper to the Duke of Buccleuch
Wilson, Robert, superintendant, Kirkbank

SEAT, &c., OF COUNTY FAMILY IN THE PARISH.

KIRKBANK.

The occasional residence of Lady John Douglas Montagu Scott

Alicia Anne), eldest daughter of John Spottiswoode, Esq., of Spottiswoode, in Berwickshire (*see* p. 642); married, 1836, Lord John Douglas Montagu Scott (younger brother of the present Duke of Buccleuch), a Deputy-Lieutenant and Justice of Peace for Warwickshire, and sometime a Captain in the Grenadier Guards, and M.P. for Roxburghshire (he died January 3, 1860).*

English residence—Causton Lodge, Dunchurch, near Rugby.

MAINHOUSE.

Situated about 4 miles from Kelso, on the Morebattle road—the property of Alexander Cameron, Esq., solicitor, Elgin ; occasionally occupied.

Mr, Cameron, after the Dukes of Buccleuch and Roxburghe, is the only proprietor in the parish of consequence.

REGISTERED VOTERS (Non-Resident).

Dalkeith, Earl of, M.P. for Edinburghshire (*see* p. 151)
Scott, Lord Henry J. Douglas Montagu, M.P. for Selkirkshire (*see* p. 395)

---

* Lady John Scott is the composer, &c., of the following popular ballads:— "Annie Lawrie," music and last verse of the words—the first verses are by Allan Cunningham ; " Douglas, tender and true," music only ; "They shot him on the nine stane rig," music only—words from Scott's Minstrelsy ; "Durrisdeer," words and music; "Shame on you, Gallants"; "The Bounds o' Cheviot;" " The Foul Fords;" "Lammermoor ;" "Ettrick, oh ! murmuring waters ;" etc.

Whenever Lady John Scott published any of her compositions, it has been for a charity. Some of them have attained an established popularity and large circulation.

LINTON.

—◆—

THIS parish is situated in the north-eastern part of the county and borders upon Northumberland. Its length is about 6 miles, and 2 miles in breadth. Its boundaries are—on the north, Sprouston ; on the east, Northumberland and Yetholm ; on the south, Morebattle ; and on the west, Eckford. The area of the parish, according to the Ordnance Survey, is nearly 6428 acres, of which $34\frac{1}{2}$ are under water, $67\frac{1}{2}$ are occupied by roads ; the remainder being land, nearly all of which is under cultivation.

" The western extremity of the parish forms part of a beautiful valley watered by the Kale, which here forms the boundary of the parish. From this valley the land rises in a somewhat undulating ascent till it reaches its highest elevation on the summit of Linton Hill. Its surface eastward is varied and uneven, and sometimes intersected by small hills, which connect those of the Cheviots with the fertile plain which extends along the southern bank of the Tweed." The principal hills in the parish are Linton Hill, in the south-east; Blakelaw, Hoselaw, and Kiplaw, in the north-west. With the exception of the first mentioned, they are all cultivated to the summits. There is a loch in the parish at Hoselaw which covers 33 acres, and abounds in perch and eels. The loch is free to the angler. The parish church* and school-house are situated near the western boundary of the parish.

---

* The pretty little church and churchyard of Linton occupy a situation on the summit of a circular hill. This eminence is generally believed to be artificial, and tradition reports it to have been the work of two sisters, who, to expiate a heinous sin perpetrated by their brother, removed the soil from a hollow still shown in the vicinity.

Above the porch of the church is an ancient stone with a carving of a man on horseback, having a long spear in his hand, which is thrust into the mouth of an animal resembling a dragon. This stone is said, also, at one time, to have borne the following inscription :—

" The wode Laird of Larieston,
    Slew the worm of Wormieston,
    And won all Linton parochine."

This refers to a monstrous serpent, wolf, or bear, which infested the neighbourhood and committed great devastation ; its den is still pointed out, under the name of " The Worm's Hole ; " and the field in which it is situated, receives the name of "Wormington." The animal was killed by William de Somerville, ancestor of Lord Somerville, who obtained Linton as his reward, and the memorial of this event is still preserved on the crest of his arms, which retains, among other allusions to it, the following inscription—" The Wode Laird."

Thomas Pringle, a poet of some note, and the first editor of Blackwood's Magazine, was a native of this parish.

The nearest post and market town is Kelso, about 6 miles distant from the parish church.

Population of the parish in 1861, 608; who comprised 104 families, 3 of whom were returned as living in houses of one window, 57 in houses of two windows, and 44—a large proportion—as living in houses of three and more windows.

Assessed property in 1863-4, £7717 : 12 : 3.

Formerly there were two villages in this parish—Hoselaw and Linton, but both have entirely disappeared, and the parish is now without one. The principal proprietors are—R. K. Elliot, Esq., of Clifton, who owns nearly a half of the whole parish; Robert Oliver, Esq., of Blakelaw (Lochside); Thomas Scott, Esq., of Graden; Andrew Wauchope, Esq., of Niddrie-Marischal; and G. Humble, Esq., of Old Graden. CLIFTON PARK, the seat of R. K. Elliot, is the only mansion house in the parish.

Those marked thus (*) are Registered Voters.

RESIDENT JUSTICE OF THE PEACE—Robert K. Elliot, Esq., of Clifton.

POST OFFICE—There is no Post Office at Linton parish, but the post between Morebattle and Kelso passes daily.

PUBLIC OFFICES—Registrar of Births, Marriages, and Deaths, Inspector of Poor, Session Clerk and Kirk Treasurer—Robert Henderson.

Medical Officer and Public Vaccinator—Vacant.

CLERGY—Presbytery of Kelso, Synod of Merse and Teviotdale. Patron—*R. K. Elliot, Esq., of Clifton.

Established Church—*Rev. Thomas Leishman (Inducted 1855). Sittings, 160.

FAST DAYS—Wednesday preceding the last Sabbaths of June and December.

SCHOOL†—Parochial—*Robert Henderson, master. Aver. attend. 60.

PAROCHIAL BOARD—Robert K. Elliot, Esq., Chairman. No. of Poor on Roll, 18. Assessment, 4½d. per £. Total Assessment for 1863-4, £148 : 16 : 10. Poor House—Kelso Combination.

CORN MILL—George Smith.

CONVEYANCE—Morebattle carriers and postrunner (which see); N. B. Railway, Kelso Station, distant about 5½ miles from the centre of the parish.

---

† Children in the parish from 5 to 15, attending school during the first week of April 1861, 147; of all ages, 154.

RESIDENTS, FARMERS, &c. IN THE PARISH.

*Burn, George, farmer, Bankhead
*Bell, Alexander, do., Linton
*Borthwick, John, do., Greenlees
*Humble, Geo. (of 13 Brisbane Place, Kelso), of Old Graden
 Purves, William, do., Burnfoot
 Roberton, Andrew, do., Hoselaw
 Stavert, George, blacksmith, Hoselaw
*Scott, Andrew, farmer, Frogden†
*Turnbull, William J., farmer, Graden
 Walker, Andrew, farm-steward, Clifton Park
 Winter, Robert, joiner, Dryburn
 Young, John, blacksmith, do.

SEAT, &c., OF COUNTY FAMILY IN THE PARISH.

CLIFTON PARK.

The residence of Robert Kerr Elliot, Esq. of Clifton and Harwood, eldest son of the late William Elliot, Esq., of Harwood (in Hobkirk parish); born 1805; succeeded to Harwood on the death of his father in 1835, and to Clifton, as heir of entail, in 1843; married, 1833, Mary Anne, daughter of Charles Claude Clifton, Esq., of Tynmaur; and has issue—

William Claude, born 1835; and other sons and daughters, including Mary Ann Frances, who married, 1859, Sir Edward Claude Cockburn, Bart. of Downton, Herefordshire, and has issue—a son, Robert, born 1861.

Mr. Elliot is a Deputy-Lieutenant and Justice of Peace for the county of Roxburgh, and was formerly an officer in the army.

REGISTERED VOTERS (Non-Resident)

Roberton, John, farmer, Harpertown
Scott, Thomas, Esq., of Graden, Broom House, Beale, Northumberland

---

† Mr. Dawson, who rendered essential services to the agriculture of Scotland, by the introduction of turnip husbandry, etc., farmed Frogden while introducing many of his improvements.

SPROUSTON.

———◆———

THE parish of Sprouston is situated in the north-eastern part of the county, and on the south bank of the river Tweed. Its boundaries are—Tweed on the north, Carham on the east, Linton on the south, and Eckford and Kelso on the west. In shape it is nearly square, being about 4 miles each way. The area, according to the Ordnance Survey, is a little over 8731½ acres, of which 33¾ are occupied by the North-Eastern Railway, 134⅛ by roads, public and private, and 96 by water. Two elevations of gradual ascent cross from north-east to south-west. The soil is rich, especially near the river; indeed this parish is famous for its fertility, and is everywhere highly cultivated.

The salmon fishings in the Tweed along this parish are very productive, and are much resorted to by anglers from all quarters. Trout fishing is free.

The climate varies with the elevation, being bracing on Lempitlaw,—the highest point—bleak on Haddenrig, and mild and salubrious along the river.

Hadden Stank and Redden Burn, in this parish, were frequently chosen as meeting places betwixt the Scotch and English commissioners for settling disputes.

There are two villages in the parish—Sprouston and Lempitlaw—the former being the larger of the two. Sprouston is situated in the north-western part of the parish, near the river. It is almost entirely agricultural. Good accommodation can be got here for strangers who come to fish. And here are the parish church and school.

The hamlet of LEMPITLAW is a very small one, in the south-eastern extremity of the parish; and is also entirely agricultural. At one time it was a separate parish. Its churchyard still continues to be used as a burial place, but its church has utterly disappeared.

Kelso is the nearest market and post town—about 2½ miles distant from the village of Sprouston. There is a station of the North-Eastern Railway close to this village.

Population of the parish in 1861, 1295; of the village of Sprouston only, 379. Number of families in the parish at the same date, 274; of whom 99 were returned as living in houses of one window, and 110 in houses of two windows. Assessed property in 1863-4, £13,064 : 1 : 5.

Superior of Sprouston and principal proprietor—Duke of Roxburghe. The other principal proprietors are— the Duke of Buccleuch, Sir William Eliott of Stobs, and Sir George H. S. Douglas, Bart. of Springwood Park—all of whom are non-resident.

———————

Those marked thus (*) are Registered Voters.

POLICE OFFICER—Andrew Cook, Lempitlaw.

POST OFFICE—John Bruce, postmaster. Daily Post to and from Kelso. Arrival, 12-10 a.m.; Departure, 3-10 p.m. Ralph Wright, messenger.
    Post Runner to Lempitlaw—Philip M'Leod, who arrives about 1 p.m., and returns for Kelso about 2.

PUBLIC OFFICES—Heritors' Clerk, Registrar of Births, Marriages, and Deaths, Session Clerk and Kirk Treasurer, and Inspector of Poor—James Brown.
    Medical Officer and Public Vaccinator—Dr. Hamilton, Kelso.

CLERGY—Presbytery of Kelso, Synod of Merse and Teviotdale. Patron —Duke of Roxburghe.
    Established Church—*Rev. Robert Orange Bromfield (Inducted 1843). Sittings, 420. Average attend. at Sabbath School, 120.
    Free Church (Sprouston) see Kelso.

FAST DAYS—Wednesday before the first Sabbaths of May and Nov.

SCHOOLS †—Parochial—*James Brown, master; average attend., 80.
    Private School (Sprouston)—Miss Gray.
    Subscription School (Lempitlaw)—John Lyle, teacher; average attendance, 75.
    Subscription School (Hadden)—George Patterson, teacher; average attendance, 60.

PAROCHIAL BOARD—Robert Darling, Esq., Broomlands, Chairman. Rate of Assessment, 9d. per £. Total Assessment, 1863-4, over £500. No. of Poor on Roll, 50. Poor House—Kelso Union.

CONVEYANCE—North British and North-Eastern Railways. Stations: Sprouston; Carham, distant 2 miles; Maxwellheugh, distant 2¼ miles. The junction of these railways is in the parish, about a mile west from the village.

CORN MILL—Banff Mill—*James Lindsay, farmer, Whitmuirhaugh.

———————

TRADES.

Sprouston.

Bruce, John, (*Post Office*), general merchant
Brown, John, clothier
Jamieson, William, grocer and spirit dealer

———————

† Children in the parish attending school between 5 and 15, during the first week of April 1861, 232; of all ages, 243.

Johnston, Alexander, contractor
Melrose, Richard, contractor, grocer, and meal-dealer
Turnbull, James, joiner
Walker, Andrew, blacksmith
Young, George, baker and grocer

Lempitlaw

Cairns, George, blacksmith
Sheriff, David, joiner

RESIDENTS, FARMERS, &c.

*Clay, John, farmer, Kerchesters
*Culberson, John, farmer, Sprouston
*Culberson, William, do.,   do.
 Dunn, William,   do.,   Redden
*Howie, Thomas,   do.,   Haddon
*Jamieson, George,   do.,   Nottylees
*Kerss, Thomas, fisherman, Sprouston water
*Ogilvie, George, do.,   Holefield
*Robson, Charles, do.,   Lurdenlaw
*Scott, John,   do.,   Lempitlaw
*Smith, Robert,   do.,   Kersquarter
*Smith, William,   do.,   Windywalls
*Stark, Thomas,   do.,   Mellendean
 Stark, John, Mellendean
 Stark, William, do.
 Stark, Miss,   do.
*Turnbull, James, farmer, Lempitlaw Eastfield.
*Turnbull, Mark,   do.,   Lempitlaw
*Watson, George,   do.,   Easter Softlaw

REGISTERED VOTER (Non-Resident).

Douglas, Sir G. H. S., Bart. of Springwood Park, Kelso.

EDNAM.

THE small parish of Ednam is situated on both sides of the river Eden, from which it takes its name. In shape it approaches a square, being about $3\frac{1}{4}$ miles long and about 3 broad. It is bounded on the north by Eccles, in Berwickshire, on the east by Eccles and Sprouston, on the south by Kelso and Sprouston, and on the west by Stichill and Nenthorn. The area of the parish, according to the Ordnance Survey, is 3,919.724 acres—comprising 3784 acres of land, all either under cultivation or laid out in wood; 70.263 of water; and 65.772 of roads, public and private. The soil varies, but is for the most part rich; and the farm of Edenmouth, in this parish, is considered the earliest in the locality. "The district is embellished with plantations, which cover the chief elevation in the parish, on which stands the elegant mansion of Hendersyde Park (J. Waldie, Esq.) HENDERSYDE PARK lies near the Kelso and Coldstream road, and is about 2 miles from the former place. The grounds in which it is situated are finely laid out—the house itself is a large four-fronted building, planned by the present proprietor, and built at different periods, from 1803 to 1841. The interior contains a fine collection of pictures, mosaics, and classical antiquities; besides a library,* which, as a general collection, is " the most extensive

---

* Sir Walter Scott (in *Lockhart's Life*) describes himself as having been greatly indebted to the Waldie Library in the time of the present proprietor's grandmother, who, when he was attending the school at Kelso, generously allowed him its free use—his aunts, with whom Sir Walter then resided at the Cottage (*see* p. 110), being intimate friends of Mrs. Waldie; a strong intimacy having existed between the families for several generations. Charles Ormiston, jun. (quaker), maternal great-grandfather of the present proprietor was the originator of the Library, and the purchaser of the Hendersyde estate, in 1715; and although now so beautifully wooded, fertile, and renting higher than any other estate of equal size in the county, was then such a waste of moor and morass, that in the '45, when Prince Charles passed through Kelso, the only plunder which his Highland followers procured from the then small holdings on the estate, was a few half-starved sheep, oats, and oatmeal. They shot the sheep, drank the warm blood, skinned and carried off the carcases; the oatmeal they compelled the women of the farms to make into cakes, which they ate half-baked off the fire as made; and tradition states that some of the plunderers were lost in the extensive moss, which then existed in the neighbourhood, and which was subsequently drained to form the present Kelso race course (*see* p. 92).
" Mrs. Waldie belonged to her father's community, and the style of life

N

and best preserved in the county;" while, as a Fine Art collection and Private Library, it is perhaps unequalled in Scotland. Orders for admission to see the interior of the house can be procured from Messrs. Smiths and Robson, Kelso.

The village of Ednam—the only one in the parish—a pretty and clean little place, is pleasantly situated on the river Eden. This village is celebrated as being the birth-place of the poet Thomson, whose father* was minister of the parish. A stumpy looking obelisk, 52 feet in height, has been erected to the poet's memory, on a hill about a mile from the village in the Kelso direction. The village also claims to be the birth-place of the father of James Cook, the famous circumnavigator.

The Eden is an excellent trouting stream, and from Ednam to its mouth, a distance of over two miles, is free to anglers; above Ednam it is mostly preserved—(*see* p. 73).

The village is about 2¼ miles north-east from Kelso, which is the nearest railway station, and which is also the post town.

Population of the parish in 1861, 599; who comprised 125 families, 46 of whom were returned as living in houses of one window, 52 in houses of two windows, and 27 in houses of three and more windows.

Assessed property in 1863-4, £8,136 : 19 : 5.

Principal proprietors—John Waldie, Esq., of Hendersyde Park—resident; —— Douglas Moffat, Esq., of Harpertoun, Admiral Sir William Dickson of Sydenham, Lord Dudley and Ward—non-resident.

Superior of the village—Lord Dudley and Ward.

---

and manners depicted in the household of Joshua Geddes of Mount Sharon, and his amiable sister, in some of the sweetest chapters of "Redgauntlet" is a slightly decorated edition of what he [Sir Walter as a boy] witnessed under her hospitable roof."—*Lockhart's Life.*

A century since the community of Quakers was a comparatively numerous and highly respectable one in the locality of Kelso; it has since become extinct, and their meeting-house at Kelso, after having been used as a school of arts, mechanics' institute, &c., is now the church of the small community of Congregationalists (*see* p. 79). In the little burial ground attached lie several generations of the Ormistons, including Mrs. Waldie. The property belongs to Mr. Waldie, of Hendersyde Park, the present representative.

* A recent writer in the ephemeral publication, the "*Border Magazine,*" states that the house in which Thomson was born still exists as the outhouse of a farm-steading, after having been used for several years as the village school. Of the poet, the parish cannot be expected to furnish any traditionary recollections; when he was only nine or ten weeks old his father was transferred to Southdean parish, and it is most improbable that Thomson had any subsequent connection with Ednam. For many years the anniversary of Thomson's birth used to be celebrated by a number of gentlemen (the *Ednam Club*) dining in the village inn. The last meeting was held September 1819. A miniature of the poet, presented to the club by the then Earl of Buchan, is kept in the manse, and handed down from one incumbent to another. This miniature is from a large portrait of the poet by Slaughter, in the possession of the Buchan family.

Those marked thus (*) are Registered Voters in the parish.

CLERGY—Presbytery of Kelso, Synod of Merse and Teviotdale. Patron —the Crown.
  Established Church—*Rev. Wm. Lamb (Inducted 1844). Sittings, 260. Average attendance at Sabbath School, 30.

FAST DAYS—Wednesday before the first Sabbaths of May and November.

SCHOOL† (Parish)—John Brown, interim master.

PUBLIC OFFICES—Heritors' Clerk, Session Clerk, Kirk Treasurer, Inspector of Poor, and Registrar of Births, Marriages, and Deaths —John Brown, interim.
  Medical Officer and Public Vaccinator—John Bookless, surgeon, Kelso.

PAROCHIAL BOARD—James Roberton, Esq , Ladyrig, Chairman. No. of Poor on Roll, 29. Poor House—Kelso Union. Average Assessment, about 3d. per £. Total ditto, 1863-4, £192 : 15 : 5.

POST OFFICE—Daily Post to Kelso. Arrival, 8-30 a.m. Departure, 2 p.m. Alexander Henderson, messenger.

MILLS—East Mill—Corn—Andrew Rutherford. West Mill—Corn— *Robert Broomfield. Sharpitlaw—Saw Mill—Hay & Rutherford.

BREWERY—John Stenhouse.

TRADES, &c.

Brotherston, James, spirit dealer
Fairbairn, Edward, blacksmith
Hall, Alexander, tailor
Main, James, shoemaker
Ovens, Robert, joiner

RESIDENTS, FARMERS, &c.

*Broad, William, farmer, Clifton Hill
*Burn, John,   do.,   Ednam West Mains ‡
*Glass, James, farmer, Hendersyde
*Pringle, Mrs., do.,   Springhall
*Ross, James,   do.,   Newtonlees
*Rannie, M. G., do.,   Edenmouth
Roberton, John, farmer, Harpertoun
Smail, John, head-gardener, Hendersyde Park

---

† Children in the parish between 5 and 15, attending school during the first week of April 1861, 122; of all ages, 127.
‡ The old mansion of the Edmonstones,—a family who held the estate of Ednam for many centuries—is now converted into the thrashing mill of this farm.

*Thompson, Thomas H., farmer, Highridgehall
*Tully, Thomas, farmer, Ferneyhill
*Whitehead, William, farmer, Houndridge

SEAT, &c , OF COUNTY FAMILY IN THE PARISH.

HENDERSYDE PARK.

The residence of John Waldie, Esq., of Hendersyde and Hay-hope; born 1st May 1781; succeeded his father, the late George Waldie, Esq., in 1826. Mr. Waldie is a Deputy-Lieut. for the county of Roxburgh. *Heir Pres.*—his nephew, George Richard Griffith, Esq., of Pencraig, Anglesea, and of Burnhall in Berwickshire.

Mr. Griffith is the son of Sir Richard-John Griffith, Bart. of Munster, Grillagh, County Londonderry, and Maria Jane, Mr. Waldie's eldest sister. Mr. Griffith was born January 1820; married, April 1849, Eliza, youngest daughter of Nicholas P. Leader, Esq., M.P., Dromagh Castle, county Cork, and has issue—a son, Richard-John, born 24th April 1850; and a daugter, Maria-Mona.

REGISTERED VOTER (Non-Resident).

Thomson, William (late of Glasgow), China

STICHILL AND HUME.

———◆———

OF the united parishes of Stichill and Hume, the former is in Roxburghshire and the latter in Berwickshire. The united parish is bounded on the north by Greenlaw and Gordon, on the east by Eccles, on the south by Ednam and Nenthorn, and on the west by Nenthorn and Earlston. It extends to about 5½ miles in length, and has an average breadth of about 4½. The surface is for the most part elevated, averaging nearly 500 feet above the level of the sea; from this height it gradually declines to the south. The areas, according to the Ordnance Survey are—Hume (including a small detached portion in the parish of Earlston, which measures nearly 39½ acres), 4103 acres — of which 60 acres are in public and private roads, and about 3¾ in water; Stichill, nearly 2804 acres—of which nearly 45½ are in roads, and 5 in water. Nearly the whole of the parish is under cultivation. Near the southern boundary of the parish is the village of Stichill. It consists of one street, and has a rather decayed appearance; but its situation is beautiful and could scarcely be better placed for health; and yet, curiously, it was the first place in the county visited by cholera in 1832, when two fatal cases suddenly occurred; since then the epidemic has not visited the parish;—Hume it has never visited. For its size the village of Stichill has always had a large proportion of very old inhabitants.

Stichill has greatly decreased in population and importance since the end of last century, when it had double its present population and twice its present extent. It was long celebrated for its open-air preachings or "Holy fairs" in connection with the Secession Church. These used to be held on the hill near to the present church, which was well suited for the purpose (it being then unplanted), and formed on the south side a sort of amphitheatre. While the religious services went on at the hill, a sort of secular fair was being held at the public house in the village. [For an exaggerated account of similar proceedings, *see* Burn's Holy Fair.] A relic of these proceedings existed to within the last thirty-five years in the *tent* preachings held on the green at the Stichill U. P. Church on sacramental occasions.

At the west end of the village is the entrance to STICHILL HOUSE. The latter, on a beautiful eminence, is a grand building in course of erection, on the site of the old Stichill House, long the seat of the Pringles, baronets of Stichill, the former proprietors of Stichill parish, and also lands in Hume, as at present possessed by George Baird, Esq. The new building is intended to have a tower of above 100 feet in height, from the top of which the view will be grand and varied, commanding a radius of over 30 miles.

The Eden, which forms the southern boundary of the parish, is an excellent trouting stream, but in which fishing is restricted. In its course it forms the beautiful cascade of STICHILL LINN; which has a height of about 40 ft., and a situation highly romantic. This and the adjacent grounds of Newton Don (see Nenthorn parish) are often visited by sight-seers from Kelso, from which they are distant about 3 miles, and may either be approached by walks through the fields or by the public roads. Above the Linn the trouts of the Eden are considered to be of a better quality than they are below it, or in any of the neighbouring streams; and their flesh has a redness of colour nearly approaching that of the salmon. No fish of the salmon genus surmount the fall, but eels make their way up by the help of the damp moss which covers the rocks at the edge of the falling water; and during the season, at the expense of a drenching by the spray, small specimens may be picked out by the hand in any quantity. The effect of the Linn depends very much on the state of the river; it is always picturesque and beautiful, but when the river is in flood, it has a considerable degree of sublimity.

It may be of interest to the naturalist to state that the bullfinch, a somewhat rare bird in Scotland, is found in considerable numbers in the woods of Stichill. In spring this bird is exceedingly destructive in gardens, the flower buds of fruit trees being its favourite food at that season; and it often completely strips the apple, plum, and other trees, and small fruit bushes.

The hamlet of HUME is situated in the centre of its parish, at the foot of the rocky eminence on which Hume Castle stands. The castle was the residence of the Earls of Home; and was for long a very important fortress. There is nothing of it now but the walls, which are modern and built upon the old foundations, to resemble the old castle; they form one of the most prominent features in the county, being seen from all points.

Each parish has its own parochial board, and in each village there is a parish school. The church stands in the village of Stichill, which is over 2 miles from the hamlet of Hume.

Kelso is the nearest market and post town, being about 3 miles from Stichill. Population of the parish of Stichill* in 1861, 425; of the parish of Hume, 420; total, 845—who composed 169

families, 1 of whom was returned as living in a house having no windows, 87 in houses of one window, 50 in houses of two windows, and 31 in houses of three and more windows.

Assessed property in 1863-4, Stichill, £4196:5:6; Hume, £5000:7:6.

Sole proprietor of the parish of Stichill, George Baird, Esq. of Stichill and Strichen. Proprietors of Hume parish—the Earl of Haddington; Sir Hugh H. Campbell, Bart. of Marchmont; and George Baird, Esq. of Stichill.

Those marked thus (*) are Electors Registered in the parish for Roxburghshire, and those marked thus (†) for Berwickshire.

POLICE OFFICER—William Hunter, Stichill.

POST OFFICE—Daily Post to and from Kelso. Arrival at Stichill, 1 p.m.; Arrival at Hume, every other day, 2 p.m. Departure from Hume, every other day, 2 p.m.; Departure from Stichill, 3 p.m. Messenger—George Fairbairn.

PUBLIC OFFICES (Stichill)— Kirk Treasurer, Inspector of Poor, Registrar of Births, Marriages, and Deaths, and Session Clerk— Adam Douglas. (Hume)—Inspector of Poor and Registrar— James Cook.
    Medical Officer and Public Vaccinator for Stichill—Dr. Mackenzie, Kelso. Hume—Dr. Robertson, Greenlaw.

CLERGY, &c.—Presbytery of Kelso, Synod of Merse and Teviotdale. Patrons—Crown and Sir H. H. Campbell, Bart. of Marchmont. Established Church ‡ (Stichill)—†*Rev. Dugald Macalister (Inducted 1846). Sittings, 320. Average attendance at Sabbath School, 25.
    U. P. Church (Stichill)— *Rev. David Cairns (Inducted 1855). Sittings, . Average attendance at Sabbath School,

FAST DAYS—Thursdays before second Sabbaths of February and July.

SCHOOLS §—Parochial (Stichill)—*Adam Douglas, master; average attendance, 75.
    Parochial (Hume)—†James Cook, master; average attend., 65.

MORTIFICATION—(STICHILL)—The late Mrs. Col. Robertson (sister of the present Sir John Pringle, Bart.) left the sum of £150, the interest of which is to be distributed among poor persons above 50 years of age in the village.
    Do. (HUME)—The late Sir William Campbell of Marchmont, by settlement, left the sum of £25 annually for behoof of the poor of the parish of Hume; the distribution of which is at the dis-

---

* Wallace and Hislop who were unjustly executed at Jedburgh, at the end of the last century, were natives of Stichill; various traditions respecting their execution are still current in the district.

‡ Redpath, the author of the "Border History," was minister of Stichill for many years; he died there 31st January 1772, leaving behind him a county history of Berwickshire in MS., which has never been published.
§ Children in Stichill parish between 5 and 15, attending school during the first week of April 1861, 76; of all ages, 78; in Hume, 56; of all ages, 62.

cretion of the proprietors of Marchmont and the Minister of the parish for the time being.

There is also a Bequest of £100, by a Captain Home in 1743, the interest of which is annually divided between the poor of the village of Hume, and the parish schoolmaster for the teaching of poor scholars.

PAROCHIAL BOARD (STICHILL)—James S. Darling, Esq., Kelso, factor for George Baird, Esq.; Rev. D. Macalister. No. of Poor on Roll, 4. Poor Rate, 2d. per £. Total Assessment 1863-4, £57. Poor House—Kelso Union.

Do. (HUME)—James Low, Esq, Berrywell, factor for Sir H. H. Campbell; James Darling, Esq., factor for George Baird, Esq.; Robert Swan, Esq., factor for the Earl of Haddington; and Rev. D. Macalister. No. of Poor on Roll, 14. Poor Rate, 6½d. per £. Total Assessment 1863, £136.

LIBRARIES of limited extent are attached to both the Stichill congregations.

CONVEYANCE—(*see* Kelso carriers).

CORN MILL—Stichill—*Mark and *James Hallowell, millers.

INSURANCE AGENT—Scottish Union Fire and Life—William Hume, Baillieknowe.

PROFESSIONS, TRADES, &c.

Stichill Parish

*Douglas, Adam, schoolmaster, Stichill
*Gray, Charles, farmer, Stichill Mains
 Gray, William, wright, Stichill
 Hermiston, George, blacksmith, Stichill
 Kinghorn, Alexander, mason, Stichill
*Lillie, John, farmer, Queenscairn
 Paterson, Robert, shoemaker, Stichill
+*Shiel, Rutherford, farmer, Sweethope
*Stuart, Gilbert,   do.,   Runningburn
 Hume, William, farmer, Baillieknowe
 Rae, John, farmer, Caldronbrae
 Wilson, William, manager, Stichill home farm

Hume Parish

 Brownlees, James, joiner, Hume
 Clark, Robert, blacksmith, do.
+Johnston, Alexander, farmer, Todrig
 Leitch, James, joiner, Hume
+Logan, George, farmer, Humehall
+Lithgow, John, do.,   Coldside
+Ormiston, Henry R., farmer, Hardies Mill Place

+Ormiston, William, farmer, Hardies Mill Place
+Rankin, Richard,   do.,   Stenmuir
+Roberton, John, jun., do.,   Fallsidehill
+Turnbull, George,   do.,   Homebyres

SEAT, &c., OF COUNTY FAMILY IN THE PARISH.

STICHILL HOUSE.

The intended residence of *George Baird, Esq. (son of the late Alexander Baird, Esq. of Lockwood, county of Lanark).

Mr. Baird succeeded to the Stichill estates on the death of his brother David in 1860.

REGISTERED VOTERS (Non-Resident).

Stichill Parish

*Black, John, farmer, Burnbrae, Nenthorn.

Hume Parish

+Roberton, John, sen., farmer, Harpertoun

SMAILHOLM.

—◆—

A SMALL agricultural parish situated in the north-eastern part of the county. It is bounded partly on the east and south by Kelso, and partly on the south by Makerstoun; the county of Berwick forms the remainder of its boundary on all sides. The parish extends in length to about 4 miles, and its greatest breadth is 3½ miles. Its area, according to the Ordnance Survey, is rather over 4202 acres, of which nearly 62 are occupied by public and private roads, and about 8 by water; of the remainder nearly the whole is either under cultivation or consists of plantations. The surface of the parish consists of a variety of high and low grounds. The greatest height to which it attains is about 600 feet above the sea. The climate of the parish is peculiarly healthy; but it has no accommodation for visitors.

Nearly in the centre of the parish is the small ancient straggling village of Smailholm, consisting of three separate parts —East-Third, West-Third, and Overtown.

The parish enjoys ample communication in all directions by means of its excellent turnpike and branch roads. Kelso, 6 miles distant, is the nearest market and post town. The nearest railway station is at Fans Loanend, nearly 4 miles from the village, on the Earlston and Dunse line

The river Eden, a first-rate trouting stream, but in which angling is restricted (*see* p. 183), bounds the parish a considerable distance on the north-east. In the south-west corner of the parish, perched on, and in the midst of a cluster of rocks, stands Sandyknowe, or Smailholm Tower. This place was the scene of Sir Walter Scott's "Eve of St. John," which he has also beautifully described in "Marmion," and where the great bard and novelist resided when a child with his grandfather, who was the farmer of Sandyknowe. It is the property of Lord Polwarth, and has recently been repaired, so that easy access may be had to the top, from which an extensive and delightful view may be had on all sides.

Population of the parish in 1861, 554; who composed 110 families, 63 of whom were returned as living in houses of one window, 26 in houses of two windows, and 21 in houses of three and more windows.

Assessed property in 1863-4, £5492 : 3 : 11.

Lord Polwarth is proprietor of most of the west portion of the parish, the Earl of Haddington most of the east portion. The Duke of Roxburghe is also a proprietor, but to a small extent. None of these proprietors are resident in the parish.†

————

Those marked thus (*) are Registered Voters in the parish.

POLICE OFFICER—Alexander Turner.

PUBLIC OFFICES—Inspector of Poor, Collector of Rates, and Registrar of Births, Marriages, and Deaths—Thomas Wood.
Kirk Treasurer and Interim Heritors' Clerk—Rev. David Swan.
Public Vaccinator—Dr. Robertson, Kelso.

POST OFFICE—James Ord, postmaster. Daily Post to Kelso. Arrival, 8-35 a.m.; Departure, 2 p.m. John Mather, Kelso, messenger.

CLERGY, &c.—Presbytery of Lauder, Synod of Merse and Teviotdale. Patron—Earl of Haddington.
Established Church‡—*Rev. David Swan (Inducted 1843). Sittings, 282.

FAST DAY—Wednesday before the first Sunday in May.

SCHOOL §—Parochial—*Thomas Wood, master; average attend., 80.

PAROCHIAL BOARD—Robert Swan, Esq., Kelso, Chairman. Committee—Messrs Curle & Erskine, Melrose, and Robert Darling, Esq., Broomlands, Kelso. No. of Poor on Roll, 12. Rate of Assessment, 4d. to 6d. per £.; Total Assessment 1863-4, £105. Poor House—Kelso Union.

SOCIETIES—Total Abstinence—George Melrose, President; Robert Grieve, jun., Secretary.
Smailholm and Whitrig Mutual Improvement Association—Hon. Walter H. Scott of Humbie, President; Mr. John Brough, New Smailholm. Vice-President; Mr. Robert Grieve, jun., West Third, Smailholm, Secretary.

LIBRARY—An excellent library, free to all the parishioners, was lately presented to the village by the Countess of Haddington. Mr Thomas Wood, Librarian.

CARRIERS—Kelso, Adam Scott and Thomas Kinghorn, Friday.

————

† The manor house of Smailholm, built by the Dons in the seventeenth century, is now occupied by Mr. Thomson, the tenant of the town-farm of Smailholm.
‡ The very ancient church of Smailholm, dating its orign in Catholic times, is ivy covered, and otherwise one of the neatest in the district, and one of the most comfortably seated.
§ Number of children from 5 to 15, attending school during the first week of April 1861, 103; of all ages, 106.

TRADES.

Grieve, Robert, sen., road contractor
Hogg, John, blacksmith, East-Third
Hunter, George, wright,   do.
Luke, George, wright, Westfield
Melrose, George, tailor
Purves, James, manure agent, carter, &c.
Vallance, John, corn dealer and road contractor
*Whillans Aaron, corn merchant, Smailholm
Whillans, James, dyke contractor
Wilkie, William, blacksmith, Westfield

RESIDENTS, FARMERS, &c.

Brockie, James, manager of the farm of Bettyfield, for
   Mr. Broad, lessee
*Brough, John, farmer, New Smailholm
*Dickie, Samuel, feuar West Third
*Heweit, James, farmer, Sandyknowe
*Mann, Andrew, do.,   Easter Girnick
*Ord, James,   do.,   Smailholm
*Smith, George, portioner, Smailholm
*Smith, Peter,   do.   do.
*Tait, James, farmer, Smailholm Mains
 Thomson, Thomas, Smailholm House
*Wotherspoon, Archibald, farmer, Spotsmains

REGISTERED VOTERS (Non-Resident).

Cockburn, Henry, farmer, Fans Loanend
Dickie, Henry, Whitehouses, Cumberland
Dickie, William, joiner, Yetholm
Dunlop, James, farmer, Rachelfield
Robeson, Robert, farmer, Springwells
Roy, Frederick Lewis, Esq. of Nenthorn
Scott, Henry F., of Harden [Lord Polwarth]
Simson, George, farmer, Courthill

MAKERSTOUN.

———◆———

A SMALL agricultural parish on the north bank of the river Tweed. It is bounded on the north by Smailholm, on the east by Kelso, on the south by the river Tweed, and on the west by Mertoun. Its length from east to west is about 4 miles, and its breadth from 2 to 3 miles. Its area, according to the Ordnance Survey, is nearly 2913 acres, of which 46½ are in roads, and 48 under water. The land gradually ascends from the banks of the river. It is all in a high state of cultivation. About 3½ miles of the Tweed belong to this parish, and within this is contained some of the finest salmon casts on that river. Trow Crags, the wildest part of all Tweed, is near the foot of Makerstoun water; "here the water way, in all ordinary states, is entirely within four splits or gullets through the great mass of trap rock; and the river for a short distance splits, chafes, and roars, in a manner similar to some of the wild ironbound streams of the Highlands." *

The church and school-house are near the centre of the parish; it contains no village, and there is only one mansion-house—MAKERSTOUN HOUSE—a seat of the late Lady Makdougall Brisbane. It occupies a beautiful and commanding position on the banks of the Tweed. The woods around it are finely laid out. The observatory erected by Sir Thomas, but now dismantled of its valuable apparatus, is close to the house.

Nearest post and market town, Kelso, 5 miles distant. The nearest railway stations to the parish are Rutherford and Roxburgh,—access can be had readily to the former by the ferry-boat at Rutherford, but that of Roxburgh is not very accessible; and although at a greater distance, that of Kelso is more convenient than either.

Population of the parish, 1st April 1861, 380; who composed 68 families, 1 of whom was returned as living in a house of no windows,† 23 in houses of one window, 21 in houses of two windows, and the others in houses of three or more windows.

Assessed property in 1863-4, £5001, 1s.

The greater part of the parish is owned by Miss Scott Makdougall, and the remainder by the Duke of Roxburghe.

---

* To step across the river at these gullies used to be a frequent although hazardous feat. A poor woman having been drowned in the attempt, the late Sir Thomas Brisbane, to prevent similar accidents, caused one of the steps to be blown up. The gullies can still be crossed by a good and daring leaper, and were thus occasionally crossed by old Rob Kerss, long the favourite resident fisherman on the Makerstoun water. The upward leap from the north is the most difficult, but Rob could accomplish it both ways.

† A vagrant family who slept that night in an outhouse.

Those marked thus (*) are Registered Voters in the parish.

POLICE OFFICER—Alexander Turnbull, Smailholm.

PUBLIC OFFICES—Inspector of Poor, Session Clerk, and Registrar of Births, Marriages, and Deaths—David Dodds.
Kirk Treasurer—Rev. Andrew Mackie.
Medical Officer and Public Vaccinator—Dr. Robertson, Kelso.

POST OFFICE—David Dodds, postmaster—Daily post to and from Kelso. Arrival, 8 a.m.; Despatch, 2-30 p.m. J. Mather, runner.

CLERGY, &c.—Presbytery of Kelso, Synod of Merse and Teviotdale, Patron—Duke of Roxburghe.
Established Church—*Rev. Andrew Mackie (Inducted 1844). Sittings, 150. Average attendance at Sabbath School, 35.
Free Church†—*Rev. David Dobbie (Inducted 1848). Sittings, 250. Average attendance at Sabbath School, 45.

FAST DAYS—Thursday before second Sabbath of May, and Wednesday before first Sabbath of November.

SCHOOL‡—Parochial—*David Dodds, master; average attend., 75.
Female School—The girls attending the Parochial School are taught sewing and knitting without any extra charge. Miss Isabella H. Dodds, sewing mistress. Average attendance, 15.

PAROCHIAL BOARD—Chairman, R. Swan, Esq., Kelso, factor for Miss Scott Makdougall. No. of Poor on Roll, 8. Rate of Assessment, 3½d. to 5d. per £.; total Assessment 1863, £92.

TRADES.

Rutherford, William, blacksmith
Stoddart, William, mason
Whitehead, John, joiner

RESIDENTS, FARMERS, &c.

Bruce, *Alexander and *James, farmers, Wester Muirdean
Fife, Mrs., Greatridgehall farm
Gray, George, gardener, Makerstoun House
*Murray, William, farmer, Charterhouse
*Usher, John,   do.,   Stodrig
*Wilson, Thomas,   do.,   Haymount

SEAT, &c., OF COUNTY FAMILY IN THE PARISH.

MAKERSTOUN HOUSE.

The property and residence of Miss Maria Scott Makdougall, Lady of the Barony of Makerstoun; who succeeded, 1864, her cousin, the late Miss Henrietta Hay Makdougall.

† This church, along with an excellent manse, was erected by the late Miss Elizabeth Makdougall, of Makerstoun, who also at her decease, in 1852, bequeathed £1500 sterling for its partial endowment.
‡ Children in the parish between 5 and 15, attending school during the first week of April 1861, 74; of all ages, 77.

ROXBURGH.

—◆—

A VERY irregularly shaped parish lying on the south side of the Tweed. It is bounded by Makerstoun and Kelso on the north, Maxton on the west, Ancrum on the south, and Crailing and Eckford on the east. The extreme length of the parish is about 8 miles, and its breadth varies from 1 to 5 miles. The area, according to the Ordnance Survey, is 7924¼ acres, of which 53¼ are occupied by the railway, 99½ in public and private roads, and 143¾ are under water. The surface of the parish is generally flat, and has a gentle slope to the Tweed on the north, with the Teviot intersecting it from north to south. In the south-west is Dunse or Doune Law, a hill about 500 feet high. Around this height the ground is moorish, but with this exception the parish has a rich soil and is well cultivated.

Near the centre of the parish and close to the Teviot is the village of Roxburgh. Here there is a station on the N. B. Railway, and a junction is here formed with the Jedburgh branch, which here strikes off along the north side of the Teviot. On the opposite side of the river, at the distance of about a mile, is the village of HEITON. Both villages are entirely agricultural, and both are small. Close to the village of Roxburgh a magnificent and lofty viaduct of fourteen arches carries the railway across the Teviot. Attached to the viaduct and near the water level is a free foot bridge, which has superseded the old ferry of Roxburgh.

The only mansion houses in the parish are—SUNLAWS, near the centre of the parish, a handsome Tudor edifice with a lofty tower, the residence of W. Scott Kerr, Esq.; and FAIRNINGTON, near the eastern boundary, the residence of Henry Rutherfurd, Esq. The gardens and grounds of Sunlaws are laid out with great taste.

At the north-eastern extremity of the parish are the ruins of Roxburgh Castle, once the most important stronghold in the south of Scotland (*see* p. 71).* (*see* p. 71) Close to the village of Rox-

* A beautiful walk by the side of the river Teviot leads from the ancient castle of Roxburgh to the village which now bears that name. The distance is about two miles; and in summer a more delightful stroll could not be found. . In the churchyard of the village is the grave of Andrew Gemmels, the original of Edie Ochiltree, the "Blue gown" of Sir Walter Scott's "Antiquary." The place is marked by a tombstone bearing the following inscription:—Andrew Gemmels, alias Edie Ochiltree, was interred here; he died at Roxburgh Newtown in 1793, aged 106 years.

burgh are the remains of an old keep, which has received the name of Wallace's Tower, but from what circumstance is not known. Within the policy of Sunlaws, overlooking the Teviot, are several artificial caves, supposed to be over 1000 years old.

A fine stretch of the Tweed for salmon fishing is in this parish, the greater part of it running through the Duke of Roxburghe's property. [*See* paragraph about permission to fish in the Teviot for salmon at p. 73, which applies to this parish, as also do the remarks there made about trout fishing.]

Kelso is the nearest market town, and is distant about 3 miles from the village of Roxburgh and 2 from Heiton.

The population of the parish in 1861 was 1178, consisting of 244 families, 205 of whom were returned as living in houses of one and two windows.

Assessed property in 1863-4, £10,441 : 3 : 8.

The principal landed-proprietors in the parish are—the Duke of Roxburghe, Sir George S. Douglas, Bart., W. Scott Kerr, Esq. of Sunlaws, Henry Rutherfurd, Esq. of Fairnington, the Merchant Maiden Hospital, Edinburgh, and Sir Edmund Antrobus, bart., of Stockstruther.

Those marked thus (*) are Registered Voters.

RESIDENT JUSTICE OF THE PEACE—Wm. Scott Kerr, Esq. of Sunlaws.

POLICE OFFICER—William Barnes, Heiton.

POST OFFICE—Heiton—John Sinclair, Postmaster. Daily Post from Kelso at 7 a.m. ; despatch, 3.30 p.m. Letters are delivered daily in Roxburgh, Fairnington, Rutherford, etc., by Michael M'Ghee, rural messenger. Letters should be addressed by Kelso ; goods to Roxburgh Station.

PUBLIC OFFICES—Registrar of Births, Marriages, and Deaths—*William Laidlaw, Roxburgh.
Heritors' Clerk, Kirk Treasurer, Inspector of Poor, and Session Clerk—Robert C. Maxwell, Roxburgh.
Medical Officer and Public Vaccinator—Dr. Hamilton, Kelso.

CLERGY—Presbytery of Kelso, Synod of Merse and Teviotdale. Patron—Duke of Roxburghe.
Established Church—*Rev. William Lee (Inducted 1843). Sittings, 400. Average attendance at Sabbath Schools, 200.

FAST DAYS—Wednesday before the first Sunday of May and Nov.

SCHOOLS†—Parochial (Roxburgh)—Robert C. Maxwell, master ; Miss Stuart, teacher of sewing. Average attendance, 90.
Heiton Side School—Miss Sloan, teacher. Average attend., 95.
General Assembly's School (Fairnington)—Patrick Marshall, teacher. Average attendance, 43.

---

† Number of children in the parish between 5 and 15 years of age attending school during the first week of April 1861, 199 ; of all ages, 222.

PAROCHIAL BOARD—Jas. Roberton, Esq., Ladyrig, Chairman. No. of Poor on Roll, 37. Rate of Assessment, 3¼d. per £ ; total Collection for 1863, £367. Poor House—Kelso Union.

LIBRARIES—Roxburgh—Robert C. Maxwell, Librarian. Heiton—Miss Sloan, Librarian. Fairnington—Mr. Marshall, Librarian.

WORK SOCIETY—Mrs. Lee, Patroness.

CONVEYANCE—North British and Jedburgh Railways at Roxburgh—Station-master—John Trotter.

CARRIERS—Roxburgh to Kelso, John Fair, Friday ; Heiton to Kelso, Eckford, and Jedburgh, Carriers twice a week, and the Post-Runner daily.

CORN MILLS—Heiton—*Robert Hogarth. Sunlaws—*Michael Turnbull.

TRADES.

Village of Roxburgh

Aitken, George, smith
Bell, Robert, tailor
Campbell, John, builder
Hay, James, shoemaker
Hogg, Henry, joiner
Scott, Alexander, grocer

Village of Heiton

Affleck, Robert, tailor
*Bruce, Robert, farmer
Hay, Thomas, mason
Herron, William, tailor
Quarry, James, smith
Logan, Peter, grocer
Red Lion Inn, Alexander Waugh
Scott, James, grocer
Sinclair, John, meal-dealer and grocer
Tait, William, sen , joiner
Tait, William, jun., joiner

RESIDENTS, FARMERS, &c., IN THE PARISH.

*Buckham, George, farmer, Kersmains
*Burn, James,   do.,   Roxburgh Newtown
Dunlop, Mrs., Roxburgh Rig
*Hubback, Thomas, do.,   Sunlawshill
Innes, James, Cairnmount
Logan, Miss, Roxburgh Mill House
M'Lean, Jas., factor for Sir E. Antrobus, Stockstruther
*Mein, Benjamin, farmer, Roxburgh Barns
Moffat, John (late tutor), Heiton
Noble, Thomas, Floors fisherman, Daniel's Den

*Roberton, James, farmer, Ladyrig
*Simson, James,   do.,   Trows
*Thomson, Jas. S. do.,   Over Roxburgh
*Thomson, Willm., do.,   do.
*Thomson, And.,   do.,   Whitehillfoot
 Wemyss, Alexander, land-steward, Sunlaws

REGISTERED VOTERS (Non-Resident).

Dickson, Sir William, of Sydenham, Bart.
Dunn, William, Redden
Hubback, Joseph, merchant, Liverpool
Logan, Abraham, farmer, Hassington Mains
Waugh, John, Langshaw

SEATS, &c. OF COUNTY FAMILIES IN THE PARISH.

SUNLAWS.

The residence of William Scott Kerr, Esq., of Chatto and Sunlaws, only son of the late Robert Scott Kerr, Esq.; born 1807; succeeded 1831; married (first), 1837, Hannah Charlotte, only daughter and heiress of Henry Scott, Esq., and widow of Sir John James Douglas, Bart. of Springwood; and had issue a daughter (now Mrs. Ramsay). Lady Douglas died 1850. Mr. Scott Kerr married (second), 1855, Frances Louisa, daughter of Robert Fennessy, Esq., of Belford, and has, with other issue, Robert, born 1859.

Mr. Scott Kerr, who is a Justice of the Peace and Deputy-Lieutenant for Roxburghshire, is descended from the Scotts of Thirleston.

FAIRNINGTON.

The property of Henry Rutherfurd, Esq., Barrister-at-Law, of the Middle Temple, London; born 19th January 1831; succeeded his father, the late Thomas Rutherfurd, Esq., in 1863. Occupied by *John Munro, farmer.

Mr. Rutherfurd, who is a Justice of Peace for Roxburghshire, is descended in the male line from the Rutherfurds of that Ilk and Edgerston—of which family he is now the representative.

FAIRNINGTON COTTAGE.

On the Fairnington estate—the residence of Mrs. Rutherfurd (widow of the late Thomas Rutherfurd, Esq.), and the Misses Rutherfurd; and the occasional residence of Henry Rutherfurd, Esq , the proprietor.

ANCRUM.

—◆—

THIS is an entirely agricultural parish, delightfully situated on the north bank of the river Teviot, and completely intersected by Ale water. It is about six miles in length, and four in breadth; and contains, according to the Ordnance Surve measurements, 10,389 acres, of which 10,102 are land, 93 water, 131 public roads, 25 private roads, and 37 occupied by railway.

The appearance of the parish is romantic and picturesque in a very high degree. Although there are no hills the surface is very irregular, breaking out into considerable eminences. In the southern part of the parish the soil is very rich ; and generally throughout the parish it is good. The Teviot and Ale afford capital sport to the angler, both for salmon and trout. Angling accommodation can be had in the village, for which it affords a good centre. Otters numerously frequent the streams of the parish, and are often hunted.

The somewhat decayed looking village of Ancrum, from which the parish takes its name, is pleasantly situated on the south side of Ale water, about a mile from its confluence with the Teviot. In the middle of the village green stands the ruins of the Cross—supposed to have been originally surmounted by the Arms of Scotland. There are three mansions in the parish—all worthy of special notice—the proprietors of which are all resident.

ANCRUM HOUSE, the seat of Sir William Scott, Bart., M.P., is a fine old baronial looking mansion, standing in the midst of an extensive park, "attractive with spots of verdant lawn, craggy knolls, and scattered trees, some of which are the finest in the south of Scotland, and whose picturesque effect is much increased by the additional beauty of a numerous herd of deer." CHESTERS, the residence of William Ogilvie, Esq., is a large and handsome building, erected over sixty years ago, and delightfully situated on the banks of the Teviot. KIRKLANDS, the seat of John Richardson, Esq., occupies a most romantic position on a wooded height over the water of Ale. This is a modern house in the Tudor style of architecture.

On the grounds opposite to Ancrum House, and for a considerable way up the Ale, are to be seen various caves, amounting in all to fifteen, hewn out of the rocky banks of the river; many of them must have been used as places of concealment, being not only extremely difficult of discovery and access, but having been provided with fire places, with apertures in the roof to carry off the smoke, and commanding a plentiful supply of water ; one of them is known as Thomson's cave, from its having been a favourite retreat of the author of the " Seasons," when he was a frequent inmate at the manse of Ancrum during the incumbency of his friend Mr. Cranston. About a mile and half to the north of the village is the scene of the battle of Ancrum Moor, now best remembered in connection with the death of "Maid Lilliard ;" there, in honour of her memory, and marking the spot where she fought and fell, has been raised a monument.* The locality is known also by the name of Lilliard's Edge.

The nearest market and post town is Jedburgh, about 4 miles distant from the village ; and the nearest railway stations are Nisbet and Jedfoot, each about 2 miles off, on the Jedburgh branch of the North British Railway. The Hawick line of the North British intersects the western portion of the parish, and has a station at New Belses, over three miles from the village.

In the north-western part of the parish is the hamlet of LONGNEWTON,† which once formed a chapelry for the barony of Longnewton. Of the church there are now no remains, but the burying ground is still made use of by some of the inhabitants of the locality.

Population of the village in 1861, 538 ; of the entire parish, 1511, who composed 322 separate families; 7 of whom were returned as living in houses having no windows, 153 in houses of one window, and 86 in houses of two windows.

Assessed property in 1863-4, £12,498 : 17.

The principal proprietors non-resident are Sir George H. S. Douglas, Bart. of Springwood Park (proprietor of the Longnewton barony), the Duke of Roxburghe, the Earl of Minto, the Trustees of the late Honourable John Elliot of Belses, Marquis of Lothian, and the Trustees of the late Roderick M'Kenzie, Esq. of Pinnacle.

Those marked thus (*) are Registered Voters.

RESIDENT JUSTICES OF THE PEACE.

Sir William Scott, Bart. of Ancrum ; William Ogilvie, Esq. of Chesters ; and John Richardson, Esq. of The Kirklands.

Police Officer—James Ross, Ancrum.

---

* The monument bears the following inscription :—

Fair Maiden Lilliard lies under this stane,
Little was her stature, but great was her fame ;
Upon the English loons she laid mony thumps,
And when her legs were cutten off she fought upon her stumps.

† John Younger, the celebrated angler of St Boswell's, was a native of Longnewton.

POST OFFICE.

Robert Turnbull, postmaster

Arrivals from Jedburgh, 7-30 a.m. and 12-20 p.m. Departures to, 8-15 a.m. and 2-35 p.m. Alexander Grierson, messenger ; William Riddell, country messenger.

Letters for the locality of Longnewton are forwarded by Newtown St Boswell's (*see* p. 147). Arrival and despatch about noon. James Thomson, messenger.

PUBLIC OFFICES.

Heritors' Clerk, Inspector of Poor, and Registrar of Births, Marriages, and Deaths—Alexander G. Catto.

Medical Officer and Public Vaccinator—Jas. Falla, surgeon, Jedburgh.

CLERGY, &c.

Presbytery of Jedburgh, Synod of Merse and Teviotdale.
Patron—Sir William Scott, Bart.

ESTABLISHED CHURCH—*Rev. John Paton (inducted 1832). Sittings, 520. Average attendance at Sabbath School, 50.

FREE CHURCH—Rev. Mr. Rattary (Inducted 1864). Sittings, 330. Average attendance at Sabbath School, 40.

FAST DAYS—Thursday before last Sabbaths of January and July.

SCHOOLS.†

Parish—*Alexander G. Catto, master. Average attendance, 120.
Auxiliary (Longnewton)—Supported by Sir G. H. S. Douglas, Bart. William Readman, teacher. Average attendance, 75.
Private School—Mrs. Phaup, Ancrum.

PAROCHIAL BOARD.

Chairman—— —— Otto, Esq., factor to the Marquis of Lothian.
No. of Poor on Roll, 33.

Rate of Assessment, 3½d. per £ ; total Assessment for 1863-4, £320.
Poor-House—Jedburgh Union.

---

† Children in the parish attending school from 5 to 15, during the first week of April 1861, 291 ; of all ages, 325.

MORTIFICATION.

Mr. James Craig, schoolmaster of Thrybergh, in the West Riding of the county of York, by his will and testament dated 30th November 1799, and subsequently on the 18th April 1811, bequeathed the sum of £160 for the education of eight poor legitimate boys at the parish school established at Nether Ancrum, for the term of three years, each commencing at the age of seven years; such children to be nominated from time to time by the minister of the parish for the time being.

SOCIETIES, &c.

MECHANICS' INSTITUTE—H. W. Scott, Esq., President; John Clark, Secretary; Wm. Mabon, Treasurer; Robt. Turnbull, Librarian. 400 vols. Subscription, 2s. per annum.

HORTICULTURAL SOCIETY—Henry Scott (Saw Mills), Preses. Competitions, first Saturdays of July and September.

TOTAL ABSTINENCE SOCIETY—George Fiddes, Secretary.

CROW CLUB—Sir William Scott of Ancrum, Bart., M.P., Patron; William Scott, yr. of Ancrum, President; James Dodd, Mossburnford, Vice-President; James Cumming, Banker, Jedburgh, Secretary and Treasurer.

INSURANCE AGENT—Life Association of Scotland, and Scottish Union Fire—Alex. G. Catto.

CARRIERS—Jedburgh, Belses, Melrose, and Selkirk—James Davidson, Tuesday, Thursday, Friday, and Saturday; Jedburgh and Jedfoot—Alexander Grierson, post-runner, twice a day.

CORN MILLS—Ancrum—*Andrew Purves. Belses—T. Oliver. Longnewton—David Porter. Nether Ancrum—Robert Scott.

ANCRUM SAW MILL—Henry Scott, wood merchant.

TRADES.

Ancrum.

Aimers, Anthony, cooper.
*Bearhope, Andrew, joiner.
Bell & Co., shoemakers
Black, George, grocer
Commercial Inn, Jessie Ford
Cross Keys Inn—John Gray
Fiddes, George, blacksmith
Gordon, Douglas, tailor
Hardie, George, shoemaker
Hogg, George, baker and grocer
*Kennedy, James, tailor

Learmonth, James, flesher
Mabon, William, blacksmith
Oliver, Jane, grocer
Scott, Thomas, joiner
Scott, William, joiner
Smith, Peter, tailor
Temple, George, grocer
*Thomson, James, portioner and church officer
Turnbull, Archibald, grocer
Turnbull, James, tailor
Turnbull, Robert, shoemaker
*Turnbull, Walter, mason
*Turner, Thomas, flesher

Longnewton.

Mill, John, blacksmith
White, John, joiner

RESIDENTS, FARMERS, &c.

Blythe, James, farmer
*Carmichael, George R., farmer, Longnewton Place
*Church, Alexander,   do.,   Pinnacle
Clephane, Peter, gardener, Kirklands
Davidson, J. S., M.D , R.N., of Aln Bank
*Davidson, Thomas, farmer, Ancrum West Mains
*Davidson, W. S., Victoria Cottage
*Faickney, James, Ancrum
*Gladstone, Andrew, Bloomfield
Gowanlock,   Standhills
*Horsburgh, John, farmer, Chesters Grange
*Hume, John,   do.,   Broom
*Ingram, William,   do.,   Copland
*Little, John,   do.,   Old Belses
*Mills, George,   do.,   Greenend
*Mills, William,   do.,   Herrietsfield
M'Queen, Peter, gardener Chesters
*Murdie, Andrew, farmer, Whitehouse
*Porter, David,   do.,   Longnewton Mill
*Pringle, Thomas,   do.,   Belses Muir.
Rae, Andrew, Chesters Craig
Renton, William, farmer. Palacehill
*Robson, Archibald, of Asmeburn
*Rutherford, Andrew, farmer, Barnhills
*Rutherford, Thomas, farmer, Sandystanes
*Rutherford, William, do.,   do.
Rutherford, Walter, of Ancrum Crag

Scott, James, farmer, Lilliard's Edge
Scott, John, do., Howden
*Scott, Thomas, do., Furlongs
Stewart, Alexander F., Rawflat
*Stodart, Thomas, farmer, Ancrum Woodhead
*Thomson, George, farmer, Hopton
*Turnbull, James, do., Chesterhall
Weaver, James, forrester to the Marquis of Lothian, Bridge-End.
*Wilson, James, farmer, Belses Quarry
Wyld, John, do., New Belses

SEATS, &c. OF COUNTY FAMILIES IN THE PARISH.

ANCRUM HOUSE.

The residence of Sir William Scott, Bart.; born 26th July 1803; succeeded as 6th baronet 1814; married, 1826, Elizabeth, daughter of David Anderson, Esq. of Balgay, Forfarshire, and has issue :—

William Monteith, born 1829, who married, 1861, Amelia Murray, eldest daughter of General Monteith Douglas of Stonebyres, in Lanarkshire.
John, captain, Scots Fusilier Guards, who died 10th Feb. 1859.
*Henry Warren, born 1833.
*Arthur, born 1835.
Three daughters—Elizabeth, Harriet, and Louisa.

Sir William Scott is a Justice of Peace and Dep.-Lieutenant for Roxburghshire, and is Member of Parliament for the same county, a Magistrate for Forfarshire; and was formerly an officer in the 2d Life Guards.
William Monteith Scott, younger, is Captain of the Jedburgh Corps of Rifle Volunteers.
Other residences—Balgay, near Dundee (occupied by Henry W. Scott, Esq.). London address—Brooks' and Travellers' Club, S.W.

KIRKLANDS.

The property of the Trustees of the late John Richardson, Esq., of Kirklands (who died 1864); factor for the estate—George Rutherford, Esq., The Scaurs, Jedburgh.—See next column.

CHESTERS.

The residence of *William Ogilvie, Esq.; born 1785; succeeded 1831, his father, the late Thomas Elliot Ogilvie, Esq.;

married, 1818, Alexina, daugter of Alexander Falconar, Esq. of Woodcot Park, East Lothian, and has, with other issue—

*Thomas Elliot, yr. of Chesters, born 1821.
*William Falconer, late captain 69th Regiment B.N.I., 33 Chepstow Place, London.
*Alexander, resident at Chesters.
George, resident at Holefield.
Francis Dashwood, in India.
And a daughter—Alexina.

Mr. Ogilvie was called to the Scottish bar in 1808, is a Justice of Peace and Deputy-Lieutenant for Roxburghshire, Lord of the Manor of Chesters, and Chamberlain to the Duke of Buccleuch, for the estates of His Grace in the district—that office having been in Mr. Ogilvie's family for over one hundred years. Mr. Ogilvie was formerly Major of the Dumfries Militia.

Chamberlain's residence—Branxholm, near Hawick.

REGISTERED VOTERS (Non-Resident).

Hay, Sir Adam, of Haystone
Hay, Lieut.-Gen. C. Murray
Horne, Donald, Athole Crescent, Edinburgh
Ogilvie, Alexander, Chesters
Potts, William, merchant, 17 Downie Place, Edinburgh
Purves, John, Kittyfield, Melrose

Romanes, Robert, writer, Lauder
Scott, Geo., wright, Bonjedward
Scott, Aurthur, Major 5th foot
Scott, Captain W. Monteith
Scott, H. W., Balgay
Smith, P., land-steward, England
Thomson, Andrew, late 70 Abbey Hill, Edinburgh

KIRKLANDS.

(See preceding column.) Presently occupied by William Monteith Scott, Esq., yr. of Ancrum; married, 1861, Amelia Murray, eldest daughter of General Sir Thomas Monteith Douglas, of Stonebyres, Lanarkshire, K.C.B.; and has issue—
William Michael Augustus, born July 1865;* and a daughter, Constance-Emily.

* Lineal descendant of Michael Scott *the Wizard—see* pp. 70, 374, 399.

SOUTHDEAN.

———◆———

A large irregularly shaped parish in the southern part of Teviotdale.* Its boundaries are Jedburgh on the north, Oxnam and Jedburgh on the east, Castleton and the county of Northumberland on the south, and Hobkirk on the west. The area, according to the Ordnance Survey, is 27,983½ acres, of which nearly 104 are in roads—the turnpike roads from Hawick and Jedburgh for the south, traversing the parish—and 55 are under water.

The southern and south-eastern parts of the parish are wild and mountainous, including some of the Cheviot range of hills. The principal heights are—Carter Fell, 1815 feet; Carlintooth Fell, 1802 feet; Peel Fell, 1964 feet; and Wolflee Hill, 1250 feet. The more northern part of the parish is also hilly, but in the centre the ground is more level. A considerable part is under cultivation, but the bulk of the parish is pastoral. From the Carter and one or two more of the high fells in this locality rise the rivers Tyne, Liddal, Jed, Rule, and Reed.

The Jed and several of its tributaries take their rise among the hills in the southern district, and the Rule bounds the parish to the west, and some of its sources are also in the parish. The trouting in both is good and unrestricted, and is best with the worm; the scenery of both streams is romantic, and they have interesting associations—(see Hopekirk).

Both the Jed and the Rule in this locality are much frequented by otters. In many of the districts of Teviotdale this species of game has greatly increased of late years.

There are still in existence the ruins of several towers, or peels; and also traces of ancient encampments.

A little north of the middle of the parish is the hamlet of CHESTERS, in which the parish church and school are situated. Several of the residents occupy small farms, held of the Countess of Home; but the village has greatly decreased in population within the last twenty years. In the manse of Southdean, situated on the banks of the Jed, nearly a mile from the village, the poet Thomson spent most of his youthful days: and underneath a *thruch-stone* in the churchyard at Chesters, the inscription on which is almost wholly obliterated [but which the heritors are about to renew in a marble tablet], rest the ashes of the poet's father, who was minister of the parish—(see Ednam parish, p. 178). Chesters is the only village in the parish. The ruins of two old churches exist—one at Southdean, whence the name of the parish, the other at Abbotrule; and there is a churchyard attached to each.

The nearest market town is Jedburgh, about 8 miles distant from the hamlet.

Population of the parish in 1861, 687 (in 1851 it was 845); the number of families at the census was 128—one of whom lived in a house with no windows, and 63 in houses of one and two windows. Assessed property in 1863-4, £8922 : 3 : 3.

The principal landed-proprietors in the parish are—Walter Elliot, Esq., of Wolflee; and David Henderson, Esq., of Abbotrule—resident; the Countess of Home (Hirsel, Coldstream), and James Robson Scott of Ashtrees (Belford, Morebattle)—non-resident.

———————

Those marked thus (*) are Registered Voters.

RESIDENT JUSTICES OF THE PEACE—David Henderson, Esq. of Abbotrule; Walter Elliot, Esq. of Wolflee.

POST OFFICE — School-house, Chesters — Neil Taylor, postmaster. Letters for Glendouglas, Bairnkine, Woodhouse, Cleethaugh, Mervinslaw, Wooplaw, and Letham, should be addressed by Jedburgh; all others by Bonchester, Hawick, where they are taken up by the respective runners.

PUBLIC OFFICES—Registrar of Births, Marriages, and Deaths, Session Clerk and Kirk Treasurer, Heritors' Clerk, and Inspector of Poor—Neil Taylor.

Medical Officer and Public Vaccinator—Mr. James Falla, surgeon, Jedburgh.

CLERGY—Presbytery of Jedburgh, Synod of Merse and Teviotdale. Patrons—Crown, and Countess of Home.

Established Church—*Rev. John Mair (Inducted 1847). Sittings, 200. Average attendance at Sabbath School, 50.

Wolflee Free Church—see Hopekirk parish.

FAST DAY—Thursday before the second Sabbath of June.

SCHOOLS †—Parochial—*Neil Taylor, master; average attend., 65. Subscription—(Glendouglas)—Thos. Turnbull, teacher; average attendance, 80.

PAROCHIAL BOARD—Walter Elliot, Esq. of Wolflee, Chairman. No. of Poor on Roll, 5. Rate of Assessment, 1d. per £; total Assessment, 1863-4, £73, 4s. Poor House—Jedburgh Union.

———————

* Southdean follows Castleton and Teviothead as the third largest parish in the county.

† The number of children in the parish between 5 and 15, attending school during the first week of April 1861, was 139; of all ages, 142.

LIBRARY—Parish—School-room, Chesters. 450 vols.

CONVEYANCE—North British Railway, per Hawick and Jedburgh.

CARRIERS—Once a week to Jedburgh—*see* Jedburgh lists.

CORN MILL—*George Bell, miller and farmer.

TRADES.

Amos, Gilbert, joiner, Chesters
Anderson, William, tailor, do.
Waugh, John, blacksmith, do.
Yule, William D., blacksmith, Smailcleugh

RESIDENTS, FARMERS, &c.

*Brown, Thomas, farmer, Ruletownhead		
*Common, Andrew, do.,	West Shiels	
*Davidson, Douglas, do.,	Wooplaw	
*Hymers, Edward do.,	Ashtrees	
*Mein, Thomas, do.,	Broomhill	
*Pringle, Robt. B., do.,	Bairnkine	
*Pringle, Jas. H., do.,	Hyndlee†	
*Scott, James, do.,	Southdean Glebe	
*Scott, Thomas, do.,	Mervinslaw	
*Telfer, William, do.,	Roundabouts	

SEATS, &c., OF COUNTY FAMILIES IN THE PARISH.

WOLFLEE.

Situated on the Rule Water, on the western boundary of the parish to the north, and opposite to Wauchope, in Hobkirk parish—the residence of *Walter Elliot, Esq.; born 1803; succeeded his father, the late James Elliot, Esq., 1855; married, 1839, Maria Dorothea, eldest daughter of Sir David Hunter Blair, Bart. of Blairquhan, Ayrshire, and has issue:—

James Thomas Spencer, born 1845; and others.

Mr. Elliot was formerly in the civil service of the H.E.I.C., and senior member of the Council of Madras.
London address—Travellers' Club, S.W.

† In Hyndlee long resided Mr. James Davidson, supposed to be one of the originals of Sir Walter Scott's "Dandy Dinmont," and the proprietor of the famous "Mustard" and "Pepper" terriers. To this day foxes are hunted in the parish as described in the fox-hunting scene in "Guy Mannering."—*See* introductory account of Castleton parish.

ABBOTRULE.

Situated on a tributary of the Rule Water, toward the western boundary of the parish to the north—the residence of *David Henderson, Esq., and of his brother Charles.

GLENDOUGLAS.

At the extreme north of the parish, on the Jed—the property of the Countess of Home; occupied by *Andrew Scott, Esq., factor for her ladyship.

REGISTERED VOTERS (Non-Resident).

Elliot, Henry, farmer, Greenriver
Elliot, Rev. J. E., rector of Whalton, Northumberland
Scott, Charles, farmer, Wauchope
Scott, James Robson, of Ashtrees, Belford
Tod, Thomas, advocate, Edinburgh

LILLIESLEAF.

———◆———

THIS parish is situated in the north-western part of the county, and is about 6½ miles in length and 2½ in breadth. It is bounded on the north by the parishes of Selkirk and Bowden, on the east by Ancrum, on the south by Minto, and on the west by Ashkirk and Wilton. The total area, according to the Ordnance Survey, is nearly 6707½ acres, 4¼ of which are occupied by the railway, 61 by roads, and nearly 35 by water. "There are several elongated eminences in the parish, which generally run from east to west a considerable distance, in the form of ridges, the highest rising to about 600 feet above the level of the sea. The declivities on the sides of these ridgy eminences are fertile and well cultivated. There are also rich valleys and gently sloping banks, interspersed with thriving plantations and hedge rows;" but beyond its agricultural beauty the parish possesses little of interest.

The Ale water, after intersecting the parish, forms its northern boundary for about two miles. The angling in this river is good, and the trouts are of a good size. The climate of the parish generally is good.

There are traces throughout the parish, but more especially in the village, of many fortresses or peels, some of them of considerable strength. From its retired situation, Lilsly (or Lilliesleaf) Moor was the resort of numerous conventicles.

In the northern part of the parish, on the banks of the Ale, is the thriving agricultural village of Lilliesleaf ("with much taste for floriculture"), the only one in the parish. It consists of one street, which contains some very handsome houses and shops. There are no markets here; the nearest market towns from the village are Hawick (8 miles), Melrose (7 miles), and Selkirk (6 miles). The nearest railway station is at Belses, 3 miles distant from the village on the Hawick line. Goods sent by rail should be addressed to Belses station, and letters by Selkirk.

Population of the village in 1861, 325; of the entire parish, 772, who composed 177 families; 65 of whom were returned as living in houses of one window, and 59 in houses of two windows, the others in houses of three and more windows.

Assessed property in 1863-4, £6923 : 16 : 3.

The principal landed-proprietors are—Mark Sprot, Esq. of Riddell, who is Superior of part of the village; the Earl of Minto; Lord Polwarth; William Currie, Esq. (Linthill, Bowden); G. Hutton Riddell, Esq.; Peter Pennycook, Esq.; Trustees of the late John G. Stewart, Esq. (of Hermiston), Cotfield; John C. Scott, Esq, of Satchels (Sinton, by Hawick); and Archibald Dickson, Esq, of Greenhouse (Bughtrig, Berwickshire). Except Mr. Sprot all are non-resident.

———

Those marked thus (*) are Registered Voters.

RESIDENT JUSTICE OF THE PEACE—Mark Sprot, Esq., of Riddell.

POLICE OFFICER—James Oliphant, Lilliesleaf.

PUBLIC OFFICES—Registrar of Births, Marriages, and Deaths, Session Clerk, Heritors' Clerk, and Inspector of Poor—James W. Mackay.
Medical Officer and Public Vaccinator—H. S. Anderson, M.D. Selkirk.

POST OFFICE—Thomas Turnbull, Postmaster. Daily Post to Selkirk. Arrival, 12 noon; Departure, 6.45 a m. Joseph M'Gregor, Messenger.

CLERGY—Presbytery of Selkirk, Synod of Merse and Teviotdale. Patron—Duke of Roxburghe.†
Established Church—*Rev. Adam Gourlay (Inducted 1842). Sittings, 320. Average attendance at Sabbath School, 28.
United Presbyterian Church—*Rev. William Young (Inducted 1857). Sittings, 350. Average attend. at Sabbath School, .

FAST DAYS—Wednesday before the last Sabbath of April and first Sabbath of November.

SCHOOLS‡—(Parochial) *Jas. West Mackay, master. Av. attend., 105. Currie Female School‖—Miss Wilson, teacher. Av. attend., 55.

PAROCHIAL BOARD—Mark Sprot, Esq., Chairman. No. of Poor on Roll, 23. Rate of Assessment, 3½d. per £; total Collection for 1863, £161 : 5s. Poor House—Hawick Combination.

LIBRARIES—The Lilliesleaf Library, open Wednesdays and Saturdays. T. Turnbull, Librarian. 1500 vols. Annual Subscription, 4s. Parish Library—The Minister, Librarian. 600 vols. Free.

TOTAL ABSTINENCE SOCIETY—Joseph Park, President; T. Turnbull, Secretary; William Turnbull, Treasurer.

CONVEYANCE—North British Railway, Belses station, 3 miles distant.

———

† This is the only interest the Roxburghe family has now in the parish; formerly they were a large landed-proprietors, and still retain the church patronage.

‡ Children in the parish from 5 to 15 attending school during the first week of April 1861, 118; of all ages, 125.

‖ William Currie, Esq. of Linthill, who died in 1858, bequeathed a house in the village, and money to put it in proper order for a school for girls, a house for the teacher, and an apartment for a public library. The house not being considered worthy of repairs was taken down and a neat, substantial, and commodious set of buildings were erected for these purposes—attached to which are a play-ground for the children, and a garden for the teacher.

INSURANCE AGENT—Edinburgh Life—Thomas Turnbull.

AUCTIONEER—Robert Scott.

CORN MILL—Riddell—Alexander Lauder, farmer.

CARRIERS—Newtown, James Henry, Monday and Thursday; Hawick, Thomas Davidson, Thursday; Selkirk, Ancrum, and Jedburgh, James Davidson, Wednesday.

TRADES AND RESIDENTS.

Brown, Robert, tailor
Burns, William, blacksmith
Cavers, William, shoemaker
Carrie, George, millwright
Cross Keys Inn, William MacIvor
Davidson, Thomas, grocer
Fairgrieve, John, grocer
Falla, Mary, grocer
Goodfellow, James, grocer
Graham, David, grocer
*Gray, Andrew, portioner
*Henry, James, grocer
Irvine, George, gardener, Linthill
King, Andrew, joiner
Law, Ann, grocer
*Lunn, John, draper
Manuel, John, blacksmith
*Minto, Andrew, farmer
Moodie, William, millwright
Murray, Alexander, cattle dealer
Nichol, William, factor for Riddell estate
Oliver, John, flesher
Ormiston, Archibald, shoemaker
*Park, Joseph, shoemaker
Plough Inn, Mrs. Robson
*Redford, James, farmer
Redford, William, clothier
*Riddell, James, carter
*Riddell, William, joiner
*Robinson, Walter, mole-catcher
*Robson, George
Scott, George, cattle-dealer
Steele, Thomas, mason
Stirling, Peter, tailor
*Turnbull, Thomas, saddler and ironmonger
Walker, George, mason
Wilson, James D., baker

COUNTRY RESIDENTS, FARMERS, &c.

*Aitken, William, farmer, Friershaw
*Alexander, George, do. Easter Lilliesleaf
*Brown, Archibald, do. Craggs
*Drummond, Alex., do. Bewlie
*Dryden, John, do. Firth
*Dryden, Robert, do. Firth
*Elliot, Andrew, do. Boose Mill
*Gourlay, David B., do. Bewlie Hill
Gray, John, do. Harlaw
*Hislop, Robert, do. Catshaw Hill
*Hislop, William, do. Raperlaw
*Henderson, James, do. Netherraw
*Horsburgh, Alex., do. Greenhouse
Johnstone, Willm., do. Hillhead
*Lambert, Andrew, do. Clerklands
*Lambert, William, do. Clerklands
*Oliver, Andrew, do. Chapel
*Oliver, Thomas, do. Chapel
*Orr, Thomas, do. West Riddell
*Preston, John, do. Middles
*Redford, John, do. Greenhill
*Stewart Francis, do. Hermiston
Stewart, John, do. Hermiston
*Thomson, Wm., do. Bewlie Mains
Turner, James, gardener, Riddell
*Young, Adam, farmer, Dunstone

REGISTERED VOTERS (Non-Resident).

Boyd, Edward, Esq., of Merton Hall
Cathcart, David, Esq., Alloway
Dodds, Rev. Andrew, Avon Bridge, Falkirk
Falla, Robert, builder, Hassendean Common
Gray, Peter, farmer, Hilton's Hill, St. Boswell's
Hogarth, Robert, Esq., Edinburgh
Law, Archibald, St. Boswell's
Law, Robert, Gloster House, Banagher, Ireland
Martin, John, Ireland Island, Bermuda
Matthewson, John, v.-surgeon, Ashkirk
Miller, Boyd, Esq., of Clapham Common
Minto, Andrew, jun., Childknowe
Scott, Hon. Francis (late M.P. for Berwickshire), Sandhurst, Ripley, Surrey
Scott, John Corse, Esq., of Sinton, Ashkirk
Spott, James, Esq., Dunbar

P

Stoddart, Captain Pringle, R. N.
Young, William, Lasswade

SEATS OF COUNTY FAMILIES IN THE PARISH.

RIDDELL.

Situated a mile to the west of the village—the property and residence of *Mark Sprot, Esq., eldest son of the late John Sprot, Esq., who purchased the estate about 1820; born 1802; married, 1829, Elizabeth, daughter of John Shewell, Esq.; and has, with other issue, a son—John, Captain 83d Foot; born 1830.

Mr. Sprot is a Deputy-Lieutenant for Roxburghshire, a Justice of the Peace for Selkirk and Roxburgh shires, Lord of the Manor of Riddell, and Vice-President of the North British Railway Company.

COTEFIELD

At the southern boundary of the parish on the Hassendean road—the property of Mrs. J. G. Stewart, 5 Arniston Place, Newington, Edinburgh; present occupant, J. C. Macintosh, Esq., of Manchester.

BOWDEN.

A HIGHLY cultivated and very fertile agricultural parish, situated to the south of the Eildon Hills, one of them being in the parish. Bowden is bounded on the north by Melrose, on the east by St. Boswell's, on the south by Lilliesleaf, and on the west by Selkirk. The total area, according to the Ordnance Survey, is over 7682 acres; consisting of 7588½ acres land, 15¼ acres water, and 79 acres public roads.

" The general surface of the parish may be well described as consisting of a series of parallel ridges, lying from west to east, and from the parallel elevations from which the Eildon Hills arise, lessening in height towards the south,—with intermediate valleys more or less wide, each having its own rill, which runs eastward to the Tweed, about two miles distant from the middle of the parish." The Eildon hill lying within the parish has an elevation of 1216 feet.*

The climate from the general elevation of the parish is cold, but healthy. The height of the village of Bowden above the level of the sea is nearly 600 feet, and Bowden Moor over 900.

There are two villages in the parish—Bowden, close to the eastern boundary of the parish, and MIDLEM (originally Midholm), situated more in the centre. Near the former village, which is the larger of the two, is the parish church and school. In the centre of this village there is a stone cross —when erected is unknown; and a handsome fountain with a good supply of water has lately been erected for the convenience of the inhabitants. The church of Bowden is extremely prettily placed. Part of it is very ancient, but a new front wall, erected last century with common windows, mars its appearance. A vault, beneath what may have been the chancel, contains the remains of many members of the ducal house of Roxburghe, one of whose ancestors acquired, about the beginning of the sixteenth century, Holydean in this parish, where the family no doubt once resided. The old building, which was strongly fortified, is now in ruins. Some remains of the stone dike of the great deer park of Holydean, enclosing about 500 acres, built about 300 years ago, still exist. The Cavers gallery pew in the church is a curious canopied seat of a very

---

* The centre and east hills lying within Melrose parish have elevations of 1385 and 1327 feet.

antique character, with the family arms and some quaint lines on a beam underneath. The three immense ash trees which grew in the churchyard have all yielded (the last only lately) to the storms which for ages they must have been exposed to. The roots and small portions of the trunks still, however, remain.†

The nearest market towns are—Melrose, about 3¼ miles distant from Bowden by the turnpike road (a nearer road to Melrose for foot-passengers is by the Eildon Hills), and Selkirk, about 3 miles from Midlem.

The population of the parish, including the villages of Bowden and Midlem, in 1861, was 864, who composed 206 families, 14 of whom were returned as living in houses having no windows,‡ and 147 in houses of one and two windows.

Assessed property in 1863-4, £7543 : 17s.

The principal landed-proprietors in the parish are—The Duke of Roxburghe, the Duke of Buccleuch, Thomas Kerr, Esq., of Millrighall (of Craighouse, Earlston), Nicol Milne, Esq., of Faldonside, Captain Riddell, of Prieston, John Boyd, Esq., of Maxpoffle, George Wm. Hay, Esq., of Whiterigg, Mark Sprot, Esq., of Riddell, P. Pennycook, Esq. of Newhall, (Hallrule, Hobkirk), Walter Riddell Carre, Esq. of Cavers Carre, Rev. John Seton Karr, of Kippilaw, William Currie, Esq. of Linthill, William Brunton, Esq. of Eastfield (Ladhope House, Galashiels), Robert G. Thomson, Esq. of Templehall (Rutherford, Maxton).

Superior of Bowden and Midlem—Duke of Roxburghe.

Those marked thus (*) are Registered Voters.

RESIDENT JUSTICES OF PEACE—W. Riddell Carre, Esq., of Cavers Carre ; Thomas Alexander Riddell Carre, yr., of Cavers Carre.

POLICE OFFICER—James Burnet, St. Boswell's.

PUBLIC OFFICES—Heritors' Clerk, Inspector of Poor, and Registrar of Births, Marriages, and Deaths—John Dodds.

Session Clerk and Kirk Treasurer—Thomas Keen.

Medical Officers and Public Vaccinators—Drs. Anderson and Ballantyne, Selkirk.

POST OFFICE (Bowden, by Newtown, for the northern localities)—

† There is also a burial place in the churchyard belonging to the estate of Midlem Mill, once the property of the Elliots of Midlem Mill, from which family the noble house of Minto springs. It is now a corn mill with a small farm attached. In former times it was a considerable estate, and combined with what was then called "Unionhall," now forms the modern estate of Linthill.

‡ Railway labourers then living in huts, but who have all now left the parish.

Mrs. Grant, postmistress. Runner (William Rutherford) twice a day to Newtown, St. Boswell's. Arrivals, 10-30 a.m. and 6 p.m. ; Departures, 6-30 a.m. and 3-15 p.m.

Pillar Box (Midlem, by Selkirk, for the southern localities)— Letters are delivered and taken up daily by the Runner (Joseph M'Gregor) to Lilliesleaf in the forenoon, and on his return to Selkirk in the afternoon.

CLERGY, &c.—Presbytery of Selkirk, Synod of Merse and Teviotdale. Patron—Duke of Roxburghe.

Established Church—*Rev. James M. Allardyce, M.A. (Inducted 1844). Sittings, 400. Average attend. at Sabbath School, 40.

Free Church—*Rev. James Pirie, A.M. (Inducted 1853). Sittings, . Average attendance at Sabbath School,

Original Secession Church (Midlem)—Rev. W. F. Aitken (Inducted 1854). Sittings, 100.

FAST DAYS—Thursday before last Sabbath in June, and Thursday before third Sabbath in December.

SCHOOLS†—Parochial (Bowden)—*John Dodds, master ; average attendance, 70.

Parochial (Midlem)—Robt. Nisbet, teacher ; average attend., 55.

PAROCHIAL BOARD—Hon. Major Baillie, Dryburgh, Chairman. Average Rate of Assessment, about 4d. per £ ; total Assessment 1863, £238 : 15s. No. of Poor on Roll, 29.

MORTIFICATIONS—There are two Mortifications connected with this parish—one of £500, for the poor, known as "Mr. Brunton's Bequest ;" the other of £75, for educational purposes : the origin of this latter bequest is not known.

CONVEYANCE—North British Railway from Newtown Station, 1½ miles distant from the village of Bowden, and Selkirk, 3 miles from Midlem.

CARRIERS—George Scott, from Bowden to Newtown Station, every lawful day except Saturday, when he goes to Selkirk. John Aitchison, from Midlem to Selkirk, Wednesday and Saturday.

CORN MILLS—Bowden—William Dodds, farmer ; Midlem—Thomas Weir, farmer.

TRADES AND RESIDENTS.

Bowden

Bonnington & Wallace, joiners
Burn, James, blacksmith
Grant, Mrs., grocer
*Grieve, Robert, mason
Nicol, James, shoemaker

† Number of children in the parish, between 5 and 15 years of age, attending school during first week of April 1861, 137 ; of all ages, 138.

*Scott, Andrew, portioner
*Suddens, John, do.
Thomson, Jean, grocer
Thomson, Thomas, tailor
*Wallace, William, joiner
Wood, Mrs. C., grocer

Midlem

Beattie, Janet, innkeeper
Cochrane, George, farmer
*Dove, James, portioner
Dove, John, shoemaker
Gray, William, farmer
*Haldane, William, do.
Harvie, Andrew, joiner
Hume, Walter, tailor
*Mabon, John, portioner
Muir, Mrs., do.
*Murray, Andrew, do.
Ormiston, James, blacksmith
*Stenhouse, John, portioner
*Sword, George, do.
*Sword, James, do.

COUNTRY RESIDENTS, FARMERS, &c.

*Ainslie, James, farmer, Curling
*Blaikie, Andrew, do., Holydean
*Brack, George, do., Houdshall
*Brack, James, do., Clarilaw Moor
*Brodie, Patrick, do., Clarilaw
 Brunton, John (of Hilton's Hill, St. Boswell's), Eastfield
 Dalgleish, Walter, farmer, Bowden Moor
 Dodds, William, do., Bowden Mill
*Henderson, John, do., Millrighall
*Hislop, John, do., Friarshaw Moor
*Jeffrey, T., do., Shawburn
 Knox, Mrs. Chesterhall
*Little, Andrew, farmer, Langside
 Lambert, Miss, Toftbarns
*Madder, James, farmer, Faughhill
*Murray, James, Midlemburn
*Scott, John, farmer, Newhall
 Scott, Thomas, do., Kersknowe
 Scott, William, blacksmith, Clarilaw Burn
*Turnbull, James, farmer, Prieston
*Turnbull, William, do., do.

SEATS OF COUNTY FAMILIES IN THE PARISH.

CAVERS CARRE.†

Situated in the southern part of the parish—the residence of *Walter Riddell Carre, Esq., who succeeded to the property on the death of his uncle, Vice-Admiral Carre in 1860.

Mr. Riddell Carre married, in 1830, Elizabeth Riddell, only surviving child of Lieut.-Col. M'Lachlan, of the 10th Regiment of Foot, descended from the M'Lauchlans of Fassiefern, and has one son—Thomas Alexander, late H.E.I.C.S., now Captain and Instructor of Musketry, Ayrshire and Wigtonshire Militia, and Lieutenant 3rd Roxburghshire Volunteers.

The founder of the family (1524) was Ralph *Ker*, brother of Thomas, abbot of Kelso, and the renowned Sir Andrew of Fernieherst, whose descendant, Lord Jedburgh, changed the orthography to *Carre*, which this branch adopted—one of its members having married his kinswoman, Jane, second daughter of the second Lord Jedburgh; and her son, John Carre of Cavers, became heir of line of his uncle the third Lord Jedburgh, who died without issue.

Edinburgh Address—New Club.

LINTHILL.

In the southern portion of the parish and near to the village of Lilliesleaf—the property of William Currie,‡ Esq., of Linthill; at present occupied by Major J. P. Briggs and family, of Her Majesty's Army of India (formerly of Fifeshire, and the author of "Heathen and Holy Lands," published in 1859.)

KIPPILAW.

Situated in the centre of the parish towards the east—the property of the Rev. John Seton Karr‖; at present occupied by *Charles Murray Barstow, Esq.

---

† The postal address for Cavers Carre, Linthill, and that locality, is—Lilliesleaf, Selkirk.

‡ William Currie, Esq., only surviving son of the late William Currie, Esq. of Linthill; born 1831; succeeded 1858. Mr. Currie is a Justice of Peace for Roxburghshire, and Lieutenant in the Edinburgh Queen's Light Infantry Militia. Town Addresses—United Service Club, Edinburgh, and Oriental Club, London.

‖ Rev. John Seton Karr of Kippilaw, Roxburghshire, eldest son of the late Andrew Seton Karr, Esq.; born 1813; succeeded 1832; married, 1855, Anna, daughter of Archibald Douglas, Esq. of Glenfinert, Argyleshire, and widow of Richard Campbell, Esq.

Mr. S. Karr is a Magistrate for the county of Gloucester, and Vicar of Berkeley, in the same county.

Heir Pres.—his nephew Andrew, born 1849, eldest son of the late George Seton Karr, Esq. of the Indian Civil Service.

WHITERIGG.

The property of George W. Hay, Esq., factor for Lord Vernon, Sudbury ; occupied by *Richard Stirling, Esq., and family (formerly of Australia).

REGISTERED VOTERS (Non-Resident).

Anderson, Robert, herd, Old Faldonside
Cowan, James, farmer, Whitmuir
Currie, William, of Linthill, Edinburgh
Dalgleish, John, Scremerston, Berwick
Elliot, James, mason, Riddell Mill
Falconer, George, Esq., yr. of Carlowrie
Hay, Geo. W., Esq., Sudbury, Derby
Karr, Rev. John Seton, of Kippilaw
Ker, Thomas of Craighouse, Earlston
Murray, Rev. William, Melrose
Paterson, Robert, merchant, Edinburgh
Pennycook, Peter, Esq., Hallrule, Hobkirk
Riddell, G. W. Hutton, Esq. of Muselee, Capt. 16th Lancers
Robertson, John, forester, Humbie
Scott, Gideon, Singlee, Selkirk
Scott, James Mitchell, tweed merchant, Galashiels
Wight, Rev. George, Whampray

MAXTON.

A PARISH entirely agricultural, and situated on the south bank of the river Tweed, which forms its northern boundary throughout its entire length. Its other boundaries are—St. Boswell's and Ancrum on the west, and Roxburgh on the south and east. It is of an oblong figure, and is about 4 miles long and 1¾ broad. Its area, according to the Ordnance Survey, is nearly 4494¾ acres. Of this about 36 are occupied by the North British Railway, 71½ are in public and private roads, and 72½ are in water.

In the southern part of the parish the soil is thin, but possesses at Muirhouselaw a clay of excellent quality for the manufacture of tiles and bricks. In the northern part where it gradually slopes down to the Tweed, the soil is rich and well cultivated.

The salmon fishings on the Tweed in this parish are very valuable. They belong to Lord Polwarth of Mertoun, Miss Ramsay of Maxton Cottage, and Sir Edmund Antrobus of Rutherford. The Rutherford salmon fishings contain some excellent casts. Trout fishing is restricted in some parts of the parish.

The village of Maxton, situated on the turnpike road from Melrose to Kelso, is the only one in the parish. Although at one time the village seems to have been a very considerable place, it now possesses no features of interest, except the remains of a cross standing in front of the smithy. A short distance from the village there is a station on the North British Railway, and at Rutherford, in the north-eastern extremity of the parish, is another.

The school-house is situated about a mile below the village, as being more central for the parish generally Near to it is the ruin of Littledean Tower, formerly a place of note, and long possessed by the Kers of Littledean and Nenthorn—a branch of the Roxburghe family. The situation is very pretty, and near to the river ; it is now the property of Lord Polwarth. There is also a circular camp, almost entire, defended by a triple rampart, on the bank of the Tweed, at the north-east extremity of the parish—an outpost probably of a larger camp which existed in the large field opposite, and now entirely obliterated by the plough ; but the tower is the only place of real interest in the parish.

The nearest market towns are—Kelso, Jedburgh, and Melrose—all about 7 miles from the centre of the parish. The post town for the village of Maxton is Newtown, St. Boswell's; for Rutherford Mains and that locality— Kelso. Goods for the village should be addressed by Maxton station.

Population of the parish in 1861, 497, comprising 95 separate families, 53 of whom were returned as living in houses of one and two windows.

Assessed property in 1863-4, £5431 : 4s, exclusive of the North British Railway.

The principal landed-proprietors in the parish are—the Duke of Roxburghe, Lord Polwarth, Sir Edmund Antrobus of Rutherford (146 Piccadilly, London), John Ord, Esq. of Muirhouselaw (Upper Nisbet), and Miss Williamson Ramsay of Maxton Cottage (St. Boswell's parish)—none of whom are resident.

Those marked thus (*) are Registered Voters.

PUBLIC OFFICES—Heritors' Clerk, Session Clerk, Kirk Treasurer, Inspector of Poor, Registrar of Births, Marriages, and Deaths—William Chisholm.

   Medical Officers and Public Vaccinators—Drs. Brown and Smith, St. Johns, Melrose.

POST—The Runner from St Boswell's (James Thomson) arrives at Maxton and departs in the forenoon ; and in the neighbourhood of Rutherford, by way of Roxburgh (Michael M'Ghee), also in the forenoon. Both the runners deliver and collect letters.

CLERGY, &c.—Presbytery of Selkirk, Synod of Merse and Teviotdale. Patron—Charles Balfour, Esq., Newton-Don.*

   Established Church—*Rev John Thomson (Inducted 1810). Sittings, 150.

FAST DAY—Thursday before second Sabbath of July.

SCHOOL†—Parochial—*William Chisholm, master ; aver. attend., 60. Female School (Rutherford)—Agnes Brotherston, teacher ; aver. attendance, 30.

PAROCHIAL BOARD—Chairman—John Ord, Esq., of Muirhouselaw. No. of Poor on Roll, 18. Rate of Assessment, 2¼d. per £. ; total Assessment 1863-4, £150 : 8 : 8¾. Poor House—Kelso Union.

---

* The patronage belonged to the Dons, formerly proprietors of Rutherford. When the late Sir Alexander sold the Rutherford estate about the beginning of the century, he retained the patronage, and thus it came to be sold along with the estate of Newton-Don n 1847, when it was bought by Mr. Balfour. Mr. Balfour has no other interest in the parish.

‡ Number of children between 5 and 15 years of age attending school during the first week of April 1861, 90 ; of all ages, 95.

MORTIFICATION—The Rev. Robert Edgar, a former minister of the parish, bequeathed, in 1714, the sum of £70, which, with some addition by the kirk-session, is invested in the stock of the National Bank of Scotland. The dividend (amounting last year to £4 : 6 : 8) is for the benefit of the "Godly puir, etc."

CONVEYANCE—By North British Railway, Maxton Station ; George Anderson, station-master. Rutherford Station—John Pagan, station-master.

CARRIER—Robert Clark, St. Boswell's, passes every Friday for Kelso.

MILL, &c.—Rutherford—Corn—*Adam Ormiston, miller and cattle dealer. Muirhouselaw Tileworks—William Dodds.

TRADES IN THE VILLAGE.

Davidson, Walter, grocer
Davidson, Walter & Robert, wrights
*Fairbairn, Charles, blacksmith and farrier
Moffat, John, grocer and innkeeper

RESIDENTS, FARMERS, &c., IN THE PARISH.

Aitken, John, Rutherford Boat-House
Bookless, John, farmer, Morridgehall
Currie, George, forester, Maxton Cottage
*Dodds, William, farmer, Muirhouselaw
Dodds, William, jun., commission agent, Muirhouselaw
Douglas, George, farmer, Riddleton Hill
Robertson, Mrs., Maxton West End Farm
*Thomson, Robert G. (of Templehall, Bowden), farmer, Rutherford
*Thomson, George, farmer, Ploughlands
*Thomson, John,   do.,   Maxton East End
*Thomson, Walter, do.,   do.
*Wight, Walter,   do.,   Maxton

REGISTERED VOTERS (Non Resident).

Antrobus, Sir E. Bart. of Rutherford
Ord, John, Esq. of Muirhouselaw, Nisbet
Scott, Hon. W. H., *Master of Polwarth*, Humbie House

CRAILING.

THE parish of Crailing occupies a delightful situation on both sides of the river Teviot, which divides it into two nearly equal portions. The parish is bounded on the north by Roxburgh, on the east by Eckford, on the south by Jedburgh, and on the west by Ancrum. Its length is about 4 miles, and its breadth 3¾ miles; and its area, according to the Ordnance Survey, is 6043¼ acres, of which 5903¼ are land, 78 are water, 51½ are public roads, and 10½ are occupied by railway.

The parish is fertile and highly cultivated, and is well watered both by the Teviot and the Oxnam waters. The trout fishing in the parish is very good, but is restricted within the policies of Mounteviot and Crailing House. The general appearance of the parish is that of a wide basin, sloping gently up on either side of the Teviot, and terminating in "three considerable eminences, on the top of one of which, called Pinielheugh, a monument of cylindrical form, with a spiral staircase, was erected by the late Marquis of Lothian and his tenantry, to commemorate the Battle of Waterloo." In height it is 150 feet, and this altitude, taken with that of the hill, which is 774 feet above the level of the sea, enables the spectator from the summit to command a magnificent view in every direction, and embracing some of the loveliest portions of Teviotdale.*

There are two very small villages in the parish—Crailing, on the south side of the Teviot, where are the church, manse, and school-house; and NISBET on the north side, where is the railway station, and where a bridge has lately been built, replacing a previous ferry, for the accommodation of the district. "Nisbet was formerly a place of some importance, and a separate parish. Of the church scarce a trace remains, but the churchyard is still used as a burying ground by the inhabitants

on that side of the river; it was the scene of the ministry of Calderwood, the church historian, and the birth-place of the celebrated Samuel Rutherford whose religious writings [his ' Letters' especially] still continue to be praised."

The parish contains nothing memorable in the way of antiquities. Near Nisbet, to the west, on the Teviot, is MOUNTEVIOT, a seat of the Marquis of Lothian who possesses the entire north side of the parish. Near to Crailing is CRAILING HOUSE, the residence of John Paton, Esq., who possesses nearly the entire south side of the parish. Crailing House is a plain modern building, and stands beautifully on a rising ground, with the Oxnam winding below; and the interest and beauty of the pleasure-grounds is much increased by the course of this mountain stream, which forms a sweet little glen, having its banks thickly covered with wood.

On the opposite side of the Oxnam, over against Crailing House, remains of caves have lately been discovered; the greater part of them appear to have been destroyed by slips from the cliff, caused by the action of the Oxnam at its base. There are indications of some of them having been used for cattle, and one for cooking. The cliff has not yet been fully explored.

The branch line of the North British Railway to Jedburgh intersects the parish by the north side of the Teviot.

The nearest market town is Jedburgh, about 4 miles off. Kelso is the post town, 6 miles off.

The population of the parish in 1861 was 673, who composed 134 families, 2 of whom were returned as living in houses having no windows, and 99 in houses of one and two windows.

Assessed property in 1863-4, £7994 : 17s.

Besides the Marquis of Lothian and Mr. Paton, the Earl of Minto owns a small portion of the parish; and Thomas Turnbull, Esq. (of Briery Yards by Hawick) owns the property of Palace.

Those marked thus (*) are Registered Voters.

RESIDENT JUSTICES OF THE PEACE—John Paton, Esq. of Crailing, and John Ord, Esq, Upper Nisbet.

POLICE OFFICER—   Brown, Crailing.

PUBLIC OFFICES—Kirk Treasurer, Session Clerk, Inspector of Poor, Registrar of Births, Marriages, and Deaths—Richard Amour.

Medical Officer and Public Vaccinator—Dr. Falla, Jedburgh.

POST OFFICE—Mrs Bell, postmistress. Arrival, 8-30 a.m.; Departure, 2-10 p.m.; Sundays, 9 and 9-40 a.m. Messenger—James Tait.

---

* The monmument bears the following inscription: "To the Duke of Wellington and the British Army. William Kerr VI. Marquis of Lothian and his tenantry dedicate this monument, xxx June, MDCCCXV." This is the date on which the foundation of the *first* monument was laid, and which, owing to faulty construction, fell, when nearly completed, with the noise and force nearly resembling that of an earthquake. As the accident occurred during the night nobody was injured. The construction of the present monument was then immediately commenced, and to this date has never been thoroughly finished.

CLERGY, &c.—Crailing is in the Presbytery of Jedburgh, and Synod of Merse and Teviotdale. Patrons—The Crown and Marquis of Lothian.

Established Church—*Rev. Adam Cunningham (Inducted 1843). Sittings, 300. Average attendance at Sabbath School,
Free Church—Rev. T. S. Anderson (Inducted 1844). Sittings, 262. Average attendance at Sabbath School, 55.

FAST DAYS—Thursday before the last Sabbath of April and first Sabbath of November.

SCHOOLS† (Parish)—*Richard Amour, master. Average attend, 90.
Industrial (in connection with the Parish School)—Mrs. Amour, teacher. Average attendance, 18.
Nisbet (supported by the Marquis of Lothian)—William Gray Innes, teacher. Average attendance, 45.

PAROCHIAL BOARD—John Paton, Esq., Chairman. No. of Poor on Roll, 11. Rate of Assessment, 2½d. per £; total Assessment 1863, £96 : 15s. Poor House—Jedburgh Combination.

MOUNTEVIOT CURLING CLUB—Secretary and Treasurer, John Munro, Fairnington. Entry-Money, 5s. Annual Subscription, 5s. Curling Pond at Nisbet.

CORN MILLS—Crailing—Richard Frater, miller; Nisbet Mill—Corn and Bone—*Francis Walker, farmer.

CONVEYANCE—Railway Station at Nisbet. Station-master—W. Hill.

CARRIERS—Thomas Richardson, occasionally to Edinburgh; Thomas Robson, to Jedburgh and Kelso, Tuesdays and Fridays.

TRADES, &c.

Brown, James, joiner, Nisbet
Dodds, John, blacksmith, Crailing
Edmonds, William, tailor, do.
Fox, Andrew, cattle dealer, do.
Huggan, Andrew, joiner, do.
Ormiston, John, shoemaker, Crailing
Purves, Agnes, dressmaker, Nisbet
Paton, Nichol, carter, Crailing
*Richardson, Thomas, grocer, Crailing
Scott, Janet, grocer, Nisbet
Turnbull, Robert, builder, Old Nisbet Cottage
Young, Adam, blacksmith, Nisbet

RESIDENTS, FARMERS, &c.

Burnet, Miss, Crailing Manse
Dodd, Mrs. and Miss, West Nisbet
Dodd, Nicholas, farmer, West Nisbet

Innes, William, head gardener to the Marquis of Lothian, Mounteviot
Kerse, Robert and James, gamekeepers   do.,   do.
Ord, John, Esq. (of Muirhouselaw, Maxton parish), farmer, Upper Nisbet
*Pringle, John, farmer, East Nisbet
Richardson, *John, and *Robert, farmers, Crailing Nook
*Robson, George, farmer, Crailingbraeheads
*Rutherford, Wr.,   do. and oil-cake mercht., Crailing Tofts
*Scott, James,   do.   Ploughlands
*Thomson,   do.   Palace
*Turnbull, John,   do.   Kirkmains
*Wood, Alexander,   do.   Littledonlees
Wilson, John, gardener, Crailing Orchard

SEATS, &c., OF COUNTY FAMILIES IN THE PARISH.

MOUNTEVIOT.

The occasional residence of William-Schomberg-Robert Kerr, Marquis of Lothian, Earl of Ancrum and Earl of Lothian, Viscount of Briene, Baron Newbattle, and Baron Jedburgh, iu the peerage of Scotland; Baron Kerr of Kerrsheugh, Roxburghshire, in the peerage of the United Kingdom; born 12th August 1832; married, 12th August 1857, Lady Constance Talbot, daughter of the Earl of Shrewsbury; succeeded his father as 8th Marquis, 14th November 1841. *Heir Pres.—* Lord Schomberg Kerr—(see Bonjedward House, Jedburgh parish).

Other Seats—Newbattle, in Mid-Lothian; Blicking Hall, in Norfolk. London Residence—16 Upper Grosvenor Street.

CRAILING HOUSE,

The property and residence of *John Paton, Esq.

REGISTERED VOTERS (Non-Resident).

Jones, Edward, merchant, Liverpool
Paton, George, Sandkeys, Liverpool
Paton, James, Captain 4th Foot, Malta
Paton, William J., 36 Inverness Terrace, London.
Turnbull, Thomas, Esq., of Briery Yards

† Children in the parish from 5 to 15, attending school during the first week of April 1861, 102; of all ages, 106.

HOUNAM.

◆

THE parish of Hounam, situated amongst the Cheviot Hills, is bounded on the north and east by Morebattle, on the south by the county of Northumberland, and on the west by the parishes of Oxnam, Jedburgh, and Eckford. In length it is about 8 miles, and in breadth about 6. Its area, according to the Ordnance Survey, is 15,107¼ acres, of which 15,042¾ acres are land, 33¼ water, and 31¼ roads.

"The appearance of the parish exhibits, in general, little else than an assemblage of hills, chiefly appropriated to pasture; and forming part of the range of Cheviot Hills." The proportion of land fit for cultivation is very small. The hills are very beautiful and the pasturage on them is both extensive and valuable; some of the best grazing farms in the district are to be found in this parish. Hounam Law, partly in Morebattle and partly in this parish, attains an elevation of 1472 feet. Cranshawlaw, near the centre of the parish, is 1152 feet; and Humblemoor Hill, more to the south, is 1191 feet; Beefstand Hill, partly in Northumberland, is 1191 feet. The parish is traversed by good roads, kept in repair by the statute labour fund. The parish is intersected by numerous burns, "romantic in scenery and abounding in trout," which take their rise among the hills; but the only stream worth mention is the Kale, flowing in a northerly direction, and cutting the parish into nearly equal halves. It abounds in trout, and is an unrestricted resort for anglers (see Morebattle parish). "A little to the westward of the village the Kale forms a cascade, called 'the Salmon leap,' and which, when the stream is flooded, becomes an object of interest. An excellent road pursues nearly the whole line of the stream." In no parish in the south of Scotland does the remains of so many old camps—British and Roman—exist, as in that of Hounam. One of them, especially, on' Bughtrig farm, is entire. The Roman road bounds the parish its entire length, on the east.

The village, or rather hamlet of Hounam, is the only one in the parish; it occupies a very pleasant and healthy site on the east side of the Kale. Here the parish church and school are situated. Near the village is GREENHILL, a favourite retreat of His Grace the Duke of Roxburghe. There are no markets or fairs held either in the village or parish. At Pennymuir, in the south-western part of the parish, but on the Oxnam side of the boundary line, two trysts are held (see Oxnam).

The nearest market towns are Jedburgh, about 9 miles distant, and Kelso about 12 miles. The latter is the most convenient for the hamlet either as a market town or railway station, and is the post town.

Population of the parish in 1861, 289; who composed 56 families, 34 of whom were returned as living in houses of one and two windows.

Assessed property in 1863-4, £6907 : 12 : 9.

The principal landed-proprietors in the parish are—His Grace the Duke of Roxburghe; James Dickson, Esq., of Chatto (Bughtrig, Berwickshire); William Scott Kerr, Esq., of Over Chatto (Sunlaws); Christopher Douglas, Esq., of Chesterhouse (Drummond Place, Edinburgh); Sir John Warrender, of Whitton (of Lochend, Bart.); John Ord, Esq., of Over Whitton (Nisbet, Kirkbank); Mrs. John Stavert, of Philogar (Melville Street, Edinburgh); and John Wilson, Esq., of Bughtrig (Otterburn, Morebattle)—all non-resident.

———

Those marked thus (*) are Registered Voters in the parish.

DISTRICT POLICE OFFICER—Alexander Douglas, Morebattle.

PUBLIC OFFICES—Inspector of Poor, Registrar of Births, Marriages, and Deaths, and Kirk Treasurer—Alexander Davidson.

Medical Officer and Public Vaccinator—Dr. Falla, Jedburgh.

POST OFFICE—Post Town, Kelso; from which letters are forwarded by runner, *via* Morebattle, three times a week.

CLERGY, &c.†—Presbytery of Jedburgh, and Synod of Merse and Teviotdale. Patron—J. B. Kidston, Esq. of 50 West Regent Street, Glasgow.

Established Church—Vacant. Sittings, about 200.

FAST DAY—Second Thursday of July.

SCHOOL ‖ (Parochial)—*Alex. Davidson, master; aver. attend., 59.

Towford School—Supported by the proprietors of Hounam and Oxnam, for the benefit of the upper districts of the two parishes —(*see* Oxnam).

PAROCHIAL BOARD—John Ord, Esq., Chairman. No. of Poor on Roll, 4. Rate of Assessment, about 1½d. per £; total Assessment, £63. Poor House—Kelso Combination.

CONVEYANCE—To and from Kelso and Jedburgh, weekly, by Carrier.

CARRIERS—Kelso, thrice a week, Thomas Edmonston; A. Riddell, Friday; Jedburgh, A. Riddell, Tuesday.

———

† While this sheet of the "Register" was at press (October 30, 1864), there died the Rev. George B. Rutherford, who had been minister of Hounam since the year 1818. Last year the patronage was sold to Mr. Kidston by Sir John Warrender. Except the patronage, Mr. Kidston possesses no interest in the parish.

‖ Children in the parish from 5 to 15 attending school during the first week of April 1861, 59; of all ages, 61.

TRADES IN THE HAMLET.

*Hall, Samuel, blacksmith
*Meikle, William, labourer
Shepherd's Inn, *William Paton

RESIDENTS IN THE PARISH.

*Douglas, George S., farmer, Hounam Mains
 Gray, William,   do.   Sharplaw
*Phillips, George,   do.   West Grange
*Scott, George,   do.   Nether Chatto
*Shiel, George,   do.   Over Whitton
*Shiel, James,   do.   Beerhope

REGISTERED VOTERS (Non-Resident).

Douglas, Christopher, W.S., Edinburgh
Dickson, Archibald, yr. of Bughtrig, Eccles
Kerr, W. Scott, of Sunlaws, Kelso
Warrender, Sir John, Bart., of Lochend, Edinburgh
Warrender, George, yr.   do.   do.

OXNAM.

A LONG irregularly shaped parish, bordering on Northumberland, from which it stretches for nearly 10 miles in a north-westerly direction. Its breadth varies from 3 to 5 miles It is bounded on the north by Jedburgh, on the east by Hounam, on the south by Northumberland and parish of Jedburgh, and on the west by Jedburgh and Southdean. The area, according to the Ordnance Survey, is about 21,223¼ acres, of which 109 are in roads, and 33¼ under water.

The southern part of the parish is mountainous, part of the Cheviot range extending into it. To the northward and in the centre of the parish the ground is very much diversified, sometimes rising into considerable eminences, which are intersected by numerous narrow ravines. The principal of these eminences are Hindhopehill, 1394 feet; Grindstonelaw, 1535 feet; and Brownhart, 1664 feet. The soil varies, but the prevailing kinds are a loamy, clayey, and gravelly nature. The northern portion of the parish, wherever the surface admits it, is highly cultivated—principally in the valleys of the Jed and Oxnam; but the southern, and by much the larger portion, is entirely pastoral. The breed of Cheviot sheep receives great attention in the parish, and is probably brought to as great perfection within its limits, as it is in any other parish in the district.

There are the remains of some Druidical circles and old camps in the parish, but its principal antiquarian object of interest is the remains of the Roman road which bounds the parish to the north-east for its entire length, and dividing it from the parishes of Hounam and Jedburgh. Within the limits of the parish this spacious road is in many parts in good order, and is still used as a drove road.

The parish has no particular feature of beauty to recommend it. The upper waters of the Kale (*see* Hounam parish), which rise among the hills in the southern part of this parish are pretty, and so are many parts of the Oxnam which flows through the parish almost its entire length. The Jed forms part of its western boundary. They all abound in trout, and are free to the angler (*see* Jedburgh).

In the northern extremity of the parish, on the Oxnam water, is the hamlet of Oxnam, the only one in the parish.

The nearest market and post town is Jedburgh, about 4 miles distant from the hamlet. Jedburgh is also the nearest railway station.

FAIRS.—*Pennymuir Lambs and Wool* (held at Pennymuir, alongside of the old Roman road, and on the confines of Hounam parish)—31st July, or the Monday after, if the date falls on a Sunday. The wool sold is very trifling ; but for lambs the fair is of great local importance, and has superseded that at the Rink (*see* Jedburgh). The description of lambs principally shewn is Cheviots and three-parts and half-bred Leicesters ; the Cheviot stock have lately shewn a falling off. This fair was established about thirty-three years ago on account of the want of room and the inconvenience attending the Rink Fair. The ground is granted by the Duke of Roxburghe, free of all dues for stock ; and for the accommodation of visitors he has lately expended a considerable sum of money in improving the accommodation and stabling at the Inn. The railway station nearest to the fair ground, by the direct route of the Roman road, is that of Jedfoot on the Jedburgh branch line, over 10 miles distant. The Jedburgh station, by way of Oxnam village, is about the same distance. For the convenience of business, the Jedburgh bank agents attend at the fair ground.

Pennymuir Sheep and Cattle (held as above)—15th October, or the Monday after. Cheviots, draft ewes, and wethers are the stock shewn. The cattle exposed are so few as to be unworthy of notice. As a local fair this of the sheep is of equal importance to that of the lambs.

Population of the parish in 1861, 592, who composed 107 families, 29 of whom were returned as living in houses of one window, and 41 in houses of two windows leaving 37 (or one-third) living in houses of three or more windows.

Assessed property in 1863-4, £10,526 : 0 : 8.

The principal landed-proprietors in the parish are—the Duke of Roxburghe, the Marquis of Lothian, W. O. Rutherfurd, Esq., of Edgerston ; A. Scott, Esq. ; Miss Scott, of Fala ; John Scott, Esq., of Riccalton ; Mrs. John Stavert, of Cunzierton ; and John Oliver, Esq., Hardacres—none of whom are resident.

Those marked thus (*) are Electors Registered in the parish.

DISTRICT POLICE OFFICER—Allan Mitchell, Oxnam.

POST OFFICE—W. Hogg, messenger Daily to and from Jedburgh. Arrives about 11-50 a.m. ; leaves about 1 p.m.

PUBLIC OFFICES—Heritors' Clerk, Kirk Treasurer, Inspector of Poor, Registrar of Births, Marriages, and Deaths, and Session Clerk —Matthew Little.

Medical Officer and Public Vaccinator—Dr. Falla, Jedburgh.

CLERGY, &c.—Presbytery of Jedburgh, Synod of Merse and Teviotdale. Patron, the Crown.

Established Church—*Rev. William Burnie, (Inducted 1859). Sittings, 250. Average attendance at Sabbath School, 54.

FAST DAYS—Thursdays before the first Sabbath of April and last Sabbath of October.

SCHOOL† (Parochial)—Matthew Little, master. Aver. attend., 70.

Towford School (Non-Parochial)‡—Peter Carruthers, master. Average attendance, 30.

PAROCHIAL BOARD—W. E. Otto, Esq., factor for the Marquis of Lothian, Chairman. No. of Poor on Roll, 16. Rate of Assessment, 1¾d. per £ ; total Assessment, 1863-4, £182 : 12 : 7. Poor House—Jedburgh Union.

MORTIFICATION—Lady Yester, according to her letters of Mortification, dated 4th November 1630, and 14th March 1638, bequeathed for behoof of the poor, one cottage, called the Alms' house, and the sum of £1000 Scots ; the annual rent and interest of which, £4, 3s. 4d., is distributed in small portions among such indigent individuals as have not been admitted permanently to the benefit of the assessment.

LIBRARY (Parish)—Open monthly. Annual Subscription, 2s. 530 vols. G. White, Librarian.

CONVEYANCE—North British Railway, Jedburgh Station, distant 6 miles from the village.

CARRIER—James Bruce, Jedburgh, Tuesday and Saturday ; Kelso, Friday.

CORN MILL—Swinside—James Davidson, farmer.

TRADES IN THE HAMLET.

Bennet, John, shoemaker
Huggan, Robert, joiner
Pateson, Robert, tailor
Story, John, blacksmith

FARMERS, &c., RESIDENT IN THE PARISH.

Barrie James, farmer, Harden Mains
*Bell, John,   do., Oxnam, Millheugh
*Dickison, William, do., Cleuchside
*Douglas, Andrew, do., Swinside Hall
*Douglas, James,   do., Swinside Townfoot
*Douglas, Thomas, do., Swinside Townhead
*Elliot, Thomas,   do., Easter Hyndhope
*Hall, Robert,   do., Newbigging Birks
*Hall, James D.,   do.,   do.

---

† Children in the parish from 5 to 15, attending school during the first week of April 1861, 91 ; of all ages, 95.

‡ Erected in 1862 near Pennymuir Inn, at the joint expense of the owners and occupiers of the parishes of Oxnam and Hounam, for the accommodation of the upper districts of the two parishes.

Pennymuir Inn, Walter Tinline
*Riddell, James, farmer, Cappuck
*Riddell, Thomas, do., Oxnam Nook
*Simson, David, do., Oxnam Row
*Simson, Robert, do., Newbigging Bush
*Swan, Samuel, do., Overton Bush
*Wyllie, James, do., Newbigging
*Wyllie, Robert, do., do.

REGISTERED VOTERS (Non-Resident).

Dodd, Nicholas, farmer, West Nisbet
Douglas, George, farmer, Riddletonhill
Oliver, John, Esq., of Overton Bush (Hardacres, Berwickshire)
Scott, Alexander, Hopetoun House, South Queensferry

CASTLETON.

THIS is the largest parish in the south of Scotland, being 18 miles long, 14 broad, and occupying fully a seventh of the map of Roxburghshire. It is bounded on the north by the parishes of Teviothead, Hobkirk, and Southdean; on the east by Northumberland, on the south by Cumberland, and on the west by Dumfriesshire. In shape it is an irregular triangle. The total area of the parish, according to the Ordnance Survey measurements, is nearly 68,152½ acres, of which there are 294 acres water, 177¾ acres of public roads. The remaining part (about 67,680½ acres) is mostly mountainous and hilly, saturated with superfluous moisture, and nearly all affording, as yet, only excellent pasturage for sheep.

"The parish has yet to be brought under the action of the plough. Here is abundance of lime, and plenty of coal to burn it, and a strong clay-soil, interspersed, no doubt, with patches of moss—everything, indeed, that the most sanguine reclaimer might wish for—yet wide pastoral ranges and lonely shepherds' cots attest that the footprints of the reclaimer are in Liddesdale yet unknown. The amount of rain-fall in Liddesdale would doubtless, in some degree, be a barrier to cereal cultivation; but a thorough drainage would mitigate this evil; and as it is, turnips and grasses—crops most luxuriant in a moist climate—are now the most profitable crops to cultivate. The latter mode—viz., an alternate system of grass and turnip husbandry—has indeed been most successfully carried out in some upland districts, and holds out to the land-improver surer and richer rewards for outlay than can be obtained in the wide range of pastoral farming."*

Four years ago Mr. Brackenridge, Yorkshire, before a committee of the House of Commons, gave an opinion that the parish contained 35,000 acres capable, with little expense, of being made fit for any agricultural purpose, and that much land had already yielded to the influence of the plough, bearing corn in some instances to the extent of 60 imperial bushels per acre.

Some of the hills rise to a considerable elevation—the principal of them are—Tudhope Fell, of 1830 feet, Millenwood Fell and Windhead, both nearly 2000 feet high; Larriston Fells,

* Sanderson's Prize Essay on the Agriculture of Roxburghshire and Berwickshire.

1524 to 1679 feet; Din Fell, 1735 feet; Hartsgarth Fell, 1806 feet; Saughtree Fell, 1421 feet; Greatmoor Hill, 1964 feet; Hermitage Hill, 1321 feet; and Peel Fell, 1964 feet.

The climate is damp, but mild; and except on such hills as Peel Fell and Greatmoor snow storms are less severe than on the Cheviots and the Selkirkshire hills.

For romantic and interesting associations, the parish of Castleton (not even excepting the more frequented and better known parish of Yarrow) excels any other in the south of Scotland. The remains of antiquity are very numerous, and the halo of romance which lingers around many of them has been perpetuated by the ballads gathered up and placed on permanent record, particularly by Sir Walter Scott. Chief among these antiquarian remains is the Castle of Hermitage, founded in the year 1244, long a notable Border fortress, and still one of the finest specimens extant of ancient baronial architecture. The castle is pleasantly situated on the left bank of the Hermitage water, and is surrounded by strong ramparts and ditches. About two hundred yards to the westward, is an old cemetery with the remains of a chapel, in which once worshipped the Lords of the Hermitage with their retainers. Outside the wall of the churchyard is a mound ten or twelve feet long, said to be the grave of the Cout of Keildar, who was treacherously murdered by Soulis of Hermitage; and near it is the pool where tradition says "the Cout" who was charmed against steel, was borne down and drowned. Hermitage is five miles from Newcastleton, and two from Steele Road Station, on the Border Union Railway, from which there is a good road. About two miles from Hermitage to the north-east, on a ridge, designated "the nine-stane-rig," is a circle of standing stones, obviously Druidical; but on which, according to the ballad, Lord Soulis, the notorious chief of Hermitage, was boiled in a sheet of lead. The view from this point southward into Cumberland and Westmoreland is magnificent. Near Hermitage, there lately stood the old farm-house of Millburnholm, the first Liddesdale house that Sir Walter Scott entered, and in which then lived Willie Elliot, supposed by many to have been at least one of the prototypes of Dandie Dinmont. The farm is now a part of Hermitage, and the old house has been replaced by a couple of new houses for farm servants. But the vale of the Liddell, even more than that of the Hermitage, abounds in antiquarian remains. Near its source are the ruins of the Wheel Church. Farther down stood Clintwood, a residence of the Soulises, but of which nothing now remains. Dinlabyre, an old-fashioned mansion, now a farm house, was the site of another chapel; and at the junction of the Hermitage and Liddell is the parish church. Here also was "the Castle of the Liddell," and the "town" which has given its name to the parish. The churchyard is

on an eminence about a mile up the river.[*] Two miles farther down the river is the village of Newcastleton. South of the village is Caerby Hill, on the top of which is a remarkably complete and extensive ancient encampment. Near the village, also, are the ruins of Mangerton tower, the ancient fortress of the Armstrongs; and near the road-side at Milnholm is a stone cross, eight feet four inches high, with a sword and several letters carved on the south side. Tradition says that this cross marks the spot where the corpse of one of the Armstrongs of Mangerton, who had been murdered at Hermitage, was rested on its way to be buried at Ettleton, while the retainers went for refreshments to the "Tower." On the hill-side above is the churchyard of Ettleton, a very old cemetery, and on the tomb-stones one observes the names of Elliots, Armstrongs, Nixons, Jardines, and others famous in the district. The salubrity of the climate is proved from the fact that some of the dead have considerably passed 100 years of age, one reaching the extraordinary age of 114. Farther to the westward is the dwelling-place of John Armstrong, celebrated in the ballad as "Jock o' the Side," and in the glen beyond are the remains of Puddingburn Ha', the scene of another ballad called "Dick o' the Cow."

Cut off from Teviotdale by a high and stormy ridge of hills, and sloping gradually but uninterruptedly down toward the Solway, Liddesdale is naturally connected with England rather than Scotland, as a consequence of which we find an approximation to the English dialect spoken in the district. Over "the edge," as it is called, into Teviotdale, there are now two main roads—one leading towards Jedburgh; the other towards Hawick, besides the railway opened in the summer of 1862, so that travelling is easy and comfortable. But till a comparatively recent period there were no roads, and persons little past middle age can remember since the Plashetts coal was carried to Hawick on the backs of ponies. Sir Walter Scott made seven annual *raids* into Liddesdale, commencing with 1792, and on the last occasion he drove a gig part of the way, which

* In the churchyard are some rather nice monuments, amongst which is one to the memory of Dr. John Armstrong (who was a native of the parish), author of "The Art of Preserving Health ;" a poem of considerable merit and celebrated in its day, but now entombed in the voluminous collections of poetry in fashion about the beginning of the century. William Scott, author of "Border Exploits," etc., is also buried here. On the opposite side of the road from this churchyard, in a pasture field, is still to be seen the base of an old stone cross, it being the place where the people in the district used to meet to hire their servants and transact their public affairs, in times long before the village of Newcastleton had a beginning, and where many a bloody fight used to be among the stalwart lads of Liddesdale.

is stated to have been the first wheeled carriage seen in the district. On the first of these visits Scott started from Abbotrule, along with Mr. Robert Shortreed, sheriff-substitute of the county, who knew the locality thoroughly; and the primitive condition of the inhabitants is obvious from the sensation which Scott's biographer describes as having occurred at Millburnholm, the first farm-house that the couple visited. When informed that Scott was an advocate, the farmer received him with great ceremony and insisted on himself leading his horse to the stable. Shortreed accompanied Willie, however, and the latter, after taking a deliberate peep at Scott, "out-by the edge of the door-cheek," whispered, " Weel, Robin, I say deil hae me if I'se be a bit feared for him now; he's just a chield like ourselves, I think." Of this decent man Lockhart says : " According to Mr. Shortreed, this good man of Millburnholm was the great original of Dandie Dinmont. As he seems to have been the first of these sheep farmers that Scott ever visited, there can be little doubt that he sat for some parts of that inimitable portraiture; and it is certain that the James Davidson, who carried the name of Dandie to his grave with him, whose thoroughbred death-bed scene is told in the Notes to ' Guy Mannering,' was first pointed out to Scott by Shortreed himself, several years after the novel had established the man's celebrity all over the Border; some accidental report about his terriers and their odd names having alone been turned to account in the original composition of the tale."

But Liddesdale and its people have changed for the better since Scott and his companion lingered over the punch-bowl with Willie of Milburnholm till they were "half-glowrin'." Now there are good roads and handsome conveyances. The farm-houses are generally comfortable and elegant, with tidy well-trimmed gardens attached, and the inhabitants are not a whit behind others of the same class in point of intelligence, refinement, and attention to the comforts and amenities of life. The working classes are honest, industrious and well conducted, and young women from Liddesdale who come " ower the edge" to serve, are generally very highly esteemed.

The principal rivers in the parish are the Liddell and Hermitage, the former of which gives to the district the popular name of Liddesdale. The Hermitage joins the Liddell in the lower part of the parish, at the junction of which, and between them, on the banks of the Liddell, stands the Established Church. Besides the Liddell and the Hermitage, the parish contains the following streams—the Kershope (which divides the two kingdoms), the Tweedon, the Tinnes, and the Blackburn. Till within the last few years these rivers were plentifully stored with trout, but from some cause or other their numbers have recently diminished. An association of proprietors of fishings in the Esk and Liddell, having its headquarters at Langholm, has undertaken to protect the waters, and no one above fourteen years of age is allowed to fish with rod and line without leave granted. A small charge is made for the season. To enforce this law a policeman is stationed at Newcastleton. On the Tweedon, and Blackburn, both of which fall into the Liddell near to Castleton, are several beautiful waterfalls—especially on the Blackburn The valleys of the Liddell, and the Hermitage are very beautiful, and contain materials of great interest to the antiquary and geologist.

The parish has long been celebrated for its sulphurous springs. The Deadwater near the head of the Liddell, and " unfortunately situated in the middle of a vast morass," used to be much frequented by persons affected by cutaneous and scrofulous complaints, who received great benefit; but for some years it has been shut up by the proprietor. Another very powerful one, famous for its petrifying qualities, is on the Tweedon; and a third is at Lawstown; besides these there are others of inferior note dispersed over the parish.

The North British Railway Company having completed their Hawick line to Carlisle, *via* Liddesdale (Waverley route), this important district, rich in minerals, and capable of high cultivation, will be opened up, and through traffic secured between the north of Scotland and the English markets. A connection with the Border Counties' Railway has also been formed in this parish, by which the valley of North Tyne, rich in coal and iron, is available, and a way opened up to Newcastle and other important towns in the north of England. There are three railway stations in the parish—Riccarton, Steel Road, and Newcastleton; the first is the junction of the Border counties' with the Waverley route.

In the centre of the lower part of the parish is the modern village of NEWCASTLETON, with a population of 1124. It was commenced in 1793 by Henry Duke of Buccleuch, is very regularly built, and consists of one principal street nearly a mile long, in which, at equal distances, the houses form three squares, of which the centre one, Douglas Square, occupies 2 acres.*

Newcastleton by road is 26 miles from Jedburgh, 20 from Hawick, 10 from Langholm, and 9 from Canonbie. Good turnpike roads communicate with all these places. By rail it is 24 miles from Carlisle, 21 from Hawick, 17 from Langholm, 10 from Canonbie, and 50 from Jedburgh.

Great Hiring Days—Men, second Friday of April ; Women, Fridays before the 17th of May and 8th of November.

FAIRS.—*Lambs* (held on the hill behind the town), Friday

---

* The first feuars who commenced building were. Mr. William Nichol, father of the late Dr. Walter Nichol, Edinburgh, and Mr. Robert Murray, blacksmith.

before the second Wednesday of September: at which from 14,000 to 15,000 of the stock of the district are generally shewn.

Ewes and Lambs (held on the hill), Thursday before second Tuesday of October.

Cattle and small Lambs (held in the square of the town), third Friday of November.

The population of the parish in 1861 was 3688, being an increase since 1851 of 1558; but this is greatly accounted for by the influx of railway labourers into the parish when the census of 1861 was taken—1250 of the increase being males (*see* remarks on the population of the district, p. 52). The total population of the parish for 1861, was returned as constituting 735 families, 162 of whom lived in houses of no windows (labourers' huts), 154 in houses of one window, and 294 in houses of two windows, which leaves 125 living in houses of three and more windows —a small proportion compared to some other parishes, even after deducting the 162 huts, which may be considered an exceptional incident.

Assessed property 1863-4, £17,218.

Superior of the Village—His Grace the Duke of Buccleuch, who is the principal landed-proprietor in the parish; the other principal proprietors are—William O. Rutherfurd, Esq. of Dinlabyre (Edgerston, by Jedburgh); William Keir, Esq. of Whithaugh; John Jardine, Esq. of Thorlieshope; William Elliot Scott, Esq. of Peel; Robert Elliot, Esq. of Redheugh; James Jardine, Esq. of Larriston; Robert Jerdan, Esq. of Liddell Bank.

RESIDENT JUSTICE OF THE PEACE—None.

POLICE OFFICERS—John Gordon; James Reid, Newcastleton.

POST OFFICE.

Margaret Murray, postmistress.

Despatches.	Arrivals.
To Hawick, 9 a.m.	From Hawick, 6-28 p.m.
To Carlisle, 6-10 p.m.	From Carlisle, 9-19 a.m.

Robert Armstrong, Langholm Street, town-deliverer.

James Nichol, A Street, messenger to Dinlay and Saughtree.

PUBLIC OFFICES.

Town Committee of Management—Mr. Thomas Wilkie, farmer; Mr. Andrew Mitchelhill, farmer, and Mr. James Murray, farmer.

Registrar of Births, Marriages, and Deaths, Inspector of Poor, Collector of Poor Rates, Heritors' and Session Clerk—John Brown.

Town Clerk—John Nichol.

Inspector of Nuisances—John Elliot.

CLERGY, &c,

Castleton is in the Presbytery of Langholm, and Synod of Dumfries.

Patron—Duke of Buccleuch.

ESTABLISHED CHURCH†—Rev. James Noble (Inducted 1861). Sittings, 820. Average attendance at Sabbath School, 80.

FREE CHURCH—Rev. Neil Shaw Ure Inducted 1861). Sittings, 250. Average attendance at Sabbath School, 85.

U. P. CHURCH—Rev. John Black (Inducted 1829). Sittings, 600. Average attend. at Sabbath School (including private class), 100.

A class for the young, in connection with the U. P. Church, held every Friday evening. Average attendance, 60.

CONGREGATIONAL CHURCH—Vacant. Sittings, 148. Average attendance at Sabbath School, 12.

FAST DAYS—Fridays before the second Sabbaths of June and Nov.

SCHOOLS.‡

Parochial (Newcastleton)—John Brown, C.T., master; Female Teacher, Miss M. Lithgow. Average attendance, 140.

Auxiliary (Burnmouth)—John Hardie, teacher; average attend., 32.

Auxiliary (Saughtree)—Alexander M'Gregor, teacher; average attendance, 40.

Auxiliary (Hermitage)—James Scott, teacher; average attend., 85.

Female School (Castleton Church)—Miss Telfer, teacher.

SUNDRIES.

PAROCHIAL BOARD—William Keir, Esq., of Whithaugh, Chairman; No. of Poor on Roll, 46. Rate of Assessment, 6d. per £.; total collection 1863-4, £700. Poor House—Jedburgh Union.

LIBRARIES—Castleton Library, containing 1469 vols.; Annual Subscription, 10s.—John Brown, librarian. Juvenile Library, containing upwards of 1240 vols.—Anne Oliver, librarian. U. P. Sabbath School Library, containing several hundred volumes— Rev. J. Black, librarian.

LIDDESDALE CURLING CLUB (admitted into the R.C.C.C., 1863)—Annual subscription, 2s. Patron—Lord Henry Scott, M.P.; President—William Keir, Esq., of Whithaugh; Vice-President—Robert Elliot, Esq., of Redheugh; Treasurer and Secretary—Mr. John Scott, Newcastleton; Chaplain—Rev. Jas. Noble, Castleton.

MEDICAL PRACTITIONERS—William Murray and Thomas C. Taylor, surgeons.

INSURANCE AGENT—Edinburgh Life—John Brown.

LIDDESDALE TURNPIKE TRUST, extending from Limekilnedge and Not-of-the-Gate to Forge Bridge, parishes of Castleton and Canonbie—Qualification, £100 Scots—Messrs. Oliver, Hawick, Clerks; Andrew Wilson, Hawick, Surveyor.

---

† The parish church and manse are situated about 2 miles to the north of the village of Castleton, at the junction of the Liddell and Hermitage; all the other churches are in the village.

‡ The children in the parish from 5 to 15, attending school during the first week of April 1861, was 334; of all ages, 368.

LIDDESDALE STATUTE LABOUR TRUST—Qualification of Trustees, £100 Scots; comprehends the parish of Castleton only—George and James Oliver, Hawick, Clerks; Andrew Wilson, Hawick, Surveyor.

BANK—A Branch of the British Linen Company's Bank is open at Castleton every Monday for public business, by Thomas Stevenson, Agent, Langholm.

FISHING ASSOCIATION (Langholm)—President, His Grace the Duke of Buccleuch; Secretary and Treasurer—H. Dobie, Esq., Langholm.

CARRIERS—Hawick, Wednesday, William Scott; Langholm, Tuesday and Friday, James Nichol; Jedburgh, Thursday, John Martin.

TRADES, RESIDENTS, &c.

Those marked thus (*) are Registered Voters in the parish.

Doncaster Street

Pringle, John, grocer

Douglas Square

Armstrong, Robert, shoemaker
Beattie, William, road-contractor
Benson, William, general merchant
*Brown, John, schoolmaster
Parochial Board and Registrar's Office
Commercial Inn, John Scott
County Police Station
Crown Inn, *Richard Murray
*Dodd, William of Greenholm
Edgar, James, merchant
Elliot, John, inspector of nuisances
Elliot, Ninian, road-contractor
Grapes Inn, John Elliot
Hall, George, cattle dealer
*Little, John. blacksmith
Mackay, William, saddler
Nichol, Thomas, baker
Scott, James, draper, clothier, grocer, etc.
    Cutter—James Forster
Scott, James, gardener
Scott, Miss Jane, grocer
Simpson, Thomas, shoemaker
Taylor, Thomas C., surgeon
Telfer, Mark, meal-dealer
Ure, Rev. Neil Shaw
Wilkie, Thomas (bailie), farmer

Hermitage Street (North)

Armstrong, Mrs., merchant
Armstrong, William, flesher
Black Bull Inn, Jane Mitchellhill
Crozier, Mrs., draper
Elliot, Robert, late carrier
Hall, Mrs. Thomas
*Little, Robert, stone-dyker
Little, William, flesher
Mitchellhill, Andrew (bailie), farmer
*Murray, James (bailie), farmer
*Nichol, Adam, mason
Nichol, John, mason
Nichol, Robert, grocer
Oliver, Adam, joiner
*Pott, Robert, feuar
Smith, John, gardener
Turnbull, Margaret, grocer

Hermitage Street (South)

Armstrong, Hugh, cattle dealer
Beattie, Walter, builder
Blaikie, Robert, saddler
Crozier, Robert, clogger
*Elliot, Adam, mason
Elliot, Thomas, grocer
Inglis, Frank, builder
Inglis, James, grocer
Murray, Margaret, draper
Murray, William, surgeon
Nichol, John, town-clerk
Oliver, Murray, tailor
Post Office, M. Murray, postmistress
*Robson, Adam, feuar
*Scott, Francis
Scott, Andrew, shoemaker
Scott, Archibald, joiner
Scott, John, builder
Storie, Thomas, blacksmith
Underwood, Arthur, butcher

Langholm Street

Elliot, Henry, joiner
Nichol, James, carrier
Nichol, William, sheep-dealer

Liddel Street

Armstrong, John, mason
Dickson, John, blacksmith
U. P. Manse, *Rev. John Black

Montague Street

Cowan, James, lime and coal agent
Kerr, Robert, tailor

Stafford Street

Nichol, William, blacksmith

Whitchester Street

*Scott, Walter, feuar (late of Hawick)
Vivens, Robert, joiner

Railway Stations

Newcastleton—J. Singleton, station-master
Steel Road—Alexander Aitken, do.
Riccarton Junction—John Elwes, do.

RESIDENTS IN THE PARISH.

Armstrong, Mrs., Sorbietrees Farm
Armstrong, James, farmer, Riccarton Mill
*Armstrong, James, do.,   Yethouse
*Ballantyne, John G., do.,   Shaws.
*Barrie, John,   do.,   Hartsgarth
*Dickson, Robert, do.,   Dinley
*Douglas, James,   do.,   Roan
Elliot, Mrs., The Flatt
*Elliot, John,   farmer, Flatt
*Elliot, Andrew, do.,   Twislehope
*Elliot, John (of Binks, by Hawick), farmer, Burnmouth
*Elliot, Robert, farmer, Powisholm
*Elliot, Thomas, do.,   Mangerton
*Elliot, Walter, do.,   Hermitage
*Elliot, John, shepherd, Newcastleton
*Graham, James, farmer, Braidlee
*Hislop, William, do.,   Gorrenberry
*Jardine, Charles, do.,   Riccarton
Johnston, Hugh, gamekeeper, Newlands
*Kyle, William, farmer, Leehaugh

*Mason, Thomas, farmer, Milnholm
*Mark, Joseph,   do.,   North Greenholm
Moffat, Arthur, do.,   Cottage
*Murray, James, do.,   Whisgills
*Murray, John,   do.,   Burnmouth
*Murray, Robert, do.,   Castleton
*Routledge, John, do., South Greenholm
*Scott, Thomas, do.,   Demainholm
*Scott, William Elliot, of Peel, Kirndean
*Snowdon, William, farmer, Mains
*Stavert, Andrew,   do.,   Dykecrofts
*Stavert, Archibald, do.,   Saughtree
Thomson, James, forester, Sandholm
*Wilson, John, quarrier, Fairloans

REGISTERED VOTERS (Non-Resident).

Elliot, Thomas, yr., of Redhaugh, Dumfriesshire
Irvine, John, of Newbie
Jardine, John, of Thorlieshope, Arkleton, Ewes
Jardine, Robert, of Liddelbank, Castle Milk, Lockerby
Murray, George, Bedlington, Northumberland
Oliver, John, farmer, Carlenrigg
Rutherfurd, William Oliver, of Edgerston
Smith, James, draper, Newcastle-on-Tyne
Wilson, Andrew, surveyor, Hawick

SEATS, &c. OF COUNTY FAMILIES AND SMALLER RESIDENCES.

DINLABYRE.

A house of considerable size but antiquated appearance, situated by the side of the Jedburgh road, near the left bank of the Liddell, and about four miles from Newcastleton—the original seat of the Rutherfurds of Edgerston, now occupied by *Robert Douglas & Sons (*James and *George), farmers, Dinlabyre and Bridge House.

LARRISTON.

The property of *Jas. Jardine, Esq. (of Dryfeholm, Lockerby), is situated on the south of the Liddell, about two miles above Dinlabyre. Mr. Jardine and family are occasionally resident.

THORLIESHOPE.

The property of John Jardine, Esq. (of Arkleton, Ewes), is also on the south side of the Liddell, about a mile above Larriston. The proprietor is non-resident.

REDHEUGH

Is pleasantly situated on the right bank of the Hermitage water, a short distance above its confluence with the Liddell—the property and residence of *Robert Elliot, Esq.

WHITHAUGH.

Situated on the south side of the Liddell, opposite to the village of Newcastleton—the property and residence of *William Keir, Esq.

LIDDELL BANK.

The property of Robt. Jardine, Esq. (of Castle Milk, Lockerby), acquired by purchase from the Trustees of the late Archibald Maxwell, Esq.—situated among woods on the north side of the Liddell, about four miles below Newcastleton, one of the finest situations in Liddesdale. Here the vale begins to expand, and a little farther on it opens into the magnificent scenery of Canonbie on the one side and Netherby on the other. The estate is occupied by *William Brakenridge, Esq., who rents the whole of the estate, including the shootings.

LIDDESDALE COURSING CLUB (Instituted 1864).

The first meeting of this Club took place near Newcastleton, in December 1864 [after the first part of the Castleton lists had been printed], when 16 Dogs were entered and run.

Secretary—Mr. John Scott, Newcastleton.

Judge—Mr. Jamieson, jun., Nottylees, Kelso.

JEDBURGH.

THE parish of Jedburgh consists of two parts, detached by intervening portions of the parishes of Oxnam and Southdean. The larger part, in which the burgh of Jedburgh is situated, is bounded on the north by Ancrum, Crailing, and Eckford; on the east by Oxnam and Hounam; on the south by Oxnam and Southdean; and on the west by Bedrule. The smaller portion, lately converted into a *quoad sacra* parish, to which small portions of the adjacent parishes of Oxnam and Southdean have been attached, lies to the south. In this portion the hamlet of Edgerston is situated, and gives the name to the new parish. Its boundaries are—north and east, Oxnam; west and south, Southdean and England. The general figure of the parish is exceedingly irregular—the largest piece is about 7 miles long, and 5 miles broad; the upper part is about 5 miles long and 4 broad. The total area of the *civil* parish of Jedburgh, according to the Ordnance Survey, is 22,670¾ acres; of which 22,300 are land, arable, and moor, 135½ are water; 221¾ are public roads; and 13½ are occupied by the railway. The surface is much diversified—the southern part extending to the Cheviot Hills is mountainous, and includes the following hills—Greenknowes, 955 feet; Hareshaw Knowe, 965 feet; Browndean Laws, 1309 feet; Lumlair Edge, 1341 feet; Hoplaw Nip (or Hophills Nob), 1173 feet; Knock Hill, 1176 feet; Ark's Edge, 1468 feet; and Leap Hill, 1542 feet. This part of the parish gradually descends with a fine undulating surface, rising sometimes into beautiful green hills. The northern portion has the same undulating hilly surface, but has nothing mountainous in its character, with the exception of Lanton Hill (923 feet), lying on its western boundary and encroaching on Bedrule parish. The Dunion, on the north-east base of which the burgh of Jedburgh is built, has its peak and most of its base in Bedrule parish, and is 1095 feet high. Almost the whole of the parish, except the most southerly part, is under a high state of cultivation.

The Jed which rises in the neighbouring parish of Southdean, flows through nearly the whole length of the parish. It is a tributary of the Teviot, which it joins about 2 miles below the town. The Oxnam water, another tributary of Teviot, bounds the eastern portion of the parish. In both these streams the fishing is best after a flood, and both improve the nearer the angler gets to their sources. In the burns which flow into the Jed, the fishing is very good.

Occupying a beautiful situation on the Jed, is the royal burgh of Jedburgh,* situated in 55° 26′ north lat., and 2° 31′ west long. It is a place of great antiquity. It was originally built by Ecgred or Egred, Bishop of Lindisfarne, in the early part of the ninth century : its castle being mentioned in the earliest Scottish annals. In 1523, the Earl of Surrey, laid siege to the town, and met with a desperate resistance. He describes it as " well builded, with many honest and fair houses in garrison, and six good towers therein."† During the time of the Border wars it was repeatedly assaulted. Jedburgh was a place of considerable importance, from its situation on the borders of England, the strength of its castle, the richness of its abbey, the safe retreat afforded to its friends and foes by its vast and impenetrable forest ; but since these were destroyed and the changes that have taken place since the Union, it has been reduced in importance to a respectable county town. The town is in general well built, and from being partly situated on the hillside possesses great diversity of levels. The height above the sea level at the outer jail gate is 388 feet, 276 feet at the Market Place, 253 feet at the Townfoot Bridge, and 219 feet at the Railway Station. The four principal streets cross at right angles and meet in a market place, of limited extent, where is situated the County Buildings, containing the Council House and the Justiciary and Sheriff Court Rooms. Jedburgh is the county town of Roxburghshire ; and the Circuit Court of Justiciary for the south-east of Scotland (which includes the counties of Roxburgh, Berwick, Selkirk, and Peebles) is held here twice a-year. The principal branch of industry is the manufacture of woollens, Cheviot and Saxony Tweeds, etc., which are here produced to a considerable extent. An extensive trade is also carried on in the buying in of wool clips for the Bradford market.

Jedburgh, as is well known, was the place where James Thomson, author of " The Seasons," received a considerable part of his education when a youth. The place in which he received his first instalment of classical education is said to have been the small aisle within the abbey, in which Dr. Sommerville now lies buried, it being then used as the "Latin School." It is a fact also, that the town-councils of Dumfries and Jedburgh were the only two public bodies which appreciated the genius of Robert Burns during his life, so far as

to bestow municipal honours upon him. This the Jedburgh town-council did on the occasion of the poet's visit in 1787, when he was invited to an entertainment, and appeared in all his eminently social and convivial qualities. We may mention that the justly celebrated Mrs. Mary Sommerville was born in the manse of Jedburgh, and that Sir David Brewster, whose father was rector of the grammar school, was born in the house No. 40 Canongate. The town-council recently conferred on Sir David the freedom of the burgh.

The climate of the parish varies considerably. In Jedburgh and the valley, which are sheltered by the banks of the river, it is mild and temperate ; whilst in the higher and more exposed parts it is colder. The town of Jedburgh might be remarkably healthy : the soil on which it stands is fine and dry, and the situation, on the sides and haughland of a narrow valley, gives it the full ventilation of fresh south-west breezes from the Border hills. Ten years ago the town was laid with a complete system of sewerage pipes, at a cost of £1400. The cholera, which in the year 1832 severely visited both Kelso and Hawick, did not then enter the parish ; but on the two subsequent occasions, when it visited the locality, Jedburgh did not escape, although the visitations were mild compared with the neighbouring towns. As might be expected from the natural salubrity of the climate, numerous instances of longevity have occurred in the parish. It must be confessed, however, that the town has not kept the position in sanitary arrangements which might have been expected. Naturally the declivity of the situation is remarkably well adapted for the outflow of sewage impurities ; yet public health has not improved. Disease in several offensive forms has been frequent of late years. By the ordinary laws of health and disease this must be owing to a laxity of police rule. The state of the lodging houses is bad, and manure is allowed to accumulate in the closes. Houses are allowed to remain disconnected with the sewerage drains, thereby revealing an improper want of water-closet conveniences ; and, above all, water is quite insufficiently supplied.

A great desideratum is a public park. This has been occasionally hinted at as an object of Jedburgh ambition, and no more worthy object of public good could be aimed at ; and that the inhabitants could raise the funds to purchase with liberality and promptness, is shown by instances of their recent surpassing liberality in church matters.

The soil and situation of the town are particularly congenial to the growth of fruit trees, and many old and celebrated orchards exist in and around it. The pears are the most esteemed. It must be admitted, however, that the fruit crop is much more uncertain than it used to be ; and the district shares in the supply of foreign fruit so liberally provided by the trading facilities with fruit growing countries of late years.

---

* For Parliamentary particulars of the Burgh, see p. 60.
† Amongst the relics preserved by the Burgh is a standard taken from the English at the Battle of Bannockburn. This was preserved by the Weavers' Corporation till that body became defunct, and it is now deposited in the Museum. The Burgh also possessed an ancient corporation standard, but about eighteen years ago it was unfortunately lost by the town officer on his return from St. James's Fair, where it used to be regularly displayed when the Fair was proclaimed.

The principal object of attraction in the town is the fine Abbey, of which the best general view is obtained from the banks of the river. It was founded by David I., and, though a considerable part of it is in a ruinous condition, it still exhibits an outline of its original magnitude and magnificence. The nave has been fitted up as the parish church, or rather the parish church has been fitted up in the nave, a combination which has been much condemned by critical visitors. Still, however, this part of the ruins makes a most imposing place of worship, such as is rarely to be seen in Scotland; and it is possible that the abbey has its present state of careful preservation from the fact of its containing the church.

In the Backgate, which runs parallel to the High Street, there is an object of interest to the visitor, being no less than the mansion occupied by Queen Mary, during an illness of several weeks, in October 1565, occasioned by fatigue in consequence of her visit to Bothwell at Hermitage Castle in Liddesdale. The house is of considerable size, and is still in good repair. It is altogether a curious survivor of old times, and has an antique and venerable air.*

To the south the scenery of the Jed is picturesque in the extreme; the road winding from side to side of the river for several miles, sometimes overhung with spreading boughs, and at other times leading through open haughs. On the south side of the town, and near to it, opposite Allars Factory, and close on the bed of the river, is exposed a fine section of rock, highly interesting to geologists, as shewing the junction of the greywacke formation with the old red sandstone. It is one of the most perfect instances of the combination to be met with, and was first pointed out by Dr. Hutton in 1769. About a mile on the Jedwater road stands the Capon Tree (an oak), one of the largest and most venerable trees in the district. Its age has been computed at more than a thousand years.† About a mile above the Capon Tree is Ferniehirst Castle, which occupies a sequestered position, and is reached by a road leading off a little to the east of the fourth bridge. It was long the seat of the Kerrs, ancestors of the Marquis of Lothian. The present pile, built in 1598, presents a massive appearance, lifting its grey turrets above the tops of the tall venerable trees by which it is surrounded. It has been long used as a farm house. Near to Fernieherst is another celebrated tree (also an oak), known as the *King of the Wood*. A short distance below the fourth bridge is the glen of Lintalee Burn, which, for fine woodland scenery on a limited scale, is not surpassed by any glen in the district. Immediately above the fourth bridge

Blackburn, a small rivulet, falls into the Jed. The scenery in this glen is exceedingly rich, and of quite a different character from that of Lintalee Burn. Burns, when on his Border tour, visited this glen; and when he afterwards wrote of

"Eden scenes on crystal Jed,"

there can be little doubt that the charming scenery of Blackburn would rise before his memory. The Hundalee Caves are likewise objects of interest, and are supposed to have been used as hiding-places in ancient warfare. The principal one is accessible from the edge of the cliff; and although now much exposed to view, it can be observed how complete a place of concealment it must have been when the rock was less broken and the quantity of brushwood greater.

There are several mansions in the parish, the principal of which is HARTRIGGE, near Jedburgh, approached by a fine avenue of stately trees; it is a fine specimen of the Old Scotch Baronial style, formed out of an older mansion of a plainer style, by tasteful and extensive additions. For several years it was the residence of its proprietor, the late Lord Chancellor Campbell, whose son now owns the property. His lordship does not reside at Hartrigge. The next in importance is EDGERSTON HOUSE, about 6 miles from Jedburgh, and in the detached portion of the parish, the seat of William Oliver Rutherfurd, Esq., the sheriff of the county.

The burgh is governed by a provost, three bailies, a dean of guild, a treasurer, and a council, elected by the parliamentary electors.

There are two villages in the larger portion of the parish: BONJEDWARD, near the junction of the Jed with Teviot, and LANTON in the western extremity of the parish. The latter has over 200 inhabitants.

General Holidays—New Year's Day, and Wednesday after hiring day in May.

Handball Match—Fastern's E'en Tuesday. This match takes place in the town, the opposing sides being those who have been born to the west of the cross, and those who have been born to the east of it. On this occasion there is a half-holiday.

Market Days—Tuesday, weekly (corn and general); monthly (fat cattle and sheep), third Thursday during the season (November to May). Jedburgh does but a small corn trade (sales by sample), and its Corn Exchange is of importance principally as a place for meetings, exhibitions, and sales—*see* lists, Corn Exchange.

Great Hiring Days—Hinds, first Tuesday of March; Girls and Young Men, first Tuesdays of May and November. These

---

* The proprietor is Lieut.-General Robert Lindsay Armstrong, Director of the Imperial Mint at St. Petersburg.

† It is specially noticed in "Gilpin's Forest Scenery."

hiring days rank in importance with those of Kelso, as the principal hiring markets in the district.

Cattle and Horse Fair (held in the town)—first Tuesday after the 26th of May—not important.

Cattle, Horses, and Shearers (held in the town)—20th August, if a Tuesday; if not, the Tuesday before.

St. James' Fair (at Kelso)—5th August, of which the burgh of Jedburgh shares the right of superiority—*see* p. 74.*

Rink Wool Fair—held two days after St. Boswell's (*see* p. 121). Much of the Cheviot wool left over from St. Boswell's is here disposed of. The *Rink Sheep Fair*, formerly of great importance, is now extinct—*see* Pennymuir fair, p. 229.

Rood Day, Cattle and Horses—Sept. 25. This old and important tryst, like the other Jedburgh fairs, is held in the streets, which, owing to the throng, form an uncomfortable place for the transaction of business. The market causes much annoyance to shopkeepers and others, who have to keep on their shutters the whole forenoon. The stock shown are principally feeding cattle belonging in the majority of instances to farmers in the hill district. A few cows are also shown—generally farrow. The show of horses has fallen off greatly; the few still brought forward are mostly young and ordinary work horses. It is the very general opinion amongst those interested, that it would be a great advantage if this fair and the Kelso Lean Cattle Market, held the day previous, were joined into one important tryst, and held in some spacious convenient locality—such as St. Boswell's Green.

Cattle and Horses (held in the town)—first Tuesday of November (hiring day). Not important.

Population of the Burgh (by the census of 1861), 2450; of the Parliamentary bounds beyond, 978; of the landward district (not including Edgerston), 1835—total, 4911; Edgerston, 225—grand total of the *civil* parish, 5263. The portions of Southdean and Oxnam, added to Edgerston, to form a separate parish, contain 107 inhabitants; making a total for Edgerston of 332. When the census was taken, the parish (exclusive of Edgerston) contained 1157 separate families, 3 of whom were returned as living in houses without windows, 523 in houses with one window, 294 in houses of 2 windows, and the remainder (337, or less than one-third) in houses of three or more windows. Edgerston contained 70 separate families, 30 of whom lived in houses of one window, 24 in houses of two windows, and the remainder (16, or less than one-fourth) in houses of three or more windows.

The annual value of real property within the Parliamentary burgh, for the year to Whitsunday 1865, was £9855 : 0 : 2. The amount of assessed property in the parish for the year 1863-4, is £22,168 : 15 : 10.

Jedburgh is 46 miles direct S.E. from Edinburgh, 10 miles S.W. from Kelso, and the same distance N.E. from Hawick, with all of which there is now roundabout railway communication by way of Roxburgh, where a single line for Jedburgh joins the Kelso branch of the N. B. line. By railway the distances are—Edinburgh 56¼ miles, Kelso 10¾, and Hawick 18½. To Carlisle by rail the distance is 64 miles, to Newcastle (by Hawick) 126 miles do. (by Berwick) 116 miles, Berwick 34⅓, Newtown 15¾, Glasgow 104½ miles. The Jedburgh station is small and inconveniently placed in the outskirts, beyond Bongate, and over half a mile from the market place. It is a matter of regret that the line has not been completed by being carried into the town.

The following principal landed-proprietors are resident in the parish :—William T. Ormiston, Esq. of Glenburnhall ; James S. E. Fair, Esq., of Langlee ; James James, Esq., of Samieston ; A. W. Mein, Esq , of Hunthill.

The Earl of Minto, the Marquis of Lothian, and the Countess of Home (non-resident) are also large proprietors.

MAGISTRATES AND COUNCIL.

The Town Council administer the General Police Act of 1850, which has been adopted in the Town for several years.

Provost—William Deans, Esq.

Bailies—William Elliot, saddler ; William Millar, solicitor ; Andrew Easton, bookseller.

Dean of Guild—J. S. Turnbull, banker. Treas.—W. Brown, mercht.

COUNCILLORS.

James Thomson, cabinetmaker	G. Chisholm, manufacturer
Adam Hope, ironmonger	John D. Storry, grocer
Peter Paterson, blacksmith	Alexander Guthrie, currier
Robert Story, surveyor	James Turnbull, joiner
William Elliot, solicitor	

James Stedman, Town Clerk.   John Lee, Procurator-Fiscal.

Police Rates, 1s. 2d. per £., exclusive of Water—*see* Water Company. Collector of Police Rates—John Lee.

COURTS.

JUSTICIARY—Generally held in April and September ; the days are fixed by the Judges who are to preside.

JUSTICE OF PEACE COURTS are held on the last Tuesday of each month.

POLICE COURTS are held as occasion requires.

---

* Since the sheet containing page 74 was printed, an endeavour is being made to revive St. James's as a sheep and lamb fair.

SHERIFF AND COMMISSARY COURTS are held during Sessions,† viz.,—on Monday and Thursday.

SHERIFF SMALL DEBT COURTS are held every Thursday during Session.

ACTING JUSTICES OF THE PEACE.

Those marked thus (*) are Resident in the parish.

Sir William Scott of Ancrum, M.P. ; William Ogilvie of Chesters ; *A. W. Mein of Hunthill ; J. Paton of Crailing ; J. Ord of Muir-houselaw ; *W. T. Ormiston of Glenburnhall ; *Jas. S. E. Fair of Langlee ; *Sheriff of the County ; *Sheriff-Substitute ; *R. S. E. Fair, yr. of Langlee ; *Jas. James of Samieston ; the *Provost of Jedburgh ; the *Senior Bailie of Jedburgh.

PUBLIC OFFICES.

Billet Master—James Stedman, County Buildings.
County Rates, Collector of—Gideon Pott, County Buildings.
Heritor's Clerk—William Millar, 24 High Street.
Inland Revenue Excise Office (Harrow Inn), Officer, William Edward Cheese.
    Do.   Collector of, Archibald Jerdon, High Street.
Income Tax, Assessor of—Walter Clark, High Street.
Justice of Peace Clerk—James Stedman, County Buildings.
Jedburgh Abbey, Custodier of—Andrew Watson, Abbey Close.
Lieutenancy, General Clerk of—William Millar, 24 High Street.
Medical Officer and Public Vaccinator—James Falla, surgeon, 4 High Street.
Police and Prison Assessment, Collector of—John Lee, County Buildings.
Police Treasurer—William Veitch, Paradise Vale.
Poor, Inspector of—James Sloan, 33 High Street.
Poor Rates, Collector of—William Scott. Office, 27 High Street.
Prison Board, Clerk to—A. O. Turnbull, Exchange Buildings.
Prison, Governor of—Charles Sprunt.
Procurator-Fiscal for Burgh—John Lee. Office, County Buildings.
Procurator-Fiscal for County—Jas. Stevenson, and Jas. C. Stevenson, County Buildings.
Registrar of Births, Marriages, and Deaths—Thos. Grieve, Kenmuir.
Session Clerk—A. C. Mounsey, Abbeybridge-end.
Sexton—William Henshelwood, Abbey Place.
Sheriff-Clerk—George Rutherford, County Buildings.
Sheriff-Clerk Depute—John M'Dougall, County Buildings.
Sheriff-Officers—Thomas Wight, 19 Castlegate ; George Robertson, 34 Castlegate ; Henry Hewat, 41 High Street.
Stamps and Taxes, Distributor and Collector of—Archibald Jerdon, High Street.
    Do.   Surveyor of—Edward Henderson, Melrose.
Town Clerk—James Stedman, County Buildings.
Town Crier—John Hope, Castlewood.

† "During Sessions"—viz., First Session commences 15th January and ends 15th March ; Second Session commences 3d or 4th April and ends 31st July ; Third Session commences 1st October and ends 15th December.

POST OFFICE (18 High Street).

ANDREW EASTON, Postmaster.

DEPARTURES.	Despatched at.	Box Closes.
Hawick, Denholm, Galashiels, Selkirk, Kelso, Coldstream, &c.	7-15 a.m.	7 a.m.
Edinburgh and the North, Melrose, &c.	9-40 a.m.	9-30 a.m.
Berwick	12-45 p.m.	12-35 p.m.
Edinburgh and the North and Melrose	2-55 p.m.	2-40 p.m.
Berwick, London and the South, Hawick, Kelso, Crailing, Coldstream, &c.	4-10 p.m.	3-55 p.m.
Edinburgh and the North	6-50 p.m.	6-35 p.m.

On Sundays, bags for Hawick, Kelso, and Melrose, will be despatched at 7-5 a.m., and for Edinburgh and the North, Melrose, Berwick, Carlisle, London, and North-Western Railway and Midland Railway Post-Offices, will be despatched at 5 p.m. Letters must be posted at 4-45 p.m.

ARRIVALS.	Arrival.	Delivery begins
Edinburgh and the North, Hawick, Melrose, Kelso, Coldstream, Berwick, and Railway Post-Office	9-45 a.m.	10-15 a.m.
Berwick, and Midland Railway Post-Office	12-5 p.m.	6-10 p.m.
Edinburgh and the North, Hawick, Melrose, and Kelso	6-20 p.m.	6-40 p.m.
London, Carlisle, Midland and North-Western Railway Post Offices	9-40 p.m.	7 a.m.

Thomas Armstrong, Letter-Carrier.

On Sundays bags from London, Edinburgh, Melrose, Hawick, Kelso, Berwick, London and North-Western, and Midland Railway Post-Offices will be received at 10.35 a.m., and bags from Berwick, &c., will be received at 7-50 p.m. A delivery by letter-carrier will be made, beginning at 2-30 p.m., and the office window will be open from 10 to 11 a.m., and 2 till 3 p.m.

The Jedwater Messenger is despatched at 10-15 a.m., and returns at 3-45 p.m. Anthony Temple, Messenger.

The Oxnam-water Messenger is despatched at 10-15 a.m., and returns at 5-45 p.m. W. Hogg, Messenger.

The Ancrum and Belses Messenger is despatched at 6 a.m., and returns at 10 a.m. ; and is again despatched at 10-15 a.m., returning at 3-45 p.m. A. Greirson, Messenger.

The Wells Messenger, via Lanton, Newton, Spittal, Bedrule, Wells, &c., arrives at 9-30 a.m., and is despatched at 10-15 a.m. Thomas Best, Messenger.

CLERGY, &c.

Jedburgh is the Seat of a Presbytery, in the Synod of Merse and Teviotdale. Patron—The Crown.

PARISH CHURCH—Rev. George Ritchie (Inducted 1843). Sittings, 1000. Average attend. at Sabbath School, 100 ; Superintendent—Rev. Mr. Ritchie ; Church Treasurer—Chas. Anderson, banker ; Session Clerk—A. C. Mounsey ; Church Officer—Andw. Watson.

QUOAD SACRA CHURCH—At Edgerston (see Edgerston).

FREE CHURCH—Rev. John Purves (Inducted 1832). Sittings, 650.

Average attendance at Sabbath School, 70. Precentor—Thomas Wight, 19 Castlegate; Treasurer Local and Foreign Missions—Mr. J. R Stewart, 1 Burnwynd; Treasurer Sustentation Fund—Mr. A. Easton, bookseller; Superintendent of Sabbath School—Mr. William Elliot, saddler; Church Officer—Thomas Grieve.

UNITED PRESBYTERIAN CHURCH (Blackfriars)—Rev. J. Polson (Inducted 1856). Sittings. 1108. Average attendance at Sabbath School, town classes, 60; country classes, 30; Bible Class by Mr Polson, 33. Precentor—George Brown, shoemaker, Bongate; Church Treasurer, general and local—Mr. William Hope, 5 Bridge Street; President of Managers—Mr. Wm. Deans, S.S.; Church Officer—Henry Twig.

UNITED PRESBYTERIAN CHURCH (High Street)—Rev. William Barr (Inducted 1841). Sittings, 1050. Average attendance at Sabbath School, 60; Bible Class by Mr Barr, average attend.. 30; Superintendent of Sabbath School and Session Clerk—Mr. Robert Oliver; Precentor, George Maclean, shoemaker, Abbey Place; Treasurer—Mr. George Hilson, solicitor; Treasurer for Missionary purposes—Mr. W. Fergrieve, ironmonger; Chairman of Managers—Mr. James Thomson, cabinet maker; Church Officer — John Rutherford.

EPISCOPAL CHURCH—Rev. John Moir (Inducted 1861). Sittings, 250. Average attendance at Sabbath School, .

CONGREGATIONAL CHURCH—Rev. George Peel (Inducted 1863). Sittings, 300. Average attendance at Sabbath School, 100. Church Treasurer—Mr. John Boyd, 26 Canongate.

ROMAN CATHOLIC CHAPEL—Rev. Francis M'Kerrel (Inducted 1856).

FAST DAYS—Thursday before first Sunday of July, and regulated by best moonlight in December.

UNITED PRESBYTERIAN CHURCH (BLACKFRIARS) MISSIONARY ASSOCIATION.

President—Rev. John Polson   Treasurer—Mr. William Hope.
Average Annual Subscriptions, £100.

COLPORTAGE SCHEME (estab. 1863).

Secretary and Treasurer—Archibald Jerdon, Esq., Jedfoot House.
John Henderson, Bongate, Colporteur.

The parishes visited by the Jedburgh Colporteur are those of Jedburgh, Ancrum, Bedrule, Hopkirk, Oxnam, Southdean, and part of Crailing; a portion of the last parish having been previously occupied by the Kelso Colporteur. It is contemplated also to extend his operations to the parish of Hounam. The income of the society for the year it has been in existence was £31, 13s. The Colporteur has sold 215 bibles and 138 testaments since the commencement of the scheme; besides books, and periodicals; and tracts, supplied by the Religious Tract and Book Society of Scotland, to the extent of 200 per month, have been distributed.

EDUCATIONAL INSTITUTIONS.*

Grammar Schools—Mr A. Mounsey, Rector; Henry Telfer, assistant; average attendance, 110.

Sessional School, (established 1851)—Mr Muckersie, master; average attendance, 100.

Side Schools (see Lanton and Edgerston).

"The Nest Acadamy," (established 1842) for Board and Education of Young Gentlemen—Proprietors, Miss Millar, and Mr Fyfe; Assistants, Mr Rutherford and Herr Schmit.

St. John's Episcopal Church School—Mr Walter Scott, master; Edward Robinson, assistant; average attendance, 130.

Private School, and Boarding Establishment for Young Ladies—Miss Kennedy, Canongate.

Day School for Young Ladies—Miss Clarkson.

Infant School—Mrs. Muckersie, Teacher; Misses Veitch and Waldie, assistants.

PAROCHIAL BOARD.

Chairman—Andrew W. Mein of Hunthill.

COMMITTEES.

General—Provost Deans; A. W. Mein of Hunthill; William E. Otto, Jerdonfield; Andrew Scott, Glendouglas; J. S. E. Fair of Langlee; William T. Ormiston of Glenburnhall; George Rutherford, Sheriff-Clerk; William Millar, solicitor; George Balfour, grocer.

Control of Nuisances—Bailie Elliot; William E. Otto, Jerdonfield; J. S. E. Fair, of Langlee; George Balfour, grocer; Robt. Oliver, grocer; Andrew Easton, bookseller; Alexander Jeffrey, solicitor.

Clerk—James Sloan.   Convener—Bailie Elliot

Number of Poor on Roll, . Rate of Assessment—A somewhat intricate method of assessment is followed in this parish, but the usual half, amounting to 5½d. per £. is charged against the proprietors at an average rate throughout the assessment roll; the other half is charged against tenants and occupants, according to the following scale, which, we presume, averages 5½d. per £. on the whole—

Tenants and Occupants of Dwelling-houses, 1s. 1d. per £.
Places of Business   ..   ..   ..   8¼d. ,,
Agricultural subjects   ..   ..   ..   3¼d. ,,

For some years the assessment was rated by the income, but it was found not to work smoothly.

Total Assessment, 1863-4, £1300.

The Board retains the management of Edgerston poor.

---

* Total number of children in the civil parish, between the ages of 5 and 15, attending school during the first week of April 1861, 852; of all ages, 1029.

UNION POORHOUSE.

The Poorhouse was erected in 1851 by the Parochial Board of Jedburgh, and has since been formed into a Union Poorhouse for the Parishes of Ancrum, Bedrule, Castleton, Crailing, Jedburgh, Oxnam, and Southdean. It is fitted up to hold at least 72 inmates.

COMMITTEE OF MANAGEMENT.

Chairman—J. S. E. Fair of Langlee.   Vice-Chairman—Provost Deans.

And. Scott, factor, Glendouglas.	Robert Young, shoemaker.
Wm. E. Otto, factor Jerdonfield.	A. O. Turnbull, solicitor.
W. T. Ormiston of Glenburnhall	Rev. John Purves, Jedburgh.
A. W. Mein of Hunthill.	William Millar, solicitor.
William Elliot, solicitor.	Rev. William Burnie, Oxnam.
John Paton of Crailing.	

Secretary and Treasurer—William Millar, solicitor.

Governor—John M'Robbie.   Matron—Mrs M'Robbie.

Medical Officer—Dr Falla.   Chaplain—Rev. W. Scott.

Average No. of Inmates, 45.

CASTLEWOOD CEMETERY GROUND.

(Parochial, not subject to the Act.)

Purchased in 1854, by the Heritors of the Parish of Jedburgh, Landward and Burghal. It is under the charge of the following Committee :—

J. S. E. Fair of Langlee ; W. T. Ormiston of Glenburnhall ; Andrew Scott, Glendouglas ; William Millar, solicitor ; Provost Deans.

Secretary and Treasurer—William Millar, solicitor.

Price of Layer in the reserved ground, 10s, ; common ground, 2s. 6d.

DISPENSARY (estab. 1807).

President and Patron—The Most Noble the Marquis of Lothian.

VICE-PRESIDENTS.

His Grace the Duke of Buccleuch ; the Right Honourable the Earl of Minto ; Sir William Scott of Ancrum, Bart., M.P. ; William Oliver Rutherfurd, Esq. of Edgerston.

COMMITTEE OF MANAGEMENT.

W. O. Rutherfurd of Edgerston.	Andrew Scott, Glendouglas, factor to the Earl of Home.
William E. Otto, Jerdonfield.	
J. Shortreed E. Fair of Langlee.	G. Rutherford, sheriff-clerk.
Rev. George Ritchie, Jedburgh.	Archd. Jerdon, Jedfoot House.
James Stevenson, solicitor.	James Cumming, banker.

Treasurer and Secretary—A. O. Turnbull, solicitor.

Medical Officer—James Falla, surgeon.

Average number of patients treated at the Dispensary, 120; at their homes, 240.

Accumulated funds, £350 and the Dispensary property.

CHARITABLE BEQUEST

Mortification of Two Hundred Pounds Scots, founded by Dame Margaret Kerr, Lady Yester, and others, so far back as the 17th century, for the use and behoof of the Schoolmaster of Jedburgh and his successors, "for learning and instructing of 12 bairns of such persons as were not able to pay for their bairns' learning within the burgh of Jedburgh ; and for helping to sustain the poor within the said burgh." The administration of this fund is claimed by the session of the Parish Church of Jedburgh.

JEDBURGH SOUP KITCHEN.

President—William Deans, Esq., Provost.

Lady Patronesses—The Most Noble Cecil Marchioness of Lothian, and Lady Scott of Ancrum.

Secretary—George Hilson, jun.   Treasurer—J. R. Stewart.

Average Annual Income, £27, 10s.

MUTUAL BENEFIT SOCIETIES.

FIRST YEARLY—Walter Clark, Secretary and Treasurer. Average number of members, 220.

THIRD YEARLY—R. O. Edmonstone, Secretary and Treasurer. Average number of members, 70.

These societies are the same in principle as those of Kelso and Melrose (see pp. 86, 135), but differ in the details of payments. Thus, the Jedburgh members pay from 6d. to 2s. per week to the general funds, and the usual 2d. per week for sick and funeral money ; while the payments to members on the sick list are, 6s. per week for the first six weeks, followed by 3s. per week to the end of the society's financial year. For funerals at the death of a member the definite sum of £2 is paid, and £1 on the death of a member's wife, but no payments are made in the event of a member's child dying. When money is advanced to members from the society's general fund, 1d. per £. per month is the rate of interest charged.

ST. JOHN'S LODGE OF FREEMASONS, No. 104 (estab. 1767).

R. W. Master—Robert Simpson.

Past-Master—George Mearns, Lisburn, Ireland.

Secretary—W. E. Cheese.   Treasurer—Robert Lauder.

TOTAL ABSTINENCE SOCIETY (estab. 1848).

President—Rev. John Polson.

Vice-Presidents—Rev. George Peel ; Thomas Oliver, clothier.

Secretary—Sam. Crosbie.   Treasurer—R. Young, leather merchant.

MUSEUM (Instituted March 1857).

President—The Most Noble the Marquis of Lothian.
Vice-Presidents—Sir Wm. Scott of Ancrum, Bart. ; William O. Rutherfurd of Edgerston.

COUNCIL.

The Sheriff-Sub. of the County.	Jas. James, Esq. of Samieston.
The Provost of Jedburgh.	Andw. Scott, Esq., Glendouglas.
Hon. H. Campbell.	William Oliver, Esq. of Langraw.
John Ord, Esq. of Muirhouselaw.	Rev. T. S. Anderson, Crailing.
A. Jerdon, Esq., Jedfoot House.	Mr. John R. Stewart, draper
G. Rutherford, Esq., Sheriff-Clerk.	

Treasurer—Charles Anderson, banker.
Secretary—John S. Turnbull, banker.
Curator—Adam Matthewson, 50 High Street.

Open gratuitously on Tuesdays and Saturdays.

LIBRARIES.

Blackfriars United Presbyterian Church Library, established 1832.
Contains 2500 vols. Annual subscription 2s. for seat-holders, 3s.
for others. T. Telfer, Boundaries, Librarian.

T. Smail's Select Library, established 1853. Contains 1500 vols of
modern literature. Annual subscription, 21s. ; Second Class,
7s. 6d. ; Magazine Club, 7s. 6d.

Mechanics' Library, established 1841. Annual subscription, 3s. ;
Apprentices, 2s. Thomas Grieve, Librarian. (See Mechanics'
Institute.)

London Library Company (limited).—Agents—A. & W. Easton.

NEW READING ROOM (Instituted 1864).

President—George Rutherford, Esq.
Vice-Presidents—A. C. Mounsey, rector ; J. Fiddes, cabinet maker.
Secy.—Jas. Lawrie, clerk. Treas.—J. R. Stewart, draper.
Annual subscription, 10s., 4s., and 2s.—at the option of subscribers.

MECHANICS' INSTITUTE.

Established in 1841 for the instruction of the Members in literature,
science, and general useful knowledge, the rational amusement of
the members, and the cultivation of their tastes. The Library, which
is an excellent one, has recently been re-arranged. The payment of
2s. by apprentices, and 3s. by others, constitutes membership.

President—John Hilson, manufacturer
Vice-Presidents—James Boyd and John R. Stewart.
Auditors—Walter Clark and John D. Story.
Secretary—John Lee, burgh procurator fiscal.
Librarian and Treasurer—Thomas Grieve.

YOUNG MENS' MUTUAL IMPROVEMENT SOCIETY (Inst. 1861).

Meets every Tuesday evening at 8-30 in the Sessional School.
Objects much the same as the Kelso Society—see p. 88.

President—Jas. Manson. Vice-President—Wm. H. Elliot.
Secy. and Treas.—Mr. T. Hastie. Journalist—Robert Gentles.

In connection with this Society, an interesting Annual Meeting
takes place generally in November, in the Corn Exchange ; intended
as a wind-up of its season's proceedings, and as a preliminary to the
excellent annual Course of Lectures, to which the public are admitted.

UNITED ROXBURGHSHIRE AND JEDBURGH AMATEUR HORTICULTURAL SOCIETY (estab. 1815).

Marquis of Lothian, Patron.
Provost William Deans, President and Treasurer.
George Maclean and James Scott, Secretaries.

Exhibitions (in the Corn Exchange) take place in May, July,
September, and November. Average annual amount of prizes, £40.
This society was the first in this district to give prizes for bouquets
of *native* wild flowers.

AGRICULTURAL SOCIETY (estab. 1862).

President—Marquis of Lothian.
Vice-Presidents—The Earl of Minto ; Sir William Scott of Ancrum,
Bart., M.P. ; Walter Elliot, Esq., of Wolfelee.
Secretary—James Stedman. Treasurer—James Cumming.

The third exhibition of this Society took place on Tuesday the 6th
September 1864, in a field near the railway station, granted for the
occasion by Mr. Stedman, when prizes for the usual classes of stock
were given. One peculiarity of this show is the prizes it gives for
shepherd's stock and cottager's pigs.[*]

BORDER COUNTIES' SOCIETY FOR IMPROVEMENT OF DOMESTIC POULTRY, PIGEONS AND CANARIES.

Chairman—W. T. Ormiston, Esq , of Glenburnhall.
Patron—His Grace the Duke of Buccleuch.

COMMITTEE.

J. S. E. Fair of Gilliestongues	William Veitch, millwright.
Samuel Swan, farmer, Bush.	John Thomson, cabinet maker
J. R. Stewart, draper.	T. E. Boog, farmer, Lanton

Secretary—J. Craw, merchant. Treasurer—J. U. Somner, brewer.
Auditor—George Rutherford, The Scaurs.

The Annual Exhibition takes place on the third Wednesday and
Thursday of January, when the average amount of prizes given

---

[*] See foot-note, *Hawick Farmer's Club*, **n** the Hawick lists.

amounts to nearly £100 for Poultry, £10 for Pigeons, and £7 for Canaries.

This is the most important Poultry Show in Scotland, and attracts specimens for competition from the most celebrated exhibitors and breeders in the kingdom.

CORN EXCHANGE COMPANY—(Limited).

Established 1860.

Directors.

John Ord of Muirhouselaw, Chairman.	A. W. Mein of Hunthill.
John Usher Somner, brewer, Jedburgh.	George Simson, Bedrule.
	William Deans, Provost, Jedburgh.
William Riddell, Hundalee.	

Secretary—A. O. Turnbull.   Custodier—John Rutherford.

Rates for Sales of Furniture or Goods by Auction.

Not exceeding £25	..	..	..	0	10	6
Exceeding £25 but not exceeding £50				1	1	0
..	50	..	..	75	1 11	6
..	75	..	..	100	2 2	0
..	100	..	..	200	2 12	6
..	200	..	..		3 3	0

Rent of Stalls (13 of which are let), 5s. per annum.

Use of the Exchange for Concerts, £2, 2s. for the first night, and £1, 1s. for every other, or £3, 3s. for a morning and evening concert ; for Balls, £2, 2s. ; for Sales of heritable properties by auction, 5s. ; for Public Meetings where any company or individual interest is involved, £2, 2s. ; where no pecuniary interest is involved, 10s. ; Use of the Small Hall for Meetings, 5s. ; besides fire and gas.

The amount of corn business done in Jedburgh Exchange is small. The building is of most importance as a place for meetings, exhibitions, and concerts—see p. 248.

Amount of Stock, £2500.

GAS COMPANY (estab. 1834).

Chairman—Provost William Deans.

Directors.

James Stevenson, solicitor.	William Brown, grocer.
A. W. Mein of Hunthill.	James Thomson, cabinet maker.
William Millar, solicitor.	Charles Anderson , solicitor.
Andrew Easton, bookseller.	William Elliot, saddler.

Charles Anderson, Secretary.   William Millar, Treasurer.

Manager—John Alston.

Price 7s. per 1000 feet.   Amount of Stock, £1500.   Pays 10 per cent

WATER COMPANY (estab. 1845).

Directors.

George Hilson, jun., solicitor.	Alexander Rutherfurd, saddler.
Geo. Chisholm, manufacturer.	William Brown, merchant.
Andrew Easton, bookseller.	Archibald Hobkirk, grocer.
William Millar, solicitor.	James Stevenson, solicitor.
George Balfour, merchant.	Jas. Thomson, cabinet maker.
John Sinton, cooper.	

George Hilson, jun., solicitor, Secretary and Treasurer.
William Veitch, millwright, Master of Works.

Amount of Stock, £1000 (nominal).   Pays 4 per cent.

MUTUAL PLATE GLASS SOCIETY.

Originated in 1857, on the same principles as the Kelso Society (see p. 92).

President—Thomas Smail, bookseller.
Secretary and Treasurer—Robert Lauder.

Entry Money—A deposit of 4 per cent. on the value of his glass is taken from each member as security and returned when he leaves.

JED FOREST COURSING CLUB.

President—Lord Binning.
Judge—Mr. M. Charlton, jun., Brundenlaws.
Hon. Secretary—Thomas Elliot, Esq., Hindhope.
Corresponding Secy. and Treas.—J. S. Turnbull, banker, Jedburgh.

BOWLING CLUB (estab. 1860).

Patron—The Marquis of Lothian.   Vice-Patron—Sir W. Scott, Bart.
President—William Veitch, millwright.
Vice President—Archibald C. Mounsey, Rector of Grammar School.
Secretary—Adam Turnbull, solicitor.
Treasurer—John S. Turnbull, banker.
And Eight Directors.

Entry Money, £1.   Ordinary Subscription, 10s. ; Subscription of yearly members, 15s. ; Subscription of members residing two miles from the Green, 5s.

CURLING CLUB.

Sir William Scott, Bart. of Ancrum, M.P., Patron.
W. T. Ormiston, President.   Dr Falla, Vice-President.
J. U. Somner and James Brown, joiner, Castlegate, Representative Members.
Adam Turnbull, Treasurer.   James Brown, Secretary.

Entry Money, 5s.   Annual Subscription, 5s.

The Pond is on the Lanton road, behind Tudhope plantations, on the property of the Marquis of Lothian.

JED FOREST ANGLING ASSOCIATION.

Treasurer—James Cumming, B. L. Coy.'s Bank.

JED FOREST CRICKET CLUB (estab. 1863).

Captain—John Turnbull, tailor. Lieutenant—Walter Easton. Treasurer—James Brown, clerk. Secretary—William Oliver, clerk. Auditor—William Shiel, accountant.

JED-FOREST INSTRUMENTAL BAND.

Head-Quarters—Nag's Head.

President—Bailie Elliot. Vice-Pres.'and Conductor—G. Maclean. Honorary Secretary—John R. Stewart.

1ST ROXBURGHSHIRE RIFLE CORPS.

Head-Quarters—Dean's Close, Canongate. Captain—Willam Scott, yr. of Ancrum. Lieutenant—J. S. E. Fair, Gilliestongues. Ensign—John Turnbull, The Brae. Secretary and Treasurer—William Millar, Solicitor. Drill Instructor—Myles Bamford. Bandmaster—George Maclean. Honorary Members 36. Enrolled Strength 107.

BANK BRANCHES.

BANK OF SCOTLAND (established 1864)—A. O. & A. Turnbull, Agents ; George Crabb, teller.

ROYAL BANK OF SCOTLAND (established 1857)—Charles Anderson, Agent ; Thomas Douglas, Accountant.

BRITISH LINEN COMPANY (established   )—James Cumming, Agent ; Archibald M. Yair, Accountant.

NATIONAL BANK OF SCOTLAND (established 1825)—George Rutherford, Agent ; William Mason, Assistant Agent.

CITY OF GLASGOW BANK (established 1855)—George Hilson, jun., Agent ; Thos. Hastie, Accountant.

LONDON AND SCOTTISH BANK—Limited—(opened 1864)—John S. Turnbull, Agent ; William Shiells, Accountant.

NATIONAL SECURITY SAVINGS' BANK*—William Scott, Actuary ; James

* Originally established in 1815 as a District Savings' Bank—the first of the kind in the south of Scotland. In 1836 it was handed over, with the concurrence of the depositors, to the Commissioners for the Reduction of the National Debt, and established as a National Securities Savings' Bank. Its accumulated deposits far exceed any other Bank of the kind in the district.

Cumming, Treasurer ; A. O. Turnbull, Secretary ; Adam Turnbull, Auditor ; Henry Thomson, paid official ; Amount of Deposits, Nov. 1863, £41,477 : 13 : 8. Depositors, 1453. Interest allowed, £2 : 18 : 6 per cent. per annum.

INSURANCE AGENTS.

ACCIDENTAL DEATH	George Hilson, solicitor.
	Samuel Crosbie, 30 High Street.
ALLIANCE	James Stedman, solicitor.
ARGUS	James Stevenson, solicitor.
CALEDONIAN	A. O. Turnbull, solicitor.
	W. Millar, solicitor.
CITY OF GLASGOW	W. Clark, Inland Revenue Office.
COMMERCIAL UNION	John S. Turnbull, banker.
EDINBURGH LIFE	W. Elliot, solicitor.
ENGLISH AND SCOTTISH LIFE ASSOCIATION	James Sloan, inspector.
INSURANCE CO. OF SCOTLAND	James Stedman, solicitor.
	William Elliot, solicitor.
LIFE ASSOCIATION	William Millar, solicitor.
NATIONAL	Hislop & Oliver, drapers.
NORTH BRITISH	Charles Anderson, banker.
NORWICH UNION	James Stevenson & Son, solicitor
NORWICH AND LONDON ACCIDENT AND CASUALTY OFFICE	J. C Stevenson, solicitor.
RAILWAY PASSENGERS' ASSURANCE COMPANY	John S. Turnbull, banker.
ROYAL LIVERPOOL	George Balfour, grocer.
	Alexander Jeffrey, solicitor.
SCOTTISH EQUITABLE	James Stevenson, solicitor.
SCOTTISH FIRE INSURANCE CO.	James Sloan, inspector.
SCOTTISH PROVIDENT	George Hilson, solicitor.
SCOTTISH UNION	W. Scott, N. S. Savings Bank.
	George Rutherford, banker.
STANDARD	George Rutherford, banker.
SUN FIRE	George Hilson,, solicitor.
SCOTTISH WIDOWS' FUND	William Mason, banker.

PROCURATORS, NOTARIES PUBLIC, &c.

Anderson, Charles, N.P., office and house, 38 High Street.

Hilson, George, jun., N.P., High Street ; house, Sunnyside.

Elliot, William, 39 High Street ; house, Mount Ulston.

Jeffrey, Alexander, office and house, 24 Castlegate.

Millar, William, 24 High Street ; house, Bellevue.

Rutherford, George, N.P,, County Buildings ; house, The Scaurs.

Stedman, James, N.P., County Buildings ; house, Bankhead.

Stevenson, James, N.P., County Buildings ; house, Friar Bank.

Turnbull, Archibald O., N.P., Corn Exchange ; house, Allerton.

Stevenson, James Charles, County Buildings ; house, Friar Bank.

Turnbull, Adam, Corn Exchange ; house, 2 Canongate.

MEDICAL PRACTITIONERS.

Robert Ballantyne, M.D., Glenfriars ; James Falla, Surgeon, 4 High Street ; John Hume, Surgeon, 24 High Street ; William Jeffrey, M.D., Glenfriars ; William Logan, Surgeon, Canongate.

NEWSPAPER.

The "Teviotdale Record and Jedburgh Advertiser," price 1½d., stamped 2½d. (established 1855), published every Saturday ; Office, 18 High Street. Proprietor and Publisher, William Easton, 6 Abbey Place.

PUBLIC BATHS AND WASH-HOUSES (Old Bridewell).

These Baths were erected by the Marquis of Lothian. The Wash-Houses are much used by all classes.

RATES.

One Penny per Hour for Washing.
Cold Shower Bath, 3d. : Warm Bath, 4d.

WOOLLEN MANUFACTURERS, MILLS, &c.

Canongate Mill—Cheviot and Saxony Tweeds—George Hilson & Son.
Kenmore Lodge Dye Works—James Boyd.
Bongate Mills—Cheviot and Saxony Tweeds—John & William Hilson.
Allars Mill   do.   do.   Chisholm & Elliot.
Abbey Bridge-end do.   do.   Alexander Spence.
    Medical Inspector—William Logan, surgeon, Canongate.

Abbey Mill—Corn and Flour—†James Andison.
Bonjedward Flour Mill—*William Young.
Bongate Flour and Saw Mills—William Dodd (11 Abbey Place).

EMIGRATION AGENTS.

Andrew Easton, 18 High Street ; Thomas Smail, 16 High Street.

AUCTIONEER.

James Brown, 2 Blackhill's Close, Canongate.

PORK CURING ESTABLISHMENT, &c.

William Dodd, pork curer, 11 Abbey Place.
Canongate Skinnery—Richard Allan, farmer (of 10 Crown Lane).

CARRIERS.

ANCRUM—Alex. Greirson, daily ; and G. Black, Tuesday, Mr Noble's.

ANCRUM AND SELKIRK—J. Davidson, Tuesday and Friday, T. Young, baker, 10 High Street.

BIRKHILL, REED WATER, AND OTTERBURN—J. Herdman, Tuesdays and Fridays, Market Place.

BONCHESTER BRIDGE AND RULE WATER—Archibald Scott, Tuesday, Market Place.

CAMPTOWN, RINK, &c.—J. Herdman, Tuesdays and Fridays, Market Place.

COQUET AND REED WATER—Walter Laurie, alternate Mondays, Mr Balfour's, merchant, High Street.

HAWICK AND DENHOLM—T. Robson, Wednesday and Saturday.

HOBKIRK—William Tait, Tuesday, Mr Wallace's, 19 High Street.

HOWNAM KIRK—Adam Riddell, Tuesday, H. Oliver, Nag's Head.

KELSO—Thomas Robson, Tuesday and Friday.

LANTON—Geo. Davidson, Mondays, Wednesdays, and Fridays.

OXNAM—Jas. Bruce, Tuesday and Saturday, Mr Young's, Baker.

REED WATER—John Herbertson, Monday.

SOUTHDEAN AND CHESTERS—Thomas Douglas, Mr Brown's ; Arch. Scott, Market Place—both Monday ; Andrew Short, Mr Craw's, Tuesday.

CONVEYANCE BY RAILWAY.

By N. B. Railway to Edinburgh, Glasgow, and all parts of Scotland and England daily. Station Master—William Hartley.

Omnibuses from the Eagle and Harrow Inns attend all the trains.
Fares, 6d. and 3d.

STATUTE LABOUR ROADS OF THE DISTRICT OF JEDBURGH

Comprehending the parishes of Jedburgh, Ancrum, Minto, Bedrule Hobkirk, Southdean, Oxnam, and Crailing.

J. M'Connell, Surveyor, Penrith, Cumberland.
William Finlay, 26 Castlegate, Jedburgh, Assistant.
William Elliot, 39 High Street, Jedburgh, Clerk.

DIRECTORY.

TRADES, RESIDENTS, AND PUBLIC OFFICES.

Those marked thus (†) are Registered Voters for the Burgh, and those marked thus (*) are Registered Voters for the County.

Abbey Place

Abbey Corn Mill, †James Andison
Anderson, Mrs., Abbey Green
7 Clark, Mrs.
9 Dodds, Henry, blacksmith
11†Dodd, William, corn merchant
6 Easton, Mrs., sen.
7†Forrest & Sons, gunmakers and fishing-rod and tackle makers
3†Goudie, Thomas, watchmaker
Grammar School, Archibald C. Mounsey, rector
5 Halliburton, Mrs.
 †Hilson, John (of J. & W. H.), of Lady's Yards
 †Hilson, William (of J. & W. H.), of Abbey Grove
2 *Jedburgh Arms Inn*, Agnes Thomson
10*†Laurie, Walter, carrier
10* Laurie, James, clerk
8 Lowther, Miss
5†Lunn, John, grocer
1†Maclean, George, shoemaker
6 Scott, John, watchmaker

Abbey Bridge End

Abbey and Parish Church (Rev. George Ritchie's, *see* p. 252)
5†Adams, George, joiner
4†Elliot, Thomas (of Chisholm & E., manufacturers)
 Lowe, John, traveller to John & William Hilson
8†Mounsey, Archibald C., *Rector of Grammar School*
10†Spence, Alexander, manufacturer

Abbey Close

12†Fyfe, George (of " The Nest ")
 Millar, Miss (of " The Nest ")
13 Ritchie, Rev. George, *The Manse*
 The Nest Academy—Mr. Fyfe and Miss Millar.
 Young, Miss, dressmaker

Bridge Street

Gas-Works, John Alston, resident manager
5†Hope, Robert, corn dealer
4†Simson, Robert, mason
6†Turnbull, John, grocer

Burnwynd

Bank of Scotland, A. O. & A. Turnbull, agents.
15†Burns, John, coal merchant
8 *Cannon Inn*, †Robert Jack
21†Charters, George, plumber and slater
23 Cheese, William E., officer of Inland Revenue
7-9 *Corn Exchange*, J. A. Rutherford, custodier
12 Laidlaw, John, mason
11 *London and Scottish Bank*, *†John S., Turnbull, resident agent
4†Miller, Jasper, confectioner
 Museum, Adam Matthewson, conservator
1 Stewart, J. R., & Co., drapers
   He d-shopman—John Borthwick
1†Stewart, John R. (of J. R. S. & Co.)
10 Turnbull, A. O. & A., solicitors, writing chambers (*see* Allerton and 2 Canongate)
   Head-Clerk—Andrew Newlands
 Turnbull, William, tailor
6†Veitch, James, baker
15 Waugh, William, slater
11†Wright, John, shoemaker

Bongate

 Alexander, George (late farmer)
Bongate Corn and Saw Mill, William Dodd
Bongate Woollen Mills, John & William Hilson
   Mill Foreman—James Herbertson
   Machineman—James Thorburn
Catholic Chapel and School
 Davidson, Jonathan, dairyman, Bankend
25†Elliot, John, grocer
10 Halliburton, Mrs.
20†Johnston, John, joiner
2†M'Kerrel, Rev. Francis
30†M'Master, James, *chief-constable*
 Oakvale Nursery
29 Oliver, Miss
1†Scott, Thomas, labourer
15†Story, Robert, surveyor

14†Tait, Andrew, gardener
21†Tait, George, joiner
 †Turnbull, James, joiner
27 Veitch, Misses

Boundaries (suburb of)—see p. 272

Castlegate

 *†Brown, William, merchant
  †Brown, James, cabinet maker, *Blackhill's Close*
40†Brunton, William, grocer
  Chief Constable's Office, James M'Master, chief constable
  Alexander Porter, superintendent
  County Buildings
48†Craw, John (of 10 Market Place)
37†Currie, Thomas, labourer
  Dunn, Misses, dressmakers
  †Fairbairn, John, innkeeper, *Cornelius Close*
26 Finlay, William, road surveyor
46 Gentles, Mrs.
53†Goudie, Thomas, watchmaker
65 Hamilton, Miss
  Hardie, William, hairdresser, *Cornelius Close*
£7†Harvey, James, shoemaker
23†Hobkirk, Archibald spirit dealer
36†Hollands, William, baker
22 Hush, Robert, flesher
  Jedburgh Castle, Charles Sprunt, keeper
24 Jeffrey's Alexander, writing chambers and house
31 Jones, Charles, china merchant
  Justice of Peace Clerk's Office, James Stedman
66†Lee, John, *Burgh Procurator-Fiscal*
97†Mabon, William, jun., gardener
61 Mabon, George, tailor
  Manson, James, cutter
61 Middlemas, James, basket maker
45†Muckersie, David, teacher
44†Murdie, John, farmer
15 *Nag's Head Inn*, Janet Turnbull
63 Ormiston, Mrs.
  Procurator-Fiscal's Office,†James Stevenson
34 Robertson, George, *sheriff-officer*
71†Robson, William, shoemaker
  Rutherford, Robert, shoemaker
10 Rutherford, Samuel, shoemaker
12 Rutherford, Walter, flesher
29-31 Rutherford, George, joiner
 5 Scott, Mrs. coffee rooms

11 Scott, James, painter
65†Scott, William (of Savings Bank)
  Sessional and Infant School
  Sheriff Clerk's Office, George Rutherford (house, the Scaurs)
  Smith, A. & R., plasterers, *Blackhill's Close* (house, Paradise Cottage)
  Stevenson, James, solicitor, writing chambers (house, Friar Bank)
  Stevenson, James C., solicitor, writing chambers (house Friar Bank)
12 Thomson, Mrs.
55 Thomson, Miss, of Glenbank
 1 *Town-Clerk's Office*, James Stedman (House, Bankhead
33†Turnbull, William, cabinetmaker
90 Turnbull, John
38 Turnbull, Mrs. (late of Harden)
26†Watson, James, grocer
 7†Weatherstone, John, baker
35 Webb, John, shoemaker
19†Wight, Thomas, baker
  Vanhegan, Misses, staymakers
  †Veitch, William, millwright, Paradise Vale
45 Young, Mrs.

Canongate

39†Aitken, Andrew, shoemaker
  Allan, Richard, wool merchant (farmer, Howden)
16†Baird, Alexander, tailor and clothier
11†Beattie, George, draper
  Head-shopman— Francis Dickson
13†Black, John & †Thomas, nurserymen
  Black Bull Inn, †James Minto
26†Boyd, John, candle maker
 1 Brown, Margaret, china merchant
  Servant's Register
57 Brown, Mrs.
  Canongate Woollen Mill, George Hilson & Son
 6 Dick, Mrs., grocer
 8 Edmonstone, Robert, tailor
28†Fiddes, William, baker
36 Halliburton, Graham, watchmaker
21-23 *Harrow Inn*, Mrs. A. Horsburgh
25 Henderson, Adam, shoemaker
55†Hilson, George, sen. (of G. H. & Son)
55†Hilson, John G. (of G. H. & Son)
 4†Hope, Adam, ironmonger and ironfounder
 7 Horsburgh, Miss, grocer
  Horsburgh's Hotel, Mrs. Horsburgh

20 Johnston, E., repository
65 Kennedy, Miss, *Boarding Establishment*
27†Laidlaw, Walter, spirit dealer
53†Little, James, mason
38 Logan, William, surgeon, Canongate House
10 Minto, James, grocer
30†Murray, William, brewer
12 Noble, Robert, grocer
    Public Reading Room
42 Robertson, Miss
14†Rutherford, Walter, watchmaker
57 Scott, Mrs., grocer
30†Scott, George, commercial traveller (of G. Hilson & Son)
 2 Turnbull, Adam, writer
53 Turnbull, Mrs.
19†Young, William, baker

Crown Lane

10 Allan, Misses (Howden)
10 Charlton, Misses (Brundenlaws)
11†Waldie, Edward, v. surgeon

Duck Row

2 Elliot, Mrs.
5†Rennilson, Robert, grocer

Friargate

10†Ballantyne, Robert, M.D., Glenfriars Villa
6†Barr, Rev. William (*High Street U. P. Manse*), Friars Vale
    Congregational Church (Rev. George Peel's, *see* p. 253)
7 Guthrie, Mrs., Friars Cottage
  †Guthrie, Alexander (of G. & Sons)
  †Guthrie, James G.   (do.)
  Hume, Mrs., sen. (late of Yetholm), *Friars Lane*
  †Moir, Rev. John, The Parsonage (*see* foot-note, p. 272)
4 Nicol, Mrs.
5 Robson, Miss, Friars Mount
  Scott, Walter, teacher, St. Johns' School
2†Stevenson, James, *Procurator-Fiscal*, Friar Bank
  Stevenson, James C., solicitor
8†Story, Robert, sen., gardener

High Street

38†Anderson, Charles, solicitor, writing chambers
51†Balfour, Alexander, baker
15†Balfour, George, tea, wine, and spirit merchant

30†Bell, William, druggist and photographer
30 Bennett, Mrs.
42 *Blackfriars U. P. Church* (Rev. J. Polson's, *see* p. 253)
40 *British Linen Company's Bank*, †James Cumming, resident
    agent
 1 *City of Glasgow Bank*, George Hilson, jun., agent
71†Clark, Walter, accountant
 3†Davidson, John, flesher
  Donaldson, Peter, blacksmith
18 Easton, A. & W., booksellers, &c.
18†Easton, Andrew (of A. & W. E.)
21†Elliot, William, saddler
39 Elliot's, William, writing chambers (house, Mount Ulston)
    Head-Clerk—James Laurie
 4†Falla, James, surgeon
13†Fergrieve, William, ironmonger
    Friars Burn Brewery, †John U. Somner
    Foreman Maltster—Walter Swanston
29-31 Guthrie & Sons, curriers (house, Friars Cottage)
 9 Halliburton, Thomas C., grocer
28†Harkness, John, cabinet maker and upholsterer
41†Henderson, Robert, shoemaker
41 Hewat, Henry, messenger-at-arms
    High Street U. P. Church (Rev. W. Barr's, see p. 253)
 3 Hilson, George, solicitor, writing chambers (house, Sunny-
    side)
 8 Hislop & Oliver, drapers and clothiers
    Head-Shopman—W. H. Elliot
    Cutter—   Johnstone
24 Hume, Dr.
27 *Inland Revenue Office* (Stamps and Taxes), Archibald Jer-
    don, distributor and collector (house, Jedfoot House)
 6 Irving, Mrs., tobacconist
37 Jackson, Miss
 4 *Jedburgh Dispensary*, J. F. Peters, manager
57†Johnston, William, smith
22 Lauder, Elizabeth, milliner
    Agent for Littlejohn's confectionery
22†Lauder, Robert
50†Matthewson, Adam, *Curator of Museum*
24½Millar, William, solicitor, writing chambers (house, Bellevue)
    Head-Clerk—William Oliver
26 *National Bank of Scotland*, William Mason, resident agent
27 *National Security Savings' Bank*, William Scott, actuary
32 Neil, James, gardener
27 *Office of Collector of Poor's Rate*, William Scott, collector
 5†Oliver, Robert, grocer
12†Oliver, J. & †T., clothiers

8†Oliver, William (of Hislop & O.)
  †Peters, Alexander (of J. R. Stewart & Co.), 3 *Smith's Wynd*
42†Polson, Rev. John, *First U.P. Manse*
18 *Post Office*, †Andrew Easton, postmaster
49 Purves, Agnes, plumber
52 *Railway Tavern*, T. Oliver
28 *Royal Bank of Scotland*, Charles Anderson, resident agent
14†Rule, Walter, watchmaker
17†Rutherfurd, Alexander, saddler
11†Scott, William, flesher
  Scott, J. & T., gardeners and game-dealers
33†Sinton, John, cooper
33 Sloan, James, *Inspector of Poor*
16†Smail, Thos., bookseller, stationer, bookbinder, librarian, &c.
  Smith, Jane, grocer
20 *Spread Eagle Hotel*, †Adam Scott
18 *Teviotdale Record Office*, W. Easton, proprietor
34†Thomson, John, cabinetmaker
36†Thomson, James, cabinetmaker
45 Thomson, Mrs., milliner
2†Turnbull, John, draper and clothier (house, The Brae)
    Head-Shopman—Robert Grieve
    Cutter—James Manson
    Millinery Department—Miss Hunter
18 *U. K. Electric Telegraph Office*, A. & W. Easton, agents
19†Wallace, John, baker
46†Wark, Adam, grocer
31†Wight, Andrew, flesher
27 Wilson, Miss
55†Wright, James, painter
23†Wood, Alexander, shoemaker
7†Young, Robert, shoemaker and wool-dealer
10†Young, Thomas, baker

Market Place

8 Cowan, Mrs.
10†Craw, John, tea, wine, and spirit merchant (house, 48 Castlegate)
    Head-Shopman—William Murdoch
12†*Deans, William, seedsman. Nurseries—Oakvale and Hillside, Bongate (house, Anna Cottage)
    Nursery Manager—Benjamin M'Garrie
    Book-Keeper—James Gray
8†Elliot, William, gunsmith, and fishing-rod and tackle maker
5†Knox, Archibald, china merchant
7†Rawdin, Joseph, chemist
1†Robertson, James ironmonger
6†Robson, James & Sons, shoemakers

9 Storrie, R., & Son, grocers (*see* farmers)
9†Storrie, John D. (of R. S. & Sons)

Pleasants

Gas-Works—John Alston, manager
†*Deans, William, S.S. (of 12 Market Place), Anna House
Episcopal Chapel, (Rev. J. Moir's—*see* foot-note)‡.
Episcopal School
†Robson, Thomas, Hawick and Kelso Carrie
  Rutherfurd, Miss

Queen Street

3 Armstrong, Miss (*Queen Mary's House—see* p. 247)
6†Barton, James, roper
15 Caverhill, Mrs.
16 Henderson, Robert, shoemaker
8†Learmond, Adam, gardener
†Spence, Peter, roadman

Richmond Row

  Laidlaw, John, coal agent
  Nicol, Miss Ann

Suburb of Boundaries [or Bourtrees]

  Bell, Mrs. Dr., Boundary Bank
†Boyd, James, dyer, Kenmuir Lodge
5 Cranston, Mrs.
  Free Church (Rev. John Purves', *see* p. 252)
3†Herbertson, Andrew, mason
†Huggan, William, millwright, Allerly Brae
1 vine, Misses, Allerly Brae
†Paterson, Peter, smith, Old Bridge End
†Purves, Rev. John, *Free Church Manse*
  Registrar's Office, Thomas Grieve
  Thomson, Mrs., Kenmuirbank
  Thorburn, Mrs., Allerly Brae

---

‡ The following information, in connection with St. John's Church was received after the Lists at p. 252 had been printed off :—

Sittings, 200 ; attendance at Sabbath School, 40, under the superintendance of Rev. John Moir ; Organist—Walter Scott, teacher ; Managers—Mr. Gordon, Mr. J. C. Stevenson, and Rev, J. Moir ; Treasurer—J. C. Stevenson ; Church Officer—Walter Hall, Queen Street.

Turnbull, Miss, Boundary Place
†Turnbull, John (of 2 High Street), The Brae
Turnbull, A. O., solicitor, Allerton
Wood, John, thatcher, Old Bridge-end
Young, Andrew, 3 Old Bridge-end

Railway Station

(Beyond Bongate Bridge—over half a mile from the Market Place—
a good fifteen minutes' walk ; road level and good.)

Resident Station-Master, Manager of Goods' Department, and
N. B. Railway Company's Coal Agent—William Hartley

OFFICES AND DEPOTS.

Burns, John, coal, lime, and tile agent, and contractor for de-
livery of railway goods in Jedburgh
Johnston & Co. (Berwick-on-Tweed), of Scremerston and
Shoreswood collieries, and lime and manur eagents—Thomas
Wylie, agent
Laidlaw, John, coal agent
Turnbull, J. S , agent for the Marquis of Lothian's coal, lime,
tiles, &c.

Village of Lanton

(2¼ miles from Jedburgh by a very hilly road, 4 miles from Ancrum,
and 5 miles from Denholm.)

SCHOOL (Parochial, Side)—Thomas Scott,‡ schoolmaster. Average
attendance, 50.

*Bell, David, wright
*Bell, John, joiner
Boog, T. E , farmer
Davidson, George, grocer
*Davidson, John, portioner
Furness, Robert, joiner
*Hall, John, portioner
Huggan, William, grocer
*Storrie, George, smith
*Storrie, William, agricultural implement maker
*Scott, Adam, portioner
*Scott, James, do.
Smail, Thomas, grocer
*Turnbull, William, farmer, Lanton Mill
Veitch, Miss

---

‡ Mr. Scott is Inspector of Poor, Collector of Poor Rates, and
Heritors' Clerk, for Bedrule parish, and Collector of Minister's Stipend
for Jedburgh parish.

Hamlet of Bonjedward

(2 miles from Jedburgh on the Kelso turnpike road.)
Brown, George, joiner
Borthwick, David, station-master at Jedfoot
Dodds, John, smith
Douglas, William, carter
Flour Mill, *William Young

COUNTRY RESIDENTS, FARMERS, &c.

Parish of Jedburgh—larger portion

*Allan, Richard, farmer and wool merchant, Howdean
Allars Factory (opposite Inchbonny)
*Black, William, of Netherwells
†Chisholm, George (of C. & Elliot), Allars
*Dodds, Andrew, farmer, Hardenpeel
*Dodd, James,   do.,   Mossburnford
†Elliot, William (solicitor, Jedburgh), Mount Ulston
*Fair, James A., yr. of Gilliestongues
†Gladstone, James, farmer, Rennieston.
*Haldane, William,   do.,   Roundhaugh
*Handyside, John B., do.,   Fernieherst
*Herbertson, Thomas, do,, Hundalee Braehead
*Herriot, William,   do., Easter Ulston
*†Hilson, George, jun. (banker, Jedburgh), of Sunnyside
*Hope, Andrew,   do , New Mill
†Hume, William, steward, Harestanes
†Hunter, Robert, farmer, Hindhousefield
*Johnston John,   do.,   Crailinghall
*Lockie, Jas., sen., do.,   Camphouse
*Mein, Alexander, do.,   Tudhope
†Middlemas, George, Inchbonny
*†Millar, William (solicitor, Jedburgh), Bellevue
*†Millar, Robert, farmer, Todlaw
*Rathie, Walter, do ,   Thickside
†*Riddell, William, do., Hundalee
*Richardson, John, do.,   Lanton Craig
*Richardson, Geo , do.,   Upper Samieston
*Rutherford, Robert, of Pleasance
*Rutherford, Wm.. farmer, Fernieherst Mill
*Scott, John (of Upper Samieston), Dolphinston
*Scott, John, farmer, Ancrum Howden
*Scott, William, do., Timpendean
*Sinton, Willm., do., Monklaw
*Story, Robert, do., (of R S. & Sons, grocers, Jedburgh)
   farmer, Netherwells
*Stedman, Js. (town-clerk, Jedburgh), Bankhead, Sharplaw

T

*Story, John D. (of R. S. & Sons)—*see* 9 Market Place
*Story, Thomas, Lanton Hill
†Turnbull, A. Oliver (solicitor, Jedburgh), Allerton
†Veitch, William, millwright, Inchbonny
*Wyllie, Thomas, farmer, Lochend
*Young, John,   do.,   Woodend
    Young, Walter, blacksmith, Mossburnford

SEATS OF COUNTY FAMILIES AND SMALLER RESIDENCES IN LARGER PORTION OF PARISH.

BONJEDWARD HOUSE.

(Formerly the property of the late Archibald Jerdon, Esq.) on the Kelso road, near the northern extremity of the parish—the dowery house of the Dowager Marchioness of Lothian ;‡ at present unoccupied.

GILLIESTONGUES.

Situated about 2 miles south from Jedburgh, on the Blackburn (*see* p. 248)—the property and residence of *†Jas. Shortreed E. Fair, Esq.

GLENBURN HALL.

In the immediate neighbourhood of Jedburgh—the property and residence of †*William T. Ormiston, Esq.

HUNDALEE COTTAGE.

On the high banks of the Jed, about 2 miles above Jedburgh—the residence of Mrs Kerr (widow of the late Charles Kerr, Esq., Merchant, London).

HUNTHILL.

Situated about 2 miles to the south-east of Jedburgh—the residence of Mrs. Mein (widow of the late James Mein, Esq.) and family, and Andrew Whitelock Mein, Esq., joint-proprietors of the estate.

JEDBANK.

Situated on the high ground beyond the Episcopal Church—the property of John M. Craigie, Esq., formerly Sheriff-Substitute for the county, and now occupied by Francis Russell, Esq., the present Sheriff-Substitute for the county ; appointed 1861.

‡ Lady Cecil Chetwynd Talbot, only daughter of Earl Talbot ; married, 19th July 1831, John-William-Robert, 7th Marquis of Lothian, who died 14th November 1841.—*See* Crailing parish, p. 221.

HARTRIGGE.

The property of Lord Stratheden and Campbell,‡ occupied by Thomas Gordon, Esq. (formerly of India).

JEDFOOT HOUSE.

Situated on the Jed, near to Jedfoot station—the property of the Marquis of Lothian, and the residence of Archibald Jerdon, Esq. (son of the late Archibald Jerdon, Esq., of Bonjedward), Distributor of Stamps and Collector of Taxes for the county.

JERDONFIELD.

Near Jedfoot—the property of the Marquis of Lothian, and the occasional residence of Wm. E. Otto, Esq., factor to his Grace.

LANGLEE.

Situated about 3 miles south from Jedburgh, on a bank overhanging the Jed—the property of James Shortreed Elliot Fair, Esq. of Gilliestongues ; occupied by *Godfrey H. Baker, Esq.

LINTALEE.

On the Lintalee Burn (*see* p. 247), about 2 miles above Jedburgh—the property of the Countess of Home, and the residence of Mrs. Scott, widow of the late Walter Scott, Esq. of Wauchope, who died in 1857 (grandfather of Mr. Walter Macmillan Scott, the present proprietor of Wauchope—*see* p. 286), and Charles Scott Esq., fourth son of Mrs. Scott and the late Walter Scott of Wauchope ; born 1819 ; married 1863, Margaret-Amelia, daughter of the late Brown Roberts, Esq.

SAMIESTON (Easter).

Situated at the source of the Cessford burn in the eastern corner of the parish—the property and residence of *James James, Esq., M.D., of Samieston and Rennieston. Mr. James purchased Samieston in 1852 from the late Robert Selby, Esq. ; married, 1856, the eldest daughter of John Edward Broadhurst, Esq., of Crow Hill, Nottinghamshire, and has issue—one son, William Lancelot, and two daughters Susan-Eleanor and Ethel-Elizabeth.

Mr. James was formerly in the F.I.C. Service.

‡ William Frederick Campbell, Baron Stratheden of Cupar, Fifeshire, Baron Campbell of St. Andrews, Fifeshire, succeeded to his mother's title of Stratheden, 25th March 1860, and his father as 2nd Lord Campbell, 23d June 1861. London Residence—Stratheden House, Knightsbridge, W. The first Lord Campbell (born 15th September 1781) was successively Solicitor-General, Attorney-General, Lord Chancellor of Ireland, Chancellor of the Duchy of Lancaster, Chief-Justice of the Queen's Bench, and Lord Chancellor of Great Britain. He was descended from a younger branch of the ducal house of Argyll.

THE SCAURS.

Situated on the Jed, a mile above Jedburgh, a recently erected villa in the Elizabethan style—the property and residence of †George Rutherford, Esq., Sheriff-Clerk of the county.

Quoad Sacra Parish of Edgerston.

PRINCIPAL LANDED-PROPRIETOR—W. O. Rutherfurd, Esq., of Edgerston

RESIDENT JUSTICES OF THE PEACE—W. O. Rutherfurd, Esq. of Edgerston ; W. A. O. Rutherfurd yr. of Edgerston.

PUBLIC OFFICES—Mostly retained by the civil parish of Jedburgh.

Kirk Treasurer, Session Clerk, and District Registrar of Births, Marriages, and Deaths—Thomas Oliver.

POST OFFICE—Messenger from Jedburgh (Anthony Temple) daily—arrives at 1.30 p.m. ; departs at 4 p.m.

CLERGY, &c.—Presbytery of Jedburgh.   Patrons—the three chief heritors in Edgerston, viz,—W. O .Rutherfurd, Esq. of Edgerston, Marquis of Lothian, and Countess of Home.

Quoad Sacra Church—*Rev. John Fergusson (Inducted 1855). Sittings, 200. Average attendance at Sabbath School, 40.

PAROCHIAL SCHOOL (Rink)—Thomas Oliver, Teacher.

SAW MILL (Edgerston)—James Hill, joiner.

Farmers, Trades, &c., in the Quoad Sacra Parish.

Amos, George, joiner, Dovesford
*Charlton, Matthew, farmer, Brundenlaws
*Davidson, John,   do.,   Arks
 Greirson, John, blacksmith, Rink
*Hall, John, farmer, Earlsheugh
 Hood, Mrs.   do., Edgerston Rig
 Pringle, James, do., Cleethaugh
*Scott, Thomas, do , Old Jedward
*Scott, Walter, do., Edgerston Tofts
 Scott, Thomas, do., Mervinslaw
 Swan, Samuel, do., Bush
 Turnbull, William, blacksmith, Dovesford
 Wheelans, A., weaver, Camptown
 Yule, John, blacksmith, Smailcleuchfoot

Family Residence.

EDGERSTON HOUSE.

Situated on the Edgerston burn, about 7 miles from Jedburgh —the property and residence of William Oliver Rutherfurd, Esq. of Dinlaybyre (in Castleton) and Edgerston, and nephew of the late John Rutherfurd, Esq., whom he succeeded and whose surname he assumed ; born 1781 ; succeeded his father in 1830, and his uncle in 1834; married, 1804, Agnes, daughter of Alexander Chatto Esq. of Mainhouse, and by her, (who died in 1859) has, with other issue—

*†William Alexander, born 1818 ; married, 1861, Margaret Jane, only daughter of the late Edward Young, Esq., and has, issue, a son—William Edward Oliver Rutherfurd, born 1863, and a daughter, Katherine Violet

Archibald John, Major, 70th Regiment; born 11th December 1820 ; married, 1860, Catherine Jane Rawlinson, and has issue, two daughters—Alice and Edith.

Mr. Oliver Rutherfurd was appointed Sheriff-Depute for Roxburghshire in 1807, and he is now the oldest sheriff on the Scottish Bench. He is a Justice of the Peace and Deputy-Lieutenant for Roxburghshire, and is Convener for the same county.

REGISTERED VOTERS FOR THE BURGH,

Living within the voting limits.

Elliot, Hon. Charles Gilbert John Brydon, Minto (Rear-Admiral, R.N., now Commander-in-Chief on S. A. station)
Ewen, Rev. John, Hobkirk
Fiddes, George, smith, Ancrum
Mack, John, mason, Denholm
Mills, George, farmer, Greenend
Pringle, Robert, Bairnkine
Rutherfurd, William A. O., of Edgerston
Scott, Sir W., Bart. of Ancrum, M.P.
Selby, Ephraim, Hassendeanbank
Stephenson, William, joiner, Cessford
Turnbull, William, groom, Minto

COUNTY VOTERS (Non-Resident).‡

Registered in Jedburgh Parish.

Dodds, Anthony, schoolmaster, Hawick
Elliot, Hon. Charles G. J. B., Rear-Admiral, S. A. station

‡ County Voters are not disqualified by any distance of residence.

Elliot, Hon. Henry George, British Minister in Italy
Elliot, Hon. Gilbert, lieut-colonel, at present stationed at Buttevant in Ireland.
Elliot, Hon., George F. Stewart, private secretary to Earl Russell, Minto House and London
Forbes, Sir John Hepburn, of Pitsligo, Bart., of Fetter-cairn House, Fettercairn
Gray, William, farmer, Sharplaw, Hounam
Jackson, John, farmer, Ewes, Langholm
Jerdan, David, bookseller, Dalkeith
Kerr, Lord H. F. C., Huntly Burn, Melrose
Kerr, Lord Charles
Kerss, Robert, gamekeeper, Mounteviot
Lang, John (of Overwells), sheriff-clerk, Selkirk
Oliver, George, writer, Hawick
Oliver, George, sen , Cross Keys, Kelso
Pringle, William, Esq., Edinburgh
Scott, Thomas Rennie, Castlemains, Lanarkshire
Talbot, Hon. G. C.
Veitch, William, 7 North-west Circus Place, Edinburgh

BEDRULE

—◆—

Is situated nearly in the centre of the county, along the banks of Rule water and the Teviot; by these streams the parish is surrounded to the extent of nearly one-half on the west and north-west. It is bounded on the north by Minto and Ancrum, on the east by Jedburgh, on the south by Hobkirk, and on the west by Hobkirk and Cavers. The length of the parish from north to south is about 4 miles, and its breadth about 2 miles. The total area of the parish, according to the Ordnance Survey, is 3952¼ acres ; of which 3875¾ are land, nearly 35 water, and 41½ public roads. In the lower grounds the land is fertile and well cultivated ; the higher consist mostly of pasture and moorland. The climate is in general dry and healthy.

The antiquities of the parish are the site of the Castle of Bedrule near the Church, formerly the residence of the Turnbulls, and the head quarters of the family, a strong border clan, famous for their predatory habits in ancient times ; and Fulton-Peel, towards the south side of Bedrule farm. The Peel is situated on a grassy slope which gently descends to the Rule, on the other side of which "dark Ruberslaw" rears its shaggy crest : the walls are still tolerably complete. The prospect of the surrounding country is very extensive, and exhibits a combination of mountain and glen scarcely to be equalled in the district. In the parish, and also worthy of notice, are the remains of a very fine avenue on the property of Mr. Robson Scott of Newton, of very old ash and elm trees, which are now carefully preserved.

The Dunion, the best known hill in the parish, situated in its eastern boundary where it joins the parish of Jedburgh, rises 1095 feet above the level of the sea. The appearance of this hill is very striking. Of a round symmetrical shape, and apparently stuck on to the end of a lofty ridge, it suggests the idea of a huge mole-hill that had been burrowed up in some early age of our world's history. When visited the hill is seen to be very rocky, the trap being covered only with a thin casting of earth, on which grows a scanty herbage. Till lately it stood in an extensive moor, but the enterprise of modern farming has now carried cultivation close up to its base on all sides. The view from its summit is one of the most magnificent in the Border counties, and will amply repay a walk from Jedburgh in the immediate proximity of which it is situated. The resting of the clouds on the Dunion and Ruberslaw in moist weather, has suggested to the inhabitants of the district the following rhyme :—

> " When Ruberslaw puts on its hat,
> And Dunion on its head,
> All the old wives of Rule water
> May expect a flood."

There are no villages in the parish. Bedrule is merely a hamlet consisting of the parish church, school house, smithy, and a farm-house, with the attached cottages. Jedburgh, which is over 3 miles distant from the hamlet, is the nearest market, and the post town. Jedfoot is the nearest railway station for the east side of the parish, and Hassendean on the Hawick line is the nearest for the west side of the parish.

Population of the parish in 1861, 222; who composed 41 families, 35 of whom were returned as living in houses of one and two windows.

Assessed property in 1864-5, £3782, 10s.

The principal landed-proprietors in the parish are—Sir William Francis A. Eliott of Stobs and Wells, Bart.; Thomas Robson Scott, Esq. of Newton ; Gideon Pott, Esq. of Knowesouth ; Thomas Cockburn, Esq., of Menslaws ; and William Oliver Rutherfurd, Esq. of Edgerston.

Those marked thus (*) are Registered Voters in the parish.

RESIDENT JUSTICES OF THE PEACE—Gideon Pott, Esq. of Knowesouth ; Thomas Robson Scott, Esq. of Newton.

DISTRICT POLICE OFFICER—John Buglass, Denholm.

POST OFFICE—Daily Runner from Jedburgh, who leaves and takes up letters throughout the parish.

PUBLIC OFFICES—Heritors' Clerk and Inspector of Poor—Thomas Scott, Lanton, Jedburgh.

　Kirk Treasurer—Rev. Archibald Craig.

　Session Clerk, Registrar of Births, Deaths, and Marriages—William M'Neill.

　Medical Officer and Public Vaccinator—William Blair, M.D., Denholm.

CLERGY, &c.—Presbytery of Jedburgh, Synod of Merse and Teviotdale. Patron—James Ross Hume (minor), of Ninewells.‡

　Established Church—*Rev. Archibald Craig (Inducted 1832). Sittings, 150.

FAST DAY—Thursday before first Sunday of July.

---

‡ Who represents a former proprietor (one of the Carres of Cavers) of Bedrule estate, but by an oversight the patronage was overlooked when the estate was sold to the Hon. William Eliott (who died in 1818, and was succeeded by the late Sir William Eliott of Stobs, in the Bedrule and Wells estates.)

SCHOOL (Parish)—*William M'Neill, master ; average attendance, 43.‡

PAROCHIAL BOARD—Gideon Pott, Esq., Chairman. No. of Poor on Roll, 6. Rate of Assessment, 2d. per £ ; total Assessment 1863, £60. Poor House, Jedburgh Union.

CONVEYANCE—North British Railway—Jedburgh Station, distant 3 miles ; Hassendean Station, distant 4 miles.

RESIDENTS, FARMERS, &c , IN THE PARISH.

　Armstrong, William, farmer, Bedrule Mill
　*Murdie, Henry,　　do , Lanton Mains
　Oliver, W., blacksmith, Bedrule
　*Simson, George, farmer, do.

SEATS, &c. OF COUNTY FAMILIES IN THE PARISH.

KNOWESOUTH.

Near the extreme north—the property and residence of *Gideon Pott, E-q., of Dod (in Teviothead parish), collector of county Rates for the county.

MENSLAWS.

On the Teviot, at the western extremity—the property and residence of *Thomas Cockburn, Esq., who purchased the property in 1860.

NEWTON.

The property and principal residence of *Thomas Robson Scott, Esq. of Newton ; succeeded to the estate in 1858, on the death of his uncle, the late John Scott Esq. of Riccalton and Ashtrees, and whose surname he assumed.

REGISTERED VOTER (Non-Resident).

Scott, William, portioner, Lanton

---

‡ Children in the parish from 5 to 15 attending school during the first week of April 1861, 41 ; of all ages, 43.

‡ James Robson Scott, Esq., Belford (Morebattle), succeeding to Ashtrees, and John Elliot Scott, Esq., Buckholm (Galashiels), succeeding to Riccalton.

HOBKIRK.

——◆——

THIS parish is bounded on the north by Bedrule and Cavers, on the east by Southdean, on the south by Castleton, and on the west by Cavers. Its length is about 11 miles, and its breadth averages 3 miles. Its area, according to the Ordnance Survey, is 16,242 acres. This is sub-divided into 16,113¾ acres of land, 49 acres under water, and 79 acres in roads. The general appearance of the parish is hilly, especially in the southern part, where Windbrugh Fell rises to a height of 1662 feet, and Fanna to a height of 1643 feet. Near the northern extremity is "dark Ruberslaw"—partly in this parish and partly in Cavers—rising to an altitude of 1392 feet. Bonchester Hill, a beautiful grassy, round-shouldered eminence, near the centre of the parish, has an altitude of 1059 feet; and near its summit are numerous remains of ancient encampments. The larger portion of the parish is pastoral, but in the valley of the Rule the soil is deep and fertile. A great extent of pasture land has lately been brought under cultivation with good results, particularly on the Wolfelee estate and on the farms of Gatehousecote and Hallrule. In all these cases the hill sides are now waving with grain, where formerly there was only rough heather or benty grass. Rule water, formed by the junction, in the parish, of the Catlee and Harrot burns, flows northward through its entire length, and some of its scenery is very beautiful. (*See* Southdean parish, p. 203).

There is no village deserving the name in the parish—the only approach to it being a very small collection of houses at BONCHESTER BRIDGE, at a distance of three-quarters of a mile from which are the church, manse, and school-house, where Thomson spent part of his early life with his friend the Rev. Robert Riccalton, then minister of the parish; and he is said to have drawn from the neighbourhood much of the scenery of his "Seasons." Foxes are plentiful in the parish, and otters are known to exist; and a heronry (the only one in the district) exists at Wells, on the property of Sir William F. A. Eliott. As a whole, the climate of the parish is damp, the heights swampy and often overhung with mists.

Hawick and Jedburgh are the nearest market towns. The nearest railway stations are—Shankend, on the Border Union line within 6 miles of Bonchester Bridge and close upon the south-western extremity of the parish, and Hassendean on the N. B. line is about 4 miles from its northern point.

Population of the parish in 1861, 771; who composed 137 families, 6 of whom were returned as living in houses of one window, and 53 in houses of two windows, leaving the high average of more than a half living in houses of three or more windows.

Assessed property in 1863-4, £9008 : 14 : 9.

The principal landed-proprietors in the parish are—Walter Elliot, Esq. of Wolfelee; the Hon. Lord Sinclair of Stonedge and Greenriver (Nisbet House, Dunse); R. K. Elliot, Esq. of Harwood; William Oliver, Esq. of Langraw; W. M. Scott, Esq. of Wauchope; Sir William F. A. Eliott of Stobs and Wells; David Henderson, Esq. Abbotrule; and Captain Cleghorn, of Weens.

————————

Those marked thus (*) are Registered Voters in the parish.

JUSTICE OF THE PEACE—Captain Cleghorn of Weens.

POLICE OFFICER—James Rankin, Forkins, by Bonchester Bridge.

PUBLIC OFFICES—Heritors'-Clerk, Registrar of Births, Marriages, and Deaths, Inspector of Poor—William Sibbald.
    Medical Officer and Public Vaccinator—Dr. M'Leod, Hawick.

POST OFFICE (at Bonchester Bridge)—Thomas Renwick, postmaster. Arrival, 1 p.m. ; Despatch, 7 a.m. Post town, Hawick. Messenger, James Watson. The post town for Wells and the northern districts of the parish is Jedburgh. Messenger—Thomas Best.

CLERGY, &c.—Presbytery of Jedburgh, Synod of Merse and Teviotdale. Patron—the Crown.
    Established Church—*Rev. John Ewen (Inducted 1834). Sittings, 360. Sabbath School attendance, 20.
    Free Church (Wolfelee)—Rev. Robert Milligan (Inducted 1863). Sittings, about 200. Average attend. at Sabbath School, 25.

FAST DAYS—Wednesdays before the longest and shortest Sundays of the year.

SCHOOL†—Parochial—*John Malcolm, master. Average attend., 85. Girls' School—Cleughhead (established under the auspices of Mrs. Elliot of Wolfelee)—Miss Gibson, teacher.

PAROCHIAL BOARD—Wm. Oliver, Esq., Chairman. Rate of Assessment, about 2¼d. per £; total Assessment 1863-4, £167 : 0 : 4. No. of Poor on Roll, 17. Poor House—Hawick Combination.

LIBRARY—William Sibbald, librarian. 1500 Vols. Annual Subscription, 3s. by members, and 4s. by occasional readers.

CARRIERS (calling at Bonchester Bridge)—Jedburgh, Tuesday, and Hawick Thursday—William Tait, Langhaughwalls; Hawick, Thursday—Archibald Scott, Chesters.

CORN MILLS—Hallrule—*William Bell. Hartshaugh—*Jas. Laidlaw.

SAW MILLS—Harwood—*James Smith, farmer, Templehall. Wells—David Davidson.

————————

† Children in the parish from 5 to 15 attending school during the first week of April 1861, 133; of all ages, 138.

TRADES, &c., IN THE PARISH.

Amos, Robert, joiner, Blackley
Bell, William, mason, Wolflee Glen
Brunton, John, do., Doveshaugh Cottage
Deans, Walter, mason and grocer, Hobkirk
Henderson, Daniel, grocer, Bonchester Bridge
Pow, William, blacksmith, Blacklee
Rutherford, Thomas, do., Bonchester Bridge
Scott, David, mason, do.
Tait, William, grocer and carrier, Langhaughwalls
Taylor, Douglas, joiner and wire-fence contractor, Bonchester Bridge

RESIDENTS, FARMERS, &c.

Armstrong, John, farmer, Westlees
*Barrie, Robert, do., Hawthornside
*Barrie, Walter, do., do.
Boog, Thomas E., do., Tythe House
Christie, William, head gardener, Wells
Dickson, Robert, farmer, Weensmoor
*Elliot, Henry, do., Greenriver
*Fairbairn, James, do., Easter Fodderlie
*Laidlaw, William, do., Bonchester
Mabon, William, do., Town o' Rule
*Mather, Daniel (of Falty Park, Ballinasloe, Ireland), farmer, Hallrule
Morrison, James, head gardener, Wauchope
Morrison, John, do., Weens
*Taylor, Walter, farmer, Howahill
*Telfer, David, do., Braidhaugh
*Thomson, Andw., do., Billerwell
*Thorburn, Geo., do., Stonedge
*Turnbull, Jas., do., Wester Fodderlie
*Turnbull, T., do., Midburn
*Usher, John, jun., do., Gatehousecote
*Wilson, James, do., Cleughhead

SEATS OF COUNTY FAMILIES IN THE PARISH.

WELLS.

Situated on the Ru'e near the northern point of the parish, in the midst of beautiful scenery and magnificent wood—the seat of Sir William Francis Augustus Eliott, Bart., of Stobs and Wells; born 1827; succeeded his father the late Sir Wm. Francis Eliott, F.R.S., in September 1864, as 8th baronet; married Charlotte Maria, daughter of Robert Wood, Esq., Canada.

Sir William, who held a commission in the 93d Highlanders, is Chief of the ancient family of Elliot, from a younger branch of which the celebrated General Elliot, the gallant defender of Gibraltar, was descended. This branch became extinct in Sir William's cousin-german the Right Hon. William Elliot, M.P., in 1818, when the late Sir William Francis Eliott succeeded to the estates of Wells and Bedrule.—*See* note, p. 281.

WEENS.

Near to Bonchester Bridge—the property and occasional residence of *George Cleghorn, Esq.; born 1831; succeeded his father, the late George Cleghorn, Esq., in 1855; married, 1862, Mary Ann Hay, third daughter of Col. Lumsden, C.B., of Belhelvie Lodge, near Aberdeen; and has issue—George Harry Lumsden, born 1863; and another son, born 1864.

Mr. Cleghorn is a captain in the Scots Greys, and formerly held a commission in the 17th Lancers.

London address—East India United Service Club, S. W.

HALLRULE.

Situated on the Rule, two miles from Bonchester—the property of Sir William F. A. Eliott, and residence of Peter Pennycook, Esq. (of Newhall, Bowden).

GREENRIVER.

Situated on the Rule near Bonchester—the property of the Right Hon. Lord Sinclair of Stonedge; occupied by *Henry Elliot, farmer.

HARWOOD.

Situated on the Harrot burn near its source—the property and occasional summer residence of Robert Kerr Elliot, Esq., of Clifton Park and Harwood (*see* Linton parish, p. 147).

LANGRAW.

Situated on the Rule above Bonchester, and near to the church—the property and residence of *William Oliver, Esq., factor for the Wolfelee estate.

WAUCHOPE.

Situated on the Wauchope burn—the property of Walter Macmillan Scott, of Wauchope, and Pinnaclehill (near Kelso) eldest son of the late Thomas Macmillan Scott; born 1848; succeeded 1862.

REGISTERED VOTER (Non-Resident).

Elliot, Robert, Esq., Wolfelee (Southdean parish)

KIRKTON.

———◆———

THE parish of Kirkton is a long narrow irregular stripe extending to about 8 miles in length from north-east to south-west, and having an average breadth of 2 miles. It is bounded in all directions, except for about 4 miles on the south-west, by the parish of Cavers, in which it is nearly embedded; Hawick and Teviothead parishes forming the remainder of its boundary Its area, according to the Ordnance Survey, is nearly 6223 acres. This is divided into 33⅓ acres in public roads, 21¼ under water, the remainder, 6168, being land, arable and pastoral. The surface of the parish is undulating, and in the south-eastern part of the parish there are some hills rising to nearly 1000 feet.

There is no village or town in the parish. The church and school are situated near the north-eastern extremity. Dr. Leyden received most of the rudiments of his education in Kirkton school. The lonely cottage at Henlawshiel, on the farm of Nether Tofts, where he spent his childhood and youth in poverty, is now extinct.

Nearest market town, Hawick, 3¼ miles distant from the church. Hawick is also the post town.

Population of the parish in 1861, 421, who composed 69 families, 50 of whom were returned as living in houses of one and two windows.

Assessed property in 1863-4, £3065 : 13 : 3.

The principal landed-proprietors in the parish are—James Douglas, Esq. of Cavers; Sir William F. A. Eliott of Stobs; Mrs. Pringle Douglas of Haining, and William R. Dickson, Esq. of Alton.

———————

Those marked thus (*) are Registered Voters in the parish.

DISTRICT POLICE OFFICER—John Buglass, Denholm.

POST OFFICE—The messenger (James Watson) from Hawick delivers letters as he passes for Hobkirk parish, &c., about 11-30 a.m., and takes up letters on his return the following morning.

PUBLIC OFFICES—Heritor-'Clerk, Session Clerk, Kirk Treasurer, and Registrar of Births, Marriages, and Deaths—Thomas Little.

CLERGY, &c.—Presbytery of Jedburgh, Synod of Merse and Teviotdale. Patron—the Crown.
Established Church—*Rev. George Hunter (Inducted 1857). Sittings, 180.

FAST DAYS—Friday before second Sabbath of April, and third Sabbath of October.

SCHOOL‡—Parochial—*Thomas Little, master ; average attend., 38.

PAROCHIAL BOARD—George Oliver, Esq., Hawick, Chairman. Average number of Poor on Roll, 8. Average rate of Assessment, 4d. per £. Total Assessment 1864, £98 : 5s. Poor House, Hawick Combination.

CONVEYANCE—Nearest Railway Stations : Hawick for the church ; Shankend, near Stobs Castle, for the southern localities. Station Master at Stobs—James Todd.

CORN MI L—New Mill—*Thomas Turnbull, farmer.

CARRIER—James Mabel, Smithfieldhaugh and by the head of North Tyne to Hawick, once a fortnight.

———————

RESIDENTS, FARMERS, &c.

*Aitchison, Alexander, farmer, Winningtonrig
*Aitchison, George,   do.   do.
Blyth, Thomas and William, farmers, Whitrigs (see Cavers)
*Bulman, Robert, farmer, Nether Tofts
*Davidson, Wm., do., Adderstone Shiels
Deans, George and Robert, farmers, Tofts
*Grierson, Thomas, farmer, Effledge
Hogg, George and Robt., farmers, Cavers Knowes (see Cavers)
*Oliver, William, farmer, Barns
Turnbull, Thomas, do. East Middle (see Cavers)
*Turnbull, Walter, do. Acreknowe
*Welsh, John,   do.   Kirkton

———————

REGISTERED VOTER (Non-Resident).

Dickson, W. R., of Alton

———————

‡ Number of children in the parish of all ages attending school during the first week of April 1861, 49.

CAVERS.

———◆———

CAVERS is a very long and irregularly shaped parish; its length being nearly 12 miles, while in some parts it is not much over 2 miles in breadth. It is bounded on the north by Minto and Bedrule, on the east by Hobkirk, on the south by Castleton, and on the west by Hawick, Wilton, Teviothead, and Kirkton parishes. The last named parish it nearly surrounds and by it it is nearly cut in two. Previous to 1850, Cavers included much more than it does at present; but in that year a large piece of it was disjoined and, along with the adjoining portion of Hawick parish, formed into the separate parish of Teviothead. The parish consists in its north part of rich arable and well cultivated lands; but in the southern part, where it marches with Castleton it is bleak and moorish. The principal hills scattered throughout the parish are—"Dark Ruberslaw," with its south side partly in the adjoining parish of Hobkirk, 1392 feet in height, Maiden's Paps 1677 feet, Penchrise 1018 feet, Brant Craig 1253 feet, Shankend 1219 feet, and Leap Hill 1544 feeet. The conical form, and the "dark" aspect of Ruberslaw, as well as its isolation, give it altogether a peculiar appearance. It is, unlike any other hill in the district, entirely covered with heath, except where it has fallen under the plough; and the heath, so different from the green grass on other hills around, causes the dark shade of the hill. Near the summit are some splendid crags, one of which bears the name of "Peden's Pulpit;" and from this peculiar elevation the noted covenanter, Alexander Peden, is said to have harangued the crowds collected on a green grassy platform, nearly surrounded by the beetling cliffs. Hardly any place could be more suitable for such a purpose in troublous times, as a coming enemy could be seen at a great distance.

The area of the parish, according to the Ordnance Survey, is nearly 18,353 acres, comprising 18,171 acres land, arable and moor, 98¾ acres water, and 83¼ acres nearly of public roads, which are kept in good repair.

The river Teviot divides this parish for a considerable distance from where it leaves Hawick parish; the Slitrig also forms its boundary for a short distance—in both of which are good trout angling, and unrestricted.

The only village in the parish is DENHOLM, situated near its southern boundary, and remarkable alike for the beauty of its situation, and the associations connected with it as being the birth-place of the far-famed Dr. John Leyden. The village is airily situated on an eminence, which is terminated abruptly on the north by the Teviot and on the west by the streamlet which meanders down the romantic glen known as Denholm Dean. The form of the village is quadrangular. Most of the houses, are generally well built, and face the village green—a common of considerable size, neatly fenced with an iron railing, in the centre of which a monument has been erected to the memory of Dr. Leyden. Through the kindness of James Douglas, Esq., of Cavers, a piece of garden ground has recently been allotted to each cottage, and every facility is now afforded for promoting the health and comfort of the inhabitants.

But the chief attraction of Denholm to the stranger will ever consist in its fame as the birth-place of Dr. John Leyden, whose singular genius and melancholy fate have raised him to a niche among the minstrels of the Border. The humble house in which he first saw the light still exists on the north side of the village; and the handsome obelisk on the green, with its suitable inscription will keep his name and memory fresh in the district.

Terminating near the village, but extending up to the south-westward, is Denholm Dean, a glen of great beauty, finely overhung with hazel, birch, and bramble, and known to botanists for its fine specimens of fern.

Two miles to the west of Denholm is CAVERS HOUSE, the residence of James Douglas, Esq., who owns the greater part of the parish. This is a singular looking baronial residence, consisting of a large square mass of buildings, facing the north-east, with enormously thick walls and small old-fashioned windows. This remarkable old mansion virtually embodies the history of the family for centuries, having been altered and enlarged to suit the requirements of different ages, the oldest portion being a square tower erected about the year 1400 by Sir Archibald Douglas, then warden of the marches. This, however, was built on the ruins of a still older castle, in which dwelt during the twelfth and thirteenth centuries some generations of the Baliols, one of whom afterwards ascended, for a short time, the Scottish throne. In the mansion are preserved the banner carried before Douglas at the battle of Otterburn, and the trophies then captured from Percy, consisting of what seems to be a pair of lady's gauntlets, bearing the white lion of the Percies, embroidered in pearls, and fringed with filagree work of silver. These gauntlets seem to have been attached to the handle of Percy's spear, which was won by Earl Douglas, and the attempt to retake which brought on the fatal fray. In the old square tower is a double staircase "an architectural curiosity so contrived that two parties may pass up and down at the same time without meeting or scarcely even seeing each other."

U

At a little distance to the north-west of the mansion is the old church of Cavers, supposed to have existed before the Reformation, in which John Leyden studied ; and adjoining which is the churchyard, where the paternal tomb-stone commemorates the learned Doctor whose dust reposes in Java. A new church and manse have been erected about half-a-mile to the westward.

The nearest market towns are Hawick, about 5 miles from Denholm, and Jedburgh about the same distance. The communication with the western part of the country has always been much retarded by the want of bridge accommodation, and the badness of the fords across the Teviot ; but this has now been remedied by a handsome bridge at Denholm, and, in connection with it, a direct road has been made to Hassendean station, the expense of which has been raised chiefly by local subscription.

By the census of 1861 the population of the village of Denholm was 766 ; of the entire parish, 1824 ; who composed 340 families, 13 of whom were returned as living in houses of no windows,‡ 112 in houses of one window, and 145 in houses of two windows, leaving a balance of 70 living in houses of three and more windows.

Assessed property in 1863-4, £11,428 : 2 : 2.

The principal landed-proprietors in the parish are—James Douglas, Esq. of Cavers—resident ; Col. William Macdonald, of Ormiston ; and Miss Macdonald—occasionally resident ; and Sir William A. F. Eliott of Stobs and Wells ; William Scott Watson, Esq. of Bucklands ; and the Duke of Buccleuch.

Superior of Denholm—James Douglas, Esq., of Cavers.

Those marked thus (*) are Registered Voters in the parish.

RESIDENT JUSTICE OF THE PEACE—Walter Wilson, Esq., Orchard.

POLICE OFFICER—John Buglass, Denholm.

POST OFFICE—Jane Turnbull, Postmistress. Daily Post to Hawick—Arrival, 1 p.m. ; Despatch, 3-5 p.m. Messenger—Archibald Douglas. Letters for the entire parish should be addressed by Hawick.

PUBLIC OFFICES—Heritors' Clerk, Inspector of Poor, and Registrar of Births, Marriages, and Deaths—*George Moodie, Denholm.
Kirk Treasurer and Session Clerk—J. Greenfield.
Medical Officer and Public Vaccinator—William Blair, M.D.

CLERGY, &c.—Cavers is in the Presbytery of Jedburgh, and Synod of Merse and Teviotdale. Patron—James Douglas, Esq. of Cavers.

‡ Railway constructors employed at the time on the Hawick and Carlisle line, and living in huts.

Established Church (Cavers)—*Rev. Alexander Munn M'Coll (Inducted 1854). Sittings, 500. Av. attend. at Sabbath School, 56.

Free Church (Denholm)—*Rev. Jas. M'Clymont (Inducted 1847). Sittings, 364. Average attendance at Sabbath School, 65.

Independent Church (Denholm)—Rev. J. M'Robert (Inducted 1846). Sittings, 230.

FAST DAYS—First Wednesday of May, and last Wednesday of Oct.

SCHOOLS‡ : Parish (Denholm)—*John Greenfield, master ; av. at. 145. Auxiliary (Cog's Mill)—James W. Scott, teacher ; av. attend. 60. Female (Cavers, supported by James Douglas, Esq.)—Miss Telfer, teacher ; average attendance, 55.

PAROCHIAL BOARD—Robert Thomson, Esq., Hawick (factor for James Douglas. Esq., Cavers), Chairman. No. of Poor on Roll, 47. Rate of Assessment, 8d. per £ ; total Assessment 1863, £544. Poor House, Hawick Union. (See Teviothead parish.)

LIBRARY—Denholm Subscription (about 1000 vols.). Annual Subscription, 5s. Thomas Barrie, Librarian.

DENHOLM HORTICULTURAL SOCIETY—Competitions, third Saturday of July, and second Saturday of September, when a variety of prizes are given. A flourishing Society. Ebenezer Oliver, secretary ; William Oliver, tailor, treasurer. Annual Subscription, 1s.

CARRIERS—Jedburgh to Hawick, Thomas Robson, Wednesday and Saturday (see Hawick Carriers).

CONVEYANCE—North British Railway—Hassendean station on the Hawick line, in Minto parish, and the one most frequented—distant 2 miles from Denholm—Robert Watson, station-master ; and Shankend station in the parish, near Stobs Castle, on the Border Union line, James Todd, station-master.

MEDICAL PRACTITIONER—William Blair, M.D., Denholm.

CORN MILLS—Denholm—*Thomas Tait ; Spittal—James Inglis.

TRADES, &c.
Denholm

Beattie, William, baker
Beattie, Andrew, flesher
Borthwick, William, tailor
Brown, Isabella, grocer, &c.
*Bulman, Robert, sen., farmer
Crown Inn, James Elliot
Davidson, John, joiner
Elliot, James, grocer, &c.
*Fergusson, Alexander, innkeeper
Fox and Hound's Inn, *William Leyden

‡ The number of children in the parish from 5 to 15, attending school during the first week of April 1861, was 306 ; of all ages, 318.

Furness, Nicholas, joiner
*Hall, Thomas, carter
Hall, J. & G., grocers
Hope, William, draper
Hume, Robert, shoemaker
Jamieson, James, shoemaker
Laidlaw, Robert, flesher
*Little, James, mason
*Little, William, builder
*Mack, John, grocer, &c.
*Messer, William, cooper
*Miller, James, joiner
*Moodie, Robert and George, millwrights
*Nichol, Robert, hosier
*Oliver, James, stocking-maker
Oliver, William, tailor
Park, James, shoemaker
*Riddell, Thomas, stocking-maker
Robson, John, blacksmith
Robson, William, do.
*Scott, William, quarryman
Sinton, Andrew, road-contractor
Smail, George, blacksmith
*Smith, John, baker
*Tait, John, stone-cutter
Turnbull, John, joiner
Turnbull, Jane, spirit dealer
*Thomson, William, mason

RESIDENTS, FARMERS, &c. IN THE PARISH.

*Amos, Thomas, farmer, Earlside
*Ashcroft, Alexander, do. South Berryfell
Ballantyne, Henry, do. Deanbrae
*Barry, Robert, do. Spittal Tower
*Blyth, William, do. Whitrigs
*Blyth, Thomas, do. do.
*Brunton, James, do. North Berryfell
*Davidson, James, Lochend
Elliot, Robert, farm-steward, &c., Cavers
*Forsyth, George, farmer, Ashybank
*Goodfellow, Hugh, do. Trow Mill
*Gray, William, do. Ormiston
Grieve, Robert, manager, Stobs
*Haddon, Andrew, farmer, Honeyburn
*Hogg, George, do. Cavers Knowes
*Irvine, William, do. Cavers East Mains
*Jobson, George, do. and coal agent, Hummelknowes

*Laing, Walter, quarry master, Denholmhill
Riddell, John, farmer, Ormiston Mains
*Scott, James, do. Colliforthill
Scott, Robert, do. Kaingend
*Scott, Robert, do. Kinninghall and Little Cote
Tait, John, gardener, Cavers
Turnbull, James, forester, Cavers
Turnbull, James, farmer, Spittal
*Turnbull, Thomas, do. East Middle
*Veitch, William, do. Dykes
*Young, James, do. Teviothaugh

REGISTERED VOTERS (Non-Resident).

Eckford, John, grocer, Hawick
King, James, Dimpleknowe, Ashkirk
Little, James, Ashieburn, Ancrum
Smith, William, farmer, Learmouth, Cornhill
Turnbull, William, groom, Minto
Riddell, John, farmer, North Sinton

SEATS, &c. OF COUNTY FAMILIES AND SMALLER RESIDENCES IN THE PARISH.

CAVERS (see p. 290).

The property and residence of James Douglas, Esq., eldest son of the late James Douglas, Esq., of Cavers (author of "The Advancement of Society," &c); born 1822; succeeded 1861; married, 1858, Mary, youngest daughter of the late Sir Andw. Agnew, Bart. of Lochnaw, Wigtonshire.

This family is descended from Archibald Douglas, natural son of James second Earl of Douglas, who was killed at Otterburn, 1388, on which occasion Archibald carried his father's banner, still preserved at Cavers, together with the trophy* captured from Earl Percy. He was infeft in the Barony of Cavers and appointed hereditary Sheriff of Teviotdale, which office (and sometimes that of Warden of the Marches) was held with only one short interruption by his successors till 1745, when hereditary jurisdictions were abolished. The present proprietor is the 20th in regular hereditary descent from the founder.

---

* Called a *Pennon* by various writers. Sir Walter Scott committed this mistake in some of his books, but corrected it in others.

ORCHARD HOUSE.

The property of James Douglas, Esq. of Cavers; at present occupied by Walter Wilson, Esq., J.P. (of Teviot Mills, and 7 Allars Crescent, Hawick), and N. B. Railway Director.

ORMISTON.

The property and autumn residence of *Col. Macdonald of Powder Hall, near Edinburgh; and temporarily occupied by Provost Wilson of Hawick, during the rest of the year.

STOBS CASTLE.

A fine mansion in the vale of the Slitrig, about 4½ miles south of Hawick—the property and once the residence of Sir Wm. Eliott. Now occupied as a summer residence by *Nicholas Wood, Esq., M. & C.E., Newcastle-on-Tyne.

MINTO.

THE parish of Minto is situated on the left bank of the river Teviot, and extends to about 4½ miles in length, and 3½ in breadth. It is bounded on the north by Lilliesleaf, on the east by Ancrum, on the south by Cavers, and on the west by Wilton. Its area, according to the Ordnance Survey, is 5620¼ acres, nearly—30¼ of which are occupied by the North British Railway, 55 by public roads, and 19¼ by water.

"A stripe of haugh in the southern extremity forms the only level ground. The surface in other places rises in frequent undulations, with a blunt outline presenting considerable variety. The general appearance of the country is chiefly diversified by two green hills, the highest of which attains an elevation of 905 feet; and to the east of them by Minto Crags, a bold and rugged eminence 721 feet above the level of the sea, overhanging the valley of the Teviot. These heights form a ridge running lengthways east and west through the greater part of the parish. To the south the ground slopes to the river, and is further diversified by some small glens or deans watered by rivulets." Minto Crags, the most conspicuous object in the parish, commands from its summit a most extensive view on all sides.

In the centre of the parish, situated on a pleasant rising ground, is the small but beautiful village of Minto—the only one in the parish. The nearest market towns are Hawick and Jedburgh, from which it is equally distant about 5 miles. There is a railway station at Hassendean, about 1 mile from the village.

The parish possesses no antiquities, except the castle of Fatlips, which the late Earl had repaired and heightened in a becoming manner, romantically situated on the eastern and most picturesque of the Minto Crags; and the ruins of Barn-hills Castle in a glen to the east of the Crags. The only mansion of any note is MINTO HOUSE, situated near the village, the seat of the Earl of Minto, a fine building erected at the beginning of the century, but better known to fame through the talent of its family than from its own peculiar grandeur or beauty. The House is four stories in height, and the uppermost room is fitted up as a sort of museum, where many interesting family relics are preserved. From the windows of this room the view is most extensive, and it is doubtful if there is in any part of Scotland a more varied and extensive prospect. The house is beautifully surrounded by grounds, woods, and crags, including the site of an old burial place, which, instead of being left to desolation after it had ceased to be used as a place of sepulture, has been tended with the most religious care; and the finest taste, as well as floricultural skill, has contributed to make it a most lovely retreat. The library of Minto House ranks as one of the most valuable private collections in the south of Scotland.

Population of the parish in 1861, 430; who composed 83 families, one of whom was returned as living in a house with no window, 7 in houses of one window, and 54 in houses of two windows.

Assessed property in 1863-4, £4667 : 13 : 8.

The principal landed-proprietors in the parish are—the Earl of Minto; Edward Heron Maxwell, E-q. of Teviot Bank; and Miss Dickson, Hassendeanburn—resident; and the Duke of Buccleuch—non-resident.

Those marked thus (*) are Registered Voters in the parish.

RESIDENT JUSTICES OF THE PEACE—Earl of Minto, and Edward Heron Maxwell, Esq.

DISTRICT POLICE OFFICER—John Buglass, Denholm.

POST OFFICE—Daily Post from Hawick. Arrival, 12-15 p.m.; Departure, 12-30 p.m. Also from Hawick, via Denholm. Arrival 2 p.m. Letters should be addressed by Hawick. Messenger—Joseph Turnbull.

PUBLIC OFFICES—Heritors' Clerk, Inspector of Poor, Kirk Treasurer, Registrar of Births, Marriages, and Deaths, and Session Clerk —John Rankine Hamilton, schoolmaster.

Medical Officer and Public Vaccinator—William Blair, M.D., Denholm.

CLERGY, &c.—Minto is in the Presbytery of Jedburgh, and Synod of Merse and Teviotdale. Patron—Earl of Minto.

Established Church — Rev. Mr. M'Morland (Inducted 1864). Sittings, 350, exclusive of the Minto private gallery. Average attendance at Sabbath School, 24.

FAST DAY—Wednesday before the last Sabbath of April.

SCHOOLS‡—Parochial—*John R. Hamilton, master; aver. attend. 45. Female—Miss Renwick, teacher; average attendance, 20.

PAROCHIAL BOARD—Angus Mackintosh, Esq., factor for the Earl of Minto, Chairman. No. of Poor on Roll, 8. Rate of Assessment, 2¼d. per £; total Assessment, 1863, £119 : 11 : 6. Poor House —Hawick Combination.

‡ Number of children in the parish attending school during the first week of April 1861, 60; of all ages, 67.

MORTIFICATION—In 1751 the Rev. George Bruce, then minister of the parish, mortified £50 for the behoof of the poor of the parish; and in 1795, after he had been translated to Dunbar, he left, or mortified (for he died that year) a further sum of £100 for the behoof of the schoolmaster.

LIBRARY—There is one in connection with the Parish Church.

CONVEYANCE—North British Railway, Hassendean Station. Stationmaster—Robert Watson.

CARRIERS—Hawick, Thomas Davidson, Saturday; Selkirk and Lilliesleaf, John Aitchison, Friday.

RESIDENTS, FARMERS, &c.

Ainslie, Thomas, blacksmith, Minto
*Amos, James, farmer, Minto Deanfoot
*Brockie, David, do.   Minto Kaims
Deans, Gideon, joiner, Horsleyhill
*Drawhill, Thomas, farmer, Huntlaw
*Hall, Andrew, farmer, Horsleyhill
Mackintosh, Angus, factor, Cloughhead
*Mark, George, farmer, Hassendeanburn
*Nicol, William, do.   Newlands
*Selby, Robert, Hassendeanbank
Selby, Ephraim, factor for Twizel Estate, Hassendeanbank
*Shiell, John, farmer, Hassendean
*Shiell, Andrew, do.   do.
*Shiell, James,   do.   do.
*Turnbull, Wm., do.   Minto Townhead
Turnbull, William, head groom, Minto House
Williamson, George, gardener,   do.

SEATS, &c. OF COUNTY FAMILIES IN THE PARISH

MINTO HOUSE.

The principal residence of the Earl of Minto (Sir William Hugh Elliot Murray Kynynmound), Viscount Melgund of Melgund, Forfarshire, Baron Minto of Minto, and a Baronet of Nova Scotia, eldest surviving son of Gilbert second Earl of Minto, by Mary, eldest daughter of the late Patrick Brydone, Esq. (the celebrated author); born 19th March 1814; succeeded his late father, as third Earl, 31st July 1859; married, 20th May 1844, Emma Eleanor Elizabeth, only daughter of the late General Sir Thomas Hislop, Bart., G.C.B., and has issue :—

Gilbert John, Viscount Melgund, born 9th July 1845.
Arthur Ralph Douglas, born 17th December 1846.
Hugh Frederick Hislop, born 23d February 1848.
William Fitzwilliam, born 14th September 1849.

London addresses—Brooks' and Traveller's Clubs, S.W., and 48 Eaton Square.

The Earl is Deputy-Lieutenant for Roxburghshire, and was M.P. for Hythe 1837-41, for Greenock 1847-52, and for Clackmannan and Kinross 1857-59.

TEVIOTBANK.

A handsome Elizabethan villa, situated on the Teviot, about one mile farther up the river, and on the opposite side from the village of Denholm—the residence of *Edward Heron Maxwell, Esq. (who purchased the property in 1860), seventh son of the late Sir John Shaw Heron Maxwell of Sprinkell, Dumfriesshire; born 1821; married, 1847, Elizabeth Ellen, only daughter of Colonel Stopford Blair, of Penninghame, Wigtonshire; and has, with other issue, a son—John Shaw, born 1850.

Mr. Maxwell is a Deputy-Lieutenant for Dumfriesshire.

HASSENDEANBURN †

Situated on the Teviot at the south point of the parish—the property and residence of Miss Dickson. *Heir-Pres.*, Archibald Dickson, Esq., yr., of Bughtrig, Berwickshire [which *see*].

REGISTERED VOTER (Non-Resident).

Dr. Aitken, late minister of the parish

---

† It was here that the first nursery in Scotland was established, and from which the celebrated firms of the Dicksons of Hawick, Edinburgh, Chester, and Perth, derived their origin.

HAWICK (AND WILTON).

—◆—

THE parish of Hawick is (as now constituted—*see* introductory account of Teviothead) bounded on the north by Wilton and Roberton, on the south by Kirkton and Cavers, on the west by Teviothead, and on the east by Roberton. It is about 6 miles in length, and from 2 to 3 miles in breadth. The area, according to the Ordnance Survey, is 6203¼ acres, of which 6017¾ are land, 90¾ are water, and 94¼ are public roads. The surface of the parish is hilly, rising to over 800 feet in one instance; the banks of the Teviot, are more level, and the soil generally is rich and well cultivated.

Situated near the northern extremity of the parish, and partly within the adjacent parish of Wilton, is the burgh of Hawick, seated at the confluence of the Slitrig with the Teviot; by the former river the town is divided into nearly equal parts. From its proximity to the borders of England and Scotland, Hawick suffered severely in times of ancient feud, and was thrice burned. The town now consists chiefly of four long streets, on the right bank of the Teviot, with a number of minor thoroughfares on both sides of the river, well paved and lighted.

At the beginning of the present century Hawick consisted of but one parish, parochial burghal, its population was under 3000, and it was a place of comparatively small importance. So lately as 1778 its corn market was established by the Farmer's Club (founded two years previously—*see* lists). About the same time the town had no post office. Previously "the letters which were brought from Jedburgh by a common hawker, once a month, were exposed on a stall in the streets on the market, like so many cakes of gingerbread, and the people used to look at them with as much curiosity as the botanists do at a few exotic plants from Van Dieman's Land.*" It is now the most important town in the district, consisting of the three burghal parishes of Hawick (parochial), St. Mary's (quoad sacra), and Wilton (parochial), with a burgh population close upon 10,500, and is one of the most eminent manufacturing seats in Scotland. Its staple trade is lambs' wool hosiery and Tweeds, but the manufacture of shawls, plaids, blankets, etc., is also very extensive.

The environs of Hawick are much admired, the banks of the Teviot being extremely picturesque; and there are also many beautiful, wild, and romantic scenes, and places of historical interest.

Situated at the upper extremity of the town, and overlooking

---

* Wilson's "History of Hawick."

the main street, is a relic of great antiquity, which is usually denominated the Moat. This consists of an artificial mound of earth; it is circular at the base, it rises in a conical form to the height of 30 feet, the circumference being 117 feet at the top and 312 at the base; it contains about 4060 cubic yards, and is almost flat upon the top. From the examination of similar remains it is believed to have been originally formed as a place of sepulture by the early occupiers of the country, and in subsequent times, courts for the administration of justice were held upon it. Sir Alexander Ramsay, while acting in a judicial capacity upon its summit in 1342, was taken prisoner by the Knight of Liddesdale, carried to Hermitage, and there starved to death.

The vestiges of several towers or Border peels, and numerous earthworks and encampments, are still remaining in different parts of the parish; one of the most ancient of these places of strength now forms a part of the Tower Inn, celebrated as the residence in former times of the Barons of Drumlanrig, and at a later period of Anne Duchess of Buccleuch and Monmouth, whose husband was beheaded in 1685. This tower, which was anciently surrounded with a deep moat drawn from the Slitrig, was the only building in the town which escaped the devastation in 1570. Another of these peels is at present attached to the castle of Branxholm, celebrated as the ancient residence of the family of Buccleuch, and invested with additional interest of late in consequence of the prominent place which it occupies in the "Lay of the Last Minstrel" (*see* Goldielands).

Probably no provincial town in Scotland has undergone such a change in appearance and limits as Hawick of late years. It has extended its bounds on all sides, while internally, the new erections which have replaced the previous thatched and mean-looking houses, have so transformed and renovated the ancient burgh as to give it—in its main thoroughfares at least—much of a metropolitian aspect. The new banks erected, or in course of erection, and many of the shops would be a credit to the principal streets of any city; while the *well-kept* streets themselves, possess a bustle, never seen but in large commercial marts.

One of the nearest tests of the commercial prosperity of Hawick is to be found in the rapid increase in the annual rental of the parish, as disclosed by the valuation roll. Thus at Whitsunday 1843, the valuation was £12,922 : 14 : 3; while at Whitsunday 1863, in the short space of twenty years, it was £29,346 : 16 : 5.*

* The roll for 1863 was made up as follows:—

Lands	.	.	.	.	£8,285 14 3
Factories, &c.	.	.	.	4,005 0 6
Houses, &c.	.	.	.	17,055 15 8
		Total	.	£29,346 16 5

No two towns in the district present such contrasts as Kelso and Hawick—each the representative of its class: Kelso of prosperous country trade and comfortable social leisure, with energy enough, but of a very undemonstrative kind, and scarcely seen out of doors. The very streets, public buildings, and shops, partake of this character—the former systematically arranged, open and airy, but with a pavement so rough as to betray no anxiety for the expedition of traffic, and except on extra occasions, sparingly frequented by either town or country people; the houses and public buildings, as a rule, substantial but heavy looking;* the shops wealthy, but making no outside show of it. Hawick—of energetic, wealth accumulating, business activity—features apparent in the very thoroughfares, and the bustling traffic frequenting them. The thoroughfares twisted and cut up to suit the exigencies of the day, and showing no system of arrangement, but macademized to the smoothness of a bowling green; its public establishments, airy elegant structures, and its shops outwardly attractive; and, while Kelso is the head-quarters for corn Hawick is that for meal. In only one feature do they resemble each other—both towns have an inspector of nuisances, and both are alike cleanly kept—that is, apparently, and as seen by a stranger; but it is quite possible that in the back slums of both places cleanliness is not so strictly carried out as it might be.

Being situated partly on the haugh lands in the valleys of the Teviot and Slitrig, and partly on the sloping hill sides, Hawick is admirably well ventilated by the cool and refreshing breezes from the mountain ranges of the western Border. The soil is dry; and since the draining of land became so universal, the same may be said in a general way of the atmosphere. It is an average healthy town. Cholera visited it pretty severely in 1832, and very fatally in 1849, when a great many cases occurred, about one-half becoming fatal. No epidemic has since assumed what may be termed an alarming form, but like all large communities, the town has occasional visits of typhus, gastric fever, and small pox; the latter almost invariably of a mild type. The great bulk of the popu-

* The Corn Exchange and Town Hall are exceptions; but take, for instance, the five bank branches at present established. Three of these are old houses cobbled up in as substantial and gloomy looking a style as possible—and probably not much more could have been made of them; still they could have been better; but for the other two, being modern erections, there is no excuse. The Bank of Scotland especially, lately completed, is to the spectator an offence both against taste and arrangement—the style towards the street (the bank department) being that of a prison, plus windows, combined with a great waste of ground and well-built walls; while the style of dwelling-house seems the result of an idea of a modern dwelling-house, combined with some architectural features borrowed from Kelso Abbey, towards which it looks.

lation is connected with the woollen factories, and the work is of a healthy character; it having been proved, beyond doubt, that weakly children thrive and grow stout shortly after entering the factories. The water supply has for some years back been far short of the necessities of the population, and the drainage is totally insufficient; but the new water works, which are in course of construction, will thoroughly remedy the first evil, and a complete system of sewerage will follow—the estimated cost of which is above £9000. When these are carried out, the health of the town will no doubt be much improved. The dwelling houses of the working classes are, in many of the poorer parts of the town, much over-crowded; and though rents are high, house property of this description is not so remunerative as to make building a favourite investment for capital. There is now plenty of ground in the market, but there seems little disposition to purchase it for building purposes. A working men's building society—the object of which is to provide self-contained houses, with proper conveniences and gardens for the members—has been lately started, and is likely to prove successful. The health and comfort of the population will be much enhanced when better dwellings are put within the reach of the operatives.

Although situated partly on slopes of the surrounding hills, Hawick possesses in reality little variety of levels, as the following heights, supplied from the Ordnance Survey Office, will show; the heights given are above mean water :—

    Bolt in Hawick Old Parish Church .... 383 feet
    Bench Mark on Town Hall .... 352¼ ,,
    Bench Mark on Hawick Bridge, Tower Knowe .. 346½ ,,
    Bolt in north side of Buccleuch Church Tower .... 339 ,,

In this respect however, for sanatory purposes, it possesses a great advantage over Kelso, which is nearly a dead level—with one inconvenient exception, where a tunnel was required.*

* The Kelso sewerage having been completed and fairly into operation since our Kelso pages were printed, we may state that, as yet, notwithstanding the almost dead level, the drains are working perfectly, and some of them have now been in operation for three years.

The following statement shows the levels of the main drains, and may be of interest to other towns where a system of sewerage is about to be carried out :—The outflow into the river, for nearly 200 feet, is a fall of 1 foot in 40; from the outskirts of the town to the outflow, it is 1 in 250; in the principal streets and square, it varies from 1 in 156 to 200—these all consist of egg-shaped brick culverts placed at an average of 11 feet below the surface. The tunnel under the rise in Roxburgh Street, is 24 feet below the surface, at its deepest. The branch lines (fire-clay pipes) vary in their level and depth according to circumstances.

The entire cost of the sewerage was about £4000. To Mr. Brunlees, C.E., London, a native of the town, Kelso is indebted, at the cost

Dr. Grant's otter hounds regularly hunt the streams in the district during the season. The trout fishing in the Teviot and Slitrig is free; the sport is good, but the fishing is sometimes spoiled by netters.

Anniversary.—Hawick Common Riding. The common riding and races constitute the great annual festival of Hawick. It commences on the last Friday of May (old style)*, and lasts over two days; and consists of the ceremony of riding the marches, horse and foot races, leaping, wrestling, and other athletic games. The days are observed as a holiday in the burgh. The origin of the festival is ascribed to a victory obtained by a gallant band of Hawick youths over a marauding party of English, the year after the battle of Flodden. Tradition says the fight took place by the side of the Teviot, two miles below the town, and the youths resisted the marauders and captured their standard. An unmarried man is chosen annually by the town council to carry a fac-simile of this standard round the marches of the town's lands, and is escorted by a troop of young men on horse-back. The burgh lands, which were granted by Sir James Douglas of Drumlanrig, being now enclosed, the riding of the marches is a mere form; but the inhabitants take great delight in having it observed with all the pomp and pageantry of by-gone times. The first mention of races in connection with the common riding is in 1723; in 1725 the town council voted a sum for the racing plate, and in 1727 a cup was run for. Hawick race meeting is consequently one of the oldest in the three kingdoms.

Holidays.—New Year's Day, and the days following the May and November hiring fairs (*see* following paragraph); the Old Year's Day is also held by some classes, but it is not a close holiday.

Markets.—Thursday, weekly (corn, etc.). The corn is sold by sample, and the business done in it is next in importance to Kelso in the county, and next to Dunse in the district; while as a meal and flour market, it is the principal in the district. A handsome Exchange is at present in course of erection, for the accommodation of farmers and dealers. No established winter markets for the sale of fat cattle occur, but the energy of Messrs. Oliver, auctioneers, has raised Hawick to the highest rank in the district as an auction mart for this class of produce. Their sales of fat stock, milch cows, &c., now take place weekly, on Monday, in a handsome new auction market, their own property, laid out and

of mere outlay, for the plans and specifications; and the results prove them to have been carefully compiled and excellently carried out.

The water system, just completed, at an expense of £3000, the plans for which were also furnished by Mr. Brunlees, has been in operation too short a time to furnish data for general conclusions.

* That is, the Friday on or previous to the 20th.

built for the purpose. Besides the ordinary weekly sales, Messrs. Oliver hold three sales specially for lambs in August, and one in September; two sales for draft ewes in October; and sales specially for feeding and store cattle in May, October, and November. At each of these lamb sales from five to ten thousand Cheviot and half and three-parts bred lambs are shown; in fact, at the sale on the 25th August 1864, the large number of 11,257 were disposed off. The draft ewe and cattle sales are equally important in extent, from 4000 to 6000 ewes, and 300 to 400 cattle being sold at each. Messrs. Oliver's mart has now become the greatest market in the south of Scotland for milch cows; in the spring months from 40 to 60, and sometimes 100, are sold weekly. Buyers regularly attend Messrs. Oliver's sales from all the towns in the locality, and from Edinburgh and the south.

Great Hiring Days—Servants and Young Men, 17th May and 8th November (when on a Saturday, Sunday, or Monday—the Tuesday after); Shearers, first Thursday after 26th July.

Wool Fair—first Thursday after St. Boswell's (the 18th of July). At this fair much of the Cheviot wool grown in the locality is sold. Buyers attend from the Midland manufacturing districts, and here and at Jedburgh (which *see*, p. 249) the manufacturers of the district buy in their principal stocks.

Tup and Lamb Fair (held in the Brewery Haugh)—21st September (when on a Saturday, Sunday, or Monday—the Tuesday after). This is one of the oldest fairs for tups in Scotland, and one long celebrated for Cheviots. Of late years a good number of Leicesters have been shown; and these being generally not extra fed, are much sought after for hill use. The late Mr. A. Oliver, about twenty-five years ago, introduced the mode of selling by auction, which has gradually got into favour, and now the greater portion are sold in the auction ring. There are also a few lots of lambs shown at this market, but Messrs. Oliver's auction, which is held the previous week, has curtailed the show of these materially. The day previous to this fair the Tup Show of the West Teviotdale Agricultural Society takes place—*see* lists, p. 318.

Tryst (Horses and Cattle) held on North British Railway Company's ground off the Wellgate, where a suitable siding for trucking cattle and sheep has been erected—third Tuesday of October.

Cattle—8th November.

By rail, Hawick has great facilities of communication in all directions. The main branch of the North British line here joins that of the Border Union (now jointly called the "Waverley Route"); by the former passengers and goods are conveyed to Edinburgh, Glasgow, and all parts of the north; while the branch lines striking off at Newtown, convey shire, Kelso, and the east coast—by the latter to south generally, and Dumfriesshire; while the Borde line, striking off at Riccarton, conveys to Hexham, the Midland districts, and south-eastern coast.

The following are the principal distances by rail:—Edin. 53 miles, Glasgow 99, Kelso 24½, Berwick 48, Carlisle 45½, ham 55, Newcastle 97½.

The Hawick station, situated in Wilton, is one of the shabbi and most incommodious on the "route." It also lies at an incon venient distance from the centre of traffic; but in this respect it is well off compared with Kelso or Jedburgh.

According to the census of 1861 the population of the town of Hawick (not including the Wilton district) was 8138, the burghal district of Wilton 2210, and of that very small part of Hawick proper which lies within Wilton, 53; total of the burgh of Hawick as at present constituted, 10,401. Population of the *parish* as parochially constituted (Hawick and landward), 8,726.

At the census the population of Hawick parish constituted 1787 separate families, 3 of whom were returned as living in houses having no window, 868 in houses having one window, 510 in houses of two windows, 406 (or rather less than one-fourth) in houses of three and more windows.

Assessed property in the parish in 1863-4, £25,115, 18s.

The largest landed-proprietor in the parish is His Grace the Duke of Buccleuch. The other principal proprietors are—the Burgh of Hawick; James Douglas, Esq. of Cavers; B. T. G. Anderson, Esq. of Tushielaw; A. E. Lockhart, Esq. of Borthwickbrae; and Thomas Turnbull, Esq. of Fenwick.

Superior of Hawick—His Grace the Duke of Buccleuch. Superior of Wilton—Mrs. Pringle of Wilton Lodge. Hawick is a burgh of barony independent of its Superior.

WILTON PARISH.—For Parochial Board, &c., belonging to Wilton as a parish, and not as part of the burgh of Hawick, *see* Wilton lists, which immediately follow those of Hawick.

TOWN COUNCIL.

(Incorporated and remodelled by Statute 24 and 25 Vict., July 1861.)

Statute Meeting of Council, first Tuesday of each month, at 7 p.m

Provost—George Wilson.

Bailies—George H. Fraser and Andrew Waugh.

COUNCILLORS.

(1) North High Street Ward—George Wilson, provost; George H. Fraser, bailie; Thomas Laidlaw.
(2) South High Street Ward—Andrew Waugh, bailie; James Harkness; Robert Milligan.

X

(3) Slitrig Ward—William Turnbull, town treasurer; John Melrose; John Scott.
(4) Teviot Ward—Jas. Oliver, solicitor ; P. Laidlaw ; J. D. Kennedy.
(5) Wilton Ward—Walter Laing, John Wilson, Adam Laidlaw.

COMMITTEES OF COUNCIL.

1. Farm. 2. Sanitary. 3. Police. 4. Law and Finances.

Thomas Purdom, Town Clerk. William Turnbull, Town Treasurer.
Daniel Munro, Superintendent of Police, Procurator-Fiscal, and Billet Master.
James Smith and Michael Wintrup, Burgh Officers.

COMMISSIONERS OF POLICE.

The Provost, Bailies, and Town Council.
Chairman—The Provost.   Clerk—Thomas Purdom.
Treasurer and Collector—Walter Haddon, of Kirk & Haddon, writers.
Superintendent—Daniel Munro.

Police Rates, 11d. per £., made up as follows :—Watching, 4d. ; Cleaning, 3d. ; Lighting, 3d. ; Sinking Fund, 1d.
Water Rates (see p. 303)—Special Domestic, 6d. per £. ; General Domestic, 2d. ; Business, 1d. ; Owners, 1d. ; and Land, ½d.

LOCAL JUSTICES OF THE PEACE.

Those marked thus (*) are resident in Hawick or Wilton parishes ; the others act regularly.

*William Ogilvie, Esq., of Chesters.
*Walter Wilson, Esq., Orchard.
*William S. Watson, Esq., yr of Bucklands
A. E. Lockhart, Esq., of Borthwickbrae, Roberton.
*David Pringle, Esq., of Wilton Lodge.
Edward Heron Maxwell, Esq. of Teviot Bank, Minto.

The Earl of Minto.
*J. S. Chisholme, Esq. of Stirches.
Wm. Elliot Lockhart, Esq. yr. of Borthwickbrae
*Thomas Elliot Ogilvie, Esq., yr. of Chesters.
Geerge Pott, Esq. of Todrig.
*The Provost of Hawick for the time being.
*The Senior and Junior Bailies of Hawick for the time being.

COURTS.

POLICE COURTS are held in the Town Hall every lawful day when there is business. Judges—the Provost and Bailies. Assessor—the Town Clerk.
THE BURGH CIVIL COURT sits when required. Judges—the Provost and Magistrates. Assessor—the Town Clerk. Jurisdiction—the same as of Royal Burghs.
JUSTICE OF PEACE COURTS are held on third Thursday of each month.
SHERIFF SMALL DEBT COURTS are held on first Tuesdays of February, April, June, August, October, and December.

PUBLIC OFFICES.

(Burghal and Parochial Parish of Hawick).

County Police Station, Slitrig Crescent—Sergt. John Ainslie, Officer.
Fire Engine House—Town Hall.
Heritors' Clerk—Andrew Irvine, 26 High Street.
Income Tax, Assessor of—Thomas Purdom, 31 High Street.
Inland Revenue Officer (Excise)—John C. Hawkins, Slitrig Crescent.
Inspector of Nuisances—Daniel Munro, Police Office.
International Telegraph Company's Agent—Thomas Cathrae, Buccleuch Street.
Justice of Peace Clerk Depute—C. M. Wilson, S.S.C.
Medical Inspector of Factories for the Burgh—D. M'Leod, Buccleuch Street.
Medical Officer and Public Vaccinator for the Parish—D. M'Leod.
Police Office—Town Hall.
Poor, Inspector of—W. N. Kennedy (Office, 6 Kirkstyle Place).
Prison, Crosswyndhead—Michael Anderson, Governor.
Procurator-Fiscal Justice of Peace Court—James Carmichael.
Registrar of Births, Marriages, and Deaths—Anthony Dodds (Office, Buccleuch Street).
Session Clerk and Kirk Treasurer—Anthony Dodds, Buccleuch St.
Sextons—See Parochial Burial Grounds.
Sheriff-Clerk Depute—Walter Haddon, 3 Buccleuch Street.
  Do. Officer—John Guild, Teviot Crescent.
Stamps and Taxes—Walter Haddon, Collector and Sub-Distributor, 3 Buccleuch Street.
Town Clerk—Thomas Purdom, 31 High Street.
Town Crier—Michael Wintrup, 2 Manse Lane.
Town Treasurer—William Turnbull, 3 Howgate.
Valuation Act—Assessor for the Hawick District of County—Edward Henderson, Melrose.
Works, Master of—Daniel Munro, Police Office

For Public Offices belonging exclusively to Wilton as an independent parish, see Wilton lists.

POST OFFICE (25 High Street).

Francis Deans, Postmaster, who attests this list.

ARRIVALS.

From London, Carlisle, and the South, at 8-13 a.m. Delivered at 9-45 a.m.
  ,,   Edinburgh, Galashiels, Melrose, Kelso, and Jedburgh, at 9-18 a.m. Delivered at 9-45 a.m
  ,,   Langholm, Canobie, and Newcastleton, at 10-33 a.m. Delivered at 10-43 a.m., to callers
  ,,   Edinburgh, Galashiels, Melrose, Kelso, St. Boswell's, and Jedburgh, at 5-53 p.m. Delivered at 6-15 p.m.
  ,,   London, Carlisle and London, and North-western Railway P. O., at 8-10 p.m. Delivered at 8-20 p.m.

DESPATCHES.

To Galashiels, Melrose, Kelso, and Jedburgh, at 7-38 a.m.
  ,, Edinburgh and the North, &c., at 9-47 a.m.
  ,, Edinburgh, Galashiels, Melrose, St. Boswell's, Berwick, Midland Railway, Kelso, and Jedburgh, at 3-9 p.m.

To Carlisle, London, Langholm, Newcastleton, and Canobie, 5-5 p.m.

,, Edinburgh and the North, &c., at 7-30 p.m.

ARRIVALS ON SUNDAY.

From Carlisle, London, Newcastleton, Edinburgh, Galashiels, Melrose, Jedburgh, Kelso, and St. Boswell's, at 9 a.m.

DESPATCHES ON SUNDAYS.

To Jedburgh Kelso, Galashiels, and Melrose, at 8-12 a.m.

,, Edinburgh, St Boswells, Berwick, and Midland Railway, 5-30 p.m.

,, Carlisle, London, and Newcastleton, at 6-15 p.m.

Receiving Office, Albion Place, Wilton—James Shiel, postmaster; and Pillar Letter Box, Railway Station. Collections made at 9-15 a.m. and 4-45 p.m.

Letters can be posted by any of the above Mails 10 minutes later than the time specified, with an additional Stamp.

On Sundays the office is open from 9-45 till 10-45 a.m. A delivery takes place over the town, commencing at 9-45 a.m.

Money Order Office open every week-day from 9 a.m. to 6 p.m.

TOWN DELIVERERS.

Robert Bryce, Melgund Place ; Jas. Paterson, Green Wynd.

POST RUNNERS.

Ashkirk	James Amos
Bonchester Bridge	James Watson
Burnfoot and Minto	Joseph Turnbull
Commonside and Teviothead	William Adamson
Deanburnhaugh	David Lyon
Denholm	Archibald Douglas
Stobs	George Scott

The Post Runners are allowed to carry small parcels on their own account, but no letters or newspapers.

The Ashkirk, Bonchester Bridge, and Deanburnhaugh Messengers, are despatched at 9-45 a.m., and return the following morning at 9-30 in time for the first despatch to Edinburgh and North, &c.

The Messengers to Denholm, Minto, Stobs, and Teviothead are despatched at 9-45 a.m., and return the same afternoon in time for the despatch to the South.

CLERGY, &c.

Presbytery of Jedburgh, Synod of Merse and Teviotdale.

Patron of the Parish of Hawick—Duke of Buccleuch.

PARISH CHURCH, Hawick—Rev. John MacRae, D.D. (Inducted 1843). Sittings, 1400. Sabbath School attendance, 120 ; superintendent of do.—John Y. Scott, Hawick Mills ; Precentor—James H. Anderson, High Street. Church Officers — James Pringle, O'Connell Street ; and Peter Young, Buccleuch Street. Church Treasurer and Session Clerk—Anthony Dodds, Buccleuch Street.

PARISH CHURCH, Wilton—see Wilton lists.

ST MARY'S CHURCH (Quoad Sacra)—Rev. John Thomson (Inducted 1860). Sittings, 700. Sabbath School attendance, 130. ; Super-

intendent of do.—Minister. Precentor—Robert Elder, High Street. Church Officer—Michael Wintrup, 2 Manse Lane. Session Clerk and Church Treasurer—George Scott, 11 Sandbed.

FREE CHURCH—Rev. J. A. Wallace (Inducted 1833); Rev. John M'Gregor, colleague and successor (Inducted 1864). Sittings, 1000. Sabbath School attendance, 350. ; superintendent of do.—George Blaikie, 46 High Street. Precentor—James Ross, Cross Wynd. Church Treasurer—Andrew Borthwick, Allars Crescent. Church Officer—James Hood, Sandbed. Session Clerk—George Blaikie, 46 High Street. Clerk to Sustentation Fund—William Kedie, Old Manse.

FREE CHURCH MISSION (West Port Territorial)—vacant—in charge of the Mission Church (formed into a Mission Church 1863). Sittings, 150. Sabbath School attend., 65 ; Superintendent of do.—Andrew Cochrane, Orrock Place. Precentor—James Marchbanks, Round Close. Church Treasurer—William Kedie, Old Manse.

U. P. CHURCH (Allars)—Rev. Robert Muir, M.A. (Inducted 1864). Sittings, 750. Sabbath School attendance, 120 ; Superintendent of do.—James Ovens, Silver Street. Precentor—William Wilson, Teviot Crescent. Church Officer—Joseph Turnbull, Melgund Place. Church Treasurer—Bailie Waugh, High Street. Session Clerk and Treasurer for Missionary purposes—Bailie Waugh.

U. P. CHURCH (East Bank)—Rev. James M'Ewen (Inducted 1862). Sittings, 800. Sabbath School attendance, 230 ; Superintendent of do.—Mungo Wilson, Silver Street. Precentor—James Stainton, Melgund Place. Church Officer—Andrew Armstrong, Bridge Street. Church Treasurer, Session Clerk, and Treasurer for Mission Purposes—James Turnbull, High Street. Secretary for Mission Purposes—James Brydon, High Street. Town Missionary—Mr Fairgrieve, Bourtree Bank.—East Bank Mission Sabbath School attendance, 80. Superintendent—Mr. Fairgrieve.

U.P. CHURCH (West)—Rev. James Parlane, A.M. (Inducted 1857). Sittings, 599. Church Treasurers—Andrew Irvine and John Ballantyne ; Session Clerk—Andrew Irvine, 26 High Street ; Sabbath School attendance, 60 ; Superintendent of do.—John Ballantyne, Wilton Crescent.

CONGREGATIONALIST—Rev. William Munro (Inducted 1836). Sittings, 300. Sabbath School attendance, 70. ; Superintendent of do.—Adam Scott, Bourtree Place. Precentor—a Lady. Treasurer for Missions—Alexander Michie, 6 O'Connell Street

BAPTIST—Vacant. Sittings, 100. Sabbath School attendance, 28 ; Superintendent of do. and Church Treasurer—J. C. Hawkins, 2 Slitrig Crescent.

EVANGELICAL UNION—Rev. David Hislop (Inducted 1864). Sittings, 400. Sabbath School attendance, 100 ; Superintendent of do.—Richard Purdom, 7 Kirkstyle. Precentor—Thomas Brown, High Street. Church Treasurer—Richard Purdom. Church Officer—Andrew Byres, Howegate.

ST. CUTHBERT'S EPISCOPALIAN—Rev. John Rose Dakers (Inducted 1854). Sittings, 320. Sabbath School attendance, 100. Secretary and Treasurer to Church Society—Charles M. Wilson, solicitor. Church Officer—Francis Cavers, Slitrig Crescent.

ROMAN CATHOLIC—Rev. Patrick Taggart (Inducted 1847). Sittings, 400. Sabbath School attendance, 80 ; Superintendent of do.—Minister.

FAST DAYS—Wednesday before last Sunday of June and second Sunday of December.

NATIONAL BIBLE SOCIETY (BRANCH).

President—James Douglas, Esq. of Cavers.
Secretary—Rev. James Parlane.
Treasurer and Depositarian—James Dalgleish, bookseller.

Committee—Messrs George Blaikie, Jas. Turnbull, Andrew Waugh, Mungo Wilson, Andrew Irvine, Thos. Purdom, John Armstrong ; together with all Ministers and Missionaries who are subscribers.

COLPORTEUR MISSION (estab. 1857).

COMMITTEE.

Rev. John Thomson, St. Mary's, Hawick ; Rev. William Munro, Bourtree Place.
Secretary and Treasurer—Rev. James Stewart, Wilton.
Colporteur—John Gordon, Howdenburn, Wilton.

Subscriptions for the year 1863, £26 : 19 : 6 (which includes £10 from James Douglas, Esq,, of Cavers).

The Colporteur's sales of books and periodicals for the year 1863 numbered 97 bibles and testaments, 1747 books, 12,402 periodicals ; representing a value of £159 : 14 : 6. The books, etc., for sale, and a quantity of tracts for gratis distribution, are supplied by the Edinburgh society. The Colporteur's district is confined to Hawick, Wilton, and the surrounding locality.

YOUNG MEN'S CHRISTIAN ASSOCIATION.

Meets in the Old Parish School (Orrock Place) for the purpose of reading original essays, and discussing subjects of religious, moral, and intellectual importance.

President—John Goodfellow.   Vice-President—Adam Scott.
Secretary—R. B. Wilson.   Treasurer—George Deans.
Recording Secretary—George Mathieson.

AUXILIARY TO THE UNITED KINGDOM ALLIANCE AND TEMPERANCE ASSOCIATION.

President—David Dundas Scott, Esq.
Vice-Presidents—John Hogg and John Goodfellow.
Treasurer—John Laing.   Corresponding Secretary—John Rule.
Recording Secretary—James Borthwick.

EDUCATIONAL INSTITUTIONS.*

PARISH AND BURGH.

Grammar School (Parochial) Buccleuch Street—Anthony Dodds, Rector ; John M'Callum, Thomas Wilson, and Miss Wilson, assistants. Average attendance, 300.
St. Mary's Parish, Brougham Place—William Murray, Master.
St. Cuthbert's School, Lynnwood—Jacob Jay, C.M., teacher ; average attendance, 150.
High School and Boarding Establishment for Young Gentlemen—James C. Mudie, 13 Buccleuch Street, Head-Master ; Jas. Morrison and Miss Ferrall, assistants.
Episcopal School, Hope Park (in Wilton)—Miss Jessie Hart, C.M. Average attendance, 60.
Roman Catholic School—   , Teacher ; average attend., 50.

LADIES' SCHOOLS.

Miss Cumming, Melgund Place.
Miss Davidson, Slitrig Bank.
Misses M'Caskie, Bourtree Place Seminary and Boarding Establishment for Young Ladies.
Mrs. and the Misses Dumbreck's Boarding Establishment and Day School for Young Ladies, North Bridge Street,
Misses Rodgers' Seminary for Young Ladies, Hope Park, Wilton.
Miss Watt's, East Bank U.P. Mission House, off Dickson St., Wilton.

INDUSTRIAL RAGGED SCHOOL.

Supported by voluntary subscriptions. The property, consisting of boys' and girls' schoolrooms, house, and garden accommodation, was built in 1858, one-half by local subscription, and partly by a donation of £150 from the Fergusson Fund, and the other half by Government grant ; the ground was given by His Grace the Duke of Buccleuch, gratis.

William Ogilvie, Esq., of Chesters, President.
Rev. Dr. MacRae, Secretary. Thos. Purdom, writer, Treasurer.
James Ker, Teacher.   Average attendance, 100.

PAROCHIAL BOARD†—(OFFICE, KIRKSTYLE PLACE).

COMMITTEE.

William Munro, Esq. of Bourtree Place, Chairman.

Rev. J. Rose Dakers.	George Oliver.
Walter Laurie.	Robert Thomson.
Thomas Young.	Alexander M. Wilson.
Robert Milligan.	Andrew Robison.
William Burnet.	William Elliot, Loan.
James Sharp.	George Fraser.
William Young.	George T. Pringle.

---

* Children in the parish of Hawick, from 5 to 15, attending school during the 1st week of April 1864, 1275 ; of all ages, 1318.
† The Parochial parishes of Hawick and Cavers retain the management of the poor of the parish of Teviothead (see Teviothead).

William Norman Kennedy, Inspector and Collector.

Medical Officer and Public Vaccinator—D. M'Leod, surgeon.

Inspector of Lodging Houses and Nuisances—Daniel Munro, Superintendent of Police.

Average No. of Poor on Roll, 320.

Rate of Assessment, 11d. per £ on owner and occupier, less 25 per cent. off house property, 27½ off mills, and 12½ off lands. Total Assessment for 1863-4, £2020 : 5 : 4.

George Turnbull, accountant, Auditor.

(For Parochial Board, Wilton, *see* Wilton lists.)

COMBINATION POORHOUSE.

The Poorhouse was opened for the reception of Paupers at Whitsunday 1857. The Combination consists of the parishes of Hawick, Hobkirk, Wilton, Roberton, Cavers, Ashkirk, Minto, Lilliesleaf, Kirkhope, and Kirkton.

Chairman—William Munro, Esq. Vice-Chairman, George Oliver, Esq.

Medical Officer—D. M'Leod, Surgeon.

Governor—Mr J. Smeaton.   Matron—Mrs Smeaton.

Secretary and Treasurer—William Norman Kennedy.

The Committee consists of delegates from each of the parishes forming the combination.

Average Number of Inmates, 60.

PAROCHIAL BURIAL GROUND (HAWICK), WELLGATE.

Provided in 1863, under the Burial Ground (Scotland) Act 1855, at a cost of over £2500. Under the Act half of the ground is free. Layers in the saleable half are disposed of at £2, £1, 10s., and 7s. 6d. each.

COMMITTEE.

William Munro, Chairman.

Robert Thomson.	William Young.
Rev. J. Rose Dakers.	Walter Laurie.
Robert Milligan.	William Burnet.
George Oliver.	A. M. Wilson.
Adam Melrose.	Thomas Young.
G. T. Pringle.	Walter Laidlaw.

William Norman Kennedy, Clerk.   Adam Scott, Sexton.

(For Parochial Burial Ground, Wilton, *see* Wilton lists).

SLAUGHTER HOUSE (BURGH).

Site obtained ; buildings not yet erected.

Convener of the Committee—John Melrose.

HOUSE OF REFUGE—(LOAN).

Supported by voluntary contribution.

COMMITTEE.

Provost and the Bailies.

Messrs William Nixon.	Messrs William Munro.
John Wilson.	David Pringle.
Robert Thomson.	William M'Kie.

William Turnbull, Treasurer.   Managers—Mr. and Mrs. Smith.

Average Annual Income, £40.

FEMALE CLOTHING SOCIETY.

For supplying clothes gratis to the Ragged and West Port Mission Schools.

President—Mrs Pringle of Wilton Lodge.

INSPECTRESSES.

Miss Ewen.	Miss Mary Douglas.
Miss Margaret Moncrieff.	Mrs James Oliver.
Miss Douglass.	

COLLECTORS.

Miss Margaret Ewen.	Miss Douglas.
Miss Margaret Moncrieff.	Miss Mary Douglas.
Mrs R. Armstrong, Secretary.	Mrs Harkness, Treasurer.

Mrs Grieve, 17 High Street, Storekeeper.

DORCAS SOCIETY.

MEMBERS.

Mrs Walter Wilson, Orchard ; Mrs Watson, Wilton Bank ; Miss Watson, Wilton Bank ; Mrs George Hobkirk, Slitrig Cottage ; Mrs Charles Kirk, Buccleuch Street ; Miss M'Leod, Buccleuch Street ; Mrs John Wilson, Ladylaw House ; Mrs John Laing, Slitrig Crescent.

Treas., Sec., and Store Keeper—Mrs. John Laing, Slitrig Crescent.

CHARITABLE BEQUEST.

Orrock's Mortification (1711)—Interest of 9000 Merks to Rector and Mathematical Master of Grammar School.

Trustees (elected 1853).

Rev. Dr. MacRae, and George Oliver, Esq., Banker.

SICK AND BURIAL SOCIETIES.

Several of these exist, and although most of them bear the name of special factories, they are not confined in their operations. All are conducted on nearly the same principles. The following are those of the

FORESTERS' ANNUAL BENEFIT SOCIETY,

the most important and strongest general society in the town. Every member must pay 2d. weekly to the sick fund, and may deposit 6d. or more, weekly, if convenient. Every member when sick shall receive six shillings weekly for the first eight weeks, five shillings weekly for the six succeeding weeks, and to continue at three shillings weekly up to the 16th of May. Any member having received the sick allowance for these two first periods cannot claim them a second time, whether he may have received these sums in succession or at intervals. If a member dies, the sum of £2 shall be given as funeral money, and his heirs shall receive the full amount of his deposits, exclusive of sick money, paid to the time of his decease. The funds of the society shall be divided on the 16th day of May, when every member shall receive the full amount of his deposits, together with the share of sick money which may be in the funds, with the exception of 4d. to the clerk and 2d. to the stewards, from each member. No. of members, 235. Under the management of this society there is a

YOUNG WOMANS' YEARLY DEPOSIT AND SICK SOCIETY,

conducted on the same principles, but having a smaller class of payments. 151 members.
William Richardson, North Bridge Street, Clerk and Treasurer.

WILLIAM WILSON & SONS' SOCIETY.

No. of Members at last division, 100. Secretary—John Rule, Back Damgate.

No. 1 SOCIETY.

No. of Members at last division, 139. Secretary—John Scott, Teviot Crescent.

NIXON & M'KIE'S SOCIETY.

No. of Members at last division, 126. Secretary—Robert Scott, Langlands Place.

W. ELLIOT'S FACTORY.

No. of Members at last division, 192. Secretary—John Turnbull.

WM. WATSON & SONS' SOCIETY.

No. of Members at last division, 95. Secretary—Andrew Wallace.

MASON LODGES.

ST JAMES' BORDER UNION ROYAL ARCH, 424 (estab. 1863).

R.W.M.—Walter Lawrie, baker.
D.M.—Daniel Munro, superintendent of police.
Secretary—George Brown.   Treasurer—William Telfer.

ST JOHN'S, 111 (estab. 1763).

R.W.M.—John G. Wilson, painter.
D.M.—John Nichol.
Secretary—William Middlemas.   Treasurer—John Kyle.

TOTAL ABSTINENCE SOCIETY (Instituted 1838).

President—William Inglis, Back Damgate.
Vice-President—Robert Tough.
Recording Secretary—Andrew Borthwick.
Corresponding Secretary—James Renwick.
Treasurer—James Hardie.

ARCHÆOLOGICAL SOCIETY (ORROCK PLACE—estab. 1856).

Open on Saturdays—Admittance, 2d.

Patron—His Grace the Duke of Buccleuch and Queensberry.
President—W. N. Kennedy.
Vice-Presidents—Robert Michie and James Hogg.
Secy.—David Watson.   Treas.—John Guthrie, Bridge Street.
Curator of Museum—John Turnbull, Melgund Place.
James Bunyan, Conservator.

Annual Subscription, 2s. 6d. ; Life, £1.

LIBRARY (SILVER STREET—estab. 1762).

Committee—J. S. Chisholme of Stirches ; D. Pringle of Wilton Lodge ; Rev. Dr. MacRae ; William Watson of Bucklands, W. Nixon, and Wm. M'Kie, Esqs.
Librarian—Mrs Armstrong.   Number of Vols. 6000.
Yearly Subscriptions for Proprietors, 10s. ; Annual Readers, 15s.

READING ROOM (TOWER HOTEL—estab. 1835).

Thomas Cathrae, Secretary and Treasurer.
Annual Subscription, £1, 1s.

ECLECTIC BOOK CLUB (Instituted 1st Nov. 1858).

Treasurer—James Hogg.
Secretary and Librarian—David Watson, Teviot Crescent.
Number of Members limited to 25.   Annual Subscription, 4s.
Entry Money, 2s.

HORTICULTURAL SOCIETY.

Patron—Sir William Scott, Bart., M.P.
President—John Turnbull.   Vice-President—A. Kennedy.
Secretary and Treasurer—Peter Patterson.
Meetings for Exhibition are held in July and September.

Amount of Prizes given in 1864, £25.

FARMERS' CLUB (estab. 1776).

Meets in Tower Hotel first Thursday of each month.

Dr Elliot, Goldielands, Secretary.

Annual Subscription (which includes all expenses), £2.

"This Club [the oldest existing club of the kind in the district—probably in the kingdom] has contributed in no small degree to the furtherance of the agricultural interests." It established the Hawick Corn Market in 1778 ; the Rink Fair (in Jedburgh parish, now extinct) in the following year ; in 1826 the Hawick May Market for cattle and horses ; and in 1780, the market for hiring hinds. For some years it held ploughing matches—"the first was held on the farm of Ashiebank, 15th April 1786, when ten ploughs started ; at the following year's match first 25th January, the second premium was gained by a servant of Sir Gilbert Elliot of Minto, who ploughed with two oxen *without a driver*."* Previous to the establishment of this Club the town seems to have had no market whatever.

---

* It was customary, when ploughing with oxen, to have a driving boy to "goad" them on with a pointed stick.

We incidentally notice in a Berwick publication of the period (January 1786), that the Jedburgh Farmers' Society were to have a ploughing match on the haugh lands of Mountholy, on the first Wednesday of March 1786, when silver medals of different values were to be given to the first, second, and third, best ploughmen, "bearing a characteristical device and the name of the winner."

By a notice in the *British Chronicle* [Kelso paper] of the following 10th March, we find that the Jedburgh match had been delayed owing to the severity of the season, "the rivers Tweed and Teviot both being frozen over, and the winter amusements of skating, curling, etc., being carried on upon them" (this must have been one of the old-fashioned winters, about which the old folks talk so much about) ; but the match eventually came off on the 22d March, "upon Commodore Elliot's haugh lands at Mountholy, when 15 ploughs and ploughmen contended for victory, by ploughing each several ridges, which took up great part of the day. After they had all finished their tasks, and their work accurately examined by the judges appointed by the Society, assisted by other gentlemen, distinguished for their knowledge in agriculture, the preferences were decided as follow, viz.—the first prize or medal to Andrew M'Lean, ploughman to Mr. Alexander Roberton, tenant of Nisbet ; the second to Andrew Walker, ploughman to Mr. George Cranston, tenant of Plowland ; and the third to William Mills, ploughman to Mr. Thomas Scott, tenant of Nisbet. The judges, as well as the very numerous and respectable spectators, expressed the highest approbation of the performances in general, many of which were remarkably well done, and treated the whole competitors in so proper and genteel a manner, as gives reason to believe this *first essay* [the italics are our own] will be productive of others, and tend to promote an useful spirit of emulation among the ploughmen of the country ; profitable to themselves, their masters, and country.

To Jedburgh, therefore, belongs the credit of having initiated ploughing matches in the district. As a commentary on the prevalent opinion, that the winters in Great Britain have ceased to be so extreme, as they once were, we extract from the Berwick publication,

TEVIOTDALE FARMERS' CLUB (estab. 1859).

President—William Aitchison, Esq., Linhope.

James Oliver, Howpasley, and James Oliver, Bridge House, Joint-Secretaries.

Annual Subscription (which includes all expenses), 25s.

Meets in Tower Hotel third Thursday of each month for discussing agricultural questions.

WEST-TEVIOTDALE AGRICULTURAL SOCIETY.

Established 1835 at the suggestion of the late James Douglas, Esq. of Cavers. Comprehending the parishes of Ashkirk, Ancrum, Bowden, Bedrule, Castleton, Cavers, Hawick, Hobkirk, Kirkton, Lilliesleaf, Minto, Roberton, Southdean, Teviothead, and Wilton.

Patron—His Grace the Duke of Buccleuch.

HONORARY DIRECTORS.

The Landed Proprietors, Members of the Society.

Allan E. Lockhart, Esq. of Borthwickbrae, President of Committee.

James Oliver, Howpasley, Vice-President of Committee.

James Oliver, Bridge House, Hawick, Treasurer and Secretary.

Subscription for Landed-Proprietors, £1, 1s. ; Ordinary Subscription, 10s.

The object of this association is to promote the interests of agriculture in general, and more especially to give premiums for the most improved breeds of horses, cattle, and sheep. The society holds an exhibition of stock on the day preceding the Hawick Tup and Lamb Fair in September (*see* p. 305), when prizes are given ; amounting in 1864 to nearly £80, including a silver medal and money prizes given by the Highland and Agricultural Society of Scotland for Cheviot sheep. The exhibition takes place at the secretary's auction mart at Bourtree Place. Of late a keener interest has been taken in this show, and a higher value has been set on its honours, than was the case for some years previously, when it was very indifferently patronized by those most concerned in making it a successful gathering. Indeed the competition was often so meagre as to quality of stock and so small in numbers, that there seemed a danger of a termination to these exhibitions. The exhibition of 1864, in all classes, was pronounced to be one of the best since the establishment of the society.

A ploughing competition, under the auspices of this society, takes place in the district annually, when a silver medal and money prizes are awarded ; there is generally from 35 to 45 ploughs on the field.

---

already mentioned, this notice of the winter following, viz., that ending March 1787 :—

Berwick, April 1, 1787.—"It is a remarkable fact in the history of Scotland, that a gentleman who is extensively concerned in the salmon fisheries, and who had built a very large icehouse with a view of preserving the fish for the London market, could not procure a single particle of ice for that purpose through the winter ; *such has been the singular mildness of the season.*"

ORNITHOLOGICAL SOCIETY (estab. 1849).

For the Improvement of Fancy Canary and other Birds.

President—Walter Ballantyne.

Secretary—William Trotter.   Treasurer—James Riddell.

Annual Exhibition and Competition in November each year, when prizes of the average amount of £10 are awarded.

SOUTH OF SCOTLAND CHAMBER OF COMMERCE.

President—Walter Laing, Esq., Hawick.

Vice-President—William Brown, Esq., Gala Hill, Galashiels.

Honorary Treasurer—William M'Kie, Esq., Hawick.

Secretaries—Thomas Cathrae, Hawick ; Robert Stewart, Galashiels.

HONORARY MEMBERS.

Sir Wm. Scott of Ancrum, Bart., M.P.	Sir G. G. Montgomery, Bart., M.P.
Lord Henry J. Scott, M.P.	D. Robertson of Ladykirk, M.P.
A. E. Lockhart of Borthwickbrae	Sir H. R. F. Davie of Creedy, Bart., M.P.
J. J. H. Johnstone, of Annandale, M.P.	William Ewart. Esq., M.P.
	Richard Hodgson, Esq., M.P.

COUNCIL.

Walter Laing, Hawick	David Ballantyne, Walkerburn
William Sanderson, Galashiels	George Rutherford, Jedburgh
George Roberts, Selkirk	Robert Scott, Dumfries
George Wilson, Hawick	Robert Gill, Innerleithen
William M'Kie, do.	James Carmichael, Hawick
Walter Wilson, do.	Wm. Brown, Gala Hill, Galashiels
William Haldane, Galashiels	Adam L. Cochrane, Galashiels
John Laing, Hawick	Alexander Reid, Langholm
William Irvine, do.	Henry Brown, Selkirk
William A. Sanderson, Galashiels	George Hilson, sen., Jedburgh
D. C. Alexander, Selkirk	Walter Thorburn, Peebles
R. Byres, Langholm	

EXCHANGE COMPANY (LIMITED).

DIRECTORS.

Provost George Wilson ; David Pringle, Esq., Wilton Lodge ; John S. Chisholme, Esq. of Stirches ; A. E. Lockhart, Esq., of Borthwickbrae ; E. H. Maxwell, Esq. of Teviotbank ; Messrs G. H. Fraser, merchant ; Adam Elliot, Goldielands ; Ephraim Selby, Hassendeanbank ; Andrew Haddon, Honeyburn ; Walter Laing, manufacturer ; Robert Thomson, factor, Loan ; William Grieve, Branxholm Park ; John Melrose, engineer.

Secretary and Treasurer—James Carmichael, solicitor, Hawick.

GAS COMPANY (estab. 1830).

President—Robert Thomson.

Manager—John Young.   Clerk—James Carmichael.

Collector—James Shiel, Albion Place.

Price 6s. 3d. per 1000 feet.   Amount of Stock, £4400.

Dividend, 10 per cent.

CO-OPERATIVE STORE COMPANY (Instituted 1838).

Secretary—Robert Tough.

Depots—62 High Street, Ladylaw Place, and 7 Sandbed (which *see*).

HAWICK BENEFIT BUILDING SOCIETY (estab. 1852).

For the purpose of assisting its members to build or buy houses for themselves, the society granting advances of £75 upon every £20, held in shares by the members ; which advances are repayable by half-yearly instalments, at the rate of 8 per cent per annum, clearing off the debt in about 12 years. The society had originally 56 members, about one-half of whom have obtained houses ; there are now only 5 shareholders who have not obtained houses, the others having sold out.

President—John Richardson.   Vice-President—Thomas Tait.

Secretary—James Douglas.   Treasurer—James Inglis.

Trustees—John Laing, manufacturer ; Thomas Brunton, joiner ; William Munro, ropemaker.

WORKING MEN'S BUILDING AND INVESTMENT SOCIETY.

Instituted April 1864, with the view of increasing and improving the House Accommodation for the Working Classes, and of enabling Working Men to occupy their own Houses.

This Society, by the report of 1864, consists of 180 members, who possess amongst them upwards of 600 shares, representing a capital of upwards of £3000.

PATRONS.

His Grace the Duke of Buccleuch.	Sir W. Scott of Ancrum, Bart. M.P.
	William Nixon, Esq., Lynnwood.

DIRECTORS.

George Wilson, Esq., Provost of Hawick.	Mr. James Thoms, coal salesman, Hawick.
Rev. James Stewart, Minister of Wilton.	Mr. John Deans, gardener, Hawick.
Rev. J. R. Dakers, The Parsonage.	Mr. John Rule, warehouseman, Hawick.
Thomas Laidlaw, Esq., manufacturer.	Mr. John Bell, foreman, Hawick.
Mr. Walter Paisley, ironmonger Hawick.	Mr. James Hogg, stocking-maker, Hawick.

TRUSTEES.

The Rev. John Thomson, Minister of St. Mary's | Gilbert Davidson, Esq., Banker, Hawick.
Mr. Jas. Douglas, Brougham Place |

President—David Pringle, Esq., of Wilton Lodge.
Vice-President—Walter Laing, Esq., Spring Bank.
Secretary—Mr. Charles M. Wilson, solicitor.
Treasurer—Mr. William Martin, warehouseman.
Bankers—The British Linen Company's Bank, Hawick.

ANGLING CLUB.

(Organised in 1858 for the Protection of Fresh Water Trout in the river Teviot and its tributaries).

President—William Ogilvie, Esq., of Chesters.
Vice-President—John Turnbull, Slitrig Crescent, Hawick.
Treasurer—James Elliot, merchant, Hawick.
Secretary—James Elliot, manufacturer, Hawick.
Annual Subscription, 6d.

HAWICK AND WILTON CRICKET CLUB (estab. 1849).

Captain—William Dryden, Wilton.
Secretary—William Sharp.   Treasurer—Adam Hart, Wilton.
The Club is supported by subscriptions amongst the members.

COURSING CLUB (estab. 1864).

Takes place annually, in December, in the locality, and continues or two days. At the meeting for 1864, 48 dogs were entered.
Judge—Mr. Charlton, jun.   Secretary—Adam Wilson.

BOWLING CLUB (estab. 1854).

President—John Young Scott, Hawick Mill.
Secy.—Walter Douglas. Treas.—John Nichol, Slitrig Crescent.
Entry Money, 20s.   Annual Subscription, 7s. 6d.

CURLING CLUB (estab. 1740).

Patron—His Grace the Duke of Buccleuch.
President—John Y. Scott.   Vice-President—Adam Laidlaw.
Secretary and Treasurer—John Nichol.
Entry Money, 5s.   Annual Subscription, 5s.
Curling Pond at Hilliesland, a mile south of Hawick.

SAXHORN BAND.

Head-Quarters—Town Hall. Bandmaster—Stephen Teal.

This Band, in 1863, took the second prize, and in 1864 the fifth prize, at the Glasgow Grand National Bands' Competition.

UPPER TEVIOTDALE VOLUNTEER RIFLE CORPS.

4TH COMPANY OF ROXBURGHSHIRE BATTALION.

Head-Quarters—Mill Path.

A COMPANY.

John Scott Chisholme, Esq. of Stirches, Captain-Commandant.
William Dickson, Esq., of Wellfield, Lieutenant.
Francis Deans, postmaster, Hawick, Ensign.

B. COMPANY.

William Scott Watson, Esq , of Burnhead, Captain.
William Scott Elliot, manufacturer, Hawick, Lieutenant.
Robert Selby, Hassendeanbank, Ensign.
George W. Thomson, M.D., Honorary Assistant Surgeon.
James Carmichael, Esq., solicitor, Hawick, Honorary Secretary.
Robert Hutton, Drill Sergeant.   Francis Gray, Bandmaster.
Honorary Members—39. Effective Force—186.
Annual Subscription for Honorary Members, £1 ; Effectives, 5s.

BANK BRANCHES.

BRITISH LINEN COMPANY (opened 1799)—William & Gilbert Davidson, Agents ; William Davidson, jun., Accountant.

COMMERCIAL BANK OF SCOTLAND (opened 1820)—George and James Oliver, Agents ; Lauchlan Gentles, Accountant.

NATIONAL BANK OF SCOTLAND (opened 1852)—Thomas Purdom, Agent ; John M'Nab, Accountant.

ROYAL BANK OF SCOTLAND (opened 1856)—Jas. Carmichael, Agent ; John Turnbull, Accountant.

N. S. SAVINGS' BANK (established 1815)—Andrew Irvine, Actuary ; D. Watson, Secretary. No. of Depositors at 20th November 1864, 1214. Amount of Deposits at same period, £25,292 : 12 : 3. Interest allowed, 3 per cent.

PENNY BANK (estab. 1859)—Open in the Town Hall every Saturday evening. Actuary—Mark Currie ; Secretary—D. Watson. No. of Depositors, 1073. Amount of Deposits, £178 : 18 : 2.

INSURANCE AGENTS.

BRITON MEDICAL & GENERAL LIFE ASSOCIATION....... } Andrew Scott, 8 Buccleuch Street.
CALEDONIAN ....W. N. Kennedy, Inspector of Poor.
CITY OF GLASGOW...........T. Cathrae, Chamber of Commerce.

EDINBURGH LIFE ....James Harkness, builder.
ENGLISH AND SCOTTISH LAW }
INSURANCE CO. OF SCOTLAND } Wilson & Anderson, writers.
LANCASHIRE FIRE DEPARTMENT T. Cathrae, Chamber of Commerce.
LIFE ASSOCIATION............John Turnbull, Royal Bank.
NATIONAL GUARANTEE INSU- }
   RYSHIP ASSOCIATION ..... } Thomas Purdom, writer.
NATIONAL (OF SCOTLAND).....Thomas Purdom, writer.
NORFOLK FARMER'S CAT. IN... James Carmichael, writer.
NORTH BRITISH & MERCANTILE G. and J. Oliver, writers.
NORWICH UNION ....Andrew Scott, 8 Buccleuch Street.
NORWICH & LONDON ACCI- }
   DENT AND CASUALTY .... } James Harkness, builder.
PLATE GLASS INSURANCE Co..Wilson & Anderson, writers.
QUEEN'S....................Alex. Wemyss, commission agent.
ROYAL LIVERPOOL...........Adam Hislop, commission agent.
STANDARD LIFE ASSURANCE }
   COMPANY .... } Wilson & Anderson, writers.
SCOTTISH EQUITABLE.........Thomas Purdom, writer.
SCOTTISH PROVIDENT........Bunyan & Gentles, Com. Bank.
SCOTTISH PROVINCIAL........Andrew Irvine, Savings' Bank.
SCOTTISH UNION.............James Carmichael, writer.
SUN ....A. Oliver & Son, auctioneers.
THE EUROPEAN ASSURANCE }
   SOCIETY .... } A. Oliver & Son, auctioneers.
UNITED KINGDOM TEMPERANCE }
   AND GENERAL PROVIDENT... } Richard Purdom, Kirkstyle Place.
WEST OF ENGLAND FIRE AND }
   LIFE INSURANCE COY. .... } W. Haddon (of Kirk & H.), writer.
WESTMINSTER GENERAL FIRE }
   AND LIFE ASSURANCE CO.. } Wilson & Anderson, writers.

PROCURATORS AND NOTARIES PUBLIC.

Anderson, John (of Wilson & A.), 2 Howgate.
Carmichael, James, N.P., 12 and 14 High Street.
Haddon, Walter (of Kirk & H.), 3 Buccleuch Street.
Oliver, George, N.P. (of G. & J. Oliver), 4 Tower Knowe.
Oliver, James, N.P.,   do.,   do.
Purdom, Thomas, N.P., 31 High Street.
Wilson, Charles M. (of Wilson & Anderson), N.P., 2 Howgate.

ACCOUNTANTS, &c.

Scott, Andrew, 8 Buccleuch Street.
Scott, Robert, 43 High Street.
Thomson, Robert, factor for Cavers estate, 17 Loan.
Turnbull, George, 6 Teviot Crescent.

MEDICAL PRACTITIONERS.

Brydone, James, M.D., 4 Sandbed.
Grant, John, M.D., 47 High Street.*
M'Leod, Donald, surgeon, 14 Buccleuch Street.
Paterson, A., M.D., 8 Buccleuch Street.
Thomson, George W., M.D., North Bridge Street.

VETERINARY SURGEONS.

Andrew Bowie, 1 West Port ; James Bowie, 41 High Street.

NEWSPAPER.

"Hawick Advertiser and Roxburghshire Gazette" (established 1854), issued every Saturday ; Publishing Office, 5 High Street ; Printing Office, 9 High Street ; James Haining & Co., proprietors, printers and publishers. Advocates Social Improvement and Parliamentary Reform.

WOOLLEN MILLS (HAWICK SIDE).

TEVIOT CRESCENT MILLS—Tweeds—William Laidlaw & Sons.
LYNWOOD MILL—Yarns and Spinnings—W. Laidlaw & Sons.
TEVIOT MILLS—Hosiery and Tweeds—Walter Wilson.
WEENSLAND MILL—Tweeds and Blankets—Wilson & Armstrong.
TOWER KNOWE AND STONEFIELD MILLS—Hosiery, Blankets, and Yarns—William Elliot & Sons.
WALTER'S WYND—Hosiery—Nixon & M'Kie.
SLITRIG CRESCENT—Lamb's Wool and Merino Hosiery—John Laing.
CROSSWYND—Hosiery—R. Pringle & Son.
NORTH BRIDGE STREET—Tweeds and Hosiery—Laing & Irvine.
MILL BANK—Hosiery—Robert Ewen ; Foreman—Andw. Richardson.
           (WILTON SIDE).
DANGERFIELD—Tweeds—W. Watson & Sons.
LADYLAW—Tweeds and Hosiery—John Wilson & Son.
LANGLANDS,   Do.,   John Wilson & Son.
WILTON.   Do.,   Dicksons & Laings ; Manager— Thos. Scott.

DYERS.

Sutherland, James, Teviot Road.
Turnbull, John, & Son, Slitrig Crescent.

* Dr. Grant is representative of the eighteenth branch of the honourable family of Grant of Grant. He is the fifth descendant of Patrick, progenitor of the family of Wester Elchies, second son of James, laird of Grant, and of Lady Mary Stewart, daughter of James, Earl of Moray, by Lady Anne Gordon, daughter of the Marquis of Huntly—Anno 1663. Dr. Grant is Master of the Teviotdale Otter Hounds.

SKINNERS.

Little & Murray, High Street.	Scott, William, Slitrig Crescent.
Nichol, John, Slitrig Crescent.	Wilson & Son, Teviot Crescent.

FLOUR MILLS.

HAWICK—John Young Scott.
TROW MILL (2 miles east of Hawick on the Teviot)—Hugh Goodfellow.
ROUGHHEUGH (Wilton)—William R. Wilson.

AUCTIONEERS.

Andrew Oliver & Son, Bourtree Place.
Robert Milligan (Appraiser), 80 High Street.
Henry Paterson, 61 High Street.

PORK-CURERS.*

James Swan, 27 High Street.   Andw. Borthwick, 4 Allars Crescent.

DAIRIES.

James Stein, Hawick Muir ; William Goodwin, Kirkton. Both come daily to Hawick.

CONVEYANCE BY RAILWAY.

By North British Railway to Kelso, Jedburgh, Newcastle, etc., South and East ; and Edinburgh, etc., North. By "Waverley Route" to Carlisle, etc.

CARRIERS.

Borthwick Head—Andrew Walker, Friday morning, Mr. Walker's, Sandbed.
Borthwick Water—John Elliot, Tuesday and Friday, Ewe and Lamb.
Carlisle—M. Murray, every Monday night, Bridge Hotel.
Cavers and Kirkton—Andrew Walker, Thursday, Mr. Walker's, Sandbed.
Chesters—Archibald Scott, Thursday, Crown.
Deanburnhaugh—Robert Brown, Thursday, Bridge Hotel.
Edinburgh and Glasgow, and all parts of Scotland, by Railway, daily.
Ettrick—Thos. Jackson, every Monday alternately, Fiddler's, grocer, Old Kirk Style ; Matthew Palmer, Eskdale Muir, Bridge Hotel.
Jedburgh and Kelso—Thomas Robson, Wednesday and Saturday, Bridge Hotel.
Kelso and Berwick, and all parts of the South, by Railway, daily.

* The number of carcases cured in Hawick during the past season amounted to 1000, weighing fully 200,000 pounds, and valued at £4500. See Kelso, p. 97.

Langholm, Ecclefechan, &c.—M. Murray, Monday and Thursday, Bridge Hotel.
Lilliesleaf—John Fergrieve, Thursday, J. Campbell, baker ; Thomas Davidson, Plough Inn.
Newcastleton—William Scott, every Thursday ; James Mable, Geo. Brown's, 9 High Street, or Plough Inn.
Newcastleton, Netheroakshaw, and Branton—Per Rail.
North Tyne—Per Rail.
Selkirk—D. Chisholm, Tuesday and Friday, Ewe and Lamb ; Wm. Scott, Monday, Fiddler's, Old Kirk Style.
Sintonmossend—W. Scott, fortnightly, Wednesday, Fiddler's, Old Kirk Style.
Shankend—Andrew Walker, Monday and Thursday—Mr. Walker's, Sandbed.
Slitrig Water—James Mable, weekly, Saturday, Ewe and Lamb, or George Brown's, grocer, 9 High Street.
Southdean—Adam Short, Thursday, Victoria Inn.
Teviot every two weeks and Ashkirk every week—George Hogg, Plough Inn, every Thursday.
Teviot Water—Christopher Glendinning, Thursday and Saturday, Ewe and Lamb.
Teviot, Rule, and Slitrig—Walter Jeffrey, Wednesday, William Jeffrey, 23 High Street.
Tyne and Keilder, England—James Mable, fortnightly, Saturday, George Brown's, Grocer, 9 High Street, or Ewe and Lamb.

DISTRICT OF HAWICK STATUTE LABOUR TRUST.

Qualification of Trustees, £100 Scots. Comprehends the parishes of Ashkirk, Cavers, Hawick, Roberton, Kirkton, Wilton, and Teviothead.

George and James Oliver, Hawick, Clerks.
Andrew Wilson, Hawick, Surveyor.
Annual Meeting—Third Tuesday of April.

DIRECTORY.

TRADES, RESIDENTS, AND PUBLIC OFFICES.

Those marked thus (*) are Registered Voters for the County.

The letter (H) after the street titles designates Hawick Parish, (W) designates Wilton Parish.

Allars Crescent (H.)

Baptist Chapel (vacant—*see* p. 310)
4*Borthwick, Andrew, pork curer
17 Chesser, James, wash-house and bath lessee
6 Davidson, John, designer, modeller, dealer in cements, and
  plasterer
    Principal Modeller—Leopoldo Arrighi
13 Douglas, Walter, clerk (W. Elliot & Sons)
1 Grieve, Miss, milliner
  Hawkins, R. Y., cabinet-maker and turner
3*Hobkirk, John, joiner and cabinet-maker
4*Inglis, William, mill manager (W. Elliot & Sons)
11*Melrose, James, wool-sorter
13*Millar, William, stocking maker
12*Muir, Rev. Robert, *Allars U. P. Manse*
4 Reid, Mrs. Walter
17 Rule, Mrs. George
15 Scott, William, skinner (works, 10 Slitrig Crescent)
13 Thomson, John, clerk (John Laing, Slitrig Crescent)
2 White, John, corn merchant
10*Wilson, A. M. & J. G., painters, glaziers, &c.
7*Wilson's, Walter (of Teviot Mills) warehouse, (house, Orchard, Cavers parish)

Albion Place (W.)

*Blain, James A. H., teacher
*Brodie, Alexander, grocer.
  Hislop, Rev. R.
  Lillico, Thomas, flesher
  Marshall & Ballantyne, builders
*Marshall, John (of M. & Ballantyne)
  Post Office, James Shiel, postmaster.
  Shiel, James, *Inspector of Poor*.

Back Damgate (H.)

*Beattie, Thomas, warehouseman
  Carlyle, W., soda-water manufacturer
  Freeman, T., sinkermaker
2*Hobkirk, G., corn merchant
*Kyle, John, warehouseman
  Millin & M'Kinlay, plumbers
4 Rule, Margaret, grocer
6 Smart, William, baker

Back Row (H.)

3 Byres, Agnes, spirit dealer
8 Graham, John, spirit dealer
4*Henderson, R., dairy keeper
3 Kerr, James, tailor
7 Kyle, James, gardener
12 Pringle, George T., grocer
10*Richardson, John, china merchant
13 Taylor, John, baker

Brougham Place (H.)

*Cochrane, William
  Douglas, James, clerk (Wilson & Armstrong)
*Goold, Alexander, framesmith
*M'Ewan, Rev. James, *East Bank U. P. Manse*
*Mitchell, William, coach builder (works, Bourtree Place)
  St Mary's Parish Church School, William Murray, master
  Syme, Mrs. William

Bourtree Place (H.)

Auction Mart, A. Oliver & Son, auctioneers (chambers, Sandbed)
    Manager of Auction Mart—Adam Hogg
*Diener, Fredrick W., joiner
  East Bank U. P. Church (Rev. Jas. M'Ewen's)—*see p.*310
  M'Caskie, Misses, Bourtree House Seminary
  Munro, William, rope maker and net manufacturer
*Munro, Rev. William (of *Congregational Church*)
  Murray, Thomas, tailor
*Scott, Adam, joiner
  Scott, Mrs. Charles
*Turnbull, George (of Dickson & T., 18 High Street)

Buccleuch Street (H.)

5 Cathrae, Thomas, agent for Plashett's coals and bricks
16 Deans, John, coachman

Dickson, Mrs. W., Teviot Lodge Villa
Dodds, Anthony, rector parish school
2*Elliot, James, grocer, seedsman, and fishing tackle maker
   Free Church (Rev. Mr. Wallace's—*see* p. 310)
18 Glendinning Mrs.
10 Graham, Mrs.
20*Graham, Robert, (of Wood & G.)
19 Grieve, W., & Co., plumbers and slaters
7 Hislop, Adam, commission agent
5 *International Telegraph Company's Office*—Thomas Cathrae, agent
   Kirk & Haddon's writing chambers
6 Kyle, William, market gardener
22*Laing, A. (of L. & Irving)
17*M'Kie, William (of Nixon & M.)
14*M'Leod, Daniel, surgeon
  *M'Rae, Rev. J., D.D., *Manse*
13 Mudie, James C., head master of High School
11*Oliver, James (of G. & J. O., writers)
12 Oliver, Mrs.
   Parish Church (Rev. D. MacRae's—*see* p. 310)
   Parish School, Anthony Dodds, resident rector
8 Paterson, A., M.D.
18*Pringle Walter, (of R. P. & Son, manufacturers)
   Roman Catholic Church (Rev. P. Taggart's—*see* p. 311)
   Scott, Andrew, accountant
4 Scott, Walter, joiner
8 Scott, Mrs. Isabella
9 Scott, Mrs. Esther
19 Scott & Wight, joiners
5 *South of Scotland Chamber of Commerce*, Thomas Cathrae, secretary
3 *Stamps and Taxes*, W. Haddon, sub-collector and sub-distributor
5 Sutherland, James, dyer (works, Teviot Crescent)
15*Taggart, Rev. Patrick (of *R. C. C.*)
1*Telfer, William, grocer
   Agent for Biggs' Sheep and Lamb Dipping Composition
   Wilson, Misses, milliners

Cross Wynd (H.)

   Allars U. P. Church (Rev. Robert Muir's—*see* p. 310)
10 Brown, Thomas, flesher
13*Brown, George, carter
11*Clark, William, photographer
5 Douglas, William, saddler
  *Ewen, Robert, Millbank
5 Farquhar, Miss M.

1 Gray, Mrs. Agnes, publican (*see* No. 32 High Street)
15*Grieve, Andrew, farmer
   Hawick Prison, Michael Anderson, keeper
3 Kay, Robert, mason
6 Kerr, Mrs. M.
   Millbank Manufactory and house
16 Pringle, Robert, & Son, hosiers (*see* 1 Melgund Place)
4 Turnbull, James, shoemaker
7 Wintrup, James, shoemaker

Damside (W.)

Donaldson, A. J., chemical works.
Hogg, George, manufacturer of hosiery
Thomline, John, miner.

Dean, suburbs of—*see* p. 341

Dickson Street (W.)

Amos, Henry, cattle dealer
Clark, John, grocer
*Laidlaw, Walter, shoemaker
Millar, Robert, baker
Reid, William, farmer (formerly of Greenside Hall)
Robertson, Robert, grocer
Scott, Alexander, grocer
Yellowlees, James, grocer

Dovemount (W.)

Brydone, James, grocer
Elder, David, gardener
*Henderson, Francis, spinner
Law, Hugh, coal agent
Law, Walter, commission agent
Mathewson, George, mason
Michie, Mrs.
*Miller, Robert, spinner
Railway Hotel, Robert Learmond
Slater, Thomas, toll collector
Watson, David, clerk
Wemyss, Alexander, commission agent
Willison, Miss Agnes

Drumlanrig Place (H.)

*Glendinning, James, gardener
*Haig, David, mason
*Hunter, Thomas, farmer
*Rae, John, joiner

Fore Row (H)

7 Black, Agnes
1 Fox, Robert, grocer and spirit dealer
 Hogg, William, pavior
7 Lymburn, Hugh, spirit dealer
9*Scott, James, grocer
1*Wheelans, Andrew, grocer

Greenwynd Head (H.)

5*Andison, James, gardener

Havelock Street (W.)

*Mathieson, George, jun., mason

High Street (H.)

70 Allan, Thomas, smith
57*Anderson, James H., hatter
21 Anderson, James, soda-water manufacturer
9 Anderson, James, grocer, wine and spirit merchant
44 Anderson, Rachel, grocer
50 Bell, Mrs. Janet
17 Black, Miss Elizabeth
17 Black, Robert, bookseller and stationer
46 Blaikie, George, ironmonger
70 Borthwick, James, grocer and provision merchant
41*Bowie, James, veterinary surgeon (shop, West Port)
78 Brown, George, grocer
9 Brown, Miss Agnes
76 Brown, Thomas, bootmaker
7 British Linen Coy's. Bank, *Gilbert Davidson, resident agent
8*Brydon, James, grocer and tea merchant
29 Bunyan, George, hairdresser
61 Bunyan, John
30*Burns, William, clothier
41 Cairns, Robert, green-grocer
10*Campbell, John, baker
12-14 Carmichael, James, writing chambers
68 Charters, Francis, coal agent
68 Charters, Thomas, baker and confectioner
28*Connell, Patrick, clothier
62 Co-operative Store, John Goodfellow, manager
17 Craig, John, druggist
55 Crosbie, Elizabeth, milliner
22 Crown Hotel, Jane Grieve
5*Dalgleish, James, stationer
4 Davis, George, flesher

25 Deans, Francis, stationer
18 Dickson & Turnbulls, nursery seedsmen and florists
 Nurseries — Trinity Lands, Weensland; Laurie's Den;
 Western Nurseries
2*Easton, George, hairdresser
21 Eckford, John, merchant
3 Fiddes, John, baker
6 Fleece Inn, John Bell
40*Forsyth, Walter, flesher
46*Fraser, J. H. (of Hislop & Co.)
1 Gowans, James, watchmaker and jeweller
16*Graham, Thomas, jeweller and watchmaker
32 Gray, Agnes, publican (see No. 1 Cross Wynd)
47*Grant, John, M.D.
10 Grierson, Adam, corn merchant
17 Grieve, Mrs. Christian
25 Guild, George, tinsmith
61 Guthrie, J., & Sons, slaters and plumbers
61 Guthrie, Lewis V. (of J. G. & Sons)
61*Guthrie, J. (of J. G. & Sons)
8*Haining, James (of H. & Co.)
9 Haining, J., & Co., printers and bookbinders
20*Hall, Thomas, & Son, wool merchants
 *Hall David (of T. H. & Son)
64 Half-Moon Hotel, Mrs. Anthony Boiston
5 Hawick Advertiser Publishing Office
53*Henderson, Walter, farmer and pork dealer
6 Hill, *Robert & *James, saddlers
15 Hislop, John, & Co., drapers (see 13 Teviot Crescent)
71 Hogg, John, flesher
3*Hopper, Thomas H., druggist
26 Irvine, Andrew, heritors' clerk
67 Irving, William (of Laing & I.)
65 Jardine, Alexander, painter
23 Jeffrey, William, baker
9 Johnston, John, tailor
27 Kennedy, David, druggist
56 Kerr, George, tinsmith
74*Kyle, Francis, farmer
60 Laidlaw, Thomas, grocer
49*Laing, John, draper and coal agent
10 Laing, John, boot and shoemaker
13 Laing, Mrs.
50 Lamb, William, seedsman and florist
39 Lawrie, Walter, baker
66*Leyden, Andrew, coal agent
27 Little & Murray, skinners
39 Little, Misses, dressmakers

17 Michie, Mrs., dressmaker
80*Milligan, Robert, cabinet-maker and appraiser
25 Mitchell, Alexander, flesher
63 Moncrieff, Miss M. L. Scott
29 Murray, John, watchmaker
51*Murray, John, draper
57 Murray, John, slater, plumber, and gasfitter
75 Murray, William, china merchant
31 *National Bank of Scotland*, *Thos. Purdom, resident agent
26 *National Security Savings' Bank*, Andrew Irvine, actuary
56 Nichol, Mrs. Mary
42*Oliver, Andrew (late tobacconist)
21*Paisley, Walter, ironmonger
19*Park, David S., merchant
17 Pasley, Miss Agnes, milliner
42 Pasley, Thomas, grocer and provision dealer
20 Paterson, D. & J., fleshers and game dealers
37*Paterson, David, flesher
72 Paterson, John, jun., ironmonger
72*Paterson, John, manufacturer
55*Patterson, George, baker
61 Patterson, Henry, auctioneer, wool merchant, and corn agent
25 *Post Office*, Francis Deans, postmaster
31 Purdom's, Thomas, writing chambers
 1 Purves, William, fruiterer and confectioner
76 *Refreshment Rooms*
53 Renwick, Frank, draper
23 Revel, William, tailor
72 Richardson, Andrew, grocer
73*Richardson, James, grocer
73 Richardson, James, jun., baker
39*Richardson, William
70 Richardson, William, Tweed merchant
24 Riddle, Helen, pie baker
24*Riddle, John, clothier
30 Riddell, Walter, baker
23*Robison, Andrew, grocer, wine and spirit merchant
12-14 *Royal Bank of Scotland*, James Carmichael, resident agent
78 Rutherford, Andrew
60 Rutherford, James, tailor
59 Rutherford, Thomas, grocer
20 Rutherford & Thomson, smiths and agricultural implement makers
 6 Rutherford, W., watchmaker
13*Rutherfurd, Richard, clothier
21 Scott, Joseph, ironmonger
36 Scott, Michael, grocer
59 Scott, Misses, milliners

43*Scott, Robert, accountant
58 Shiel, John, shoemaker
59 Sinton, Adam, grocer
27*Swan, James, grocer and wine merchant
76*Tait, George, mason
24 Tait, Thomas, joiner
20 Teal, Stephen, tobacconist and china merchant
64 Temple, James, cabinet-maker
69 Thompson, J., turner
34 *Town Hall, Police Office, and Fire-Engine House*—Daniel Munro, custodier
51*Turnbull, James, grocer and wholesale and retail spirit dealer
11*Turnbull, James, draper
52 *Victoria Hotel*, *George Burns
10 Watson, Charles, painter
38*Waugh, Andrew, clothier
48 Wield, John, druggist
54*Woodcock, William, rag and china merchant
66 Young, Robert, baker
45*Young, Thomas, draper

Hope Park (W.)

Anderson, J. (of Wilson & A.)
Rodger, Misses, Boarding Seminary

Howgate (H.)

20*Barclay, George, innkeeper
 7 Blackburn, G., baker and confectioner
21 Brown, Robert, grocer and confectioner
16 Burnet, R. & *Wm., shoemakers
11 Cavers, Robert, grocer
14 Cook, Thomas, green-grocer
13 Douglas, Mrs. Elizabeth
 1 Fox, John, flesher
 4*Haldane, James, corn' merchant
18 Hislop, Jane, baker and grocer
17 Hunter, Mrs. Robert, grocer
 9*Jackson, John, clogger
17 Johnston, John, green-grocer
12*Martin, John, joiner
15*M'Kenzie, Francis, hairdresser
 4 Middlemas, William, grocer
13 Montgomery, George, shoemaker
18 Nichol, John, flesher
 2 Nisbet, William, flesher
   Purves, James, poulterer, game dealer, and fishmonger
 1*Richardson, John, china merchant

12 Riddell, John, tailor and grocer
 8 Rodger, James, flesher
19 Scott, George, grocer
18*Sheeran, Michael, clothier and licensed pawnbroker
 6*Thomson, Alexander, grocer
14 Turnbull, Thomas, contractor
 3*Turnbull, William, general merchant
 4 Watt, R. & W., shoemakers
 4 Wilkinson, Samuel, tailor's cutter
 2 Wilson & Anderson, writers, *Depute Justice of Peace Clerks*
10*Wilson, Walter, baker

Kirkstyle Place   (H.)

 9*Cochrane, James, stocking maker
   Corn Exchange (in course of erection)
 9 Fiddler, Ann, grocer
 6 *Inspector of Poor's Office*, W. N. Kennedy, inspector
3, 4, 5 Kedie, William, (Old Manse), draper
 7 Kay, George, grocer
 7*Purdom, Richard, joiner
   St Mary's Quoad Sacra Church (Rev. John Thomson's
    —*see* p. 310)

Kirk Wynd   (H)

16*Aitken, John, farmer
 2*Burnett, William, shoemaker
 1 Elliot, Alexander, shoemaker
13*Hardie, Oliver, farmer
 2 Purdie, Richard, baker (*see* 5 Loan)
20 Sharp, James, grocer
 2 Tait, John, wright

Kirk Yard   (H.)

 4*Swinton, Charles, weaver

Ladylaw Place   (W.)

Co-operative Store, Thomas Bell, manager
 Gray, James, grocer
*Hunter, John, joiner
 Richardson, John, mill foreman

Loan   (H.)

 Ballantyne, John (of Marshall & B.), builder
13*Ballantyne, Andrew, stocking maker
49*Blyth, Andrew, dyer
52*Blyth, William, labourer
   Combination Poor House, John Smeaton, governor
39*Davidson, William, plasterer

 2*Elliot, William, farmer
 9 Fleming, Thomas, carter
 4 *House of Refuge*, James Smith, burgh-officer, keeper
   Industrial School, James Kerr, resident teacher
17*Laidlaw, Robert, farmer
51 Nichol, Mrs. Margaret
 5*Purdie, Richard, baker (*see* 2 Kirk Wynd)
37*Richardson, Henry, carter
44 Riddell, Mrs. Mary
 3*Shiell, Thomas, grocer
   Spalding, George, plasterer
44*Thomline, Thomas
27 Thomson, Robert, (factor, Cavers' estate)
27 Thomson, Mrs. Rachael
32*Thorburn, John, farmer
45*Weir, John, wool sorter

Mather's Close   (H.)

 *Foley, John, drain contractor
  Murray, James, smith
 *Turnbull, W., warehouseman

Melgund Place   (H.)

 4 Ainslie, Margaret J., dressmaker
 1 Pringle, R., & Sons (*see* 16 Cross Wynd)
 5 Scott, Mrs. Elizabeth
 2*Smith, William, blacksmith
 6 Smith, Mrs. and Miss
 2 Stainton, James, nail manufacturer
 5 Temple, James, cabinet-maker

Mid Row   (H.)

 4 Brown, Elizabeth, grocer
   Cairns, Robert, grocer
10*Lamb, John, needlemaker
11 Turnbull, John, grocer

Mill Path   (H.)

Hawick Corn Mills, *John Y. Scott
 Leithead, John, farmer

Mill Port   (H.)

 Johnstone, G., shoemaker
 Scott, William, picture frame maker
 Stewart, Robert, refreshment rooms
 Thompson, Thomas (of Rutherford & T., High Street)

Myreslaw Green   (H.)

Halliday, Walter, gardener
Inglis, James, joiner
*Jardine Theodore, stocking maker
*Parlane, Rev. James, *West U.P. Manse*
Scott, Walter, clerk
*Tait, Robert, mason
*Tait, Thomas
*Tait, William, mason
    West U.P. Church (Rev. James Parlane's—*see* p. 310)
Wight, William, joiner

North Bridge Street   (H.)

*Brown, William, road contractor
7 Buchanan, Mrs.
5 Douglas, Misses
3 Ewen, Miss Jane
    Harkness, James, Builder's Yard
3 Kerr, Mrs. Gideon
5 Kyle, Miss
    Laing & Irving's warehouse; Andrew Yule, warehouseman
    Oliver, Mrs. Andrew
    Taylor, Miss, dressmaker
*Thomson, George W., M.D.
    Turnbull, Miss Jane
2*Turnbull, James (of T. & Sons, grocers)
4*Turnbull, John (of J. T. & Sons, dyers)
1*Turnbull, John (of Dickson & T.)
    Waldie, Mrs. Peter
    Waldie, Miss, dressmaker
    Waldie, William, *Station-master*
    Wood, Mrs. & Miss (of W., Graham, & Co., 12 Sandbed)

O'Connell Street   (H.)

Congregationalist Church (Rev. Wm. Munro's—*see* p. 310)
Evangelical Union Church (Rev. D. Hislop's—*see* p. 310)
8 Gibson, Gideon, stocking maker
7 Hunt, Henry, grocer
*Harkness, James, builder
3*Langton, William, framesmith
6*Michie, Robert, currier
    Munro, Daniel, *Superintendent of Police, etc.*, **Murray** Place
8*Sharp, John, framesmith

Orrock Place   (H.)

1*Anderson, Thomas, smith
    Archæological Society's Museum

Cochrane, Andrew, tailor
Ewe and Lamb Inn, Donald Cameron
M'Bean, Hector, plumber
Nichol, Barbara, grocer
Public Baths and Wash-houses
Stewart, Miss Margaret
Walker, Mrs. baker

The Path   (W.)

*Aitken, Archibald, grocer
*Davis, G., flesher (*see* Hawick)
    Easton, Miss
    M'Gregor, Rev. John, *Free Church Manse*,
    Mather, Mrs.
    Purdom, John, grocer
    Purdom, Mrs.
    Robison, Mrs. Ebenezer
    Robson, William, grocer

Path Head   (W.)

Donaldson, A. J., chemical works

Round Close   (H.)

11*Brunton, Thomas, joiner
    *Brunton, John, jun., joiner
*Cook, Thomas, grocer
    M'Cracken, William, rag merchant
    Randells & Brothers, tinsmiths
    Towns, James, Taylor

Sandbed   (H.)

1 Armstrong, George, baker
    *Armstrong, John, ironmonger
5 *Bridge Hotel*, *Andrew Patterson
4 Brydon, James, M.D.
7 *Co-operative Store Company's Depot*, G. Anderson, manager
7 Deans, Robert, printer
12 Deayell, E. & C., milliners
3 Drummond, G., meal-dealer
3*Graham, Andrew
    Hood, James, thatcher
2*Kennedy, J. D., bookseller
1 Lawson, Alexander S., watchmaker and jeweller
8*Messer, James, cooper
8 Nichol, Walter, grocer

*Oliver, James, auctioneer, &c., writing chambers (auction mart, Bourtree Place)
9 *Plough Hotel*, James Wood
6 Scott, *Charles, & Sons, shoemakers
11*Scott, George, ironmonger and gun maker
10*Tudhope, J., china merchant and tobacconist
12 Wood, Graham, & Co., drapers
12*Young, William, baker and confectioner

Silver Street (H).

5 Armstrong Mrs. Elizabeth
5 Hawkins, John C., druggist
3 Ovens, James, smith
2*White, William, shoemaker
2*White, M., stocking maker
4 Wilson, Mungo, grocer

Slitrig Bank (H).

1 Davidson, Mrs. Alison, teacher
*Rutherford, John (of R. & Thompson)

Slitrig Crescent (H).

11 Anderson, Mrs. Robert
14*Dakers, Rev. J. Rose, *Parsonage*
6 Elliot, W. & Sons, manufacturers
  Elliot, James (of W. E. & Sons)
5 Elliot, William Scott (of W. E. & Sons)
6 Elliot, Mrs. William
  Episcopal School House, Jacob Jay, resident master
  Hawick Brewery, *G. H. King (house, No. 7)
  *Kennedy, W. N., *Inspector of Poor, &c.*, Stonefield Cottage
8*Laing, John, hosiery manufacturer
  Liddle, Ebenezer, farmer, Rockville
14 Melrose, James, & Sons, millwrigh ts
14*Melrose, John (of J. M. & Sons)
13*Melrose, Adam (of J. M. & Sons)
1*Nichol, John, skinner
7 Scott, Mrs.
14 Scott, William, skin works
  St. Cuthbert's Episcopal Church (Rev. John Rose Daker's—*see* p. 310)
3*Turnbull, Alexander R. (of J. T. & Sons, dyers)
4 Turnbull, J. T., & Sons, dyers
  *Turnbull, Thomas (of J. T. & Sons)
10*Wilson, Mungo (shop, Silver Street)

Teviot Crescent (H.)

9*Aitken, John, wool-sorter
6 Dyer, Mrs.
13*Fraser, George H. (of Hislop and Co., 15 High Street)
2 Guild, John, sheriff-officer
12 Kennedy, Andrew, painter (house, Rose Bank)
5*Scott, John, mill foreman (W. Laidlaw & Sons)
13 Shiell, David grocer
12 Spiers, Andrew
6 Turnbull, George, accountant
10 Whiting, Mrs. Agnes
1*Wilson, M., & Son, skinners and wool merchants
1*Wilson, Walter (of W. & Son)
3*Wood, William (of W., Graham, & Co., 12 Sandbed)

Tower Knowe (H.)

4 *Commercial Bank*, George & James Oliver, agents
7*Kedie, William, draper (*see* Kirkstyle Place)
3 Millar, M., & Co., boot and shoe warehouse
4 Oliver, George & James, writing chambers
2 *Temperance Hotel*, Robert Murray
1 *Tower Hotel*, *William Crozier
2 Turnbull, James, & Son, grocers (*see* North Bridge Street)
6 Wood, Graham, & Co., drapers (*see* Sandbed)

Village (H.)

Purves, James, cabinet maker and upholsterer

West Port (H.)

1*Bowie, Andrew, smith
3 *Free Church Mission*, W. Kedie, custodier
3*Hall, John spinner

Wellington Street (W.)

  Bird, James, joiner
  Eckford, William, baker
*Jamieson, Andrew, stocking maker
  Maxwell, Robert, engineer
  Ormiston, Thomas, coal agent
*Patterson, Adam, grocer
*Richardson, George W., wool-sorter
  Richardson, John, warehouseman
*Richardson, Walter, warehouseman

Wellington Place   (W.)

*Barrie, James, joiner
Hogg, George, manufacturer
Michie, Hugh, clerk
Straton, Oliver, mill foreman

Wilton Grove   (W.)

Burns, John, gardener
*Laidlaw, Peter, manufacturer of hosiery, shirtings, &c.
Smith, Mrs.

Wilton Crescent   (W.)

Anderson, Mrs.
Hart, James, weaver
Hogg, Misses
*Leithead, W., warehouseman
Miller, Robert, coal agent
Reid, Mrs.
Renwick, Mrs.
Robson, James, smith
Rodgie, Mrs.
White, Mrs.

Wilton Path (see Path Head)

Wilton Place   (W.)

Bold, Mrs., grocer
*Laidlaw, Adam, builder, Kirkhouse
*Martin, Robert, tailor
Parochial School, James A. H. Blane, master
Rutherford, Thomas, grocer
Wilton Parish Church (Rev. James Stewart's—*see* p. 348)

Suburb of Dean   (W.)

Rodger, William, grocer
*Scott, John, mason
*Scott, Robert, do.
Scott, Thomas, do.
Scott, William, do.
Stewart, James, stocking maker
*Stewart, Daniel, florist
*Thomson, Thomas, labourer
*Turnbull, John, sen.
*Turnbull, John, jun.

Detached Residences in the Burgh

*Dickson, William (of D. & Laing, Wellfield)   (W.)
*Govenlock, John (late Commercial Inn)

*Kennedy, A., painter, Rosebank (W.—*see* Teviot Crescent)
*Laing, Walter, of Springbank (of Dicksons and L.)   (W.);
*Scott, Thomas, manager of Dicksons' & Laing's mill
*Stewart, Rev. James, *Wilton Manse*, Station Road   (W.)
Thomson, Rev. John, of Rosalee (St. Mary's *quoad sacra*)   (W)
Watson, Mrs., of Wilton Bank   (W.)
*Watson, Robert (of Watson & Co.), Wilton Bank
*Watson, Thomas,   do.   do.
*Wilson, John, of Ladylaw House (of J. W. and Son)   (W.)
*Wilson, George (of Wilson & Armstrong) *Provost*, Weens-
  land   (H.)
*Wilson, John Fiddes (of M. Wilson & Son, Teviot Crescent),
  Leaburn House   (H.)
Wilson, William, of Sillerbithall (of Ladylaw and Lang-
  lands Woollen Mills)   (W.)

Address and Trade unknown.

*Borthwick, Thomas (H.)

Railway Station (W)

W. Waldie, station-master, manager of goods' department, and
  N. B. Company's coal agent

OFFICES AND DEPOTS.

Cathrae, Thomas, Plashetts' coal, and brick agent
        Salesman—James Thom
Charters, Francis, coal agent
Harkness, James, free-stone, brick, and tile merchant
Jobson, George,   do.
Laidlaw, Adam, lime agent
Laidlaw, William, do.
        Salesman— R. Miller
Laing, John, coal merchant
        Salesman—D. Milne
Leyden, Andrew, coal and lime merchant
Ormston, Thomas, coal agent
Oliver, James (auctioneer), coal and lime agent
        Salesman—John Hart

COUNTRY RESIDENTS IN HAWICK PARISH

*Borthwick, Alexander, farmer, New Mill
*Elliot, Robert, farm-steward, Bucklands
*Fulton, William, Newhouses
*Grierson, Andrew, farmer, Whitchesters
*Grieve, William, farmer, Branxholm Park
*Grieve, Robert, farmer, Southfield

*Grieve, Robert, farmer, Branxholmbraes
*Hogg, James, farmer, Crumhaugh Hill
*Inglis, William, joiner, Deanbrae Bar, Cavers
*Knox, William, farmer, Meikle Whitlaw
*Lees, David, farmer, Fenwick
 Scott, Ebenezer, farmer, Burnflat
*Shiel, John, Greenabraehead
*Stein, James, farmer, Pilmuir
 Thomson, John, mole catcher, Burnflat
 Turnbull, Thomas, Crowbyres

COUNTRY RESIDENTS IN WILTON PARISH.

 Campbell, John, Sillerbithall
*Campbell, Robert, farmer, Whitehaugh
*Davidson, William, Wester Boonraw (of W. & G., bankers, Hawick)
*Easton, Andrew, farmer, Overhall
*Glendinning, Scott, Boghall
*Govenlock, Andrew, farmer, Calaburn
*Hart, James, Lockie's-edge
*Knox, David, farmer, Martinshouse
*Laidlaw, William, farmer, Clarilaw
*Lees, Richard, farmer, Drinkstone
*Liddle, Ebenezer, farmer, Rockville
 Nichol, John, farmer, Greensidehall
 Oliver, George, farmer, Borthaugh (of G. & J. O., writers, Hawick)
 Pringle, William, farmer, Newstead
*Rae, William, farmer, Scau Mill
 Reid, Thomas, mason, Dyke Neuk
*Scott, Robert, farmer, Easter Boonraw
 Scott, Thomas, farmer, Priestrig
*Scott, Walter, of Newton
 Scott, William, farmer, Burnhead
*Smart, James, farmer, Whitehaugh Moor
*Smith, Alexander, veterinary surgeon, Appletreehall
*Taylor, David, farmer, Newhouses
 Thomson, John, farmer, Muirfield
 Turnbull, James, joiner, Stirches Croft
*Turnbull, George, joiner, Appletreehall
*Turnbull, John, farmer, Burnfoot
*Turnbull, John, farmer, Wilton Burn
*Turnbull, Robert, of Galalaw
*Turnbull, Thomas, farmer, Lees
*Usher Thomas, farmer, Courthill
*Wilson, Adam, farmer, Midshiels

SEATS OF COUNTY FAMILIES, SMALLER RESIDENCES, &c., IN THE PARISHES OF HAWICK AND WILTON.

BRANXHOLM (H.)—see p. 301

About 3 miles above Hawick, beautifully situated on a sloping bank of the Teviot, looking down on the river at a narrow, sudden curve of the glen. The present edifice looks more like a peaceful mansion than a military castle; yet includes an old square tower of enormous strength. The ancient edifice was much larger than the present one, and had a far more imposing appearance, and was the master fort of the district.

It has for upwards of a century been the residence of the Duke of Buccleuch's chamberlain, and is at present occupied by William Ogilvie, Esq. of Chesters (see p. 201), who has held that appointment for several years.

BRIERY YARDS. (W.)

On the Teviot, near the eastern boundary of the parish—the property of the trustees of the late William Turnbull, Esq.; occupied by David Dundas Scott, Esq., and family.

BUCKLANDS HOUSE. (W)

(Formerly BURNGROVE), pleasantly situated on the north bank of the Teviot, near the eastern boundary of the parish—the residence of *William Scott Watson, Esq., yr. of Burnhead and Bucklands.

LYNWOOD. (H.)

Close to Hawick, on the Slitrig—occupied by *William Nixon, Esq. (late of Lynwood Mills).

GOLDIELANDS TOWER (H.)

Situated upon an eminence, on the right side of the Teviot, nearly opposite the mouth of the Borthwick Water. It commands an extensive view of the vale of the Teviot, from near its source at Teviot Stones to Minto Rocks downwards. It is one mile from Hawick and one from Branxholm, which it overlooks, and with which in former times it was intimately connected. It is one of the most perfect specimens of the Border keep or peel, that has survived the devastations of the district, but history says little regarding it.

Goldielands is the property of His Grace the Duke of Buccleuch, by whom it was fitted up as a comfortable residence, and for several years has been occupied by Adam Elliott, Esq., M.D. (formerly of H.E.I.C. Maritime Service), Secretary to the Hawick Farmers' Club (see p. 317).

SILLERBITHALL. (w.)—*see* p. 347.
see p. 347.

About ¼ of a mile north-east of Hawick—the property and residence of *Thomas Laidlaw, Esq. (of William Laidlaw & Sons, manufacturers). This is one of the finest buildings in the old baronial style in the county.

STIRCHES. (w.)

Over 1 mile to the north of Wilton—the residence of *John Scott Chisholme of that Ilk, Stirches and Whitehaugh, all in the county of Roxburgh; born 1812; succeeded his maternal uncle the late James Scott, Esq. of Whitehaugh, whose name he assumed in 1852 by patent, and his father, the late Gilbert Chisholme, Esq., in 1820; married, 1840, Margaret eldest daughter and co-heiress of the late Robert Walker, Esq. of Mumrills in Stirlingshire, and has issue :—

> John James, born 1st August 1851.
> Christina Madeline.
> Elizabeth Scott.

Mr. Chisholme is a Magistrate, etc. for the County of Roxburgh, and Captain of the 4th Roxburghshire Rifle Corps.

Town Addresses—New Club, Edinburgh; and Morley's Hotel, Trafalgar Square, London, W.S.

WILTON LODGE. (w.)

Situated on the Teviot, about a mile above Wilton—the residence of *David Pringle, Esq., fifth son of the late Alexander Pringle, Esq. of Whytbank, in Selkirkshire; born 1806; married (first) Francis, daughter of Alexander Tod, Esq., of Alderstone, who died 1856, and by whom he has one son and two daughters; married (second), 1858, Mary, only daughter and heiress of James Anderson, Esq. of Wilton Lodge.

Mr. Pringle, who was formerly in the Bengal Civil Service, is a Magistrate for the County of Roxburgh.

Mrs. Pringle, as heiress of her late father, is Lady of the Barony of Wilton.

VOTERS REGISTERED IN HAWICK PARISH,
BUT NOT RESIDENT.

Alexander, George, Castlegate, Jedburgh
Armstrong, John, Guelph, Canada West
Chalmers, Walter, of Prestonhall, near Annan
Deans, John, Alexandria, North America
Douglas, Robert, farm-servant, Teinside
Easton, John, Constantinople
Grahame, Alexander, Berwick
Hamilton, George, Edinburgh
Kerr, Robert P., seedsman, 4 Basnett Street, Liverpool
Laidlaw, Walter, India
Laidlaw, William, shoemaker, Morebattle
Lewis, Walter, farm-steward at Howgills, Ewes, Langholm
M'Robert, Rev. John, Denholm
M'Ausland, John, Albany, North America
Marrs, George, Jedburgh
Nichol, William, cattle-dealer, Kelso
Oliver, Straton, warehouseman, Edinburgh
Pearson, James Cousland, East Lothian
Purdom, Walter, farmer, Blinkbonny, Kelso
Robertson, James, writer, 17 Duke Street, Edinburgh
Scott, Andrew, Ballarat, Australia
Scott, Gideon, millwright, late 6 Albion Place, Blackfriars Road, London
Stenhouse, John, brewer, Ednam
Scott, Walter, farmer, Newcastleton
Selby, Ephraim, Hassendeanbank
Stewart, John, W.S., India Street, Edinburgh
Turnbull, Thomas, Lees, Hawick
Turner, John, late Hagging Dean, Yorkshire
Welsh, George, farmer, Ericstane, Moffat
Wight, Walter, joiner, Cavers West Lodge
Wight, William, joiner,   do.
Wilson, George, accountant, Glasgow
Wilson, James Anderson, assistant engineer, Portsea
Wilson, William, mercantile clerk, Port Louis, Mauritius

VOTERS REGISTERED IN WILTON PARISH,
BUT NOT RESIDENT.

Aitken, John, Rutherford Boathouse
Chisholme, William Scott, of Coldhouse, 15 Bruntsfield Place, Edinburgh
Cockburn, John, Curve Acre, Brampton Villa, North Devon
Dickson, James, of Chatto (Bughtrig, Eccles)
Dobson, John Easton, joiner, Stockbridge, Edinburgh
Elliot, John, Scarnook, Roberton
Hobkirk, Adam, corn merchant, Glasgow
Hobkirk, Robert, builder, Southburn, Lockerbie
Johnstone, James, Esq. of Alva
Leggat, William, America
Little, George, mason, Denholm
Little, William, mason, Denholm
Nichol, William, jun., factor at Riddell (Lilliesleaf)

Rae, Robert H. schoolmaster, Devonport
Riddell, George W. Hutton, of Muselee (Captain 16th Lancers)
Robertson, Alexander, gamekeeper, Commonside, Teviothead
Robertson, Gilbert, Captain 1st Royal Dragoons, Aldershott
Rutherford, Thomas, groom, London
Scott, Archibald, New Zealand
Stoddart, William, gamekeeper, Minto
Thomson, John, Nether Whitlaw, Galashiels
Watson, William, of Burnhead

WILTON.

THE parish of Wilton is situated on the left bank of the river Teviot, which separates it from the parish of Hawick. Its boundaries are — on the north by Minto; on the east, Cavers; on the south, Hawick; and on the west, Ashkirk and Roberton. It is about 5 miles in length, and its average breadth about 3½ miles. The area, according to the Ordnance Survey, is rather more than 8820 acres, of which 59½ are under water, 73½ are in roads, and about 40¾ are occupied by the railway. The surface of the parish is irregular, and in some instances hilly. The greater part of it, however, is under cultivation.

On the left bank of the Teviot, and opposite Hawick, is the town of Wilton. It consists of several streets containing very handsome houses. The greater part of the town is of comparatively modern erection. Although distinct from Hawick parochially, it is incorporated with it in all other respects. The two towns are connected by several bridges. Several large woollen factories are on the Wilton side of Teviot; and the railway station, at least for the present, is in Wilton; but from its being in a very inconvenient and exposed situation, there will, in all likelihood, be a new one erected nearer the town of Hawick. There has been erected in the parish, during the past year, a stately and imposing edifice, near Sillerbithall (see p. 345), the property of Thomas Laidlaw, Esq. (of W. Laidlaw & Sons, Hawick), and another in Hawick parish, at Weensland, the property of George Wilson, Esq., provost of the burgh.

In the parish there is also the small suburb of Wilton Dean,* lying about one mile above Wilton, on the Teviot (see p. 341).

---

* Wilton Dean is the supposed scene of the "Cottagers of Glenburnie."

The population of the parish of Wilton, in 1861, was 3357 (including that of the town, 2210, which is within the burgh bounds of Hawick), who constituted 703 separate families; of whom 1 was returned as living in a house having no window, 351 in houses having one window, 2214 in houses of two windows, and the remainder (127) in houses of three or more windows.

Valuation of property in 1863-4, £13,199 : 8 : 5 (exclusive of railways).

The principal landed-proprietors in the parish are—The Duke of Buccleuch; Mrs. Pringle of Wilton Lodge; John Scott, Chisholme, Esq. of Stirches; William Watson, Esq. of Bucklands; Trustees of William Turnbull, Esq. of Briery Yards; A. Dickson, Esq. of Alton; Captain Riddell of Muselee; Walter Scott, Esq. of Newton

Superior of Wilton—Mrs. Pringle of Wilton Lodge.

For MAGISTRATES, JUSTICES OF THE PEACE, and COURTS, etc., in which Wilton and Hawick as a Burgh are mutually interested, see the separate headings under HAWICK.

PUBLIC OFFICES.

Medical Officer and Public Vaccinator—D. M'Leod, surgeon, Buccleuch Street, Hawick.
Inspector of Poor, Registrar of Births, Marriages, and Deaths, and Heritors' Clerk—James Shiel, Albion Place.

CLERGY, &c.

Wilton is in the Presbytery of Jedburgh, and Synod of Merse and Teviotdale.

Patron—Duke of Buccleuch. -

PARISH CHURCH (Wilton)—Rev. James Stewart (inducted 1851). Sittings, 950. Average attendance at Sabbath School, 200. Conductor of Psalmody—Samuel Stainton, Dickson Street. Church Treasurer—the Minister. Session Clerk—William Ainslie, Pathhead.

FAST DAYS—same as Hawick (see p. 311).

PAROCHIAL SCHOOLS.†

Wilton—James A. H. Blane. Average attendance, 130.
Clarilaw (Side)—Jas. Stewart, teacher. Average attend., 65.
Stouslea (Side)—David Wells, teacher. Average attend., 38.
There is also a Juvenile School at Wilton Dean, partly supported by Mrs. Pringle of Wilton Lodge—Miss Hartley, teacher.

---

† Children in the parish of Wilton (including that portion of the burgh of Hawick situated in Wilton parish), from 5 to 15, attending school during the first week of April 1861, 496 ; of all ages, 507.

PAROCHIAL BOARD.

David Pringle, Esq., of Wilton Lodge, Chairman.

COMMITTEE.

Walter Laing.   George Oliver.
Robert Turnbull.   William Scott Watson.
Robert Thomson.

Inspector and Collector—James Shiel.

Medical Officer and Public Vaccinator—D. M'Leod, surgeon.

Auditor—James Oliver, Esq., banker.

No. of Poor on Roll, 79.

Rate of Assessment, 5d. per £ on owner and occupier, less 25 per cent off house property, 30 per cent off mill property, and 12½ per cent off lands. Total Assessment, 1863-4, £501 : 6 : 3.

PAROCHIAL BURIAL GROUND.

(Provided under the Act).

David Pringle, Esq., Chairman.

COMMITTEE.

John Wilson.   Walter Laing.
Robert Thomson.   John Marshall.
George Oliver.   Rev. James Stewart.

Clerk—James Shiel, Albion Place.   Sexton—Thomas Simpson.

The Layers in the saleable half are disposed of at £2, £1, and 10s. each   Fees for digging graves 3s., if the deceased was under 14 years of age ; and 4s. 6d. if above that age for 5 feet graves—1s. per foot additional above that depth.

TEVIOTHEAD.

—◆—

THIS is a large and chiefly pastoral parish situated in the south-western extremity of the county. Previous to 1850 Teviothead formed the southern parts of the parishes of Hawick and Cavers, but was in that year disjoined and erected into a separate parish. It is bounded on the north by Roberton and Hawick, on the east by Kirkton and Cavers, on the south by Castleton and Dumfriesshire, and on the west by Roberton. The extent of the parish is about 10 miles in length from east to west, and 8 miles in breadth from north to south. The area, according to the Ordnance Survey, is over 31,559½ acres, 64½ of which are in roads, and 101 under water. The southern half of the parish is entirely billy—the highest being Cauldcleuch-head on the border of Castleton, which attains a height of 1996 feet. The following are the other principal heights :—Millstone-edge 1857 feet, Skelfhill Pen and Fell each 1745 feet, Dod Hill 1620 feet, Wisp Hill 1950 feet, Pikethaw Hill, 1750 feet, Causeway Grain 1607 feet, Comb Hill 1687 feet ; and there are many others less elevated. The northern part of the parish though not so elevated is also hilly ; and except the vale of the Teviot, which has its rise in the extreme south-west and flows in a north-easterly direction through the entire parish, the whole may be said to be pastoral. In the narrow vale of the Teviot the ground is lower and is under cultivation. The Teviot is fed by innumerable burns, which all have their rise in this parish. The Allan water, a considerable tributary, also has its rise here and joins the Teviot at the extreme north of the parish. All these streams are free to the angler. Trouts, as a rule, are plentiful, but small. In the north-eastern part there are the remains of a good number of forts. The great road from the east of Scotland to the west of England traverses the parish, its course being along the defile of the Teviot—" a narrow and sinuous glen overhung by sheep walks and solitude."

There is no village in the parish. The church, manse, and school are situated near its centre at the confluence of the two main branches of the river Teviot.

The principal landed-proprietors are—The Duke of Buccleuch ; Sir William F. Eliott, Bart., of Stobs and Wells ; B. T. G. Anderson, Esq., of Tushielaw ; Thomas Turnbull, Esq., of Fenwick ; John Elliot, Esq., of Binks (Burnmoth,

Castleton); William Turnbull, Esq., of Merrylaw; Gideon Pott, Esq., of Dod (Knowsouth, by Jedburgh).

Hawick—9 miles distant from the church—is the nearest market and post town. The nearest railway station is at Stobs on the Border Union line; but as yet it is of no practical value, 2½ miles of road being required to connect it with the parish, which, if made, would be a great boon to the district. Under present circumstances the Hawick station is the most convenient.

Population of the parish in 1861, 438, who composed 82 families; one of whom was returned as living in a house of no windows, and 43 in houses of one and two windows, leaving nearly a half living in houses of three and more windows.

Assessed property in 1863 4, £8805 : 10 : 6.

———

Those marked thus (*) are Registered Voters in the parish.

DISTRICT POLICE OFFICER—John Middleton.

POST OFFICE—Simon Little, Postmaster.   Daily post to Hawick. Arrival, 12 55 p.m. ; Departure, 2 p.m.

PUBLIC OFFICES—Registrar of Births, Marriages, and Deaths, Session Clerk, Kirk Treasurer, and Heritors' Clerk—Simon Little.

Medical Officers and Public Vaccinators—Dr. M'Leod, Hawick, for what was formerly Hawick parish; Dr. Grant for Cavers.

CLERGY, &c.—Presbytery of Jedburgh, Synod of Merse and Teviotdale.   Patron—Duke of Buccleuch.

Established Church—*Rev. Robert Young (Inducted 1854). Sittings,

FAST DAYS—Wednesdays before the second Sabbath of April and third Sabbath of October.

SCHOOL†—Parish—*Simon Little, Schoolmaster.   Av. attend.,   .

PAROCHIAL BOARD—The management of the poor was retained, at the erection of the parish, by the Parochial Boards of Hawick and Cavers.

LIBRARY—Parochial.

CARRIER—Hawick, Christoph. Glendinning, Thursday and Saturday.

———

TRADES.

Hume, John, feuar, Gledesnest
*Miller, David, joiner, Dovecot

———

† Children in the parish between 5 and 15, attending school during the first week of April 1861, 65 ; of all ages, 71.

Murray, William, joiner, Mossieknow
Pow, Gavin, blacksmith, Hendersonsknow

———

RESIDENTS, FARMERS, &c.

*Aitchison, Wm. (of Glenkerry, Ettrick), farmer, Linhope
*Beattie, John, farmer, Harwood
*Elliot, Henry,   do.,   Coltherscleuch
*Fenwick, John, do.,   Northhouse (late *Tower Hotel*, Hawick)
Govenlock, Mrs., Mosspaul Farm
*Govenlock, Robert, farmer, Teinside
*Grieve, Wm., farmer, Skelfhill ‡
*Ogilvie, Wm. R. do., Broadhaugh
Oliver, John,   do.,   Rigg
*Riddell, Willm., do., Ramsaycleuch Burn
Scott, Archd. (of Howcleuch, etc., in Roberton), farmer, Commonside
*Scott, Walter, farmer, Bowanhill
Scott, Charles,   do.,   Priesthaugh
Robertson, Alexander, gamekeeper to the Duke of Buccleuch, Commonside Cottage
*Turnbull, William (of Merrylaw), Falnash
Turnbull, R., L., farmer, Merrylaw

———

REGISTERED VOTERS (Non-Resident).

Anderson, B. T. G., of Tushielaw (Edinburgh)
Beattie, Robert, Sinton Mill
Clark, J, T., Ilderton, by Alnwick
Welsh, Thomas, farmer, Errickstane, Moffat

———

‡ The *Fowledge*, a shepherd's cottage on this farm, is probably the highest inhabited house in Roxburghshire—height 1037 feet.— *See* foot-note, *highest inhabited houses of the district*, Ettrick parish.

ASHKIRK.

——◆——

THE parish of Ashkirk is situated mainly in the county of Roxburgh, though it includes two portions of the county of Selkirk. One of these, comprehending the Sinton estate, is completely detached from Selkirk and imbedded in Roxburgh. While, however, it forms part of the county of Selkirk for purposes of assessment, it ranks with Roxburgh in the enjoyment of the elective franchise; the other and smaller Selkirkshire portion ranks with Selkirk in the enjoyment of the franchise, and in every respect forms an integral part of that county. The boundaries are—on the north, Selkirk parish; on the west, Kirkhope; on the south Roberton and Wilton; and on the east, Minto and Lilliesleaf. It is about 7 miles long and about 3¼ in breadth. The area, according to the Ordnance Survey, is, in Roxburghshire—8285¾ acres land, 78 acres water, and nearly 53 acres public roads—total, 8416¾ acres, of which 2489¾ are arable; in Selkirkshire—3348 acres land, nearly 16 acres water, and 21 acres public roads—total, 3385 acres, of which 1202 acres are arable; total for both counties, 11,801¾ acres.

The Ale, the only river in the parish, flows through its centre, following a serpentine course through a beautiful valley of varying breadth from south-west to north-east. There are several lochs in the parish containing trout of large size and fine quality, like those found in Loch Leven; also perch and pike. These lochs have, as well as the river to which they are feeders, long been favourite resorts of the angler. The land is good turnip soil, and, from where the "haughs" terminate to the water shed of the Ettrick on the north and the Teviot on the south, presents an undulating surface; towards the south-west and north the hills rise from 800 to 1200 feet above the level of the sea,* and they afford excellent pasture for sheep. Marl is plentiful in the parish, and is of excellent quality. Skulls and horns of a race of animals long extinct, as well as wood of different kinds, have been found in peat moss overlaying the marl.

The climate is healthful and bracing. The village of Ashkirk is pleasantly situated in the centre of the parish, in Roxburghshire, on a sloping bank of the river, and at the junction of the county roads from Roberton and Ettrick with the Edinburgh and Carlisle road, which crosses the parish. Ashkirk is distant 5½ miles from Selkirk (where also is the nearest railway station), and 6½ miles from Hawick. Ashkirk was formerly a vicarage belonging to the chapter of Glasgow. The archbishop had a residence here, and a place near the manse still retains the name of "the palace walls." Five of the present proprietors pay feu to the archbishopric of Glasgow.

Population of the parish in 1861, 578; who composed 105 families, 29 of whom were returned as living in houses of one window, and 38 in houses of two windows, leaving the full average of over one-third as living in houses of three or more windows.

Assessed property in 1864-5, in the county of Roxburgh, £3788 : 4s.; in the county of Selkirk, £2188 : 0 : 3—total £5976, 4s. 3d.

The principal landed-proprietors in the parish are—the Earl of Minto; John C. Scott, Esq. of Sinton; Alexander Cochran, Esq. of Ashkirk (32 Marina, St. Leonards-on-the-sea); A. E. Lockhart, Esq., of Cleghorn and Borthwickbrae (Hawick); Col. George Pott, of Todrig and Borthwickshiels (Hawick); Mrs. Pringle Douglas, Haining (Selkirk); Geo. Combe Ainslie, Esq., of Woll; and Mark Sprot, Esq. of Riddell (Selkirk).

Those marked thus (*) are Registered Voters in the parish for Roxburghshire, and those marked thus (†) for Selkirkshire.

POLICE OFFICER—David Brown, Ashkirk.

PUBLIC OFFICES—Heritors' Clerk, Kirk Treasurer, Registrar of Births, Marriages, and Deaths, Session Clerk, and Inspector of Poor—James Smellie.
Medical Officers and Public Vaccinators—Drs. Anderson & Ballantyne, Selkirk.

POST OFFICE—William Amos, postmaster—Daily post to Hawick. Arrival, 12 noon; Departure, 7·30 a.m. Jas. Amos, Messenger.

CLERGY—Ashkirk is in the Presbytery of Selkirk and Synod of Merse and Teviotdale. Patron—Earl of Minto.
Established Church—*Rev. William G. Smith (Inducted 1861). Sittings, 180. Sabbath School attendance, 30.
Free Church—*Rev. John Edmondston (Inducted 1837). Sittings, 200. Sabbath School attendance, 25.

FAST DAYS—Wednesdays before the first Sunday of May and second Sunday of November.

SCHOOLS†—Parochial—*James Smellie, master; average attend., 55. Female—Miss Cheyne, teacher; average attendance, 22.

---

* Of these, Blackcastle Hill has a height of 908 feet, Stobshaw Hill 1051 feet, Ashkirk Hill 967 feet, Leap Hill 1047 feet, and two unnamed hills near the head of Blendhaugh Burn are given in the Ordnance Survey plans as 1126 and 1178 feet.

† Children in the parish, between 5 and 15, attending school during the first week of April 1861, 89; of all ages, 90.

2 A

PAROCHIAL BOARD—Rev. W. G. Smith, Chairman. No. of Poor on Roll, 8. Rate of Assessment, 3½d. per £ ; total Assessment 1864, £86 : 15 : 4½.

LIBRARIES—Parochial—Thos. Turnbull, librarian. 640 vols. Annual subscription—proprietors, 2s. 6d. and 1s. ; readers, 1s.

Free Church Library—Thomas Robertson, librarian. Free to all readers.

TOTAL ABSTINENCE SOCIETY—John Douglas, Easter Essenside, President. Numbers nearly 250 non-resident and resident Members.

CARRIERS—Selkirk, Ashkirk, and Hawick, David Chisholm, Tuesday and Friday ; Selkirk, Monday ; Hawick, Thursday—Wm. Scott, Sinton Mossend.

MILLS : Ashkirk—Robert Bruce, farmer.
Sinton—Robert Beattie, farmer.

TRADES, FARMERS, &c., IN THE PARISH.

Aitchison, George, mason, New Headshaw
Amos, William, shoemaker, Ashkirk
*Anderson, Thomas, farmer, Shielswood
†Brydon, William,   do.   Whitslade
Cleghorn, Andrew, wright, Sandyhall
*Douglas, John, farmer, Easter Essenside
Douglas, Willm., do. Dimpleknowe
Gowenlock, John, mason, Barbauchlaw
Gowenlock, Mrs., Greenhill farm
Gray, William, farmer, Ashkirktown
Gray, John,   do.   Bridge-end
Hogg, George,   do.   Barbauchlaw
*Inglis, William, do.   Salenside
*Inglis, John,   do.   do.
Matthewson, John, veterinary-surgeon, Ashkirk
Minto, Gavin, smith, Whitfield
*Murray, George, farmer, Castleside
Murray, William, do.,   Haughhead
*Patterson, John,   do.   Wester Essenside
*Riddell, Andrew,   do.   North Sinton
*Scott, Adam,   do.   Burnfoot
*Scott, Robert,   do.   New Woll
*Thorburn, Mungo, do.   Headshaw
Turnbull, James, stocking-weaver, Castleside
Waldie, Thomas, wright, Ashkirk
*Young, James, sen., farmer, Dryden
*Young, James, jun., do.   do.

SEATS OF COUNTY FAMILIES IN THE PARISH.

ASHKIRK HOUSE.

The property of Alexander Cochran, Esq. ; at present occupied by *George Johnstone Wainwright, Esq. (formerly of 19 Canning Street, Liverpool, and Runshaw Hall, Euxton, Lancashire).

SINTON HOUSE.

The property and residence of *John Corse Scott, Esq.

WOLL HOUSE.

The residence of *George Combe Ainslie, Esq., who purchased the property from the heirs of the late Lieut.-Col. John Scott.

REGISTERED VOTERS (Non-Resident).

*Cochran, Alexander, Esq., of Ashkirk
*Lockhart, Allan Eliott, Esq., of Borthwickbrae
*Scott, Col. Alexander C., Burnhouse, Stow
*Scott, Col. James C., Chisholme House

ROBERTON.

——◆——

THIS parish is situated partly in Roxburghshire and partly in Selkirkshire. The larger portion being in the former county, however, we have placed it under the head of Roxburghshire; and in this notice of it both parts are included. Its boundaries are—on the north-east, Wilton, Ashkirk, and a detached part of Selkirk, lying at the head of the Todrig Burn; on the south-east, Hawick and Teviothead; on the south-west Dumfriesshire; and on the north-west, Ettrick and Kirkhope. Its extreme length is about 15 miles, and its average breadth 5 miles. The area of that part of it which is in Roxburghshire is nearly 18,038¼ acres, about 43½ of which are in roads, and 102 under water. That part of it in Selkirkshire has an area of 11,628¼ acres, 40¾ being in roads, and nearly 145 under water—total for both counties, 29,666½ acres. The parish is for the most part hilly, though none of the hills attain any very great elevation. In the centre of the parish they average about 1200 feet in height, but the highest are those in the south-west near the borders of Dumfriesshire, where Crib Law, in Selkirkshire, attains an elevation of 1389 feet, Knowebog Hill 1227 feet, and Catgairedge 1421 feet; while in Roxburghshire, Muckle Knowe rises to 1394 feet, Ladder Law 1462 feet, Long Tae 1438 feet, Archie Hill 1451 feet, Stock Hill 1561 feet, Ladshaw Hill 1527 feet, and Craig Cross Hill 1482; the road which crosses Craig Cross into Eskdale-Muir rises to nearly the same height, and will be by much the highest road in the three counties. "The soil in the vale of Borthwick is of good quality. Upon the ascents on each side of the water it becomes thinner, gravelly, and dry. Towards the summits of the hills, especially in the western part of the parish, the soil is naturally wet and boggy, but much has been done lately to remedy this."

There are several lakes in the parish. That of Alemoor is a pretty circular sheet of water, about two miles in circumference, and of considerable depth. Hellmoor Loch, partly in the parish, is three times the extent of the former, but more shallow. Kingsmoor Loch is also a pretty large one. All of these lochs occur as expansions or remote sources of the Ale water, and lie in Selkirkshire. All abound in fine perch and pike, and Kingsmoor contains an excellent red trout much resembling that of Loch Leven. Fishing in these lochs, except in Alemoor and Hellmoor is restricted; in the Borthwick and Ale, which contain a number of small trout, the fishing is free. Moodlaw Loch, in the south-western part of the parish is equally divided between three parishes—Roberton, Eskdale-Muir, and Ettrick; and as each of these is in a different county, we have the curious coincidence of three parishes and three counties meeting in the middle of a loch.

Throughout the parish there are a number of ancient camps, the largest and most complete being that on the farm of Broadlee. "Harden, the ancient residence of the Scotts of Harden [represented by Lord Polwarth] stands in the north-eastern part of the parish. It has been repaired and added to during this summer (1864), and converted into a most comfortable residence. Some quaint specimens of stucco work adorn the roof of the old hall, which has been preserved, and the ceiling and other peculiarities have been restored according to their ancient pattern. A chimney-piece in one of the rooms tells of the ancient importance of the lairds of Harden,* for it bears an earl's coronet, and the letters W.E.T., the initials of Walter, Earl of Terras, a title conferred on Walter Scott of Highchesters in 1660."

There is but one hamlet in the parish—DEANBURNHAUGH, situated on the Borthwick, about 8 miles from Hawick, near the centre of the parish and on the boundary line dividing the two counties. It contains about 50 inhabitants. Roberton church, manse, and school-house are also on the Borthwick water, but about 3 miles nearer to Hawick, and also situated on the boundary line separating the two counties.†

The principal proprietors in the parish are—His Grace the Duke of Buccleuch, who owns nearly half of the parish; Lord Polwarth, Mertoun; William Richardson Dickson, of Chisholme (minor); Mrs. Stavert of Hoscote (Edinburgh); Mrs. Pringle Douglas of Haining; Capt. Hutton Riddell of Muselee (16th Lancers); Archibald Scott, Esq., of Howcleuch and Borthwick Mains (Commonside, Teviothead)—non-resident; A. E. Lockhart, Esq. of Borthwickbrae, and Col. Pott, of Borthwickshiels—resident.

Hawick, the nearest market town and railway station, is about 3 miles from the lower and 18 from the upper part of the parish. An excellent road traverses the parish its entire length.

Population in 1861, 640; who composed 116 families, 18 of whom were returned as living in houses of one window, and 42 in houses of two windows, leaving nearly a half living in houses of three and more windows—a very high average.

Assessed property in 1863-4, in the county of Roxburgh, £6318 : 7 : 11 ; Selkirk, £3488 : 8 : 8—total, £9806 : 16 : 7.

---

* Harden is the scene of Leyden's finest incident in his "Scenes of Infancy"—the discovery of the infant by the Flower of Yarrow, in Harden's plunder after a foray.

† The boundary of the two counties in the parish appears on the map as if dove-tailed—it is so irregular.

Those marked thus (*) are Registered Voters in the parish for Roxburghshire, and those marked thus (†) for Selkirkshire.

RESIDENT JUSTICES OF THE PEACE—Allan E. Lockhart, Esq., of Borthwickbrae, William E. Lockhart, yr. of Borthwickbrae, and Col. Pott, of Borthwickshiels.

DISTRICT POLICE OFFICER—Archibald M'Lean, Roberton.

PUBLIC OFFICES—Heritors' Clerk, Kirk Treasurer, Inspector of Poor, Session Clerk, and Registrar of Births, Marriages, and Deaths—Thomas Anderson,
    Medical Officer and Public Vaccinator—Dr. G. W. Thomson, Hawick.

POST OFFICE (Deanburnhaugh)—Adam Hudson, Postmaster. Daily Post to Hawick ; leaves at 6.30 a.m. ; returns about 2 p.m., taking up letters for Hawick on way down, and delivering on his return at every house within 50 yards of public road. Messenger—David Lyon.

CLERGY, &c.—Presbytery of Selkirk, Synod of Merse and Teviotdale. Patron—the Crown.
    Established Church—*†Rev. Chas. K. Greenhill (Inducted 1845). Sittings, 330.

FAST DAYS—Generally First Friday—sometimes Wednesday—of April and November.

SCHOOL ||—Parochial—†Thomas Anderson, master. Av. attend. 60.

PAROCHIAL BOARD—A. E. Lockhart, Esq. of Borthwickbrae, Chairman. No. of Poor on Roll, 10. Average Rate of Assessment, 3¼d. per £ ; total Assessment for 1863-4, £125. Poor House—Hawick Combination.

CARRIER—John Elliot, to Hawick, Tuesday and Friday, from Borthwickbrae ; Robert Brown, to Hawick, Thursday, from Deanburnhaugh.

CORN MILL—Highchesters—*John Haldane, farmer.

TRADES.

Anderson, Thomas, blacksmith, Borthwickbrae Burnfoot
Scott, William, joiner, Deanburnhaugh,
Shakelton, William, do., Roberton Woodfoot

RESIDENTS, FARMERS, &c.

*Anderson, Andrew, farmer, Woodburn
†Anderson, Thomas,   do.   Easter Alemoor
†Anderson, Thomas, schoolmaster, Roberton

|| Children in the parish from 5 to 15 attending school during the first week of April 1861, 59 ; of all ages, 61.

†Burnet, Francis, farmer, Bellendean
*†Burnet, Robert,   do.,   do.
*Brown, Robert,   do.,   Muselee
Elliott, Thomas, land-steward, Howcleuch and Mains
†Grieve, James, farmer, Borthwickbrae Burnfoot
*†Hogg, John,   do.,   Hoscote
†Moffat, John,   do.,   Craick
†Nichol, John,   do.,   Philhope
†Nichol, Willm., do.,   Wester Alemoor
*Oliver, James,   do.,   Howpasley
*Paterson, J. jun., do.,   Chapelhill
*Scott, Thomas,   do.,   Milsington
*Scott, Walter,   do.,   Girnwood
Scott, Henry,   do.,   Eildrig
Wilson, John, farm-steward, Greenbanks

SEATS, &c. OF COUNTY FAMILIES IN THE PARISH.

BORTHWICKBRAE.

Situated in the Selkirkshire portion of the parish, and near its centre—the property and residence of †Allan Eliott Lockhart, Esq., of Borthwickbrae and Cleghorn, eldest son of the late William Eliott Lockhart, Esq. of Borthwickbrae ; born 1803 ; succeeded 1832 ; married, 1830, Charlotte, daughter of the late Sir Robert Dundas, Bart., of Beechwood ; and has issue—

†William, Captain 26th Cameronians, born 1833.
David, born 1834.
Allan, Captain Royal Engineers, born 1837 ; died Sept. 1864.
Robert Dundas, Royal Artillery, born 1841.
Charles Walter, born 1850.
Six daughters—viz, Matilda, Marianne-Elizabeth, Robina-Catherine, Catherine-Henrietta, Mary-Dora, and Jane-Margaret.

Mr. Lockhart is a Justice of the Peace and Deputy-Lieutenant for the counties of Selkirk, Lanark, and Roxburgh ; and was M.P. for Selkirkshire from 1846 to 1861.
Other Residences—Cleghorn near Lanark, and Carlton Club, London.

BORTHWICKSHIELS.

Situated in the Roxburghshire portion of the parish, and about 2 miles from its northern extremity—the property and residence of *Col. George Pott, of Todrig and Borthwickshiels, eldest son of the late George Pott, Esq., of Todrig ; born 1811 ; married, 1840, Julia, youngest daughter of the late Rev. Robert Sparke, Hatchings ; and has issue a son—Robert Constantine, born 1851.

HOSCOTE HOUSE.

Near the centre of the parish and in the Selkirkshire portion of it—the property of Mrs. Margaret Stavert, 31 Melville Street,‡ Edinburgh; occupied by †Joseph, Hubback, Esq., merchant, Liverpool.

CHISHOLME.

Situated in the Roxburghshire part of the parish—lately the property of Robert Scott Chisholme, Esq., but was purchased about two years ago by the Trustees of William R. Dickson (minor);‖ presently occupied by Colonel James C. Scott (late Bengal Staff Corps), who rents the shootings on the property.

REGISTERED VOTERS (Non-Resident).

*Church, James, farmer, Sark Tower, Parkhill, Canonbie
*Dove, George,   do.,   Wark, Kelso

---

‡ While this sheet was at press, 1st April 1865, Mrs. Stavert of Hoscote died.
‖ Presently residing at 5 Regent Terrace, Edinburgh.

†Grieve, James, farmer, Branxholm Park, Hawick
†Grieve, William, do.,   do.   do.
†Hubback, Thos., do., Sunlawshill, Kelso
†Moffat, James, do., Garwald
*Patterson, James, sen., farmer, Terrona, Langholm
*†Scott, Archibald, Esq., Commonside, Hawick
*Wilson, John, farmer, Billholm, Langholm

SELKIRK PARISH

AND

GALASHIELS (LINDEAN) PARISH.

—◆—

Small portions of both these parishes are situated in Roxburghshire. They will be noticed under their proper heads in Selkirkshire.

END OF ROXBURGHSHIRE.

SELKIRKSHIRE.

THIS is a small county, of very irregular form, bounded on the east by Roxburghshire, on the west by the counties of Peebles and Dumfries, on the south by Dumfriesshire, and on the north by the county of Edinburgh. It extends from north to south 28 miles, and from east to west 17½ miles. The area of the county was formerly estimated to contain 266 square miles, or 170,313 acres; but according to the Ordnance Survey, just completed, it is 260 square miles, or 166,524 statute acres, which is close upon 16 statute acres to each of the population. Except towards the south and south-west, where the water-shed of the Dumfriesshire and Peeblesshire hills form the boundary for about one-third of its circumference, the limits of Selkirkshire are most arbitrarily and irregularly defined. Its outlines form points, promontories, peninsulas, bays, islands, mountain headlands, and level strands.

This county was formerly designated "Ettrick Forest," or shortly, "The Forest," from being in a great measure covered with wood, of which scarcely a vestige now remains. It was stocked with large herds of deer, and formed a favourite place of recreation for the Scottish monarchs. With the exception of a narrow portion on its eastern side, the county may be said to be a continued alternation of hill and dale, many of the eminences rising to a considerable height.* The principal vales are those of the Ettrick and Yarrow, with a portion of the vales of the Tweed and the Gala.

---

* "Viewed from a commanding height, the whole county seems crowded with hills, among which neither a house nor any mark of human life appears. In the lower parts of the district, where the country is more open, and the surface undulating, cultivation occupies a considerable breadth, covering the minor hills, and skirting the base of the mountains; but in the higher parts it is confined to narrow strips along the streams, and so deeply seated as to be invisible to the eye from any of the adjacent summits. The valleys are too narrow to be called dales, and are simply named from their rivers. That of Tweed being more important, has obtained the name of Tweedside; but, in the common language of the country, as if the smaller rivers had not a side on which a habitation might be placed, it is said of the people, as if they lived in waters, 'he lives in Caddon, he comes from Ale, or he belongs to Ettrick, or to Yarrow.' The hills vary in elevation from a few hundred to two thousand feet, They have an appearance of sameness in their general character, but they have often a considerable variety; in particular those

In the lower districts of the county, including the parishes of Galashiels, Selkirk, and the northern portion of the parish of Yarrow, great attention is paid to agriculture, which is here carried out as successfully and on exactly the same system as in the counties of Berwick and Roxburgh (*see* p. 43 *et seq.*). In the upper districts sheep farming has been followed with great success—Leicesters, half-breds, and Cheviots being the kinds raised, according to locality, to almost the entire exclusion of the old black-faces. Where the pastures are coarse a number of Highland cattle are grazed.† Within the last fifty years the climate and condition of the upper district of Sel-

---

around St. Mary's Loch and the Loch of the Lowes, where they rise in steep dark masses, especially towards the head of the glen, having their own tops concealed in clouds. The county has also some of the least agreeable scenery which the eye of man can endure, that of a cold, plain, black heath; which lies between Borthwick Water and the Ettrick, and which is relieved only by small lakes of no character, serving only to suggest the swampy nature of their situation." —*Remarks furnished by the late Rev. N. Paterson, minister of Galashiels, to the "Statistical Account of Selkirkshire," published 1841.*

* The following is a comparative statement of the proportional acreage of the principal crops of the three counties of the district, for the year 1857; extracted from the last report issued by John Hall Maxwell, Esq., Secretary for the Highland and Agricultural Society of Scotland; which will give an idea of the position of Selkirkshire as an agricultural county; roughly stated, the area of Selkirkshire is half that of Berwick, and a third of that of Roxburgh—rather over in both cases.

County.	Total Statute Acres.	Total acreage under Rotation of Crops.	Wheat.	Barley.	Oats.	Beans.	Peas.
Berwick	302,957	146,815	12,404	15,298	30,444	2,275	489
Roxburgh ..	428,494	124,479	8,558	12,107	28,428	1,070	398
Selkirk	166,524	14,441	261	949	4,162	18	11

County.	Tares.	Turnips.	Potatoes.	Rape.	Turnip Seed.	Hay.	Summer Fallow.
Berwick	1,128	27,300	2,117	289	141	54,232	1,184
Roxburgh ..	650	23,993	1,590	159	66	46,669	476
Selkirk	75	2,624	222	30	4	5,013	65

[For continuation of Comparative Statement, see next page.]

kirkshire have greatly improved,* and now a quality of stock is raised ; crops, fruits, and trees grown, and game harboured, which were formerly never attempted. (For fuller and interesting particulars as to this, *see* account of Ettrick parish.)

Selkirkshire is well watered by the beautiful rivers Ettrick, Yarrow, and Tweed ; it also possesses numerous lakes—the principal being St. Mary's Loch, and the Loch of the Lowes, lying at the head of the Yarrow ; the others, small and unimportant, lie about the head waters of the Ale.

The county has railway communication by means of a branch of the North British line from Galashiels to Selkirk.

Of the ten parishes constituting the county of Selkirk, only three of them, viz.—Kirkhope, Yarrow, and Ettrick, are complete within itself ; of the others, Ashkirk (*see* p. 353) and Roberton (p. 357) have their larger portions in Roxburghshire ; Selkirk (p. 371) and Galashiels, while their larger portions are in this county, have each smaller portions in Roxburghshire. Stow (*see* following pages) lies mostly in the county of Edinburgh, while Innerleithen and Peebles lie in Peeblesshire, except the out-of-the-way corners of both, which in this county consist, in the case of Peebles, of one moderately sized grazing farm, and in the case of Innerleithen of two moderately sized grazing farms and a gentleman's mansion with its surrounding grounds ; and as if to confuse the confusion, in one case at least,—in Ashkirk parish, while one portion ranks with Selkirk for the purposes of assessment, it ranks with Roxburghshire on the voters' roll. Situated as Selkirkshire is, in respect to its parishes, we presume that, excepting Nairn, it is unique amongst the counties of Scotland, if not in the kingdom.

The only towns are Selkirk and Galashiels, the former being a royal burgh and the county town. The county returns one member to Parliament.

The population of Selkirkshire in 1801 was 5388 ; in 1811, 5889 ; in 1821, 6637 ; in 1831, 6833 ; in 1841, 7990 ; in 1851, 9809 ; and in 1861, 10,449. The number of inhabited houses was 1331 ; uninhabited, 25 ; building, 9. The annual value of real property, as assessed in 1815, was £43,584 ; in 1849, £52,839 ; in 1855, £59,554 : 19 : 4 ; in 1856, £59,914 : 9 : 3 ; in 1857, £60,711 : 5 : 7 ; in 1858, £61,652 : 14 : 1 ; in 1859, £63,591, 6s. 9d ; in 1860, £65,069 : 10 : 6 ; and in 1864-5 (exclusive of railways), £73,883 : 11 : 8.

VALUATION AND AREA OF THE SEVERAL PARISHES IN THE COUNTY OF SELKIRK.

FOR THE YEAR ENDING WHITSUNDAY 1865.

Acres.	Parishes.	Real Rental from Whitsunday 1864-65.
21,517.157 }	Selkirk, . .	£11,299 9 8
	Burgh of Selkirk, .	8828 1 8
5710.569	Galashiels, . . .	14,605 16 7
3384.927	Ashkirk, . . .	2188 0 3
3578.752	Innerleithen, . .	1071 13 9
42,682.781	Ettrick, . . .	9852 19 7
11,628.223	Roberton, . . .	3503 0 8
10,017.855	Stow, . . .	4337 2 2
22,972.608	Kirkhope, . . .	6148 5 11
3172.391	Peebles, . . .	80 0 0
41,859.090	Yarrow, . . .	9964 6 5
	Railways . . .	2004 15 0
166,524.353		£73,883 11 8

LIEUTENANCY.

Lord-Lieutenant and Sheriff-Principal—Lord Polwarth (Mertoun, St. Boswell's), 1845.
Vice-Lieutenant—Vacant.

DEPUTY-LIEUTENANTS.

Ballantyne, Jas., of Holylee, 1829.
Dalkeith, Earl of, 1853.
Johnston, J., of Alva, 1824.
Lockhart, Allan E., of Borthwickbrae, 1824.
Napier, Lord, 1848.

Murray, Sir John, of Philiphaugh, 1848.
*Plummer, C. S., of Middlestead, 1848.
Scott, Hugh, of Gala, 1848.
Walker, W. S., of Bowland, 1843

Clerk of Lieutenancy—Peter Rodger, Selkirk.
Convener—A. E. Lockhart, Esq. of Borthwickbrae.

County.	Horses for Agricultural Purposes.	Milch Cows.	Total Cattle.	Breeding Sheep.	Feeding Sheep.	Lambs.	Swine.
Berwick..	5,439	3,741	16,265	85,738	59,051	87,876	5020
Roxburgh	4,441	4,361	16,192	222077	41,186	173795	4376
Selkirk ...	598	630	2,449	81,275	3,293	61,164	474

* The angler, or pedestrian tourist visiting the wilds of Selkirkshire should be careful how he sets out on any excursion without a supply of waterproof protection from the weather. Amongst the hills rain and wind come on with a suddenness and fury unknown in the plains ; the country possesses little natural shelter, while the private houses are few and the inns fewer : of the latter there are only four in the hilly district. He may also find it to his comfort to set out with a moderate supply of provisions.

PARLIAMENTARY REPRESENTATION.

Member for the County—Lord Henry J. Scott, 1861 (Conservative).
Parliamentary Constituency of the County, 499.
Auditor of Election Expenses for the County—D. C. Alexander, solicitor, Selkirk.

SHERIFF AND COMMISSARY COURT.

Sheriff and Commissary—George Dundas, Esq., Advocate, 9 Charlotte
Square, Edinburgh, 1844.
Sheriff-Substitute and Commissary Depute—James S. Milne, Esq.,
Heatherlie, Selkirk, 1861.
Procurator-Fiscal—Peter Rodger, Esq. of Elm Park.
Sheriff and Commissary-Clerk—John Lang, Esq. of Viewfield.
Depute Sheriff and Commissary-Clerk—J. Mitchell, Market Place,
Selkirk.

The Sheriff Courts for the County and Sheriff Small Debt Courts are
held at Selkirk weekly during Sessions.* Circuit Sheriff Small Debt
Courts held at Galashiels on first Tuesdays of February, April, June,
August, October, and December. Quarter Sessions are held at Selkirk on the first Tuesdays of March, May, and August, and last
Tuesday of October.

COMMISSIONERS OF SUPPLY.

His Grace the Duke of Buccleuch
and Queensberry.
James Ballantyne of Holylee.
James George Ballantyne, yr. of
Holylee.
Adam Brown of Helmburn.
John Cochrane, manufacturer,
Galashiels.
Earl of Dalkeith.
The Right Honourable Lord Elibank.
Sir Adam Hay of Smithfield and
Haystoune, Bart.
John Hay, yr. of Smithfield and
Haystoune.
James Johnstone of Alva and
Hangingshaw.
James Johnstone, yr. of Alva and
Hangingshaw.
George Lee, manufacturer, Galashiels.
A. Eliott Lockhart of Borthwickbrae.
Wm. E. Lockhart, yr. of Borthwickbrae.
Earl of Minto.
Sir John Murray of Philiphaugh.
Robert Mercer of Scotsbank.
Alexander Mitchell of Stow.

The Hon. William Napier of
Broadmeadows.
The Right Hon. Lord Napier.
The Hon. William J. Napier.
The Hon. Montolies F. Murray.
The Right Honourable Lord Polwarth.
Sir John Pringle, Bart.
James Pringle, yr.
Alexander Pringle of Whytbank.
James Pringle, of Torwoodlee.
George Pott of Todrig.
Chas. S. Plummer of Middlestead.
James G. Pott of Potburn.
William Paterson of Ettrickhall.
George Roberts, manufacturer,
Selkirk.
George Rodger of Bridgelands.
John Scott of Rodono.
Robert Sanderson, manufacturer,
Galashiels.
Hugh Scott of Gala.
The Hon. Walter Scott, Master of
Polwarth.
Archibald Scott of Howcleuch.
Henry Scott of Overkirkhope.
John Scott, yr. of Overkirkhope.
John Sibbald, manufacturer, Galashiels.

* "During Sessions"—*see* foot-note, p. 251.

T. M. Scott of Shorthope.
James Sime, manufacturer, Galashiels.
James Stalker, Factor for Hugh
Scott of Gala.
Alex. Williamson of Cardrona.
William S. Walker of Bowland.
William Walker, yr. of Bowland.
John Anderson, Lewenshope.
The Duke of Buccleuch's Chamberlain, for the time being.

The Sheriff-Depute of the County
of Selkirk, for the time being.
The Sheriff-Substitute of the
County of Selkirk, for the time
being.
The Provost of Selkirk, for the
time being.
The Senior Bailie of Selkirk, for
the time being.
The Junior Bailie of Selkirk, for
the time being.

Clerk of Supply—Robert Paton.
Collector of County Rates—Peter Rodger.

COMMISSION OF THE PEACE FOR COUNTY OF SELKIRK.

Those marked thus (*) have been qualified under the New Commission of
3d July 1853. Those marked thus (†) generally preside at Selkirk,
where the only Justice of Peace Courts for the County are held.

*His Grace the Duke of Buccleuch
and Queensberry.
Earl of Dalkeith.
Earl of Minto.
*Lord Napier.
Lord Elibank.
*William Clark of Langhaugh.
John G. Henderson of Abbotrule
John Hay, yr. of Smithfield and
Haystoune.
*†A. E. Lockhart of Borthwickbrae.
William E. Lockhart, yr. of Borthwickbrae.
*†Sir John Murray of Philiphaugh, Bart.
*Robert Mercer of Scotsbank.
Alexander Mitchell of Stow.
*†George Pott of Todrig.
*James Pringle of Torwoodlee.
James Pringle, yr. of Newhall.
*Wm. Paterson of Ettrickhall.
*Lord Polwarth.
*Alexander Pringle of Whytbank.

*†Charles S. Plummer of Middlestead.
*†James Ballantyne of Holylee.
*James G. Ballantyne, younger
of Holylee.
*†James Johnstone of Alva and
Hangingshaw.
Archibald Scott of Howcleuch.
*†Hugh Scott of Gala.
Mark Sprot of Riddell.
*Henry Scott of Overkirkhope.
Thomas M. Scott of Wauchope.
*William S. Walker of Bowland.
*The Sheriff-Depute of the County
of Selkirk, for the time being.
*The Sheriff-Sub. of the County
of Selkirk, for the time being.
*The Provost of the Burgh of Selkirk, for the time being.
*†The Senior Bailie of the Burgh
of Selkirk, for the time being.
*†The Senior Magistrate of the
Town of Galashiels, for the time
being.

Clerk to the Justices—John Lang.
Depute Clerk of the Peace—J. Mitchell.

PROPERTY AND INCOME TAX COMMISSIONERS.

COMMISSIONERS FOR GENERAL PURPOSES.

Robert Mercer of Scotsbank.
Sir John Murray of Philiphaugh
Archibald Scott of Howcleuch.
William S. Walker of Bowland.

The Sheriff.
The Sheriff-Substitute.
Charles. S. Plummer of Middlestead.

COMMISSIONERS FOR ADDITIONAL PURPOSES.
James Ballantyne of Holylee.
Robert Paton, W.S., Selkirk, Clerk.   Peter Rodger, Selkirk, Assessor.
Edward Henderson, Melrose, Surveyor.

No time fixed for Appeal Courts.

POLICE COMMITTEE OF SELKIRKSHIRE.

Under 20 and 21 Vict., cap. 72.

Chairman—A. E. Lockhart of Borthwickbrae.

Lord-Lieutenant of the County.	Jas. Ballantyne, Esq. of Holylee.
The Sheriff of the County.	Sir John Murray of Philiphaugh.
His Grace the Duke of Buccleuch.	Chas. S. Plummer, Esq. of Middle-
James Johnstone, Esq. of Alva.	stead.
Major Scott of Gala.	The Provost of Selkirk.
Sheriff-Substitute of the County.	

Clerk—Peter Rodger, writer, Selkirk.
Chief Constable—James Fraser, Selkirk.
Deputy Chief Constable—Peter Merrylees, Selkirk.

SELKIRKSHIRE PRISON BOARD.

A. E. Lockhart, Esq.	The Sheriff.
Major Scott of Gala.	The Sheriff-Substitute.
Chas. S. Plummer, Esq. of Middle-	The Provost of Selkirk.
stead.	The Senior Bailie of Selkirk.

Robert Paton, W.S., Clerk.   Peter Rodger, Collector.
Governor of Selkirk Jail—Henry Harrison.

INLAND REVENUE.

Stamp and Tax Department, Distributor of, and Collector—Robert
Thorburn, Peebles.

DEPUTES.
Selkirk—John Lang. Galashiels—Wm. Rutherford.
Surveyor of Property and Assessed Taxes—Ed. Henderson, Melrose.

EXCISE DEPARTMENT.
Collector—J. Luckie, Haddington.   Supervisor—B. F. Dun, Kelso.
Officers for the County—James Deans, Melrose, for Galashiels and
District ; and John Hawkins, Hawick, for Selkirk and District.

VALUATION OF LANDS AND HERITAGES IN SCOTLAND.

Assessor for Selkirkshire—Peter Rodger.
Assessor for Burgh—D. C. Alexander, solicitor.

REGISTRARS OF SASINES.

John Murray, Esq., W.S., Melrose, Keeper for the County.
Peter Rodger, Esq., Selkirk, Keeper for the Burgh.

PASTORAL SOCIETY OF SELKIRKSHIRE.

Instituted in 1819 by the late Lord Napier, to promote the improvement of live stock.

Patron—His Grace the Duke of Buccleuch and Queensberry.
President—John Anderson, Esq., Lewenshope.
Vice-Presidents—G. J. Scott, Esq., Singlie ; Jas. Gibson, Esq., Shaws.
Council—Hon. W. Napier, C. S. Plummer, Esq., J. Clapperton, Esq.
Secretary and Treasurer—Peter Rodger, Selkirk.

The Meetings are held annually on the first Wednesday of September, near Ettrick Bridge-end. At the forty-sixth Exhibition, held
on 7th September 1864, Prizes to the amount of £40, besides sweepstakes, etc., were given (see Kirkhope parish).

SELKIRKSHIRE ASSOCIATION FOR IMPROVEMENT OF DOMESTIC POULTRY (estab. 1863).

Patron—His Grace the Duke of Buccleuch.

COMMITTEE OF MANAGEMENT.

Bailie Dalgleish.	Mr. William Mills, Fleece Hotel.
E. Clarkson, Esq., M.D.	Mr. G. Dryden, County Hotel.
Mr. W. D. Connochie, V.S.	Mr. Thos. Wilson, auctioneer.
Mr. George Mathison, draper.	Mr. Peter Melross, shoemaker.
Sergeant Atkins.	

Secy.—Jas. Millar, watchmaker. Treas.—Robert Paton, Esq., W.S.
Auditor—Basil Henderson, accountant.

The Annual Exhibition is held at Selkirk in December. Amount
given in Prizes at the Exhibition of 1864, £26.

SELKIRKSHIRE FARMERS' CLUB.

Established 11th June 1806, for the purpose of discussing questions
of agricultural interest. Meets at Selkirk second Wednesday of every
month, except September.

Peter Rodger, Selkirk, Treasurer. John Lang, Selkirk, Secretary.
Entry-Money, 21s. An. Subscription, which pays all expenses, 21s.

SELKIRKSHIRE AND ROXBURGHSHIRE ADMINISTRATIVE BATTALION OF VOLUNTEERS. (See p. 54.)

Local Secretary—William Little.

2 B

SELKIRKSHIRE AND ETTRICK TURNPIKE ROAD TRUSTS.

John Lang, Selkirk, Clerk.

Tolls generally let on the second or third Wednesday of March.

STATUTE LABOUR ROADS,

Comprehending the parishes, or parts of parishes, of Ettrick, Yarrow, Kirkhope, Selkirk, Roberton, Ashkirk, Stow, Galashiels, Inner-leithen, and Peebles.

Statutory Meetings are held on 30th April, and second Tuesday of June, and other Meetings when required.

R. Paton, W.S., Selkirk, Clerk and Collector.

SELKIRK.

Two small portions of the parish of Selkirk are situated in Roxburghshire, but the larger part is in this county.* It is bounded on the north, by the parishes of Galashiels and the extreme south-eastern point of Stow—the river Tweed intervening; on the east, by Bowden parish in Roxburghshire; on the south, by Kirkhope; and on the west, by Yarrow. The general outline of the parish is very irregular. The length of the main part of the parish, north to south, is $7\frac{1}{2}$ miles, and its breadth, east to west, is over 8 miles. The area of the parish (exclusive of the two portions which are in Roxburghshire, but including the detached part in Selkirkshire, which consists of $1430\frac{3}{4}$ acres), according to the Ordnance Survey, is about 21,517 acres; comprising as follows :—21,068 4-5th acres land, 307 water, $135\frac{1}{4}$ public and private roads, and 6 occupied by the railway. The detached portions in Roxburghshire have a total area of $1358\frac{1}{8}$ acres. Total area of the parish in both counties, $22,895\frac{1}{8}$ acres. The parish is completely of a hilly character; but, from being all very elevated, the different peaks have not that marked appearance they otherwise would have. The most remarkable hills lie between the Ettrick and Tweed. Of these the Three Brethren Cairn is 1523 feet, Broomy Law 1519 feet, Foulshiels Hill 1454 feet, South Height 1493 feet, and Brown Knowe are 1718 feet in height. In the detached portion of the parish, cut off by Kirkhope, the ground, except along the Todrig burn, averages over 1100 feet in height The river Tweed bounds the parish throughout its entire length on the north, and the Ettrick and Yarrow intersect and have their confluence in it. At the extreme north-

---

* Although these small portions form part of the county of Roxburgh, both of them are undetached from the parish. The larger, consisting of $1280\frac{1}{2}$ acres, lies at the north-east, and contains the estate and loch of Whitmuirhall and farm of Greenhead. The other portion, consisting of $77\frac{1}{2}$ acres only, lies about $1\frac{1}{4}$ miles north of the town, on the left bank of the Ettrick, which forms its eastern boundary. Its southern boundary is the Nettly Burn, and it is bounded on the north by Ettrick Bank house and grounds. Between these two pieces of Roxburghshire, the Selkirkshire part of Selkirk, and a long finger-like piece of the Roxburghshire part of Galashiels (Lindean) intervenes. Another small portion, forming part of Selkirkshire, but lying undetached from the county, although detached from the parish, lies at the head of Todrig Burn, cut off by Kirkhope parish, and forming part of the northern boundary of Roberton parish.

east point of the parish the Tweed and the Ettrick have their confluence. All of these rivers abound in both salmon and trout. Except a stretch of the Ettrick of five miles above Yarrow foot, all the streams in the parish are free to trout anglers. In the parish are also some small lochs.

The soil is in general light and dry. The whole of the parish was in former times, in common with neighbouring parishes, covered by an extensive forest, and was used as a royal hunting ground, of which scarcely a trace now remains (*see* Ettrick parish).

Near the eastern extremity of the parish, and occupying a fine situation on an eminence on a slope on the right bank of the Ettrick, is the town of Selkirk. It is a very ancient town, a royal burgh, and capital of the county, and was formerly a place of considerable importance; not less than a hundred of its citizens having followed James IV., to the disastrous field of Flodden, where they distinguished themselves in the most gallant manner. "In revenge for their conduct the English, on some subsequent occasion, burnt the town to the ground; but to compensate for that loss a grant of 1000 acres of the adjoining land was made over by the crown to the burghers and their peasantry for ever," and now constitutes Selkirk Common (*see* lists—Selkirk Races).

Till of late Selkirk presented a dull and decaying appearance, but a spirit of improvement has become developed. Several large mills have been erected on the Ettrick; and the manufacture of woollens established on an extensive scale contributes greatly to the prosperity of the town. Some elegant private houses have lately been built: in the Market Place is a good statue of Sir Walter Scott; and a similar monument to Mungo Park, the African traveller, stands in the High Street; the streets are well paved and lighted; the population has considerably increased, and the town now presents altogether a prepossessing aspect. As yet the sanatory arrangements of the town are very imperfect, and consequently it has been subject to epidemics, but at the date of publication extensive works were in progress for providing a water supply, and those for sewerage only awaited the engineer's plans. The adoption of the cleaning provisions of the Police and Improvement Act would tend very much to the improvement of the closes and bye-ways of the town, and under proper sanatory regulations Selkirk, from its situation, should be, if not the healthiest, as healthy a town and one of the pleasantest in the entire district. That the town is well situated for thorough sanatory arrangements, is shown by the following heights, supplied from the office of the Ordnance Survey:—

Bench Mark at Bythorne Gate .... 619 feet.
Bench Mark on Corner of High St. and Tower St ...... 563.6 ,,
Bolt in Front of Tower of Selkirk Town Hall .... 561.2 ,,
Largest Gasometer at Gasworks .... 400 ,,

For fall and outflow these levels surpass those of any town in the district. The new Police Act of 25 & 26 Vic. has been adopted, to admit of carrying out the sewerage and water supply, and levying an assessment for the same—rates not yet fixed. In ordinary police matters the town has been associated with the county—3½d. per £. Other expenses connected with the burgh have been defrayed by the rents of the town property; the magistrates having had no power to assess.

The town possesses few antiquities or associations of interest, but its neighbourhood is rich in both. Near to it is the HAINING —the seat of Mrs. Pringle Douglas—delightfully situated amidst woods, with a beautiful sheet of water in front of the mansion. Another seat of interest, and frequently visited, is BOWHILL, situated up the Yarrow, 4 miles from Selkirk, and on the tongue of land near its confluence with the Ettrick, the hunting residence of His Grace the Duke of Buccleuch; the house is small for a Duke's palace, but the grounds are fine; and within their circuit, further up the Yarrow, is the ruin of Newark Castle, upon a peninsula cut out by the surrounding stream, in a situation of wild grandeur and of greater beauty than is possessed by any other Border keep. Free access to the ruin is to be had at all times by the public; and the pleasant walks along the banks of the river are, every summer, trod and enjoyed by a large number of visitors. The interest of this ruin is enhanced from its being the mansion in which Lady Anne, Duchess of Buccleuch, is made to listen to the "Lay of the Last Minstrel." Nearly opposite to Newark is Foulshiels, the birth-place of Mungo Park. The house in which the traveller was born is now uninhabited, having stood for many years in a ruinous condition. About 2 miles from Selkirk, on the north side of the Ettrick, is the plain of Philiphaugh where in 1645 Montrose was defeated by General Leslie. "Close to Newark, on the Yarrow, is a field called the Slain Man's Lee, where the Covenanters, a day or two after, are said to have put many of their prisoners to death." About 2 miles farther up the Yarrow stands the mansion-house of PHILIPHAUGH. On the Ettrick, 4 miles from Selkirk and at the southern boundary of the parish, is Oakwood Tower, said to have been the residence of the famous Sir Michael Scott, of Balweary*—now the property of Lord Polwarth. Below Yair

---

* Traditionally named *The Wizard*—a person of very extraordinary abilities, and who made a remarkable figure at the time in which he lived. His extraordinary discoveries in the science of chemistry obtained for him the character of a magician; and to this day there are marvellous tales told in the district of his communings with the evil one (*see* p. 76, and *vide* Hogg's "Three Perils of Man"). Sir Michael is honourably mentioned by Dante in his "Inferno." He died about the year 1294. From him Sir William Scott, Baronet of Ancrum, is lineally descended (*see* p. 201).

House there is a beautiful stretch of Tweed, where it is beset with rocks and forced into rapids within the limits of a hill pass.

The railway constructed between the burgh and the North British line at Galashiels has been the means of opening up the resources of the district, giving a great impulse to the trade and manufactures of the town and contributing much to its growing prosperity. The distance of Selkirk from Edinburgh by rail is 40 miles, 7 from Galashiels, and 24 from Hawick. By turnpike road Selkirk is distant from Hawick 12 miles, Peebles 22, and Moffat 34. The railway station is close under the eminence on which Selkirk is built ; the distance though comparatively short is fatiguing to walk, but omnibuses attend the trains.

Anniversary—Selkirk Common Riding—a day on which races usually take place. This is not fixed, but it generally falls on the Friday after Hawick Common Riding, about the beginning of June (*see* p. 304, and p. 380—Merchant Company).

Annual Holiday—New Year's Day.

Market Day—Wednesday, at which little business of any kind is transacted. The corn is sold by sample. The burgh has lost its old pre-eminence for shoemaking, and the large trade it did in supplying bread to Moffat during the visitors' season is now also gone : that branch of trade having been extinguished by the railway facilities between Moffat and other places.

Hiring Days—Shepherds and Hinds, first Wednesday in March ; Servants, 5th April ; Shearer's Port, 15th July ; Women, 31st October. When any of these dates fall on a Sunday the hiring is held the Monday after.

The population statistics of the parish by the census of 1861, were as follows :—of the Burgh, 3695 ; landward portions in Selkirkshire, 993 ; in Roxburghshire, 51—total, 4739 ; who composed 1039 families, one of whom was returned as living in a house having no window, 450 as living in houses of one window, 330 in houses of two windows, and 258, or one-fourth, in houses of three and more windows.

Assessed property in the parish 1864-5, £20,127 : 11 : 4.

The principal landed-proprietors are—Sir John Murray, Bart. of Philiphaugh ; Mrs. Pringle Douglas of Haining ; the Duke of Buccleuch ; Alexander Pringle of Yair ; Lord Polwarth (Mertoun, St. Boswells) ; Charles S. Plummer of Sunderland Hall ; the Burgh of Selkirk ; Hon. William Napier of Broadmeadows ; Trustees of the late Charles Dunlop, Esq., of Whitmuirhall

---

MAGISTRATES AND COUNCIL,
Who have the government of the town.

John Johnstone, Provost.

Thomas Dalgleish, Senior Bailie.   George Lewis, Junior Bailie.

Jas. Millar, Dean of Guild.   Basil Henderson, Treasurer.

Peter Rodger, Town Clerk.

COUNCILLORS.

Henry S. Anderson, M.D.	Michael Muir, draper.
Thomas Hall, joiner.	Robert Hope, mason.
D. C. Alexander, writer.	John Walker, mason.
John Scott, grocer.	William Mills, innkeeper.
Ebenezer Clarkson, M.D.	W. D. Connochie, V.S.

Police Rates, *see* p. 374.

PUBLIC OFFICES, &c.

Billet Masters—James Hall and Walter Paterson.

Burgh and County Rates, Collector of—Peter Rodger, High Street.

Chief Constable—James Fraser, Tower Street.

Fire Brigade, Superintendent of—William Robson, Gas Works.

Heritors' Clerk—Robert Paton, W.S., High Street.

Income Tax—John Lang, Collector. Peter Rodger, County Assessor. D. C. Alexander, Burgh Assessor.

Inland Revenue, Collector of—John Lang, Market Place.

Justice of Peace Clerk—John Lang. Depute—John Mitchell, Market Place.

Medical Officers and Public Vaccinators—Drs. Anderson & Ballantyne, High Street.

Nuisances, Inspector of—

Police Assessment, Collector of—John Dunn, Tower Street

Poor, Inspector of—James Hall ; office, Back Row.

Prison, Governor of, Henry Harrison.

Procurator-Fiscal for County—Peter Rodger.
    „   for Burgh—Robert Paton.

Register of Sasines Office, (Burgh)—Peter Rodger.

Registrar of Births, Marriages, and Deaths—John Dunn, chemist, Tower Street.

Sheriff-Clerk—John Lang. Depute—John Mitchell.

Sheriff-Officer—Alexander Sherriff, The Valley.

Session Clerk and Kirk Treasurer—Alex. Scott, Halliday's Park.

Sexton—Robert Currie, Chapel Street.

Stamps and Taxes, Collector of—John Lang.

Turnpike Road Trustees' Office—John Lang, Clerk.

Town Clerk—Peter Rodger.

Town-Crier—Walter Mathison, Kirk Wynd.

Town Treasurer—Basil Henderson, High Street.

POST OFFICE (Market Place).
Postmaster—George Turnbull.
Letter Carriers—Walter Dryden and Walter Ingles.

DESPATCHES.	Box Closes.
Galashiels, Hawick, Kelso, Jedburgh, &c. .	6-25 a.m.
Edinburgh and Dalkeith .	9-50 a.m.
London and all parts of England, Edinburgh, Galashiels, Melrose, Hawick, Kelso, Jedburgh, &c. .	3-20 p.m.
Edinburgh .	7-15 p.m.
Ettrick, Yarrow, Lilliesleaf, and Yair districts .	9-20 a.m.

ARRIVALS.	
London, Edinburgh, and all parts .	9-40 a.m.
Berwick, and North-East of England .	11-50 a.m.

Edinburgh, Galashiels, and Dalkeith . . . . 6 p.m.
London and all parts . . . . 9-20 p.m.
To callers, till 10 p.m. Delivery at 7 a.m. following morning.

Sundays.

Galashiels, Melrose, &c. . . . . 6-55 a.m.
London and all parts of England, Edinburgh, &c. . 5 p.m.

Office open to callers from 9-30 to 10-30 a.m., and from 2 to 3 p.m.
No Sunday Delivery.

Country.

Lilliesleaf, (Six Days a week) at 10-20 a.m. Jos. Macgregor, runner.
Kirkhope, Ettrickbridge-end, Ettrick, and Ramsaycleuch, (Tuesday, Thursday, and Saturday) at 10-20 a.m. Thomas Armstrong, runner.
Yair (Six Days), at 10-20 a.m. William Scott, runner.
Yarrow School House (Six Days), at 10-20 a.m. A. Robson, runner.
From Yarrow to Cappercleuch and Meggat (Six Days), at 1-30 p.m. ; arrives, 8-30 p.m John Brunton, runner.

Letters can be Registered to within half-an-hour of Box Closing, and Late Letters can be posted 20 minutes after Box Closing, by affixing an extra Stamp.
Money Order Office open daily, excepting Sunday. from 9 a.m. till 6 p.m.

CLERGY, &c.

Presbytery of Selkirk, and Synod of Merse and Teviotdale.
Patron—Duke of Roxburghe.*

PARISH CHURCH—Rev. James Farquharson, M.A. (Inducted 1857). Sittings, 1100. Leader of Psalmody—Thompson Aimers, West Port ; Session Clerk and Kirk Treasurer—Alexander Scott, Halliday's Park ; Church Officer—Robert Currie, Chapel Street.
FREE CHURCH—Rev. James Young (Inducted 1860). Sittings, 700. Average attendance at Sabbath School, 80 ; Superintendent of Sabbath School—G. Tudhope, Kirk Wynd ; Leader of Psalmody —William Scott, Market Place ; Session Clerk—Richard Leitch, Heatherlie Burn ; Church Treasurer—Henry Harrison, Chapel Street ; Sustentation Fund Secretary—William Brockie ; Church Officer—John Lothian, South Port.
U. P. CHURCH (First)—Rev. John Lawson (Inducted 1850). Sittings, 850. Average attendance at Sabbath School, 150 ; Superintendent of Sabbath School—John Scott, West Port ; Leader of Psalmody—James Crichton, Heatherlie ; Session Clerk—John Scott, West Port ; Secretary—Robert Steele, Halliday's Park ; Kirk Treasurer—Robert Forsyth, West Port ; Church Officer—William Brown, Fleshmarket Street.
U. P. CHURCH (West)—Rev. John Dalziel Dickie (Inducted 1861). Sittings, 490. Average attendance at Sabbath School, 80 ; Super-

* The Duke of Roxburghe possesses no heritages in Selkirk, but from time immemorial he has been patron of, and a proprietor of teinds in, the parish, and has held a family pew in the parish church. His Grace's right to a pew was on one occasion on certain grounds called in question, but the right was sustained by award of the Sheriff.

intendent of Sabbath School—Andrew Stavert, Castle Street ; Leader of Psalmody—James Scott, Back Row ; Session Clerk—Richard Turnbull, Hawthornbank ; Kirk Treasurer—Jas. Turnbull, Hawthornbank ; Church Officer—Jas. Murray, South Port.

ENGLISH CONGREGATIONAL CHAPEL—Rev. John Nichol (Inducted 1850). Sittings, 130. Average attendance at Sabbath School, 50 ; Conductor of Music—George Lewis, High Street ; Treasurer—George Lewis ; Church Officer—Archibald Anderson, Back Row.

EPISCOPALIAN CHURCH—Rev. Robert Gibson (Inducted 1859). Sittings, 110. Church Warden—Robert Tudhope, Market Place ; Organist—Miss M. Leslie, Market Place ; Clerk—H. O. Kemp, Back Row.

FAST DAYS—Thursdays before last Sabbath of April and second Sabbath of November.

BRANCH OF EVANGELICAL ALLIANCE.

Directors—Rev. Messrs. Farquharson and Lawson, Selkirk ; George Rodger, Esq., Bridgelands ; John Lee, Esq., Oakwood.
Secretary—Robert Paton, W.S.

YOUNG MEN'S CHRISTIAN ASSOCIATION (estab. 1862).

Meets every Friday evening at 8-15 (excepting May, June, and July), for the purposes of spiritually improving the mind by biblical research, and discussing religious topics.

Entry-Money, 6d. Yearly Subscription, 4s.

Hon. President—William Brown, Esq., Galahill, Galashiels.
President—Joseph Brown, Chapel Place.
Treasurer—George Bell. Secretary—John Anderson.

AUXILIARY TO EDINBURGH INSTITUTION FOR DEAF AND DUMB.

President—George Roberts, Esq., manufacturer.
Secretary and Treasurer—Robert Paton, W.S.
Committee—The Clergy of Selkirk.

AUXILIARY OF NATIONAL BIBLE SOCIETY OF SCOTLAND (Estab. 1864.)

President—George Rodger, Esq., of Bridgelands.
Treasurer—Mr. R. Leitch, Heatherlie Burn.
Secretary—Rev. James Young, Free Church Manse.

COLPORTAGE SOCIETY (estab. 1862).

Directors—Rev. Messrs. Farquharson, Lawson, Young, and Dickie.

Selkirk ; George Rodger, Esq., Bridgelands ; James Roberts, Esq., Hermitage ; John Lee, Esq., Oakwood.

Secretary—Robt. Paton, W.S.　Colporteur—T. Slater, Tower Street,

EDUCATIONAL INSTITUTIONS.*

Parochial or Grammar School—Alexander Scott, Rector ; A. Baxter, assistant ; average attendance about 220.

Burgh School—James Millar, Master ; John C. Calder, assistant. Average attendance 159.

Philiphaugh School, at Philipburn (supported by Sir John Murray, and under the superintendence of Rev. Mr. Nichol)—Andrew Cairns, Teacher, 60.

Young Ladies' Seminary—Misses Miller, High Street.

Girls' School (Backbrae Park)—Miss Laidlaw ; average attend., 60.

　　,,　　(South Port)—Miss Heatlie ; average attendance, 30.

CHARITY SCHOOL.

Supported by voluntary subscriptions.　Average income, £50. Average attendance, 80 ; three-fourths of whom are taught gratis, and one-fourth pay the nominal rate of 1d. per week.　The present premises were built in 1859, the funds for which were raised principally by a very successful bazaar in Selkirk in 1858.

Teacher—G. Dryden.　Secy.—Mr Paton, W.S.　Treas.—Mr. Rodger.

PAROCHIAL BOARD.

COMMITTEE.

George Roberts, Esq., Chairman.

Rev. James Farquharson.	Richard Leitch.
Henry S. Anderson, M.D.	Peter Rodger.
Robert Paton, W.S.	Geo. Anderson, Broomhill.
John Lang.	William Mark.
George Rodger, Bridgelands.	William Brown, jun.
Bailie Lewis.	Bailie Thomas Dalgleish.
William Brockie.	Rev. John Lawson.
William Muir, sen.	D. C. Alexander.
John Johnstone, Provost.	G. Oliver, Hawick, for the
James Millar.	Duke of Buccleuch.
Robert Hope.	

James Hall, Inspector.

No. of Poor on Roll, 68.　Rate of Assessment, 5d. per £. ; total Assessment 1864-5, £816 : 6 : 7½.　Poor House—Galashiels Combination.

DISPENSARY (Instituted 1851).

Supported by general contributions.

Annual donations about £10, the other revenue is derived from mutual subscriptions proportioned to the families of the subscribers.

* Children in the parish from 5 to 15, attending school during the first week of April 1861, 729 ; of all ages, 777.

President—Wm. Williamson.　Vice-President—Wm. Minto. Robert Douglas, Secretary.　John Armstrong, Treasurer. Medical Officers—Drs. Anderson, Ballantyne, and Clarkson.

The income of this Institution last year (1864) amounted to £152, 19s. 4½d. ; expenditure, £148 : 6 : 4.　Average number of members, 450 ; number of persons represented, 1291 ; number of prescriptions, 2205 ; number of medical visits, 7689.

LADIES' WORK SOCIETY (estab. 1854).

For supplying clothing to the necessitous Poor of the Town.

Patroness—Mrs. Pringle of Whytbank.

Secretaries—Mrs. Pringle and Miss Agnes Anderson.

Treasurer—Mrs. Paton, Shaw.

Purchasers—Mrs. G. Roberts and Mrs. J. Farquharson.

Recipients of Clothing—men, 15 ; women, 98—total, 113.

Income for 1863-4, £45 : 7 : 5 ; expenditure, £39 : 9.

MERCHANT COMPANY.

Michael Muir, Master.

Robert Paton, Secretary.　John Yellowlees, Treasurer.

Entry-Money, £1, 1s. (Ballot).　Yearly Subscription, 1s.

The Company consists of the principal professional and business men in the town, and is of very old standing—one of the books bearing the date 1694.　A small sum is paid for funeral money to the family of a deceased member, and subscriptions are bestowed yearly for benevolent purposes.　The funds are in a flourishing state.

The privileges are of a social order.　On the morning of the Common Riding day in June, the Company escort the magistrates and burgesses to the corn mills, and on their way round the marches of the burgh.　A fine flag belonging to the Company is carried on the occasion by one of the members chosen annually for that purpose. On the afternoon of the day the members dine together in the County Hotel.　Strangers are admitted to the dinner.

CHARITABLE BEQUESTS.

Mortification by Mrs Janet Scott or Campbell, 12th January 1831, for the clothing and education of six boys, sons of poor parents, burgesses of Selkirk, with a preference in favour of those of the name of Scott.　Trustees—The Provost of Selkirk, the Minister of the parish, and Minister of the First United Presbyterian Congregation for the time being.　Lang and Steedman, agents for Trustees.

Trust by Mr J. D. Oliver, sometime Schoolmaster of the parish of Selkirk, 24th August, 1824.　Annual Prize for Greek Poem and best English Scholar in the Parish School.　Trustees—The Provost of Selkirk ; Rev. J. Farquharson ; John Lang, Esq. ; John Anderson, Esq. ; the Schoolmaster of the Parish.　Lang and Steedman, agents for Trustees.

FRIENDLY SOCIETIES.

BENEFIT SICK SOCIETY.

President—Gavin Tudhope. Treas.—A. Stavert. Secy.—J. Brodie.

Average number of Members, 100.

This Society is the same in principle as those of Kelso (*see* p. 86); but the scale of payment to sick members is more liberal—viz., 5s. a-week for the first three months, and 3s. 6d. a week till the close of the financial year.

YEARLY SAVINGS SOCIETY.

Secretary—Andrew Stavert. Treasurer—Peter Melross.

Average number of Members, 100.

This Society has something of the character of a small banking establishment; its transactions are limited to the members.

ST. JOHN'S LODGE OF FREEMASONS (No. 32)

(Re-opened 19th August 1864.)

R.W. Master—Hon. William Napier of Broadmeadows.
Past Master—William Williamson.
Secretary—Alexander Forsyth. Treasurer—Dr. E. Clarkson.

WEAVERS' PROVIDENT SOCIETY (estab. 1864).

President—Andrew Anderson.
Treasurer—Peter Steele. Secretary—James Cockburn.

TOTAL ABSTINENCE SOCIETY.

President—James Ballantyne. Secretary—Joseph Brown.
Treasurer—George Turnbull, saddler.

SUBSCRIPTION LIBRARY.

(Instituted 1772.) Open Wednesday and Saturday, from 1 to 2.

Secretary—John Lang. Treasurer—John Dunn.
Librarian—James Dobson.

Share, £3. Annual Subscription, 15s. No. of Vols., about 3500.

MECHANICS' INSTITUTE, LIBRARY, AND READING-ROOM

(Established 1853).

Annual Subscription, 4s. No. of Vols, 1500.
President—Sir John Murray of Philiphaugh, Bart.
Vice-President—Robert Paton, W.S., Esq., Shaw Cottage.
Secretary—Alex. Scott, teacher. Treasurer—John Dunn, chemist.
Librarian—James Cockburn.

Reading-Room open daily from 10 a.m. till 10 p.m. Library open on Wednesday evenings from 8 to 9 o'clock, and on Saturday evenings from half-past 7 till 9 o'clock.

YOUNG MEN'S MUTUAL IMPROVEMENT SOCIETY.

(Estab. January 1861.)

Meets every Monday evening at 8-15 (excepting June, July, and August) for the purpose of reading original essays, select readings, recitations, discussing subjects of moral and intellectual importance. There is in connection with the Society a small but increasing Library, and a MS. monthly Journal. Entertainments and lectures are occasionally got up under its auspices.

Office-Bearers elected quarterly.
Secretary—William Meikle. Treasurer—Andrew Fairbairn.
Annual Subscription, 4s. 4d.

ETTRICK FOREST CLUB (estab. 1788).

Jas. Murray, Selkirk, Secretary.

CHORAL SOCIETY (estab. 1850).

Meets on Thursday evenings at a Quarter-past Eight o'Clock.

President—George Lewis. Vice-President—H. O. Kemp.
Secretary—Henry Harrison. Treasurer—Peter Steele

COTTAGERS' HORTICULTURAL SOCIETY (Instituted 1852).

President—George Roberts, Esq. of Wellwood Park.
Vice-President—Ebenezer Clarkson, Esq., M.D.
Secretary—John Brodie. Treasurer—George Lamb.

Two Exhibitions are held during the year in connection with this Society—the first on the second Saturday of July, and the other on the second Saturday of September, when a number of prizes are distributed, one of which is open to all similar societies. The prizes awarded in 1864 amounted to nearly £14.

SELKIRKSHIRE PASTORAL SOCIETY,
SELKIRKSHIRE FARMERS' CLUB,
ASSOCIATION FOR THE IMPROVEMENT OF DOMESTIC POULTRY,

See County Lists, p. 370.

GAS COMPANY.

DIRECTORS.

H. S. Anderson, M.D.   Peter Rodger, Esq.
Mr Thomas Dalgleish.   Mr William Muir, sen.
Mr William Brockie.

W. Brockie, Treasurer.   D. C. Alexander, writer, Secretary.
William Robson, Manager.

Price 6s. 3d. per 1000 feet.   Pays 10 per cent.
Amount of Stock, £1690.

CO-OPERATIVE STORE COMPANY (Limited).

President—William Davidson.
Secretary—Alexander Heard.   Treasurer—James Vair.
Auditors—Peter Steele and John Falla.
Store Manager—W. Meikle.   Depot, West Port.

Average sales nearly £8000, returning a gross profit of 15 per cent.

PROVIDENT BUILDING SOCIETY—Selkirk Branch.

Established 1859, in connection with that at Galashiels—which *see.*
Treasurer—John Scott, West Port.   Secretary—John Falla.

RACES.

Stewards—The Provost and Magistrates.
Judge—Bailie Dalgleish.
Clerk of the Course—Basil Henderson.

The Annual Meeting takes place over the Gala Rig, lying about 1½ miles to the north of the town, belonging to the burgh of Selkirk, on the second Friday of June (*see Anniversary*, p. 375, and Merchant Company, p. 380).

BOWLING CLUB (estab. 1855).

R. Paton, Esq., W.S., President.   W. Brydone, R.N., Vice-President.
Basil Henderson, Secretary.   J. Dunn, Treasurer.
Council—Messrs. Rodger, Clarkson, Smith, and Yellowlees.

Annual Subscription at present, 10s. Entry-Money, which includes the first year's subscription whatever be the rate, 20s.

CURLING CLUB (estab. 1850).

Admitted to R.C.C.C., 1854.

Patron—The Earl of Dalkeith, M.P.
Mr D. C. Alexander, President.
Mr George Anderson, Broomhill, Vice-President.
Mr Wm. Brockie, Treasurer.   Mr Jas. Millar, Secretary.

Chaplain—Rev. James Farquharson.
Council—Messrs. Rodger, Dunn, Lewis, Coutts, Mills, and Dryden.
Annual Subscription, 2s. 6d.
The matches take place on Haining Loch.

CRICKET CLUB (estab. 1852).

Captain—John Scott.   Secretary and Treasurer—Michael Stavert.
Entry-Money, 2s. 6d.   Annual Subscription, 5s.

2ND SELKIRKSHIRE RIFLE CORPS—(SELKIRK).

Head-Quarters—Armoury, High Street.

Captain—Charles Scott Plummer, Esq. of Middlestead.
Lieutenant—William Brown, Esq., Ladywell House.
Ensign—David C. Alexander, Esq., Byethorne.
Colour-Sergeant—John Brown.
Hon. Chaplain—Rev. James Farquharson, M.A., The Manse.
Hon. Surgeon—Henry Scott Anderson, Esq., M.D.
Drill Instructor—Sergeant Atkins.
Treasurer—Peter Rodger.   Secretary—John Lang.
Annual Subscription for Honorary Members, £1.
Effective Force—77.

Local Secretary of Border Rifle Association—Wm Little.—*See* p. 54.

BANK BRANCHES.

BRITISH LINEN COMPANY'S BANK (estab. 1825)—John Lang, Agent ; James Mathison, Accountant.

UNION BANK OF SCOTLAND (estab. 1853)—Peter Rodger, Agent ; Basil Henderson, Accountant.

NATIONAL BANK OF SCOTLAND (estab. 1864)—D. C. Alexander, Agent ; William Little, Accountant.

SAVINGS' BANK (estab. 1838, and converted into a National Securities Savings' Bank in 1839)—James Murray, Cashier ; Robert Paton, Actuary. Number of Depositors, 411. Deposits, 20th November 1864, £7889 : 8 : 9. Interest allowed, 2¼ per cent.

INSURANCE AGENTS.

ALLIANCE......................Lang & Steedman, writers.
BRITISH GUARANTEE.............D. C. Alexander, banker.
CALEDONIAN....................William Brockie, merchant.
EDINBURGH.....................Peter Rodger, writer.
INSURANCE Co. OF SCOTLAND......Lang & Steedman, writers.
LAND SECURITIES' COMPANY ......D. C. Alexander, banker.
LIFE ASSOCIATION...............George Lewis, bookseller.

ROYAL ....C. D. Alexander, banker.
SCOTTISH AMICABLE..............Yellowlees Brothers, ironmongers.
SCOTTISH NATIONAL INSUR. COY...Thomas Dalgleish, baker.
SCOTTISH UNION............... { Robert Paton, W.S.
                             { George Anderson, merchant.
SCOTTISH WIDOWS' FUND ....John Dunn, druggist.
SUN...........................Peter Rodger, writer.
UNITED KINGDOM TEMPERANCE }
 AND GENERAL PROVIDENT.... } Wm. Cheyne, plumber.

EMIGRATION AGENTS.

George Lewis, bookseller; John Dunn, chemist; Wm. Cheyne, plumber; Yellowlees Brothers, ironmongers.

PROCURATORS AND NOTARIES PUBLIC.

D. C. Alexander, N.P., West Port; house, Byethorne.
John Lang, N.P. (Sheriff-Clerk for the County), Market Place; house, Viewfield.
Robert Paton, W.S., High Street; house, Shaw Cottage.
Peter Rodger, N.P., High Street; house, Elm Park.
John Steedman, S.S.C. (of Lang & S.), Market Place; house, The Hermitage.

MEDICAL PRACTITIONERS.

Henry S. Anderson (of A. & Ballantyne), M.D., High Street.
Alexander Ballantyne (of Anderson & B.), M.D., High Street.
Ebenezer Clarkson, M.D., Market Place.

VETERINARY-SURGEON—William D. Connochie, Tower Street.

AUCTIONEER.

Thomas Wilson, Flesh Market Street.

NEWSPAPER.

The "Southern Reporter" (established 1855)—published every Thursday morning, George Lewis, Printer and Publisher.

WOOLLEN MILLS, &c.

Engaged principally in the manufacture of Tweeds and Shawls.

BRIDGE HAUGH MILL—Dobie & Richardson.
DUNSDALE MILL—Waddell & Turnbull.
ETTRICK MILL—J. & H. Brown & Co.
FOREST MILL—George Roberts & Co.
PHILIPHAUGH MILL—James Dobson, manager.
WAULK MILL—John Crosby.

Medical Inspector of Woollen Mills—Henry S. Anderson, M.D.

THE HAUGH—Corn Mill—William Douglas
PHILIPHAUGH—Saw Mill—Robert Yellowlees.

CARRIERS.

All put up at the *Cross Keys*, except David Chisholm, Back Row.

ANCRUM AND JEDBURGH—James Davidson, Wednesday.
BOWDEN—George Scott, Saturday.
ETTRICK—J. Hill, Monday; John Amos, Tuesday and Friday; John Murray, Wednesday.
GALASHIELS—Railway Station daily, and D. Chisholm, Monday.
HAWICK—David Chisholm, Tuesday and Friday.
INNERLEITHEN—John Christopherson, Monday.
MELROSE—David Chisholm, Monday.
MIDLEM—John Aitchison, Wednesday and Saturday.
MOFFAT—Robert Stewart, Monday and Friday.
TRAQUAIR—John Christopherson, Monday.
YARROW—John Brunton, Monday, Wednesday, and Friday.
YARROW AND MOFFAT—Robert Stewart.

CONVEYANCE.

To Galashiels, by Railway, and thence to all parts by the North British line (*see* monthly time tables). Omnibuses from the County Hotel and Fleece Inn attend all the trains. A two-horse coach is occasionally put on in summer between Selkirk and St. Mary's Loch, where it is met by other conveyances running from Innerleithen Station and Moffat.

DIRECTORY.

—

TRADES, RESIDENTS, AND PUBLIC OFFICES.

Those marked thus (*) are Registered Voters.

Back Row

*Brown, James, quarryman
Brown, Mrs. Andrew
Burgh School (new buildings in course of erection)
*Chisholm David, carrier
*Cowan, James (late Whitmuir)
Dalgleish, Thomas, forester
Dryden, George, teacher
Forsyth, R., stocking maker
Forsyth, Miss, dressmaker
*Hill, James, grocer
Hall, James, *inspector of poor*
*Inglis, Andrew, mason
Inglis, Thomas, mason
Murdoch, William, grocer
Muir, George, grocer
*Murray, Thomas, slater
Nichol, William, painter
Pow, Robert, mason
Rae, Mrs. William
Scott, James, shoemaker
Thomson, Robert, blacksmith

Castle Street

Gray, Andrew, joiner
M'Aulay, W., gardener, Haining
Scott, William, hosier
Scott, John, tailor
*Smith, John, slater
*Watson, Adam, farmer
*Watson, John, sen., carter

Chapel Street
County Jail, Henry Harrison, governor
Charity School, G. Dryden, resident teacher
Episcopal Chapel (Rev. R. Gibson's, *see* p. 378)
*Ingles, Walter, shoemaker

Ingles, Alexander, shoemaker
Little, Miss, dressmaker
Oliver, James, mason
Scott, John, painter
*Vair, James, weaver

Dunsdale Haugh

Dunsdale Woollen Mill, Waddell and Turnbull
Ettrick Woollen Mill, J. & H. Brown & Co.
  London Offices, 75 Cannon Street, W. George Scott,
  Manager.
Falla, Walter, joiner and cartwright
Hope, Thomas, mason
*Irvine, George, weaver
Martin, William, grocer
*Scott, John, foreman
Stewart, Adam, grocer

Ettrick Terrace

*Bathgate, Simeon, engineer (works, Mill Haugh)
Brydone, William, R.N., Greenbank Villa
Brown, John (of J. & H. B. & Co.), Comely Bank
*Brown, Wm., jun. (of J. & H. B. & Co.), Ladywell House
  Established Church (Rev. J. Farquharson's, *see* p. 377)
*Little, S., & Son, commission agents, &c.
Laidlaw, Miss, Back Brae Villa
*Lawson, Rev. J., Ettrick Brae, *First U. P. Manse*
Roberton, William, road-surveyor
Robertson, Misses, Bridge Park
Russell, Mrs., Bridge Park
*Waddell, William (of W. & Turnbull), Braeside Villa
  West U. P. Church (Rev. J. Dickie's, *see* p. 377)

Flesh Market Street

Fire Engine House
First U.P. Church (Rev. John Lawson's, *see* p. 377)
Little, James, cabinet maker
Scott, Thomas, sen., tailor
Turnbull, James, flesher
Wilson, Thomas, auctioneer

The Green

Meadow Green Skinnery, Sanderson & Murray, Galashiels
  Manager—William Mark

*Robertson, James, joiner
Smail, James, foreman

Halliday's Park

Brown, Mrs.
Brown, John, blacksmith
*Clapperton, Adam, plasterer
*Deans, William, joiner
*Rutherford, Andrew (of Smith & R.)
Orr, William, foreman
*Spence, James, road contractor
Scott, Alexander, teacher
Steele, Robert, mill foreman
Watson, James (late rector of Burgh School)
Welsh, Miss

High Street

*Anderson, Henry S., M.D.
Ballantyne, Mrs.
Ballantyne, Alexander, M.D.
Brown, John, watchmaker and jeweller
Carruthers, George, gardener
Coutts, William, shoemaker
County Hotel, *George Dryden
*Dickson, Robert, shoemaker
Fairbairn, Mrs.
Fair, Andrew, game dealer
Gibson Rev. Robert
*Henderson, Basil, accountant
*Heatlie, Robert, baker
*Hall, Thomas, joiner (house, Hume's Close)
Henderson, Arbor, provision merchant
Hislop, E., grocer
Johnstone, Robert, saddler
Johnston, Robert, grocer
*Johnstone & Son, clothiers
*Lewis, George, bookseller, printer, &c.
*Little, Andrew, grocer
Lawson, Miss Nancy
M'Kenzie, Robert, painter
Miller, Misses, *young ladies' seminary*
Rodger, P., writing chambers
    Managing Clerk—A. Johnstone
*Roberts, James (of G. R. & Co.)
School, Parochial and Grammar, Alexander Scott, rector
*Scott, Thomas jun., tailor
*Scott, John, baker
Scott, John, painter

Scott, George
Simpson, Elizabeth, grocer
Steedman, John, S.S.C., The Hermitage
Stoddart, Thomas, barber
Southern Reporter Office, George Lewis, publisher
    Printing Foreman—Alexander Chalmers
*Sword, George, carter
Tait, James, draper
Thomson, Andrew, flesher
Union Bank of Scotland
    Resident Accountant—Basil Henderson
Wood, Mrs., dealer in small wares
    Agent for Littlejohn's confectionery

Kirk Wynd

*Brown, Thomas, road contractor
Clapperton, George, grocer
Douglas, William, hairdresser
Henderson, John, cabinet maker
Hardie, Adam, tailor
*Ingles, John, shoemaker
*Melross, Peter, shoemaker
*Melross, John, shoemaker
*Patterson, Walter, hosier
Scott, Andrew, carter
Smith, Cairns, & Co., tailors and clothiers
Stavert, Andrew, mason
*Peebles, James, watchmaker

Long Close

*Mitchell, James, blacksmith
Rodney, Mrs., dressmaker

Market Place

Buchan, Miss
*Brockie & Mathison, drapers
Bruce, James, general merchant.
British Linen Company's Bank
    Resident managing clerk—John Mitchell
*Brunton, W., tailor
Brunton, Robert, hairdresser
Clapperton, George, grocer
*Cumming, Thomas, baker
*Clarkson, E., M.D.
Cross Keys Inn, D. Johnston
*Dalgleish, Thomas, baker
Douglas, John, tailor
Elliot, James, grocer and provision merchant

Fleece Inn, *William Mills
Hardie, James, painter
Lang & Steedman's writing chambers
    Managing Clerk—J. Mitchell
*Millar, James, watchmaker (house, Tower Street)
*Mark, William, tanner
Mechanics' Institute, Reading Room, and Library, James
    Cockburn, resident librarian
Mitchell, John, sheriff-clerk depute
*Muir, Michael, draper
    Millinery Department—Miss Darnick
    Dressmaking   do.   Miss Kinnell
Muir, William, general grocer and ironmonger
Post Office, George Turnbull, postmaster
Stoddart, Thomas, plumber
Stoddart, Hugh, meal-dealer
Sligh, David, grocer, tea, wine, and spirit merchant
Stamps and Taxes and Inland Revenue Office, John Lang,
    sub-distributor and collector
*Tudhope, Robert, wine and spirit merchant
Thomson, Mrs., wine and spirit merchant
Thomson, David, plumber
Town Hall
Turnbull, George, saddler
Temperance Coffee-House, J. S. Adamson
Temperance Coffee-House, W. Murray

Mill Street

Bathgate, S., engineer (house, Ettrick Terrace)
Bridge Haugh Mill, Dobie & Richardson
Gas Works, W. Robson, manager
Hogg, James, grocer
Railway Hotel, *Francis Hogg
Corn and Flour Mills, William Douglas
Forest Mill, George Roberts & Co.
Water Works
Waulk Mill, John Crosby (house, The Green)

Scott's Place

*Brown James, (of J. & H. B. & Co.), Knowepark
Brodie, Miss
*Gray, John, coal agent
Greig, Mrs.
Paton, Robert, of Shaw Cottage
*Rodger, Peter, town-clerk, of Elmpark
Smith & Rutherford, joiners
*Turnbull Richard, (of Waddell & T.), Hawthornbank

South Port

Brown, John, watchmaker
Blackhall, James, carter
*Currie, Ebenezer, Bog Cottage
*Heatlie, Andrew, sen., joiner
*Heatlie, Andrew, jun., joiner
*Muir, William, hosier
Watson, William, farmer

Tower Street

Alexander, David C., solicitor, Byethorne
Armstrong, John, foreman
Cheyne, William, plumber
Connochie, William D., veterinary surgeon
Crown Inn, Robert Fowler
*Dickie, Rev. John D. (of *West U. P. Church*) Edenhill
Dryden, John
Dunn, John, druggist
Fraser, James, chief constable
Free Church (Rev. James Young's, *see* p. 377)
*Hope, Robert, mason
Hogg, William, slater
*Inglis, G., builder, Rosemount Villa
*Inglis, Thomas, smith
*Kerr, Thomas, grocer
*Lambert, James, farmer, Springbank
Library, J. Dobson, librarian
Millar, James, schoolmaster, Russell Cottage
*Murray, James (of Savings Bank)
*Mitchell, Alexander P., baker
Mitchell, Thomas (late road-surveyor)
Millar, James, watchmaker (shop, Market Place)
Newton, William, coal agent, Myrtle Cottage
Paton, Robert, writing chambers
    Managing Clerk—James Murray
Pringle, Alexander, flesher
Reid, Adam (of G. Scott, draper, High Street)
Stoddart, Thomas, shoe merchant
Sturrock, Mrs.
Scott, James, Byethorne
Savings Bank—James Murray, cashier
*Walker, John, mason
Wayness, John, cooper

The Valley

*Fairbairn, Thomas, carter
Rodger, James, shoemaker
Sherriff, Alexander, sheriff-officer.

West Port

Aimers, Thompson cooper
Alexander, D. C., writing chambers
Allan, Andrew, china merchant
Atkins, Samuel, drill instructor
Brown, Mrs., bookseller
Brown, Jane, milliner
Canning, J., boot and shoe maker
Emond, Mrs.
*Farquharson, Rev. James, M.A., *The Manse*
Forsyth, Robert, flesher
Forest Inn, John Wilkinson
*Lamb, William, & Son, nurserymen and seedsmen
*Lamb, G. (of W. L. & Son)
*Melross, Andrew, shoemaker, &c.
National Bank of Scotland, D. C. Alexander, agent
Nichol, William, painter
Provision Store Company, W. Meikle, salesman
Purdie & *Gray, tailors
Queen's Head Inn, *W. Dickson
*Scott, Andrew
Scott, John, grocer
Smith, Thomas, & Co., drapers
Smith, Thomas (of T. S. and Co.)
*Scott, Thomas
*Trotter, William, grocer
Watson, Adam, plumber
*Watson, John, tinsmith
Yellowlees Brothers, ironmongers

Suburb of Heatherlie

Lying on the Philiphaugh road, mid-way between the Station and Selkirk by the omnibus route.

*Kedzie, Robert, blacksmith
*Leitch, R., Heatherlie Burn
Scott, Mrs. Francis
Scott, Mrs. Gideon, Upland Cottage
*Tait, Thomas, weaver
*Tait, William, dyer
Waddell, Thomas (of Dunsdale Mills), Heatherlie Park
*Young, Rev. James, *F.C. Manse*

Railway Station

(Situated on the Haugh, close upon the Ettrick, and under the hill on which Selkirk is built.)

Resident Station-Master and General Manager—Ralph Compton

OFFICES

Compton, John, coal agent
Dickson, R., coal and lime agent
Gray, John, coal agent
Lees, William, do.
Little, Simon, & Son, coal, lime, brick, etc., agents
Newton, William, coal agent
Yellowlees, George,   do.

FARMERS AND OTHER RESIDENTS

In the Parish of Selkirk but not in the Burgh.

Those marked thus (*) are Registered Electors for Selkirkshire, and those marked thus (†) are Registered for Roxburghshire.

Anderson, G., farmer, Broomhill
*Ballantyne, Rob., forester, Bowhill
*Beattie, Michael, farmer, Linglee
Bellany, John, farmer, South Common
*Blackburn, Robert B., Esq., advocate, Harehead
*Brown, Henry, Esq., Philipburn
*Cochrane, John S., farmer, Shawmount
Cowan, Robert, clerk of works, Bowhill
*Dickson, R., farmer, Shawburn
*Elliot, Richd, farmer, Hartwoodmyres
*Elliot, William, farmer,   do.
*Easton, A., farmer, Todrig
Fairbairn, Rt., farmer, Whitmuir
*Fletcher, Wm., farmer, Howden

Kerse, Jas., head-gamekeeper, Bowhill
*Lawrence, Jas., farmer, Raelees
*Lee, John, farmer, Oakwood
Little, Thomas, farmer, Sunderland Hall
*Matthewson, John, farmer, Williamhope.
*Matthewson, George, do.   do.
Matthewson, John, head-gardener, Bowhill
*Messer, Gideon, farmer, Smedheugh
†Mitchell, T., farmer, Greenhead
Mitchell, Thomas, jun., farmer, Middlestead
Reekie, William, factor, Bowhill
*Scott, R., farmer, Philiphaugh
*†Smith, W., farmer, Bridgeheugh
*Yellowlees, R., Philiphaugh Inn

SEATS, &c., OF COUNTY FAMILIES AND SMALLER RESIDENCES IN THE PARISH.

BOWHILL (*see* p. 374).

The hunting seat of His Grace the Duke of Buccleuch and Queensberry (Walter Francis Montague Douglas Scott), Marquis of Dumfriesshire, Earl of Buccleuch, Dalkeith, Drumlanrig, and Sanquhar, Viscount Nith, Torthorwald, and Ross; Baron Scott of Whytchester and Eskdaell, and Baron Douglas of Kinmound, Middlebie, and Dornock—in the peerage of Scotland; Earl of Doncaster (Yorkshire), and Baron Tynedale (county Northumberland), in the peerage of England; K.G., A.D.C. to the Queen, Captain-General of the Royal

Company of Archers—the Queen's Body Guard of Scotland ; Lord-Lieutenant of Edinburgh and Roxburgh shires ; Colonel of Edinburgh County Militia, High Steward of Westminster, D.C.L., and LL.D. ; born 1806 ; succeeded his father, 1819 ; married, 1829, Lady Charlotte Anne Thynne, third daughter of Thomas, second Marquis of Bath, K.G. ; and has issue—

William Henry Walter, Earl of Dalkeith, M.P. for the county of Edinburgh, etc. (see p. 151).

Henry John, born 1832, M.P. for Selkirkshire.

Walter Charles, late Captain 15th Hussars, born 1834 ; married, 1858, Anne Marie, fourth daughter of Sir W. E. Cradock Hartopp, Bart. ; and has issue—Francis Walter, born 1860, and Charles Henry, born in 1862.

Charles Thomas, R.N., born 1839.

Victoria Alexandrina, married 1865 Lord Schomberg F. Kerr, second son of the late John William Robert, seventh Marquis of Lothian.

Margaret Elizabeth.

Mary Charlotte.

His Grace is fifth Duke of Buccleuch and seventh Duke of Queensberry.

Other residences—Dalkeith Palace, Edinburghshire ; Drumlanrig Castle, Dumfriesshire ; Richmond, Surrey ; Broughton, Northamptonshire ; and Beaulieu, Hants. London residence—Sefton House, 37 Belgrave Square (Montague House, Whitehall Gardens, is being rebuilt).

BRIDGELANDS.

Situated near the Galashiels road, about 1½ miles from Selkirk—the property of *George Rodger, Esq.

BROADMEADOWS.

Near Yarrowford, 5 miles from Selkirk—the seat and residence of the *Hon. William Napier (younger brother of the present Lord Napier), who purchased the property in 1861 ; born 1821 ; married, 1854, Louisa Mary, daughter of J: H. Lloyd, Esq., London ; and has issue—Francis Horatio, born 1861 ; Charles Frederick, born 1862 ; William John, born 1863 ; and three daughters—Mary-Eliza, Beatrice, and Lilias.

Mr. Napier served nine years in the Royal Engineers, was Clerk of the Works at Hong Kong, and is Managing Director of the Lands' Improvement Company and Land Securities Company.

London addresses—Boodle Club, St. James' Street ; 54 Green St., Somerset Place.

HAINING (see p. 374).

The seat and residence of Mrs. Pringle Douglas (Margaret Violet), daughter of the late Mark Pringle, Esq., of Clifton,

the Haining, and Fairnilee ; succeeded her brother, the late Robert Pringle, Esq., of the Haining and Clifton, in 1841 ; married, 1824, Archibald Douglas, Esq., of Edderstone in Roxburghshire (who died 1860), and has issue—Ann Elizabeth, now Mrs. Pattison.

For five generations, ending with the late Robert Pringle, Esq., the Pringles of Haining represented Selkirkshire in Parliament.

ETTRICK BANK.

Pleasantly situated on the left bank of the Ettrick, about 1½ miles below Selkirk (2½ miles by the Selkirk Bridge road)—the property of Thomas Murray, Esq., merchant, London.

HEATHERLIE.
(Formerly *The Parsonage*.)

Situated at the suburb of Heatherlie—the property of Sir John Murray, and the residence of James S. Milne, Esq., Advocate, Sheriff-Substitute of the county (appointed Sept. 1861).

SUNDERLAND HALL.

Near the junction of the Tweed and Ettrick—the seat and residence of *Charles Scott Plummer, Esq., of Middlestead and Sunderland Hall, only son of the late Chas. Balfour Scott, Esq. of Woll, Roxburghshire ; born 1821 ; succeeded 1839 ; married, 1857, Sophia, eldest daughter of Joseph Goff, Esq., of Hale Park, Hants ; and has issue—

Charles Henry, born 1859 ; Joseph Walter, born 1861 ; and Jane Eliza.

Mr. Scott Plummer was called to the Scottish Bar in 1846, and is a Magistrate for Roxburghshire and a Justice of Peace and Deputy-Lieutenant for Selkirkshire, and Captain 2d Selkirkshire Rifle Volunteers ; he assumed the name of Plummer in 1839, on succeeding to the entailed estates of Middlestead and Sunderland Hall, when he relinquished the estate of Woll in favour of his uncle, the late Lieut.-Col. John Scott.

London address—Carlton Club, S.W.

PHILIPHAUGH (see p. 374).

The seat and residence of *†Sir John Murray, Bart., of Philiphaugh and Melgund, eldest son of the late James Murray, Esq., of Philiphaugh (who died 1854) ; born 1817 ; married, 1840, Rose-Mary, only daughter and sole-heiress of William-Andrew Nesbitt, Esq., of Bombay, and has issue :—

John Forbes Pringle, born 6th January 1842.

James, born 3rd February 1845.

Jessie-Rose-Mary.

Sir John, who is a Justice of Peace, a Deputy-Lieutenant, and a Magistrate for Selkirkshire, was served heir male in 1863 to Sir Albert Joseph Murray of Melgund, a Count of the Austrian Empire. "The outlaw Murray," *temp.* James IV. of Scotland, was an ancestor of the present representative of this family.

London addresses—33 Queen's Gate Terrace, Kensington, and Reform Club, S.W.

VIEWFIELD.

At Scott's Place, Selkirk—the property and residence of John Lang, Esq., of Overwells, Roxburghshire, Sheriff Clerk for the county,

WHITMUIR HALL.

Situated in the Roxburghshire part of the parish—the property of the trustees of the late Charles Dunlop, Esq., at present occupied by David M'Gregor, Esq.

YAIR HOUSE.

Situated amidst charming grounds on the banks of the Tweed, about two miles above its junction with the Ettrick—the residence of Mrs. Pringle (Agnes-Joanna, second daughter and co-heiress of Sir William Dick, Bart. of Prestonfield) and the property of her son, *Alexander Pringle, Esq. of Whytbank and Yair, only son of the late Alexander Pringle, Esq. of Whytbank and Yair (who died 1857); born 1837.

Mr. Pringle was called to the Scottish Bar 1863, is a Magistrate for Selkirkshire, and Cornet Mid-Lothian Yeomanry Cavalry. He is male representative of the original stock of the Pringles who were once numerous in the south-east of Scotland, where they held lands since the 13th century.

VOTERS FOR SELKIRKSHIRE REGISTERED IN THE PARISH

(Non-Resident).

Blackwood, John, Edinburgh
Blackwood, William, Peebles
Bogg, Thomas, Kirndean
Boylan, H. D. 16 Warwick Gardens, Kensington, London
Brown, John, Galahill
Bryden, J. M. H., London
Campbell, Sir Hugh P. H., of Marchmont, Bart.
Carmichael, Jas., writer, Hawick
Chisholme, John S., of Stirches
Clarkson, James, B., Melrose
Dobson, George, Leith
Douglas, Arch, writer, Edinburgh
Douglas, Alex. S., W.S., do.
Douglas, Christ. D., W.S., do.
Dove, James D., Audit Office, London
Dundas, Robt. of Arniston, Gorebridge
Dryden, Adam, Edinburgh
Easton, Robert, Chisholme
Elliot, William B., of Benrig, St. Boswells
Forrest, Sir John of Comiston, Bart., Mid-Lothian

Erskine, Js. of Shielfield, Melrose
Gibson, Hy. G., W.S., Edinburgh
Gibson, John, jun., W.S., do.
Glen, Andrew, Melrose
Gourlay, Rev. Adam, Lilliesleaf
Graham, William, Wilderhaugh, Galashiels
*Gray, Andrew, joiner, Lindean Cottages
Hobkirk, George. Hawick
Hope, Sir Archibald of Pinkie, Musselburgh
Horne, Th. E. O., W.S., Edinb'rgh
Hume, J. farmer, Broom, Ancrum
Inglis, Harry M. J. of Loganbank, Edinburgh
Jardine, John, Thorlieshope
Lawrie, John M. of Maxwelton, Thornhill
Leny, William M'Alpine, yr. of Dalswinton, Dumfries
Lomax, Jas., Clayton Hall, Lancashire
Macgibbon, Charles, Edinburgh
Maconochie, Robt. B., W.S., do.
Milne, Nicol of Faldonside, Galashiels
Mitchell, Alex. of Stow, Lauder
Moncrieff, David S., W.S., Edinburgh
Moncrieff, Robert S. of Fossaway, Dalkeith
Moncrieff, Rev. Wm. S., Tiverton, Devonshire
Montgomery, J. B. H., of Newton
Montgomery, Sir G. G., of Stanhope
Montgomery, T. H., Rankeillour
Napier, Hon. Major Charles, 85th Regiment of Foot
Neilson, Jas., S.S.C., Edinburgh
Ogilvie, R. G., W.S., Edinburgh
Ogilvie, Wm. of Chesters, Branxholm, Hawick
Ogilvie, G., Holefield, Kelso
Oliver, George, writer, Hawick
Oliver, James, writer, Hawick
Oliver, James, Howpasley
Oliver, James, late Drummond Street, Edinburgh
Oliver, John, Rigg, Teviothead

Park, William K., surgeon, 16th Lancers
Patterson, George, Hawick
Pitman, Fred., W.S., Edinburgh
Pott, Col. George, of Todrig, Roberton
Pringle, David, Wilton Lodge, Hawick
Pringle, Thomas, farmer, Belses Moor, Ancrum
Quin, Edward, Galashiels
Ramsay, Robert B. W. of Whitehill, Lasswade
Robertson, George, Lilliesleaf
Roberts, George, manufacturer, Galashiels
Robertson, James, Edinburgh
Scott, R. of Raeburn, St Boswells
Scott, Walter, Hereford
Scott, William J., of Eastfield
Scott, W. E. Kirndean
Scott, Rt, mason, Belses Quarry, Ancrum
Scott, James R. H. of Abbotsford, Melrose
Souter, W. S., writer, Blairgowrie
Spottiswoode, J., of Spottiswoode, Lauder
Sprot, Mark of Riddell, Lilliesleaf
Stavert, Archibald, Saughtrees
Stoddart, Andrew, flesher, Stow
Stevenson, A., writer, Langholm
Stevenson, J. Moss, Howgill, do.
Swinton, Arch. C., yr. of Kimmerghame
Sword, William B., Edinburgh
Sword, William, Hopehouse
Tait, Joseph, farmer, Lindean
Tait, Peter G., Edinburgh
Thomson, George of Burnhouse
Tod, Thomas of Drygrange
Turnbull, Thomas, blacksmith, Birkwoodfoot
Turner, Thomas, farmer, Shoestanes, Heriot
Walker, James M. of Bowland
Walker, George, of Crawford
Welsh, Thomas, of Earlshaugh
Wight, John, Edinburgh
Williamson, James, farmer, Laretburn, St. Boswell's

VOTER FOR ROXBURGHSHIRE

Registered in the Parish but not resident.

Thomas Murray, 12 Copthall Court, London.

KIRKHOPE.

—◆—

FORMERLY Kirkhope formed part of the parish of Yarrow, but was disjoined and erected into a separate parish in 1851, at the instance of the Duke of Buccleuch. It is bounded on the north by Selkirk parish, on the east by Ashkirk parish (Rox.) Roberton, and the detached part of Selkirk parish which lies on Todrig burn, on the south by Roberton and Ettrick, and on the west by Ettrick and Yarrow. Its greatest length north-east and south-west is about 9 miles, and its average breadth 5 miles The Ordnance Survey measurements are nearly 22,677 acres land, 248½ acres of water, 38 acres of public roads, and 9¼ acres of private roads—in all about 22,972¾ acres. The parish is for the most part hilly*—the exception being "a cold black heath" over 1000 feet above the level of the sea—(see foot-note, p. 363) on the east side which is more level. The river Ettrick intersects the entire parish from north to south, and is fed by numerous tributaries from the hills on both sides. There are several small lochs in the parish—Clearburn at the south, and lying partly in Ettrick parish, about a mile in circumference, is one of the feeders of the Ettrick. Shaws, Helmoor, and Ockermoor, which have an average of the same size, lie distributed to the east and form part of the group of lochs flowing into the head waters of the Ale—(see Roberton parish). Aughling in Clearburn Loch and in the Ettrick below Ettrick Bridge is strictly prohibited, but it is otherwise free in the parish. Accommodation can be had at Ettrick Bridge. The parish is nearly all pastoral, and partakes to the full of the climate of the middle district of Yarrow, from which it was disjoined (see Yarrow). In itself the parish possesses little interest except in the fact of the Ettrick intersecting it with a line of beauty, and that, with the rest of Selkirkshire, it at one time formed part of "The Forest," of which a few remains still exist on the farm of Fauldshope. Within the limits of the parish the stream may be said to have few associations. No sooner, however, does it pass into Selkirk, than it takes up the ancient reminiscences, and tells the story of Michael Scott's witcheries as it winds round the woods of Bowhill.

* The following are the principal hills in the parish:—					
		Feet			Feet
Craig Hill	..	1260	Cop Law	..	1195
Stand Knowe	..	1528	White Hill	..	1267
Wedder Lairs	..	1539	Moss Brae	..	1528
Dun Knowe ..	..	1458	Shaws Hill	..	1292

At the extreme north of the parish is the small village of ETTRICK BRIDGE, of about 150 inhabitants. Here are the parish church, manse, school, and school-house. The nearest market town is Selkirk, 7 miles from Ettrick Bridge. Selkirk is also the nearest railway station and is the post town.

Population of the parish in 1861, 555, who composed 114 separate families; 43 of whom were returned as living in houses of one window, 29 in houses of two windows, and 45 in houses of three and more windows.

Assessed property in 1863-4, £6148 : 5 : 11.

Principal landed-proprietors—the Duke of Buccleuch, Lord Polwarth, and James Johnstone, Esq., of Alva.

Those marked thus (*) are Registered Electors in the parish.

POLICE OFFICER—John Gordon, Ettrick Bridge station house.

POST OFFICE—George Hope, postmaster. Arrivals—Tuesdays, Thursdays, and Saturdays, at 12 noon. Departures—Mondays, Wednesdays, and Fridays, at 1 p.m. Messenger (who proceeds to Ettrick)—Thos. Armstrong.

PUBLIC OFFICES—Session Clerk, Kirk Treasurer, Inspector of Poor, and Registrar of Births, Marriages, and Deaths—Hugh M'-Morran.

    Heritors' Clerk—Robert Paton, Esq., W.S., Selkirk.

    Medical Officer—H. S. Anderson, M.D., Selkirk.

    Public Vaccinators—Drs. Anderson and Ballantyne, Selkirk.

CLERGY, &c.—Presbytery of Selkirk, Synod of Merse and Teviotdale. Patron—The Crown.

    Established Church—*Rev. John S. Gibson (Inducted 1851). Sittings, 300. Average attendance at Sabbath School, 20.

FAST DAY—Last Thursday of July.

SCHOOL† (Parochial)—*Hugh M'Morran, master; aver. attend., 50.

    Do. (Endowed), Redford Green, south side of the parish. Thomas Cowan, teacher. Average attendance, 12.

    Do. (Endowed), Ladyside, in the upper district of the parish. Thomas H. Amos, teacher. Average attendance, 24.

PAROCHIAL BOARD—Rev. J. S. Gibson, Chairman. No. of Poor on Roll, 14. Average Assessment, 3d. per £.; total Assessment, 1864, £179 : 6 : 7.

TOTAL ABSTINENCE SOCIETY—Charles Stewart, President; David Mitchell, Secretary; Hugh M'Morran, Treasurer.

† Children from 5 to 15 in the parish, attending school during the first week of April 1861, 83; of all ages, 85.

SELKIRKSHIRE PASTORAL SOCIETY'S SHOW—Held annually at Ettrick Bridge-end on first Wednesday of September.—*See* p. 370.

HORTICULTURAL SOCIETY—Rev. J. S. Gibson, President ; D. Mitchell, Secretary. Competitions in July and September.

CURLING CLUB—Thomas Mitchell, Esq., Newhouse, President ; H. M'Morran, Secretary

CARRIERS—Thomas Brown, to Selkirk, daily, except Tuesdays ; William Grieve and William Brydone, to Ettrick and Eskdale-muir, week about—all from Ettrick Bridge-end.

TRADES.

Ettrick Bridge-end

*Anderson, Thomas, blacksmith
*Blyth, John, mason
Brydon, William, grocer, etc.
Burton, Gilbert,   do.
Crown Inn,† William Thomson
Cross Keys Inn,† William Grieve
*Inglis, David, feuar
Kennedy, James, blacksmith
Kennedy, Mrs., grocer, etc.
Mitchell, Thomas, joiner

RESIDENTS, FARMERS, &c.

*Aitken, John, farmer, West Redfordgreen
*Brown, Adam,   do.   Helmburn
*Brown, William, feuar, Brockhillhaugh
*Boston, James, farmer, Easter Deloraine
*Dalgleish, Adam, Brookhill
*Gibson, James, farmer, The Shaws
*Grahame, James,   do.   Drycleuchlee
*Grieve, Robert,   do.   Outer Huntly
*Kennedy, Thomas, do.   Newburgh
*Mitchell, Thomas, do.   Newhouse
*Potts, John,   do.   Shiringscleuch
*Scott, Henry,   do.   Gilmanscleuch
*Scott, Gideon J., do.   Singlie
*Scott, John, jun., do.   Wester Deloraine
*Scott, William,   do.   Howford
*Scott, Thomas,   do.   Langhope
*Simson, James,   do.   Fauldshope

† Both these inns have stabling attached, and the *Cross Keys* has accommodation for a few boarders.

REGISTERED VOTERS (Non-Resident).

Grieve, Adam, Galashiels
Hogg, Adam, Deuchar Mill, Yarrow
Scott, The Hon. Walter H., *Master of Polwarth,* Humbie House, Haddingtonshire
Scott, Henry, farmer, Outfield, New Luce

Registered Voters of Yarrow and Kirkhope.

In the lists officially published the Registered Voters for Yarrow and Kirkhope are mixed up to some extent, but we give them as arranged by residents in these parishes.

YARROW.

———◆———

THE parish of Yarrow, in common with the rest of Selkirkshire, is of an entirely hilly character. It is bounded on the north-west by Peeblesshire, on the north by the parish of Traquair, on the east by Selkirk parish, on the south-east by Kirkhope, which was formerly a part of this parish (see p. 399), on the south and east by Ettrick, and on the west by Ettrick, and Megget parish in Peeblesshire. Its north-western boundary is very irregular in shape, some extremities being almost isolated from the main portion, and one entirely so, where the Selkirkshire part of Peebles parish wedges in and cuts it off—this detached portion has its north-eastern extremity resting on the Tweed, 4¼ miles below Peebles and 1½ miles above Innerleithen—both distances calculated in a direct line. Here is the farmhouse of Old Howford; the farm-house of Birks, the only other in this detached portion, lies 2¼ miles due south-west near the head waters of the Quair,* which here has its rise in Birkcairn hill; 5 miles due east the parish (undetached portion) again rests on the Tweed, at Scrogbank, and contains, within a stretch of 4¼ miles, the Elibank and Ashiesteel waters, with those of Holylee, in Innerleithen parish, on the opposite side, "scarcely surpassed on the Tweed for rippling streams and pleasant pools, and swarming with trout of superior size." Here, too, clean salmon fishing may be said to begin, those caught farther up being generally foul. The greatest direct length of the parish N.E. and S.W. is 16 miles, and it is the most extended in the south of Scotland; its greatest breadth, at its north-west extremity, is about 8 miles. The area of the parish, according to the Ordnance Survey, is 40,948½ acres land, 813 acres water, 97½ acres public and private roads—total, 41,859 acres. The detached portion, already mentioned, contains 2166¼ acres, and is included in these measurements. Many of the hills rise to a considerable elevation.† The greater part of the parish is under pasture. The valley through which the Yarrow flows is fertile, and there the cultivation is in an advanced state. The far-famed St. Mary's Loch is in the south-west extremity of this parish (it lies partly in Ettrick—which see); and the Yarrow, rendered famous in song, intersects it throughout its entire length. "More poetry, both old and recent, has been written on Yarrow than on any other Scottish vale; and most of it is plaintive or wailing." Anglers are largely attracted to the vale of the Yarrow, for fishing in St. Mary's Loch, and in the Yarrow itself and its tributaries. From St. Mary's Loch to Yarrowford, a distance of 11 miles to north-east, the Yarrow is free to the angler; beyond this the Yarrow is preserved to its confluence with the Ettrick (see Kirkhope and Selkirk parishes). A mile above the "Gordon Arms," the Douglas burn, its principal upper tributary, falls into the Yarrow. This stream is famous for its trout fishing. All the other burns in the locality are also good. In both the Yarrow and Ettrick the commencement of the fishing season is late, and fishing with fly is precarious; but the trout are well-sized and plentiful, and take readily with worm and minnow (see p. 399).* "The Gordon Arms," situated on the Yarrow, 3 miles below St. Mary's Loch, is a good angling centre for the middle waters of both Ettrick and Yarrow; and "Tibby Shiels'," at the head of St. Mary's is a good centre for all the upper waters and the two lochs (St. Mary's and the Lowes). The lochs contain pike, perch, eels, trout, and salmon, which afford excellent sport to the angler in early spring—the fishing is unrestricted. Otters are found about the streams.

"In former times the straths of Ettrick and Yarrow re-

---

* The Quair joins the Tweed in Peeblesshire, after a course of over 8 miles, a short way below Traquair House. "The trout in it are very abundant, but so small, that they are not worth catching."

† The following are a few of the principal hills in the parish, the altitudes of which are taken from the Ordnance Survey:—

Upper District of St. Mary's Loch.	Feet	Lower District of St Mary's Loch.	Feet
Longmoor	1652	Dryhope Rig	1712
Fall Law	1828	Drycleuch Rig	1581
Bowerhope Law	1570	White Law	1374
Shaw Brae, or Peat Law	1737	Blacknowe (partly in Kirkhope)	
The Wiss	1932		1806

	Feet		Feet
Meg's Hill	1438	Elibank Craig	969
Sundhope Height (partly in Kirkhope)	1684	Ashiesteel Hill	1314
		Peel Hill	991

Lower District of the Parish.		Middle District of the Parish.	
Birk Cairn Hill (detached)	2169	Mount Benger Hope	1784
Wallace's Hill (do.)	1507	Welldean Hill	1500
Dod Hill	1082	Minchmoor (partly in Peeblesshire)	1856
Plora Craig	1212		
Hare Law	1670	Black House, Black Law, Hundleshope, Glenrath, and other hills about the sources of the Douglas Burn, and lying partly in Peeblesshire, average	2200
Brown Knowe	1717		
Middle Hill	1688		

On the Tweed.			
Scrogbank Rig	961		

* "In both Ettrick and Yarrow you will find minnow a good lure; but you will require to get your bait elsewhere, as minnows are not to be found in these streams."—Hints to Anglers by Adam Dryden.

ceived the appropriate designation of ' The Forest,' of which a few stunted remains are scattered over the parish ; the name is still retained, but is no longer characteristic of the country, which is almost one continuous sheep-walk." (See p. 399 and introductory account of Ettrick.)

Near the lower extremity of St. Mary's Loch is Dryhope Tower, the birth-place of Mary Scott, the celebrated Flower of Yarrow (see p. 358). A short way farther up the loch is the site of St. Mary's kirk. The building itself has long since disappeared, but its ancient and solitary cemetery, now known by "St. Mary's Isle," still continues to be used as the burial place of several old families in the neighbourhood. Hogg "the Ettrick Shepherd" was in his youth a shepherd on Blackhouse, 2 miles up the Douglas Burn ; he afterwards for a few years occupied the farm of Mount Benger, situated near to the "Gordon Arms;" but the greater part of his life, till his death, was spent at Altrive Lake, on the opposite side of the river—a small farm, generously given him rent-free by His Grace the Duke of Buccleuch. The monument to him, lately erected, is in Ettrick parish (which see). Most of the other objects of interest are connected with the poetry of the district. In the northern part of the parish, where it is bounded by the Tweed, is Ashiesteel, long the residence of Sir Walter Scott. "While living here, he won his first laurels, and a small hillock covered with trees, beneath whose shade much of his poetry was penned, is still called the ' Sherra's Knowe.' "*

In the higher districts of the parish the climate is comparatively damp and cold ; but of late, like Ettrick, Yarrow has been greatly improved in these respects by drainage and planting ; the vicissitudes of the weather are extremely frequent (see foot-note at p. 365). In the lower districts adjoining the Tweed the climate partakes of the general character of Roxburghshire.

At THE HANGINGSHAW, near Yarrowford, one of the seats of Mr. Johnstone of Alva, the grounds contain some of the noblest trees that are to be seen anywhere in the south of Scotland.

There is no village whatever in the parish, Yarrowford being merely a small collection of detached cottages. The church, manse, and school-house are 4 miles farther up the valley ; and 2 miles beyond we come to Yarrow Feus, which are another string of detached cottages, extending over a mile in length, and contain a number of country tradesmen—see list. The road alongside the Yarrow, extending from Selkirk and continuing on to Moffat, is one of the best, free from toll, and passes through the most picturesque scenery in the south of Scotland.

The nearest railway station is Innerleithen for the upper

districts, which is 8 miles from the "Gordon Arms;" the nearest market town and railway station for the lower districts is Selkirk, about 5 miles distant from Yarrowford, about 13 from the "Gordon Arms," and 19 from "Tibby Shiels'," or St. Mary's Cottage, as it has lately been named.

Population of the parish in 1861, 643 ; who composed 134 families, 20 of whom were returned as living in houses of one window, 47 in houses of two windows, and 67, or exactly one-half, in houses of three and more windows.

Assessed property in 1864-5, £9964 : 6 : 5.

The principal landed-proprietors in this parish are—the Duke of Buccleuch, James Johnstone, Esq., of Alva, Lord Napier, of Thirlestane, Lord Elibank of Elibank, Heirs of the late Earl of Traquair (who died 1861 : title supposed to be extinct), Alexander B. Kerr Williamson, Esq., of Cardrona, Hon. Miss Russell, of Ashiesteel.

Those marked thus (*) are Registered Voters.

RESIDENT JUSTICE OF THE PEACE—James Johnstone, Esq., of The Hangingshaw.

DISTRICT POLICE OFFICER—John Simpson, Benger Burn.

PUBLIC OFFICES—Session-Clerk, Kirk Treasurer, Registrar of Births, Marriages, and Deaths—William Bell, Parochial School-House.
Heritors' Clerk—Robert Paton, W.S., Selkirk.
Inspector of Poor—William Dalgleish, Mount Benger School.
Medical Officers and Public Vaccinators—Drs. Anderson and Ballantyne, Selkirk.

POST OFFICE—William Bell, postmaster. Daily to Selkirk—Arrival, 12-50 p.m. ; Departure, 6-10 a.m—A. Robson, messenger. Daily to Megget—Departure, 1 p.m. ; Arrival, 8-30 p.m.—John Brunton, messenger.

CLERGY—Presbytery of Selkirk, Synod of Merse and Teviotdale. Patron—the Crown. (See foot-note, p. 418, Ettrick parish.)
Parish Church— *Rev. James Russell, A.M. (Inducted 1841). Sittings, 430. Average attendance at Sabbath Schools, 61.
Free Church of Yarrow and Megget (Yarrow Feus)—*Rev. Thos. M'Crindle, M.A. (Inducted 1847). Sittings, . Average attendance at Sabbath School, .

FAST DAY—Thursday before second Sabbath of July.

SCHOOLS†—Parochial—*William Bell, master. Average attend., 45.
Yarrowford (Endowed) bordering upon Selkirk parish, eastern extremity of parish of Yarrow—John Gill, master. Average attendance, 40.

---

† Children in the parish, between 5 and 15, attending school during the first week of April 1861, 124 ; of all ages, 135.

---

* Sir Walter was at that time sheriff of Selkirkshire.

Mount Benger (Endowed), west and south-west district of parish—William Dalgleish, master. Average attendance, 23.

PAROCHIAL BOARD—Rev. James Russell, Chairman. Average Rate of Assessment, about 3¼d. per £ ; total Assessment 1863-4, £216. Number of Poor on Roll, 14. Poorhouse—Galashiels Union.

LIBRARIES—Parish Subscription. 1000 vols. Wm. Bell, librarian. There are also Libraries attached to the School at Yarrowford and to the Established Sabbath School at Yarrow.

HORTICULTURAL SOCIETY—Rev. J Russell, President ; William Bell, Secretary and Treasurer. Competitions in July and September.

CURLING CLUB—Thomas Ballantyne, Whitehope, President ; William Bell, Secretary and Treasurer.

CARRIERS—John Brunton, Yarrow Feus, to Selkirk every Monday, Wednesday, and Friday. Robert Stewart, Yarrow Feus, to Selkirk every Monday and Friday ; to Moffat every Tuesday. Wr. Nichol, Sandbed, from Hawick to Yarrow, every Monday.

CONVEYANCE—During the summer a coach is generally put on from Selkirk station to St. Mary's, running twice or thrice a week in connection with conveyances from Moffat, and one is also put on from the "Gordon Arms" between Innerleithen station and St. Mary's in the same connection. Days can be known by applying at any of the stations or places mentioned.

SURGEON—William Shaw, Parochial School-House.

MILL—Deuchar Flour Mill, near the manse—Adam Hogg, miller.

TRADES.

Gordon Arms Inn, James Douglas
*St. Mary's Cottage,** Mrs. Richardson

Yarrow Feus

Brunton, Mrs., grocer
Dalgleish, John, mason
Dalgleish, Andrew, & Sons, masons
Dalgleish, Peter, mason and stone-dyker
Fleming, David, tailor
Hogg, Alexander, mole-catcher
Mathison, Alexander, shoemaker
Reid, John, blacksmith
Rutherford,   , joiner
Stewart, R., grocer

---

* *St. Mary's Cottage* is not a licensed inn, but there fishers, tourists, and travellers, can always procure refreshments in some shape, and a good bed if required. Both houses have stabling attached.

FARMERS, RESIDENTS, &c. IN THE PARISH.

*Anderson, John, farmer, Lewenshope
*Ballantyne, Thos., do.,   Whitehope
*Brown, Thomas, Esq., Elibank Cottage
*Douglas, John, farmer, Tinnis and Altrive
*Goodfellow, William, Catherwood
 Grieve, James, farmer, Ashiesteel
 Laidlaw, Alex., do.,   Bowerhope
*Laidlaw, Robt., do.,   Sundhope
*Leadbetter, Jas., do.,   Elibank
*Milne, Nichol, do.,   Dryhope
*Mills, Thomas, do.,   Mount Benger
*Mitchell, John, do.,   Peel
*Mitchell, Robt., do.,   Kirkstead
 Mitchell, Mrs. James, Crosscleuch
*Rutherford, John, farmer, Eldinhope
*Scott, William,   do.,   Ladhope and Kershope
*Thomson, John,   do.,   Catslackburn
 Yarrow Cottage (Yarrow Feus)—at present unoccupied

SEATS, &c., OF COUNTY FAMILIES IN THE PARISH.

ELIBANK.

On the Tweed, 6 miles below Innerleithen and about 8 from Selkirk—the property and occasional residence of Baron Elibank (Sir Alexander Oliphant Murray of Elibank), in the peerage of Scotland, and a baronet ; born 1804 ; succeeded his father as ninth baron in 1830 ; married, 1838, Emily-Maria, only daughter of Archibald Montgomery, Esq., and niece of Sir James Montgomery, Bart., of Stanhope ; and has issue—

Montolieu Fox, *Master of Elibank,* born 1840.
Dudley-Oliphant, born 1846.
Francis St. Hippolyte, born 1856, died 1857.
Alice, died 1852.
Ada Oliphant, died 1852.
Florence-Emily.
Blanche.

Elibank is the ancestral property of the family of Murray, and contains their old peel tower. The mansion was the birth-place of Russell, the historian of "Modern Europe."

Other Seats—Ballencrief, Haddingtonshire ; Darnhill, Peeblesshire ; Pitheavlis, Perthshire.

THE HANGINGSHAW (*see* p. 405).

The occasional residence of *James Johnstone, Esq. of Alva and The Hangingshaw, eldest son of the late James Raymond Johnstone, Esq. of Alva ; born 1801 ; succeeded 1830; married (1st), 1846, the Hon. Augusta Anne, daughter of the Hon. Fletcher Norton (a Baron of the Exchequer in Scotland), and sister of Fletcher, third Lord Grantley (she died 1859) ; (2d), 1862, Sarah-Mary, daughter of the late Lieut.-Col. L'Estrange, of Moyston, King's County ; and has issue by the former—

John Augustus James, born 1847.
Caroline Elizabeth Mary.

Mr. Johnstone was called to the Scotch Bar in 1824, is a Justice of Peace and Deputy-Lieutenant for the counties of Clackmannan, Stirling, and Selkirk, and Lord of the Barony of Alva. He was M.P. for the counties of Clackmannan and Kinross 1851-7. This family is a younger branch of the Johnstones, baronets of Westerhall.

Principal residence — Alva House, near Stirling. London address—Athenæum Club, S.W.

ASHIESTEEL (see p. 405).

The residence of Lady Russell (Katherine Mary, daughter of Sir James Hall, Bart. of Dunglass), widow of General Sir James Russell, K.C.B. (who died 1859), and the property of their eldest daughter, Miss Helen Jane Mountstuart Russell,* also residing at Ashiesteel.

Postal address for Ashiesteel and that locality—Galashiels.

REGISTERED VOTERS (Non-Resident).

Allan, William, Esq., of Hillside and Glen
Archibald, John, Duddingston House, South Queensferry
Ballantyne, John, jun., forester, Knowesly Hall, Lancashire
Bursby, George G., farmer, Innerleithen Mains
Carruthers, Alexander, Esq., of Warmanbie, Annan
Cunningham, Alexander, farmer, Morebattle Tofts
Elliot, John, Esq., of Binks, Hawick
Fox, William, sen., farmer, ⎱ (lessees of Birks), Orchard
Fox, William, jun., do., ⎰ Mains, Traquair
Gibson, William, do., lessee of Easter Plora
Gardner, Robert, do., Traquair Knowe, Peebles
Hope, John D., wine merchant, Leith
Johnstone, Charles Kinnaird, Esq.
Johnstone, George Dempster, Esq.

Johnstone, M. Cholmely, Esq.
Mitchell, James, Yair, Selkirk
Mercer, Robert, Esq. (of Scotsbank and Hyndhope), of Ramsay Lodge, Portobello
Moncrieff, John Scott, accountant, Edinburgh
Nixon, William, manufacturer, Hawick
Primrose, James, farmer, Turniedykes, Dalkeith
Robson, Charles, farmer, Lurdenlaw, Kelso
Rutherford, George, of Sunnyside, Melrose
Rutherford, George, jun., Strathallan, Auchterarder
Scott, Lord Charles T. M. Douglas
Scott, Hon. Francis, Sandhurst, Riplev (late M.P.)
Scott, Lord Henry J. M. Douglas, M.P.
Scott, Lord Walter C. M. Douglas
Scott, William Henry W. M. D., Earl of Dalkeith, M.P.
Swan, Robert, writer, Kelso
Tod, Robert, farmer, Cardrona Mains, Peebles
Williamson, Alexander B. Kerr, Esq., of Cardrona, Peebles
Williamson, William, Esq., of Laretburn, St. Boswell's

Registered Voters of Yarrow and Kirkhope.

See note, p. 402.

* *Heir-pres.*—Miss Russell's only sister, Katharine-Anne ; married, 1860, Laurence W. M. Lockhart, Esq., Captain 92d Highlanders ; and has issue one son and two daughters. Present Address—Blackburn House, Ayr.

ETTRICK.*

———◆———

THE parish of Ettrick, which has been rendered famous by Boston, Scott, Hogg, Wilson, and De Quincey, is situated in the south-western part of the county. It is bounded on the north by Yarrow, on the east by Kirkhope and Roberton, on the south by Eskdale-muir, and on the west by Moffat, Dumfriesshire. Its greatest direct length is about 10 miles, and breadth 11 miles. The area of the parish, according to the Ordnance Survey, is 42,682¾ acres; comprising 42,312¾ acres land, nearly 296 acres water, and 74 acres in public and private roads; and since Kirkhope was disjoined from Yarrow, it is now the largest parish in the county, and, next to Castleton, the largest in the district. The surface of the parish is entirely mountainous, and is covered with rich pasture to the hill tops, which supports immense flocks of Cheviot sheep; a few Highland cattle are also grazed; while very considerable numbers of the Ayrshire breed of cows are kept in the parish, and in it excellent cattle of that breed and of the short-horned are now fattened for the market. There are a few black-faced sheep in the parish, and these are very superior.

The climate of this parish, which used to be cold and damp, has, owing to the improvement of the hills and vales by extensive drainage within the last twenty years, been greatly ameliorated. The older inhabitants say that the winters are neither so cold nor the summers so moist as they used to be. In old times the climate was late, but cannot be said to be so entirely now. Within the last year an attempt has been made at Ramsaycleuch to break up the hill-sides for agriculture. The crops—oats principally, and some barley grown in the valleys and on the slopes—are of excellent quality and may be ten or fourteen days behind those in Selkirk parish, but not more; and it has been proved that excellent turnips can be raised in the parish. All the ordinary kinds of fruits and vegetables grow in full perfection—black currants, particularly, are superabundant, and without failure as to quantity and quality. Gooseberries come next in order, succeeded by apples.

* We have gratefully to acknowledge the hearty assistance given to us in the compilation of this parish by a gentleman resident in it —all the more valuable, as the previous published accounts of Ettrick are erroneous in the extreme, and such as might have suited it in the days of Boston.

At the end of last century, *except* black currants, nothing would ripen in the parish.

These remarks apply to the northern and lower part of the parish—about and above the manse for some miles, and above "Tibby Shiels'." In the extreme upper district—for instance at Potburn and Upper Phawhope, which lie at the very head of Ettrick water—cabbages and potatoes alone come to maturity. Corn is grown on these farms principally for the straw, and is known to have come but *once* to perfection on them.

Some of the hills in the parish attain to considerable elevations.*

On the borders of Dumfriesshire the Ettrick takes its rise and traverses the parish. The flanks of the stream for a few miles are a sea of hills, high but covered with the richest grass to be found at such an elevation,† and carry the healthiest stocks of sheep in all the district. About a mile-and-a-half above Ettrick church the hills open to admit a pleasant vale, with stretches of luxuriant haugh and slopes of verdant pasture. About a mile below comes in the Tema water, the principal upper tributary of the Ettrick. Three miles down, and the Rankle burn comes in, the next principal tributary. All these streams abound in trout of average small size; angling in them is unrestricted, and begins late—the worm is the most suitable lure; salmon occasionally find their way thus far in winter only when the streams are closed for angling. Below Crosslee the Ettrick reaches Kirkhope parish—which

* The following are some of the heights as given by the Ordnance Survey:—

Confines of Moffatdale and Eskdale.		Feet	Centre of the Parish.			Feet
Andrewwhinney	.. ..	2220	Mid Hill	.. ..	..	1471
Bodesbeck Law	..	2173	Peniestone Knowe	..		1870
Capel Fell	..	2223	Ramsay Knowe	..		1854
Windfell	.. ..	2180	Ward Law	..		1951
Ettrick Pen	..	2269	Thirlestane Hill	..		1475
Phawhope Kips	..	1938	Tushie Law	..		1431
Blue Cairn Hill	..	1715	Gamescleuch Hill	..		1490
			Mount Common Hill			1517
West of Loch o' the Lowes and Yarrow Water.			Sauchie Law..	..		1449
			Cauld Face	..		1750
Yearny Knowe	..	1533	Nether Craig..	..		1750
Paper Hill	..	1888	Blacknowe	..		1804
Middle Hill	..	1740	Glenkerry Hope Head	..		1697
Rattinside	..	1675	Cacra Hill	..		1546
Quarrie Brae	..	1374	Annelshope Hill	..		1415
Oxencleuch Rig	..	1320	Kirkhill	..		1293

† The tourist passing through Ettrick into Moffatdale, immediately perceives the superiority of the former, both in point of richness and beauty. Compared with the hills of Ettrick those of Moffat have a monotonous and barren look.

see. In the valley and district of the Ettrick, where the improvements, previously mentioned, principally have taken place, there are some very nice plantations of larch and fir rising up, which, by their variety, refresh the eye not a little at all seasons. In the western side of the parish, excepting about "Tibby Shiels'," where the farmers, with few exceptions, are non-resident, the country is all under grass. Moodlaw loch is partly situated in this parish, at its south-east extremity—described at p. 357 ; the Loch o' the Lowes is entirely within its boundaries ; and a part of the upper shores of St. Mary's, on the western side, is also in Ettrick ; the next stretch of a mile and the western shore of St. Mary's lies in Peeblesshire ; within this stretch the Megget water falls into the loch, "a very famous fishing ground" (*vide Noctes Ambrosianæ*). On the Megget, about a mile from the road, is situated Henderland Castle, the scene of the ballad of " the Lament of the Border Widow." The lower portion of the loch and the whole of its western side are in Yarrow parish—which *see*. Both the Loch o' the Lowes and St. Mary's are well stocked with fine large trout, perch, eels, and pike ; and in St. Mary's salmon are occasionally plentiful (*see* Yarrow). From these circumstances the locality has for many years been a favourite resort for anglers, who, along with fine sport, enjoy cozy upputting at "Tibby Shiels'." Loch Skene and Dobb's Linn lie in Dumfriesshire, but both are most accessible from Birkhill, at the southern extremity of the parish. Falconidæ of different kinds frequent, and some nest in, the district. Both the golden eagle and the osprey were frequent visitors long ago, but neither have been seen for a number of years ; and those traditionary swans which "floated double swan and shadow," have long ceased to frequent the lakes.

In the Ettrick, especially above Ettrick kirk, the angler will find splendid water and unrestricted fishing. In the Rankle burn and some of the other tributaries the fishing is indifferent, but not for the want of trout.

In olden times, except a very few grouse, there was no game in the parish, neither was there any shelter for it ; but now the plantations belonging to the Duke of Buccleuch and the woods around Thirlestane Castle form excellent cover, and there are considerable quantities of pheasants, partridges, black game, hares, rabbits, and wild ducks—enough to satisfy the proprietors, and causing no complaint on the part of the tenants.

Slate of a coarse heavy quality is found in the parish.

The parish has no village. Hopehouses, a mile below Thirlestane Castle, and beside which the fairs are held, is only a hamlet of some 40 or 45 inhabitants. The church and manse stand in a bend of the hills, in the midst of trees, on the Kirkburn, about a quarter of a mile from the public road and half-a-mile from the Ettrick, and occupy the most beautiful,

sunny, and desirable corner in the parish.* To the church is attached a heavy square tower which rises considerably above the surrounding trees.† The school-house is pleasantly placed on the side of the hill about a quarter of a mile below the church, and, like it, is conveniently situated near the centre of the parish. The school-room is close by, and is a most excellent and commodious building erected recently. About a mile below the school-house is THIRLESTANE CASTLE, beautifully situated amid extensive and thriving plantations of pine and hard wood —the seat of Lord Napier. Immediately behind the castle are the remains of the old castle, or Thirlstane Tower, as it is generally called, surrounded by a fine flower garden. On the opposite side of the valley stand the ruins of Gamescleuch Tower, also belonging to Lord Napier.‡ About 3 miles below Thirlestane and in sight of Gamescleuch, near to where the Rankle burn falls into the Ettrick, stand the extensive ruins of Tushielaw ; and on the opposite side of the vale stands the house of CACRA-BANK, the modern residence of the proprietor. The vale of the Rankle burn contains the lonely farm of Buccleuch, supposed to be the original property of that noble family ; but it does not appear to have ever been the site of a baronial residence. Here stood the ancient church of Buccleuch, now level with the ground ; and here was a burying-ground and very considerable village, of which there are abundant and clear traces ; and here the Covenanters from the neighbouring parishes of Yarrow, Kirkhope, Roberton, Eskdale-muir, and Ettrick, meet every third Sunday for public worship.§ A quarter of a

* The church occupies a very central position, being in round numbers 19 miles from Selkirk, Hawick, Moffat, and Innerleithen, and from these places all medical assistance comes and many *et ceteras* besides.

At one time the Ettrick ran near the manse and close by the foot of the glebe, but not for many years ; a Mr. Beattie, then proprietor of Ettrick Hall, cut a new course for the river at the opposite side of the vale, and in that course the river has run ever since.

† Till lately there was not a tree round the church and manse : the late Rev. Mr. Smith during his incumbency (from 1823 to 1858) planted and beautified the ground around very much, and now in summer both church and manse are almost hid amid large and beautiful trees ; and around Thirlestane Castle there was not a tree till those now surrounding it were planted by the late Lord Napier. Their effect is to render the district very beautiful, and, where their influence is felt, much more mild.

‡ Tradition says this tower was built for, but never occupied by, the then heir to the estates and titles of the Scotts of Thirlestane—he having been poisoned by his stepmother the night before his marriage.

Midway between Thirlestane and Gamescleuch stands the mill— now used as a cow-byre—in which the miller, according to tradition and Hogg, to gain possession of his goods, murdered and buried a pedler.

§ At one time the Covenanters formed a large proportion of the population of the parish of Ettrick ; but owing to emigration and

mile below Tushielaw Tower is Tushielaw Inn—the only one in the parish ("Tibby Shiels'" lies in Yarrow), and an excellent centre for anglers. Tourists can also be put up at Birkhill (which lies in Moffatdale) in a homely way. The well-known Thomas Boston, author of the "Fourfold State," died while pastor of this parish in 1732,* and a handsome monument has been erected to his memory in the churchyard. The cottage in which Hogg was born stood close by the present farm-steading of Ettrick Hall. It fell of its own accord about 1830, and about twenty years ago the stones of which it was built were removed, and the spot on which it stood now forms part of the garden at

other causes, they form now, under the name of Reformed Presbyterians, a proportion comparatively small. They are a most intelligent and excellent little community, highly esteemed by their Established Church neighbours for their superior intelligence and virtue, and beloved for their many good qualities. There is very little bigotry amongst them ; that spirit which is said to have been strong at one time having quite died away in Ettrick, as it has with them in other places. The only *congregation* of Reformed Presbyterians now in the district is at Kelso, which, through "emigration and other causes," has also greatly fallen off within the last thirty years. In the west of Scotland they are still a strong and wealthy body, eschewing pulpit robes, choirs, written sermons, the metre paraphrases, and a service of less than two hours' length.

A large proportion of the inhabitants of Ettrick parish, Kirkhope, and the wilder districts of Yarrow, are shepherds, and are perhaps the most intelligent and best read men, possessed of like means (averaging £45 a-year—this sum including perquisites, *i.e*, right to the keep of a small flock—a *pack* as it is locally termed, that is 43—of their own sheep, a cow's grass, and cottage rent free) in Scotland or anywhere else. Many of these men have the entire charge of the farm and stock—the farmer himself often living at a distance, generally on an arable farm in the lowlands ; but not an instance is known of the shepherd's gross abuse of his trust—a remark which cannot be made as regards stewards having charge of lowland arable farms. A correspondent thus writes of the shepherds of the district :—"I believe that as a class they are amongst the most honourable and faithful of servants. They continue generally very long with the same master, and some of them from father to son, and scarcely know what a 'flitting' is."

* The session records of the parish go back a long way, and in the days of Boston were kept with great care and taste. The bell of Boston's kirk is preserved in the manse—a gift in his day from one of the Scotts of Thirlestane ; and supposed to be the first bell ever rung in Ettrick. It was rung at the door of the church, in the memory of many still living, and then flung with a fearful bang into a deep recess behind the pulpit by the beadle, who paid no further attention to his duty, but allowed the minister to attend to himself. At Cossar's hill are kept, in charge of the housekeeper and shepherds, the walking staff of Boston, and other relics belonging to him and his wife ; which, like his grave, are viewed with great veneration by his admirers.

Ettrick Hall.* A stone in the wall, close by the road, with the poet's initials and date of birth, marks the spot.

Possibly few churchyards—population considered—contain a larger number of monuments than that of Ettrick ; and it is remarkable that a very large number of those whose names are recorded upon these died at ages varying from eighty to ninety-four. Besides the monument to Boston, there is one to the late Lord Napier, who died in China, but was buried in Ettrick at his own request ; one to John Beattie and his father, who together were parochial schoolmasters in Ettrick 101 years ; one to the grandfather of Hogg, who for "feats of frolic, agility, and strength, had no equal in his day ;" and one to Cunningham, "the Curate," son of the Earl of Glencairn, who died farmer of Midgehope. Here Hogg is buried, and a neat and substantial monument, erected by his widow, marks the spot.†

Midway between the Loch o' the Lowes and St. Mary's, and near "Tibby Shiels'" (which by the way is not an inn, properly speaking, as it has no licence—*see* Yarrow parish), stands the public monument to James Hogg the Ettrick Shepherd, upon a treeless, grassy, rising ground overlooking both lochs. At the head of the Loch o' the Lowes and near by Chapelhope farm-house are the remains of a burying-ground, and the foundation of the ancient chapel of Chapelhope, which, according to Hogg, was dedicated to St. Lawrence, and formed a joint curacy with Kirkhope. Kirkhope was dedicated to St. Irene, and is now called Overkirkhope. Of Kirkhope burying-ground or chapel, there is no trace, the plough having been passed over the ground. One spot never fails to produce excellent crops and first-rate potatoes, and this is supposed to be the old churchyard. Into the stone fence close by the farm-house of Overkirkhope is built a whin-stone which was picked up near this supposed burying-ground, and on which is rudely carved

* At Ettrick House, about a mile above Ettrick Hall and at the opposite side of the stream, are the remains of the foundation of one of the many "peels," or Border towers, which are found in this parish. In the days of Boston 43 families resided here—(it then constituted the village of Ettrick) ; now there is only one. On this house the sun does not shine for nearly half the year, being placed on what the people call the *dark side* of the water. The hill—a high one—comes between it and the sun.

† Tradition says that the four Covenanters who were shot by Claverhouse at Birkhill, lie in Ettrick churchyard : but of this there is no direct evidence. Under the main entrance to the church is the vault of the ancient family of the Scotts of Thirlestane (who assumed the name of Napier in 1805), closed after its desecration by Claverhouse ; who, according to Hogg, having run short of ammunition while in the district, rifled the coffins to obtain lead, and scattered their contents. The relics were shortly after gathered up, deposited in the chests, and deeply buried under the aisle floor.

a Romish priest in full canonicals with upraised hands in the act of pronouncing the benediction.

Behind Cacra-bank and on the slopes at the mouth of Rankle Burn are the remains of part of Ettrick Forest—a quantity of crooked stunted natural wood; and far up the hills by the roadside, between Tushielaw and the lochs, stands a fine but solitary tree, the last of the forest in that elevated region. Some have denied that the hills of Ettrick were ever forest lands; but those who have been long resident in the district maintain that there is abundant evidence of the fact, proved by the places on the hills on which the wood had been collected and burnt when sheep farming became the order of the day.

The parish is supplied with excellent roads.* The nearest convenient market towns are Hawick and Selkirk—both 19 miles distant from the church. Moffat is nearer, but owing to the state of the road by the top of Bodesbeck it cannot readily be reached.

Ettrick labours at the present day under various difficulties and disadvantages : (1st) The absence of a daily letter-carrier to and from Selkirk, there being no letters brought from Selkirk to Ettrick from Saturday till Tuesday night. (2d) Neglect on the part of parties in power to complete three miles of road over Bodesbeck Law and thereby connect the upper half of Ettrick with Moffat, from which it is not far distant. Were these few miles of road, which lie in Dumfriesshire, completed, pleasure parties in summer from Moffat could vary and increase the interest of their drives by driving through the interesting and beautiful vale of Ettrick, crossing into or from the loch districts by the road from Tushielaw instead of having, as at present, to drive to "Tibbie Shiel's" from Moffat and back again the same road. (3d) The want of a railway and the distance of twenty miles and upwards from a railway station. Were a railway to cross the vale at any point it would confer a great boon on all parties, but particularly on the farmers, who would improve their farms by the application of large quantities of lime, which at present cannot be done to the extent they wish. (4th) Absence of wood, particularly on estates where the proprietors and tenants are non-resident. More wood would improve the climate, add to the beauty of the parish, and to the value of property.

Fairs.—(All held at Ettrick fair grounds, near the hamlet of Hopehouses). Sale of ewes and the hiring of shepherds, last Wednesday of March, Sale of lambs and wool 30th July. Sale of draft ewes and small lambs, and for the purchasing of tups and fat sheep, 24th September. The "little fair," third Friday of November for the purchasing of fat sheep for *marts* (i.e , for

salting down) : at this fair keeping stock is sometimes exposed, and servants occasionally hired. These fairs have now dwindled away to almost nothing. About thirty years ago an extensive local business was transacted at them.

According to the census of 1861, the population of the parish was 454, who composed 78 families ; 3 of whom were returned as living in houses having one window, 19 in houses of two windows, and 56 (the large proportion of two-thirds) in houses of three and more windows.

The principal landed-proprietors in the parish are—His Grace the Duke of Buccleuch, the Right Hon. Lord Napier, Benjamin T. Anderson, Esq., of Tushielaw [Edinburgh] ; John Scott, Esq., of Rodono ; Major Pott, of Pottburn ; Henry Scott, Esq., of Overkirkhope ; Thomas Macmillan, Esq,, of Shorthope ; Captain Williamson, of Midgehope and Cossarshill ; William Paterson, Esq., of Ettrick Hall (Channel Street, Galashiels) ; William Aitchison, Esq., of Glenkerry (Linhope by Hawick).

Assessed property in 1864-5, £9852 : 19 : 7.

Those marked thus (*) are Registered Voters in the parish.

DISTRICT POLICE OFFICER—Andrew Smith, Crosslee Station.

POST OFFICE—Jas. Amos, Ramsaycleuch Shop, postmaster. Post Town, Selkirk. Departure at 9 a.m. on Monday Wednesday, and Friday. Arrives at 4 p.m. on Tuesday, Thursday, and Saturday. Thomas Armstrong, messenger.

PUBLIC OFFICES—Inspector of Poor, Session-Clerk, and Registrar of Births, Marriages, and Deaths—George Hood.

Kirk Treasurer—Rev J. Falconer.

Heritors's Clerk—Peter Rodger, Selkirk.

CLERGY, &c †—Presbytery of Selkirk, and Synod of Merse and Teviotdale. Patron—Lord Napier.

Established Church—*Rev. John Falconer (Inducted 1864). Sittings, 310. Average attendance at Sabbath School, 20

FAST DAYS—Unfixed. Generally in June and November.

SCHOOL‖ (Parochial)—*George Hood, master ; average attend., 45.

PAROCHIAL BOARD—Henry Scott, Esq., of Overkirkhope (Crosslee), the only permanent resident heritor in the parish—Chairman.

---

* Thanks to the late Lord Napier, until whose day there was scarcely a bush or trace of road in the parish.

† This parish and that of Yarrow are the richest in the south of Scotland in unexhausted teinds ; dividing between them, as they do, the ancient parish of St. Mary's of the Lowes—Yarrow having a revenue of £1100 per year, and Ettrick nearly £500. This large sum is divided annually amongst the Deans of the Chapel Royal, subject to augmentation of minister's stipends for Yarrow and Ettrick.

‖ Children in the parish from 5 to 15, attending school during the first week of April 1861, 78 ; of all ages, 81.

Average number of poor on the roll, 22. Average Assessment per £, 1½d. ; total Assessment, 1864-5, £180 : 3s †

LIBRARY—Parochial Subscription—Contains nearly 1200 volumes ; subscription, 6s. of entry-money, after that, 2s. 6d. per annum. George Hood, Librarian.

There is also an excellent Juvenile Library in the parish.

CARRIERS—Matthew Palmer, Hopehouses, to Hawick and Eskdalemuir every week ; John Amos, The Shop, Ramsaycleuch, thrice a week to Selkirk ; John Murray, Wednesday, and James Hill, Monday, from Selkirk ; —— Brydone, from Ettrick Bridge, Kirkhope, to Edinburgh, fortnightly.

TRADES.

Amos, James, draper, grocer, etc., Ramsaycleuch Shop
Blythe, William, dyker, etc., Ettrick Bridge-end
Hopkirk, John, tailor and precentor, do.
Kerr, Robert, joiner   do.
Laidlaw, John, tailor,   do.
Pringle, Walter, shoemaker,   do.
Shankie, Andrew, blacksmith,   do.
Tushielaw Inn, Elizabeth Thomson

FARMERS, &c., RESIDENT IN THE PARISH.

*Anderson, John, farmer, Braidgarhill
*Blake, Walter, sen. do.   Shorthope
*Blake, Walter, jun. do.   do.
*Blyth, Walter,   do.   Ettrickhall
*Brydon, George,   do.   Scabcleuch
*Brydon, Walter,   do.   do.
Copland, Walter, Esq., factor to Lord Napier, Thirlestane Lodge
*Dalgleish, John, farmer, Potburn ‡
Dalgleish, Simon, do.,   Over Phawhope ‡
*Elliot, Walter,   do.,   Over Kirkhope
*Grieve, Thomas,   do.,   Wester Buccleuch

---

† In the parish of Ettrick there are only 4 resident paupers—2 illegitimate children, and 2 infirm persons.
‡ These two are the highest inhabited houses in the south of Scotland, each being 1250 feet above mean water (*see* p. 352, footnote) ; Mosspaul, in Teviothead (formerly an inn), is only 827 feet ; Hunter's Hall Inn, situated in Channelkirk parish, and probably the highest in Berwickshire, is 1093 feet ; Birkhill, in Moffatdale, close to the borders of Ettrick parish, is 1101½ feet ; while the *Ale House*, at the head of Kirkston Pass in Cumberland, "the highest inhabited house in England" (so says the sign-board over the door), is given in the guide books as 1200 feet.

*Haliburton, Thos., farmer, Tushielaw
*Hall, William,   do.   Midgehope
*Laidlaw, John,   do.   Annelshope
*Little, Thomas,   do.   Gamescleuch
*Little, William,   do.   do.
*Scott, Alexander,   do.   Ramsaycleuch
Scott, Charles,   do.   Nether Phawhope
*Scott, Henry (of Overkirkhope), farmer, Crosslee
*Tully, John, farmer, Deephope

SEATS, &c., OF COUNTY FAMILIES IN THE PARISH.

THIRLESTANE CASTLE.

The seat and principal residence of Baron Napier (Sir Francis Napier) of Merchistoun, in the peerage of Scotland, and a Baronet of Nova Scotia ; K.T. and a Privy Councillor ; born 15th September 1819 ; succeeded his father, as 9th baronet, 11th October 1834 ; married 2d September 1845, Anne-Jane-Charlotte, only daughter of R. Manners Lockwood, Esq., and has issue—

William-John-George, *Master of Thirlestane*, born 1846.
John Scott, born 1848.
Basil, born 1850.
Mark-Francis, born 1852.

His Lordship having previously, from 1840, filled various diplomatic offices, was Ambassador to the United States of America, from 21st January 1857 till 13th December 1858. when he was appointed British minister at the Hague ; in December 1860 he was appointed Ambassador-Extraordinary and Plenipotentiary to the Emperor of Russia ; and in September 1864 was appointed Ambassador-Extraordinary and Plenipotentiary to the King of Prussia.

CACRA-BANK.

Situated at the junction of the Rankle Burn with the Ettrick —the property and intended summer residence of Benjamin Gaskin T. Anderson, Esq., of Tushielaw, and of Carterhope, in Tweedsmuir, in Peeblesshire ; at present unoccupied.

Mr. Anderson is a Magistrate for Peeblesshire and a Lieutenant in the Dumfries, Roxburgh, and Selkirk Militia. Mr. Anderson resides principally in Edinburgh.

RODONO.

On the shores of St. Mary's Loch about half-way between its head and the Meggat, a handsome residence is in course of erection for John Scott, Esq., of Rodono, and which it is understood Mr. Scott will call " Rodono "—he having revived the name of that ancient barony, granted to the monks of Melrose by charter of king Alexander II. in 1236. This house of Rodono will occupy one of the finest positions on St. Mary's shores, and when the grounds are properly laid out and wooded, will form a great ornament to the beautiful district in which it is situated.

Mr. Scott is the eldest son of the late William Scott of Teviot Bank, who was only son of John Scott of Midgehope and Glenormiston, who was third son of William Scott of Woll, Sheriff of Selkirkshire; born 2d October 1809; married, Anne, 2d daughter of Henry Singleton of Belpatrick, County of Louth.

London Residence—3 Chester Place, Hyde Park.

Mr. Scott is a Justice of Peace for the County of Roxburgh.

REGISTERED VOTERS (Non-Resident).

Anderson, Andrew, farmer (Cossarshall), Woodburn, Roberton
Anderson, B. T. G., Esq. (of Tushielaw)
Aitchison, William, farmer, Linhope, Hawick
Aitchison, W., jun., do.   do.
Brydon, Herbert, Thirlestanehope, Moodlaw, Eskdale-muir
Brydon, James   do.   do.   do.
Clerk, James, Esq., Penicuik
Davidson, William, banker, Hawick
Dundas, W. Pitt, Esq., advocate (Registrar-General for Scotland), Edinburgh
Elliot, Henry, farmer (Over and Nether Dalgleishes), Greenriver, Rulewater
Elliot, Jas., farmer (Over and Nether Dalgleishes), Lamberton, Berwick
Kerr, Thomas, Esq. of Craighouse, Earlston
Milne, David, Esq. of Milne-Graden, Berwickshire
Plummer, William, flesher, Dalkeith
Ritchie, Robert, farmer, Cloverhill, Biggar
Scott, John, Esq. of Rodono, W.S., Edinburgh
Scott, John, farmer, Australia
Staver, Andrew, Dykecrofts, Castleton
Tod, Walter, farmer, Cleuchfoot, Langholm
Turnbull, John, farmer Burnfoot, Hawick

GALASHIELS.

THE parish of Galashiels is situated partly in Roxburghshire and partly in Selkirkshire, the larger part being in the latter county. Its general outline is irregular—its greatest length N. W. by S. E. being about $6\frac{1}{2}$ miles, and its greatest breadth over 3 miles. On the north and north-east it is bounded, for its entire length, by Melrose parish, on the east by Bowden, on the south by Selkirk, and on the north-west by that part of Stow parish situated in Roxburghshire. The parish of Galashiels was formed out of two old parishes, Lindean (in Roxburgh) and Boldside (in Selkirk), in the early part of the seventeenth century. The site of Lindean church is still pointed out about half-a-mile south of the Lindean cottages. It appears to have been the centre of a somewhat large parish, extending along the banks of the Tweed immediately above the embouchure of the Ettrick. "Boldsyd" kirk and clachan, evidences of which still remain in the heaps of stones and house-foundations that lie amidst clumps of aged oaks, stood on the banks of the Tweed about a mile above Abbotsford, and on the other side of the river. The "deserted village" was a favourite haunt of Sir Walter Scott, and up to the end of his life he might often have been seen reclining under the branches of a giant oak that stood near the only remaining cottages, surveying the course of the river as it emerged from the woods of Sunderland Hall, or perhaps watching the trees and lands of Abbotsford as they grew into beauty beneath his hand. The formation of the present parish of Galashiels, first mooted in 1622 by the commissioners for the plantation of kirks, was consummated about 1640. Dr. Douglas, who sold Cartley-hole,* the original name

* Newharthaugh, vulgarly called Cartley Hole, was purchased by Dr. Douglas about the year 1797 or '98, and was by him cultivated, improved, and laid out into parks; and at the time it was sold to Sir Walter, in 1811, it was occupied by an improving tenant.

The Doctor was ordained minister of Galashiels (when 23 years of age), in 1770. At that time there was only one slated house in the village besides the manse. He died in 1820. He was an eminently philanthropic man, and by his advice and pecuniary assistance rendered material aid to the infant manufacturers of Galashiels, at the time when the predecessors of the present flourishing and wealthy mill owners were struggling into existence, from the condition of country weavers, which they had previously occupied; and who, to their honour be it said, never gave the Doctor cause to regret the work he had undertaken, or—we have authority for stating —lost him a shilling; and he was the unpaid banker, and sometimes broker, to the community from before 1790, when his improved circumstances enabled him to render assistance, till those he had

of Abbotsford, to Sir Walter, and was for many years honoured by his closest friendship, was minister of the parish of Galashiels; and "the manse-garden" of Galashiels has been made the subject of a well-known work by the Rev. Dr. Nathaniel Paterson, another minister of the parish, now pastor of a Free church in Glasgow. The parish presents that undulating aspect characteristic of the Border counties generally, and of Roxburghshire in particular. Its climate and soil vary considerably, from the cold bleak hill-sides at a high elevation above the sea, to those of the comparatively genial and fertile valleys that form the beds of the various rivers by which it is traversed. Among these, the Tweed, the Gala, and the Caddon may be enumerated, which with numberless little mountain rills and smaller tributaries, plentifully water the hills and valleys that alternate from end to end of the parish. Besides these, lying in Selkirkshire, its boundaries include the whole of Hollybush Loch, a sheet of water about a mile in circumference, and, lying in Roxburghshire, half of Cauldshiels Loch, a broad expanse of clear water lying like a diamond in a nook of the dark hills above Abbotsford (see p. 127). Sitting on the banks of this loch, Sir Walter Scott, after the ruin of his fortunes, composed one or two of the most beautiful and affecting stanzas that ever fell from his pen. Altogether Galashiels is one of the most picturesque parishes in the south of Scotland; and connected as it is with some of the most interesting traditions of the district, a more attractive spot for the tourist, the historian, or the antiquarian it would be difficult to point out.

The total area of the parish is nearly 8589 acres, of which about 2878½ are in Roxburghshire. According to the census of 1861, the population of the parish was 3379; but the additions which have been made since must have increased it to at least 3500 (this of course is only about one half the population of the burgh, the other part being the parish of Ladhope—see Melrose p. 130). The principal heights in the neighbourhood are—

Meigle Hill, 1387 feet (or two feet higher than the Eildons); Gala Hill, 904; Rink Hill (on which there is a singularly perfect Pictish camp), 638; Cauldshiels Hill (literally covered with ancient fortifications), 1076; Buckholm Hill, 1064; Glendearg (scene of the Monastery), 589; and Williamlaw, 1315.

The parish of Galashiels has few antiquities. The principal attraction to antiquaries is the Cat-rail, a Pictish ditch with earthen ramparts on each side, which runs a course of nearly 45 miles, and which is in this neighbourhood in remarkably good preservation. It seems to have been a fence, capable of being used as a military trench, and connecting a number of the strong circular forts defended by our barbarian ancestors. The Rink Camp, about 3 miles from Galashiels, is much valued by antiquarians on account of its perfect preservation. Near it is Fairnielee Tower, an old Border peel, now in ruins. While staying here Mrs. Cockburn (born Alison Rutherford of Fernylee, sometime about 1700) wrote the pathetic verses sung to the "Flowers of the Forest," and beginning—

"I've seen the smiling of fortune beguiling." [*]

About 4 miles off, behind Langlee Hill (in Ladhope—see p. 129), stands Hillslap Tower, chosen by Sir Walter Scott as the residence of the Glendinings, in his novel of "The Monastery." and which the present proprietor—Mr. Paterson, Galashiels—has christened Glendearg, the name given to it by the great novelist. There is a tradition that the Covenanters used to hold meetings in "Meigle Pots," two deep holes in the hill of that name, about a mile and a half from Galashiels.

The only town in the parish is Galashiels, which covers both banks of the river Gala for about two miles before it falls into the Tweed. Though of modern erection and of modern fame, Galashiels, we have good evidence for believing, was a place of some importance at a very early period. The "fayre forest of Ettrick," from the earliest times a favourite hunting-ground of the kings of Scotland, and apparently esteemed a valuable appanage of the crown, appears to have terminated somewhere about "Gallowschel," where a royal hunting station had been planted. We first come upon the name in an old charter, written very early in the 14th century; and about a hundred years after, in 1416, we find Archibald, Earl Douglas, quelling the quarrelsome Haigs of Bemersyde, from his tower at Gallowshiels. When the Princess Margaret of England, on the occasion of her marriage with James IV., received Ettrick

---

aided had in a great measure ceased to require his help, and his own increasing infirmities, including his loss of sight, made it requisite he should wind up:—this would be about 1810 or '12; but he was a man of great shrewdness, with a keen perception of character, and, with all his goodness, not a subject to be readily imposed upon. While thus engaged for the temporal good of the community, the Doctor was a model clergyman, who thoroughly performed his ministerial and parochial duties.

The weavers of Dr. Douglas's time held a high social position in the community; they were numerous, spirited, routhy, and the most of them were bonnet lairds. As a rule, they were shrewd, and, compared with the average emoluments of the time, a well paid class of tradesmen; and not to be confounded with the few poverty-stricken handloom weavers now working in the country villages at sacking and other rough jobs, whose earnings, when fully employed, seldom exceed 1s. 3d. a day.

---

[*] The other song to the same air—

"I've heard the lilting at our yowes milking,"

was by Miss Jane Elliot, daughter of Sir Gilbert, second baronet of Minto, who lived contemporary with Miss Rutherford. Sir Gilbert was great-great-grandfather of the present Earl of Minto, and is said to have introduced the German flute into Scotland.

Forest as her dowry, Sir John Murray gave her sasine of the lands near the tower and manor of Galashiels, among the witnesses being David Pringle of Galashiels. Within the memory of many still living (1865) the old peel known as "The Hunter's Ha'," stood in some of its pristine strength near the parish school; but the wants of the growing population requiring school extension, to make room, the venerable ruin was ruthlessly levelled with the ground. Part of the old Tolbooth, clad with ivy, and still a picturesque little ruin, may be seen at the edge of the Gala policy, near the residence of the baron bailie; but the Cross lies unheeded and crumbling among the outhouses of the lord of the manor.

Whatever may be said of the claims of Galashiels to importance in the olden times, there can be no doubt of its importance now. About the beginning of the present century the introduction of certain new machinery for the manufacture of woollen cloth gave an impetus to the trade which had been pursued in Galashiels from time immemorial. Machines were procured that did the work of the hand-carders, others that did away with the spinning-wheel, small mills began to spring up, new ideas were worked out, the factories were constantly enlarged, the machinery every year improved, communication with the cities quickened; the railway-engine at length bounded through the town; and the Tweed-trade, now become such an important and valuable portion of this country's commerce, sprung into existence and prosperity. This trade, which has now grown to be the main business of Hawick, Selkirk, Innerleithen, Dumfries, Jedburgh and other towns in the Border, as well as of Galashiels, is generally admitted to have had its origin in the latter place. It still maintains the distinction of producing more Tweeds than any of its rivals; and the proof of its manufacturers being the founders of the trade is still further evidenced by the fact that the mill-owners in Selkirk, Innerleithen, and Walkerburn, all hail from Galashiels. There are now about twenty large factories, comprising between sixty and seventy setts of machines, each of which is estimated to represent a turn-over of £7000 a year. In addition to the yarn produced by these machines, large quantities are procured from the Ochil district and in the vicinity. The yearly turn-over in manufactured goods in Galashiels alone can be little less than £600,000. A large portion of that, again, may be said to be twice turned over, because most of the wool used in the factories is sold by firms having their head quarters in the town.

In form the town is long and narrow, filling up the north corner of the valley formed by Meigle and Gala hills on one side, and by Buckholm and Langlee hills on the other. Gala Water, or rather the bed of the river (for the water is exclusively carried down the factory-dam during half the year), runs through the centre of the town from north-west to south-east.

The bridges over it are in every way unworthy a town of such enterprise, besides being highly dangerous to the inhabitants, and too narrow for the traffic. The centre parts of the town, as well as its extremities which border the river course, are mainly occupied with factories, shops, offices, and workmen's dwelling-houses. Abbotsford Road, Melrose Road, and the Windyknowe suburbs, however, comprise a considerable number of elegant and capacious villas, the residences of the manufacturers and other principal inhabitants. Close to the town, and within the boundaries of the burgh, are GALA HOUSE, the residence of Major Scott, the lord of the manor; and LANGHAUGH (*see* p. 152), the snugly-lying mansion of Captain Clark. The most beautiful house in the neighbourhood is undoubtedly LANGLEE, the residence of James Dalrymple, Esq., of Langlee and Greenknowe (*see* p. 153—WESTER LANGLEE). TORWOODLEE, commanding a splendid view of the whole vale, is still held by the Pringles, the present laird. Lieut. J. T. Pringle, R.N., being a lineal descendant of the Hoppringle who was summoned by the outlaw Murray when terrified by the king's approach (*see* Stow parish—portion in Selkirkshire). ABBOTSFORD (*see* pp. 126, 149) is only about a mile distant from the burgh as the crow flies, but the intervention of the Tweed makes the nearest approach to it on foot more than 3 miles. The rapid extension of the town proper rendered necessary the widening of the burgh, which was satisfactorily managed, in spite of much opposition from the outlying house owners, in 1864, in terms of the New Police Improvement Act. The burgh may now be said to contain 7500 inhabitants. New streets and new villas are being yearly added to it. There is every prospect of the town continuing to increase rapidly in size and in prosperity. In 1780 Galashiels contained only 400 inhabitants; so that in 85 years the town has increased eighteen-fold.

Galashiels is well looked after in religious matters, there being no fewer than eleven places of worship in the burgh—the parish church, Ladhope parish church, two Free churches, two U. P. churches, one Roman Catholic church, one Episcopal church, one Baptist church, one Independent chapel, and one Glassite church. With the exception of the Episcopal and Roman Catholic churches, neither of these present any architectural beauties, and some of them are architectural eyesores.

Besides private academies, of which there is a great number for the instruction of both sexes, there are two public schools—the parish school and Gala subscription school. The deficient accommodation provided in the former has long been a source of complaint on the part of the inhabitants, and a reproach to the heritors.

Galashiels, as already mentioned, is situated in the vale of the Gala, some of it being built on the slopes of the hills, but the greater part on the alluvial deposit on both sides of the channel—the direction of which is here nearly from west to east, and consequently, the town is not sheltered from the prevailing east and west winds. Though the atmosphere does not, as a rule, stagnate, yet occasionally, especially during the nights of winter, a considerable fog settles over the town. With this exception the situation of Galashiels is a healthful one. Goitre, a disease peculiar to localities where the hills are of a height great in proportion to the width of the valleys between them, is sometimes met with, but not to any considerable extent.

The water supply of the town is not in a satisfactory condition. The greater part of the water used is got from wells sunk into the gravelly subsoil over which most of the town is built. This water generally is exceedingly good, and though there exist a number of cess-pools, through the porous walls of which their fluid contents are allowed to percolate, yet no more than one or two of the wells have been rendered sensibly polluted— the others showing no indication of the presence of organic matter, even with the most delicate tests. A number of the houses in the town are served with water by a private water company. This source of supply, however, in a dry summer always fails, and the water is not of first-rate quality. On the whole, the water of Galashiels is defective, not so much in quality as in quantity. An effort is being made in the burgh for the adoption of the water clauses of Mr. Lindsay's Act, and the securing to the town of an abundant supply of water of unexceptionable purity.

In the matter of drainage, the town is also in a bad condition. There is no proper system of drains, and many of the houses have no drains whatever, the refuse of some of them being simply allowed to subside into the soil. Of the drains which do exist, some empty themselves into the mill-lead, but some into the bed of the Gala ; and as during a great part of summer this stream is almost dry, all the water being carried into the mill-lead, the sewage is not carried away, but allowed to remain a nuisance, and, no doubt, a cause of disease. It is mainly owing to the defective drainage, we believe, that the greatest amount of mortality, for some years back, has occurred in the dryest seasons. Notwithstanding these drawbacks, Galashiels is a healthy town. This must be partly owing to the abundant work and good wages attendant upon its thriving condition as a manufacturing place. There is almost no destitution ; and wanting this, the town wants one of the most frequent causes of an excessive mortality. To some extent, however, this advantage is counterbalanced by the excessive over-crowding in many of the houses occupied by the working classes. The rapid increase of Tweed manufacturers has drawn to Galashiels so many mill-workers as to have made the house accommodation much too small for the population ; and though new buildings are rising up on every side, it must be some time before this source of ill-health is fairly put an end to.

The mortality of Galashiels for 1861 2·3 was less than that of any town of similar size within a radius of 30 miles. In 1864 the figures of the Registrar-General appear not so favourable ; but the population has increased so very much since the census, that, in this year, no accurate death-rate can be calculated. As a rule, the epidemics visiting the town are not very severe. It has had two visitations of cholera, of no more than the usual mortality. Diphtheria had in the early part of 1863 a number of victims, but, excepting that period, the cases have not been numerous. Fever of the typhoid or enteric type is not an unfrequent visitor, but typhus has not been recognised for some years.

Galashiels is a burgh of barony, and up till 1850 was governed by the baron bailie representing Mr. Scott of Gala, its feudal superior. In that year, however, the Police and Improvement Scotland Act was adopted by the inhabitants ; and a Commission of nine gentlemen, elected by the householders, under the chief magistracy of William Rutherford, Esq., banker, soon effected a thorough revolution in the appearance of the town. Footpaths were constructed along the principal streets, where formerly there were nothing but large holes— dangerous traps by summer and pools of mud by winter. The thoroughfares were lit up by numerous lamps, and in a year the dark and dirty village, with its rotheaps and nuisances, had become a clean and well-ordered town, having all the modern appliances for the promotion of the public health and comfort. Much still remains to be done ; but there are prospects of the two greatest desiderata (efficient drainage and good water) being accomplished in a year or two.

At present the burgh has no central offices of its own (*see* note, Justice of Peace Courts). The Police Court and the meetings of Commissioners are held in the Public Hall, while the cells are rented from the county of Roxburgh. It is probable, however, that the Commissioners will, at an early period, combine under one roof all rooms and offices required for the administration of the burgh affairs, including houses for the superintendent of police and the constables under him. The erection of a slaughter-house, to be the property of the burgh, is also contemplated. The largest and the most elegant building open to the public, is the Public Hall, the property of a private company of shareholders. It is of two storeys, the uppermost of which is entirely occupied by the concert hall, 70 feet by 40, and 24 feet high. Beneath are committee rooms, ladies' rooms, keeper's rooms, etc. The Corn Exchange, facing the market place, and not two minutes' walk from the railway station, was finished in 1860, and has a principal hall 59 feet long by 30 broad. Both halls are well used, and the latter, which was got up with least expense, now pays a remunerative dividend. The bank branches, like those of Kelso (*see* p. 302, foot-note), are all ornaments to the town. By far the most imposing edifice in the town is the Roman Catholic Chapel, which stands at the foot of Stirling Street, in close proximity to the railway station. Even in its present unfinished state, it is an object of some interest and a good deal of admiration.

Besides the town of Galashiels, the following hamlets are, geographically or ecclesiastically, connected with the parish :— LINDEAN COTTAGES (in Lindean, Roxburghshire), now consisting of a school-house, smithy, joiner's shop, and the old churchyard ; LANGSHAW (Ladhope), *see* p. 148 ; CADDONFOOT —the greater part of this hamlet is in Stow, which *see* ; CLOVENFORDS—all in Stow.

In the Gala, on which Galashiels is situated, the angling is free ; before the opening of the railway it was a splendid trouting stream, and above the town is still good ; but now, owing to its convenience of access to Edinburgh anglers, it is overfished ; in its course of nearly 2 miles through the town there is no fishing. In the Tweed the trout angling is good and free. Cauldshiels Loch * is well stocked with perch and pike, and angling in it is freely permitted. Its waters are deep and its bottom treacherous ; and the angler or visitor should on no account place foot beyond its banks. Holybush Loch contains trout and a large quantity of eels.†

The nearest railway station to Abbotsford is that of Abbotsford Ferry, the first from Galashiels on the Selkirk line. A ferry-boat here takes the visitor across and lands him within Abbotsford grounds. The Tweed can also here be forded by conveyances.

Holidays—New Year's and Michaelmas days, and the afternoons of the March and July Galashiels fairs and the Lammas fair at Melrose.

Markets—Weekly, for grain in bulk, Tuesday, when a small business is done.

---

* *Cauldshiels Loch, i.e.,* the bleak lake, or more literally, the lake at the bleak or unsheltered folds. Till Sir Walter Scott planted trees on the Abbotsford side of the loch, it was entirely without shelter, and the name then must have been very appropriate. Except on the Abbotsford side, its shores are still " lamentably bare." Hogg, in his " Three Perils of Man," gives a different origin to the name.

† The bed of all the streams of the district literally swarms with splendid eels, mostly the Grig species, and some of the broad-nosed ; but a very general and strong prejudice exists against catching or eating them. Lampreys, locally known as *Ramper Eels,* also frequent the Tweed and Teviot during the summer to spawn ; they are regarded with a general and very senseless feeling of dread, disgust, and detestation.

Fortnightly Live Stock Sales—established this year (1865). These are conducted by Messrs. Andrew Oliver & Son of Hawick, and are held on the Saturdays ; at them a great part of the fat and other stock reared in the district is sold.

Fairs (at which a very small business is done—so small that they might almost be omitted)—Seed Corn, third Wednesday of March. Wool, 8th July.

By rail Galashiels is distant 33½ miles from Edinburgh, 81 from Glasgow, 6¼ from Selkirk, 19 from Kelso and Hawick, 4 from Melrose, 42½ from Berwick-on-Tweed, 116¼ from Newcastle by the Border Counties' line, 64¼ from Carlisle by the Waverley route.

The railway station at Galashiels is conveniently situated in the town on the Ladhope side, and is the only one on the line where the comfort of the passengers has been creditably cared for.

Population of the parish according to the census of 1861, including that part of the town situated in Selkirkshire, 3379 ; of the town, including that part of it which lies in the county of Roxburgh, 6433. The housing statistics of the parish at the same date—1 family sleeping in a house having no window, 302 in houses of one window, 262 in houses of two windows, and the small proportion of 158 (less than one-fourth) in houses of three or more windows ; total families in the parish 723 (*see* p. 130 for the family statistics of Ladhope).

The principal landed-proprietors in the parish are—Major Scott of Gala ; Mrs. Pringle Douglas, of Fairnilee (Haining, Selkirk) ; Charles S. Plummer, Esq., of Sunderland Hall ; Nicol Milne Esq. of Faldonside.

Amount of assessed property in 1864-5, in the parish, excluding the Ladhope district (which is included in Melrose— *see* p. 130), £14,605 : 16 : 7.

Superior of Galashiels—Hugh Scott, Esq. of Gala.

MAGISTRATES AND COMMISSIONERS.

The government of the town is under the Police Act 25 and 26 Vict., cap. 101. For all purposes of the Act the Burgh is held to be in Selkirkshire.

George Bathgate, Esq., Chief Magistrate.

Thomas Laidlaw, Esq.,   } Junior Magistrates.
William Haldane, Esq.,   }

COMMISSIONERS OF POLICE.

Mr Geo. Bathgate.	Mr Adam Cochrane, jun.
,, Thos. Laidlaw.	,, William A. Sanderson.
,, Thomas Roberts.	,, William Haldane.
,, W. Mitchell.	,, Thomas Clapperton
,, Hugh Roberts.	

Robert Stewart, Clerk.   John Pringle, Procurator-Fiscal.
James Beaton, Superintendent of Police,

JUSTICES OF THE PEACE (Resident in the Locality).

Hugh Scott, Esq., of Gala.
Willm. Paterson, Esq. Channel Street, Galashiels.
Js. Pringle, Esq. of Torwoodlee.

Capt. Clark, R N., of Langhaugh
The Chief Magistrate of Galashiels.

COURTS.

JUSTICE OF PEACE COURTS—None held in Galashiels.—The cases are tried either in Selkirk or Melrose, according to the jurisdiction in which they occur. *See* p. 368.

POLICE COURTS are held as occasion may require.

SHERIFF SMALL DEBT COURTS are held on the first Tuesdays of February, April, June, August, October, and December.

PUBLIC OFFICES.

Billet Master—William Sanderson, bookseller.
Heritors' Clerk—James Stalker, Elm Row.
Inland Revenue (Excise)—James Deans, Dingleton, Melrose, Officer.
Inland Revenue, Assessor of—T. J. Dunn, Melrose.
Kirk Treasurer and Session Clerk—Thomas Roberts, Elm Row.
Medical Officers and Public Vaccinators—Mr. Tweedie for Galashiels district, and Dr. Brisbane for Ladhope district.
Nuisances, Inspector of—John Murray, Hall Street.
Poor, Inspector of—John Thorburn, Albert Place.
Procurator-Fiscal—John Pringle, Bridge Street.
Registrar of Births, Marriages, and Deaths, Parish of Galashiels—George Taket, 54 Overhaugh Street.
Registrar for District of Ladhope—Thomas Paterson, teacher, Ladhope Bank.
Sextons : Ladhope—James Miller, Wilderhaugh ; Galashiels—Alex. Thorburn, Wait Knowe.
Sheriff-Clerk Depute—Robert Stewart, 1 Bridge Place.
Sheriff-Officer—James Wright, Bridge Street.
Stamps and Taxes—William Rutherford, Collector, Channel Street.
Superintendent of Police—James Beaton.
Town Clerk—Robert Stewart, 1 Bridge Place.
Town Crier—John Penman.
Town Treasurer—George Taket, 54 Overhaugh Street.
Works, Master of—John Murray, Hall Street.

POST OFFICE (Bank Street).

John Creelman, Postmaster.

DESPATCHES.

Hawick, Kelso, Melrose, &c.	.	.	.	.	7-45 a m.
Edinburgh, Glasgow, and Stow	.	.	.	.	10-50 a.m.
Edinburgh, Glasgow, and North	.	.	.	.	8-12 p.m.
Do. Do. Do.	.	.	.	.	4-5 p.m.
London, Kelso, Hawick, &c.	.	.	.	.	4-25 p.m.

Sunday.

Hawick, Kelso, Melrose, &c.	.	.	.	.	7-25 a.m.
London, Berwick, &c.	.	.	.	.	5-35 p.m.
Edinburgh, Stow, &c.	.	.	.	.	6-36 p.m.
Stow	.	.	.	.	.	5-15 p.m.

DELIVERIES.

London, all parts of England, and Selkirk . . 7-30 a.m.
Edinburgh, London, and all parts of the Kingdom 9-20 a.m.
Berwick, North-East of England, Edinburgh, Selkirk, Hawick, Melrose, &c. . . . . 5-30 p.m.

Country.

Thornilee and Clovenford—Despatch at 9-20 a.m., Arrives at 2-4 p.m. Thomas Currie, Messenger.
Langshaw—Despatch at 9-20 a.m., Arrives at 2-4 p.m. Charles Dickson, Messenger.
On Sundays the Box is open from 8-30 a.m. till 10-30 a.m.
The Pillar Boxes at Abbotsford Road and Wilderburn are cleared every week-day at 10-30 a.m. and 3-45 p.m. No collection on Sunday.
Letters can be Registered to within half an hour of the Box Closing, and late Letters can be posted 20 minutes after Box Closing by affixing an extra Stamp, with the exception of the despatch for Edinburgh at 8-12 p.m.

CLERGY, &c.

Galashiels is in the Presbytery of Selkirk and Synod of Merse and Teviotdale. Patron—Hugh Scott, Esq., of Gala.

PARISH CHURCH—Rev. Kenneth M'Lay Phin (Inducted 1841). Sittings, 800. Average attendance at Sabbath School, 170. Superintendent of Sabbath School—Rev. J. W. Gibson ; Precentor—A. Curle ; Church Officer—James Stuart.

LADHOPE—Rev. Robert Blackstock (Inducted 1858). Sittings, 900. Average attendance at Sabbath School, 120. Superintendent of Sabbath School—Minister ; Treasurer—Thomas S. Hall ; Session Clerk—James Shaw ; Precentor—James Horsburgh ; Church Officer—James Turnbull.

FREE CHURCH—Rev. James Selkirk (Inducted 1861). Sittings, 500. Average attendance at Sabbath School, 110. Superintendent of Sabbath School—Andrew Herbertson ; Treasurer—Adam Henderson ; Session Clerk—John Sibbald ; Precentor—Alexander Gellatly, Huddersfield ; Church Officer—P. Mack, Albert Place.

FREE CHURCH (Ladhope)—Rev. James Fettes (Inducted 1850). Sittings, 550. Average attendance at Sabbath School, 100. Session Clerk—John Galbraith ; Treasurer—Thos. Dickson, King Street, Buckholmside ; Precentor—Peter Crichton ; Church Officer—John Dickson.

U. P. CHURCH (East)—   (Inducted 18). Sittings, 840. Average attendance at Sabbath School, 130. Superintendent of Sabbath School—James Bell, Channel Street ; Precentor—J. Thomson, High Street ; Church Officer—Robert Broad, Island Street.

U. P. CHURCH (West)—Rev. Robert Blair (Inducted 1838). Sittings, 600. Average attendance at Sabbath School, 120 ; at Minister's

Bible Class, 60. Superintendent of Sabbath School—A. Davidson ; Precentor—John Scott ; Church Officer—William Lowrie.

CONGREGATIONAL—Rev. Alex. Brown (Inducted 1861). Sittings, 100. Average attendance at Sabbath School, 70. Superintendent of Sabbath School—James Bathgate ; Treasurer—William Gray.

EPISCOPALIAN—Sittings, 240. Average attend. at Sabbath School, 50. Superintendent of Sabbath School and Organist—Charles Lapworth ; Leader of Choir—John Goodfellow ; Church Officer —Henry Faichney.

BAPTIST—Mr. A. Thompson (Inducted 1852). Sittings, 90.

GLASSITE—

ROMAN CATHOLIC—Rev. Father Langton (Inducted 1864). Sittings, . Average attendance at Sabbath School, 80.

CADDONFOOT CHURCH (Endowed), lying in the parish—*see* Stow.

FAST DAYS—Thursdays before first Sunday of May and second Sunday of November.

LADHOPE FREE CHURCH CHRISTIAN ASSOCIATION.
(Established 1864.)

Meets every Sabbath morning, and quarterly on week-days, for spiritual improvement.

President—Rev. Mr. Fettes.   Vice-President—D. Brotherston. Secretary—James Sanderson.

AUXILIARY BIBLE SOCIETY (BRANCH—estab. 1863).

Preisdent—Mr. Sibbald.   Sec. and Treas.—Rev. Mr. Fettes.

COLPORTAGE SCHEME (estab. 1859).

Mr. Sibbald, President.
W. A. Sanderson, Treasurer.   Rev. Jas Selkirk, Secretary.
John Horsburgh, Colporteur.
COMMITTEE.

J. Riddell.	John Sibbald.
James Stalker.	William Carruthers.
William Cuthbertson.	Andrew Herbertson.
James Rankin.	Alexander Thomson.
Arthur Dickson.	George Anderson.
Robert Swan.	Thomas Ovens.
William Brown.	Dr. Somerville.

The Colporteur's sale of books, periodicals, etc., for the last five years are as follows :—

Sold in 1859,	£108	18	9½	Sold in 1862, £126	4	0
,, 1860,	116	14	2½	,, 1863, 130	7	5
,, 1861,	122	4	0	,, 1864, 204	6	2

The subscriptions for the year just closed amounted to £30 : 3 : 3. The books and periodicals sold are supplied at a reduced rate by the Tract Society, Edinburgh.

EDUCATIONAL INSTITUTIONS.*

Parochial School—Alexander Williamson, Master. Av. attend., 200.

Gala School (Supplementary, managed by Trustees—Major Scott of Gala, President)—James Duthie, Master. Av. attendance, 130.

Bridge Place Academy and Boarding Establishment—Thos. Fairley, Head-Master.

St. Peter's Episcopal School—Charles Lapworth, Teacher. Average attendance, 90. Supported by Government grant, by fees, and the Episcopal congregation. This is a handsome modern erection.

Lindean Side School—Robert Tait, Teacher. Average attend., 45.

Young Ladies' Academy—Misses Weir, Abbotsford Road.

Young Ladies' School and Boarding Establishment—Misses Stewart, Roxburgh Street.

Young Ladies' Academy—Misses Powell, Victoria Buildings.

Roman Catholic School, Stirling Street, Average attendance, 70.

Buckholmside (Private)—Thomas Paterson, Master.

Stirling Street (Private)—Walter Clapperton, Master.

Caddonfoot Side School—*see* Stow.

PAROCHIAL BOARD.

G. Bathgate, Chairman.
John Thorburn, Inspector and Collector.
Half-yearly Statutory Meetings held in June and December.
William Haldane, Clerk.
COMMITTEE OF MANAGEMENT.

Messrs Arthur Dickson	Messrs A. Herbertson
Thomas Roberts	Adam Paterson
Alex. Yellowlees	Adam L. Cochrane
William Sanderson	William Paterson

No. of Poor on Roll, 43. Average Assessment, 1s. per £, ; total Assessment for 1864-5, £642 : 3 : 6.

PAROCHIAL BURIAL GROUND.

Situated in a retired nook at Eastlands, tastefully laid out, and of considerable dimensions. Completed May 1865.

COMBINATION POOR HOUSE.

The Parishes forming the Combination or Union, are—Galashiels, Melrose, Selkirk, and Yarrow.
COMMITTEE.

For Galashiels—Major Scott of Gala, Geo. Bathgate, John Cochrane ; for Melrose—A. Stirling, John Pringle ; for Selkirk—George Roberts, George Rodger, W. Brown ; for Yarrow ——

---

* Children in the entire parish from 5 to 15 attending school during the first week of April 1861, 494 ; the Ladhope portion of the town, 583 ; *of all ages in both districts*, 1137.

Governor—John Fenwick.   Matron—Mrs John Fenwick.
Chaplain—Rev. Robert Blackstock.
Medical Officer—James Brisbane, M.D.
Secretary and Treasurer—James Stalker.

Average No. of Inmates for 1864-5 (third year), 23.

TOTAL ABSTINENCE SOCIETY.

President—Mr Brotherston, Bridge Street.
Vice-President—
Secretary—Thomas Messer.   Treasurer—William Carruthers.

TOTAL ABSTAINERS AND PERMISSIVE BILL SOCIETY.

President—James Bell, Channel Street.
Vice-President—James Foster, Albert Place.
Secretary—Thomas Högg, "Border Advertiser" Office.

MANUFACTURERS' CORPORATION.

Deacon elected annually, on the Friday nearest the 10th October, from among the Members.

W. A. Sanderson, Deacon.   W. Brown, Gala Hill, Ex-deacon.

SICK AND BURIAL SOCIETIES.

Conducted on the same principle as those of Kelso, Melrose, etc.—
(see pp. 86, 135.)

THE YEARLY MENAGE AND BENEFIT SOCIETY.

Held in the Salmon Inn every Tuesday night. Number of Members for the current year (1864-65), 286.
President—
Trustees—Mr. James Hay and Mr. Thomas Pringle.

TEMPERANCE YEARLY BENEFIT SOCIETY.

President—Thomas Armitage.
Treas.—A. Melrose, Market Street.   Secy.—G. Bowie, Queen Street.

SCOTTISH LEGAL BURIAL AND LOAN SOCIETY (Branch).

Secretary and Treasurer—John Dickson, Island Street.

The object of this Society is to provide a fund for defraying the funeral expenses of any of its members.

MASONIC LODGE—(St John's, No. 262).

A. Thomson, R.W.M.   James S. Armit, S.W.
James M'Alister, Secretary.

READING ROOM (Town's Arms, High Street).

Mr. Melville, Manager.
Annual Subscription, 10s.

MECHANICS' INSTITUTE AND LIBRARY (estab. 1840).

President—Dr. Somerville.   Vice-President—John Pringle, Esq.
Sec. and Treas.—James Armit.   Librarian—E. Gray.
Number of volumes, 780.   Annual Subscription, 3s.

COTTAGERS' HORTICULTURAL SOCIETY (estab. 1850).

PATRONS.

Lord Henry Scott, M.P.	Wm. Brunton, Esq. of Ladhope
Lord Henry Kerr	John Pringle, Esq.
Capt. Clark of Langhaugh	Sir Wm. Scott of Ancrum, M.P.
Hon. William Napier	Hugh Scott, Esq. of Gala
Jas. Dalrymple, Esq. of Langlee	William Sanderson, Esq. Oaklee

MEMBERS OF COUNCIL.

Adam Renwick	Andrew Sanderson	Andrew Hill
George Hamilton	Robert Irvine	William Robertson
James Brownlee	Jordan Chadwick	S. Metcalf
George Wayness	John Mitchell	James Brown

President—J. Hope Scott, Esq. of Abbotsford
Treasurer—Peter Paisley.   Secretary—William Douglas.

The object of this Society is the encouragement of horticulture and cottage economy among the amateurs and cottagers within the parishes of Galashiels and Ladhope; none but such being allowed to compete, unless by special permission of Council.
Meetings for exhibition in July and September. Amount of prizes given in 1864, £15.

FARMERS' CLUB.

Meets first Tuesday of every quarter.

President—William Patterson, Esq. of Ettrick Hall.
Secy.—Alex. Rutherford.   Treasurer—John Pringle.
Annual Subscription, 12s.

CORN EXCHANGE (erected 1860).

Secy.—W. Haldane, banker.   Treas.—Alex. Rutherford, banker.
Custodier—John Allan, Channel Street.

Amount of Stock, £1100.   Pays 3 per cent.

Rates for Concerts, etc.—1st night, £1, 1s.; each additional night, 10s. 6d.; for Dancing, when taken for the season, generally 5s. per night. Weddings are frequently held in it.

TOWN HALL.

Erected 1860 at a cost of £3000.　　Yearly Revenue, £100.

Chairman—George Bathgate.
Secretary—R. Stewart.　Treasurer—W. Haldane.

GAS COMPANY (estab. 1836).

Chairman—G. Bathgate.

DIRECTORS.

John Sibbald.	Henry Brown.
A. L. Cochrane.	James Sime.
Frank Rutherford.	John Pringle.

Secy. and Treas.—William Haldane.　Manager—Alex. Scott.
5s. 10d. per 1000 feet.

Amount of Stock, £4000.　Annual Dividend, 7½ per cent.

WATER COMPANY (estab. 1839).

Secretary—Robert Stewart.

Rate 1s. per £1 on Rental.

PROVIDENT BUILDING SOCIETY (estab. 1853).

Office, 36 Channel Street.

Chairman—Adam Hall.　　Secretary—William Sanderson.
Treasurer—William Brown.　Law Agents—Lees & Stewart.

Meets every fourth Monday at 8 p.m. for the transaction of business, i.e., collecting funds and granting advances to members. This Society has a branch at Selkirk—see p. 383.

The object of this Society is to collect a fund by voluntary subscriptions of its members, so that each member may obtain an advance according to the amount of shares, for the purpose of purchasing or building houses or other heritable property. Any person may become a member by taking one or more shares of £25 each, and paying into the general fund 1 per cent. thereon as entry-money. This Society has upwards of 220 members, 46 of whom have obtained advances.

PROVISION STORE COMPANY (estab. 1840).

Managed by a Committee of 14 Members, one-fourth of whom retire quarterly.

Amount of Stock, £12,172, 10s.　Pays, 1s. 7d. per £.

DEPOTS.

Western Branch, High Street; Bank Street Branch, 16 Bank Street; Eastern Branch, Market Street.

Sales for year ending 16th September 1864, £23,457 : 7 : 11½.

BOWLING CLUB (estab. 1859).

Patron—James Dalrymple, Esq. of Langlee.
Preses—Mr Frank Rutherford.　Vice-Preses—Mr James Sime.
Secretary and Treasurer—Mr William Riddell.

Entry-money and Subscription for the first year, £1, 6s. ; Annual Subscription, 15s.; Occasional Member's Subscription 5s.

CURLING CLUB.

Patron—Major Scott.　　Patroness—Mrs Scott.
President—Mr A. Scott.　Vice-President—Mr A. Stirling.
Representative Members—Messrs J. Hood, W. Hirst, A. Rutherford.
Treasurer—Mr. William Haldane.

The Pond is situated within the Gala policy, about ¾ of a mile from Galashiels.

CRICKET CLUB.

Patron—Hugh Scott of Gala.

Secretary and Treasurer—John Lees.

Annual Subscription, 21s.

1st SELKIRKSHIRE RIFLE CORPS—(GALASHIELS).

Captain—Wm. Clark, of Langhaugh.　Lieutenant—A. L. Cochrane,
Ensign—Wm. Sime.　Hon. Surgeon—Dr. Tweedie.
Secretary—John Pringle.　Effective Force—100
Drill Instructor—James Dobson.　Bandmaster—Frank Auty.

Hon. Member's Subscription, £1, 1s.

BANKS.

BANK OF SCOTLAND (Established 1857)—William & Alexander Rutherford, Agents.

NATIONAL BANK OF SCOTLAND (Established 1825)—William Haldane, Agent;　　, Accountant.

ROYAL BANK OF SCOTLAND (Established 1857).　William Paterson & Robert Stewart, Agents; John Brown, Accountant.

NATIONAL SECURITY SAVINGS' BANK (Established 1857)—John Brown, Actuary.　Amount of Deposits up to Nov. 1864, £7210 : 7 : 1.

INSURANCE AGENTS.

BRITISH GUARANTEE.............Robert Stewart, banker.
CALEDONIAN...................William Rutherford, banker.
CITY OF GLASGOW.............. Adam Thomson, merchant.

INSURANCE CO. OF SCOTLAND......Robert Stewart, banker.
LIFE ASSOCIATION...............
LONDON INDUSTRIAL & GENERAL { R. F. Fisher, at Messrs Sanderson & Murray's.
LONDON AND LANCASHIRE FIRE...Thomas Fairgrieve.
LONDON AND LIVERPOOL..........Alex. Yellowlees.
NATIONAL (OF SCOTLAND)....... { J. Pringle, writer. George Dun.
NORTH BRITISH AND MERCANTILE.James Stalker, writer.
NORTHERN.....................W. Carruthers, merchant.
PEOPLE'S PROVIDENT (LONDON).. { R. F. Fisher, at Messrs Sanderson & Murray's.
ROYAL INSURANCE COMPANY......George Anderson.
SCOTTISH EQUITABLE............John Grant, bookseller.
SCOTTISH PROVIDENT............John Pringle, writer.
SCOTTISH UNION................W. & R. Haldane, writers.
STANDARD ....Robert Stewart, banker.
UNITED KINGDOM PROVIDENT....Thomas Fairgrieve.

EMIGRATION AGENTS.

A. Yellowlees, grocer, Bank Street ; T. Fairgrieve, grocer, Bank St.

PROCURATORS, NOTARIES PUBLIC, &c.

Haldane Richard, (of W. & R. H.), 24 Bank Street.
Haldane, William, N.P. (of W. & R. H.), 24 Bank Street.
Pringle, Jn. N.P., and Procurator-Fiscal for Burgh, 12 Bridge Street.
Rutherford, Alexander, Channel Street.
Rutherford, William, N.P., Channel Street.
Stalker, James, N.P., Elm Row.
Stewart, Robert, (of Lees and S.), Bridge Place.

MEDICAL PRACTITIONERS.

Robert Sommerville, M.D. 9 Church Street ; A. C. Tweedie, 43 High Street ; James Brisbane, M.D., Sime Place.

NEWSPAPER.

The "Border Advertiser" (established 1848), published every Friday morning. Principles, liberal. Office, High Street. James Brown, Abbotsford Road, Proprietor.

WOOLLEN MILLS.

All engaged in the manufacture of Tweeds, shawls, or Tartans—mostly of the class known as Saxony.

(G) (L)—*see* note under Directory.

ABBOTS MILL, Lower Huddersfield (G)—John Sibbald & Co.
BOTANY MILL, Roxburgh Street (G)—James Sime & Son.
BUCKHOLM MILL, Buckholm (L)—Brown Brothers.

COMELY BANK MILL, Low Buckholmside (L)—Bogue & Co.
GALA MILL, Lower Huddersfield (G)—R. & A. Sanderson & Co.
GALABANK MILL, Wilderhaugh (G)—George Lees & Co.
HUDDERSFIELD MILL, Huddersfield Street—G. Paterson & Co.
LADHOPE MILL, Buckholmside (L)—Laidlaw & Fairgrieve.
MID MILL and NETHERDALE, Paton Street and Damfoot (G)—J. & W. Cochrane.
NETHERHAUGH MILL, Huddersfield Street (G)—James Bathgate & Son.
ROSEBANK MILL, Roxburgh Street (G)—John Paterson, 72 High St., Hawick.
TWEED MILL, Peebles Road (L)—P. & R. Sanderson.
VICTORIA MILL, Market Street (G)—W Roberts & Co.
WAULK MILL HEAD, Bank Street (G)—Arthur Dickson, & Co.
WILDERBANK MILLS, Wilderhaugh Street (G)—Brown & Shaw.

Medical Inspector of Mills—A. C. Tweedie, 43 High Street.

GALASHIELS CORN MILL—*John Smail.

DYER.

James Brownlee, Island Street.

SKINNERIES.

Sanderson & Murray, Roxburgh Street.
William Wood, Market Place.

TANNERY.

William Paterson, Channel Street.

ENGINEERING ESTABLISHMENT.

Thomas Aimers, Huddersfield Street.

BREWERY.

William Haldane, Low Buckholmside.

DAIRIES.

Peter Wright, Sime Place ; —— Lillie, 29 Bank Street ; A. Hobkirk, 1 Overhaugh Street ; R. Melrose, High Street ; James Lees, Island Street ; Walter Kerr,

AUCTIONEERS.

A. Oliver, Buckholmside.   A. Sutherland (of Melrose), High Street.

Fat Stock Sales, conducted by Andrew Oliver & Son, Hawick, fortnightly—*see* p. 430.

CARRIERS.

Earlston—Robert Porteous (Mrs Murray's), Thursday.

Edinburgh, Glasgow, Kelso, Berwick, and all parts North and South, by Railway, daily.

Hawick and Melrose—Railway Station, daily, and James Chisholm (Harrow Inn).

Innerleithen, by Coach—Andw. Oliver, High Buckholmside, Monday, Wednesday, and Saturday.

Lauder—Andrew Gill (Learmonth's), Monday.

Peebles—   (Harrow Inn), Thursday.

Selkirk—Railway Station, daily, and James Chisholm (Harrow Inn), Monday and Thursday.

St Boswell's and Kelso—Robert Clerk (Mrs. Murray's), Tuesday.

CONVEYANCE.

By North British Railway to Edinburgh and all places North and West, and Hawick, Jedburgh, Kelso, and the South. To Selkirk by branch line of N. B. R., in connection with all the trains from and to Edinburgh. *See* Monthly Time Tables.

DIRECTORY.

TRADES, RESIDENTS, AND PUBLIC OFFICES.

Those marked thus (*) are Registered Voters for county of Selkirk.
(For the Voters registered for Roxburghshire, living in the town of Galashiels, *see* pp. 153 and 154, Melrose parish.

The letter (G) after the street titles designates Galashiels parish, (L) that of Ladhope in Melrose district.

Abbotsford Road (G.)

*Anderson, George
*Bathgate, George, manufacturer
*Brown, James (of *Border Advertiser*)
*Cochrane, Adam Lees (of J. & W. C.)
*Cochrane, Archibald   do.
*Cochrane, John, sen.   do.
*Cochrane, Adam, jun.   do.
Cochrane, Kenneth,   do.
Cochrane, Mrs., Walter
Combat, Mrs. Alexander
Hay, Miss Agnes
*Herbertson, William,
*Lees, George, Esq., Oatlands
Lees, Mrs. Hugh
Lapworth, Charles, teacher
*Paterson, William, manufacturer
*Roberts, Henry,   do.
*Sanderson, Robert, Wakefield Bank
*Sanderson, W. A.,   do.
Sanderson, Walter
Selkirk, Rev. James (*Free Church Manse*)
*Sibbald, J. E.
*Sibbald, J. R.
*Sibbald, John (of J. S. & Co.)
St. Peter's Episcopal Church (*see* p. 433)
*Weir, Robert
Weir, Miss

Albert Place (G.)

Herbertson, A. & Sons, builders
Millar, M., dressmaker
*Tait, George, manufacturer
*Thorburn, John, *inspector of poor*
Stirling, John, grocer (*see* Stirling Place)
*Shillinglaw, Richard, joiner

Bank Street (G.)

13 Bell, John, shoemaker
22 Cleghorn, Thomas, butcher
43 Combat, Mrs. Alexander, draper
     Manager—Thomas Messer
     Millinery Department—Miss E. Cranston
20 Craighead, David, printer
 8 Creelman, John, stationer and *postmaster*
26 Cunningham, John, shoemaker
10 Fairgrieve, Thomas, grocer and provision merchant
41-42 Gray, George, spirit dealer
 3 Haldane, Misses
24 Haldane, W. & R., writing chambers
24*Haldane, William (of W. & R. H.)
25*Haldane, Richard (of W. & R. H.)
32 Heard, Robert, baker
 5 Laidlaw, William clothier
17*Melville, George, plumber
33 Mirtle, J., shoe merchant
24 *National Bank of Scotland*, Wm Haldane, resident agent
 8 Post Office, John Creelman
16 *Provision Store Company*, Thomas Dickson, salesman
  *Riddell, James, china merchant
 2 Roberts, Mrs. John
30 Robinson, James, tailor
38-39 *Salmon Inn*, George Fair
29 Scott, John, tinsmith
18 Scott, Andrew, general dealer
19 Sligh, William, baker
  United Kingdom Telegraph Office, John Creelman
  Waulk Mill Head Woollen Mill, Arthur Dickson & Co.
  Weir, Mrs. George
35*Yellowlees, Alexander, general merchant

Bridge Place (L.)

15 Carruthers, William, grocer
  Craig, Andrew, teacher
  Fairley, Thomas, *Academy*
  Fisher, R. F., manager to Sanderson & Murray
 3 Forsyth, John, flesher
11 Johnston, James, tailor
 1 Lees & Stewart's writing chambers
 4 Mackay, John, drysalter
 7 Roxburgh, Janet, grocer
  Stewart, Walter, Tweed merchant
 2 Traquair, J., fancy repository
 6 Wright, James, wine and spirit merchant

Bridge Street (L.)

  Brotherston, David, corn merchant
  Carruthers, Mrs. George
  Clapperton, George (of T. & G. C.)
  Clapperton, T.   do.
  Clapperton, George, manufacturer
25 *Commercial Hotel*, Samuel Maxwell
  Dunn, W. H., wool merchant
10 *Galashiels Museum*, James Kemp, custodier
23 Gillies, James, grocer
  Gillies, William (of G. & Williams)
  Gillies, William, agent
14 Hislop, Andrew, hosiery manufacturer
 9 Hood, John, plasterer
12 Pringle, John, solicitor
11 Sanderson, Mrs. Henry
  *Sanderson, Peter, wright
 1 Smith, David, shoe merchant

Buckholmside (High—L.)

  Arthur, Mrs, grocer
  Bain, James, innkeeper
  Buckholm Mill, Brown Brothers
  Darling, Mrs. Adam
  *Darling, Adam
  Galbraith, John
  Hood, John, jun., plasterer
  Jamieson, James, grocer
  Ladhope Mill, Laidlaw & Fairgrieve
  Macdougall, William, joiner
  Mark, George, carter
  Oliver, Andrew, carrier and auctioneer
  Paterson, Miss
  Robson, Mrs. George
  Thomson, Miss, grocer

Buckholmside (Low—L.)

  Comely Bank Mill, Bogue & Co.
  Fairgrieve, Thomas, manufacturer
  Galashiels Brewery, William Haldane
  Foreman Maltster—
  Lees, Miss
  Mercer, James (of Paterson & Co.)
  Mitchell, James & Co., Tweed merchants
  Paterson, Adam, & Co., wood and manure merchants
  Sanderson, Thomas mason
  *Tait, George
  Watson, Andrew, & Co., drysalters

Channel Street (G.)

Allan, John, letter-carrier
Bank of Scotland, *Alexander Rutherford
1 Crosbie, John grocer
24 Dixon, Thomas, commission agent
13 Lindsay, William, slater
43 Mabon, Janet, milliner
Rutherford, William, writing chambers
Scott, John, cooper
Wilkinson & Dunlop, smiths

Channel Street (G.)

3 Bell, James, painter
*Blaikie, Andrew, tobacconist
Gillies & Williams, waste merchants
60 Hall, Adam, grocer
Horne, Thomas, fishmonger
53*Mack, Thomas, clothier
4 Mitchell, William, blacksmith
16*Paterson, William, tanner
56*Sanderson, William, stationer

Church Street (G.)

Anderson, George, coal agent
Cunningham, John, shoemaker
M'Dougall, Mrs. Dr.
Parochial Church (Rev. K. M. Phin's, *see* p. 432)
Parochial School (School Close), Alexander Williamson, resident master
*Paterson, Robert, wool agent
*Phin, Rev. K. M., *Manse*
Rutherford, William, N.P.
*Rutherford, Frank, writer
Sommerville, Dr.
*Wear, William, jun., dyer

Elm Row (G.)

Bruce, John, blacksmith
*Cochrane, William, joiner
Elliot, Mrs. Walter
*Herbertson, Adam
Herbertson, Adam, jun.
*Herbertson, Andrew (of A. H. & Son)
Herbertson, Andrew, jun.
14 Johnston, John, grocer
Kerr, James, clerk

*Lees, Alexander, wool sorter
*Paterson, Adam, manufacturer
*Rankine, William
Roberts, Thomas, mill-overseer
Stalker, James, N.P., factor for Major Scott
*Young, William, baker

Green Street (G.)

Stirling, R. & A., builders
*Stirling, Adam (of A. & R. S.)
*Stirling, Robert,   do.
Wilson, George, meal dealer

High Buckholmside—see *Buckholmside*, p. 444.

High Street (G.)

19 Bell, James, tailor and clothier
6 *Border Advertiser Office*, James Brown, publisher
   Printing foreman—Thomas Hogg
   Brown, James, bookseller and stationer (house, Abbotsford Road
17*Brown, Andrew, flesher
1 Dickson, Mrs., confectioner
   Douglas, Thomas, grocer
2 Hall, Mrs., shoemaker
7 Hogg, George, baker and grocer
9 Kemp, Mrs. James, ironmonger
4 M'Donald, James, china merchant
21*Milne, William, ironmonger
25 Murray & Hepburn, smiths
5 Spavin, John, fishmonger
   Thomson, John, grocer

High Street (L.)

56 Alexander, Robert, coal agent
81 Brown, Robert H., hair dresser and fancy merchant
74 Clark, Charles, china merchant
71 Cowan, Adam, saddler
   Dixon, Robert, draper
77 Dodgson, R., hatter
48 Dorward, Mrs.
33 Douglas, George, tailor
72 Easton, James, shoemaker
95 Fairbairn, George, butcher
   Frier, Mrs., grocer
47 Gowans, James, watchmaker
57 Grant, John, bookseller, stationer, and bookbinder

51 Gray, Edward, house painter
22 *Harrow Inn*, James Walker
80 Hood, Mrs. E., grocer
93 Hutchinson, Miss, confectioner
59 Kerr, David, flesher
31*Laidlaw, Thomas, wine and spirit merchant
46 Mackay, John, chemist
   Melrose, Robert, cow-feeder and dairyman
34 Mirtle, Peter, shoemaker
14 Muir, James, draper
88 *National Securities Savings' Bank*, John Brown, actuary
50 Nisbet, James, plumber and gas-fitter
39 Paisley, George, corn merchant
67*Paisley, Peter, baker
87 *Provision Store Company*, Robert, Scott, salesman
52 Quin, Edward, china merchant
   Reading Room, J. Grant, proprietor
   Branch of Edmonston & Douglas's Book Club (Edinburgh)
82 Richardson, James, shuttlemaker
88 *Royal Bank*, William Paterson and Robert Stewart, agents
   Resident accountant—John Brown
   Sanderson, David, wright
24 Sanderson, James, cap maker
   Sanderson, Miss, straw hat maker
45 Somers, Mrs., grocer
103 Tait, Andrew, baker
26 Tait, Alexander, shoemaker
41 Tait, Misses, grocers
23 *Town Arms Inn*, George Melville
   Town Hall, William Spence, custodier
36 Turner, James, shoemaker
41 Tweedie, Dr.
64 Tweedie, John, plumber, gas-fitter, and tinsmith
   U. P. Church (East)— *see* p. 432
   U. P. Church (West—Rev. Robert Blair's), *see* p. 432
   Victoria Buildings—
      12 Cochrane, John, jun., draper
         Macintosh, James, druggist
         Powell, Miss, academy
         Scott, Walter, druggist
85 Walker, Alexander, stationer and bookseller
76 Walker, William, draper, tailor, and clothier
84 Watson, Henry, & Co., drapers and milliners
   Manager—James S. Armit
44 Watt, Gavin, house painter
58 Wood, James, draper and milliner
   Manager—James Scott

Huddersfield Street   (G.)

Abbots Mill, John Sibbald & Co.
*Aimers, Thomas, millwright, founder, etc.
*Dickson, Arthur, (of D. & Co.)
Gala Mill, R. & A. Sanderson & Co.
Huddersfield Mill, George Paterson & Co.
*Mather, Jesse
Roberts, James, manufacturer
Scott, James
*Sibbald, David

Hall Street   (G.)

Sanderson, James, manufacturer

Island Street   (L.)

Aitken, Miss, milliner
8 Aitken, Robert, watchmaker
*Brown, William (of B. & Shaw), manufacturer
Brownlee, James, dyer
1 Dun, John, seed merchant, etc.
14 Forsyth, David, tailor and clothier
Freee Church (L —Rev. James Fettes's), *see* p. 432
Hall, Robert, & Son, builders
Hall, Thomas S. (of Hall & Son)
Halley, Mrs.
28 Hunter, William, grocer
M'Allister, James (clerk to Hall & Co.)
Murray, Miss
27 Nisbet, James (*see* 50 High Street)
42 Rankine, James, cabinet-maker and upholsterer
13 Scott, George, baker
20 Thomson, Mrs., grocer
37 Wilson, William, grocer

Johnston's Close   (L.)

Johnston, Mrs., and Miss Kemp, milliners

King Street   (L.)

Brown, George, spirit merchant
Cleghorn, Mrs., grocer

Ladhope Bank.

Paterson, Thos., teacher and *Registrar for Ladhope district*

Ladhope Vale

Aikman, Stuart, and M'Innes, tweed merchants
Brown & Co., tweed merchants

Free Church (G.)—Rev. James Selkirk's, *see* p. 432
Hall & Murray, builders
Metcalfe, Stephen, game dealer
Scott, Walter, druggist
Parochial Church (L.)—Rev. R. Blackstock's, *see* p. 432
Victoria Mill, William Roberts & Co.
Wilson, Alexander, slater

Low Buckholmside—see *Buckholmside*, p. 444.

Market Street (G.)

38 Auty, Frank, tobacconist
   Broad, William, baker
   Brown, William clothier
   Bruce, John, blacksmith
   Gray, William, grocer, tea, wine, and spirit merchant
*Learmonth, Robert, corn merchant
15 Melrose, Adam, hardware merchant
   Provision Store Company, Alexander Inglis, manager
1 Smail, Robert, baker
   Temperance Hotel, Mrs. Hymers
* Wood, William, tanner

Market Street (L.)

Ireland, Michael, saddler
Ovens, Thomas, guano, cake, and seed merchant (house, Lynwood)
Railway Hotel, Mrs. Murray
Victoria Hotel, Walter Scott

Overhaugh Street (G.)

43 Anderson, John, grocer
  *Brown, Henry, baker and confectioner
  Corn Exchange, John Allan, letter-carrier, custodier
  *Crichton, John, weaver
6 Gilligan, Patrick, shoemaker
33*Gladstone, Archibald, wright
10 Henry, Edward, broker
  *Johnston, James
44 Lockhart, John, shoemaker
53*Mitchell, William, smith
47 Moffat, J., grocer
  *Pringle, Thomas
32 Robertson, William, grocer
  Scott, George, grocer
  Scott, Robert, manufacturer

Smith, William, innkeeper
5 Smith, Catherine, grocer
54*Taket, Geo., *Registrar for parish of Galashiels*
54 Taket, Mrs., grocer

Paton Street (G.)

Anderson, James, grocer
*Bathgate, James, manufacturer
Cochrane, Archibald commission agent
Gas Works, Alexander Scott, resident manager
Gill, Miss
Mid Woollen Mill, J. & W. Cochrane
Robertson, W. & J., fleshers
Thorburn, Thomas, wright
Tweed Mill, P. & R. Sanderson

Peebles Road (L.)

Dickson, Arthur, Wheatland
Lees Robert (of Fens, St. Boswell's), of Leebrae
*Sanderson, Peter (of P. & R. S.)

Roxburgh Street (G.)

Armstrong, Misses
Botany Mill, James Sime & Son
Duthie, James, teacher
*Monteith, Robert, weaver
Rosebank Woollen Mill, John Paterson (Hawick)
Sanderson & Murray, wool merchants
   Alexander Michie, manager of skin works
Sanderson, Miss Jane
*Sime, William (of J. S. & Son)
Stewart, Misses, teachers, Rosebank

Roxburgh Street (L.)

Douglas, John, wright
Glassite Chapel, see p. 433
Grieve, Adam
Ormston, Thomas, shoemaker
Ronald, John, glazier

School Close (G.)

Parochial School (*see* Church Street)
*Williamson, Alexander, schoolmaster

Sime Place (L.)

Bogue, George (of B. & Co., of Comely Bank Mill)

Brisbane, James, M.D.
*Roberts, Hugh, manufacturer
*Sime, James (of J. S. & Co.)
Thomson, Adam, grocer
Wright, Peter, cowfeeder and dairyman

Stirling Place (L.)

Stirling, John, grocer and family wine and spirit merchant

Stirling Street (L.)

Abbotsford Hotel, John Toward
Baptist Chapel, (Mr. A. Thomson's), *see p.* 433
Brady, Miss, teacher
Burns, George, millwright
Clapperton, Walter, grocer
Gibb, William, slater
Paterson, Mrs. Euphemia
Pringle, George, shoemaker
Roman Catholic Church (Rev. Father Langton's), *see* p. 433
Saddler, Thomas, stocking maker
Scott, J., grocer
Tait, James, baker
Whitley, Rev. Robert, of *Roman Catholic Chapel*

Union Street (G.)

Congregational Chapel (Rev. A. Brown's), *see p.* 433
Gala Supplementary School. James Duthie, master
*Lockhart, John
*Lockhart, William
*Renwick, Andrew, weaver
*Shaw, James (of Brown & S.)
Shiell, David, coal agent

Wilderhaugh (G.)

Gala Bank Mill, George Lees & Co.
Hall, John, Wilderburn
Wilderbank Mills, Brown & Shaw

Wilderhaugh (L.)

Anderson, George, commission agent
Stewart, Robert (of Lees & S., writers)

Windyknowe (L.)

*Blackstock, Rev. Robert, *Ladhope Manse*
Blair. Rev. Robert, *East U. P. Manse*
Darling, Miss

Paterson, Mrs. Adam
*Sanderson, Robert, Knowpark

Miscellaneous

*Cooper, Andrew, labourer, Damside
*Young, Adam (address unknown)

Railway Station Road

Morrison, J. & R., Tweed merchants

Railway Station (L.)

Robert White, station-master, manager of goods depart-
ment, and N. B. Railway coal agent
OFFICES.
Robert Alexander, coal agent
Francis Dalgleish, coal merchant
David Grant, coal agent
James Scott,   do.
David Shiell,   do.
Thomas Taylor, do.

RESIDENTS, &c., IN THE VICINITY.

*Anderson, George, cow feeder, Old Town
Brodie, Alexander (late millwright)
Brown, Adam, of Helmburn
Brown, Henry, Buckholmburn
*Brown, William, of Galahill (of Brown Brothers)
Brunton, William, of Ladhope (*see* p. 151)
*Brydone, Adam, farmer, Netherbarns
*Clark, Captain, of Langhaugh (*see* p. 152)
*Elliot, Walter, farmer, Hollybush
Fettes, Rev. James (of *Ladhope F.C.*), Edinburgh Road
Geddes, Robert, fisherman, Boldside
*Haldane, Robert, farmer, Fairnilee
Hall, Robert, farmer, Kilnknowe
Leithead, James, farmer, Langheugh
Morrison, J. & R , Tweed merchants, Cascade
*Murray, John (of Sanderson & M.), of Ashwood
Ovens, Thomas, of Lynwood (office, Market Street)
*Riddell, George, farmer, Rink
*Roberts, William, manufacturer. Springwood Bank
*Sanderson, James, sen., farmer, Meigle
*Sanderson, James, jun.,   do.,   (and of Manchester
Buildings, London)
*Scott, William, farmer, Mossilee
Sanderson, William (of S. & Murray), of Oaklea
Stirling, Adam, of Laurel Bank
*Thorburn, Thomas, wright, Wighton

SEAT OF COUNTY FAMILY (ROXBURGHSHIRE).

GALA HOUSE.

The seat of *Hugh Scott, Esq. ; born 1822 ; succeeded 1840 his father, the late John Scott, Esq. ; married, 1857, Elizabeth-Isabella, daughter of Capt. Johnstone Gordon of Craig, and has issue—John-Henry-Francis-Kinnaird, born 1859.

Mr. Scott, who is a Justice of Peace and Deputy-Lieutenant for the county of Selkirk, was formerly Captain in the 92d Highlanders, Major in the Dumfries, Roxburgh, and Selkirk Militia, and also formerly Captain 1st Selkirk R.V.

Mrs. Scott now represents the family of Gordon of Craig and Kincardine, as successor to her mother, the late Elizabeth Johnstone Gordon, who died at Nice, 20th January 1863.

The following particulars were received too late for insertion at p. 434 :—

PAROCHIAL BURIAL GROUND (East Land).

Provided in 1865 under the Burial Ground (Scotland) Act 1855, at a cost of over £1600. Under the Act half of the ground is free. Layers in the saleable half are disposed of at £2, £1, and 10s. each.

COMMITTEE.

Mr. George Bathgate, Chairman.

Rev. K. M. Phin, Messrs. John Cochrane, Thomas Roberts, William Sanderson ; with the addition of the following members of the Board :—Hugh Scott, Esq., of Gala, or in his absence, Mr. Stalker ; Messrs. George Lees, Alexander Yellowlees, and William Sanderson, stationer.

W. Haldane, writer, Clerk. A. Herbertson, builder, Superintendent. Alexander Thorburn, Sexton.

NOTE.—In our foot-note pp. 422, 423, the statement that most of the weavers in Dr. Douglas's time were bonnet lairds requires qualification. None of the Galashiels weavers who wrought at blankets and *Galashiels Gray* (a coarse woollen cloth) were ; but nearly all the weavers of the time resident in Darnick, Gattonside, and Kelso—all of whom wrought at linen—were lairds. Our present statement may also require qualification, as we give it from hearsay, and the facts have already become almost traditional ; but if it is correct it would imply that the linen weavers had been the better paid and wealthier class of tradesmen ; while the fact that the latter have either sunk into poverty or died out, and the former have risen to be the most important trading community in the locality, suggests interesting speculations on the ups and downs of the world and the causes which lead to them.

In Kelso the Corporation of Weavers was the oldest of the incorporated trades ; it was the strongest, and, we understand, the most wealthy. At this date (June 1865) there is only one weaver in Kelso earning a living by his trade.

The last of the Darnick weavers were William and Thomas Boston (brothers), who, finding their trade fluctuating and gradually falling off, determined, about the year 1820—work at the time having become more than ordinarily scarce—to visit a married sister settled near London, in Upper Canada. Taking Sheffield on their way to the place of embarkation, they purchased a large stock of needles ; after landing at New York they *walked* on to Canada and peddled the needles along the route. They thus saw the country, and, what is more to the purpose, the needle sales cleared more than their voyage and journey expenses. Arrived at their sister's, they took to the weaving as temporary employment, when, by their producing checked ginghams with which to clothe their sister's children, they created quite a demand for their productions. This induced them to purchase land and settle ; William returning the following year to Darnick, to sell the family property and take away his mother and a widowed sister. The Bostons are a very old family in the locality. One of their little lairdships in Gattonside (now sold out of the family) was held by charter from the monks of Melrose.

LINDEAN COTTAGES,

Situated in the Roxburghshire part of the parish about 4 miles from Galashiels by the turnpike, and near to the Lindean railway station.

---◆---

Post Office—Selkirk. William Scott, Messenger, arrives daily about 10.30 a.m.

Lindean School—Robert Tait, Master. *See* p. 434.

Lindean Mill—†William Smith, corn merchant and farmer.

Station-Master—John M‘Donald.

 Gray, Andrew, joiner
 Scott, James, blacksmith

RESIDENTS IN THE DISTRICT OF LINDEAN.

Being that part of the parish of Galashiels which is in Roxburghshire.

Those marked thus (*) are Registered Voters for Roxburghshire.

*Porteous, Thomas, farmer, Nether Whitlaw
*Tait, Joseph, farmer, Lindean
*Turner, Thomas, farmer, Over Whitlaw

VOTER IN LINDEAN (Non-Resident)

Charles S. Plummer, Esq. of Sunderland Hall (*see* p. 396)

SEATS IN LINDEAN †

OLD FALDONSIDE.

Very pleasantly situated near Cauldshiels Loch, and about half a mile east from the Melrose and Selkirk road—the property and residence of *Nicol Milne, Esq., of Faldonside.

NEW FALDONSIDE.

On the Tweed, opposite Boldside Ferry—the property of Nicol Milne, Esq.; at present unoccupied.

VOTERS FOR SELKIRKSHIRE (Non-Resident).

Aubrey, Rev. G. H. W., late incumbent of Galashiels Episc. Ch.
Ballantyne, Henry, manufacturer, Tweedvale Mills, Walkerburn, Innerleithen
Ballantyne, George,   do.   do.
Barstow, Charles Murray, Kippilaw, Bowden
Blaikie, James, Glasgow
Brown, John, America
Cunningham, Charles A., farmer, Grahamslaw
Crichton, David, banker, Thornhill, Dumfriesshire
Ewan, Rev. John, Hopkirk
Gill, Robert, manufacturer, Innerleithen
Goodfellow, John, grocer, Hawick
Grant, Alexander W. T., Bonjedward House
Harper, Robert, farmer, Catpair
Hobkirk, William, farmer, Craiglockhart, Edinburgh
Hobkirk, John, corn merchant, Chapel Street, Edinburgh
Hope, Hugh, 3 Princes Street, London
Hope, Thomas, Captain R.N,
Leitch, John Turner, late The Bow, Edinburgh
Murray, Robert, dyker, Sunnyside, Herriot
Millar, William, writer, Jedburgh
Meiklam, John, of Gladswood, Melrose
Patterson, John, Hawick (of Rosebank Woollen Mills)
Purdie, Adam, Ettrick Bank
Purdie, John, Pavilion
Purves, John, Kittyfield, Melrose
Purves, William, farmer, Burnfoot, Morebattle
Rutherfurd, W. A. O., yr., of Edgerston, Jedburgh
Scott, Archibald, Captain Mid-Lothian Militia
Scott, Francis Stevenson, Woolwich
Scott, Walter,   do.
Stevenson, Thomas, Langholm
Turnbull, William, accountant, Royal Bank, Edinburgh
Wear, William, sen., Cambusbarron, Stirling
Young, William, baker, Hawick

† Post town, Melrose.

PORTIONS OF PARISHES IN SELKIRKSHIRE.

STOW.

—◦—

OF this parish rather more than a fourth is in this county, the remainder being in Edinburghshire. The portion in Selkirkshire situated at the northern extremity of the county, measures, according to the Ordnance Survey, nearly 10,018 acres; of this 48½ acres are under water 47 acres consist of public and private roads and 12¼ acres are occupied by the N. B. Railway. Its extreme length south-east and north-west is close upon 7 miles; its average breadth in its north-west and hilliest district is nearly 2 miles; at the south-east where it borders on Galashiels parish, it expands to a breadth of 3½ miles. The surface is hilly * and pastoral; "and consists almost solely of the vale and hill streams of the Caddon water"—a stream in which there is unrestricted angling, and in which fairish sport may be had after a flood.† The only village in the parish is the straggling one of Stow, situated in Edinburghshire, and at which is a station of the North British Railway; in the Selkirkshire portion there is the small hamlet of CLOVENFORDS, situated near its southern border on the Caddon burn about 1 mile from where it joins the Tweed and 3 miles by the road, west from Galashiels. It is a good centre for anglers, both for the Caddon itself, and for the Tweed, whose trouting streams in the vicinity are amongst its best (*see* p. 403). CADDONFOOT is a locality which may be considered as belonging, geographically, to Clovenfords; it lies straggling a mile up and down the Tweed, from the mouth of the Caddon, and includes the church,

---

* The following are the principal hills :—

	Feet			Feet
Deaf Heights	1844	Maiden Law	..	1648
Scroof Hill	1623	Great Law	..	1666
Fernieherst	1644	Knowes Hill	..	1222
Red-Car Law	1837	Crosslee	..	1157

† "Caddon water is worth the angler's attention, especially in exceptional states of water, when the Tweed is unfishable. After rain, smaller waters are often falling into the best condition for angling just when the main river is rising to its height, and a minnow or worm may be deadly in the Caddon when the Tweed is roaring from bank to brae, and the sickened and terrified trouts are thinking only of their safety as they keep to the edge of the yellow flood that is covering haugh and holm."—*Border Angler.*

manse, and school-house in Galashiels, and the farm of Caddon-lee and its cottages in Stow.

At the census of 1861 the population of the Selkirkshire portion of Stow parish was 363. The returns do not give its housing accommodation apart from that of the entire parish, which we give in a foot-note.*

Assessed property in 1864-5, £4337 : 2 : 2.

The principal proprietors of this portion of the parish are—James T. Pringle, Esq., of Torwoodlee; Alexander Pringle, Esq., of Whytbank; Alexander Mitchell, Esq., of Stow, Carolside; and Sir John Pringle, Bart., of Newhall.

STOW OFFICIALS, &c.—

Justice of the Peace, resident in the Selkirkshire portion—James T. Pringle, Esq., of Torwoodlee; do., in the Edinburghshire portion—John Borthwick, Esq., of Crookstone.

Established Church (Stow): Patron—The Crown. Rev. David Waddell.

Fast Days—Wednesdays before the second Sabbaths of July and December.

Registrar of Births, Marriages, and Deaths, and Inspector of Poor—Mr. John F. Walker.

Parochial Board—Henry Inglis, Esq., of Torsonce, Chairman. Average Rate of Assessment, 3½d. per £.

Statute Labour Roads—Stow parish—Jas. Walker, Stow, Clerk. Thomas Mitchell, Melrose, Surveyor. Meets at Stow 5th April.

Hamlet of Clovenfords and locality of Caddonfoot

Post Town for the district—Galashiels. Thomas Currie, messenger. Leaves Galashiels daily for Clovenfords and Thornielee at 9.20 a.m., and returns at 2.4 p.m. There is no local postmaster.

Caddon Mill—*Robert Pace, miller.

Caddonfoot Church† (*Quoad Sacra*—Endowed)—Rev. Robert Small. Sittings, 260. Sabbath School attendance, 35. Precentor—Thomas M'Donald, Church Officer—John Turnbull; Kirk Treasurer —Rev. R. Small.

---

* Total population, 2171, constituting 414 families; 4 of whom were returned as living in houses having no window, 99 in houses of one window, 12 in houses of two windows; leaving 179—the full proportion of one third—living in houses of three or more windows.

† The ecclesiastical district of Caddonfoot church consists of the outlying portions of Galashiels (in Selkirkshire, in which the church is situated, on the Tweed, about half a mile down from the Caddon mouth); Selkirk (in Selkirkshire), lying on the opposite side of the Tweed; Yarrow, also on the opposite side of the Tweed and within 1½ miles; Stow, same side of the Tweed but above the Caddon burn; Innerleithen, same side of the Tweed, beyond Stow and within 2 miles.

Fast Days—*see* Galashiels, p. 433.

Caddonfoot Side School—James Dodds, Teacher. Aver. attend., 60.

Caddonfoot Literary Association (Instituted 1860)—Alex. Pringle, Esq., of Whytbank, President; Rev. R. Small, Vice-President; James Dodds, Treasurer; A. Donaldson, Secretary.

Caddonfoot Subscription Library (Instituted 1865)—Open every Sunday at 11-30 a.m., and on Wednesdays from 12 noon to 1 p.m. 250 volumes; James Dodds, Librarian.

Caddonfoot Pence Savings Bank—A. Pringle, Esq., President; Rev. R. Small, Treasurer; Mr James Dodds, Secretary. Open every Monday.

Darney, James, joiner, Clovenfords
Donaldson, Gavin, blacksmith, do.
Parkend, Mary, innkeeper   do.

FARMERS, RESIDENTS, &c.

Those marked thus (†) are resident in that part of the parish which belongs to Selkirkshire; those marked thus (§) in that part of it which belongs to Peeblesshire, in the case of Innerleithen and Peebles, and Edinburghshire in the case of Stow; those marked thus (‡) do not reside in the locality; and those marked thus (*), whether resident or non-resident, are Registered Electors for Selkirkshire.

Anderson,   , gardener, Torwoodlee†
*Borthwick,[1] John, Esq. of Crookstone §
*Clapperton, James, farmer, Caddonlee†
*Dun, George W., farmer, Laidlawstee†
*Dun, John,   do.   do.   †
*Elliot, Robert, gardener, Bowland
*Elliot, Andrew Taylor, farmer, Newhall†
*Elliot, Thomas,   do.   Blackhaugh†
*Gibson, Robert,   do.   Windydoors†
*Gibson, Thomas,   do.   Fernieherst §
*Hall, Thomas,   do.   Crosslee†
*Hope, James Park,   do.   Caddonhead§
*Hope, Thomas Park,   do.   do.
*Pringle,[2] Sir John of Newhall, Baronet‡

---

[1] John Borthwick, Esq., of Borthwick and Crookstone, Midlothian, eldest son of the late John Borthwick, Esq., of Borthwick; born 1825; succeeded 1846; married 1854, Elizabeth Mason, eldest daughter of the late Vice-Admiral Pringle, of Torwoodlee. Is a Magistrate for Midlothian. This family is the nearest male representative of Borthwick, Baron Borthwick, in the ancient Peerage of Scotland, as decided by the House of Lords A.D. 1814.
Residence—Crookstone House, Stow. London Address—Grosvenor Hotel, S.W.

[2] Sir John Pringle, Bart., of Newhall, Selkirkshire, eldest son of the late Sir James Pringle, Bart., of Newhall, and Stichill; born

*Scott, John, Elliot (of Riccalton), Buckholm, Galashiels
*Scott, Hon. and Rev. Wm. Hugh, Maiden Newton, Dorset
*Walker,[1] William, Stuart, Esq. of Bowland†
*Walker, William Campbell, Esq., younger of Bowland
*Walker, James, Scott, Esq., 25 Austin Friars, London ‡
*Young, Thomas, farmer, Redhead †
*Young, William,   do,   do. †

COUNTY FAMILY SEATS.

TORWOODLEE.

Finely situated on the Gala, at the south-eastern extremity of Stow parish, and about 2 miles north-west of Galashiels—the property and residence of *James Thomas Pringle, Esq., eldest son of the late Vice-Admiral James Pringle of Torwoodlee; born 1832; succeeded 1859; is married and has issue—

Mr. Pringle is a Magistrate for Selkirkshire and a Lieutenant R.N. This family represents the Hop Pringles, and is the oldest branch of the numerous families of Pringle in the locality.

1784: succeeded 1809; married same year, Emilia Anne, daughter of General Norman Macleod, of Macleod, and had issue—

James, yr. of Stichill.
Norman (drowned in the Thames 18   ).
John Robert, in the Madras Civil Service.
Katharine, married Archibald Campbell Swinton, Esq. yr. of Kimmerghame (see Edrom parish).
Anne Crawford, married, July 1854, to the Hon. Charles St. Clair, Commander, R.N., second son of the late Lord Sinclair, of St. Ella's Lodge, Eyemouth (which see).
Eliza (dead), Emily, Mary.

Sir John married 2nd, 1831, Lady Elizabeth Maitland Campbell, daughter of John, 1st Marquis of Breadalbane, and has issue. Sir John is a Justice of Peace and Deputy-Lieutenant for the county of Berwick, and Vice-Lieutenant of the county of Roxburgh; was formerly Capt. 12th Light Dragoons. See Langton House, Berwickshire.

---

[1] William Stuart Walker, Esq., of Bowland, Midlothian, eldest son of the late Brigadier-General Alexander Walker, of Bowland; born 1813; succeeded 1831; married 1836 Eliza, daughter of William Loch, Esq., H.E.I.C. Civil Service, and has, with other issue—

William Campbell, yr., of Bowland, born 1838.

Mr. Walker, who was called to the Bar at Edinburgh 1840, and appointed Secretary to the Scotch Poor-Law Board 1853, is a Justice of Peace and Deputy-Lieutenant for the counties of Edinburgh and Selkirk. This family is descended from the Walkers of St. Fort, county Fife.

Residences—Bowland, near Stow; 35 Heriot Row, Edinburgh.
London Address—Carlton Club, S.W.

LAIDLAWSTEEL.

Situated half-way between the Tweed and the Caddon, about 4½ miles due west from Galashiels and about 3½ from Bowland station—the property and residence of Mrs. Mitchell, sen. of Carolside (see Earlston parish)

London Residence—Great Stanhope Street.

INNERLEITHEN.

[As the parishes of Innerleithen and Peebles have so small an area, and otherwise have so little interest in the county, the compiler has not considered it necessary to insert any of the officials of these parishes.]

Of this parish 3578¾ acres, including 19 acres under water and 12 acres public and private roads, are in the county of Selkirk. It lies at the northern extremity of the county, and consists of two portions, the smaller (836¼ acres of the lands of Priesthope), lying detached—the county of Peebles cutting it off by a belt varying from half to three-quarters of a mile in breadth from the larger (2472¼ acres). It is bounded its entire length—a distance of 5 miles—north-west by the Selkirkshire portion of Stow, and by the Tweed for about 2 miles to the south, which there divides it from Yarrow parish, (see Yarrow, page 403). Its breadth is irregular, but averages 1 mile. Both portions are almost entirely composed of hills, rising in the case of Glede Knowe to 1936 feet, and Priesthill to 1802 feet, in the detached portions; while Windlestrawlaw, in the larger portion, rises to 2161 feet. The hills are for the most part covered with a rich pasture. The village of Innerleithen, which is a favourite watering place, stands on the Leithen water, near its junction with the Tweed, and situated in Peeblesshire.

At the census of 1861 the population of this part of the parish was 73.

Assessed property in 1864-5, £1071 : 13 : 9.

The proprietors of this piece of the parish of Innerleithen are—James Ballantyne, Esq., of Holylee and Priesthope; A. Mitchell, Esq., of Thornielee (see Carolside).

COUNTY FAMILY SEAT.

HOLYLEE.

Situated near the Tweed, in the southern district of the parish in Selkirkshire—the property and residence of *James

Ballantyne, Esq., eldest son of the late Thomas Ballantyne, Esq.; born 1789; succeeded 1824; married 1821, Anne, daughter of Andrew Henderson, Esq., of Midgehope, and has issue—

*James George, yr., of Holylee, born 1837; Lieutenant 98th Regiment, at present stationed at Umballa, Bengal.

Three daughters—Helen Turnbull, Elizabeth Burnet, and Ann Williams.

Mr. Ballantyne is a Justice of Peace and Deputy-Lieutenant for the counties of Selkirk and Peebles.

*James Roxburgh, farmer, Thornielee†

PEEBLES.

OF this parish 3172¼ acres, including nearly 7 acres in private roads, are in the county of Selkirk. It lies at one of the northern extremities of Yarrow and detaches a small portion of that parish, the sources and most of the whole of the Glensax burn, a small tributary of the Tweed, is contained within its limits. Its shape is irregular; it consists entirely of hill pasture, and contains the following elevations :—Deadside 1712 feet, Kirkhope Law 1758 feet, Hundleshope and Glenrath heights both lying partly in Manor parish, 2349 and 2347 feet; the only habitation on it is a shepherd's house. The town of Peebles lies on the north side of the river Tweed, and in the county of Peebles.

At the census of 1861 the one house in this portion of the parish was uninhabited, but at the census of 1851 it contained a population of *six*.

Assessed value of property in 1864 5, £80.†

The sole proprietors of this portion of the parish are—Sir Adam Hay, Bart., and Robert Hay, Esq., yr.

*Hay,[1] Sir Adam, of Haystoune §
*Hay, Robt., Esq. yr., of Haystoune, Hay Lodge§
*Melross, Peter, farmer, Newby§

Ashkirk—*See* p. 353.
Roberton—*See* p. 357.
Selkirk and Galashiels parishes; *see* note, p. 362.

† *Only 6d and a fraction per acre for part of the Vale of the Tweed!* The returned rental has been at the same figure since we commenced the publication of the REGISTER (1856). We have written to different parties to explain its insignificance; but, except a suggestion that the acreage might be erroneous, we have received none. We know that the acreage given is strictly accurate, as we had it measured from the plans at the Edinburgh Survey Office, under our own inspection. Curious to know how the other parishes of the two counties stood the test per acre. we compiled the following table (*see* next page). We wonder if any other parish, or distinct part of parish. in Scotland, south of the Forth, has as small a rental as this piece of Peebles?

[1] Sir Adam Hay, Bart., of Smithfield and Haystoune (created 1635), third son of the late Sir John Hay, Bart., of Haystoune, (who died 1830); born 1795; succeeded his brother as 7th Bart. 1838; married 1823, Henrietta Callander, daughter of the late William Grant, Esq., of Congleton. Is Vice-Lieut. for the county of Peebles, and a Magistrate for the counties of Midlothian, Perth, and Selkirk; was M.P. for the Lanark Burghs 1820-30. This family is descended from a common ancestor with the Earl of Erroll. *Heir,* his son Robert, yr. of Haystoune, born 1825; married 1858, Sally, daughter of Alexander Duncan, Esq., of New York, and has issue—four sons and a daughter.

Residence—King's Meadows, near Peebles.

END OF SELKIRKSHIRE.

COMPARATIVE TABLE

Showing the Gross Value per Acre of each of the Parishes in Roxburgh and Selkirk shires (including house property and water), as per the Valuation returns; the Rise per Acre since 1856; and the Net Agricultural Value per Acre.

No		Parish.	Average Real Rental per Acre.			Rise per Ac. since 1856.		Agricultural value per Acre.		
			£	s.	d.	s.	d.	£	s.	d.
1	I.—Town.	Galashiels	2	11	2	9	3½	1	7	0
2		Selkirk	1	1	3	3	4¼	0	18	0
3		Hawick and Wilton	2	11	0	10	0	0	18	5
4		Jedburgh	1	7	8½	2	3¾	0	18	2½
5		KELSO	5	18	6	1 19	5½	3	0	1
6		Melrose	1	10	9	5	6¼	0	15	5¾
7	II.—Village Agricultural.	Ancrum	1	4	0¾	3	1½	1	0	7
8		Bowden	0	19	7½	2	8½	0	16	0¾
9		Cavers	0	12	5	1	6¼	0	10	9
10		Lilliesleaf	1	0	7½	1	8¾	0	18	0¾
11		Morebattle	0	11	6½	1	0¼	0	10	7½
12		Roxburgh	1	6	4	2	0	1	2	10½
13		St. Boswell's	2	0	0	5	2	1	7	8
14		Smailholm	1	6	1½	5	0¼	1	2	10
15		Sprouston	1	9	11	3	0½	1	6	0¾
16		Yetholm	1	6	9	2	7¾	1	2	1¾
17		*Crailing*	1	6	5	—		1	3	8¾
18		Eckford	1	1	3½	1	9¾	0	18	11½
19		EDNAM	2	1	6	3	11	1	9	7
20	III. Agricultural.	Lindean	0	15	7¾	2	0½	0	15	1¾
21		Linton	1	4	0	3	8½	1	1	9¾
22		Makerston	1	14	4	3	7¾	1	8	10
23		Maxton	1	4	2	1	5¼	1	1	0¾
24		Minto	0	16	7	1	11¾	0	14	7¾
25		Stichill and Hume	1	6	7½	3	9¾	1	3	6
26	IV.—Grazing.	Ashkirk	0	12	4¾	1	10½	0	10	7½
27		Ettrick	0	4	7	0	8½	0	4	3¾
28		Innerleithen	0	5	11¾	0	4¾	0	5	5¾
29		Kirkhope	0	5	4	0	6½	0	4	7¾
30		*Peebles*	0	0	6	0	0	0	0	6
31		Roberton	0	6	7	1	9¾	0	5	11½
32		Stow	0	8	7¾	2	2¼	0	7	0¼
33		Yarrow	0	4	9	0	9¾	0	4	1¾
34		Bedrule	0	18	7	1	4	0	16	9¼
35		Hobkirk	0	11	1	2	1¼	0	9	9
36		Hounam	0	9	1½	1	1½	0	8	7½
37		Kirkton	0	9	10	0	10¾	0	8	5¾
38		Oxnam	0	9	11	1	2½	0	8	11½
39		Teviothead	0	5	6¾	1	2¾	0	5	1
40		Southdean	0	6	4½	0	9¾	0	5	5¼
41		Castleton	0	5	0½	1	0¾	0	4	1

NOTES

ON THE PRECEDING TABLE HAVING REFERENCE MORE ESPECIALLY TO THE COLUMN, "AGRICULTURAL VALUE PER ACRE."

Our arrangement of parishes in the preceding Table may appear arbitrary, and in some instances not altogether fair (*see* note, 7-25—Ancrum to Stichill), but it is to the best of our judgment. Our system of arriving at conclusions also for the net column will to many seem more ingenuous than correct. Still, we think that the conclusions arrived at will be found so near the mark, in the main, as to entitle the results to some degree of confidence (and tested by the burgh returns of Jedburgh and Selkirk, they are). To those admitting the conclusions as even possibly correct, their interest will be at once established; but whether or not accurately correct the whole table will serve as a standard for future comparisons computed on the same basis. It is quite possible that some of the items are erroneously cast up; but any one can test the parish in which he is interested, by turning up the details, making the necessary deductions, and finally dividing by the qualified acreage.

The corresponding table for **BERWICKSHIRE** will be found after the lists of that county. A table of the Comparative Sanatory Condition of the different towns in the district, having reference more especially to their Housing statistics; Death rate of the different parishes, Poor rates, Illegitimacy, etc — appears at the end of the volume.

1. GALASHIELS (that part of the town and parish situated in Selkirkshire only—*see* No. 6, Melrose, and No. 20, Lindean).—Manufacturing and agricultural. We arrive at the net annual agricultural value per acre by allowing **£2** for the house accommodation of each inhabitant and deducting the value of 71 acres for roads (the net amount) and 40 acres for railways* (double the net amount). The streams and rivers in the parish we pass, as being of equal value, on account of water privileges or fisheries, with the soil.

* We should mention that railways are not included in the parish valuations; roads we are not sure about, and cannot stop the press while we enquire, but take for granted that they also are not included. [If we are wrong in this, the agricultural value per acre should appear proportionally lower in all the parishes; but this would leave their *comparative* value little affected.] Consequently our allowance of so much for roads is really doubling that stated, and for railways four times that stated; our reason for this is, that the vicinity of roads and railways adding greatly to the rentable value of agricultural property, we make a charge for (what we may here term) the fictitious advantages.

2. SELKIRK, all its portions.—Manufacturing, trading, agricultural, and grazing   The population of this parish is better housed than that of Galashiels ; we presume house property in it will not have so high a rentable value ; but we allow £2, 5s. for house accommodation, as it contains many seats ; * and while the value of 130 acres (the net amount as before) is deducted for roads, we add 100 for land under water (lochs), as surface included in the acreage but making no rent return. The 6 acres of railway we pass unnoticed—its short length within the parish, and recent construction, can have had little effect, especially as yet, in adding to the value of agricultural rental. Streams, pass.

3. HAWICK and WILTON.—Manufacturing, half agricultural, and half grazing.   £2 allowed for house accommodation, and the value of 168 acres for roads and 160 for railways deducted. Although the railway is but recently carried through Hawick, we conclude, from the peculiarities and energy of the locality, it will already have had an effect on rental, especially on town property, and have allowed accordingly.

4. JEDBURGH (including EDGERSTON, which should have been grouped in the grazing parishes, but we have not its separate valuation).—Manufacturing, trading, partly agricultural, partly grazing, and, to a small extent, horticultural† and suburban.‡   £2 10s. allowed for housing accommodation ; the value of 188 acres for roads and 25 acres for railways deducted.

5. KELSO.—Trading, agricultural, largely horticultural, and largely suburban.   £3 10s. allowed for housing accommodation ; the value of 121 acres of roads and 69 acres for railways deducted   As yet the railway has had no effect on the rental of town property in Kelso parish ; but it has had largely upon land. It will be observed how highly Kelso figures in all the columns.

6. MELROSE (including the Ladhope part of Galashiels, the valuation of which is not separately given—properly this part of the parish should have been with Galashiels).—Manufacturing, trading, largely suburban in the Melrose portion, agricultural, including some portions horticultural, and half grazing.   £3 allowed for the housing accommodation in Melrose, £2 in Ladhope ; the value of 324 acres for roads and 120 acres for railways deducted.

7-25. ANCRUM to STICHILL.—Agricultural. In agricultural parishes the house accommodation has a comparatively small rentable value (however really valuable it may be as house property—although as a rule the population is badly housed), £1 is only allowed for each inhabitant ; but deductions are made for roads and railways on the same principle as that followed in the town parishes. This principle places those parishes of this class, through which the railway passes at a disadvantage in the net scale ; in the case for instance of St. Boswell's, Sprouston, and Minto, where deduction is made for railway advantages ;

---

* See following note—horticultural.
† By horticultural we mean, not a country of gardens in the proper sense of the word, but of high-class farms, nursery grounds, gardens, properly so called, and finely kept gentlemen's policies.
‡ By this we mean largely consisting of high-class dwelling houses, —street, or villa.

---

compared with parishes so near to the line as to possess the full advantages—instance Bowden and Lilliesleaf ; or partial advantages—Linton, Ednam, Makerstoun, which have no deductions made on that score ; but it will be evident that we cannot go into excessive minutiæ and fine drawn distinctions, while the arbitrary rules we have followed are close enough for popular comparison.

13, 19, and 22. ST. BOSWELL'S, EDNAM, and MAKERSTOUN.—Agricultural, but being also to some extent suburban or horticultural. £2 allowed for each inhabitant's house accommodation.

17. CRAILING.—This parish has the peculiarity of having fallen in its rental since 1856. This is accounted for by the fact that four of its farms pay a grain rent. In the year in question wheat, quoting from the fiars' prices, was 49s. per boll ; last year, the date of the valuation returns, which we take as the basis of our calculations with the Roxburghshire parishes—(we take the returns of the present year for those of Selkirkshire)—wheat probably averaged 30s. (this year it is still less), but the real returned difference is so small that it is evident, while grain rental has fallen, money rental has increased ; the net decrease per acre being only 6¼d.*

26-40. ASHKIRK to SOUTHDEAN.—Grazing. In grazing parishes the house accommodation of the population being better than in the agricultural, and also of higher rentable value, we allow £1 10s. for each of the population. For roads, nothing is deducted ; we let them pass as so much surface, which to the parish is all they are worth, although of great service to the community at large—as in the case of Yarrow ; but for all the purposes of a grazing farmer—as a farmer—a drove road is as really useful as a turnpike. The streams in the grazing parishes we pass as of equal value with the soil, but we allow for lochs and lakes making no rent return—in Ettrick, 296 acres ; Kirkhope, 248 acres ; Roberton, 144 acres ; and Yarrow, 813 acres.

30. PEEBLES.—See foot-note, p. 462.

41. CASTLETON.—Its long continued isolated position has greatly retarded the condition of this parish ; at present it may be described as grazing, but it is capable of a high state of cultivation (see p. 232), and the net result of 4s. 1d. per acre must not be taken as its real agricultural value. As its house accommodation is low in the scale, we have put it in that respect on the footing of agricultural parishes—viz., £1 for each of the population, which we take at only 3320, thus excluding the 1250 influx of male railway labourers who were in the parish when the census was taken. In this, as in the grazing parishes, we deduct nothing for roads, but as the valuation has risen £100 since the railway opened—supposing that the railway may have caused the rise, we deduct for that £100.

* Gross rental (1856)	.	.	.	£8144 1 3
do. (1864)	.	.	.	7994 17 0
Gross difference	.	.	.	£149 4 3

NOTES.—See pp. 58 and 366 for the rental returns which we take as the basis of our calculations.

For COMPARATIVE RENTAL OF THE THREE COUNTIES, see pp. 470, 471.

BERWICKSHIRE.

BERWICKSHIRE, the most south-easterly county of Scotland, is bounded on the east by the North Sea, and on the west by the counties of Edinburgh and Roxburgh ; on the north it is separated from the county of Haddington by the range of the Lammermoor hills ; on the south it is bounded by Roxburghshire and Northumberland, having a detached portion of the county of Durham on its south-eastern limits ; and at its south-east corner the Liberties of Berwick-on-Tweed. Its form is an irregular oblong, measuring from east to west 35 miles, and from north to south 22 miles. The area of the shire was formerly estimated (see par. following) at about 483 square miles, or 309,375 acres. It is divided into three districts : the Merse, Lammermoor, and Lauderdale—the largest and most valuable being the Merse,* which occasionally gives name to the whole county ; it is the most compact and extensive piece of level ground in Scotland, comprising nearly 130,000 acres ; and being everywhere in a high state of cultivation, presents the appearance of a vast garden. Lammermoor, which consists of nearly 90,000 acres, is chiefly pastoral, and runs on the northern border of the Merse, dividing the valley of the Tweed from the counties of Edinburgh and Haddington. The district of Lauderdale, containing about 67,000 acres, ranges along the banks of the Leader Water, and it comprises a mixture of hill and dale, the land in the valleys being arable. Many beautiful rivers and streams flow through this county, and include the Blackadder, Whitadder, Leader, and Eye. There is railway communication by the North British line, from Berwick-on-Tweed by Cockburnspath, Dunbar, Haddington, etc., to Edinburgh, with a branch line from Reston station to Dunse and Earlston, which will, when completed, join the Hawick branch

---

* " One topographical feature of Berwickshire is worthy of notice. The valley of the Merse forms a great basin, having its lowest point about Coldstream, which is some fourteen miles from the sea, and from whence there is a great rising of the land towards the seaboard, with the exception only of the narrow gorge through which the Tweed finds its outlet. The Leet Water, for instance, flowing from near Whitsome to Coldstream, has a south-westerly course from the sea inwards. The Till river also, in Northumberland, has a similar course, and falls into the Tweed near Coldstream. The bed of the Whittadder, six miles from the sea, is higher than the bed of the Tweed at Kelso, which is twenty-four miles inland. It is to the basin-like form of the district that its original water-logged condition was due, and for which it obtained its name *Merse*—that is *Marsh*."—*Sanderson.*—(*See* Whitsome lists.)

of the same line near to Newtown station. The coast line of Berwickshire has a direct length north-westerly of 8¼ miles, from its commencement at Lamberton to St. Abb's Head ; or, allowing for headlands, 9¼ miles. From St. Abb's Head to the mouth of the Dunglass burn, where it terminates, is another direct length, nearly due west, of 8½ miles ; or again allowing for headlands, 9½ miles. Most of this coast is of great geological interest, and consists of bold rocky precipices, sometimes rising, as at St. Abb's Head, to an altitude of striking sublimity. In all this stretch of nearly 20 miles there is only one harbour or safe refuge for ships (Eyemouth) ; and a few boat harbours, constructed in some instances at great expense by Government assistance. From the peculiar geological construction of Berwickshire, all its streams, except the Eye and a few burns, find their way to the sea as tributaries to the Tweed (*see* foot-note, preceding page).

Berwickshire comprises thirty-one parishes, and two parts of parishes (Stichill and Hume—*see* p. 182, and Oldhamstocks), several towns and villages, and one royal burgh (Lauder), which, in conjunction with Haddington, Dunbar, North Berwick, and Jedburgh, sends one member to Parliament. The county returns another. Greenlaw is the county town, and contains 800 inhabitants ; but many of the county offices having been transferred to Dunse, as being more central, most of the county business is now transacted there, and there also most of the county officials reside.

The white fishery on the coast is of great excellence, and, since the opening of railway communication by the coast line, has been energetically cultivated at some of the stations—*vide* Eyemouth for particulars.

The district included in the "REGISTER" is entirely destitute of mines. Berwickshire has sandstone of a superior quality over most of its area. A red stone, which first shows itself on the Morriston estate in Ledgerwood, extends easterly through the centre of the county to the sea-coast. Of this stone Ayton Castle, which forms so conspicuous a feature in the landscape, is built. Another stone, more generally used for outside walls and carvings, on account of its colour (a delicate cream or yellowish gray), extends along the vale of the Tweed from the Roxburghshire boundary ; underlaying Eccles, Coldstream, Ladykirk, Swinton, and Whitsome, and cropping into Edrom, Hutton, and other surrounding parishes. The quarries of this stone are extensive and valuable. In the Lauder district of the county, north of Ledgerwood, whinstone is quarried. The sandstone quarries of Roxburghshire are of little importance.* There is no want

---

* One exception to this is the quarry of Denholm Hill in Cavers parish, which has a very durable and valuable stone.

of stone in many localities; but, as a rule, it is poor—often not worth the working. Roxburghshire possesses some very good whinstone in its higher districts. Selkirk may be said to possess no sandstone, but its whinstone is of the best description —beautiful in colour, pure as possible in quality, and capable of being raised in very large blocks.

If we follow out a series of comparisons between the counties of Berwick and Roxburgh, we find that while the former has its seaboard with its interesting geological formations and valuable white fishery, and extensively distributed beds of sandstone; the latter takes precedence in most other qualities of industry, produce, or interest; thus Berwickshire is greatly the inferior in general beauty* and its antiquities, except Dryburgh—situated at an extreme point of Mertoun parish, which juts singularly into Roxburghshire—are of little interest. Neither has it such names as those of Scott, Thomson, or Leyden in its obituary of men lately eminent, although it can boast of Boston and others of more ancient but now nearly forgotten date. As a manufacturing county it is almost *nil*, and it is almost the only county in the empire, certainly the only one of equal importance, which has no newspaper; "and strange to say the county of Berwick has no fairs of great importance. Dunse fairs for ewes and lambs, and Earlston for cattle, are all gradually declining."† Berwickshire contains a larger arable surface than Roxburghshire by 20,000 acres ; ‡ but, as a rule, Roxburghshire is now the more successfully farmed county (*see* p. 44, "Similarity of the two counties"). We say *now*, as the reverse was the case till within the last 30 or 40 years. Berwickshire then, with its superior wheat soil and the high prices obtained for grain, had inducements to high farming which Roxburghshire had not, and of which it was indeed scarcely considered capable; but the late extension of turnip culture and its consequent effect on sheep farming, combined with the reduced price of grain, has changed this. Roxburgh is now the favoured county, and has naturally gone a-head. Berwickshire also labours under the disadvantage of an isolated position—boxed up,

---

* Elihu Burritt, the learned blacksmith of America, describes the view from Bemersyde Hill as the most magnificent he ever saw in Scotland, excepting the one from Stirling Castle—"so truly beautiful as to be beyond description." But although Bemersyde Hill is in Berwickshire, it is Roxburghshire that fills the eye.

† Sanderson's *Essay*.

‡ The proportions stand thus :—
ROXBURGH, total area, 428,494 acres; arable. 130,000 acres—or less than one-third. This estimate includes the parish of Castleton, which occupies one-seventh of the map of Roxburghshire, and which may be considered as entirely pastoral.
BERWICK, total area, 303,000; arable, 150,000 acres—or one-half nearly. This estimate includes the Liberties of Berwick-on-Tweed, amounting to 5790½ acres.

as it were, into a corner of the kingdom; her communications intercepted by hills or rugged shores; she is crossed by no great lines of traffic ; and within her borders she has no busy manufacturing hives, by the want of which she is free from some disagreeable phases of society, but by it she loses the energizing stimulus which such a society creates.

The area of Berwickshire according to the Ordnance Survey, just completed, is 473 miles, or 303,000 statute acres, which is rather more than 8¼ acres to each of the present population.

The population of Berwickshire in 1801 was 30,206 ; in 1811, 30,893; in 1821, 33,385; in 1831, 34,040; in 1841, 34,238; in 1851, 36,297; and in 1861, 36,613. The number of inhabited houses in 1861 was 6385.

The total value of real assessed property, as assessed in 1815, was £245,379; in 1849, £265,890; in 1855, £288,963, 17s. 5½d.; in 1856, £302,924:14:4½; in 1857, £295,554:14:8; in 1858, £312,070:15:1; in 1859, £313,091:7:3; in 1860, £329,018:4:6; in 1861, £332,745:14s; and in 1863-4, £333,778, 7s. 9d.

Following out the series of comparisons, suggested by the valuation and population returns, we find that while the rental of the two counties in 1815 was nearly the same—Roxburgh being £254,180 and Berwick £245,379: a difference of only £8801 [or reducing each county to its value per acre we find Berwick gives 16s. 2d. and Roxburgh 11s. 9d.] In 1849--34 years—Roxburgh had increased 20¼ per cent. on the period, while Berwick had only increased 8½ per cent ; the counties then standing—Roxburgh £306,315, Berwick £265,890. Reducing these figures also to the value per acre, we have for Berwick 17s. 6d., while Roxburgh has got up to 14s. 3½d—the rise exceeding that of Berwick by 1s. 2½d. Since 1849 the rise in value of both counties has been greatly more uniform and rapid; the returns for the fourteen years ending 1863 from Roxburgh show an average annual rise of £5377 or 24½ per cent. for the period; from Berwick they show an average annual rise of £4849, or nearly 26 per cent. for the period. The totals of each, then are—Roxburgh £381,597, Berwick £333,778; or per acre over head—Berwick 22s., Roxburgh 17s. 9¾d.; the rise in Berwick on this occasion exceeding that of Roxburgh by 1s. 11½d.

The landed properties in Berwickshire are much more equally divided than those of Roxburgh. Most of the estates in the former run from £5000 to about £18,000 per annum; in the latter they run as high as about £28,000 per annum. So far as the interests of the country are concerned this may be considered as an advantage to Berwick.

The population of the two counties at the census of 1801—the first taken under the present system—was, Roxburgh 33,726, Berwick 30,206 : a difference of only 3520. In 1851 Roxburgh numbered 51,642, a decennial increase of 8 and four-fifths per cent. for the period;* for the decade ending 1861 the increase was 2477, or 4 and seven-tenths per cent.† In 1851 the population of Berwick numbered 36,297, a decennial increase of only 3⅓ per cent.* The decade ending 1861 shows a gross rise of only 316 (306 *of whom were an addition to the female population*—*see* p. 52), or 1 and one-eighth per cent.† Total 1861—Roxburgh 54,119, Berwick 36,613.

Not so much for the purpose of comparison as to complete our series for the district, we add the particulars of the rental and population of Selkirkshire (the *civil* county—which excludes Ladhope, Lindean, and all the other Roxburghshire, etc., portions of parishes, but includes that portion of Ashkirk which, though civilly belonging to Selkirk, belongs politically to Roxburgh—*see* p. 353).

In 1815 the returned rental of Selkirk was £43,584, or per acre over head, 5s. 3¼d. In 1849 it had increased to £52,839, or 6s. 3d. per acre; the rise per cent for the period being 21—or one-half per cent. higher than Roxburgh and 12½ higher than Berwick. We have not the Selkirk returns for 1863; but taking them for the following year (1864-5), we find an extraordinary rapid rise in the value of this county — the fifteen years being equal to 36 per cent. (or, taking the average, 33¾ per cent. for the 14 years ending 1863, which is 9½ per cent. higher than Roxburgh, and 7¾ per cent. higher than Berwick for the same period); per acre over head, 8s. 3d.

Comparative Rise in Value of the three counties 1815-63.—Selkirk, over a half; Roxburgh, fully a half; Berwick, over a third.

The population of Selkirkshire in 1801 was 5388; in 1851 it numbered 9809, having increased decennially with the following curious irregularity:—1811, 9 per cent.; 1821, 12 per cent.; 1831, 3 per cent. (*all males*—all the other periods show a very equal proportion of sexes); 1841, 17 per cent.; 1851, 23 per cent.—the average decennial rise being 12½ per cent.* For the decade ending 1861 the increase was 640, or 6½ per cent.†; the total then standing 10,449 — the population having nearly doubled in 60 years.‡ Increase of Roxburgh in the same period, over a half; of Berwick, one-sixth.

Statute Acres to each of the Population in 1861.—Roxburgh, 8; Berwick, 8¼; Selkirk, 16.

---

* The average decennial increase of Scotland for the period being 10 and one-fifth per cent.

† Average increase of Scotland for the period being only 6 per cent. which the Census Report designates a *startling fact* (*see* foot-note, pp. 51, 52).

‡ Of all the counties in Scotland, Linlithgow shows the greatest rise per cent for the decade ending 1861, viz., 28 and one-third. Lanark

---

VALUATION AND AREA OF THE SEVERAL PARISHES IN THE COUNTY OF BERWICK,

FOR THE YEAR TO WHITSUNDAY 1864-65.

Acres.	Parishes.	Amount.
4826.843	Parish of Abbey St. Bathans .	£1862 0 0
6832.154	,, Ayton . .	15,019 5 11
9256.430	,, Bunkle . .	10,508 11 1
14,202.587	,, Channelkirk .	7135 4 3
5594.079	,, Chirnside . .	11,651 13 7
12,951.761	,, Cockburnspath .	10,013 8 6
24,325.326	,, Coldingham .	26,633 4 8
8534.499	,, Coldstream .	18,921 13 10
8738.245	,, Cranshaws .	1715 4 4
11,474.740	,, Dunse . .	22,495 5 8
18,009.566	,, Earlston . .	11,119 0 0
12,488.876	,, Eccles . .	22,846 4 2
9634.238	,, Edrom . .	18,879 12 1
1079.541	,, Eyemouth .	5624 14 1
4668.847	,, Fogo . .	7202 2 8
3298.124	,, Foulden . .	5563 2 10
9738.979	,, Gordon . .	8347 9 11
12,200.121	,, Greenlaw . .	10,253 3 5
4103.034	,, Hume . .	5123 5 10
5648.285	,, Hutton . .	10,626 19 6
3446.787	,, Ladykirk .	6851 2 11
7150.871	,, Langton . .	7344 11 0
34,981.026	,, Lauder (Parish) .	17,531 11 3
	,, (Burgh) .	2272 12 0
8817.108	,, Ledgerwood .	6920 19 3
19,604.533	,, Longformacus .	6634 9 0
6536.201	,, Mertoun . .	8768 5 4
3069.864	,, Mordington .	3717 6 0
3478.562	,, Nenthorn . .	5641 3 10
8012,991	,, Polwarth . .	2624 2 0
5571.657	,, Swinton . .	10,993 9 7
14,643.878	,, Westruther .	7212 16 11
4896.779	,, Whitsome . .	8976 11 11
2347.287	Pendicles . . .	1395 10 0
		£326,153 6 5
	North British Railway .	10,832 11 0
	Berwickshire Railway .	1200 15 0
297,162.819		£337,186 12 5

LIEUTENANCY.

Lord-Lieutenant and Sheriff-Principal—David Robertson, Esq. of Ladykirk, M.P., 1860.

Vice-Lieutenant—Lord Binning, 1864.

---

follows with 19 and one-tenth per cent. The latter county increased 34 per cent for the decade ending 1841—the highest on record. The next highest is Dumbarton, 33 per cent. for the same period.

DEPUTY-LIEUTENANTS.

Anderson, David, of Moredun.
Campbell, Sir Hugh H., of Marchmont, Bart.
Greig, George, of Eccles, 1861.
Haddington, Earl of.
Hamilton, Major Robert Baillie, Lennel House, 1864.
Hay, William, of Dunse Castle.
Home, Earl of.
Home, David M., of Milne Graden.
Hood, John, of Stoneridge.
Innes, A. M., of Ayton, 1864.
Lauderdale, Earl of.
Macbraire, Js., of Broadmeadows, 1864.
Mitchell, Alex., of Stow, 1861.

Miller, William, of Manderston, M.P., 1864.
Polwarth, Lord.
Pringle, Sir John, Bart.
Renton, Major Archibald Colin Campbell, of Mordington, 1864.
Seymour, Harry Ernest Clay Ker, of Morriston, 1864.
Sinclair, Lord, of Nisbet.
Spottiswoode, John, of Spottiswoode.
Swinton, John Campbell, of Kimmerghame.
Turnbull, John, of Abbey St. Bathans.
Wilkie, John, of Foulden.

Clerk to Lieutenancy—Alexander Weatherhead, Dunse, 1811.

PARLIAMENTARY REPRESENTATION.

Member of Parliament for the County—David Robertson, Esq. of Ladykirk, 1859 (Liberal). Constituency for the County—1248.
For the Burgh of Lauder, (forming part of the Haddington District of Burghs)—Sir H. R. F. Davie, Bart. of Creedy, 1857 (Liberal). Constituency for the Burgh—65.
Auditor of Election Expenses for the County—William Stevenson, accountant, Dunse.
Assessor of County Voters' Registration Act—David M'Watt, Dunse.

SHERIFF AND COMMISSARY COURT.

Sheriff and Commissary—And. Rutherford Clark, Advocate, 17 Great Stuart Street, Edinburgh, appointed 1843.
Sheriff-substitute and Commissary-depute—Geo. Dickson, Advocate. Dunse, appointed 1843.
Commissary-depute and Sheriff-clerk—William T. Kellie, Dunse.
Depute-Sheriff-clerk—J. B. Kellie, Dunse.
Sheriff Procurator-fiscal—James C. Robson, Dunse.
Commissary-clerk—Robert Romanes, Lauder.
Inspector of Weights and Measures—J. Kerr, Dunse.

The Sheriff and Commissary Courts are held at Greenlaw the last Thursday of every month, and at Dunse on every other Thursday, as well as every Tuesday, during Sessions.* Sheriff Small Debt Courts are held at Ayton on the Monday before the last Thursday of March, the last Monday of May, the Monday before the last Thursday of July, and the first Monday of November; at Lauder on the Wednesday before the last Thursday of March, July, and October; at Coldstream on the Saturday after the last Thursday of March, the last Wednesday of May, the Saturday after the last Thursday of July, and the last Wednesday of November; at Dunse on the third Thursday of Janu-

* "During Sessions"—see foot-note, p. 251.

ary and February, the Tuesday before the last Thursday of March, the first Thursday of May and June, the Tuesday before the last Thursday of July, and the first Thursday of October, November, and December; at Greenlaw on the last Thursday of January, March, May, June, July, October, and November. Quarter Sessions are held at Greenlaw on the first Tuesday of March, May, and August, and last Tuesday of October.

COMMISSIONERS OF SUPPLY.

Convener for the County—William Hay of Dunse Castle.

Allan, Joseph, of Quixwoode
Allan, Thomas, of Slighhouses
Allan, John, yr. of Slighhouses
Allan, William H., of Allanbank
Baillie, Charles, Lord Jerviswoode
Baillie, Rev., The Hon. John
Baillie, The Hon. Major Robert
Baird, George, of Stichill
Balfour, Charles, of Newton Don
Binning, Lord
Boswall, Sir Geo. A. F. Houston, of Blackadder, Bart.
Borthwick, John, of Crookston
Broadwood, David, of Fulfordlees
Broomfield, Wm., of Old Greenlaw
Broughton, Robert H., of Rowchester
Brown, David, of Park
Brownlow, Earl
Buchan, Geo. W. F., of Kelloe
Carnegie, James, of New Edrom
Cotesworth, Robert, of Cowdenknowes
Campbell, Sir Hugh H., of Marchmont, Bart.
Cosens, Geo. Weir, of Peelwalls
Cosens, Robert, of Bogangreen
Cranstoun, Geo. C. T., of Dewar
Curle, Alexander, of Morriston
Dalrymple, James, of Langlee and Greenknow
Darling, James S., W.S., as factor for George Baird of Stichill
Dickson, James, of Chatto
Dickson, Arch., yr. of Chatto
Dickson, William, of Whitecross
Dummond, H. Home, of Blair-Drummond
Drummond, George Home, yr. of Blair Drummond
Dunglass, Lord
Dunlop, J. Renton, of Mayfield
Erskine, James, of Shielfield

Elcho, Lord
Fairholme, Wm., of Chapel
Forster, Ralph, of Whitsome Hill
Greig, George, of Eccles
Grieve, John M'Lean M'Kenzie, of Huttonhall
Haddington, The Earl of
Hall, Sir James, of Dunglass
Hardie, Henry R., of Stoneshiel
Hay, William, of Dunse Castle
Hay, Jas. W., yr. of Dunse Castle
Hepburn, Sir Thomas Buchan, of Smeaton, Bart.
Herriot, Alexander T., of Coldinghamlaw
Herriot, James, of Herriotbank
Hood, John, of Stoneridge
Hood, Thos. H., yr. of Stoneridge
Hood, William, of Sunnyside
Home, David Milne, of Wedderburn
Home, D. M., yr. of Milne Graden
Home, Earl of
Home, Lieut.-Col. G. L., of Broomhouse
Home, William, of Fairlaw.
Home, Major John H. F. of Bassendean
Hume, George, of New Mains
Hunter, James W., of Thurston
Hunter, William King, of Pilmuir
Hunter, Matt. D., of Antons Hill
Innes, Alex. M., of Ayton
Landale, Thomas, of Templehall
L'Amy, J. Ramsay, of Dunkenny
Logan, Abram., of Burnhouses
Lauderdale, Earl of
Low, James, of Laws
Lumsdaine, Edwin S., of Blanerne
Lumsdaine, F. E. S., yr. of Blanerne
Lundie, William C., of Spittal
Macbraire, Jas., of Broadmeadows
Hume, M. N. M'D., of Ninewells
Mack, William, of Berrybank

Marjoribanks, Sir John, of Lees, Bart.
Meiklam, John, of Gladswood
Morton, Earl of
Miller, William, of Manderston
Milne, Admiral Sir Alexander
Milne, Nicol, of Faldonside
Mitchell, Alexander, of Stow
Munro, Captain Alexander, of Craiglockhart
Nisbet, Col. Robert, of Mersington
Nisbet, Captain Thomas, yr of Mersington
Ogilvie, William, of Chesters
Polwarth, Right Hon. Lord
Pringle, Sir John, of Newhall, Bart.
Purves, Col. J. H., of Purveshall
Renton, Major. A. C. C., of Lamberton
Robertson, David, of Ladykirk
Roxburghe, Duke of
Roy, Frederick L., of Nenthorn
Roy, Fred. L yr., of Nenthorn
Scott, the Hon. Francis
Scott, Hon. and Rev. John
Scott, Hon. W., Master of Polwarth
Scott, Hon. William
Simson, Charles, of Threepwood
Smith, Major W. H., of Cruickshield
Smyth, James, of Whitchester

St Clair, James, Lord Sinclair
Spottiswoode, John, of Spottiswoode
Stuart, Charles, Lord Blantyre
Swan, Robert, writer, Kelso
Swinton, J. C., of Kimmerghame.
Swinton, Archibald Campbell, yr. of Kimmerghame
Suttie, Sir George Grant, of Balgone, Bart.
Suttie, Jas. Grant, yr. of Balgone
Tait, James, of Langrigg.
Tawse, John, W.S.
Thomson, Alex. C., of Grueldykes
Trotter, Richard, of Mortonhall
Tod, Thomas, of Drygrange
Turnbull, James, of Hillend.
Turnbull, John, of Abbey St Bathans
Tweeddale, Marquis of
Warrender, Sir J., of Lochend
Weatherly, James, of Monynut
Webster, George, of Hallydown
Wemyss, Earl of
Wilkie, John, of Foulden
Wilson, George, of Georgefield
Wilson, John, of Cumledge
The Sheriff of Berwickshire
The Sheriff-Substitute of Berwickshire
The Chief Magistrate for the Burgh of Lauder for the time being.

Head Meetings of the Commissioners are held at Greenlaw 30th April, and 1st Tuesday in October.

Clerk of Supply—George Peat, of Wellnage, Dunse.

Collector of County Rates—Alexander Crawford, Dunse.

County Auditor—J. MacAllan, W.S.

COMMISSION OF THE PEACE FOR THE COUNTY OF BERWICK.*

Duke of Roxburghe.
Marquis of Tweeddale.
Marquis of Bowmont.
Earl of Morton.
Earl of Home.
Earl of Haddington.
Earl of Lauderdale.
Earl of Wemyss and March.
Charles A. H., Lord Dunglass.
Lord Binning.
Lord Elcho.

Lord Somerville.
Lord Sinclair.
Lord Polwarth.
Master of Polwarth.
Sir Hugh H. Campbell of Marchmont, Bart.
Sir J. Pringle, Bart., of Newhall.
Sir George G. Suttie of Balgone, Bart.
Sir Thomas Buchan Hepburn of Smeaton, Bart.

* A new Commission is in preparation.

Sir J. Marjoribanks of Lees, Bart.
Sir George A. F. H. Boswall of Blackadder, Bart.
Thomas Allan of Slighhouses.
Joseph Allan of Quixwoode.
William H. Allan of Muircleugh.
Thomas Anderson, Shawbraes
Charles Balfour of Newton Don.
David Broadwood of Fulfordlees.
William Broomfield of Old Greenlaw.
John Borthwick of Crookston.
Major David Brown of Park.
Col. G. W. F. Buchan of Kelloe.
Rt. H. Broughton of Rowchester.
R. B. F. Brown of Whitsome Newton.
A. J. Balfour of Whittinghame.
James Carnegie of New Edrom.
G. R. Carnegie, yr. of New Edrom.
George C. T. Cranstoun of Dewar.
R. Cotesworth of Cowdenknowes
George W. Cosens, yr., of Kames.
William Dickson of Whitecross.
Henry H. Drummond of Blair Drummond.
George Home Drummond, yr. of Blair Drummond.
John R. Dunlop of Mayfield.
James Dickson of Chatto.
Archibald Dickson, yr. of Chatto.
James Erskine of Shielfield.
William Fairholme of Greenknowe.
George Fairholme, Old Melrose.
Ralph Forster of Whitsome Hill
John M'Lean M'Kenzie Grieve of Hutton Hall.
George Greig of Eccles.
William Hay of Dunse Castle.
Rt. Home of Coldingham Law.
William Home of Fairlaw.
George Home of Newmains.
John Hood of Stoneridge.
William Hood of Sunnyside.
James W. Hunter of Thurston.
Matthew D. Hunter of Antons Hill.
John C. Hopkins of Rowchester.
Matthew N. Macdonald Hume of Ninewells
Charles John Baillie Hamilton of Rumbleton Law.
Sir James Hall, of Dunglass.
Wm. J. Hay, yr. of Dunse Castle.
Lieut.-Col. George L. Home of Broomhouse and Edrom.

David Milne Home of Wedderburn.
T. H. Hood, yr., of Stoneridge.
A. T. Herriot of Coldingham Law
D. M. Home, yr., of Wedderburn.
Alexander Mitchell Innes, of Ayton.
James Low, of Laws
Edwin S. Lumsdaine of Lumsdaine and Blanerne, Clerk.
F. G. S. Lumsdaine of Blanerne.
Wm. Compton Lundie of Spittal, Clerk,.
Thomas Landale of Temple Hall.
Jn. Ramsay L'Amy of Dunkenny and Netherbyres.
Wm. MacIntyre of Temple Hall.
Alexander Mitchell of Stow.
Rear-Admiral Sir A. Milne, R.N.
Alex. Munro, of Craiglockhart.
Capt. A. D. M'Laren, Coldstream.
Jas. Macbraire of Broadmeadows.
William Mack of Berrybank.
Robert Nisbet of Mersington.
Capt. T. Nisbet, yr. of Mersington.
William Dickson of Chesters.
James J. Oswald of Edrington Castle.
Sir H. Preston, Bart., of Valleyfield and Lutton.
George Peat of Wellnage.
Lieut.Col. J. H. Purves of Purves.
James Pringle, yr., of Newhall.
Frederick L. Roy of Nenthorn.
David Robertson of Ladykirk.
Archibald C. C. Renton of Lamberton.
Capt. F. Ramsay, Paxton House.
J. Spottiswoode of Spottiswoode.
J. C. Swinton of Kimmerghame.
Major William Hope Smith of Wester Cruicksfield.
Archibald C. Swinton, yr. of Kimmerghame.
Charles Simson of Threepwood.
James S. Smyth of Whitchester.
J. Grant Suttie, yr., of Balgone.
Thomas Tod of Drygrange.
Richard Trotter of Charterhall.
John Turnbull of Abbey St Bathans.
Alexander Thomson of Whiterig.
James Tait of Langrigg.
Alex. C. Thomson of Grueldykes.
Hy. Trotter, yr., of Mortonhall.
James Turnbull of Hillend.
John Wilkie of Foulden.

John Wilson of Cumledge.
Captain James Wood of Nunlands
The Sheriff of Berwickshire and Haddingtonshire, for the time being.

The Sheriff-Substitute of Berwickshire, for the time being.
The Chief Magistrate of the Royal Burgh of Lauder, for the time being.

Clerk to the Justices—Jonathan Melrose, writer, Coldstream.

DEPUTE-CLERKS—Ayton, Charles David Colville ; Lauder, Thomas Broomfield ; Dunse, Alex. Weatherhead.

PROCURATOR-FISCAL for the District of Dunse—D. Fergusson, Dunse ; for the districts of Earlston and Lauder, R. Romanes, Lauder ; for the district of Ayton, J. Bowhill, Ayton ; for the district of Coldstream, Geo. Brown, Coldstream.

Quarter Sessions of the Justices are held at Greenlaw on first Tuesdays of March, May. and August, and last Tuesday of October.

The Justice of Peace Court for the district of Dunse is held on first Monday of every month ; for the districts of Earlston and Lauder, are held at Lauder on the third Friday of February, April, June, August, October, and December ; for the districts of Ayton and Eyemouth, are held at Ayton on the first Thursday of every month ; for the district of Coldstream, are held at Coldstream on the third Wednesday of every month.

PROPERTY AND INCOME TAX COMMISSIONERS.
GENERAL PURPOSES.

Frederick L. Roy of Nenthorn.
Lieut.-Col. George L. Home of Broomhouse.
J. Spottiswoode of Spottiswoode.
Robert Cotesworth, yr. of Cowdenknowes.
Thomas Tod of Drygrange.
David M. Home of Wedderburn.
George Wilson, of Georgefield.
Archibald Campbell Swinton, yr. of Kimmerghame.
Col. G. W. Fordyce Buchan of Kelloe.
A. T. Herriot of Coldingham Law.
William Mack of Berrybank.
Sir H. H. Campbell, Bart., of Marchmont.
John Meikleham of Gladswood.
Major John Hutchison Ferguson Home of Bassendean.

John Hood of Stoneridge.
George C. T. Cranstoun of Dewar.
Alex. M. Innes, of Ayton.
Thomas Landale of Templehall.
Major A.C.C. Renton of Lamberton.
John Wilkie of Foulden.
Major William Hope Smith of Cruicksfield.
William H. Allan of Allanbank.
The Sheriff and Sheriff-Substitute of Berwickshire.
Charles Simson of Threepwood
James Dickson of Chatto.
Alexander Mitchell of Stow.
Sir J. Marjoribanks of Lees, Bart.
James Nisbet of Lambden.
William Miller of Manderston.
F. L. Roy, yr. of Nenthorn.

ADDITIONAL COMMISSIONERS.

John Wilson, Edington Mains.
David Logan, Ferneycastle.
Captain M'Laren, Coldstream.
James Cunningham, Coldstream.

Thomas Thomson, Dunse.
Robert Forester Hardy, Dunse.
James Thomson, Dunse.
William King Hunter, Dunse

Clerk—Geo. Peat, Dunse. Assistant Clerk—Wm. Jeffreys, Dunse.
Inspector—Alexander Paterson, Edinburgh.

Surveyors—Alexander M'Lean, Haddington, for the first district—comprehending Ayton and Dunse ; Edward Henderson, Melrose, for the second district—comprehending Coldstream, Greenlaw, Lauder, etc.
Collector of Assessed Property and Income Taxes—Alexander Crawford, Dunse.
Assessors—T. Broomfield, Lauder, for the district of Lauder ; C. Watson, Dunse, for the district of Ayton ; and D. M'Watt, Dunse, for the district of Dunse and Coldstream.

LANDS VALUATION COMMITTEE.
Convener—A. C. Swinton, yr. of Kimmerghame.

Maj. W. H. Smith, of Cruicksfield.
Archibald Campbell Swinton, yr., of Kimmerghame.
John Spottiswoode of Spottiswoode.
John Turnbull of Abbey St Bathans.

Geo. Dickson, sheriff-substitute.
Lt.-Col. G. W. Fordyce Bucahn of Kelloe.
John Hood of Stoneridge.
D. M. Home of Wedderburn.
Major Logan Home of Broomhouse.

Assessors under the Act—Thomas Broomfield for the Lauder district ; Charles Watson, for Ayton district ; William Stevenson for Dunse district ; David M'Watt for Coldstream district.

BERWICKSHIRE POLICE COMMITTEE.
Lieut.-Col. George Logan Home of Broomhouse, Convener.

Sir Hugh H. Campbell of Marchmont, Bart.
Sir George Houston Boswall of Blackadder, Bart.
Frederick L. Roy of Nenthorn.
Lord Binning.
M. D. Hunter of Antons Hill
The Bailie of Dunse
Maj. W. H. Smith of Cruicksfield.
J. Turnbull of Abbey St. Bathans
William Hay, of Dunse Castle.
John Hood of Stoneridge.

Lieut.-Col. Fordyce Buchan of Kelloe.
David Milne Home of Wedderburn.
J. Spottiswoode of Spottiswoode.
Alex. Mitchell Innes of Ayton.
The Lord Lieutenant of County.
Archibald Campbell Swinton, yr. of Kimmerghame.
Sheriff of Berwickshire.
Sheriff-Sub. of Berwickshire.
The Bailie of Coldstream.

William Stevenson, accountant, Dunse, Clerk.

BERWICKSHIRE PRISON BOARD.
Lieut.-Col. G. W. Fordyce Buchan, of Kelloe, Chairman.

Arch. C. Swinton, yr. of Kimmerghame.
Chief Magistrate of Dunse.
John Hood of Stoneridge.
Sir Hugh H. Campbell of Marchmont, Bart.
Lieut.-Col. George L. Home of Broomhouse.

George C. T. Cranstoun of Dewar.
Sir George Houston Boswall of Blackadder, Bart.
Major William Hope Smith of Cruicksfield
The Sheriff of Berwickshire, and in his absence the Sheriff-Substitute.

Governor of Greenlaw Prison—William Smith.

    ,,   Dunse Prison—Thomas Simpson.

Clerk to the Prison Board—James C. Robson, Dunse.

Chief Constable—G. H. List, Dunse.

Superintendent—William Grant.

Sergeant of Constables—   Monro.

Sheriff Officer at Dunse—John Pilmer.

    ,,   Ayton—James Thompson.

    ,,   Coldstream—

    ,,   Eyemouth—Peter Nisbet.

    ,,   Coldingham—David Buglas.

    ,,   Lauder—William Malloy.

BERWICKSHIRE DISTRICT LUNACY BOARD.

(See District Information, p. 53.)

INLAND REVENUE.

Stamp and Tax Department, Distributor and Collector—Alexander Crawford, Dunse.

SUB-DISTRIBUTORS AND COLLECTORS OF TAXES.

Coldstream—John Halliburton.

Ayton—Thomas Carter.

Lauder—Thomas Broomfield.

Eyemouth—James Bowhill.

EXCISE DEPARTMENT.

Collector—J. Luckie, Haddington. Supervisors— Probyn, Kelso, for the northern district; and John Somerville, Dunbar, for the southern district.

Officer at Chirnside—G. B. Allice; Coldstream—George Bannerman; James Deans, Melrose, for the Lauder and Farlston districts; William Wight, Kelso, for the localities of Nenthorn and Hume.

ELLEM FISHING CLUB.

INSTITUTED 1829.

Preses—John Turnbull, Esq., of Abbey St. Bathans.

Members of Council—G. C. Trotter Cranstoun, Esq., of Dewar; A. Campbell Swinton, Esq.; Major William Hope Smith of Cruicks-field; Rev. James Logan, Swinton.

Chaplain—Rev. James Logan.

Assessor—Archibald Campbell Swinton, Esq., yr. of Kimmerghame.

Artist—William Smellie Watson, Esq., R.S.A., Edinburgh.

Secretary—James Turnbull, Esq. of Hillend.

Annual Subscription, 5s. Life-Membership, £3.

The annual meeting and competition take place at Dunse in May.

BERWICKSHIRE FISHING CLUB (estab. 1861).

President—William Crawford, Esq., Dunse.

Vice-President—Adam Calder, Esq., West Blanerne.

Secretary and Treasurer—Charles Watson, Esq., Dunse.

Annual Competition alternately on last Monday of April and last Monday of June.

Annual Meeting for election of members, etc., at Dunse, second Thursday of March. Annual Subscription, 7s. 6d. Entry-Money, £1, payable in advance.

BERWICKSHIRE NATURALISTS' CLUB.

(Instituted 1831.)

President—Elected Annually.

Joint Secretaries and Treasurers—Dr. Embleton, and George Tate, Esq., Alnwick.

Meets four times a year during the summer and autumn—per circular from the Secretary. The Annual Subscription is determined by the expenses incurred in printing the proceedings. These contain some papers of great merit on local subjects, and complete sets of them are scarce and valuable.

BERWICKSHIRE FIRST ADMINISTRATIVE BATTALION OF RIFLE VOLUNTEERS.

(Head-Quarters, Dunse.)

Lieutenant-Colonel—The Honourable A. F. Cathcart, of Caldra.

Major—Sir John Marjoribanks, Bart., of Lees.

Capt. and Adjt.—Geo. Renny, late B.-Major 73d Regt., Edrom House.

Hon. Quartermaster—T. Broomfield.

Hon. Surgeon—R. C. M'Watt, M.D., Dunse.

The Battalion is composed of the following corps :—

Corps.		Commanding Officer.	Strength.
1st or Dunse	Capt.	the Hon. A. F. Cathcart....	80
2d or Coldstream	,,	Sir John Marjoribanks	79
3d or Ayton	,,	David Popplewell	66
4th or Greenlaw..	,,	J. H. Home, Major	65
5th or Lauder....	Lieut.	William Fairholme	92
6th or Earlston ..	Capt.	Alexander Mitchell	77
7th or Chirnside..	Lieut.	Robert Slight	47

Total strength of Battalion (July 30, 1864) 506

1ST BERWICKSHIRE ARTILLERY CORPS (Eyemouth).

Captain Commanding—Lieut. Peter Tod, of Redhall.

Effective Force, 50.

2D ARTILLERY CORPS (Coldingham).

BERWICKSHIRE PROVINCIAL GRAND LODGE OF FREE MASONS.

Alexander Mitchell, Esq., of Stow, P.G.M.
Substitute, G.M. (Vacant).
Mark Liddle, builder, Lauder, S.W. Thomas Hogg, Coldstream, J.W.
A. Crawford, Dunse, Secretary.

BERWICKSHIRE HORTICULTURAL SOCIETY.

Properly a Dunse Society—*see* Dunse lists.

BERWICKSHIRE ROAD TRUSTS.

(*See* district information, p. 56.)

COLDSTREAM.

THIS parish is situated on the banks of the river Tweed, which forms its eastern and south-eastern boundary and here separates England and Scotland ; Swinton and Ladykirk parishes bound it on the north-east, and Eccles on the west and south-west. The parish is of an irregular shape, and on the map looks not unlike a boy's kite. Its greatest length is $6\frac{1}{2}$ miles, and breadth about 5 miles ; and, according to the Ordnance Survey, contains $8534\frac{1}{2}$ acres ; of which $149\frac{1}{2}$ are in public and private roads, and $214\frac{1}{3}$ are under water. Its general appearance is flat, but well cultivated and enclosed, and sheltered at equal distances by the Cheviots and Lammermoors. The former name of the parish was Lennel ; and situated about one mile to the north of the town of Coldstream, on a high bank overhanging the Tweed, there is a village called Lennel Newtown, to distinguish it from the former village of the name, of which nothing now remains except the burying ground and the ruins of the church. This burying ground is the only one in the parish, and lies a short way beyond the present village.

On the north bank of the Tweed, and occupying a delightful, low-lying, and sheltered situation, is the town of Coldstream, irregularly built, but containing a number of excellent houses, and public buildings, of which the British Linen Company Bank, the Bank of Scotland, Mechanics' Institution, the Free and Parish churches, are all very creditable specimens. The Tweed is here crossed by a fine bridge, designed by Smeaton, the engineer ; commenced in July 1763, and opened in October 1766. It consists of five arches, which, though of different apertures, are portions of the same circle, by which means they were all built on one centre. The views both up and down the river from the bridge are very fine ; that downward in the direction of Lennel House being—next to that of Kelso Bridge, looking up—one of the best on the Tweed. This bridge forms a nominal division of Scotland and England, and in consequence of the proximity of Coldstream to the latter, it was long noted for the celebration of runaway marriages, and is so still to some extent, but which a late Act has now rendered illegal.* At the east end of the town is a chaste and hand-

---

* These marriages generally took place at the Coldstream bridge toll-house (now a small shop)—the first house in Scotland ; occasionally also in any convenient house in Coldstream. It is a remarkable circumstance that no fewer than three Lord Chancellors of England were married in this irregular way, namely, Lords Eldon, Erskine, and Brougham, who was married in the head inn.

some monument, exected in 1834 to the memory of Charles Marjoribanks, Esq., the first M.P. for the county in the Reformed Parliament. About a mile from Coldstream, situated on the Leet water, is HIRSEL, the seat of the Earl of Home—a place of much beauty amid a profusion of noble trees. Within the grounds is a fine artificial lake, in which large pike are occasionally caught. The other mansions in the parish are—LENNEL HOUSE, a seat of the Earl of Haddington, a recent erection on the site of a previous mansion, which was inhabited for many years by Patrick Brydone, author of the "Tour in Sicily and Malta," and father of the present Countess of Minto; MILNE GRADEN, the seat of David Milne Home, Esq.; and LEES, the residence of Sir John Marjoribanks, Bart. In the parish some interesting vegetable fossils have been discovered. "It is well known that General Monk, before the restoration of Charles II., raised here the regiment of Foot-Guards, which still bears the name of the parish." The house occupied as the head-quarters of the regiment, situated at the east of the market place, was taken down and rebuilt this year (1865); it bears the following tablet—" Head-quarters of the Coldstream Guards 1659; rebuilt 1865." Across the Tweed, and 5 miles south of the town, in Northumberland, is the celebrated field of Flodden, memorable as one of the most destructive conflicts recorded in British history; and 3 miles east is, by many, the supposed site of Chevy Chase, where Douglas went to hunt Percy's deer, and which led to the battle of Otterburn, where both Percy and Douglas fell—localities which attract many visitors from Coldstream, and excursionists from all quarters.* A ford of the Tweed in the vicinity of Coldstream, the first one of moderate depth above Berwick, was the passage by which Edward I. entered Scotland in 1296, and by which many armies, both English and Scotch, made invasion from that period till 1640, when the Covenanters crossed it to make war against Charles I. A wealthy Cistercian nunnery, of which not a vestige now remains, was founded at Coldstream by the first Earl of Dunbar; and the bodies of the most distinguished of the Scottish heroes who fell at Flodden were interred in its burying ground. The nunnery stood on a spot a little eastward from the market place, where there are still some peculiarly luxuriant gardens.

* " A mile above Coldstream, on the south side of the Tweed, but readily accessible by a ferry boat, is the ancient village of Wark and the ruins of Wark Castle. The latter was demolished at the Union, and now consists of a few ruined fragments without any appearance of strength or interest. Anciently it was a fortalice of great importance and figured much in the sieges of the Border strifes. Froissart assigns the origin of the Order of the Garter to an incident at a ball at Wark Castle given by Edward III."

Coldstream has lately had the advantage of having had a thorough sewerage system and water supply introduced. Owing to the lowness of its level, Coldstream is in a considerable degree exempt from rain and cold, and, compared with some other parishes, does not suffer much from the scourging influence of the easterly blast : hence the climate is mild and salubrious. Coldstream is the head-quarters of the Earl of Wemyss' fox-hounds, which regularly hunt both sides of the Tweed, and is the principal pack in the district. The salmon fishing on the Tweed is good for both rod and net. Trout fishing on the Tweed is good and unrestricted ; it is also good in the Leet, which flows through the parish, but within the limits of the parish it is mostly preserved. The Leet also contains pike and very large eels.* From Cornhill are also accessible the Glen, the Till, the Bowmont, and other streams in Northumberland. Inn accommodation and lodgings can readily be had in the town by sportsmen and visitors.

CORNHILL, a village about a mile to the east (in England), contains an excellent inn (the Collingwood Arms), and for visiting Chevy Chase and Flodden, and for angling in the Northumberland waters, is an excellent centre.

General Holidays—New Year's Day, and an unfixed day in June.

Market Days—(fat cattle and sheep, *see* p. 469) held once in four weeks during the winter months—on Mondays; they are fixed by the bailie so as not to fall on the Kelso cattle market day. Owing to the farmers in the district selling their stock at home, the number of stock brought forward is not so large as hitherto.

Fairs and Great Hirings—none held in Coldstream ; but one is at Cornhill on the first Monday of March for hiring farm servants, and there the following important fair is held.

Cornhill Lamb and Wool Fair—(held in a field convenient to the village and railway station)—July 3 (or the Monday after when the date falls on a Sunday). This is the first fair of the kind in the district, and its business transactions are looked forward to with considerable interest by farmers and dealers, as the prices realised here assist in a great measure in regulating the terms of the other fairs which take place in the Border counties during the course of this and the following month. The number of lambs annually exposed varies greatly : thus in 1862 there were shown over 4000, in 1863 under 3000, and for last year (1864) little over 1000. This falling off seems to have been caused by the farmers having had good offers at home. A few sheep and cattle are also exposed. The wool sold is Leicester, full, half, and three-parts bred ; and although lots

* Eels—*see* foot-note, p. 429.

do not largely change hands, the transactions are of importance, as a *feeler* for the fair at Kelso (which is the principal fair for the sort of wool in the district—*see* p. 74) on the second Friday of the month. The sale of lambs begins about dawn, that of wool about 10 o'clock forenoon.

A little beyond Cornhill, at a very inconvenient distance from Coldstream, is the nearest railway station, on the Berwick and Kelso branch of the North-Eastern line. Coldstream is 64 miles from Edinburgh by rail, 12 from Kelso, and 14 from Berwick.

According to the census of 1861, the population of the town of Coldstream was 1834, of the entire parish, 2823, who constituted 670 separate families ; 4 of whom were returned as living in houses having no window, 289 in houses of one window, 205 in houses of two windows, and 172 (or rather less than a fourth) in houses of three or more windows.

Assessed property in 1864-5, £18,696 : 4 : 11.

The principal landed-proprietors in the parish are—the Earl of Home, Sir John Marjoribanks, and David Milne Home, Esq. (resident), and the Earl of Haddington, and Sir Hugh Hume Campbell of Marchmont (non-resident).

Superiors—Earls Haddington and Home.

LOCAL ACTING JUSTICES OF THE PEACE.

Those marked thus (*) are Resident in the parish.

*The Earl of Home.	*Lord Dunglass, The Hirsel.
*Sir John Marjoribanks, Bart., of Lees.	James Dickson, Esq. of Chatto, Bughtrig.
David Robertson, Esq. of Ladykirk, M.P.	George Greig, Esq., of Eccles.
*Archd. Dickson, Esq., of Castlelaw.	M. D. Hunter, Esq. of Antons Hill.
	*David Milne Home, Esq. of Milne Graden.
John Hood, Esq. of Stoneridge.	*Captain M'Laren, of Hope Park.
Clerk—Jonathan Melrose.	Procurator-Fiscal—Geo. Brown.

BAILIE AND COMMISSIONERS OF POLICE,

By whom the town is governed under the Act.

William Cunningham, Esq., Baron Bailie.

COMMISSIONERS OF POLICE.

Peter Robson.	John Halliburton.
John Allison.	M. J. Turnbull, M.D.
Robert Henderson.	Wm. Douglas.
J. S. M'Dougal.	Thomas Melrose.

William Douglas, Treasurer to Commissioners of Police.

George Brown, Clerk.

Police Rates, which do not include the water rates (*see* Companies) but includes the sewerage, averages 1s. per £. Total Assessment about £170.

COURTS.

JUSTICE OF PEACE SMALL DEBT COURTS are held on the third Wednesday of each month.

SHERIFF SMALL DEBT COURTS are held on the Saturday after the last Thursday of March, the last Wednesday of May, the Saturday after the last Thursday of July, and the last Wednesday of November.

POLICE OFFICERS—Sergeant Brown, William Gordon, and an assistant for the Tweed Protection.

PUBLIC OFFICES.

Billet Master—George Brown, solicitor.
Clerk of the Peace—Jonathan Melrose, solicitor.
Heritors' Clerk—William Cunningham, solicitor.
Poor, Inspector of, and Collector of Poor Rates—A. Y. Henderson.
Procurator-Fiscal, Coldstream District—George Brown, solicitor
Registrar of Births, Marriages, and Deaths—John Allison.
Session Clerk—John Allison, parochial schoolmaster.
Stamps and Taxes, Collector and Distributor of—John Halliburton, postmaster.
Sheriff Officer—
Statute Labour, Collector of—Jonathan Melrose, solicitor.
Town and Relieving Officer—

POST OFFICE.

John Halliburton, Postmaster.

Town Deliverer—James Reid, High Street (West).

DEPARTURES.

First Mail for South, at 2-35 p.m.	Second, at 6-30 p.m.
Do. North, at 8-25 a.m.	Second, at 4-15 p.m.
Do. Kelso, at 8-25 a.m.	Second, at 6-30 p.m.

ARRIVALS.

First Mail from South at 10-15 a.m.	Second, at 8-30 p.m.
Do. North, at 11-15 a.m.	Second, at 8-30 p.m.
Do. from Kelso, at 11-15 a.m.	Second, at 4-15 p.m.

Town Deliveries—at 11-30 a.m., and 8-30 p.m. On Sundays, 8-30 p.m.

Sundays.

DEPARTURES—Mail for South, 6-30 p.m. ; Do. for North and Kelso, 4 p.m. ARRIVALS First Mail from North, South, and Kelso, 8-30 p.m.

Office open on Sundays from 9-30 till 10-30 a.m., and from 1-30 till 2-30 p.m.

LOCAL POSTS.

To Presson, by Wark, Carham, &c., at 11-30 a.m. Returns at 5-30 p.m. James Reid, runner.

To Leitholm at 11-30 a.m. Returns at 6-15 p.m. Alex. Scott, runner.

To Etal and Ford, by Cornhill, &c., at 10-15 a.m. Returns at 6 p.m. Peter Brown, runner.

To Birgham and Eccles at 11-30 a.m. Returns about 5-30 p.m. Jas. Scott, runner.

To Kilham at noon. Returns next day at 11-15 a.m. James Spence, runner.

To Twizel four days a-week, at 10-15 a.m. Returns at 2 p.m. J. Reid, runner.

To Swinton at 11-30 a.m. Returns next morning, at 8-30 a.m. D. Reid, runner

---

CLERGY, &c.

Coldstream is in the Presbytery of Chirnside, and Synod of Merse and Teviotdale. Patron—Earl of Haddington.

ESTABLISHED CHURCH—Rev. Archibald Nisbet (Inducted 1860). Sittings, 1100. Average attendance at Sabbath School, 150. Superintendent of Sabbath School—Rev. A. Nisbet; Session Clerk and Kirk Treasurer—John Allison, parochial teacher; Precentor—Somerville Mercer, High Street; Church Officer—Wm. Hann, Church Lane.

FREE CHURCH—Rev. Alexander Rodger (Inducted 1847). Sittings, 600. Average attendance at Sabbath School, 100. Superintendent of Sabbath School and Session Clerk—Adam Y. Henderson; Treasurer—Walter Davidson, accountant; Precentor—George Deans, Wark; Church Officer—William Johnston, New Road.

UNITED PRESBYTERIAN (East)—Rev. James Porteous (Inducted 1840). Sittings, 700. Average attendance at Sabbath School, 100. Superintendent of Sabbath School—A. Robb, merchant; Treasurer—James Porteous; Precentor—John Davidson, Market Street; Church Officer—Walter Johnston, Abbey Lane.

UNITED PRESBYTERIAN (West)—Rev. Peter Mearns (Inducted 1846). Sittings, 1000. Average attendance at Sabbath School, 180. Treasurer — Robert Carmichael, merchant; Precentor — John Dalgleish, jun., High Street; Church Officer—William Shannon, Cornhill.

NEW ROAD CHAPEL—Various. Sittings, 150.

FAST DAYS—Wednesday before first Sunday of May and, for a long time past, a Wednesday before October, but not definitely fixed.

EDUCATIONAL INSTITUTIONS.*

Parochial School—John Allison, Master; average attendance, 225.
Do.   Mrs. Hewitson, teacher of Sewing School.

---

* Children in the parish from 5 to 15, attending school during the first week of April 1861, 501; of all ages, 537.

Boarding Academy for Young Gentlemen—Adam Y. Henderson. Assistants—Henry Todd and D. Munro.

Girls' School—Miss White, Market Place.

Side School at Milne Graden—Jas. Sked, teacher; aver. attend, 100.

Ladies' Seminary and Boarding Establishment—Miss J. M. Henderson

---

PAROCHIAL BOARD.

COMMITTEE.

William Cunningham, Chairman.

R. Carmichael.	Thomas Hogg.
Robert Tait.	George Smith.
Robert Henderson.	George Wilson.
Thomas Hood.	J. S. M'Dougal.

Adam Young Henderson, Inspector and Collector.

Average No. of Poor on Roll, 100. Average Rate of Assessment, 9d. per £.; total Assessment 1864-5, £1236 : 2 : 9.

DISPENSARY.

Supported by subscriptions from the Gentry in the district and the Parochial Board.

MEDICAL ATTENDANTS.

Alex. Brown, Surgeon. | M. J. Turnbull, M.D.

George Gillies, Surgeon.

George Wilson, Chemist to Dispensary.

Wm. Douglas, banker, Treas.   Wm. Cunningham, solicitor, Secy.

CHARITABLE BEQUESTS.

Charles Marjoribanks, Esq., M.P., of Lees, who died in 1833, bequeathed the sum of £1000, the interest of which to be applied for behoof of the aged and industrious poor of the town and neighbourhood. The distribution is managed by Mr. James Cunningham, banker; Mr. Robert Tait, Lees Mill; and Mr. John Halliburton, Post Office, in half-yearly payments, on the 25th January and 25th July. Number on list 40, who each receives £1.

Mr. John Bell of Berwick-upon-Tweed, who died about 1810, bequeathed the sum of £800, the interest of which to be applied in providing clothing, and educating, and otherwise assisting the children of the poor in the town. Managers—Kirk Session.

YEARLY BENEFIT SOCIETIES.

The same in principle as those of Kelso (see page 86), but with a more liberal payment to sick members viz.—6s. a week for the first three months, 3s. a week for the second three months, and 1s. 6d. a week till the close of the financial year of the Society.

HIGH STREET—meets in West U. P. Vestry.
George Tait, Secretary.   William Scott, Treasurer.

DUKE STREET—meets in Masonic Hall.
Gabriel Wood, Secretary.   Walter Johnson, Treasurer.

FEMALE CLOTHING SOCIETY.

Mrs. Nisbet, Manse, President.
Mrs Wilson of Georgefield, Secretary.   Mrs M'Dougal, Treasurer.

Established to purchase clothing for the poor of the town. Supported by voluntary subscriptions.

ST. JOHN'S LODGE OF FREE MASONS.
(Established 1825.)

Alexander Cameron, W. Master.   Thomas Pike, Treasurer.
George Brown, Secretary.

Masonic Hall, Duke Street—erected 1861, and the property of the Lodge.

MECHANICS' INSTITUTE.

The building is just completed, but the affairs of the Society are not yet arranged.

TRUSTEES OF BUILDING (commenced 1863).

William Cunningham, bailie.   Andrew Robb.
James Cunningham, banker.   M. J. Turnbull, M.D.
William Douglas, banker.   James Noble.
Robert Henderson.

TOTAL ABSTINENCE SOCIETY.
(Recently re-organized.)

President—Rev. Peter Mearns, West U. P. Church.
Secretary—Mr. Murray, Gas Lane.
Treasurer—Mr. Henderson, Academy.

READING ROOM AND LIBRARY.

W. Cunningham, Esq., President.

DIRECTORS.

Rev. Archibald Nisbet.   J. S. M'Dougal.
Rev. P. Mearns.   James Porteous.
Rev. A. Rodger.   Peter Robson.
John Allison.

Andrew Robb, Librarian.   William Douglas, Treasurer.

Annual Sub.—Reading Room, 10s. 6d., 5s., and 2s.   Library, 2s.

The Library contains upwards of 2000 volumes, and is open every Monday and Thursday evenings from 7 to 9 o'clock for giving out and receiving books from members. The annual meeting of the subscribers is held on the first Wednesday in November, and quarterly meetings on the first Wednesdays of February, May, and August.

BORDER HORTICULTURAL SOCIETY.

Patron—The Right Hon. the Earl of Home.
President (elected annually) for 1865—Sir John Marjoribanks, Bart, of Lees.
Vice-President—William Cunningham, Esq., Bailie.
Chaplin—Rev. Archibald Nisbet.
Treasurer—Mr. Thomas Henderson, Bank of Scotland.
Secretary—Mr. Allison, Parochial Teacher.

Competitions are held in the beginning of July and September. Average annual amount of prizes £30. The annual general meeting of the members is held in January.

UNION AGRICULTURAL SOCIETY.

The general exhibition of stock of this Society is held annually in March, at Kelso and Coldstream alternately. The exhibition of this year (1865) took place at Coldstream—see p. 89.

PLOUGHING CLUB (estab. 1858).

Patron—The Earl of Home.
President—Sir John Marjoribanks, Bart., of Lees.
Vice-President—William Cunningham, Bailie of Coldstream.
Hon. Secretary and Treasurer—William Calder, Esq., M.D., Oxenrig.

Annual Competition takes place on a suitable day about the end of December, when prizes to the amount of £9 are given away.

LITHTILLUM AND COLDSTREAM CURLING CLUB.

Patrons—The Earl of Home and Sir John Marjoribanks, Bart.
President—James Cunningham, Esq., banker, Coldstream.
Vice-President—Archibald Dickson, Esq., of Castlelaw.
Secretary—John Dove, Esq., Eccles Newtown.

Curling Pond at Lithtillum Loch, about 3 miles west from Coldstream.

GAS COMPANY

DIRECTORS.

William Douglas, Chairman.

John Halliburton, Coldstream.	Robert Carmichael, Coldstream.
William Dunn, Long Birgham.	Thomas Hogg, do.
Robert Henderson, Coldstream	J. S. M'Dougal. do.
M. J. Turnbull, do.	

William Cunningham, Clerk.   John Halliburton, Treasurer.

6s. 8d. per 1000 feet.

Dividend, 8 per cent in 1864.

We have not got the date of this gas company, but it was the first established in the district.

WATER COMPANY.

The Commissioners of Police, Ex-Officio.

WATER RATES.

Rents under £20,   2s. 6d. per Annum.

,,   from £20 to £30,   3s. 6d.   do.

,,   above £30,   5s. 0d.   do.

2ND BERWICKSHIRE RIFLE CORPS—(COLDSTREAM.)

Major Sir J. Marjoribanks, Bart., Captain. Thos. Hood, Lieutenant.
John Allison, Ensign.   Alex. Brown, Surgeon.
James Porteous, Quarter-Master, and Hon. Secretary and Treasurer.
Sergt.-Major Rogers, Drill Instructor and Resident Armourer.

Effective Force—65.

Armoury, and residence for Drill Instructor, Old School Buildings.

BANKS.

BRITISH LINEN COMPANY (opened 1820)—William Douglas, Agent ; W. Davidson, Acountant ; A. E. Jones, Clerk.

BANK OF SCOTLAND (opened 1855)—James Cunningham, Agent ; Thomas Henderson, Teller ; Alexander Laurie, Clerk.

SAVINGS' BANK (estab. 1842)—James Porteous, Actuary ; William Douglas, Treasurer. Open every Monday evening at 7 o'clock, in the Vestry of the Parish Church, for receiving and paying deposits. Amount of deposits November 1864, £3984 : 15 : 7. No. of depositors, 256. Interest allowed, £2 : 18 : 4.

POST OFFICE SAVINGS' BANK—John Halliburton, postmaster.

INSURANCE AGENTS.

ALLIANCE....................Wm. Cunningham, writer.
BRITISH GUARANTEE.........Jonathan Melrose, writer.
EDINBURGH LIFE...........Robert Henderson, merchant.
GENERAL....................Miss Scott, stationer.
INSURANCE CO. OF SCOTLAND..Wm Cunningham, writer.
LIFE ASSOCIATION............Ts. Henderson, Bank of Scotland.
LONDON & LIVERPOOL, AND }
    GLOBE................} A. & R. Robb, merchants.
NATIONAL (OF SCOTLAND).....Wm. Douglas, banker.
NATIONAL ALLIANCE ACCI- }
    DENTAL................} James M. Dewar, draper.
NORTH BRITISH.............Hogg and Wood, merchants.

PROVINCIAL.................George Gillies, surgeon.
SCOTTISH AMICABLE ....John Allison, teacher.
SCOTTISH EQUITABLE.........Jonathan Melrose, writer.
SCOTTISH UNION.............John Halliburton, stationer.
SCOTTISH PROVINCIAL (for- }
    merly Aberdeen).... .. } James M. Dewar, draper.
STANDARD...................Robert Carmichael, merchant.
SUN........................Jonathan Melrose, writer.

ASSOCIATION FOR THE PROMOTION OF THE FINE ARTS IN SCOTLAND.

John Halliburton, Esq., Hon. Secretary.

PROCURATORS AND NOTARIES PUBLIC.

George Brown, house, High Street (West).
William Cunningham, office and house, Rosybank.
Jonathan Melrose (of M. & Porteous), N.P., office, Dunse Road ; residence, Newbigging, Northumberland.
James Porteous (of Melrose & P.), office, Dunse Road ; residence, High Street (East).

MEDICAL PRACTITIONERS.

Brown Alexander, (of Turnbull & B.), High Street (East).
Gillies, George. High Street, (West).
Purves, J. High Street, (West).
Turnbull, M. J. (of T. & Brown), M.D., High Street, (East).

VETERINARY SURGEON—Robert Watson, High Street.

MILLS.

LEES (Coldstream)—Corn and Flour—Robert Tait.
TWEED MILL*—Corn and Meal—William M'Laren.

QUARRIES.

SOUTH QUARRY—the property of John Fair, Esq., Edinburgh ; let to Smith and Brown, masons, Coldstream.

NORTH QUARRY—the property of James Cunningham, Esq , banker, Coldstream ; unlet.

MILNE GRADEN—the property of David Milne Home, Esq. ; unlet. The stone of this quarry is the finest in the locality.

* Situated about 3 miles below Coldstream—the last mill on the Tweed.

CARRIERS.

BERWICK—A. Younger, every other day, Market Place.
DUNSE—A. Mack, Mondays,   do.
GREENLAW—Robert Richardson, Mondays, William Tait's.
KELSO—A. Mack, Tuesdays and Fridays, Market Place.
WOOLER—John Turnbull, Mondays, William Tait's.

CONVEYANCE BY RAILWAY.

Trains leave station at Cornhill for Kelso and the North, and for Berwick and the South, several times daily. See Time Tables. An Omnibus from the Newcastle Arms Hotel attends all the Trains— Fare, 6d. Station-master at Cornhill—William Deans.

STATUTE LABOUR ROADS.

Coldstream is in the Swinton district, which *see.*

CORNHILL DISTRICT OF ROADS.

Clerk—J. Melrose, Solicitor.
Surveyor—James Cunningham, Bank of Scotland
Surveyor of Coldstream Bridge—James Cunningham.

DIRECTORY.

——

TRADES, RESIDENTS, AND PUBLIC OFFICES.

Those marked thus (*) are Registered Voters.

Abbey Lane

Gilkie, Miss, Abbey House

Church Lane

Armoury of the Coldstream Corps of Rifle Volunteers, Old School Buildings. Resident—Sergeant-Major Rogers
Hann, William, church officer
Ruffle, James, saddler
Shiell, Ellen, innkeeper

Duke Street

*Briggs, James, joiner and implement maker
Brown, Peter, post-runner to Ford, &c.
Davidson, J. & A., brewers, grocers, wine and spirit merchants
Assistant manager—Henry Fairgrieve
*Davidson, A. (of J. & A. D.)
*Ewart, Samuel, fenar
Henderson, Thomas, teller, Bank of Scotland
Henderson, R., baker
*Kerse, William, mason
Masonic Hall
*Melrose's, Thomas, currying premises
*Murray, William, blacksmith
*Oliver, Archibald, plumber and gas-fitter
White, John, joiner

Dunse Road

Dewar, Walter, slater
Hogg, Mrs. (late of Bogangreen)
Melrose & Porteous, solicitors, writing chambers
*Plenderleith, George, bootmaker
Queen's Head Inn, William Brady
Robson, John, cattle salesman
Service, Mrs., farmer
The Old Manse, Alexander Cameron

Gas Lane

Gas Works, George Murray, resident manager
Laidlaw, James, cow keeper
*Lamb, John, roper

High Street (East)

*Baird, William, blacksmith
Bank of Scotland, *James Cunningham, resident agent
Blue Bell Inn, Robert Sked
*Brady, John, bootmaker
British Linen Company Bank, *William Douglas, resident agent
Brown, Robert (of Smith & B.), mason
Burns, James, tinsmith
*Carmichael, Robert, grocer, wine and spirit merchant, and seedsman
    Managing assistant—Alexander Cockburn
Carmichael, Thomas, wholesale grocer, furnishing ironmonger, and iron merchant
    Assistant manager—Robert Swan
*Collingwood, Henry, saddler
Commercial Inn, L. Shaw
Dewar, James M., draper
Donaldson, Mrs., & Sons, fishmongers and game dealers
East U. P. Church (Rev. James Porteous's—see p. 487)
Established Church (Rev. Arch. Nisbet's—see p. 487)
Foster, William, saddler
Foster, John, photographic artist
Free Church (Rev. Alexander Rodgers's—see p. 487)
Gray, Andrew, boot and shoemaker
    Bootmaker to the late Prince Consort
Hair, Miss, dressmaker
*Halliburton, John, bookseller, stationer, and sub-distributor of stamps and taxes
*Henderson, Robert, grocer, wine, and spirit merchant
    Assistant manager—James Shiel
*Hogg, Thomas (of H. & Wood, Market Place)
Hogg, William, butcher
*Johnston, Alexander, boot and shoe maker
Johnston, George, market gardener
Johnston, William, boot and shoemaker
Lawson, Mrs.
M'Cankie, Thomas, merchant
*M'Dougal, John S., saddler and harness maker, and net and rope merchant
    Assistant manager— Henry Collingwood
Mechanics' Institution
News Room and Reading Room, Miss Tait, keeper

Nisbet, Colonel Robert, of Mersington *
Nisbet, Robert, jun., of Mersington
*Nisbet, Rev. Archibald, The Manse
O'Brian, J., painter and paper-hanger
Palmer, Thomas, baker
Pike, Thomas, grocer, wine and spirit merchant
Porteous, Rev. James, East U. P. Manse
Porteous, James (of Melrose & P.)
Post Office, John Halliburton, postmaster
*Purves, John, surgeon and druggist
Ramsay, William, joiner
Richardson, Mrs.
Robb, A. & R., grocers, booksellers, &c.
    Servants' Register Office
Robson, Mrs., Monument Cottage
Smith, George, ironmonger
Smith, Mrs. Janet, merchant
    Servants' Register Office
Stamford, Thomas, & Son, drapers, tailors, clothiers, &c.
*Stamford, Thomas, draper
Stamford, William (of T. S. & Son)
Stamp and Tax Office, John Halliburton, collector
*Steel, William, grocer and spirit merchant
Steelyard, Alexander Smart, keeper
Swan, Misses, dressmakers
Tait, William, innkeeper
Taylor, J., horse trainer
Turnbull, Robert, jeweller, watch and clock maker
Walker, John, joiner, implement maker, etc.
Wallace, George, baker
Watson, Robert, veterinary surgeon
*Whitelaw, Francis, feuar
*Wilson, George (of Georgefield), medicine warehouse

High Street (West)

Baird. Mrs. (late of Yetholm Manse)
Bay Horse Inn, Mrs. Moore
*Bennet, Andrew, cabinet-maker and upholsterer
*Bennet, Robert, cabinet-maker and upholsterer
Brown, Alexander (of Turnbull & B.), surgeon
Brown, George, solicitor
Clark, Misses, dressmakers
Cockburn, Mark, china merchant
Coldstream Boarding Academy, A. Y. Henderson, rector
Common, James, & Son, watchmakers
County Police Office, William Brown, police sergeant

* See Seats, Eccles lists.

Cunningham, Peter, teacher of dancing, &c.
*Dalgleish, John blacksmith
Ford & Son, plumbers
*Gillies, George, surgeon
*Henderson, Adam Young, *rector, Coldstream Academy,*
    and *Inspector of Poor*
Henderson, William, general drapery establishment
    Assistants—Robt. Robertson and W. Henderson, junr.
Hogarth, Peter, painter and paper-hanger
Kay, James, painter and paper-hanger
Ladies' Seminary, Miss Jane M. Henderson
*Mearns, Rev. Peter, *West U. P. Manse*
Medical Hall, Nicholas Dodds, chemist
*Melrose, Thomas, leather merchant, tanner, etc.
    Assistant—George Plenderleith
*Mercer, Somerville, boot and shoemaker
Newcastle Arms Hotel, Mrs. Margaret Hume
Paterson, Mrs., merchant
Reid, Joseph, baker
Reid, James, post runner and town deliverer
*Scott, James, cow-keeper
Smart, James, carter
Smith, Mrs. (late of Westfield)
Smith, David, baker
*Tait, Robert, grocer, miller, and grain merchant
*Tait, William, game dealer and merchant
Town Hall and Court House, Miss Tait, resident keeper
*Turnbull, Dr. M. J. (of T. & Brown), surgeon
West U. P. Church (Rev, P. Mearns's, *see* p. 487).
Whitehead, James, plasterer

Home Place

*Allison, John, *Registrar, Session Clerk,* etc.
*Beloe, W. L. teacher of dancing and fishing-tackle maker
Carlisle, Robert, stud groom to Lord Wemyss
Carmichael, John (late of Tilmouth)
*Davidson, Walter, (accountant, B. L. Company's Bank)
    Quarry Cottage
Dodds, James, millwright, Quarry Houses
Parochial School, J. Allison, master
    Sewing Mistress, Mrs. Hewitson
*Rodger, Rev. Alexander, *Free Church Manse*

Market Place

Aimers, Alexander, merchant
Black Bull Inn, James Weatle
Clarke, A. G. butcher

Coldstream Brewery, J. & A. Davidson
    Brewer—John Stoddart
*Dippie, James, candlemaker
Dodds, William, gardener
Dunn, David, merchant and shoemaker
*Fish, Alexander, grocer, wine, and spirit merchant
    Assistant—P. Meikle
*Guthrie, Thomas, carter
Heard, William, cattle dealer, &c.
Hogg & Wood's seed stores and offices.   Nurseries—High
    Street and Lees Lodge
    Resident Clerk—Peter Thompson
Livingstone, Miss Jane
*Luke, Harry, horse dealer
*Luke, William, cooper
Mack, Andrew, carrier to Berwick, Kelso, Wooler, and
    Dunse
Shiel, George, joiner and implement maker
Smeaton, J., baker
Turner, John, slater
Wood, Alexander, grocer and pork curer

Market Street

Davidson, George, butcher, farmer, &c.
Dunn, Mrs., merchant
Laidlaw, William, town crier and bill poster
Mill, Robert, hair dresser
*Neilans, John, grocer, meal dealer, and farmer
Oliver, Margaret, merchant
Red Lion Inn, Mrs. Ann Young
Scott, Miss, bookseller
Ternent, Thomas, tailor
*Wight, John, commission agent

New Road

Dalton, Christopher, sweep
*Hume, James, mason
Infant School, Miss White, teacher
Kedie, Miss, dressmaker
Matthew, Peter, carter
Melrose, Thomas, tannery (*see* p. 497)
New Road Chapel
*Noble, James, joiner, undertaker, &c.
*Robson, Peter, tailor and clothier
Smith, William (of S. & Brown, masons)
Weatherston, Andrew, carter
Weatherston, John, carter

Wood, Gabriel, merchant
Younger, Adam, carrier to Berwick, etc.

Roseybank

*Cunningham, Wm., Esq. (baron bailie), solicitor, writing chambers
Managing assistant—George Brown, solicitor

Village of Lennel Newtown

*Gray, John, grocer and feuar
Hogg, Archibald, blacksmith
Renton, John, joiner
*Salmon Inn, Andrew Scott
Scott, Robert, fishmonger and game dealer
Scott, William, fisherman
*Sim, John, gardener
*Skeene, James, labourer
Storey, Mrs., Lennel Bank
Wilson, Alexander, grocer and meal dealer

RESIDENTS, FARMERS, &c., IN THE PARISH.

*Bauchope, John, farmer, Milne Graden Westmains
*Calder, Turnbull,   do. Oxenrig, M.D.
*Davidson, Thomas,   do. Westmains
*Davidson, William,   do.   do.
*Dodds, George,   do. Fireburnmill
*Fairbairn, John,   do. Todhillrig
*Hood, Thomas,   do. Coldstream Mains,
*Hutchison, John, of Ruthven
Hutchison, William, farmer, Ruthven
Hutton, Arthur, factor, Milne Graden
*Lauder, James, grocer, etc., Bridge-end
*M'Laren, William, miller, Tweed Mill
*Somerville, Alexander, do. Hawkslaw
Shaw, James, farmer, Skaithmuir
Smith, George, factor for Hirsel, The Crooks
*White William, farmer, Lennelhill
*Young, Thomas, farmer, Little Todrig

SEATS, &c., OF COUNTY FAMILIES IN THE PARISH.

CASTLE LAW.

About 2 miles west from Coldstream—the property and occasional residence and home farm of Archibald Dickson, Esq., (see Eccles parish), J. P.

THE HIRSEL.

About a mile from the town of Coldstream, on the south side of the Leet, surrounded by fine woods—the seat of the Earl of Home (Cospatrick Alexander Home), Baron Home and Baron of Dunglass in the peerage of Scotland, and representative peer for Scotland ; born 27th October 1799 ; succeeded his father, the late Alexander 10th Earl of Home, 21st October 1841 ; married 1832 the Hon. Lucy-Elizabeth, daughter of Henry James, late Lord Montagu (ext.), and has issue—

Charles Alexander, Lord Dunglass, born 11th April 1834 ; a Justice of Peace and Deputy-Lieutenant for Lanarkshire, Justice of Peace for Berwickshire, and Captain Queen's Own Royal Glasgow Yeomanry Cavalry.
James Archibald, born 20th January 1837.
Montagu Cospatrick, born 9th June 1840 (died 1st June 1859).
William Sholto, born 25th February 1842.
Cospatrick, born 2d May 1848.
George Douglas, born 4th October 1853.
Elizabeth-Eleonora Ada.
Charlotte-Lucy.

His Lordship is a Justice of Peace and Deputy-Lieutenant for Berwickshire.
Other seats of the Hirsel family—Douglas and Bothwell Castles, Lanarkshire. London Addresses — Carlton Club, S.W. ; 6 Grosvenor Square, W.

HOPE PARK.

At Dunse Road, Coldstream—the residence of *Captain Alexander Donald M'Laren, J.P.

THE LEES.

Close to Coldstream, on a peninsula formed by the junction of the Leet with the Tweed—the seat and residence of *Sir John Marjoribanks, Bart., of Lees ; born 1830 ; succeeded 1834 ; married, 1858, Charlotte-Mary, daughter of R. Trotter, Esq., of Mortonhall, Midlothian.
Heir pres., his brother William, born 1832 ; who married Frances Anne, daughter of the late Baldwin Duppa Duppa, Esq., of Hollingbourne House, Kent.

LENNEL HOUSE.

About 1 mile below Coldstream on a high bank overhanging the Tweed, and occupying the site of the ancient convent of Lennel—the property of the Earl of Haddington, and occupied by the Earl of Wemyss as a hunting seat.

MILNE GRADEN.

A modern mansion finely situated on the Tweed amidst extensive grounds at the east end of the parish, and about $3\frac{1}{2}$ miles from Coldstream — the seat and principal residence of David Milne Home, Esq. of Billy and Wedderburn, eldest son of the late Admiral Sir David Milne, G.C.B., of Milne Graden; born 1803; succeeded 1845; married 1832, Jean, eldest daughter and co-heir of the late William Foreman Home, Esq., of Paxton House (Hutton parish, which *see*), and has issue—

*David, born 25th September 1838; Cornet, Horse Guards.

Five daughters — Jean, Grace, Margaret, Georgina, and Susan.

Mr. Milne Home was called to the Scottish Bar 1826; appointed Advocate Depute 1838; is a Justice of Peace and Deputy-Lieutenant for the county of Berwick, a Magistrate for Midlothian, and author of several treatises on astronomy and geology. This family came originally from Invernessshire.

Other seats in Berwickshire—Wedderburn Castle, near Dunse; Paxton House, near Berwick. Town Addresses—10 York Place, and New Club, Edinburgh; Carlton Club, London, W.S.

REGISTERED VOTERS (Non-Resident).

Allen, Ralph, v. surgeon, Holystone, Newcastle
Davidson, James, carter, Wark
Donaldson, Alexander, feuar
Dunn, William, farmer, Birgham, Eccles
Fairbairn, James, feuar, West Fireburnmill
Harvey, Gavin, clerk, London
Hogarth, George (of Marlefield), Eccles Tofts
Inglis, Craigie Charles H., of Cramond, near Edinburgh
Liddle, John, surgeon, London
Logan, William, Belford
Lorimer, Alexander, M.D., *Dep. Inspector General of Hospitals*, 11 Brunswick Street, Edinburgh
Melrose, Jonathan (of M. & Porteous, Coldstream), East Newbigging, Northumberland
Purves, Jas., watchmaker, 4 Victoria Place, Edinburgh
Scott, James, carter, Wark
Sibbald, John Robertson, (of Lechend), M.D., 8 Newington Terrace, Edinburgh
Trotter, John W., seaman
Turnbull, Matthew, Belhaven, Dunbar

LADYKIRK.

------◆------

THE parish of Ladykirk, formed by the ancient parishes of Horndean and Upsettlington, containing some of the finest and richest pasturage in Scotland, or indeed in Great Britain, is situated in the eastern part of the county, about 10 miles from the sea, on the north bank of the river Tweed, which there forms the boundary between England and Scotland. It is bounded on the north and east by Hutton, on the north and west by Whitsome and Swinton, and on the south-west by Coldstream. Its length is upwards of 4 miles and its average breadth about 2 miles. The area of the parish, according to the Ordnance Survey, is $3446\frac{3}{4}$ acres; of this $54\frac{1}{2}$ are occupied by public and private roads, $66\frac{1}{2}$ woods and plantations. The surface gently rises from the Tweed, and is diversified with swelling slopes, especially from the river, which skirts the parish for $4\frac{1}{4}$ miles. The soil throughout is very fertile, and under a high state of cultivation. The late Mr. Robertson of Ladykirk in 1788 introduced the famous short-horned breed of cattle into Berwickshire; for which that county, as well as north Northumberland owe him a very great debt of gratitude. The climate, from the fine exposure to the south, and being greatly protected from the north and east winds, and the land being thoroughly drained, is very healthful. On the Tweed, which bounds the parish its entire length, there are several valuable salmon fisheries, one half the extent of which—upwards of 2 miles—the present Mr. Robertson most handsomely allows to be open for angling, both for salmon and trout, to all the respectable residents or visitors in the neighbourhood. There are three small villages in the parish, viz.—HORNDEAN, to the north, having a population of 160; Ladykirk, in the centre, merely a few cottages belonging to the farm; and UP-SETTLINGTON, in the south, consisting of cottages containing the work people on the Ladykirk estate. Ladykirk church, an interesting Gothic edifice, especially within, was built in the year 1500 by James IV. of Scotland, who returning with his followers from a raid on the English Borders, having vowed if he got safe over the Tweed, at the ford there, he would build a church and dedicate it to the Virgin—a promise which he fulfilled—and called it Ladykirk. This church has recently undergone a thorough repair at the expense of the heritors, and a handsome three-light stained window, by Wailes of Newcastle, has been inserted in the east end, at the sole expense of Mrs. Robertson. The ford was always a dangerous one, and the present Mr. Robertson, in 1839, with the aid of Dr. Gilly, Lord Home, Lord Frederick Fitzclarence, Lord Haddington, Mr. Wilkie of Ladythorn, and others, completed the good work of building a bridge between Ladykirk and Norham, of stone piers with a wooden superstructure. Within the park are perhaps the finest stables and riding school in the kingdom. The house is large and modern, and beautifully situated, commanding a fine view and reach of the river.* Within the policies of Ladykirk House, a very fine sandstone quarry (Bannockburn Quarry), from which the extensive buildings on the estate have been wrought. This stone is part of the valuable strata which underlays all this part of the county (see p. 468).

The post town is Berwick-upon-Tweed, 10 miles distant. The nearest market town is Coldstream, about 6 miles from the centre of the parish. The nearest railway station is at Norham on the south side of the river, 2 miles distant on the Berwick and Kelso branch of the North-Eastern railway

The population of the parish in 1861 was 565; who constituted 121 separate families.

Assessed property in 1864-5, £6851 : 2 : 11.

The principal landed proprietor in the parish is—David Robertson, Esq., M.P., Lord-Lieutenant for Berwickshire.

---

* Connected with the locality, but lying across the Tweed, in Northumberland, is Norham village and castle. The village is a single wide street of 919 inhabitants, with a green, queer pyramidal cross, and church dedicated to St. Cuthbert, which is a handsome building having a massive tower and Norman zig-zag arches, and modern stained glass windows. The philanthropic Dr. Gilly, author of "Waldensian Researches," was the late rector of Norham. The Castle is a massive red sandstone keep, rising above the river, with many vaults and fragments of other edifices, enclosed within an outer wall of great circuit. Sir Walter Scott's description of this ancient fortress as it stood in the days of its strength, with which his poem of "Marmion" opens is familiar to all. Norham Castle is chiefly remarkable as being the place where Edward I. disclosed his ambitious designs against the independence of Scotland, when the rival claims of Bruce and Baliol to the Scottish throne were referred to his decision. The Scottish barons assembled at Upsettlington, to weigh his claim to be considered the Lord Paramount of Scotland ; and, however doubtful of its validity, being unprepared for resistence, were forced to deliver into his custody the whole fortresses of the kingdom. The Castle was taken, through the advice of a traitor, by James IV. in 1513, who, after demolishing its outworks and ravaging the country round, took up a position at Flodden, six miles distant, when that fatal engagement took place in which he fell, with the flower of his nobility. From Norham down the bank of the river and through the fields, a pleasant footpath extends to the village of Horncliff, beyond which about a mile the Union Chain Bridge spans the Tweed (see Hutton parish) close to Horncliff a glen strikes off the Tweed which terminates at a picturesque solitary mill and dripping petrifying spring—a spot occasionally visited by tourists and others from Berwick.

Those marked thus (*) are Registered Voters.

RESIDENT JUSTICE OF THE PEACE—David Robertson, Esq.

DISTRICT POLICE STATION at Swinton.

PUBLIC OFFICES—Heritors' Clerk, Inspector of Poor, Kirk Treasurer, Session Clerk, and Registrar of Births, Marriages, and Deaths —Joseph Hutton Thomson.
Medical Officer and Public Vaccinator—Dr. Paxton, Norham.

POST OFFICE—Post Town, Berwick. Robert Alder, Ladykirk, Postmaster ; Robt. Trotter, Messenger. Arrival, 10 a.m. and 8-30 p.m. Despatch, 2-30 and 5-30 p.m., six days a week.

CLERGY, &c.—Ladykirk is in the Presbytery of Chirnside, and Synod of Merse and Teviotdale. Patron—The Crown.
Established Church—*Rev. William Dobie (Inducted 1853). Sittings, 270. Average attendance at Sabbath School, 34.
United Presbyterian Church (Horndean)—*Rev. John Stark (Inducted 1849). Sittings, 450. Average attendance at Sabbath School, 30.

FAST DAYS—Thursday before last Sabbath of February and second Sabbath of July.

SCHOOL†—Parochial—*J. H. Thomson, Master. Aver. attend., 65.

PAROCHIAL BOARD—Rev. W. Dobie, Chairman. No. of Poor on Roll, 23. Average Rate of Assessment, 3½d. per £ ; total Assessment for 1864-5, £218 : 16 : 8.

CHARITABLE BEQUEST—Margaret Lyal, in 1804, bequeathed the sum of £100, the interest of which to be laid out in educating poor children belonging to the parish whose parents are unable to give them any.

LIBRARIES—A Congregational Library at Horndean, a Library supported by Mr. Robertson, Ladykirk, and Sabbath School Library.

FAIR—Held at Ladykirk on 5th April (25th March o. s.). This fair is of very ancient date, and was once a great place for the sale of cloth (linen and woollen), lint, seeds, and plants. It has now dwindled down to "sweeties," crockery, coopers' goods, tinsmith's wares, etc.

CARRIER—Thomas Dyer, New Ladykirk, to Berwick every Saturday

TRADES, &c.

Village of Horndean

Alison, Robert, shepherd
Bennet, Thomas, watchmaker
Blair, George, general dealer
Burnet, James, gardener
Carse, Adam, baker
Cockurn, George, joiner

---

† Children in the parish from 5 to 15 attending school during the first week of April 1861, 99 ; of all ages, 101.

Gillies, Sergeant, innkeeper
Hay, William, shoemaker
Henderson, John, smith
*Henderson, William, shoemaker
Robertson, John, innkeeper
Steel, Isabella, dressmaker
Wight, Joseph, tailor

Ladykirk
Cairns, William, blacksmith

RESIDENTS, FARMERS, &c., IN THE PARISH.

Bird, James, Horndean Cottage
Herriot, Mrs. Fellowhills farm
*Jeffrey, Alexander, farmer, Walterstead
*Stenhouse, John, farmer, Old Ladykirk
*Straughan, James, do. Ramrig
*Straughan, William, do.   do.
*Unthank, Thomas, do. New Ladykirk
*Webster, John,   do. New Horndean

SEAT OF COUNTY FAMILY.

LADYKIRK HOUSE.

A modern building, very finely situated on the banks of the Tweed, and surrounded by a magnificent park, beautifully wooded, extending to upwards of 150 acres—the seat and principal residence of David Robertson, Esq., youngest son of the late Sir John Marjoribanks, Bart., M.P., of Lees, and uncle of the present baronet; born 1797; married 1834, Mary Sarah, eldest daughter of the late Sir Thomas Haggerston, Bart., and granddaughter and heiress of the late W. Robertson, Esq., of Ladykirk, whose name they assumed, and has issue—

Thomas Haggerston, born November 1843, died 1861.
Sarah, married 1856, Watson Askew, Esq., of Pallinsburn, Northumberland, and has issue.
Alicia-Margaret, married 1862, to Henry Day Ingilby, Esq. younger of Ripley Castle, Yorkshire, and has issue.

Mr. Robertson is Lord Lieutenant and M.P. for the county. London Address—56 Upper Brook Street, W.

REGISTERED VOTERS (Non-Resident).

Grant, John, farm-servant, Lumsdaine
Rattery, Rev. Alexander, Craigend House, Glasgow
Wilson, John (farmer, Ladykirkshiels), Loanend Cottage, Horncliff

EARLSTON.

THIS parish was originally called Ercildoune, the origin of which is uncertain. It appears to have attracted considerable notice at a very early period, probably from its vicinity to Melrose and Dryburgh. It is bounded on the north by Legerwood and Gordon, on the east by Smailholm and Nenthorn, on the south by Mertoun, and on the west by Melrose. Its greatest length, from a point west of Carolside to its extreme north east corner, is 7¼ miles; its greatest breadth, along its western boundary, is 4 miles; and, according to the Ordnance Survey, it contains 10,009½ acres, of which 151 are occupied by public and private roads, and 41 are under water; there is also a detached portion of about the fortieth part of an acre lying on the west side of the Leader, and on which is situated a thatched cottage belonging to the farm of Craigsford.* Part of the parish is hilly, and contains no elevated ranges; the only remarkable hill is "Earlston Black Hill," which rises to the height of 1031 feet, and bears signs of a Roman encampment. The soil of the parish varies a good deal, the arable part being a rich loam, which is in high cultivation. The climate of the parish is mild, and the atmosphere dry. In the Leader, which separates the parish from Melrose, trout are plentiful; indeed it is one of the best tributaries of the Tweed for the angler. The Eden, another very good trouting stream, also flows through part of the parish. In both these streams angling is partly restricted. In the vale of the Leader the scenery on either side is very fine. The Edinburgh and Kelso coach road intersects the parish throughout its entire length. This, as well as the other roads (with which the parish is very well provided) are well kept.

Beautifully situated near the western boundary of the parish is the small town of Earlston, in a rich valley, surrounded by hills of a moderate height. It is celebrated as having been the residence of "Thomas the Rhymer," a small part of whose dwelling, called Learmont Tower (now the property of Charles Wilson, Esq., manufacturer), still remains; and Cowdenknowes, a delightful residence, the scene of the ancient song, "The Bonnie Broom," is near the town. Earlston possesses one ex-

---

* How this moiety of Craigsford comes to be part of Earlston parish we have been unable to discover. The rest of the farm belongs to Melrose parish.

tensive woollen manufactory,—the only one in the county—and also produces quantities of the well-known "Earlston ginghams." There is no other place in the country where the same class of ginghams is made.

Earlston itself is remarkably healthy. It is also thoroughly drained, and it had a fine supply of water recently laid down.

Earlston is 31 miles from Edinburgh by the old coach road which passes through the village, 11 from Kelso, and 7 from Lauder. The new branch of the North British railway from Dunse to Newtown is now open for traffic to Earlston, and that part of it extending to Newtown is in rapid progress. This, when completed, will be of considerable service to Earlstoun, as well as the whole county of Berwick, as it opens direct communication with the north-west of England.

About 2 miles south from the town of Earlston, in the south-western part of the parish on the Leader, is the ancient hamlet of REDPATH, consisting mostly of a few thatched houses. Near to FANS, formerly a village, but now merely an extensive farm steading, occupying an eminence in the north-eastern part, is a goods or mineral station on the Berwickshire branch of the N. B. railway.

In the eastern extremity of the parish is MELLERSTAIN, a seat of the Earl of Haddington. The house occupies a very fine position on a rising ground close to the river Eden, which here widens into a beautiful loch. The grounds are very finely laid out, and the house is embosomed in magnificent woods, which surround it on all sides. COWDENKNOWES, already mentioned, is the seat of R. Cotesworth, Esq. CAROLSIDE, the seat of A. Mitchell, Esq., occupies a very pleasant and pretty site on the Leader about a mile to the north of the town of Earlston. There is a fine well stocked deer park belonging to it. This, and the one at Ancrum are the only deer parks in the three counties.

Holidays.—Few holidays are held, and these at irregular periods.

Fairs.—The June fair falls on the 29th, or Monday after if the date be a Sunday. The October fair falls on the third Thursday of the month. These fairs are for _feeding cattle, cows,_ and _horses,_ and are held on the easter and wester greens of the town. Like most fairs in small towns, they have fallen off considerably within the last twelve or fifteen years. At one time these were great fairs in the district; and for grazing cattle still attract both buyers and sellers from a distance. The cows and horses have only a local interest. It is confidently expected that these fairs will revive their ancient importance with the through opening of the railway (in August), which will open up a large stock district, of which Earlston will then form the centre. A few early sales and consignments of wool are made at the June fair.

Lately a fortnightly sale of stock has been commenced in Earlston, conducted by Mr. Alexander Shiels, Kedslie. So far as it has gone, it promises to be a success. The sale is held every alternate Saturday.

Grain Market.—At a large and influential meeting of farmers held in Earlston on 24th August 1864, among others, the following resolutions were unanimously passed.—"That this meeting resolve that a grain market be opened at Earlston;" and "that the market shall be weekly, and shall be opened on the completion of the Berwickshire railway." Mr. James Smail, banker was appointed hon. secretary; and a large committee was appointed, with a view to carrying out the resolutions at the proper time.

According to the census of 1861, the population of the town of Earlston was 980, and consisted of 444 males and 536 females.[*] The population of the entire parish was 1825, who constituted 399 families, of whom 152 were returned as living in houses having one window, and 130 in houses having two windows—leaving 52, or as nearly as possible a fourth, who lived in houses of three or more windows.

The assessed property of the parish in 1864-5 was £11,119.

The principal landed-proprietor in the parish is the Earl of Haddington, who possesses about two-thirds of the rental; the other principal proprietors are—Thomas Tod, Esq., of Drygrange (_see_ Melrose, p. 151); Alexander Mitchell, Esq., of Carolside; Robert Cotesworth, Esq., of Cowdenknowes; and Major Brown, of Park.

Superior of Earlston—the Earl of Haddington.

Those marked thus (*) are Registered Voters.

BARON BAILIE.

Robert Swan, Esq., Kelso.

LOCAL ACTING JUSTICES OF THE PEACE.

The Earl of Haddington.	Thomas Tod of Drygrange.
Lord Binning, Mellerstain.	R. Cotesworth of Cowdenknowes.
Alexander Mitchell of Carolside.	

Police Officer—Alexander Shaw.

Justice of Peace Courts for the district are held at Lauder—which _see._

---

[*] A redundancy of females equal to 19 per cent.—_see_ Chirnside lists, and Melrose, p. 130.

COURT OF BOURLAWMEN.

Mr Joseph Ker ; Mr James Mather.

The men holding this somewhat rare office are sworn when appointed to give judgment, to the best of their knowledge and ability, in cases that come before them, and their decision is understood to be absolute in point of law. Their work as Bourlawmen consists of fixing the amount of damages done by straying or pounded cattle and the like.

PUBLIC OFFICES, &c.

Burgh Officer and Billet Master—James Black.
Heritors' Clerk—Daniel Aitkenhead.
Gas Works—George Wood, manager and proprietor.
Poor, Inspector of—Robert Smith.
Kirk Treasurer—Robert Smith.
Registrar of Births, Marriages, and Deaths—Robert Smith.
Session Clerk—Daniel Aitkenhead.
Stamps, Sub-Distributor of—Ralph Dodds, merchant.
Medical Officer and Public Vaccinator—Robert Riddell, surgeon.

POST OFFICE.

Earlston is a Sub-Office under Melrose.
William Crockett, Postmaster and Deliverer.
Arrivals—10·40 a.m., 7 p.m. ; Departures—6·30 a.m., 3 p.m.
Post Runners—David Swanston and David Trotter.
Letters are delivered over the town immediately after arrival.

CLERGY, &c.

Presbytery of Lauder, Synod of Merse and Teviotdale.
Patron—The Crown.

ESTABLISHED CHURCH—Rev. D. W. Gordon (Inducted 1808). Assistant—Rev. Robert Horne. Sittings, 800. Average attendance at Sabbath School, 80. Precentor—Robert Lees ; Church Officer—Thomas Sudden.

UNITED PRESBYTERIAN CHURCH (East)—Rev. Alexander Henderson (Inducted 1854). Sittings, 400. Av. attend. at Sab. School, 44. Superintendent of Sabbath School—Minister ; Kirk Treasurer—Mr. William Mercer ; Precentor—Henry Wallace, shoemaker.

U. P. CHURCH (West)—Rev. John Kechie (Inducted 1851). Sittings, 200, Average attendance at Sabbath School, 55. Superintendent of Sabbath School—Mr. William Hislop ; Session Clerk—Mr. W. Hislop ; Kirk Treasurer—Mr. Johnstone M'Vitie ; Precentor—George Young ; Church Officer—David Trotter.

FAST DAYS—In February and July—unfixed.

SCHOOLS.†

Parochial (Earlston)—Daniel Aitkenhead, master. Av. attend., 120.
Auxiliary (Redpath)—John Walker, teacher. Av. attend., 58
Mellerstain School—supported by Lord Haddington. ——· Mitchell, teacher. Av. attend., 60.
Free Church School (Earlston)—M. Berry, teacher. Av. attend., 106.
Female School (Earlston)—Miss Phin, teacher. Av. attend., 35.

PAROCHIAL BOARD.

Chairman—R. Swan, Esq., Kelso, factor for the Earl of Haddington. Number of Poor on Roll, 56. Average Rate of Assessment, 8d. per £. Total Assessment 1864, £586 : 12s. Poor House—Kelso Combination.

CHARITABLE BEQUESTS.

The Honourable Mrs Baillie of Jerviswoode bequeathed in 1798 £100, the Interest to be applied for the benefit of the poor of the parish. Trustees—The Minister of Earlston, and Factor on the Estate of Mellerstain.—Also the interest of £50, to be paid to the Minister of Earlston, upon his administering the Sacrament twice in the year.

John Tod, Esq. of Kirklands, in 1798, bequeathed £182, the Interest to be applied for the purchase of coals for the poor of the parish. Trustees—The Minister and Kirk Session, and Factor on the Estate of Mellerstain.

—— Dick, above a century ago, bequeathed £30, the Interest to be applied for the education of poor scholars in the parish. Trustees—The Kirk Session.

In 1815, Thomas Wilson, E.I.C.S., Superintending Surgeon at Bombay, bequeathed, " for the better management of Earlston Grammar School," £550, to be called " a gratuity for the benefit of the said School." Trustees—The parish Minister, two of the Justices of the Peace, Heritors, with the Clerk of Court at Earlston.

In 1859, Mr James Walker (deceased, second son of Mr. David Walker, retired schoolmaster of Earlston), formerly of Earlston, afterwards in London, bequeathed £200, the annual proceeds to be expended in the purchase of coals for the poor of the parish not receiving Parochial Relief. Trustees—The Kirk Session.

YEARLY FRIENDLY SOCIETY—Henry Wallace, Treasurer. Number of Members, .

READING ROOM AND LIBRARY (Inst. 1856).

President—Major R. Baillie, Dryburgh. Vice Pres.—C. Wilson, sen. Secretary—George Wood. Treasurer—William Robertson.

Librarian John Aitchison. Annual Subscription, 2s. 4d.

† Children in the parish between 5 and 15, attending school during the first week of April 1861, 317 ; of all ages, 333.

HORTICULTURAL SOCIETY—Patrons—Earl of Haddington, Lord Binning, Alexander Mitchell, Esq.; Patroness—Mrs. Cotesworth, Cowdenknowes; President — Charles Wilson, Esq., sen.; Vice-President—George Wood; Secretary—John Thomson; Treasurer—Daniel Macdonald. Competitions take place annually in July and September, when prizes to the amount of £10 are given away.

6TH BERWICKSHIRE RIFLE CORPS—(EARLSTON).

Alexander Mitchell, of Stow and Carolside, Captain.
James Smail, banker, Lieutenant.
Charles Wilson, jun., manufacturer, Ensign.
Hon. Secretary—Daniel Aitkenhead, schoolmaster.
Hon. Treasurer—Charles Wilson, sen., manufacturer.

BANK BRANCH—Commercial Bank of Scotland (opened 1862)—James Smail, Agent.

INSURANCE AGENTS—Caledonian—Jas Wood, draper; Norwich Union—Geo. Scott, ironmonger; Scottish Provident—James Smail, banker; Scottish Provincial (Fire Department)—James Smail, banker; Life Association—William Robertson, saddler; North British—George Wood, gas manufacturer.

MEDICAL PRACTITIONERS—Robert Riddell, James Gibson, and James Philp, surgeons.

MANUFACTURERS—Woollen—Charles Wilson & Sons; Ginghams—William Clendinnin & Co., and Thomas Gray.

CORN MILL—William Moffat.

AUCTIONEER—Alexander Shiels, farmer, Kedslie.

CARRIERS—To Edinburgh—Widow Thomas Kerr, Tuesday; A. Simpson, Tuesday. To Kelso—Widow Thomas Kerr, Friday; A. Simpson, Friday.

CONVEYANCE—Omnibus to Newtown Station every morning and evening, from Commercial Inn.

EARLSTON DISTRICT ROADS.

Parishes of Earlston, Mertoun, Gordon, and Nenthorn.
Jas. Erskine, Esq., Melrose, Clerk. Th. Mitchell, Melrose, Surveyor.
Meets at Earlston on or about the 20th April.

TRADES, OFFICES, PRINCIPAL RESIDENTS, &c.

Aitken, James, shoemaker
*Aitkenhead, Daniel, *Parochial School*
*Anderson, William, Town Farm
Berry, Morrison, teacher
Black Bull Inn, A. Fairbairn
Blyth, Alexander, tinsmith
Broomfield, Misses, grocers
*Brownlee, Alexander, timber merchant, Haughhead
Clendinnin, Thomas, clothier
Clendinnin, William, & Co., manufacturers of ginghams
Commercial Inn, *George Wallace
Cranstoun, Miss
Crocket, William, grocer
*Dodds, Ralph, grocer
Dewar, Miss, dressmaker
Fairbairn, A. innkeeper
Fairbairn, William, grocer
*Favey, William
Fisher, George, painter
*Glendinning, David, innkeeper
*Gordon, Rev. David W. *Manse*
Gray, James, bookseller, stationer, and printer
Gray, John, farmer
Gray, John, joiner
*Gray, Thomas, manufacturer
Haig, George, baker
*Henderson, Rev. Alexander, *East U. P. Manse*
Hewat, Mrs. Dr.
*Hunter, James, (late joiner)
Jamieson, David, carrier
Johnston, John, horse dealer
*Kechie, Rev. John, *West U. P. Manse*
Ker, G. & J., boot and shoe makers
*Ker, James, carrier
Ker, Joseph, flesher
Kerr, Miss, dressmaker
Lee, Robert, blacksmith
Lees, Miss, dressmaker
*Leslie, Andrew, clothier
Martin, Alexander, cattle dealer
Martin, James, cattle dealer
Martin, William, bread and biscuit baker
*Mercer, William, draper and clothier
Moffat, James, flesher
Morton, Miss, draper
Mollison & M'Vitie, millwrights (Kelso and Earlston)
M'Vitie, Johnstone (of Mollison & M'V.)

M'William, Mrs. grocer
Murdison, A., slater, etc.
Newton's Hotel, John Newton
*Paterson, Stewart, mole-catcher
Police Station and Lock-up,   Shaw, policeman
Pringle, Alexander, flesher
Porteous, Robert, grocer
Pringle, John, watchmaker
*Purves, David, feuar
*Riddell, Robert, surgeon
Robertson, Miss, grocer
Robertson, William, saddler
Rodger, William, & Co., builders
*Runciman, John
Scott, Alexander, & Son, grocers, etc.
Scott, George, farrier
Scott, Miss
*Simpson, Alexander, carrier
Smail, James, banker
Sudden, Thomas, blacksmith and sexton
*Smith, Robert, general merchant
*Sanderson, Christopher, merchant and corn dealer
Temperance Hotel, J. Webster
Thomson, John, thatcher
Tinline, Alexander, grocer and spirit merchant
*Walker David (late parochial schoolmaster)
*Wallace, George, *Commercial Inn*
Wallace, John, joiner
*Wallace, Henry, shoemaker
Watson, William, baker
Webster, J., *Temperance Hotel*
White Swan Inn, *David Glendinning
Wilson, Charles, & Sons, manufacturers
*Wilson, Charles (of C. W. & Sons)
Wilson, Mrs. James
*Wood, George, gas manufacturer
Wood, James, draper
Wood, Miss, dressmaker
Young, George, shoemaker

Railway Station

Benjamin Thompson, station-master and general manager

OFFICES.

Robert Newton, coal agent
George Lidster,   do.
James Webster,   do.

Village of Redpath

POST OFFICE—Letters by Messenger (A. Johnston) are despatched from Melrose at 9-10 a.m. ; arrives at Redpath at 12 noon ; departs from Redpath at 2-20 p.m.

Fairbairn, Miss, grocer
Simpson, John,   do.
Walker, John, schoolmaster

Fans-loan-end Station

For goods and minerals. No resident manager.

RESIDENTS, FARMERS, &c., IN THE PARISH.

*Bayne, Alexander, farmer, Georgefield
Bone, Alexander,   do., and manager of Cowdenknowes estate, Craigsford
*Brown, John,   do.,   Hallidean Mill
*Cockburn, Henry,   do.,   Fans-loan-end
*Dunlop, James,   do.,   Rachelfield
Elliot, James,   do.,   Chapel Mains
*Fairbairn, John,   do.,   Grizzelfield
*Fairbairn, Willm.,   do.,   Redpath (east end)
Fleming, John,   do.,   Craigsford Mains
*Frier, Richard S.,   do.,   Fans
*Frier, Thomas,   do.,   do.
*Forsyth, Andrew,   do.,   Cowdenknowes Mains
Goodall,   , head gardener, Mellerstain
Hogg, William, farmer, Clackmae
*Kerr, Thomas, of Craighouse
*Lillie, Allan, farmer, Yarlside
Logan, Mrs, Birkhillside
Logan, John, farmer, Legerwood
Logan, Robert, do.,   Birkenside
*Mather, James, do.,   Earlston Mains
*Messer, Andrew, do., Purveshaugh
*More, Alex.,   do., Covehouse
*M'Dougall, William, farmer, Sorrowlessfield Mains
M'Dougall, George,   do.   do.
*M'Dougal, John, farmer, Whitefield
*M'Dougal, Robert, of Summerfield
Newton, John, land-steward, Mellerstain estate
*Rutherford, James, farmer, Lightfield Moss-side
*Wilson, James,   do. Carneymount

SEATS, &c., OF COUNTY FAMILIES IN THE PARISH.

MELLERSTAIN (*see* p. 507).

The occasional residence of the Right Hon. the Earl of Haddington (George Baillie Hamilton), and Baron of Binning and Byres, in the peerage of Scotland; and Representative Peer for Scotland; son of the late George Baillie, Esq., of Jerviswoode (Lanarkshire) and Mellerstain; born 14th April 1802; succeeded as 10th Earl at the decease of his kinsman Thomas 9th Earl of Haddington, 1st December 1858; married 16th September 1824, Georgina, daughter of the Venerable Robert Markham, Archdeacon of York; and has issue—

George, Lord Binning.*

Robert, Major in the Army, born 8th October 1828; married, 18th July 1861, his cousin, Mary Gavin, daughter of Sir John Pringle, Bart. (*see* Gavinton), at present abroad.

Clifton, born 5th March 1831, died 3d April 1857.

Henry, Lieutenant R. N., Knt. of the Medjidie; born 20th August 1832.

Percy, died an infant, 1835.

Arthur Charles, in holy orders; born 16th February 1838.

Mary, married to the Hon. and Rev. Henry Douglas, third son of Sholto, 18th Earl of Morton, and brother of the present Earl, Hanbury Rectory, Worcestershire, and has issue.

Frances.

Georgina Sophia, married, 17th October 1861, to Harry Foley Vernon, Esq., of Hanbury Hall, Worcestershire.

His Lordship has obtained a royal license, dated 24th March 1859, to add Hamilton, the original surname of his family, to that of Baillie, which was assumed by his grandfather upon inheriting the estates of *his* maternal grandfather George, who was the son of Robert Baillie, the celebrated Covenanter, and

---

* Mellerstain is also the permanent residence of the Earl of Haddington's eldest son, George, Lord Binning; born 26th July 1827; married 17th October 1854, Helen, daughter of Sir John Warrender, Bart., and his wife the Hon. Frances Henrietta Arden, daughter of Lord-Chief-Justice Alvonley; and has issue—

George, born 24th December 1856.
Richard, born 28th August 1858.
Henry, born 4th October 1862.
Ruth, Isabel (died an infant), and Grisell.

Lord Binning, by royal license dated 31st December 1858, was authorised to take the surname of Arden in addition to Baillie, and to bear the arms of these families quartered. Lord Binning is Capt. of one of the Haddingtonshire Yeomanry Cavalry.

Seat—Eaton Banks, Tarporley, Cheshire.

---

the husband of the no less locally celebrated Grizzel, daughter of Sir Patrick Hume of Polwarth.

His Lordship is Lieut.-Col.-Commanding East-Lothian Yeomanry Cavalry.

Other Seats—Tyninghame, Haddingtonshire (principal residence); Lennel House, Coldstream; and Langshaw Cottage, Melrose parish. *See* Seats, Mertoun parish.

CAROLSIDE (*see* p. 507).

The property and residence of *Alexander Mitchell, Esq. of Stow and Carolside, eldest son of the late Alexander Mitchell, Esq.; born 1831; succeeded 1839; married, 1856, Fanny Georgiana, daughter of Richard Hasler, Esq., of Aldingbourne, Sussex.

Mr. Mitchell is a Magistrate for the counties of Berwick, Edinburgh, and Selkirk; Deputy and Provincial G.M. of the Freemasons of Berwickshire; was formerly a Captain in the Grenadier Guards, and served through the siege at Sebastopol; he is now Captain of 6th Berwickshire, or Earlston, corps of Rifle Volunteers.

Mr. Mitchell's family represents the late Gilbert Innes, Esq., of Stow, and succeeded to his estates. The family of Ayton Castle (*see* Ayton parish), Berwickshire, which has adopted the name of Innes, is a younger branch of this family.

London Addresses—Guards' Club, S.W.; Brooks' Club; 6 Great Stanhope Street, May Fair, W.

COWDENKNOWES.

Situated on the Leader, and about a mile from the village to the south—the property and residence of Mrs. Cotesworth, sen., and residence of Mr. and Mrs. Robert Cotesworth.

KIRKLANDS.

Situated at the extreme south-west point of the parish, on the Leader, and close to its junction with the Tweed—the property of Thomas Tod, Esq., of Drygrange, and the residence of his sisters, the Misses Tod.

PARK.

Situated in the southern district of the parish, about 2 miles from the village by the road—the property of Major Brown;† at present occupied by *James Weatherly, Esq. (of Nether Monynut, Oldhamstocks), farmer.

---

† Present address—Manse of Ratho, Edinburgh.

REGISTERED VOTERS (Non-Resident).

Baillie, George, of Jerviswoode [now Earl'of Haddington]
Barrie, James, cattle-dealer, Newtown
Brown, Major David, of Park
Dalziel, John, Australia
Freer, Allan, writer, Melrose
Johnston, Thomas, clerk, Edinburgh
Laidlaw, James, joiner, Innerleithen
M'Dougal, William, farmer, Sorrowlessfield Mains
Stalker, James, factor, Galashiels
Swan, James, late of Meilerstain Mill
Tod, Thomas, of Drygrange, Melrose
Young, Thomas, Edinburgh

LAUDER.

————◆————

THIS is the largest parish in the county, its greatest length being 10½ miles, or, including a detached portion lying south from the larger portion and nearly surrounded by Melrose parish, about 12½ miles ; its greatest breadth is 8 miles (the detached portion has a breadth of nearly 2 miles, and in shape is nearly square), and covering, according to the Ordnance Survey, 34,981 acres (this includes the detached portion consisting of 1302¾ acres which contains the mansion house of Chapel and farm of Kedslie); of these 164 acres are occupied by public and private roads, and 83 are under water. It is bounded on the north by the county of Haddington, on the east by the parishes of Longformacus, Cranshaws, and Westruther, on the south by Legerwood parish and Melrose in Roxburghshire, and on the west by Channelkirk and Mid-Lothian ; the detached portion has the Leader skirting its eastern side of about 2 miles, beyond which is Earlston parish. About two-thirds of the whole parish is coarse moorland, the surface of the country being almost one mass of hills ; of these the highest are to the north, and constitute part of the Lammermoor range.* The vale of the Leader is the best land of the parish. The Leader and its tributary streams intersect the parish in all directions, and afford good trout fishing, mostly unrestricted. The climate of the parish, though variable, is healthy. Throughout the parish there are traces of Roman and Pictish camps. There is one town in the parish, viz.—Lauder. This ancient royal burgh is situated in the vale of the Leader, on the main road from Edinburgh to Kelso. It consists chiefly of one long street and a shorter one, at the intersection of which stands the Town House. The charter constituting Lauder a royal burgh, granted by William the

---

* The following are some of the principal elevations, as given by the Ordnance Survey :—

			feet.				feet.
Crib Law	..	..	1670	Blytherig	..	..	1412
Scenes Law	..	..	1683	Hog's Law	..	..	1470
Hart Law (north)	..	..	1578	Scouredrig	..	..	1191
,, (south)	..	..	1437	Wheelburn Law	..	..	1090
Waddelscairn	..	..	1490	Brownrig on Lauder Com-			
Wedderlaw	..	..	1460	mon is 1063 ; the general			
Huntlaw	..	..	1625	altitude of the Common			
Wedderlairs	..	..	1593	is 905 feet			
Riddel Law	..	..	1271				

Lion, was renewed in 1502. The government is now vested in two bailies and seven councillors, chosen annually from amongst the burgesses. By the Reform Act it is joined with Jedburgh, Haddington, Dunbar, and North Berwick, in returning one member to Parliament (*see* p. 245). The burgesses possess considerable landed property, including Lauder Common, which extends to about 1700 acres. Close upon the town is THIRLESTANE CASTLE, the seat of the Earl of Lauderdale, a splendid building—partly ancient and partly modern— beautifully surrounded by extensive woods, and occupying a fine lawn on the right bank of the Leader. The decorations are mostly in the style in vogue at the time of Charles II.

Lauder is 25 miles from Edinburgh, 17 from Kelso, 7 from Earlston, and about 5 from Stow, where is the nearest railway station.

Lauder has no weekly market.

Hiring Days—Hinds and Herds 1st Tuesday of March ; Domestic Servants, sixth Tuesday after 1st Tuesday of March (occurs about the middle of April) and 4th Friday in October.

Lamb Fair— Friday immediately before 12th August. The lambs sold—chiefly Cheviots and a few half-breds— are mostly from Lauder hill, the property of the burgesses.

Population of the burgh in 1861, 1137 ; of the parish (including burgh), 2198 ; who constituted 476 separate families, 3 of whom were returned as living in houses having no window, 184 in houses of one window, 140 in houses of two windows, and the remainder (149), or rather less than one-third in houses of three or more windows.

Assessed property in the burgh in 1864 5, £2241 : 14 ; in the parish (exclusive of burgh), £17,531 : 11 : 3 ; total, £19,804, 3s. 3d.

The principal landed-proprietors in the parish are — the Earl of Lauderdale, the Marquis of Tweeddale ; Alexander Mitchell, Esq., Carolside ; William Fairholme, Esq. of Chapel ; James Erskine, Esq. of Shielfield ; W. H. Allan, Esq., Allanbank.

MEMBER OF PARLIAMENT FOR THE BURGH—Sir H. R. F. Davie (*see* p.60).

MAGISTRATES.

Robert Symington, watchmaker, Chief Magistrate   Alex. Jamieson, grocer, Junior Magistrate.

LOCAL JUSTICES OF THE PEACE.

Those marked thus (*) are Resident in the parish.

*William H. Allan, Esq., of Allanbank ; *the Chief Magistrate of Lauder ; Charles Simson, Esq., of Threepwood ; and *William Fairholme, Esq., of Chapel-on-Leader.

COURTS.

JUSTICE OF PEACE COURTS are held on the third Friday of every second month. First of the year in February.

SHERIFF SMALL DEBT COURTS are held on the Wednesday before the last Thursday of March ; the Wednesday before the last Thursday of July ; and the Wednesday before the last Thursday of October.

Summonses issued at the office of Thos. Broomfield, writer, Lauder.

SHERIFF OFFICER—Wm. Malloy.   POLICE OFFICER—John Henderson.

PUBLIC OFFICES.

Burgh Treasurer—Mark Liddell.
Burgh Voters' Assessor—Thomas Broomfield.
Clerk to the District Road Trustees and Statute Labour Conversion, Collector of—Robert Romanes.
Heritors' Clerk—Thomas Broomfield.
Income Tax, Assessor of, for Western District of Berwickshire— Thomas Broomfield.
Justice of Peace Clerk—Thomas Broomfield.
Keeper of the Register of Sasines and Commissary Clerk for Berwickshire—Robert Romanes.
Lands Valuation Assessor for Burgh of Lauder, and for the Western District of Berwickshire—Thomas Broomfield.
Poor Inspector of—Thomas Broomfield.
Procurator-Fiscal for Burgh—Thomas Broomfield.
Procurator Fiscal for District of Lauder and Earlston—Robt. Romanes.
Registrar of Births, Marriages, and Deaths—John Lindsay.
Session Clerk—John Lindsay.
Stamps and Taxes, Collector and Sub-Distributor of—Thomas Broomfield.
Town Clerk and Billet Master—Robert Romanes.

POST OFFICE.

Miss Janet Romanis, Postmistress.

Mails arrive at 10 a.m., and leave at 3-30 p.m.

Sub-Post to Oxton, Blainslie, and Westruther daily, at half past 10 a.m. The Oxton and Westruther Runners bring letters to Lauder at 10 a.m., and the Blainslie Runner returns to Lauder at half-past 3 o'clock. No Post on Sundays to these districts.

CLERGY, &c.

Lauder is the seat of a Presbytery, in the Synod of Merse and Teviotdale. Patron—The Earl of Lauderdale.

ESTABLISHED CHURCH—Rev, James Middleton, M.A. (Inducted 1862). Sittings, 773. Average attendance at Sabbath School, 130. Superintendent of Sabbath School—Minister ; Kirk Treasurer and Session-Clk.—John Lindsay ; Precentor—Robt. Watson ; Church Officer—Hugh Weddell.

FREE CHURCH—Rev. Thomas Waters (Inducted 1843). Sittings, 450. Average attendance at Sabbath School, 40. Superintendent of Sabbath School—Minister; Precentor—W. Keppie; Church Officer—James Wilson.

UNITED PRESBYTERIAN CHURCH—*Rev. Geo. Robson (Inducted 1834). Sittings, 600. Average attendance at Sabbath School, 50. Superintendent of Sabbath School— Mr. Robson ; Treasurer—Mark Liddell ; Precentor—James M'Pherson ; Church Officer—James Brotherstone.

FAST DAYS—Wednesday before last Sunday of June, and Wednesday before Full Moon in December.

EDUCATIONAL INSTITUTIONS.†

Parish School—John Lindsay, Master. Average attendance, 115.
Side School at Cleekhimin—Alexander Kinlayside, teacher.
Free Church School—William Alexander, Teacher. Aver. attend., 90.
Boarding School for Young Ladies—Miss Romanis.

Do.	Do.	Miss Haswell.
Do.	Do.	Miss Paterson.

Industrial School—Miss Helen Roberts, Teacher.

PAROCHIAL BOARD.

Wm. H. Allan, Esq., Chairman.

COMMITTEE.

Rev. J. Middleton.	William Cuthbertson.
Robert Romanes.	James Ballantyne.
George Watson.	Chief Magistrate for the time
Mark Liddell.	being.

Thomas Broomfield, Inspector of Poor for Burgh and Parish, and Collector of Poor Rates.

No. of Poor on Roll, 60. Rate of Assessment, 10d. per £ ; total Assessment, 1864-5, £841 : 18 : 9.

COMMITTEE OF HERITORS.

Robert Romanes, Lauder.	Wm. Henry Allan of Allanbank.
Rev. Thomas Waters.	Chief Magistrate of the Burgh for
Mark Liddell, builder.	the time being.

CLOTHING SOCIETY (estab. 1841).

Mrs Romanes, Preses.

† Children in the parish from 5 to 15 attending school during the first week of April 1861, 391 ; of all ages, 410.

ST. LUKE'S LODGE OF FREE MASONS (estab. 1772).

Thomas Gray, Grand Master.
Secretary—W. M'Leod. Treasurer—R. A. Smith, draper.

TOTAL ABSTINENCE SOCIETY (estab. 1841).

William Wilson, clothier, Secretary.

PUBLIC SUBSCRIPTION LIBRARY.

President—Mark Liddell.
Vice-President—James Whitton, Thirlestane Castle.
Secretary—W. D. Aikman. Treasurer—J. M'Pherson.

Number of volumes, 436.

A course of Lectures is given during the winter in connection with this library.

LAUDERDALE AGRICULTURAL SOCIETY (estab. 1829).

Thomas Broomfield, Secretary and Treasurer.

The exhibition of this Society is held annually in Spring. That for 1865 took place on Saturday, April 1, when prizes amounting to £19 were given, besides £5 for implements. An exhibition is held in Autumn also for sheep stock ; premiums in 1864 amounted to £17.

LAUDERDALE HORTICULTURAL SOCIETY.

Secretary and Treasurer—Peter Scott.
Committee—W. Armstrong, J. M'Pherson, and W. M'Lyon.

Competitions take place annually in July and September.

GAS COMPANY (estab. 1842).

COMMITTEE.

James Hay.	William Cuthbertson.
James Ballantyne.	George Sommerville.

Thomas Broomfield, Secretary and Treasurer.
Price 10s. per 1000 feet.
Stock, £885. Dividend, 5 per cent.

WATER COMPANY (estab. 1830).

R. A. Smith, Preses.
Thomas Broomfield, Secretary and Treasurer.

Rate, 6d. per £ for first £2 of rent, and 3d. per £ thereafter.

CURLING CLUB (estab. 1850).

Earl of Lauderdale, President.

Mark Liddell, Secretary.   Thomas Broomfield, Treasurer.

The Curling Pond is situated within ¼ of a mile of the town, on burgh property.

5TH BERWICKSHIRE RIFLE VOLUNTEERS—(LAUDER).

W. Fairholme, Esq., of Chapel, Captain.

Robert Romanes, Lieutenant.   Thomas Broomfield, Sec. and Treas.

Sergeant Alexander M'Leod, Drill Instructor.

Effective Force, 88.   Hon. Members, 10.

Annual Subscription of Hon. Member, 21s.

BANK BRANCHES.

BANK OF SCOTLAND (opened 1833)—Robert Romanes, Agent ; Thomas Edgley, Teller.

CITY OF GLASGOW BANK (opened 1855)—Thomas Broomfield, Agent. John Wilson, Accountant.

INSURANCE AGENTS.

ALLIANCE...........................A Torrie, merchant.
CALEDONIAN.......................Robert Romanes, writer.
INDISPUTABLE.....................R. A. Smith, draper.
LIFE ASSOCIATION.................George Watson, merchant.
ROYAL FARMERS' FIRE............Thomas Carson, merchant.
SCOTTISH PROVINCIAL...... ....Thomas Broomfield, writer.
STANDARD LIFE ....W. D. Aikman.

ROYAL ASSOCIATION FOR PROMOTION OF FINE ARTS.

Thomas Broomfield, writer, Hon. Secretary.

PROCURATORS AND NOTARIES PUBLIC.

Thomas Broomfield ; Robert Romanes.

MEDICAL PRACTITIONERS.

*Simon Hunter ; Robert Riddell.

VETERINARY SURGEON—James Baillie.

AUCTIONEER.

Alexander Shiels, Kedslie, by Earlston.

CORN MILLS.

ST. LEONARDS—W. Brown, miller.

LYLESTONE MILL—Charles Stewart, miller.

CONVEYANCE.

A 'bus runs between Lauder and Stow Station once a day, leaving Lauder at 6.30 a.m. in connection with the first train for Edinburgh passing Stow at 7.40 a.m. ; returning from Stow at 7.57 a.m. on arrival of the first train from Edinburgh. G. Henderson, proprietor.

CARRIERS.

To Stow railway station, and thence to all parts—Mark Liddell, daily. To Dalkeith, every Monday—John Cowe.

STATUTE LABOUR ROADS, LAUDER DISTRICT.

Comprising the parishes of Lauder, Channelkirk, Westruther, and Legerwood, and the Burgh of Lauder.

One Meeting annually (day not fixed, but generally about the 16th October).

Robert Romanes, writer, Lauder, Clerk and Collector. Thomas Mitchell, Melrose, Surveyor.

DIRECTORY.

TRADES, PUBLIC OFFICES, RESIDENTS, &c.

Those marked thus (*) are Registered Voters for the County, and those marked thus (†) are for the Burgh.

†Aikman, William D., draper
†Anton, Thomas, tailor
Alexander, William, *Free Church School*
*Anderson, George, shopman
Baillie, James, veterinary surgeon
†Bain, Alexander, mason
*†Ballantyne, James, grocer
Black Bull Inn, †Henry Hinks
Brodie, Matthew, steward to Lord Lauderdale
Broomfield, Thomas, solicitor
Brotherstone, Andrew, grocer
†Brown, John, grocer
†Carson, Thomas, grocer, ironmonger, and seedsman
*Chisholm, Walter
Cockburn, George, cooper
Commercial Inn, †Joseph Brown
*†Cuthbertson, William, labourer
†Darling, Archibald, plumber
Darling, Robert, slater
Darling, William, grocer
*†Dickson, Adam, labourer
*†Dickson, John,   do.
*Dickson, Alexander
†Dickson, William, carpenter
*†Dodds, William
Donaldson, Charles, shoemaker
†Downie, George, joiner
†Dunlop, John, saddler
Eagle Inn, †David Keppie
†Geddes, William S., labourer
*†Gillies, Thomas, baker
*†Graham, James, sen., mason
Haldane, Andrew, grocer
†Haldane, Andrew
Haldane, Mrs. James
Haswell, Miss, *Boarding Establishment*
Hay, James, labourer
†Henderson, George, stabler
*Henderson, William, slater

Henderson, James, flesher
Henderson, Thomas, do.
†Hinks, Henry, innkeeper
Hislop, Thomas, builder
†Hogg, Alexander, grocer
Hume, John, millwright
*†Hunter, George, grocer
*Hunter, Hugh
*Hunter, Simon, surgeon
*†Jamieson, Alexander, grocer
Jeffrey, James, blacksmith
Johnston, Robert, flesher
†Keppie, William, baker
*†Kelly, John
*Laidlaw, Alexander
Lee, Robert, joiner
*†Liddell, Mark, builder
*†Lindsay, John, *Parish School*
*†Middleton, Rev. James, *Manse*
*Miller, Andrew, shoemaker
*†Miller, James, labourer
†Morrison, John, blacksmith
*Munro, Andrew, labourer
Murdison, Robert, slater
*†Murray, Robert, watchmaker
*†Murray, Thomas, labourer
Murray, Thomas, grocer
*†Murray, William, shoemaker
M'Gan, Peter, china merchant
*†M'Lachlan, Thomas, labourer
M'Leod, Sergeant A., drill instructor
†M'Pherson, James, tailor and grocer
*†Ness, William, carter
Nisbet, John, cooper
Patterson, Miss, *Boarding Establishment*
*Paterson, James, labourer
Post Office—Miss Romanis
*Purves, Andrew
Rae, James, tobacco and snuff manufacturer
Reid, Robert, printer and stationer
Riddell, Robert, surgeon
Roberts, Miss Helen, *Industrial School*
*†Robson, Rev. George, *U. P. Manse*
*Romanes, Robert, solicitor
Romanis, Miss, *Boarding Establishment*
*Runciman, Richard, baker
*†Runciman William,   do.
†Simpson, Andrew, grocer
*†Sligh, Peter, labourer

†Smith, Ralph A., draper
*Smith, Robert, labourer
*†Somerville, George, shoemaker
*Somerville, John, do.
*†Spence, William R., labourer
Sudden, Mrs. Jane, milliner
*†Symington, Robert, watchmaker
*†Symington, Robert, jun., grocer
Temperance Hotel, *†Robert Stoddart
　　Do　　　Do.　Margaret Torrie
*†Thomson, Andrew, carter
†Torrie, Andrew, draper
*Vallance, William
Waddell, John, saddler
*†Waters, Rev. Thomas, *Free Church Manse*
†Watson, George, draper and clothier
†Wilson, William, clothier
†Wilson, Thomas, mason
*Wilson, James, do.
*White, William, labourer

FARMERS AND RESIDENTS IN THE PARISH.

Bertram, Alexander, gardener, Chapel
Brodie, 　　　land steward, Thirlestane Castle
*Brydon, Walter, farmer, Burncastle
*Bone, William, 　do.　Blackburn
Brockie, George, Woodheads
*Brown, William, farmer St. Leonards
*Bathgate, James, 　do.　Overbowerhouse
*Dickenson, Willm., do.　Longcroft
*Dickson, John, 　do.　Easter Addinston
Dods, Alexander, 　do.　West Mains
Elliot, James, 　do.　Chapel Mains
Fortune, William, gamekeeper to W. Fairholme, Esq. of Chapel
Hogg, Mrs., Whitlaw
*Hogarth, William, farmer, Shielfield
*Hume, Nathaniel, 　do.　Blue Cairn
*Harper, Thomas, 　do.　Newbiggingwalls
*Johnston, James, 　do.　Huntington
*Johnston, Walter, 　do.　Inchkeith
Laing, Mrs. Wester Addinston farm
Lee, Mrs., New Mills farm
*Murray, John, farmer, East Mains
*M'Dougal, Geo., farmer, Blythe
*M'Dougal, James, do.　Lylestone

*Pringle, John, farmer, Haugh
*Pringle, James, do.　do.
Romanes, Robert, of Harryburn
*Runciman, James, farmer, Wantonwalls
Scott, Barlo, gamekeeper to Lord Lauderdale
*Stewart, Charles, farmer, Lylestone Mill
*Shiels, Alexander, do. and auctioneer, Kedslie
*†Smail, Adam, 　do.　Trabroun
Taylor, Mrs., Thirlestane
*Tillie, William, farmer, Trabroun Hill
*Tod, William, 　do.　Pilmuir, and merccht. Manchester
*Taylor, John, 　do.　Burnmill
*†Watherstone, Thomas, farmer, Loanend
*Waddell, George, 　　do.　Muircleugh
*Welsh, John, 　　do.　Trabroun
*Weddell, John W., 　　do.　Lauder Barns
Whitton, James, gardener, Thirlestane Castle

SEATS, &c., OF COUNTY FAMILIES IN THE PARISH.

ALLANBANK.

Close to the town—the property and pretty residence of *†Wm. H. Allan, Esq., J.P.

CHAPEL-ON-LEADER.

In the detached portion of the parish—the seat of *William Fairholme, Esq., of Chapel-on-Leader, eldest son of the late George Fairholme, Esq., of Greenknowe, Berwickshire; born 1819; succeeded 1846; married 1853 Grace Penelope, eldest daughter of the late Wray Palliser, Esq., of Derrylaskan, county Tipperary, and Comragh, county Waterford, and has issue—

Anne Gledstanes, Caroline-Grace, Mary-Elizabeth-Eleanor, Louisa-Margaret, and Katherine-Harriett.

Mr. Fairholme is a Magistrate for the county of Berwick, and Captain 5th Berwickshire Rifle Volunteers; and formerly held a commission in the 71st Highlanders.

Addresses—New Club, Edinburgh; Athenæum Club, London.

THIRLESTANE CASTLE.

The seat of the Right Hon. the Earl of Lauderdale (Sir Thomas Maitland), Viscount of Lauderdale and Maitland, and Baron of Thirlestane, Boltoun, and Lauderdale of Thirlestane, in the peerage of Scotland; a Knight Bachelor, a Baronet of Nova

Scotia, Rear-Admiral of the Red, C.B., and Knight of Charles III. ; born 3d February 1803 ; succeeded his cousin Anthony, with whom the English honours of the family became extinct, as 11th Earl, 22d March 1863 ; married 1828 Amelia, 3d daughter of Wm. Young, Esq., of Rio Janeiro, and has had issue—

Thomas Mordaunt, born 1838 (died 7th August 1844).
Isabel Anne (died 3d May 1854).
Mary Jane.
Alice-Charlotte (died 30th January 1833).

The Earl of Lauderdale is Hereditary Standard Bearer for Scotland, and is a Deputy-Lieutenant for Berwickshire ; he was Commander-in-Chief of the Fleet in the Pacific, and served in the East Indian and Chinese coasts, and also on the Spanish coast 1835-7.

Other Residence—Dunbar House, East Lothian.
London Address—17 Upper Hyde Park Gardens.

COUNTY REGISTERED VOTERS (Non-Resident).

Anderson, John, Selkirk
Allan, Henry John, England
Coldwells, William, Galashiels
Durie, Robert H., farmer, Barney Mains
Erskine, George Pott, Melrose
Scott, Hon. Francis, late M.P.
Simson, Charles, Tasmania
Stevenson, Andrew, farmer, Halls

BURGH VOTERS

(Non-Resident but living within the voting limits).*

Simson, Charles, Threepwood
Wight, William, Carfrae

* County voters are not disqualified by any distance of residence, but Burgh voters must live within 7 miles (see p. 278).

CHANNELKIRK.

THIS parish is the most westerly of Berwickshire ; it is situated in the upper district of Lauderdale, and is generally of a high and bleak nature. It is bounded on the north by the parish of Falla in East Lothian, on the east and south by Lauder parish, and partly on the south by Stow parish, and on the west by Stow and Falla. Its general outline is triangular ; its greatest direct length, measuring the base of the triangle from its northern point to south of Collie Law, is nearly 8 miles ; its greatest breadth, due east and west, is exactly 5 miles. The total area, according to the Ordnance Survey, is 14,202½ acres, of which about 3000 are under cultivation, 12 are under water, 66 are in roads, and the remainder are rough hilly pasture. The parish consists of hills and valleys, with a small portion of flat land in the southern part, forming the vale of the Leader, many of whose upper branches have their rise in this parish. The hills belong to the Lammermoor range, which here terminates. The most elevated points are Clints Hill in the southwest, which rises to 1535 feet, and Ninecairn Edge in the north extremity, which attains a height of 1479 feet. Hartside Hill and Headshawlaw, situated more in the centre of the parish, are respectively 1340 and 1349 feet high ; Collie Law, near the south, is 1255 feet ; while Soutra Hill, which lies partly in the parish on the north-eastern boundary, is about 1209 feet at its highest point. The old coach road from Edinburgh to Newcastle runs through the centre of the parish from north-west to south-east, reaching a height of nearly 1100 feet, and is the only turnpike road in the parish. The climate, although subject to sudden changes of temperature, is healthy. The district is well watered by the many tributaries of the Leader. They are all mere hill streams of no great size, in which trout are plentiful but small ; to angling there is no restriction. There are but few remains of antiquity in the parish ; there are remains of a few camps on the tops of several of the hills, and a fine spring to the west of the parish church, called the Well of the Holy Water Cleugh. The road by which the monks went from Melrose to Edinburgh passes through the western part of the parish ; and a few miles west of the church are the ruins of an old building called "Restlaw Ha'," at which it is said monks and pilgrims used to stop for refreshments. There is no market town in the parish, the nearest being Lauder, at a distance of over 5 miles from the centre of the parish, and 4 from the village of Oxton.

2 M

The village of OXTON is in the south-east part of the parish, and contains about 200 inhabitants. About a mile to the west of Oxton are the parish church and manse, and near to them are the remains of the ancient village of Channelkirk.

Oxton Annual Holiday—see Total Abstinence Society.

Population of the parish in 1861, 641 ; who composed 137 families, 64 of whom were returned as inhabiting houses of one window, and 30 houses of two, leaving 43 who lived in houses of three or more windows.

Assessed property in 1864-5, £7135 : 4 : 3.

The principal landed-proprietors in the parish are—the Marquis of Tweeddale; Lord Lauderdale (of Airhouse); John Borthwick, Esq. of Crookston; Sir Hugh P. H. Campbell, Bart., of Marchmont; Mrs. Grace Niddrie (of Over Howden), Edinburgh ; Jas J. H. Parker, Esq. (of Justice Hall), 4 Brandon Street, Edinburgh; and Robt. Mason, Esq. of Heriotshall.

Those marked thus (*) are Registered Voters.

POST OFFICE (Oxton)—Jas. Mathewson, postmaster. Letters arrive from all parts, by Lauder daily, at 12-5 noon. Despatch to all parts daily at 7-30 a.m. William Lockie, messenger.

PUBLIC OFFICES—Heritors' Clerk, Session Clerk, Kirk Treasurer, Registrar of Births, Marriages and Deaths, and Inspector of Poor—Alexander Davidson.

 Medical Officer and Public Vaccinator—Robert Riddell, surgeon, Lauder.

CLERGY, &c —Channelkirk is in the Presbytery of Lauder, and Synod of Merse and Teviotdale. Patron—Sir Hugh P. H. Campbell
 Established Church—*Rev. James Walker (Inducted 1862). Sittings, 300. Average attendance at Sabbath School, 30.

FAST DAYS—Last Wednesday of June, and an unfixed day in December.

SCHOOL†—Parochial (Oxton)—*Alex. Davidson, master. Av. at., 36.
 Subscription (Oxton)—Alex. Denholm, master. Av. attend., 65.

PAROCHIAL BOARD—Robert Romanes, Lauder, factor for Lord Lauderdale, etc., chairman. No. of Poor on Roll, 27. Rate of Assessment, 4½d. per £ ; total Assessment in 1864-5, £260.

PAROCHIAL LIBRARY—300 vols. John Waddell, librarian. Yearly Subscription, 3s.

OXTON FRIENDLY SOCIETY—Established 1801 for the purpose of assisting working men during sickness, and defraying burial expenses at death. Each member pays 6s. per annum, and during sick-

† Children in the parish from 5 to 15 attending school during the first week of April 1861, 83 ; of all ages, 86.

ness gets 5s. per week for 10 weeks ; 3s. for the next 10 weeks ; and 2s. for 32 weeks ; after this he is allowed 1s. per week till his sickness terminates. Superannuated members are allowed 1s. per week for life. The business is conducted by nine of a committee, chosen annually, who meet on the first Saturday of each quarter.

OXTON BOVIAL SOCIETY—Instituted 1835 for the purpose of helping working men, such as hinds and shepherds, in the event of their cow dying, to get another. Each member, on an average, pays 4s. per annum ; and if his cow dies he is allowed £8 to help to get another. Farmers may enter the Society, and any number of cows may be entered by one individual on the rolls for insurance, but practically the transactions are limited to the risk of single animals. Business is conducted by a committee of nine members, chosen annually, who meet on the first Wednesday of June and December.

TOTAL ABSTINENCE SOCIETY (Instituted 1840). Business is conducted by a committee of eight members, who meet twice a year. The Society have an annual soiree in January and a rural excursion and pic-nic in July.

CONVEYANCE—The nearest railway station to Oxton is Fountainhall on the North British line, about 5 miles due west by a hilly road ; the Stow station by way of Lauder is about 10 miles distant, but the road is better.

CARRIERS—James Brown on Monday and Robert Thomson on Tuesday—both to Edinburgh.

TRADES, &c., IN OXTON.

Bell, John, bootmaker
Bell, William, cartwright
*Campbell, Andrew, grocer
Campbell, John, cartwright
Forrest, Mary Ann, milliner and dressmaker
Macintosh, Robert, grocer
Matthewson, James, grocer, seedsman, and ironmonger
Murray, John, blacksmith
Reid, James & Alexander, blacksmiths
Richardson, Adam, tailor and clothier
Scott, David, bootmaker
*Scott, John, baker
Scott, Thomas, bootmaker and grocer
*Swan, James, draper
Waddell, John, tailor
Waddell, William, tailor and clothier
Walkingshaw, Robert, grocer and spirit dealer
*Watson, Adam, grocer
Watson, Robert, cartwright

RESIDENTS, FARMERS, &c., IN THE PARISH.

Annfield Inn, Matthew T. Chalmers
*Archibald, John, farmer, Glengelt
*Armstrong, William, do. Wiselaw Mill
Bathgate, James, Bower House
*Bell, James, farmer, Herriotshall
Bertram, James, do. Hartside
*Binnie, William, do. Over-Howden
Carfrae Mill Inn, *George Jamieson
*Graham, John, farmer, Clints
*Hope, James,   do.   Kirktonhill
Hunter's Hall †
*Sharp, James, farmer, Justice Hall
*Shiels, William, do. Headshaw
*Stewart, Andrew, do. Collielaw
*Taylor, Alex.,   do.   Hillhouse
*Taylor, Thos., jr., do. Threeburnford
*Tweedie, David, do. Nether-Howden
*Waldie, George, do. Airhouse Mains
*Walkinshaw, Dvd. do. Airhouse Parkfoot
*Wight, William, do. Carfrae
*Wilson, Robert,   do.   Oxton Mains

REGISTERED VOTERS (Non-Resident).

Archibald, John, Wester Duddingston, So. Queensferry
Borthwick, John, Esq., of Crookston
Fairgrieve, James, labourer, Lauder
Mason, Robt. (of Heriotshall), Morton Mains, Edinburgh
Ogilvie, William, Esq. of Chesters, Ancrum
Parker, John James, Esq. of Justice Hall
Pringle, James Thomas, Torwoodlee
Scott, Thomas, joiner, Crichton

---

† Formerly an inn, now a shepherd's house, situated on the top of Soutra hill, at an elevation of 1093 feet above mean water, probably the highest inhabited house in the country—*see* p. 419, foot-note.

LEGERWOOD.

—◆—

A HILLY agricultural parish in the western part of Berwickshire. It is bounded by Lauder and Westruther on the north; Gordon and Westruther on the east; Earlston on the south; and the detached part of Lauder parish, and Melrose, in Roxburghshire, on the west. Its greatest length is over 5 miles, its greatest breadth about 4 miles, and its total area, according to the Ordnance Survey, is 8817 and one-tenth acres; 107 of which are occupied by public and private roads, and $27\frac{3}{4}$ are under water. "The greater part of the parish lies high, the northern part especially, which may be described as forming with Westruther on the east, a table land of considerable elevation. The surface of this portion is not level, but consists of three ridges of hills, with high valleys intervening—the two southernmost of these ridges, stretching from east to west, and the northern, striking off from them, in a northerly direction, and terminating in a round massive height, named Boon Hill, which rises 1070 feet above the level of the sea. The southern part of the parish is entirely occupied by Legerwood Hill, which rises to the height of about 1000 feet. The soil varies considerably, but the greater part of the parish is under a high state of cultivation. The Leader, which is a good fishing water, skirts the parish on the west; the Eden, here quite a burn, takes its rise on the farm of Boon. There are in the parish the remains of two towers—Corsbie and Whitslaid—and traces of two British encampments. The climate though cold and unsheltered is not unhealthy. Near the centre of the parish, on a tributary of the Leader, is the small hamlet of Legerwood. The parish church, manse, and school house are here. Earlston is the nearest town and railway station for passengers, and is distant from the hamlet about 3 miles. Fans-loan-end, for goods and minerals, is only 2 miles distant. Between Fans-loan-end and Earlston stations the Berwickshire railway cuts across the extreme south point of the parish.

The population of the parish by the census of 1861 was 599; who constituted 97 separate families, 1 of whom was returned as living in a house having no window, 57 in houses of one window, 25 in houses of two windows, and the balance (14) in houses of three or more windows.

Assessed property in 1864-5, £6920 : 19 : 3.

The principal landed-proprietors in the parish are—Mrs.

Clay Ker Seymer,* of Morriston ; Marquis of Tweeddale ; John Spottiswoode, Esq. of Spottiswoode ; Alexander Curle, Esq. of East Morriston ; and Alexander Mitchell,† Esq. (of Stow and Carolside) of Whitslaid—none of whom are resident.

Those marked thus (*) are Registered Voters.

DISTRICT POLICE OFFICE—Earlston.

PUBLIC OFFICES—Heritors' Clerk, Session Clerk, Kirk Treasurer, Inspector of Poor, and Registrar of Births, Marriages, and Deaths—John Smith.
Medical Officer and Public Vaccinator—Dr. Riddell, Earlston.

POST OFFICE—Letters arrive six days a week from Earlston. Runner—David Trotter.

CLERGY, &c.—Legerwood is in the Presbytery of Lauder, and Synod of Merse and Teviotdale. Patron—Mrs. Clay Ker Seymer, of Morriston.
Established Church—*Rev. Archibald Brown (Inducted 1859).
Sittings, 300. Average attendance at Sabbath School, 30.

FAST DAYS—In summer, Thursday before the fourth Sunday of July ; in winter, variable.

SCHOOL‡—Parochial—John Smith, master. Aver. attend., 50.

PAROCHIAL BOARD—Rev. Archibald Brown, Chairman. No. of Poor on Roll, 13. Rate of Assessment, 3d. per £ ; total Assessment in 1864-5, £145 ; average Assessment, £120.

LIBRARIES—One in connection with the Sabbath School.

QUARRY : East Morriston—Alexander Curle, Esq., proprietor ; Wm. Rodger & Co., builders, Earlston, lessees.

TRADES IN THE PARISH.

Rutherford, John, blacksmith, Legerwood
Romanes, William, joiner,   do.
Stewart, Adam, meal-dealer, Dodmill

---

* Mrs Gertrude Clay Ker Seymer (born 1843) represents the old family of the Kers of Morriston ; she succeeded her father, the late Henry Ker Seymer, Esq., to the entailed lands in Legerwood and Swinton parishes in May 1864 ; married, January 1864, Harry Ernest Clay, Esq (who then assumed the name of Ker Seymer), second Secretary of the British Legation at Paris ; and has issue a son, Evelyn, born March 1865. Paris residence—37 Avenue des Champs Elysées (or British Embassy). London residence—26 Montague Square.
The old mansion of Morriston, the foundations of which can now only be traced, stood near the present farm house.
† Since our sheet containing p. 516 went to press Mr. Mitchell has been elected M.P. for Berwick-on-Tweed in the Liberal interest.
‡ Children in the parish from 5 to 15 attending school during the first week of April 1861, 94 ; of all ages, 96.

RESIDENTS, FARMERS, &c., IN THE PARISH.

*Haig, Thomas, farmer, Kirkhill
*Halliday, Francis, miller, Bridgehaugh Mill
*Harper, James, farmer, Whitslaid
 Lockie, William, West Morriston
 Lockie, Mrs.   do.
 Logan, Mrs., Boon
*Logan, John, farmer, Legerwood
*Logan, Robert, do.   Birkenside
 Logan, Mrs., Birkhillside
 Logan, Robert, farmer, Corsbie
*Milne, John,   do.   East Morriston
*Mill, Allan,   do.   Dods

REGISTERED VOTER (Non-Resident).

Curle, Alexander, Esq., Abbey Park, Melrose

GORDON.

AN agricultural parish, in the western district of the Merse, —bounded on the north-west by Westruther and Legerwood, on the east by Greenlaw, on the south by Earlston and Hume, and on the west by Legerwood. Its extreme length is over 6 miles from east to west, and its greatest breadth from north to south is 4½ miles. The general outline is an irregular square. The area of the parish, according to the Ordnance Survey, is nearly 9739 acres; of which about 105 are occupied by roads, nearly 26 are under water, and of the remainder about one-fourth consists of unreclaimed moor. That part of it which is arable is under a high state of cultivation. The parish lies high, but none of the rising grounds are entitled to the name of hills. The atmosphere is clear and salubrious, owing to the general high situation. The parish of Gordon was formerly the residence of the noble family of the same name.* When they removed to their possessions in the north they seem to have transferred some of the names of their former possessions to the new. Greenknowe Tower is the only ruin of any interest in the parish; it stands in a hollow at the foot of the hill, on which is built the village of Gordon. Nothing now remains but the walls, which, however, are very entire. Green-knowe was the residence of a zealous covenanter of the name of Pringle. The Eden water, the only one of importance in the parish, divides from north to south into two nearly equal parts; the trout fishing in it is excellent, but it is partly restricted. The Blackadder skirts the parish for about a mile at its southern extremity, and is here a good

* " Now represented by the Duke of Richmond and Lennox and the Marquis of Huntley, the male line of Gordon (of this family) terminating in an heiress, who, by marriage, carried the estates into a branch of the Setons; the new line adopted the name of Gordon. They acquired the Marquisate of Huntley, and subsequently the Dukedom of Gordon; but the latter title has become extinct, most of the estates passing to the Duke of Richmond and Lennox, nephew of the late Duke; while the title of Huntley devolved on a collateral of the Gordon-Seton line. The territory of Gordon (in Berwickshire) was anciently of great extent, and included Gordon, Faunys, Fogo, Huntly, Melowistanes and (in Roxburghshire) the barony of Stichell. They seem to have settled about Gordon in the eleventh or twelfth century; in the fourteenth century they began to acquire possessions in the north, from which date their interest and possessions in Berwickshire gradually decreased (see Chirnside parish, p. 626, for the only instance of a *Gordon* estate now in the district). "In Normandy there is a manor called Gordon, belonging to a family of the same name."—*Spectator*, Sept. 2, 1865.

fishing water—trouts large and of excellent quality, but not plentiful; it requires fine tackle; and from here downward no water requires greater care on the part of the angler, to whose sport there is here no restriction. For some miles, both above and below, where the Blackadder skirts the parish, the district through which it winds is very lonely; with the exception of a single farm house or shepherd's cottage there is no sign of human life. The turnpike road from Dunse to Earlston, and one of the old coach roads from Edinburgh to Kelso, pass through the parish, crossing each other at right angles in the centre of the village.

The only village in the parish is Gordon,* already named; it occupies the summit of a hill near the Eden. It consists of one long street, in which are some very good shops and houses. The population is for the most part agricultural. Gordon has now a station quite close to it, on the Berwickshire branch of the North British Railway. From the increased facilities thus opened up, the parish and village may be expected to reap considerable advantages. The village is surrounded with small enclosures, the property of the villagers; at the foot of the hill, on which Gordon stands, is a very extensive moss, from which peats to a very large extent are dug. Gordon is 8 miles from Kelso, 5 from Greenlaw, and 6 from Earlston. Kelso is the nearest market and post town.

The population of the parish in 1861 was 931, who constituted 186 separate families; of whom 39 were returned as inhabiting houses of one window, 57 in houses of two windows, and the remainder (36) as inhabiting houses of three or more windows.

Assessed property in 1864-5, £8347 : 9 : 11.

The principal landed-proprietors in the parish are—Earl of Haddington; James Erskine, Esq. of Nether Huntlywood (The Priory, Melrose); James Dalrymple, Esq. of Greenknowe (Wester Langlee, Galashiels); Heirs of the late Charles John Baillie Hamilton, Esq., of Rumbleton Law; David Robertson Esq. of Middlethird and Fawside (of Ladykirk).

There are no mansion-houses in the parish, but Mr. Robertson has a shooting box called Fawside Cottage on Fawside farm.

Those marked thus (*) are Registered Voters.

DISTRICT POLICE OFFICER—James Pirie, Gordon.

PUBLIC OFFICES—Heritors' Clk., Session Clk., Inspector of Poor, and Registrar of Births, Marriages, and Deaths—Nicholas Dodds.
    Kirk Treasurer—Rev. William Stobbs.
    Medical Officer and Public Vaccinator—James Gibson, Earlston.

* More correctly *West* Gordon, as given in the Survey maps, and to distinguish it from *East* Gordon, also in the parish, once a village, but now only a farm-steading.

Post Office—Nicholas Dodds, postmaster. Daily post to Kelso. Departure, 6-20 a.m. Arrival, 2 p.m. Messenger, George Scott. A rural messenger (William Lockie) delivers letters through the parish daily.

Clergy. &c.—Gordon is in the Presbytery of Lauder, and Synod of Merse and Teviotdale. Patron—The Crown. Established Church—*Rev. William Stobbs (Inducted 1855). Sittings, 400. Average attendance at Sabbath School, 70. Free Church—*Rev. John Fraser (Inducted 1843). Sittings, 250. Average attendance at Sabbath School, .

Fast Days—Wednesdays before the first Sabbath of July, and a Sabbath in December (unfixed).

Mortification.—Bruce of Slogaries' bequest.—see p. 85.

School†—Parochial—*Nicholas Dodds, master. Aver. attend., 135.

Parochial Board—James Erskine, Esq., Chairman. No. of Poor on Roll, 41. Rate of Assessment, 5½d. per £ ; total Assessment in 1864-5, £327 : 6 : 6. Poor House—Kelso Combination.

Library—Village Library, open on Saturdays. Annual Subscription, 3s. James Brotherston, Librarian.

Corn Mills : Mid Mill—Christopher Sanderson, farmer. Nether Mill—James Wilson, miller. Mack's Mill—*George Burnett, farmer.

Carriers—John Frisken, Edinburgh on Monday—Kelso on Friday ; Ralph Robertson, Kelso, Tuesday and Friday ; Thomas Shiell, Dunse, Tuesday—Galashiels and Kelso on alternate Fridays ; Thomas Jack, to Galashiels every Saturday during summer, and to Earlston every Monday and Tuesday.

Conveyance to all parts by Berwickshire branch of the North British Railway. Station-Master, General Manager, and Railway Coal Agent—John Domin. Offices—James Wood, coal agent ; David Weatherhead, coal agent. For arrival and departure of the Trains, see Monthly Time Tables.

TRADES IN THE VILLAGE.

*Aitchison, John, grocer and feuar
*Allan Richard, feuar
Cochrane, James, fishing-tackle maker
Cockburn, Peter, tailor
Cockburn, Robert, blacksmith, East Gordon
Harvey, Joseph, joiner
Frisken, John, grocer and carrier
Gibson, John, inkeeper and carrier
Henderson, Agnes and Mary, innkeepers
Hunter, George, joiner, East Gordon
Jack, Thomas, grocer and carrier
Kennedy, Oliver, flesher
*Lockie, Robert, mason and feuar

---

† Children in the parish from 5 to 15 attending school during the first week of April 1861, 178 ; of all ages, 180.

*Lockie, Thomas, mason and feuar
Middlemas, Thomas, cooper
Miller, James, tea dealer and grocer
M'Dougall, George, tea dealer
Murray, Aaron, baker
Murray, John, shoemaker
Pringle, Helen, dressmaker
Pringle, John, tailor and clothier
Pringle, Margaret, milliner
Smith, Agnes, milliner
Smith, Steven, shoemaker
Waldie, George, blacksmith
Wood, David, tailor
Wood, Isabella, draper and dressmaker

RESIDENTS, FARMERS, &c., IN THE PARISH.

*Allan, David, farmer, Gordon East Mains
*Burnett, John, do. Fawside
*Clark, Thomas, do. Gordon Cottage
Gibson, George (late innkeeper), Gordon
Gray, Mrs., of Anchor Hill
*Hay, John, feuar, Gordon
*Henderson, Jn., farmer, Middlethird
*Henderson, Geo., do. Huntlywood
*Henderson, Geo., do. East Gordon
*Hay, William, farm-steward, Nether Huntlywood, feuar
*Lockie, Alexander, U.P. preacher, feuar
*Lyal, Robert, farmer, Greenknowe
*M'Dougall, do. Gordon West Mains
*Nisbet, John, do. Rumbleton
Rutherford, Aw,, do. Rumbletonlaw
Rutherford, Mrs., Rumbletonlaw

REGISTERED VOTERS (Non-Resident).

Baillie, Charles, Lord Jerviswoode, Bemersyde House
Baillie, The Hon. Major Robert, Dryburgh Abbey
Baillie, The Hon. and Rev. John, Elsden Tower Rectory, and Canon of York
Dalrymple, James, Esq. of Langlee, Galashiels
Erskine, James, Esq. of Shielfield, Melrose
Ford, James, labourer, Westruther, (feuar)
Hamilton, Charles John Baillie, Esq. of Rumbletonlaw
Henderson, John, feuar
Usher, Robert, Australia
Waldie, James, Craigo Mill, Kinross

GREENLAW.

—◆—

THE parish of Greenlaw lies almost in the centre of the Merse. It is bounded on the north by Longformacus, on the east by Polwarth, Fogo, and Eccles, on the south by Eccles and Hume, and on the west by Gordon and Westruther. Its length N.W. by S.E. is about 8 miles, and its average breadth is less than 3 miles; the total area of the whole parish, according to the Ordnance Survey, is 12,200¼ acres: of these 121¼ are occupied by public and private roads, and 51 are under water. "The surface of the parish is generally level, but in the north-west it is heathy and moorish. In the upper part of the parish a gravelly ridge, about 50 feet wide and 30 or 40 feet high, called the 'Kaimes,' crosses the moor, extending nearly 2 miles in length. On the north of this ridge the ground is boggy, and on the south of it is Dugden Moss, about 500 acres in extent." The Blackadder, which is carefully preserved over most other parts of its course, intersects the parish for nearly 5 miles, and here is free to the angler; on its banks are extensive quarries of red sandstone, from which was built the railway bridge at Leader foot, and most of the stones required on the Dunse and Earlston Railway were procured from them (*see* p. 468). The climate is generally good—mild in the southern part of the parish; but in the northern part the winds in autumn and spring are keen and penetrating. Near the centre of the parish is the small town of Greenlaw (of 800 inhabitants), the county town of Berwickshire, situated in a valley on the north bank of the Blackadder, and consisting of an extensive square from which diverge three or four short streets, containing a few good houses and shops, and a very handsome county inn. In the square are also the old county buildings and jail; to the west of the town a new and commodious county jail has been erected, and new county buildings have lately been erected at Dunse. Being near the centre of the shire, it was, by Act of Parliament, in 1696, ordained head burgh of the county, but by an Act lately passed, part of its privileges was transferred to Dunse, where most of the county officials reside, and some of the courts are held. Greenlaw is 36 miles from Edinburgh, 21 from Berwick, 16 from Kelso, and 8 from Dunse. It has a railway station on the Berwickshire branch of the North British line.

Fairs—Half-yearly, on 22d May and last Thursday of October, principally for the sale of cows; they are only of local importance. No other fairs for Greenlaw exist, although several appear in the different almanacs.

According to the census of 1861, the population of the entire parish was 1371; who constituted 318 separate families, 111 of whom were returned as living in houses of one window, 89 in houses of two windows, and the large proportion of 118 as living in houses of three and more windows.

Assessed property in 1864-5, £10,253 : 3 : 5.

The principal landed proprietors in the parish are—Sir Hugh P. H. Campbell, Bart., of Marchmont, who owns over two-thirds of the parish, and is Superior of the town; R. H. Broughton of Rowchester, William Bromfield of Old Greenlaw, and James Nisbet of Lambden.

RESIDENT JUSTICES OF THE PEACE—William Bromfield, Esq. of Old Greenlaw, and R. H. Broughton, Esq., of Rowchester.
Baron Officer—James Richardson.

COURTS.

THE SHERIFF ORDINARY and SMALL DEBT COURTS are held on the last Thursdays of January, March, May, June, July, October, and November.

COMMISSARY COURTS are held on the same days as the Sheriff-Courts.

JURY COURTS and COUNTY MEETINGS are held in the County Buildings.
Police Officer—Alexander Aitchison.

PUBLIC OFFICES, &c.

County Jail—William Smith, Governor.
Land and Assessed Taxes, Sub-Collector of—Allan Purves.
Medical Officer and Public Vaccinator—Patrick Kynoch, M.D.
Poor, Inspector of, Session Clerk, Kirk Treasurer, and Registrar of Births, Marriages, and Deaths—John Williamson.
Sheriff-Officer—John Pilmuir, residing at Dunse.
Stamps and Taxes—Allan Purves, Sub-Collector and Distributor.
Sheriff-Clerk Depute—Allan Purves.

COUNTY TOWN OFFICIALS—*see* County Lists, pp. 472, 473, and Dunse Lists, p. 550.

POST OFFICE.

Mrs J. Miller, Postmistress.

Mails arrive by Dunse at half-past 2 p.m., and leave at half-past 5 a.m. James Sutherland, Deliverer. A rural Runner (William Dawson) leaves, after the arrival of the Post, on a circuit of about 12 miles, leaving and taking up letters in the parish.

CLERGY, &c.

Greenlaw is in the Presbytery of Dunse, and Synod of Lothian and Tweeddale.

Patron—Sir Hugh Hume Campbell, Bart.

ESTABLISHED CHURCH—Rev. John H. Walker (Inducted 1844). Sittings, 476. Average attendance at Sabbath School, 70. Superintendent of Sabbath School—Mr. Broomfield ; Precentor—Geo. Common ; Church Officer—James Richardson.

FREE CHURCH—Rev. John Fairbairn (Inducted 1842). Sittings, 450. Average attendance at Sabbath School, 50.

UNITED PRESBYTERIAN CHURCH—Rev. John Milne, A.M. (Inducted 1854). Sittings, 450. Average attendance at Sabbath School, 45. Superintendent of Sabbath School—Minister ; Precentor and Kirk Treasurer—George Pringle, tailor ; Church Officer—Alexander Allan.

FAST DAYS—Wednesdays before first Sunday in November and first Sunday in May.

SCHOOLS.†

Parochial—John Williamson. master. Average attendance, 100.
Free Church—Quentin Kerr, master. Average attendance, 120

PAROCHIAL BOARD.

Sir H. H. Campbell, Bart., Chairman.
No. of Poor on Roll, 55. Average rate of Assessment, 8d. per £ ; total Assessment in 1864-5, £583.

CHARITABLE BEQUESTS.

£50 annually, left by the late Sir W H. Campbell of Marchmont, in 1821, is intrusted to the parish minister to be distributed in meal and coals to the poor of the parish in the months of November and February.

£7 annually, left by the late Mr. Broomfield, in 1734, for the education of the poor of the parish ; administered by the Kirk Session.

‡TH BERWICKSHIRE RIFLE CORPS—(GREENLAW.)

Major Fergusson Home of Bassendean, Captain.
James Wood, Whiteside, Lieutenant.
Ensign—J. Turnbull, Grizzlerig.
Assistant Surgeon—Dr. Kynoch.
Drill Instructor—Sergeant-Major J. Conn.
Enrolled Force 85.
Subscription for Honorary Members 10s. ; Ordinary, 2s. 6d.

† Children from 5 to 15, in the parish, attending school during first week of April 1861, 231 ; of all ages, 250.

LIBRARY.

Annual Subscription, 4s. No. of vols., 1000. Librarian—Robert Gibson, clothier. Open Tuesdays and Fridays.

BANK.

CITY OF GLASGOW BANK (Opened 1850)—Allan Purves, Agent.

INSURANCE AGENTS.

SCOTTISH UNION................William Hume, Baillieknowe.
NORTHERN ASSURANCE..........Allan Purves, banker.
NORFOLK CATTLE INSURANCE.....A. Purves, Do.
SCOTTISH MUTUAL PLATE GLASS INSURANCE .... } A. Purves, Do.
EDINBURGH LIFE ASSOCIATION OF SCOTLAND............. } Henry Miller, merchant.

MEDICAL PRACTITIONER—Dr. Kynoch.

CORN AND FLOUR MILLS : Castle Mill—James Wilson, miller ; Greenlaw—David Robinson, miller.

QUARRY : Greenside—Sir Hugh H. Campbell of Marchmont, proprietor ; at present leased by Mr. Lanton, railway contractor.

CARRIERS : Coldstream—John Richardson, Monday ; Edinburgh—John Richardson, Tuesday ; Dunse—John Dick, every alternate Tuesday ; Kelso—John Dick, Friday.

CONVEYANCE—Railway to all parts.

GREENLAW TURNPIKE ROAD TRUST.

SOUTHERN DISTRICT.

Meets at Greenlaw on the 24th October, or thereabouts.
James C. Robson, Dunse, Clerk. Thos. Mitchell, Melrose, Surveyor.

EASTERN DISTRICT.
James Cunningham, Coldstream, Surveyor.
Jonathan Melrose, Clerk.

STATUTE LABOUR ROADS.

DISTRICT OF GREENLAW.

Consisting of the parishes of Greenlaw, Polwarth, and Hume.
District Clerk—J. Williamson, Greenlaw.
No fixed Surveyor or days of meeting.

TRADES AND RESIDENTS IN THE TOWN.

*Anderson, William, road contractor
Aldcorn, Robert, baker
Alexander, Misses, dressmaker
Alexander, Miss A., do.
Allan, Alexander, tailor
Aimers, Thomas, Tweed warehouse
Anderson, James, grocer
*Brown, William, cartwright
Brownlees, Alexander, blacksmith
Carr, James, Millwynd
Castle Inn, Mrs. Learmonth
Clarke, Robert, blacksmith
Clarke, William, cattle dealer
Common, George, shoemaker
Clark, Isabella, grocer
Clark, Miss, milliner
*Cossar, William
Crown Inn, John Gray
Dodds, Catherine, dressmaker
Dodds, George, butcher
*Dodds, James, saddler
*Fairbairn, Rev. John, *Free Church Manse*
Frater, Peter, shoemaker
*Frater, George, builder
Frater, Thomas, sculptor
*Gardener, James, undertaker
*Gibson, Robert, tailor and clothier
Grosset, Thomas, joiner
Haig, Miss, confectioner
Henderson, Janet, dressmaker
Hislop, Andrew, millwright
Hogg, John, tailor
Henderson, James, joiner
*Johnston, James, late *Governor of Prison*
Johnston, John, grocer
Kay, James, ironmonger
*Kerr, James, shoemaker
*Knox, John
Kynoch, Patrick, M.D.
Kerr, Q., *F. C. schoolmaster*
Laidlaw, George, watchmaker
Lamb, Peter, thatcher
*Lamb, William, tailor and clothier
Lillie, Mrs., Millwynd
*Lumsden, James, millwright
Lyall, Alexander, slater and glazier
Lyall, Alexander, jun., slater

M'Donald, Mrs., grocer
Martin & Scott, woollen manufacturers
Matthewson, John, blacksmith
*Miller, Henry, draper and grocer
*Milne, Rev. John, M.A., *U. P. Manse*
*Moscrip, William, innkeeper and coal agent
Pringle, George, tailor and clothier
*Pringle, William, tailor
Purves, Allan, banker
Purves, William, tailor
Richardson, David, shoemaker
Richardson, Robert, cattle dealer
Rogerson, George, butcher
Shillinglaw, Mrs., china merchant
Sligh, Archibald, provision dealer
Smart, William, baker
Smith, William, *Governor of County Jail*
Sprightly, Francis, shoemaker
Stark, William, shoemaker
*Sutherland, George, grocer
Tait, Archibald, shoemaker
Thomson, Miss, Flora Bank
Tocher, Alexander, watchmaker
Turnbull, George, The Cottage
Turnbull, Miss, Lochiel House
Waddell, Janet, grocer
Waldie, Mrs., Millwynd
Walker, Rev. John H., *The Manse*
Weir, Miss, dressmaker
*Williamson, John, schoolmaster
Wilson, Alexander, builder
Wood, John, joiner

———

Railway Station, William Glasgow, station-master
    Thomas Hogarth, coal agent

———

RESIDENTS, FARMERS, &c , IN THE PARISH.

Black, Miss, Greenlaw Dean
*Burton, James, farmer, Angelraw
*Dodds, Willm.,   do.   Elwartlaw
*Grieve, Alex.,   do.   Eastfield
*Johnston, George, do.   Howlaws
*Jamieson, George, do.   Catmoss
*Lauder, Robert,   do.   Slegdean
*Lauder, George,   do.   Polwarth Woodheads
*Lithgow, Edward, do.   Bedshiel
Robertson, James, manager, Greenlaw Dean

Robertson, John, Clerkinvale
*Simpson, Peter, farmer, Gordonbank
*Stevenson, Willm., do.   Crumrig
Walker, Andrew, do.   Cowrig
Watson, James,   do.   Hallyburton
*Wood, James,   do.   Whiteside
Wood, Mrs., Whiteside

SEATS, &c., OF COUNTY FAMILIES IN THE PARISH.

LAMBDEN.

Situated on the Lambden Burn, which bounds the parish its entire length, south-east, and divides it from Eccles—the property and residence of *James Nisbet, E-q. ; born 1841 ; succeeded his father, the late Robert Nisbet, Esq., 1861. Lambden is also the residence of Miss Nisbet, the aunt of the proprietor, and of the Misses Nisbet, his sisters. The Lambden property is partly in Eccles parish.

OLD GREENLAW.

Situated about 1 mile south-east from Greenlaw—the property and residence of *William Bromfield, Esq.
Heir—his son William-John, also resident at Old Greenlaw.

ROWCHESTER.

A fine building erected by the late proprietor, situated near the south of the parish—the residence of *Robt. H. Broughton, Esq., who purchased the property in 1858 from John C. Hopkins, Esq., formerly of Rowchester, now of Redcar, Yorkshire ; born 7th May 1829.

REGISTERED VOTERS (Non-Resident).

Campbell, Sir Hugh P. H., Bart , of Marchmont
Logan, James, innkeeper, Leitholm
Ovens, John, Gunsgreen, Eyemouth
Rae, Robert, Whitrighill, Mertoun
Scott, Hon. and Rev. William Hugh, Rector of Maiden Newton, Dorset
Stobie, William, tailor, 17 Greenside St., Edinburgh
Thomson, James, baker, Dunse
Turnbull, John, sen., Homebyres
Watson, Adam, road-maker, Lander
Watson, George, farmer, Easter Softlaw
Watson, John, labourer, Polwarth
Warrender, George, Polmont House, Lasswade

DUNSE.

———•———

THIS is an irregularly shaped parish, extending from the Lammermoor Hills southwardinto the rich fertile vale of the Merse. In length it is about 6 miles from north to south, and its mean breadth is about 3½ miles. The area of the parish, according to the Ordnance Survey, is 11,474¾ acres, of which 78¼ acres are under water, 120 are roads, public and private, and 24¼ are occupied by the railway. The northern part into which the southern ridge of the Lammermoors extends, consists of rough hilly pasture, unfit for cultivation. Here Cockburn Law, the highest hill in the parish, rises to 1065 feet. The remainder of the parish is fertile and highly cultivated. The Blackadder and Whitadder, both of which skirt the parish for a considerable distance, abound in trout of a very fine quality. Salmon ascend the Whitadder in considerable numbers, but are seldom seen in the Blackadder. The former of these streams is free to the angler ; the latter is partly restricted.

Near the centre of the parish is the town of Dunse, with a population of 2256—a burgh of barony, and the principal town in Berwickshire. It lies nearly in the centre of the county, on a fine plain, under the skirts of Dunse Law, a beautiful hill, which rises to the height of 700 feet. The town is of great antiquity and was frequently destroyed in the Border wars. It now contains a number of excellent shops and houses, an elegant town hall, which stands in the centre of the Market Place, a corn exchange and new county buildings in Newtown Street. The suburbs are very pretty, and contain several handsome villa residences ; about half a mile to the north is DUNSE CASTLE, the seat of Mr Hay, a splendid modern mansion in the castellated style. The grounds surrounding Dunse Castle are very beautiful, and contain an artificial loch of small dimensions, which is well stocked with tench, perch, and eels, and at certain seasons, is greatly frequented by wild fowl. Dunse has been the birth-place of several eminent men, among whom were the Rev. Thomas Boston, author of the "Fourfold State" and other works ; Abraham Robertson, LL.D., Regius professor of astronomy at Oxford ; Thomas M'Crie, D.D., the historian ; and John Black, late editor of the *Morning Chronicle ;* and it is generally acknowledged that here Joannes Duns Scotus was born in 1274. The house where Boston was born still exists in Newtown Street, where a tablet in the wall points it out.* The town is governed by a baron bailie ; the feuars manage, by a council of nine, the property vested in them;

* For interesting particulars of Boston *see* Ettrick parish, pp. 414-17.

and the police commissioners superintend the business of lighting, paving, cleaning, etc., and other matters connected with the burgh.

The sanitary condition of the town may be regarded as very good. Epidemic fevers in the form of typhus are rare; and the district altogether will vie with the most favoured localities in this respect. It must be confessed, however, that the death rate of the parish, as shown by the Registrar-General's returns, is unfavourable—*see* Table. The town is well supplied with water.

The North British Railway Company is progressing rapidly with its Dunse extension line to Newtown, St. Boswell's. It is now open as far as Earlston, and, when finished, will, from the facility of communication with England, prove of immense benefit to the town and district.

General Holidays—New Year's Day and a day in June (unfixed.)

Market Day—Tuesday, when a large corn business in bulk is done. Second only to Kelso in importance in the district (*see* p. 304). Fat cattle and sheep—first Fridays of the month.

Great Hiring Days—For Hinds, first Tuesday of March; for Women and Lads, second Tuesday before 26th of May and first Tuesday of November.

FAIRS*—*Cattle, Sheep, and Horses*, first Thursday of June. This fair is the oldest, and for long was the most important in Dunse. Owing to the establishment of the monthly cattle markets it has greatly decreased within the last eight or ten years, but it is still an important fair, and excites a general interest. It is of a very miscellaneous character; the cattle shown being of all kinds—fat, feeding, grazing, and generally a few lots of Irish; sheep—fat and lean clipped, ditto rough—bred, half-bred, and blackfaced; cows—a plentiful supply of good and indifferent; horses—generally a small and inferior supply.

Lambs, Wool, and Cattle, second Tuesday of July. The lambs exhibited are principally three-parts and half-bred Leicesters; very few cattle are shown of any kind; the wool sold is of a very miscellaneous description — including Leicester, Cheviot, and black-faced. This fair is attended by a good number of wool merchants from the south. The sale of lambs, &c., begins early; that of wool about 2 p.m.

Cattle, Lambs, and Horse, and for Hiring of Shearers (hence the name of *Hook* fair, by which it is known)—26th August, or Tuesday after when the date falls on a Saturday, Sunday, or Monday. The most important feature of this fair is a sale of tups by auction at its termination. The show of horses is gene-

* All the Dunse Fairs are held in the town—*see* paragraph on the Berwickshire fairs, generally, p. 469.

rally good, but, as it invariably happens, the demand for them is dull. In cattle, "no business of note" occurred at the market of 1864; and lambs showed a falling off from the previous year.

Ewe Tryst, third Thursday of September. This is probably the most important fair in Berwickshire; and being the first of the ewe fairs in the district, its transactions are regarded with considerable general interest. Ewes—half and three-parts bred Leicesters, and Cheviots are the stock mostly shown; lambs of the same kinds follow in importance, then grazing cattle. After the fair, in the afternoon, an important district tup sale takes place; at the fair of 1864, 61 Leicester rams were thus sold.

Cattle &c., 17th November, or Tuesday after when that date falls on a Saturday, Sunday, or Monday. For the sale of wintering cattle (principally stirks and two-year olds) and horses, and when a small and irregular trade in lambs and sheep takes place.

According to the census of 1861, the population of the entire parish of Dunse was 3595; who constituted 857 separate families, 3 of whom were returned as living in houses having no window, 315 in houses of one window, 225 in houses of two windows, leaving 314 (or rather less than two-fifths) living in houses of three or more windows.

Assessed property in 1864-5, £22,495 : 5 : 9.

The principal landed-proprietors in the parish are—William Hay, Esq. of Dunse Castle; William Miller, Esq., of Manderstone, M.P.; Jn. Wilson. Esq., of Cumledge; Capt. Alexander Monro of Cockburn (Craiglockhart, near Edinburgh); David Milne Home, Esq., of Wedderburn; Lady Elizabeth Pringle of Langton; William King Hunter, Esq. of Wellfield (Barnken, Dunse); Abraham Logan, Esq., of Burnhouses (Caverton Mill, Kelso); Geo. Denholm, Esq. of Broomhill.

Superior of Dunse—William Hay, Esq.

MAGISTRATES AND COUNCIL.

The government of the town is under the Police Act 3 and William IV. cap. 46.

COMMISSIONERS OF POLICE.

Chairman Ex-officio—Alexander Crawford, Bailie.

John Young, painter.	John Kerr, bookseller.
John Tait, surgeon.	John Cockburn, baker.
Robert Webster, draper.	T. Wilson, Temperance Hotel.
Geo. Johnston, stationer.	John Waite, inspector of poor.
John Cockburn, druggist.	

Treasurer—Geo. Swan.   Clerk—Charles Watson.

Collector—A. Weatherhead.   Officer—A. Cormack, Newtown Street.

Police Rates, 1s. per £.

ACTING JUSTICES OF THE PEACE.

Those marked thus (*) are Resident in the parish.

Sir Hugh H. Campbell, of March-
mont, Bart.
Sir Geo. A. F. Houston Boswall,
of Blackadder, Bart.
Geo. C. Trotter Cranstoun, Esq. of
Dewar.
*John Wilson, Esq. of Cumledge.
Archd. C. Swinton, Esq., younger
of Kimmerghame.
Col. G. W. F. Buchan, of Kelloe.

Major Wm. H. Smith of Cruiks-
field.
Lieut.-Colonel George L. Home of
Broomhouse.
John C. Swinton, Esq. of Kim-
merghame.
*Wm. Hay, Esq. of Dunse Castle.
*George Peat, Esq., of Wellnage.
*George Dickson, Esq., Sheriff-
Substitute of Berwickshire.

A. Weatherhead, Depute Justice of Peace Clerk for Dunse District.

COURTS.

JUSTICE OF PEACE COURTS held first Monday of every month—Alex. Weatherhead, writer, Clerk.

SHERIFF AND COMMISSARY COURTS, held every Tuesday and Thursday during Sessions,* with the exception of last Thursday of each month.

SHERIFF SMALL DEBT COURTS held on the third Thursday of January, and February, the Tuesday before the last Thursday of March, the first Thursday of May and June, the Tuesday before the last Thursday of July, and the first Thursday of October, November, and December.

PUBLIC OFFICES.

Billet Master—Thomas Holywell, Market Place.
Clerk of Lieutenancy Office—Alexander Weatherhead, Barniken, Clerk, Murray Street.
Clerk of Supply Office, (County Buildings,) Clerk to the Trustees of Middle District of Roads, and Clerk to Commissioners of Income Tax and Assessed Taxes—George Peat, of Wellnage.
Commissary Clerk Depute—William T. Kellie, Clouds.
Collector of County Rates—Alexander Crawford, South Street.
Income Tax Assessor—A. Maclean, Haddington.
Justice of Peace Fiscal—David Ferguson, writer.
Justice of Peace Clerk—Alexander Weatherhead, Barniken.
Police, Inspector of—James Grant, County Buildings.
Police Office, (County Buildings)—G. H. List, Chief Constable.
Police Rate, Collector of—A. Weatherhead, Barniken, Murray Street.
Poor, Inspector of, and Collector—John Waite, East Street.
Procurator Fiscal's Office (County Buildings)—James C. Robson, of Southfield.
Registrar of Births, Marriages, and Deaths—Thomas Holywell.
Session Clerk and Kirk Treas.—John Mercer, Church Yard Square.
Sexton—William Ross, Caste Street.

* "During Sessions"—see foot-note, p. 251.

Sheriff Clerk's Office, (County Buildings)—William T. Kellie, Sheriff Clerk ; John B. Kellie, Depute.
Sheriff Officer—John Pilmer, South Street.
Stamps and Taxes, Distributor of—Alexander Crawford.
Town Crier—John Crawford, Market Place.
Valuators under Lands Valuation Act—Charles Watson, Clouds, (Ayton District); David M'Watt, Currie Street (Coldstream District) ; William Stevenson, South Street (Dunse District).
Weights and Measures, Inspector of—John Kerr, Castle Streeet.

POST OFFICE, (Easter Street.)

M. D. Jeffreys, Postmistress.

| Box closes at 8-35 a.m. | Arrival—10-10 p.m. |
| ,,   4-10 p.m. | ,,   10-40 a.m. |

Sundays—Delivery, 8 a.m.

FOOT POSTS.

Departure—Greenlaw, 12 noon.	Arrivals—Greenlaw, 8 a.m.
,, Charterhall, 6 a.m.	,, Charterhall, 12-10 p.m.
,, Ellemford and Abbey 6 a.m.	,, Ellemford and Abbey, 1-30 p.m.
,, Longformacus and Cranshaws, 6 a.m.	,, Longformacus & Cranshaws, 11-10 a.m.
,, Chalkielaw, 6 a.m.	,, Chalkielaw, 9.30 a.m.

Town Deliverer—John Lawrie.

RUNNERS.

James Sutherland for Greenlaw, A. Elliot for Charterhall, James Gillies for Ellemford, W. Fraser for Longformacus, J. Holywell for Chalkielaw.

CLERGY, &c.

Dunse is the seat of a Presbytery, in the Synod of Merse and Teviotdale.

Patron—William Hay of Dunse Castle.

PARISH CHURCH—Rev. John M'Leod (Inducted 1863). Sittings, 1200. Average attendance at Sabbath School, 220. Session Clerk and Kirk Treasurer—John Mercer. Organist—— Barker, Berwick. Church Officer—W. Symington.

BOSTON FREE CHURCH—Rev. John Fordyce (Inducted 1858). Sittings, 650. Average attendance at Sabbath School, 102. Session Clerk—Robert M'Lean ; Precentor—John Thompson.

UNITED PRESBYTERIAN CHURCH (East)—Rev. William Ritchie (Inducted 1839). Sittings, 650. Aver. attend. at Sab. School, 102. Superintendent of Sabbath School—Philip Wilson : Session Clerk—Thos. Thompson ; Treasurer—John Wilson ; Precentor—Thos. Dunbar; Church Officer—John Lawrie.

UNITED PRESBYTERIAN CHURCH (South)—Rev. Daniel Kerr, M.A. (Inducted 1840). Sittings, 640. Average attendance at Sabbath

School, 80 ; Superintendent of do.—Minister ; Session Clerk—Robert Wilson ; Treasurer—George Aitken ; Church Officer—W. Ross.

UNITED PRESBYTERIAN CHURCH (West)—Rev. Charles Miller (Inducted 1841). Sittings, 400. Average attendance at Sabbath School, 60.

EPISCOPALIAN CHURCH—Rev. Augustus E. Crowder (Inducted 1850). Sittings, 200.

FAST DAYS—Thursday before second Sunday of July. Winter unsettled.

EDUCATIONAL INSTITUTIONS.†

Boarding Seminary for Young Ladies—Misses Doubleday.
Hawthorn Boarding Seminary for Young Ladies—Misses Hamilton.
Parochial School—John Mercer, Master. Average attendance, 125.
Free Church School—Robert Lillie, Master ; Aver attendance, 130.
Wellfield Boarding Academy, East Street—James Wood, University, Edinburgh. Assistant—Philip Wood.
Industrial School (held in the evening for educating the young who cannot attend school during the day). Supported by voluntary subscriptions. John King and Andrew Stenhouse, male teachers ; Miss Dickson, female teacher ; Philip Wilson, corn merchant, Secy. and Treas.
Private Schools—James Swan, Miss Pringle, Miss Turner.

DUNSE AND LANGTON INFANT SCHOOL.‡

President—John Campbell Swinton, Esq. of Kimmerghame.
  Secretary—Mr. William R. Wait.
  Treasurer—Mr William Stevenson.
Teacher—Miss Davidson. Average attendance, 100.

PAROCHIAL BOARD.

John Wilson, Esq. of Cumledge, Chairman.

James Thomson, Dunse.	Thomas Holywell, Dunse
Alexander Crawford, Dunse.	George Johnstone: do.

John Waite, East Street, Inspector.
Rate of Assessment, 7¼d. per £ ; total Assess. in 1864-5, £1115 : 10 : 9.
Average number of Poor on Roll, 131.

LADIES' CLOTHING SOCIETY (estab. 1833).

Committee—Miss Johnstone, Miss Mary Stuart, Miss Trotter. Mrs. William Purves, Secretary and Treasurer.
Supported by voluntary subscriptions for supplying warm clothing to the poor of the parish.

† Children in the parish from 5 to 15 attending school during the first week of April, 1861, 568 ; of all ages, 670.
‡ This institution has no connection with Langton, although the name is here associated with that of Dunse.

SAILORS' SOCIETY (estab. 1848).

Secretary and Treasurer—Mrs. Mercer, Church Square.
Supported by voluntary subscriptions for supplying the means of Grace to fishermen.

BENEFIT SOCIETY (estab. 1856).

President—John King.
J. Cockburn, baker, Treasurer. Robt. Lillie, teacher, Secretary : John Kerr and Robert Rankine, Auditors.

" This Society shall be conducted by twelve members, two auditors and a president, secretary, and treasurer. Each member on entering shall pay 1s. as entry-money, and shall continue to pay weekly a sum not less than 6d. ; and shall receive when sick 5s. per week for the first 13 weeks, and 3s. for the second 13 weeks."—*Extract from Rules.*

Number of Members for 1864, 184, who partook of the following scheme of division at the end of the financial year, after paying all expenses of management and sick money :—

Depositors of 3s. 2d. per week received	£8	5	11.
Do. 2s. 2d. do.	5	12	11.
Do. 1s. 8d. do.	4	6	6
Do. 1s. 2d. do.	3	0	0.

This statement shows that the depositors received more than their payments—a fact that speaks largely for the general health of this community.

LODGE OF FREE GARDENERS (estab. 1812).

T. N. Fairley, Master. Thomas Scoular, Past Master.
Depute Master—John Brown.
John Purves, Senior Warden. John Brown, Junior Warden.
John Whitehead, Secretary. G. Pringle, Treasurer.

MASON LODGES.

DUNSE LODGE, No. 23 (estab. 1758).
James Watson, Master.
Charles Watson, Secretary. Wm. Jeffreys, Treasurer.

CALEDONIAN ROYAL ARCH-CHAPTER OF FREE MASONS.
Estab. 1792 by Royal Charter from Kilwinning.
No. 25, holder of the Supreme Grand R. A. C. of Scotland.
Thomas Holywell, 1st Principal ; William Dickson, 2d Principal ; David Duns, 3rd Principal. Scribe—Wm. Symington.

CHARITY.

The Grieve Fund belonging to the Dunse Mason Lodge for decayed members of said Lodge, consisting of house property left by the late Miss Grieve, Eyemouth ; the rents to be divided amongst the poorer members.

SUBSCRIPTION LIBRARY (Town Hall—estab. 1768).

James Thomson, Chairman.
Wm. Stevenson, Treasurer.   J. Kerr, Librarian.   No. of vols. 2000.
Yearly Subscription, 10s.   Shares, £4.

MECHANICS' INSTITUTE (estab. 1840).

Presidents—W. Crawford, Alex. Weatherhead, George Young, Philip
Wilson, and Dr. M'Watt.
Secretary—William H. Waite.
Corresponding Secretary and Treasurer—Robert Brown.
Librarian—John Cockburn.
Yearly Subscriptions—Members, 2s. ; Family Tickets, 5s. ; Appren-
tices, 1s.

BOSTON F. C. YOUNG MEN'S CHRISTIAN ASSOCIATION.

President—William Crawford.
Secretary—John Virtue.   Treasurer—Thomas Lillie.

Meets in the Free Church vestry every Monday evening during winter for mutual improvement.

BERWICKSHIRE AMATEUR HORTICULTURAL SOCIETY

(estab. 1842).

Jas. Thomson, Esq., President.   Charles Watson, Clouds, Secretary.
George Wilson, Treasurer.

Competitions take place annually in July and September.

CORN EXCHANGE (opened 1856).

DIRECTORS.

James Thomson, Chairman.   Thomas Hood.
John Elliot.   John Wilson.
W. T. Kellie, Treasurer.   David Ferguson, Secretary.
Rental, £64.   Pays 3 per cent.

GAS COMPANY (estab. 1825).

James Thomson, Chairman.   J. C. Robson, Treasurer.
William Thompson, Manager.   David Ferguson, Clerk.
6s. 8d. per 1000 feet.
Capital, £1400 ; Dividend, 8 per cent.

WATER COMPANY (LIMITED—estab. 1858).

A Chairman and nineteen Directors.
W. K. Hunter, Secretary and Treasurer.
John Lawrie, Officer.
Capital £2000, in 4000 shares.

CHORAL SOCIETY.

President—Rev. D. Kerr.   Treasurer—R. C. Lochhead.
Secretary—Robert Brown.   Conductor—David Lamb.
Yearly Subscription for Male Members, 2s. ; Females, *nil.*   60
members.

FLUTE BAND

President—John Cockburn.
Treasurer—James Edgar   Secretary—John Virtue.
Leader—Thomas Ormiston.   24 members.
Supported by Voluntary Subscriptions.

FISHING CLUB (estab. 1850).

President—Peter Dunbar.   Secretary—John Gray.
The annual competition is on the day after the May hiring.

CURLING CLUB.

Instituted 1807, and admitted into Royal Caledonian Curling Club
in 1856,
Sir H. H. Campbell, Bart , of Marchmont, Patron.
Lady Campbell, Patroness.
Alexander Weatherhead, Chairman.
J. B. Kellie, Vice-Chairman.   Rev. A. E. Crowder, Chaplain.
Alexander Warden, Treasurer.   Charles Watson, Secretary.
Curling Pond—"The Hen Poo"—at Dunse Castle, about half-a-
mile north of the town.

1ST BERWICKSHIRE RIFLE CORPS—(DUNSE.)

Hon. A. F. Cathcart, Colonel.   Major Rennie, Capt. and Adjutant.
David Ferguson, Lieutenant.   Philip Wilson, Ensign.
Robert C M'Watt, M.D., Surgeon.   Walter Nisbet, Drill Instructor.
Effective Force, 80.

GYMNASTIC CLUB.

President—A. Campbell Swinton, yr. of Kimmerghame.
Treasurer—John Kerr.   Secretary—W. H. Waite.

The Games are held in August in a field adjoining the town.   The
prizes given in 1864 amounted to £11.

BANKS.

BANK OF SCOTLAND (opened 1833)—George Peat and R. F. Hardy,
Agents ; B. Mackenzie, Teller.

BRITISH LINEN COMPANY* (opened 1784)—James Wylie, Agent.
CITY OF GLASGOW BANK (opened 1850)—Johnston and Robson, Agents ; R. Lochhead, Accountant.
ROYAL BANK OF SCOTLAND (opened 1856)—William King Hunter, Agent.

INSURANCE AGENTS.

BRITISH GUARANTEE................Johnston and Robson, writers.
CALEDONIAN...................... ...William Kinghorn, merchant.
CITY OF GLASGOW .... { William Kinghorn.
                                 { Wm. Jeffreys, County Buildings.
EDINBURGH LIFE...................Robert Brown, merchant.
ENGLISH AND SCOTTISH LAW........J. C. Robson, procurator-fiscal.
FARMERS'.........................Robert Webster, merchant.
INDISPUTABLE LIFE................
INSURANCE CO. OF SCOTLAND.......J. B. Kellie.
LIFE ASSOCIATION .. ..R. F. Hardy.
LIVERPOOL & LONDON & GLOBE ....Charles Watson.
NORTH BRITISH ....James Wylie, banker.
NORWICH UNION FIRE............ William Crawford.
NORTHERN ....Alex. Weatherhead, writer.
PHŒNIX..........................George Johnston, bookseller.
ROYAL INSURANCE CO..............William Stevenson, accountant.
SCOTTISH AMICABLE...............Robert Wilson.
SCOTTISH PROVIDENT..............William K. Hunter, banker.
SCOTTISH UNION.................. { David M'Watt.
                                { William K. Hunter, banker.
STANDARD............ ....Alexander Crawford
SCOTTISH WIDOWS' FUND.......... }
SUN .... } Philip Wilson, corn-factor.
UNITED KINGDOM TEMPERANCE AND } Robert G. Swan.
    GENERAL PROVIDENT .... }

EMIGRATION AGENTS

John Young, draper ; John Cockburn, baker ; Thomas Holywell.

PROCURATORS, NOTARIES PUBLIC, &c.

Alexander Crawford, Mountview, South Street ; Wm. Crawford, Mountview, South Street ; David Ferguson, N.P., Newtown Street ; W. King Hunter, Market Place ; Jas. Curle Robson, Market Place ; Charles Watson, N.P., Clouds ; Alexander Weatherhead, Barniken, Murray Street.

MEDICAL PRACTITIONERS.

William W. Campbell, M.D., Newtown Street ; Robert C. M'Watt, M.D., Haymount ; John Tait, surgeon, Market Place.

VETERINARY SURGEONS.

William Lothian, North Street ; William Blair, Castle Street.

* Next to the Bank of Scotland at Kelso (see p. 94), this is the oldest in the district.

MILLS.

Those marked thus (*) are Registered Voters.

COCKBURN MILL—Corn—*William Darling, miller
DUNSE MILL—Corn—*James Swanston, farmer.
PUTTON MILL—Corn—*J. Smith, miller.
NISBET MILL—Corn—John Ford, farmer.

CUMLEDGE MILL—Woollen—*William Laidlaw, jun.
TILE WORKS—

AUCTIONEERS.

Archibald Jamieson, Peelrig.   Robert G. Swan, Albert Cottages.

STATUTE LABOUR ROADS.

DUNSE DISTRICT.

Comprising the parishes of Bunkle, Cranshaws, Dunse, Edrom, Langton, Longformacus, and Abbey St. Bathans.

Clerk—William Stevenson, Accountant.
Surveyor—James D. Harmon.

Meetings are held in April and October.

CARRIERS.

ABBEY ST. BATHANS—Peter Aitchison, Tuesday and Friday, Mrs. Gibb's, baker, South Castle Street.
BERWICK—By Rail, daily ; Robert Edgar, Saturdays, North Street.
EARLSTON—By Rail, daily.
EDINBURGH,   do.
COLDSTREAM—Andw. Mack, Monday, Market Place.
CRANSHAWS—Robert Laurie, Tuesday, Red Lion.
GARVALD—Robert Guy, Tuesday, Market Place.
GORDON and GALASHIELS—Thomas Shiels, Tuesday.
GREENLAW—By Rail, daily ; John Dick, Tuesday, Plough Inn, North Street.
KELSO—By Rail, daily ; John Dick, Tuesday, Plough Inn, North St. ; and Andw. Mack, Saturday, Market Place.
ORMISTON—George Dickson, Tuesday, Market Place.
SWINTON—L. Short, Tuesday,   do.
WESTRUTHER—J. Brotherston,   do.
WHITSOME—John Middlemiss, Tuesday.

CONVEYANCE BY RAILWAY.

Dunse Branch of North British line, joining the main line at Reston, lately extended to Earlston, and in progress to Newtown. David Wilson, Station-Master.

DIRECTORY.

___

TRADES, RESIDENTS, AND PUBLIC OFFICES.

Those marked thus (*) are Registered Voters.

Albert Cottages

Aitchison, Jasper, merchant
Aitchison & Rae, slaters
Swan, Robert G., auctioneer
Maxwell, John
*Kinlayside, James, joiner
Blackie, John, pavior

Black Bull Street

Black Bull Hotel, *James Lauder
Cockburn, Mrs, straw hat-maker
Grinlaw, Andrew, watchmaker
Mills, Miss,
Paxton, George, tinsmith
Rathie, Miss, china merchant
Temperance Hotel, *Thomas Wilson
*Young, George, plumber

Bridge End

*Burgoine, Joseph, grocer
*Crombie, John, joiner
*Wilkinson, Richard, farmer

Castle Street (North)

Alexander, W., coal agent
Blaikie, James, tailor
Blair, W. & D., blacksmiths
Cross Keys Inn, Thomas Wilson
Dickenson, D., millwright
*Dickinson, William, painter
*Dodds, Alexander, builder
Galbraith, Miss, grocer
Industrial School (see p. 553)
*Kay, James, feuar
*M'Leod, Rev. John, *The Manse*
*Penny, Walter, carrier

*Scott, John, joiner
*Scott, David, joiner
Turner, M ss, teacher
Vallance, William, flesher
White, Alexander, tailor

Castle Street (South)

*Dunbar, Peter, tailor and clothier
Edgar, Mrs.
Haggerty, Joseph, china merchant
Gibb, Mrs., baker
Guthrie, Robert, fishmonger
Ingram, Miss, strawhat-maker
Kerr, John, bookseller and surveyor
*Lauder, John, baker
Martin, William, fishmonger
*Oliver, James, butcher
Stoddart, Mrs., green-grocer
Swan, James, teacher
Swan & Co., booksellers
Weatherhead Miss

Church Yard Square

Parish Church (see p. 552),
Parochial School, *John Mercer, resident master

Clouds

*Dodds, David, mason
Kellie, W. T., *sheriff-clerk*
Miller, Rev. C. (*West U. P. Church*)
Scott, George, *town missionary*
*Watson, James, N.P. (*baron bailie of Coldingham*), house and writing chambers
West U. P. Church (see p. 552)

Currie Street

Fortune, Thomas, slater
M'Watt, David, valuator
Newbigging, John, tailor
Purves, John, tailor

Easter Street

*Blackhall, Thomas, grocer
*Cockburn, John, baker
Darling, Mrs.
Darling, William

Dickison, James, wheelwright
East U. P. Church (see p. 552)
Ford, Miss, dressmaker
Guthrie, George, cabinet-maker
Hall, William, watchmaker
*Jack, William, plasterer
*Jeffreys, William, writer
Johnston, Miss, dressmaker
Johnston, William, tinsmith
*Norris, James, china merchant
Oliver, A. & J., millwrights
Post Office, Miss Jeffreys
Red Lion Inn, Robert Fairbairn
Purves, Misses, dressmakers
*Ritchie, Rev. William, *East U. P. Manse*
Simpson, John, blacksmith
Swan, Thomas, & Son, joiners
*Swan, Robert George (of S. & Son)
*Thomson, Andrew
Thompson, James, baker
*Waite, John, surveyor, and *inspector of poor*
*Wood, James, Wellfield Academy

Elm Bank

Wilson, Mrs.
Houliston, Miss
Blythe, John

Golden Square

Moffatt, Miss, baker
Rutherford, M., grocer
*Rutherford, William, flesher

Gourlay's Wynd

*Duns, David, } builders and architects
*Duns, William } lessees of Swinton Quarter Quarry
Walkinshaw, J., baker
Whitehead, Thomas, blacksmith

Haymount

Johnston, Miss
M'Watt, Robert C., M.D.
Purves, Mrs. W.
Trotter, Miss

Langton Gate

Dunse and Langton Infant School (see p. 553)
Miller, George E., grocer, wine and spirit merchant

Moffat, Jane, grocer
*Wilson, Robert, baker and meal dealer

Market Place

*Allan, Nicol, flesher
Brown, Robert, grocer, wine and spirit merchant
Cockburn, John, druggist
*Cockburn, Thomas, shoemaker
Crawford, John, *town crier*
City of Glasgow Bank, James C. Robson, agent
Farnington, William, coal agent
Falconer, Allan, ironmonger and fishing-tackle merchant
Forbes, Thomas, painter
Graham, J. & W., ironmongers and general merchants
*Graham, James (of J. & W. G.)
*Graham, William   do.
Grey Horse Inn, William Patterson
Gunn, William, druggist
*Hill, Davidson, baker
*Hollywell, Thomas, *parish registrar*
Hunter, Wm. King, writing chambers
Kinghorn, William, seedsman
Marshall, Robert, bell-hanger
Mitchell, John, candlemaker
*M'Lean, Robert, draper
Robson, James C., writing chambers (house, Southfield)
Royal Bank of Scotland, W. K. Hunter, resident agent
*Stephenson, Richard, saddler and ironmonger
Sutherland, Alexander, grocer
Swan, George, grocer
Swan Hotel, George Hownam
Tait, Thomas, flesher
Temperance Hotel, Mrs. Edgar
    Do.   Do. Andrew Wallace
*Turnbull, John, draper
*Veitch, James, pharmaceutical chemist
*Waddell, John, grocer, tea, wine, and spirit merchant
*Webster, Robert, draper
    Managing Assistant—John Ford
*Whitelaw, John, shoemaker
Wilson, Matthew, grocer, wine and spirit merchant
Wilson, John, & Son, drapers
Wilson, John, merchant
Wilkie, J. M., bookseller and printer
Young, John, draper

Murray Place

Heatley, Mrs.
Dickson, George, sheriff-substitute

Murray Street

Dewar, James, cabinet-maker
Fairbairn, David, shoemaker
Farnington, William, coal agent
Gibson, George, watchmaker
*Johnston, George, bookseller and printer
Lamb, W. G., seedsman
*Peat, George, Esq., of Welnage, J.P.
Rankin & Aitchison, drapers, clothiers, and silk mercers
South U. P. Church (see p. 552)
Webster, R., draper (see Market Place)
*Weatherhead, Alexander, of Barniken, house and writing chambers

Newtown Street

*Aitken, George, sawyer
Bank of Scotland, R. F. Hardy, resident agent
*Blaikie, Andrew, paver
British Linen Company's Bank, James Wylie, resident agent
*Campbell, William W., surgeon
Ferguson David, N.P., writing chambers (house, Todlaw)
Free Church School, Robert Lillie, resident master
*Hillston, James, bank agent
Horn Inn, John Wilkinson
Hunt Inn, David Moffat
*Lawrie, John, weaver
Martin, William, manufacturer
Paterson, Robert, blacksmith
Regan, William, grocer
Sanderson & Co., cutlers and hedge knife manufacturers
Managing partner—Thomas Scoular
Scott, William, slater
Scoular, Miss, dressmaker
Smith, William, plasterer
Thomson, Janet, grocer
Thompson, John, baker
*Thomson, Thomas, writer
*Virtue, John, shoemaker
White, Mrs., Clock Mill
Wilson, Miss, strawhat-maker
*Young, John, painter

North Street

*Broomfield, John, carter
*Brown, William, baker
Christison, William, tailor

Cowe, Robert, shoemaker
Doughty, John, fishmonger
Edgar, Robert, grocer
*Edington, James, watchmaker
Palmer, Misses, dressmakers
Plough Inn, Mrs. Hill
*Pringle, George, sawyer
Rae, James, shoemaker
Rathie, Miss, china merchant
Virtue, David L., blacksmith
Virtue, Peter, cutler

South Street

Aitchison, William, slater
*Brown, Alexander, grocer
Bruce, George, plumber and photographic artist
Crawford, Alexander, of Mountview, bailie of Dunse, house and writing chambers
Ewart, Alexander, saddler
*Galbraith, Thomas, coachbuilder
Low, Mrs., dressmaker
Pringle, Gilbert, shoemaker
Pringle, Miss, teacher
Purves, R. A., baker
Stamp Office, Alexander Crawford, distributor
Stevenson, William, accountant
Strauchon, George, grocer
Wastle, William, clogger
Watson, George, green-grocer

Teindhill Green

Dewar, Alexander, cabinet-maker
Episcopal Church (see p. 553)
Gillies, Nichol, manufacturer
Kerr, Rev. D., South U. P. Manse
*Thomson, James, feuar

Todlaw

Doubleday, Misses, boarding establishment
*Ferguson, David, writer
*Fordyce, Rev. John, F. C. Manse
Hogg & Wood, nurserymen and seedsmen
Manager—Rob. Lidgate (see Coldstream, p. 498)

Whillis Wynd

Duff, Robert, blacksmith
Rodgers, James, ironfounder

Miscellaneous Villas

Brown, Misses, Trinity Lodge
Cunningham, Mrs., Briery Bank
Hamilton, Misses, *The Hawthorn Boarding Academy*
Johnston, Thomas, Wellfield Cottage
Robson, James C., of Southfield, *procurator-fiscal*
*Wilson, George, merchant, View Law Villa

Railway Station

Situated between Toll-Bar and Cheeklaw.

Wilson, David, station-master, manager of goods' department, and N. B. Railway's coal agent

OFFICES AND DEPOTS

Alexander, William, coal agent
Farnington, J.,   do.

Boston Free Church (*see* p. 552)
Crowder, Rev. A. E., *Episcopal Manse*

FARMERS AND RESIDENTS IN THE PARISH

Aitchison, Mrs., Cheeklaw farm
Allan, Misses, Crunklaw
*Bell, John, farmer, Cockburn
Blair, Peter, manager, home farm, Dunse Castle
*Brash, Richd., do. Cairnhill
*Cossar, Mark, do. Greenknowe
*Denholm, George, of Broomhill
*Fender, Robert, farmer, Rulesmains
*Fortune, John,   do.   Easter Winshiel
Gibson, George,   do.   Grueldykes
*Gray, Alexander, farmer, Elfhole
*Hastie, John, farmer, Chapel
*Haig, Joseph, of Kaysmuir
*Hownam, George, farmer, Brieryhill
Jamieson, Archibald, auctioneer, Peelrig
Kellie, John B., Ladywell
*Lindsay, David Baird, Oxendean
Macfarlane, Thomas, farmer, Crumstane
*Paterson, William, farmer, Castlemains
*Robson, Andrew,   do.   Broomhill
*Robson, William,   do.   do.
Scott, George, farmer, Kidshielhaugh
Slight, Robert Nicholson (of the firm of Young Trotter

& Son, Chirnside Paper Mill (*see* p. 558), Turtleton.
Smyth, Mrs., Ellem Cottage
*Smyth, James (of Whitchester), Ellem Cottage
*Webster, James, overseer, Manderston

SEATS OF COUNTY FAMILIES AND SMALLER RESIDENCES IN THE PARISH.

BERRYWELL.

In the immediate neighbourhood of Dunse—the property of William Hay, Esq., of Dunse Castle, and occupied by James Low, Esq., of Laws (*see* Seats, Whitsome parish).

CAIRNBANK.

In the immediate neighbourhood of Dunse—the property and residence of the Misses Logan.

CUMLEDGE.

Situated on the Whitadder, where it skirts the parish 1½ miles north from Dunse—the property and residence of John Wilson, Esq., J.P.; born 1799; succeeded 1836.

DUNSE CASTLE (*see* p. 548)

The seat of *William Hay, Esq., eldest son of the late Robert Hay, Esq., of Drumelzier, Whittinghame, and Linplum; born 1788; succeeded 1807; married, 1816, Mary, daughter of John Bradstreet Garstin, Esq., of Harold House, county Bedford, and by her, who died in 1863, has, with other issue—

*William James, formerly in the Bengal Civil Service; born 26th May 1827; married, 1865, Caroline, daughter of the late William Hay, Esq., of Hopes.
Alexander Charles, born 24th February 1829; married 18th April 1860, Annie daughter of Major Dobbs, of the Mysore Commission.
*Robert Mordaunt, born 4th October 1833; lately in the service of Sir James Brooke, Borneo.
Mary, married August 1840, to George Home Drummond, Esq., jun., of Blair Drummond, and died 4th April 1855.
Christian Henrietta
Ann Elizabeth, married, 15th February 1855, to Robert Graham Moir, Esq., of Leckie, Stirlingshire; died 1864.
Cordelia, married 28th June 1848, to John Bargus Yonge, Esq., of Pushlinch, Devonshire; died 1864.

Janet Matilda, married, October 1856, to Charles Thomas Constantine, eldest son of John Grant, Esq., of Kilgraston, Perthshire.

Harriet Scott.

Mr. Hay, who is a Justice of the Peace, a Deputy-Lieutenant and Convener of the county of Berwick, and Colonel of the Berwickshire Militia, was in the 16th Light Dragoons 1806-11; he served in the Peninsula, and was present at the battles of Talavera, Busaco, Fuentes d'Onor, etc. The family is descended from the Hon. William Hay, younger son of John, 1st Earl, and brother of the 1st Marquis of Tweeddale.

MANDERSTON.

Situated about 1½ miles from Dunse, due east—the property and seat of *William Miller, Esq., M.P., of Manderston, second son of the late James Miller, Esq., of Leith; born 1809 married, 1858, Mary-Anne, daughter of John Farleigh Leith, Esq., Barrister-at-Law, and has issue a son, born 1863.

Mr. Miller was formerly a merchant and Honorary British Vice-Consul at St. Petersburg; he was elected M.P. for the Leith Burghs in 1859, re-elected 1865; in 1864 he purchased the estate from the trustees of his late brother, Richard Miller, Esq., Leith.

London Residence—135 Piccadilly.

WEDDERBURN CASTLE.

Situated near the eastern extremity of the parish—the property and one of the residences of David M. Home, Esq., of Billie and Wedderburn (*see* p. 501).

WELLFIELD HOUSE.

The property of William King Hunter, Esq., of Pilmuir (Coldingham parish); at present occupied by James Wood, Esq., M.A., as a boarding school for young gentlemen.

Mr. Hunter is agent for the Royal Bank of Scotland—a large and handsome building in the Market Square; he is also a solicitor, and holds various other appointments.

REGISTERED VOTERS (Non-Resident).

Brown, Peter, commercial traveller, Glasgow
Carlisle, Robert, groom, Amisfield, Haddington
Darling, William, engineer, Inchicove
Dodds, James, tailor, Gavinton
Fairbairn, John, draper, Edinburgh
Ford, John, Hutton
Forrester, William, farmer, late Wedderburn Mains
Hamilton, Right Hon. Robert A. C. Nesbit, of Belhaven and Dirleton
Hodgson, Richard, of Carham Hall
Hodgson, Thomas, of Morris Hall
Home, Patrick, writer, Edinburgh
Hudson, John, Ash Grove
Hume, Peter, commercial traveller, Glasgow
Hunter, William A., York Place, Edinburgh
Johnston, Rev. George, Lanark
Knox, James, stationer, Dunbar
Learmonth, William, Glasgow
Logan, Abraham, farmer, Caverton
M'Gregor, Hugh, seedsman, Reston
Munro, Alexander, of Wester Winshiel
Scott, William, joiner, Edinburgh
White, George, farmer, Duddo, Northumberland
White, George, jun.,   do.   do.
White, Thomas,   do.   do.
Wilkie, James, grocer, Haddington

LANGTON.

—◆—

THIS parish lies partly in the Merse and partly among the Lammermoors, a range of which, called Langton Edge, runs through its northern part from east to west. Langton is bounded on the north by Longformacus and Dunse, on the east by Dunse and Edrom ; on the south by Polwarth, Fogo, and Edrom ; and on the west by Polwarth and Longformacus. Its greatest length pointing N. W. is over 6 miles, and breadth over 3 miles. Its area, according to the Ordnance Survey, is nearly 7151 acres, of which 58 acres are occupied by roads, and nearly 12 acres are under water. The northern half of the parish is used as pasture land, and some of the hills in this portion have a considerable elevation—Harden Hill is 1056 feet, Blacksmill, 905 feet ; the remainder varying from 500 to 900 feet in height. The lower part of the parish has a fertile soil, and is all well cultivated and finely enclosed. The atmosphere is clear, and the climate is healthy. There are one or two small hill streams in the parish, but none of any size. There is one village in the parish—GAVINTON, so called in honour of Mr. Gavin, maternal grandfather of the late Marquis of Breadalbane, who built the village in 1760, to supersede the ancient village of Langton, which stood half-a-mile to the north. The village is a neat place, and laid out on a regular plan. In the immediate neighbourhood of Gavinton, situated on the Langton burn, and surrounded by extensive woods, is LANGTON HOUSE, a grand edifice in course of erection ; commenced in 1862 by the late Marquis of Breadalbane, after designs by David Bryce, Esq., R.S.A. It will contain, in virtue of a special bequest by his lordship, a splendid gallery of pictures, which he recommended his heirs to allow to be open for the inspection of lovers of art. Nearest market town to the village is Dunse, distance 2 miles north-east, where is also the nearest railway station ; the nearest railway station in the west or Earlston direction is at Marchmont, a little over 2 miles.

Population of the parish in 1861, 502, who constituted 116 separate families ; 26 of whom were returned as living in houses of one window, 53 in houses of two windows, and the remainder (37) as living in houses of three or more windows.

Assessed property in 1864-5, £7344, 11s.

Superior of Gavinton—Lady Elizabeth Pringle, who owns nearly the whole of the parish.

Those marked thus (*) are Registered Voters in the parish.

DISTRICT POLICE OFFICE—Dunse.

PUBLIC OFFICES—Heritors' Clerk, Session Clerk, Kirk Treasurer, Inspector of Poor, and Registrar of Births, Marriages, and Deaths —John Gow.

Medical Officer and Public Vaccinator—John Tait, M.D., Dunse.

POST OFFICE—John Lillie, Gavinton, postmaster. Daily Post to Dunse, James Sutherland, post runner. Arrival and Despatch, 12.30. p.m.

CLERGY, &c.—Presbytery of Dunse, and Synod of Merse and Teviotdale. Patron—Lady Elizabeth Pringle.

Established Church—*Rev. Robert Stormonth Darling (Inducted 1864). Sittings, 300. Average attend. at Sabbath School, 30.

Free Church—Rev. William Logan (Inducted 1849). Sittings, 300. Average attendance at Sabbath School, 30.

FAST DAYS—Last Thursdays of April and October.

SCHOOL‡—Parochial—*John Gow, master ; average attendance, 60.

DUNSE AND LANGTON INFANT SCHOOL, see Dunse lists, p. 553.

PAROCHIAL BOARD — Lawrence Davidson, Esq., W.S., Edinburgh, Factor for the Langton Estates, chairman. No. of Poor on Roll, 14. Rate of Assessment, 5d. per £ ; total Assessment 1864-5, £314 : 2 : 7.

LIBRARY—Parochial—

LANGTON AND MIDDLE OF BERWICKSHIRE AGRICULTURAL SOCIETY— Alexander Lawrie, overseer, Langton, Preses and Treasurer. Has an annual meeting after harvest, when prizes for ploughing are given.

CORN MILL : Langton—*William Weir, miller.

———

TRADES.

Village of Gavinton

Cooper, George, shoemaker
Dodds, James, tailor
Duns, William E., veterinary surgeon
Lawrie, Andrew, joiner
Lillie, John, blacksmith and *postmaster*
Lyal, Isabella, general dealer
Mercer, George, innkeeper
Middlemas, John, baker
Polwarth, James, general dealer
Purves, James, farmer
*Rae, Robert, slater

———

‡ Children in the parish from 5 to 15 attending school during the first week of April 1861, 90 ; of all ages, 92.

Sanderson, William, joiner
Smith, Janet, general dealer
*Spiers, John, builder
Tully, George, flesher
*Waddell, James, (of A. & J. W., builders)
*Waddell, Alexander,   do.

RESIDENTS, FARMERS, &c., IN THE PARISH.

Allan, Nicol, farmer, Middlefield
*Allan, Thomson, do. Ladyflat
Fair, Peter, Gavinton
Lawrie, Alexander, overseer, Langton
Logan, Mrs. Woodend, farm
*Patterson, John, farmer, Hardens
*Taylor, John,   do.   Raecleughhead
Waddell, Misses, Gavinton

SEAT IN THE PARISH.

LANGTON HOUSE.

The property and intended residence of Lady Elizabeth Pringle (Elizabeth Maitland Campbell); married, 19th October 1831, to *Sir John Pringle, Bart., of Newhall, in Selkirkshire (*see* p. 458), and has issue:—

Mary Gavin, married 18th July 1861, to Robert (second cousin), second son of George 10th and present Earl of Haddington, at present abroad.

Magdalene Breadalbane, married, July 9, 1863, to Alexander Anderson, Esq., of Newstead, Australia.

Lady Elizabeth Pringle succeeded to the Langton estates on the death of her brother, the late Marquis of Breadalbane, 8th November 1862, when the Marquisate and Barony of Breadalbane, in the peerage of the United Kingdom, became extinct; and the Scotch honours passed to his cousin, John Alexander Gavin Campbell, Esq., of Glenfalloch, Perthshire—now 6th Earl of Breadalbane, in the peerage of Scotland.

Principal residence—Undermount, Bonchurch, Isle of Wight.
Temporary residence—Ninewells, Chirnside parish.

REGISTERED VOTERS (Non-Resident).

Clay, John, farmer, Kerchesters, Kelso
Gibson, George, do. Grueldykes, Dunse
Paterson, George, land-steward, Marchmont House
Peacock, George, farmer, Papple, Haddington
Swinton, Archibald C., yr. of Kimmerghame
Swinton, James Rannie, 33 Warwick Square, London

EDROM.

THIS parish lies along the south bank of the Whitadder. Its general outline is irregular, its greatest, length S.W. by N.E., is 8 miles; greatest breadth at its southern boundary 6 miles. Its boundaries are—on the north the parishes of Bunkle and Chirnside; on the east Hutton; on the south Whitsome, Swinton, and Fogo; and on the west Dunse. The total area of the parish, according to the Ordnance Survey, is 9634¼ acres; of which 19½ are occupied by railway, nearly 152 by roads, public and private, and about 89½ are under water; the remainder, except what is laid out in beautiful plantations, consists mainly of arable land in a high state of cultivation. Immense boulders are scattered about in the alluvial soil. On the estate of Kimmerghame, there is a shell marl bog of considerable extent. The climate throughout the parish is good. The Whitadder which skirts the parish on the north, and the Blackadder, which, after cutting the parish in two, falls into the Whitadder, abound in good trout. Salmon and sea-trout also are plentiful in the Whitadder—angling restricted.

The mansion-house on the estate of Broomhouse was built in 1813, on the site of an ancient castle of the same name. Several skeletons were found in digging the foundations. The mansion-house of NISBET is a fine old building in the castellated form. KIMMERGHAME, on the banks of the Blackadder, is a fine edifice, erected by the present proprietor in 1851, after a design by David Bryce, Esq., R.S.A. At BLACKADDER HOUSE there is a fine conservatory, built in the form of a Gothic chapel, the frame-work of which is entirely of cast-iron, and part of the glass beautifully stained. The situation of EDROM HOUSE and the parish church is very beautiful.

The hamlet of Edrom—"a place of much antiquity"—is situated on the Whitadder near the south-western extremity of the parish. Here are the parish church, manse, and school-house; and close at hand is Edrom House (already noticed). The distance south-east, of Edrom from Dunse, is about 3½ miles. Two-and-a-half miles east from the hamlet of Edrom, and about 5 from Dunse, situated at the junction of the Blackadder and Whitadder is the village of ALLANTON. Near Allanton is Chirnside Bridge paper mill, used for the manufacture of the highest class of printing and plate papers. The Dunse branch of the North British Railway crosses the parish, and has a station about half-a-mile east from the hamlet of Edrom.

Population of the parish in 1861, 1592, who composed 301 families; of whom 78 were returned as living in houses with one window, and 127 in houses with two windows, leaving 96 living in houses of three or more windows.

Assessed property in 1864-5, £18,879 : 12 : 7.

The landed-proprietors in the parish are—Lord Sinclair of Nisbet; Sir G. A. F. Houston Boswall, Bart. of Blackadder; John Campbell Swinton, Esq., of Kimmerghame; George W. F. Buchan, Esq., of Kelloe; James Carnegie, Esq., of Edrom Newton; Colonel Logan Home of Broomhouse; George C. Trotter Cranstoun, Esq., of Chirnside Bridge.

Those marked thus (*) are Registered Voters.

RESIDENT JUSTICES OF THE PEACE—Sir George Houston Boswall, Col. Fordyce Buchan, Lieut.-Col. Logan Home, John Campbell Swinton, A. Campbell Swinton, George C. Trotter Cranstoun, of Dewar.

DISTRICT POLICE OFFICE—Dunse.

PUBLIC OFFICES—Heritors' Clerk, Kirk Treasurer, Session Clerk, Registrar of Births, Marriages, and Deaths, and Inspector of Poor—Charles Airth.

Medical Officers and Public Vaccinators — Drs. M'Watt and Stuart, Dunse.

POST OFFICE—David Wilson, Edrom, postmaster. Letters arrive daily from all parts, by Ayton, at 10.30 a.m.; Despatched at 8.40 a.m. Daily from Dunse, &c., at 4-40 p.m.; Despatched at 9-40 p.m. *Local Posts*: Bunkle—Despatch, 11 a.m.; Returns, 2 p.m. David Wilson, messenger. Berryhill—Despatch, 11 a.m.; Returns, 1-30 p.m. Mary Laurie, messenger.

Post Town for Allanton, *see* Chirnside.

CLERGY, &c.—Presbytery of Chirnside, and Synod of Merse and Teviotdale. Patron—The Crown.

Established Church (Edrom)—*Rev. James Wilson (Inducted 1849). Sittings, 600. Aver. attend. at Sabbath School, 44.

Free Church (Allanton) — Rev. John C. Fairbairn (Inducted 1844). Sittings, 450. Aver. attend. at Sabbath School, 30.

FAST DAYS—Thursday before second Sunday in May and November.

SCHOOLS†—Parochial—*Charles Airth, master; av. attend., 65.

Auxiliary (Allanton)—Andrew Kelly, master; av. attend., 58.

Do.   (Kimmerghame)—Jas. Sharp, master; av. attend., 62.

PAROCHIAL BOARD—Col. Fordyce Buchan of Kelloe, Chairman. Average number of Poor on Roll, 48. Rate of Assessment, 2¼d. per £; total Assessment 1864-5, £448 : 8 : 8.

---

† Children in the parish between 5 and 15, attending school during the first week of April 1861, 245; of all ages, 257.

MORTIFICATION—Five Pounds annually, left by the late Mrs. Carr in 1812, for the industrial poor of the estate of Nisbet.

QUARRY—Todhaugh—   , proprietor.   Thomas Dodds, mason, Dunse, lessee.

CORN MILLS : Allanbank—*James Dickison, miller; Nisbet—*John Ford, farmer.

PAPER MILL—Chirnside Bridge—Young Trotter & Son, paper makers (*see* pp. 565 and 575).‡

CONVEYANCE—By North British Railway to all parts. Jas. Mitchill, station-master and N. B. Railway Company's coal agent.

TRADES.

Village of Allanton

Carter, Thomas, grocer
*Dickson, William, weaver
Darling, Thomas, smith
*Hillson, Alexander, slater
Johnston & Melrose, builders, lessees of Whitsome and Swinton Quarries
Patterson, John, grocer
Purves, William, tailor
Robertson, Robert, shoemaker

RESIDENTS, FARMERS, &c., IN THE PARISH.

*Aitchison, Peter, farmer, Shannobank
*Bell, William,   do.   Todbaugh
*Bertram, James,   do.   Mid-Edrom
*Black, John,   do.   Edrom Mains
*Brodie, John D.,   do.   Bellshiel
*Brown, Walter,   do.   Swallowdean
*Brydon, Adam,   do.   Craigswalls
*Calder, Robert,   do.   Kelloe Mains
*Carnegie, James, jun., Esq. of Edrom Newton
*Carnegie, George R.,   farmer,   do.
*Dodds, Robert,   do. Blackadderbank

---

‡ The former paper mill at Bromhouse was razed in 1841, when the lease of the present firm, which had occupied them since 1790, expired; the property of Chirnside Bridge was then acquired, and the present extensive first-class mill built. The English edition of the Emperor Napoleon's "Life of Cæsar" was printed on paper made here

*Elliot, Francis, farmer, Middlestots
*Forrest, Robert, do.   Stuartslaw
*Glendinning, R. W., farmer, Broomdykes
 Grosset, Thomas, joiner, Sinclair's Hill
*Herriot, David, farmer, Whitelaw
*Moffat, George,   do.   and innkeeper, Mount Pleasant
 M'Laren, John, joiner, Kelloe Bastle
 Patterson, William, blacksmith, Sinclair's Hill
*Pringle, James,   do. Nisbet Hill
*Robson, William   do. Kimmerghame Mains
*Ross, John,   do. Reedylock
 Thomson, James,   do. Mungoswells
 Turnbull, Henry,   do. Blackadder Westside
*White, Joseph,   do. Blackadder Eastside

SEATS OF COUNTY FAMILIES IN THE PARISH.

ALLANBANK.

Situated on the west bank of the Blackadder and opposite Blackadder House—one of the mansions of Sir George A. F. Houston Boswall, Bart.

BLACKADDER HOUSE (see p. 572).

Situated on the Blackadder near the centre of the parish, and about 5 miles from Dunse—the seat and residence of *Sir George Augustus Frederick Houston-Boswall, Bart., of Blackadder and Allanbank, elder son of the late General Sir William Houston, Bart., G.C.B. ; born 1809 ; succeeded as second baronet 1842 ; married, 1847, Euphemia, daughter of Thos. Boswall, Esq., of Blackadder, whose name he has assumed, and by whom he has issue—

George Lauderdale, born 11th December 1847.
William, born 11th April 1849.
Thomas Alford, born 21st July 1850.
Robert, born 11th December 1852.
Alfred } twins, born 13th February 1854
Evelyn }

Sir George, who is a Justice of Peace and Deputy-Lieutenant for the county of Berwick, and a Colonel unattached, was formerly Lieut.-Col. Grenadier Guards. Sir George's family descend from a common ancestor with the Houstons of Houston, Renfrewshire; and he is heir-male of the ancient family of the Houstons of Cotrioch, heritable bailies and justiciaries of the barony of Busbie, Wigtonshire, and of Calderhall, Midlothian.
    London Address—Maurigny's Hotel.

BROOMHOUSE (see p. 572).

Situated at the north-western boundary of the parish, on the banks of the Whitadder and about 2 miles north from Dunse—the property and residence of *Colonel George Logan-Home, of Broomhouse and Edrom, only surviving son of the late Major George Logan, of Edrom, by Helen only daughter of the late William Home, Esq., of Broomhouse (who served on the staff of Prince Charles Edward at Culloden); born 1805 ; succeeded his uncle, Lieut.-General James Home, 1849 (when he assumed the name of Home by royal sign manual); married 1844 Annie, eldest daughter of Major Doran, 18th Royal Irish Regiment, and has issue—

William James Home, born 1847.
Cospatrick Robert, died young.
George John Ninian, born 30th January 1855.
Ferdinand Cospatrick, born September 1861.
Henry Waldeve, born November 1863.
Helen Georgina.

    Mr. Logan-Home, who entered the Royal Marine Artillery 1823, retired on half-pay as Captain 1848; is a Magistrate for the county of Berwick, Lieut.-Colonel-Commandant Haddington and Berwick Militia Artillery, and a Knight of the Legion of Honour, and of the Order of the Redeemer of Greece; he served in the Mediterranean at the siege of the Morea Castle in 1828, and in Spain with the British Legion in 1836-37. This family is a junior branch of the Homes of Wedderburn, Patrick of Broomhouse being the 7th son of Sir David Home of Wedderburn, slain at the battle of Flodden.
    Town Addresses—New Club, Edinburgh ; Junior Carlton Club, London.

CHIRNSIDE BRIDGE HOUSE.

The property and residence of *George Cranstoun Trotter Cranstoun, Esq., of Dewar (in Edinburghshire) ; born 1801 ; succeeded his father, the late Young Trotter, Esq., to the Chirnside Bridge property in 1841, and to the maternal properties in Midlothian of Dewar and Harvieston in 1848.
    Chirnside Bridge Paper Mill, to which the house is closely situated, forms part of Mr. Cranstoun's property.
    Edinburgh Address—New Club.

EDROM HOUSE (see p. 572).

Situated about one mile east of Broomhouse, and also on the Whitadder—the property of Colonel George Logan-Home ; at present occupied by Major Renny, Adjutant of the Berwickshire Rifle Volunteers (formerly of the 73d Regiment).

KELLOE.

Situated on the Blackadder, near the centre of the parish, and about 4 miles from Dunse—the property and residence of *Col. George William Fordyce Buchan, second son of the late Thomas John Fordyce, Esq. of Ayton; married, 1858, Anne, daughter of General Sir Hew Dalrymple Ross, G.C.B.; succeeded his uncle, George Buchan, Esq., 1856, when he assumed the additional name of Buchan.

Col. Fordyce-Buchan served in the Kaffir war in 1851 with the 74th Highlanders, and in the Crimea in 1854 and 1855 with the Scots Fusileer Guards, from which regiment he retired in 1856. He is a Justice of the Peace for the county of Berwick.

Edinburgh address—New Club. London addresses—United Service Club, and Junior Carlton Club.

KIMMERGHAME HOUSE.

Situated near the southern extremity of the parish, and about 3 miles south-east from Dunse—the seat and residence of John Campbell-Swinton, Esq., of Kimmerghame, eldest son of the late Archibald Swinton, Esq., H.E.I.C. Service; born 1777; succeeded to Kimmerghame in 1850 on the death of his aunt Miss Mary Campbell (who had re-purchased the estate in 1846, which had been sold by his father), when he assumed the additional name of Campbell; married 1809, Catharine, only daughter of James Rannie, Esq., merchant, of Leith, and has issue—

Archibald, formerly Professor of Civil Law in the University of Edinburgh, born 1812; married, 1st, 1845, Katharine Margaret, second daughter of Sir John Pringle, Bart., of Newhall and Stichill (she died 1846, leaving one daughter); 2d, 1856, Georgiana Caroline, third daughter of the late Sir George Sitwell, Bart., of Renishaw, Derbyshire, by whom he has issue three sons and one daughter.

James Rannie, artist; married 11th July 1865, the Honble. Blanche Fitzgerald De Ros, daughter of Lord and Lady de Ros. Residence—33 Warwick Square, London.

Catherine.
Mary.
Henrietta, married Henry Davidson, Esq. of Muirhouse, near Edinburgh.
Agnes, married Rev. Geo. Murray, Vicar of Dedham, Essex.

Mr. Campbell Swinton, sen., is a Justice of Peace and Dep.-Lieutenant for the county of Berwick, and Lord of the Barony of Kimmerghame; he was formerly an officer in the army. This family is a branch of the ancient family of Swinton, of Swinton, (see Swinton parish).

Edinburgh address—New Club.

NISBET HOUSE.

Situated about 2 miles south-east from Dunse, on the Swinton road—one of the seats of the Right Hon. Lord Sinclair; † at present temporarily occupied by William Kippen, Esq.

REGISTERED VOTERS (Non-Resident).

Preston, Captain Sir Henry, R.N., of Valleyfield and Lutton
Cockburn, Thomas, jun., wine merchant, Berwick-on-Tweed
Hepburn, Sir Thomas B., Bart. of Smeaton
Trotter, Charles Young, surgeon, Australia
Trotter, John P., sheriff-substitute of Dumfriesshire

† Baron Sinclair (James St. Clair, the second of this line who holds the title), in the Peerage of Scotland; late Captain Grenadier Guards; born 3d July 1803; succeeded his father (who preferred his claim to the dormant barony of Sinclair, which, after investigation by the House of Lords, was acknowledged 25th April 1782) as 11th Lord Sinclair, 30th September 1863; married, 14th September 1830, Jane, eldest daughter of Archibald Little, Esq., of Shabden Park, Surrey, and has issue—

Charles William, *Master of Sinclair*, Major 56th Regiment, born 8th September 1831.
Archibald, R.N., born 2d October 1833.
James Chisholm, Madras Civil Service, born 21st November 1837.
Lockhart Matthew, born 25th July 1855.
Mary Agnes.
Helen, who died 19th August 1849.

Lord Sinclair's family dates from William Sinclair, Lord of Roslyn, the companion in arms of King Robert Bruce, and who perished along with James Lord of Douglas in battle against the Moors in Spain, in 1330, while carrying that monarch's heart to the Holy Sepulchre at Jerusalem.

Other seats—Herdmanston, Haddingtonshire (principal residence); Greenriver, Hobkirk parish, Roxburghshire.

WHITSOME.*

———◆———

THIS parish, entirely agricultural, is situated in the eastern part of the Merse. It is bounded on the north by Edrom, on the east by Hutton, on the south by Ladykirk and Swinton, and on the west by Swinton and Edrom. It measures, east by west, 4¾ miles long, and is 2¾ broad. It contains, according to the Ordnance Survey, 4896¾ acres ; of which over 75¼ are occupied by public and private roads, and little more than 1 is under water. The easterly and northerly parts of the parish are generally flat ; a belt of low land also stretches along the course of the Leet† (which rises in the parish), while an undulating surface diversifies the remainder. Hilton churchyard,‡ which lies about a mile east from the village, is the highest point in "the How of the Merse." The parish has everywhere the beautifully enclosed and richly cultivated appearance which so generally distinguishes the district. The road from Berwick to Dunse, and the north road from Berwick to Kelso, both traverse the parish. There is but one small village in the parish—Whitsome, which is exactly in the centre, and contains 93 inhabitants. At short intervals to the westward of the village are the schoolhouse, church, and manse. Whitsome is 10 miles from Berwick, 9 from Coldstream, 15 from Kelso, 6½ from Dunse, and 4 from Chirnside.

Population of the parish in 1861, 640, who constituted 129 separate families ; 1 of whom was returned as living in a house having no window, 38 as living in houses of one window, 44 in houses of two windows, and the remainder (46, the full average of one-third) in houses of three or more windows.

Assessed property in 1864-5, £8976 : 11 : 11.

The principal landed-proprietors in the parish are—Marquis of Tweeddale (Yester House, Gifford) ; Sir George Houston Boswall, Bart., of Blackadder (by Chirnside) ; Richard Trotter, Esq. of Morton Hall (Liberton) ; Mrs. Gertrude Ker Symer or Clay (London) ; James Low, Esq. of Laws (Berrywell, by Dunse) ; Ralph Foster, Esq., of Whitsome Hill (The Temple, London) ; James Tait, Esq., of Langrigg (Edenside, Kelso) ; Robert Brown Forsyth Brown, Esq., of Whitsome East Newton (Junior United Service Club, London) ; Thos. Allan, Esq., of Whitsome West Newton (Blackhouse, by Edrom) ; James Herriot, Esq., of Herriot Bank (Leetside, by Chirnside)—only the last of whom is resident in the parish.

———

Those marked thus (*) are Registered Voters.

POLICE OFFICER FOR THE DISTRICT—Robert M'Kenzie, Swinton.

PUBLIC OFFICES—Heritors' Clerk, Inspector of Poor, Session Clerk, and Registrar of Births, Marriages, and Deaths—Jn. Turnbull. Medical Officer and Public Vaccinator—Charles Stuart, M.D., Chirnside.

POST OFFICE—Postmaster—John Turnbull, schoolmaster. Post Town, Chirnside. Departure 6-45 a.m. ; arrival, 1-5 p.m. Andrew Patterson, runner. No Post on Sundays.

CLERGY, &c.—Whitsome is in the Presbytery of Chirnside, and Synod of Merse and Teviotdale. Patron—David Logan, Esq.,† Ferney Castle, Reston.
Established Church—*Rev. John Robertson (Inducted 1843). Sittings 245. Precentor—Jas. Trotter ; Beadle and Gravedigger—Angus Robertson. Average attendance at Sab. School, 55 ; at Bible Class of Rev John A. Robertson, jun. 35. Superintendent of Sabbath School—John Turnbull.

FAST DAY—Thursday before last Sabbath of June.

SCHOOLS‡—Parochial—*John Turnbull, master. Aver. attend., 95.

PAROCHIAL BOARD—James Low, Esq., chairman. No. of Poor on Roll, 20. Rate of Assessment, 1½d. per £ ; total Assessment in 1864-5, £220.

LIBRARY—Whitsome Subscription Library, opened in 1858. 310 vols. Annual Subscription, 2s. Thomas Brown, Librarian.

QUARRY—Whitsome Newton—Johnston and Melrose, masons, Allanton, lessees ; Robert Brown Forsyth Brown, Esq., proprietor.

CONVEYANCE—North British Railway, Edrom or Chirnside Stations, distant each 5 miles. North-Eastern Railway, Norham Station ; distant 6 miles.

CARRIER—John Middlemiss, Berwick on Saturday, and Dunse on Tuesday.

———

TRADES IN WHITSOME VILLAGE.

Ainslie, William, blacksmith, Hilton
Aitchison, Jasper, innkeeper

———

* Ecclesiastically known as Whitsome and Hilton.
† The Leet, which intersects the parish, is the only stream in Berwickshire which flows a considerable distance to the west. This peculiarity depriving it of sufficient fall, has caused it to give annoyance by frequent overflows to the farmers through whose land it passes. It is now, however (1865), having its channel deepened, so that the annoyance will most probably cease.
‡ The use of this burial-ground was practically abandoned in the notorious "resurrection" times : the erection of a watch-house in the burial-ground at Whitsome having made it more secure against sacrilege.

† Mr. Logan has no other interest in this parish.
‡ Children in the parish from 5 to 15 attending school during the first week of April 1861, 98 ; of all ages, 112.

Aitchison, William, baker
Brown, Thomas, roadman
Dippie, James, blacksmith
*Grieve, James, shoemaker
Grieve, James, innkeeper
*Hume, Alexander, tailor
Hume, Peter, joiner
Middlemiss, Andrew, joiner
Middlemiss, Elizabeth, dressmaker
Middlemiss, John, grocer
Mitchell, John, gardener
Purves, Isabella & Agnes, dressmakers
Robertson, Angus, mason
Simson, William, grocer
*Smith, William, grocer
Spark, Margaret, grocer and dressmaker
Trotter, Robert, mason
Wright, Thomas, shoemaker

RESIDENTS, FARMERS, &c., IN THE PARISH.

*Balmer, Thomas, farmer, Hiltonhill
*Balsillie, Balfour, do.   Dykegatehead
Clay, John,   do.   Winfield
*Cowe, Peter,   do.   Jardinefield
*Craw, James,   do.   Whitsomehill
Crow, Adam, tailor Langrigg
*Denholm, George, Eagle Hall
*Herriot, James, farmer, Leetside and Herriot Bank
Purves, James, farmer and carter, Drummond's Lands
Scott, Henry, Herriot Bank
*Simson, John, farmer, Whitsome West Newton
*Simson, Thomas, do.   do.
*Spark, George,   do.   Frenchlaw
*Tait, John,   do.   Langrigg and Ravelaw
*Taylor, Peter,   do.   Whitsome East Newton
*Torrance, Thomas, do.   Laws
*Trotter, James,   do. and carter, Heritage, Whitsome East Newton
Turnbull, William, gardener, Jardinefield
Webster, Patrick, do.   Hilton

SEATS OF COUNTY FAMILIES.

None—but Mr. Low intends to build on his estate of Laws.

REGISTERED VOTERS (Non-Resident).

Brown, Robt. Brown Forsyth, Esq. of Whitsome East Newton
Foster, Ralph, Esq. of Whitsomehill
Low, James, Esq. of Laws, Berrywell, Dunse
Lugton, Andrew (farmer, of South Laws), Swinton.
Tait, James, Esq. (of Langrigg), Edenside, Kelso
Wilson, James, Esq., East Chevington

ABBEY ST. BATHANS.

— ♦ — —

THIS parish is situated in the midst of the Lammermoor Hills. In shape it is irregular, and is cut into two by a detached portion of the parish of Longformacus; it has also, lying quite detached in the north of Cockburnspath parish, another small portion. Its average length is 3¼ by 2½ miles broad; and it contains, according to the Ordnance Survey, nearly 4827 acres, including all the portions.* Its boundaries are—on the north, the parishes of Innerwick in Haddingtonshire, and Oldhamstocks and Cockburnspath in Berwickshire; on the east, Coldingham and Bunkle; on the south Bunkle and Dunse; and on the west Longformacus. Though in the Lammermoor district, none of the remarkable elevations of that range are in the parish. The higher grounds rise to a height of 300 or 400 feet above the level of the plains; while Abbey Hill and Barnside Hill (respectively 943 and 865 feet above the sea level) are the most elevated points. In the higher parts of the parish, the surface is for the most part barren, and covered with coarse heathy pasture. The lower grounds, in the neighbourhood of the small streams which drain the parish, are generally fertile and well cultivated. The Whitadder, here a considerable stream, winds through the parish in an easterly direction, and is fed by numerous hill streams. It abounds in trout of the best quality. The banks are beautifully wooded to a considerable height. The roads are generally narrow and in some places steep, but are kept in tolerable repair. In a beautiful valley, watered by the Whitadder, lies the hamlet of Abbey St. Bathans, sheltered on every side by finely wooded hills. A fine wood and iron bridge, suspended on strong stone piers, spans the broad channel of the Whitadder, and forms a pleasing object in the landscape. On the south side of the water are the old parish church, the manse on the height above among the trees, the farm-house, and farther to the east, ABBEY ST. BATHANS HOUSE, an elegant building in the cottage style, lately erected; while on the other side, the school and school-house stand in a pleasant situation, where a little stream joins the Whitadder. The east and north walls of the church are the only remains of the ancient abbey, from which the parish took its name. The style of architecture is that of the 13th century. On the

* Largest portion (west), containing the hamlet, mansion-house of Abbey St Bathans, the estate of Barnside, &c., 3045¼ acres; second portion (east), containing the estate of Quixwoode, &c., 1685 acres; third portion (north), containing the old farm-house of Potts, 97½ acres.

Monynut, a tributary of the Whitadder, is situated Godscroft, once the residence of David Hume, the friend of Melville, who died in 1620. Dunse, about 7 miles distant from the parish church by the road, is the nearest market and post town, and there, on the Dunse line, is the most convenient railway station. The station at Grant's House, on the N. B. coast line and nearly due north, is only 5 miles off, but the road to it is bad.

The population of the parish in 1861 amounted to 179, who composed 27 families, 6 of whom were returned as living in houses of one window, 4 in houses of two windows, and the large proportion of 17 as living in houses of three and more windows.

Assessed property in 1864-5, £1862.

The principal landed-proprietors are—John Turnbull, Esq., of Abbey St. Bathans (W.S., Edinburgh); Joseph Allan, Esq. of Quixwoode (Ayton); Thomas D. M'Gregor, Esq. of Barnside (The Brunt, near Dunbar); David Milne Home, Esq. of Godscroft (Milne Graden, Coldstream); Sir Hugh Hume Campbell, Bart. of Shannabank (Marchmont House); and Adam Landells, Esq. of Bankend (in New Zealand).

Those marked thus (*) are Registered Voters.

DISTRICT POLICE OFFICES—Longformacus and Cockburnspath.

PUBLIC OFFICES—Registrar of Births, Marriages, and Deaths, Session Clerk and Kirk Treasurer, Heritors' Clerk, Inspector of Poor, and Collector of Road Money—George Watson, schoolmaster. Medical Officer and Public Vaccinator—Dr. M'Watt, Dunse.

POST OFFICE—Post town, Dunse. James Gillies, messenger, comes to Abbey St. Bathans three days a-week—Tuesday, Thursday, and Saturday at 9-30, and leaves at 10-30 a.m.

CLERGY, &c.—Presbytery of Dunse and Synod of Merse and Teviotdale. Patron—the Crown. Established Church—*Rev. Thomas Davidson (Inducted 1843). Sittings, 140. Average attendance at Sabbath School, 14.

FAST DAYS—Third Sabbaths of July and December.

SCHOOL†—Parochial—*George Watson, teacher. Av. attendance, 36.

PAROCHIAL BOARD—Mr. James Aitchison, Abbey farm, Chairman. Average Assessment, 6d. per £; total Assess. 1864-5, £79 : 1 : 2. No. of Poor on Roll, 7.

LIBRARY—Contains 320 volumes. Annual subscription, 2s. Librarian—George Watson.

CARRIER—Peter Aitchison, to Dunse on Tuesdays and Fridays, and to Grant's House on Wednesdays and Saturdays.

MILLS : Strathfontane—Corn—*George Aitchison.

† Children in the parish from 5 to 15 attending school during the first week of April 1861, 20; of all ages, 25. On 1st Jany. 1865, 33.

TRADES.

Luke, John, blacksmith
Mack, Robert, joiner

RESIDENTS, FARMERS, &c.

*Aitchison, David, farmer, Quixwoode
*Aitchison, William, do.,   do.
*Aitchison, James,   do.,   Abbey
*Aitchison, Peter,   do.,   Shannabank
*Hume, Captain Joseph, Bankend
*Hunter, William, farmer, Godscroft
*Wright, Robert,   do ,   Barnside

SEAT.

ABBEY ST. BATHANS HOUSE.

The property and principal residence of *John Turnbull, Esq., W.S. ; born 1821 ; succeeded 1855.
Mr. Turnbull is a Deputy-Lieutenant and Justice of Peace for Berwickshire, and Lord of the barony of Abbey St. Bathans. Edinburgh addresses—49 George Square, and 16 Thistle St.

REGISTERED VOTERS (Non-Resident).

Allan, Joseph, of Quixwoode, Ayton
Landels, Adam, Esq., of Bankend

CRANSHAWS.

—◆—

A PASTORAL and thinly populated parish in the northern part of the county, and in the heart of the Lammermoor hills. It consists of two distinct pieces of the county, separated by the parish of Longformacus; the northern part is in shape pentagonal, measuring over 2 miles in every drection—this part is bounded on the south and east by Longformacus. All its other boundaries are in Haddingtonshire. The southern part is of an irregular shape, measuring about 5 miles long, by 2 miles broad—this part is bounded by Longformacus parish for fully two-thirds of its circumference; its other third, south and south-west, is bounded by Westruther and Lauder respectively —over more then half its length towards the west, but gradually expanding to a breadth of over 3 miles at its eastern boundary. The total area of both portions, is 8738¼ acres ;* of this 8½ acres are in roads, and 30½ are under water ; the remainder, with the exception of about 900 acres, which are under cultivation, consists of hills belonging to the Lammermoor range. Some of these hills have a considerable elevation. The principal of them, Cranshaws Hill, in the northern division of the parish, is 1245 feet high. The northern peak of this hill, known as the Doglaw, is 1049 feet, the southern peak, or Mainslaughterlaw, 1381 ; and in the southern and larger part are Dunside Hill, 1298 ; Scarlaw, 1185 ; and Blyth Edge, partly in the parish, 1522. The climate is cold and damp, being subject to very dense fogs, especially in the spring and autumn months, but it is decidedly salubrious. The only streams of any size are the Whitadder, which bounds the northern portion of the parish, and the Dye, which bounds the southern portion. Both streams unite a little to the south-east, in Longformacus parish. The Whitadder and its tributaries at this point swarm with small trout : fishing begins late ; worm is the best lure. The waters of the Dye, which rises in Longformacus parish, are famous for small trout.† CRANSHAWS CASTLE, once a hold of the Douglasses, is in the northern portion of the parish, the property of the Earl of Morton. The parish

---

* The largest part being 6149¼ acres, and the smaller 2589 acres.
† About a mile beyond the boundaries of the parish, in Haddingtonshire, the Whitadder receives the Fasney water, " a very sequestered stream, quite in a state of nature. It teems with trout probably more than any other stream within the basin of the Tweed, and is all open to the angler ; but its trout, though of good size, are of the heather-burn kind, black, ill-shaped, and poor."—*Land of Scott.*

has no village. The parish church, manse, and school-house, are situated near the Whitadder, where it skirts the eastern boundary of the northern part of the parish.

Population in 1861, 134 ; who composed 22 families, 10 of whom were returned as living in houses of one window, and 6 in houses of two windows, leaving 6 who lived in houses of three or more windows.

Assessed property in 1864-5, £1715 : 4 : 4.

The principal landed proprietors in the parish are—the Duke of Roxburghe, Lord Aberdour, and A. C. Stuart, Esq. of Rawburn and Scarlow (Eaglescarnie, Haddington).

Those marked thus (*) are Registered Voters in the parish.

DISTRICT POLICE OFFICER—James Aitchison, Longformacus.

PUBLIC OFFICES—Heritors' Clerk, Session Clerk, Kirk Treasurer, Inspector of Poor, and Registrar of Births, Marriages and Deaths—Robert Pringle.

    Medical Officer and Public Vaccinator—Dr. M'Watt, Dunse.

POST OFFICE—Post Town, Dunse. Postmaster and Messenger—Robert Lawrie. Arrivals, 9.30 a.m. ; Despatches, 7.15 a.m. daily, except Sunday.

CLERGY, &c.—Cranshaws is in the Presbytery of Dunse, and Synod of Merse and Teviotdale. Patron—Lord Aberdour.

    Established Church—*Rev. William M. Hutton A.M. (Inducted 1853). Sittings, 120. Average attend. at Sabbath School, 28.

FAST DAYS—Second Sabbath of July ; in winter variable

SCHOOL†—Parochial—*Robert Pringle, master. Aver. attend., 40.

PAROCHIAL BOARD—Robert Craise, manager, Cranshaws farm, Chairman. No. of Poor on Roll, 1. The Rates of Assessment are paid by the interest of legacies ; total expenditue in 1864-5, £18 : 11 : 9.

CHARITABLE BEQUESTS—On or about the year 1841, Captain Charles Hope Watson, R.N., bequeathed £100 ; and in 1841, William R. Watson, Esq. of Langton, £1000 for the poor of this parish.

PAROCHIAL LIBRARY—containing 250 vols. Quarterly Subscription, 6d. Librarian—Robert Pringle.

LAMMERMOOR PLOUGHING CLUB—Patron—John Turnbull, Esq. of Abbey St. Bathans. Hon. Secretary—John S. Bertram, Cranshaws. Annual competition takes place on a suitable day in December, January, or February. Embraces the parishes of Longformacus, Cranshaws, and Abbey St. Bathans, and outlying portions of several East-Lothian parishes. Premiums are annually given to the amount of £3 at least, and Highland Society's Medal. Arrangements are made by a Committee of three, retiring annually.

---

† Children in the parish, of all ages, attending school during the first week of April 1861, 35.

CONVEYANCE—The nearest railway stations are at Dunse, on the Dunse and Earlston line, and Innerwick on the Coast line—both fully 10 miles off ; there are proper cart roads to each place, but to no where else.

CARRIERS—Robert Laurie, to Dunse every Tuesday ; David Rattray, from Edinburgh by Garvald every Monday ; and Thomas Shiell, from West Gordon every Monday.

RESIDENTS, FARMERS, &c.

Bertram, John, Cranshaws farm

    Mr. Wilson, Edington Mains (Chirnside), is lessee of Rawburn, and two small portions of land in the parish are sub let.

SEAT.

CRANSHAW CASTLE.

One of the seats of Sholto John Douglas, Earl of Morton.* At present unoccupied. The shootings are rented by David Anderson Paterson, Esq., Leith.

REGISTERED VOTER (Non-Resident).

Stewart, A. C., Esq. of Eaglescarnie

---

* Sholto John Douglas, 18th Earl of Morton, born 1818 ; succeeded 1858 ; married, 1st, 1844, Helen, daughter ot the late James Watson, Esq., of Cranshaws, and of Saughton, Mid-Lothian (who died 1850), and has issue—

Sholto George Watson, Lord Aberdour, Cornet Mid-Lothian Yeomanry Cavalry, born 1844.

    The Earl married, 2d, 1853, Lady Alice Ann Caroline, daughter of John George, 1st Earl of Durham.

    His Lordship is a Deputy-Lieutenant for Mid-Lothian and county Argyle, a Magistrate for county Fife, and Lieut.-Col. Mid-Lothian Yeomanry ; was formerly Lieutenant 11th Dragoon Guards.

    Principal residences—Dalmahoy, near Edinburgh ; Bonaw, Argyleshire. London address—47 Brook Street, W.

COCKBURNSPATH

———◆———

THIS parish is situated in the N.W. part of Berwickshire. It is bounded on the north by the German Ocean, on the west by East Lothian, on the south by Abbey St. Bathans, and on the east by Coldingham. In outline the parish may be described as very nearly a square of $4\frac{1}{4}$ miles; although its greatest length is nearly $7\frac{1}{2}$ miles. The total area, according to the Ordnance Survey, is $12,951\frac{2}{3}$ acres; of which $81\frac{3}{4}$ are in roads, $18\frac{1}{2}$ are under water, $50\frac{1}{2}$ are occupied by the railway (the North British) and $281\frac{1}{2}$ are "Fore Shore."

"The general aspect of the parish is varied and uneven, being diversified by hill and dale, and intersected by occasional deep and picturesque ravines, through each of which a little river works its troubled way into the sea. But though thus generally uneven, a very marked distinction in point of scenery is apparent: that part of the parish lying nearest to the sea being arable and highly cultivated, while, as it recedes from the coast it becomes more hilly and is principally adapted for pasture. This latter division may be considered as a continuation of the range of hills known as the Lammermoors, the north-east of which terminates a little beyond the boundaries of this parish, in the bold rocky promontory of St. Abbs" (see Coldingham). The general appearance of this hilly tract is smooth and rounded, the hills rise from 500 to 700 feet, and in one instance (Ecclaw Hill) to 909 feet; and these are intersected by deep valleys, some of them very picturesque. The most remarkable of these valleys are—Dunglass Dean, which is here the boundary between the counties of Berwick and Haddington, and is crossed by a magnificent railway viaduct of six arches, of which the one that spans the Dean is $124\frac{1}{2}$ feet in height from the bed of the stream to the top of the parapet, and has a span of 135 feet. This, with the exception of the celebrated viaduct at Ballochmyle in Ayrshire, is the loftiest and greatest in Scotland.* The whole work is executed in the most substantial manner, and forms an object of great architectural beauty; the scenic effect being heightened by the presence of two other bridges over the Dean, one on each side, on the old and new roads, and by the picturesque accessories of wood and water. The Tower Dean, so named from an old castle over-hanging it;

Edmond's Dean; and the Pease or Peath's Dean, the most remarkable of all, from its great depth and bold rocky heights which rise on either side. Across this glen or ravine is the Pease Bridge. This bridge, built in 1786, is 300 feet in length, 15 feet wide, and 127 feet in height above the stream over which it passes, and was long celebrated as the highest bridge in Scotland, and for any thing we know it may be so still.* On the eastern slopes of the high ground above the Pease burn is probably the most extensive oaken coppice in the three counties. Throughout the parish, but especially in the vicinity of the deans just mentioned, are the remains of many British camps. Besides being rich in natural beauty, along the sea-line of the parish occur some very interesting and striking pieces of coast scenery. Of these, one of the most picturesque is the Cove Harbour, situated about a mile from the village of Cockburnspath, a little bay surrounded by precipices of above 100 feet. "Various other very interesting coast scenes might be described, one especially in the neighbourhood of Redheugh in the eastern part of the parish, named Siccar point, the geological phenomena of which are celebrated. The natural and scientific beauties of this place have been rendered accessible to strangers by means of a winding foot-path cut along the sides of the steep sea-bank. Here the geological appearances are remarkable as to strike at once, even those who are least acquainted with geology as a science; no wonder, therefore, that they were thought sufficient to attract at one time three of the most eminent men of their day—we mean Dr. Hutton, Professor Playfair, and the late Sir James Hall, Bart. of Dunglass."† Near to Siccar point are the ruins of St. Helen's Church—a piece of simple Saxon architecture, supposed to have been erected so early as the seventh century; its position, in a field not far from the steep sea bank, commands an extensive and fascinating view.

Cockburnspath is well provided with good public roads which traverse it in all directions. In the north-west of the parish, close to the North British Railway, which has a station here, is the neat little village of Cockburnspath, containing 261 inhabitants. Although small, it is of considerable importance to the neighbourhood, there being no town of any consequence nearer than Dunbar on one side, 8 miles off, and Dunse and Ayton on the other, both of which are about 14 miles distant. Its distance from Edinburgh by rail is $36\frac{1}{2}$ miles; Berwick on-Tweed, 21 miles.

---

* The viaduct of Ballochmyle has a span of 184 feet and a height of 193 The span of Chester bridge over the Dee is 200 feet, and is probably the greatest stone arch in Britain, but its want of height, by throwing it out of proportion, mars its effect and, besides, gives it an appearance of weakness.

---

* Some accounts make it only 123 feet high—the difference probably arises between measuring from the roadway and from the top of the parapet. We have seen an old statement making this bridge to be 240 feet high, and *the highest in the world*. It will be observed we here make a distinction between a *bridge* and a *viaduct*.

† Late Rev. A. Baird in the Statistical Account of Scotland.

By the census of 1861 the population of the parish was 1194, constituting 232 families ; 68 of which were returned as living in houses of one window, and 87 in houses of two windows, leaving 77 as living in houses of three or more windows.

Assessed property in 1864-5, £10,013 : 8 : 6.

Superior of the village—Sir James Hall, Bart. of Dunglass. Dunglass* is on the borders of the parish, but in the neighbouring county of Haddington.

The principal landed-proprietors in the parish are—Sir Jas. Hall, Bart. of Dunglass ; Sir George Grant Suttie, Bart. of Prestongrange ; James W. Hunter, Esq. of Thurston ; Duncan Wright, Esq. of Blackburn (Altiery, Glenluce) ; and David Broadwood, Esq. of Fulfordlees (Crowhill, Innerwick).

Those marked thus (*) are Registered Voters in the parish.

DISTRICT POLICE OFFICER—James Forbes, Cockburnspath Station.

JUSTICES OF THE PEACE for the County Resident in the Neighbourhood—James W. Hunter, Esq., of Thurston ; and David Broadwood, Esq., Crowhill (*see* Coldingham lists).

PUBLIC OFFICES—Heritors' Clerk, Session Clerk, Kirk Treasurer, Inspector of Poor, Registrar of Births, Marriages, and Deaths—Andrew W. Henderson.

Sexton and Bellman—Andrew Cowe.

Medical Officer and Public Vaccinator—James Black, surgeon.

COAST-GUARD STATION (near Redheugh, 3 miles along the coast east from Cove)—William Kendall, Chief Boatman in charge ; Commanding Officer—Hon. Captain F. Charteris, Edinburgh.

POST OFFICE—Agnes Crooks, postmistress ; Local Post Messengers——James Nisbet and Robert Stewart. Letters from all parts arrive at 9-55 a.m., and 7-30 p.m. ; despatch to all parts at 9-20 a.m., 3 p.m., and 7 p.m. On Sundays, Letters from Edinburgh at 9-50 a.m., and 7.30 p.m. ; from London at 5-40 p.m. ; despatched to Edinburgh 5 p.m., to London 7 p.m.

CLERGY, &c.—Presbytery of Dunbar, Synod of Lothian and Tweeddale. Patron—The Crown.

Established Church—*Rev. William Patterson (Inducted 1843). Rev. J. M. Buchanan, assistant and successor (Inducted 1863). Sittings, 400. Average attendance at Sabbath School, 70.

Free Church (belongs ecclesiastically to Cockburnspath, but is situated at Oldhamstocks village in Haddingtonshire, about 2½ miles from Cockburnspath village)—Rev. Andrew Wallace (Inducted 1846).

U. P. Church (Stockbridge, about a mile south-west from the village)—Rev. David M. Inglis (Inducted 1819). Sittings, 420. Average attendance at Stockbridge Sabbath School, 20 ; Do. at Old Cambus, conducted by William Cairns, 25.

FAST DAYS—Thursdays before first Sabbath of March and second Sabbath of July.

SCHOOLS*—Parochial—Andrew W. Henderson, master ; av. at., 85.

Old Cambus (supported by Sir James Hall, Bart.)—Wm. Cairns, master ; average attendance, 50.

PAROCHIAL BOARD—Sir James Hall, Bart., Chairman. No. of Poor on Roll, 29. Rate of Assessment, 6d per £ ; total Assessment, 1863-4, £250. Poor House—Linton Combination.

PUBLIC LIBRARY—1228 volumes. David Hardy, tailor, Librarian. Annual subscription, 6s.

DUNGLASS AND COCKBURNSPATH CURLING CLUB—Patron—Sir James Hall, Bart., of Dunglass ; President—John Hood, Old Cambus Townhead ; Vice-President—John Aitchison, Blackburn ; Representative Members—John Hood, and William Hardy, Horsley ; Secretary—Philip Wilson (H. M.) ; Treasurer—John Allan, Redheugh. Members on the Roll, 40. Annual Subscription, 2s. The Curling Pond is situated at Ewieside.

COCKBURNSPATH HORTICULTURAL SOCIETY—Patroness—Lady Hall, of Dunglass. Secretary and Treasurer—Mr. Mitchill, factor, Dunglass.

PLOUGHING CLUB†—Secretary and Treasurer—John Hood, Old Cambus Townhead.

CARTER'S MEETING—This Society, consisting of farmers and their servants (next to the Hawick Farmers' Club the oldest in the three counties *see* p. 317), was established November 6, 1779, to keep in force certain rules and regulations as to the driving of sea-weed from the shore ; the charter was granted by Sir James Hall, Bart., of Dunglass (Lord of the Manor, and grandfather of the present baronet), and to this date the rules and regulations have been strictly enforced. It is limited to the Dunglass barony, and at each meeting two farmers require to be present. Sea-weed being very much used for manure in the locality, the collecting and driving of it is a matter of importance.

MEDICAL PRACTITIONER—James Black, Cockburnspath, surgeon.

SURVEYOR OF ROADS FOR THE DISTRICT—John Wilson, Chapelhill.

MILLS : Pease—Corn—William Lawson, Dunglass, miller.

CONVEYANCE—By Rail to all parts per North British Railway. Station-master and North British Railway Coal Agent—Alex. Deas.

---

* Dunglass House, the seat and principal residence of Sir James Hall, Bart., of Dunglass, Haddingtonshire, eldest son of the late Sir John Hall, Bart of Dunglass, born 1824 ; succeeded as 6th Bart., 1860 ; is a Magistrate for the counties of Berwick and Haddington. London addresses—Carlton Club, S.W. ; 63 Lowndes Square, S.W. *Heir Pres.*, his brother Douglas, born 182-.

* Children in the parish from 5 to 15, attending school during the first week of April 1861, 191 ; of all ages, 202.

† There existed in the parish an Agricultural Society to award prizes to the best ploughmen, as far back as 1806. It was re-established in 1843.

TRADES IN COCKBURNSPATH VILLAGE.

Aitchison, James, grocer, &c.
Anderson, John, smith
Black, James, surgeon
*Christison, William, innkeeper
Crooks, Agnes, draper and grocer
Grieve, Thomas, bootmaker
Hardie, David, tailor
Johnston, Hugh, baker
Laing, Peter, tailor
Paterson, James, slater
Pringle, William, tailor
Reid, Thomas, grocer, tailor, and clothier
Renton, William, boot and shoemaker
Robertson, George, flesher
Smith, James, contractor and mason
Tricket, John, smith
Turner, William, joiner

———

Cove Fishing Station, William Thorburn, fish-curer

Old Cambus

Hay, William, smith
Shearer, George, grocer

———

RESIDENTS, FARMERS, &c., IN THE PARISH.

*Aitchison, John, farmer, Blackburn
*Allan, John, do. Redheugh
*Allan, William do. Bowshiel
 Burdus, Robert, forester (to Sir James Hall, of Dunglass), Penmanshiel Cottage
*Cockburn, George, farmer, Whiteburn
 Cranston, James, do. Pathhead
 Hardy, Arthur, do. Penmanshiel
*Hardy, George, do. do.
 Hardy, James, Oldcambus West Mains
 Hardy, William, Horsley
 Hood, Mrs., Cove
*Hood, John, farmer, Oldcambus Townhead
*Hood, Robert, do. Linhead
*Johnston, Jas., do. Fulfordlees
*Miller, James, do. Blackburn Mill
*Smith, Fred. C. do. Hoprig

*White, William, Oldcambus East Mains
*Wight, George, farmer, Edmonsdean and Ecclaw
*Wilson, Philip, do. Chapelhill

———

REGISTERED VOTERS (Non-Resident).

Broadwood, David, Crowhill, Innerwick, Dunbar
Forbes, Sir Charles, of Newe and Edinglassie
Hall, Sir James, Bart., of Dunglass
Hunter, James, of Godscroft
Hunter, James William, of Thurston
White, Alexander, Causewaybank
Wright, Duncan, Altiery, Glenluce

AYTON.

—◆—

THIS parish, situated on the coast of Berwickshire, is about 4 miles long by 4 broad. It is bounded on the north by the parishes of Eyemouth and Coldingham, on the east by the German Ocean, on the south by the parishes of Mordington and Foulden, and on the west by Chirnside and Coldingham. The eastern boundary of the parish comprehends about 2 miles of a bold rocky sea-coast, which at one place rises to the height of 339 feet. The south-western part of the parish is hilly, the highest point being Ayton Hill, 654 feet above sea-level. In the northern part of the parish the ground, although elevated, is much lower than in the southern. The area of the parish, according to the Ordnance Survey, is 6832 acres ; of which 26½ are under water (¼ of an acre being tidal), 96¼ are public roads, 37 are occupied by the railway, and nearly 106 consist of " foreshore." The remainder, in the lower districts of the parish, is under the highest state of cultivation ; the hilly portions are covered with fine plantations.

The streams in the parish are—the Eye, which skirts at first its southern boundary, then flowing north intersects the parish ; and the Ale, which, before joining the Eye, skirts the boundary from the parish of Eyemouth. The Eye contains a few trout of good quality ; the scenery on its banks is very pretty and varied. The roads to Eyemouth from Ayton, on either side of the Eye, are very pleasing ; and there are some fine views to be had from Flemington, Millerton, and Camp Hills—all within a mile from the village. In the parish are some British remains.

Near the centre of the parish, and situated on the Eye, is the cleanly and pleasant village of Ayton. It is about a quarter of a mile from the station of the same name, on the North British Railway. It is very regularly built, and contains a number of good houses and shops. Good accommodation is also to be had in the different inns. The neighbourhood of the village is dotted over with some very fine residences—among which are AYTON CASTLE, the seat of Alexander Mitchell Innes, Esq., occupying nearly the site of the ancient castle, which was formerly a place of considerable importance. The new building, which was finished in 1851, is a splendid mansion in the Scottish Border style, beautifully situated in the midst of fine woods, and from its commanding position, forms a very prominent object in the landscape (*see* p. 468). GUNSGREEN

HOUSE, an excellent mansion, is situated close to the sea-side, at a short distance from the harbour of Eyemouth. This house is said to have been built by a wealthy smuggler. NETHERBYRES, formerly the property of Captain Brown, whose name is well known in connection with suspension bridges, now the residence of John R. L'Amy, Esq.

A new parish church is at present being built to hold 750 sitters. The site is the field between the toll and the bridge, which Mr. Innes, with his well known liberality, has gifted for the purpose. The building is to be in the pure Gothic style, richly carved, with a spire 130 feet high, and to have painted windows of the Nativity, etc. The heritors give £1500, and Mr. Innes contributes the remainder, which it is supposed will cost him upwards of £3000—in all, besides the field, £4500. It is expected to be opened in about six months from this date (August 1865).

About 2¼ miles from Ayton, on the coast, is the small fishing village of BURNMOUTH. It is romantically situated in a deep cove at the bottom of a steep ravine, and has a good boat harbour ; also a station on the N. B. Railway. The fishery is thriving, and consists of cod, ling, haddock, whiting, flounders, halybut, turbot, mackerel, and other kinds, which are sent off to the English markets.

Ayton is about 7 miles from Berwick-on-Tweed, and about 11 from Dunse—with both of which there is communication by rail, the North British line intersecting the parish from east to west.

Annual Holidays—New Year's Day, and generally the last Tuesday in June.

Population in 1861 of the village of Ayton, 875 ; of the parish including the village, 2014 ; who composed 436 separate families ; of these 3 were returned as inhabiting houses having no window, 172 in houses of one window, 165 in houses of two windows, leaving a balance of 96 living in houses of three or more windows.

Assessed property in 1864-5, £15,019 : 5 : 11.

Amongst the principal landed-proprietors resident in the parish are—Alexander Mitchell Innes, Esq., of Ayton Castle ; and John R. L'Amy, Esq., of Netherbyres ; non-resident—Trustees of Sir William Fettes of Whiterig, Dr. Patrick Home of Gunsgreen, Earl Brownlow of Fairneyside (Belton House, Grantham) ; and Captain Cosens of Peelwalls.

———————

Those marked thus (*) are Registered Voters in the parish.

POLICE OFFICER—James Steer, Sergeant.

  Police Assessment same as County—2d. per £.

ACTING JUSTICES OF THE PEACE.

David M. Home of Wedderburn.	Thos. Landale of Templehall.
Alexander M. Innes, of Ayton.	Maj. L'Amy, Netherbyres House.
Jas. Jeffreys Oswald of Edring- ton Castle.	James Grant Suttie, younger of Balgone, Maines House.
G. C. Trotter Cranstoun of Dewar.	Alex. T. Herriot of Coldingham- law.
John Wilkie of Foulden.	
Major A. C. C. Renton of Lam- berton.	Thomas Anderson of Shawbraes. William Mack of Berrybank.

Charles D. Colville, Ayton, Clerk.   James Bowhill, Ayton, J.P.,
Procurator-Fiscal

COURTS.

JUSTICE OF PEACE COURTS are held on the first Thursday of each month, except September.

SHERIFF SMALL DEBT COURTS are held at Ayton on the Monday before the last Thursday of March ; the last Monday of May ; the Monday before the last Thursday of July ; and the first Monday of November, in the Red Lion Inn.

PUBLIC OFFICES.

Billet Master—James Thompson.
Collector of Poor Rates, Registration and Sanitary Rate, and Statute Labour Rates—Charles D. Colville.
Heritors' Clerk—William G. F. Tod.
Inspector of Poor—Thomas Thompson.
Justice of Peace Clerk—Charles D. Colville.
Medical Officer and Public Vaccinator—Dr. Jeffrey.
Registrar of Births, Marriages, and Deaths—Chas. D. Colville.
Session Clerk—Rev. Daniel Cameron, pro tem.
Sexton—John Connal.
Stamps and Taxes—Jas. Bowhill, District Collector of Taxes. Walter Carter, Sub-Distributor of Stamps.

INLAND REVENUE.

Office at Red Lion Inn.

James Luckie, Haddington, Collector.   —— Tomlinson, Clerk.
Collection made every Six Weeks.

POST OFFICE.

MONEY ORDER OFFICE AND SAVINGS BANK.

George Wood, Postmaster.
Robert Grieve, Letter Carrier.

POST OFFICE HOURS.

			Box Closes.
Edinburgh and the North—First,	.		8-30 a.m.
Do.,	Do.—Second,		6-30 p.m.
Berwick	. . . .	.	10-50 a.m.
Berwick and the South—First,	.		3-20 p.m.
Do ,	Do.—Second,		7-20 p.m.
Dunse, Chirnside,	&c.—First,	.	8-30 a.m.
Do.	Do.—Second,		8-10 p.m.
Eyemouth,	.	. —First,	. 10-30 a.m.
Do.	. . .	. —Second,	8-10 p.m.
Reston, Auchincrow, & Burnmouth			10-30 a.m.
Coldingham,	. . .	.	10-30 a.m.

Deliveries—11 a.m., 4-25 and 8-30 p.m., and on Mondays at 7 a.m.

RURAL MESSENGERS.

James Paterson, for town and district : Robert Spence, jun., for Coldingham ; William Mason, for Auchencraw ; and Thomas M'-Vicar for Eyemouth.

CLERGY, &c.

Presbytery of Chirnside, and Synod of Merse and Teviotdale. The United Presbyterian Churches are in the Presbytery of Berwick. Patron—The Crown.

ESTABLISHED CHURCH—*Rev. Daniel Cameron (Inducted 1843). Sittings, 500. Average attendance at Sabbath School, 60 ; at Minister's Bible Class, 50. Superintendent of Sabbath School—Minister ; Church Officer—John Connal.
U. P. CHURCH (West)—Rev. James Stark (Inducted 1819). Sittings, 300. Average attendance at Sabbath School, 40. Session Clerk —Robert Clark ; Precentor—Thomas Renton.
U. P. CHURCH (Summerhill)—*Rev. Thomas Montgomery (Inducted 1846). Sittings, 560. Average attendance at Sabbath School, 50.

FAST DAYS—Thursdays preceding last Sundays of Feb. and July.

EDUCATIONAL INSTITUTIONS.†

Parochial School—*William G. F. Tod, master ; average attend., 80.
Female and Infant School (in connection with Parochial School)—Miss Morrison, teacher ; average attendance, 80.
Burnmouth School (Parochial)—A. Falconer, master ; av. at., 75.
Odd Fellows' School—P. Sheddon, master ; average attendance, 75.
Girls' School—Mrs. Hume, teacher ; average attendance, 20.

PAROCHIAL BOARD.

James Bowhill, Chairman.
No. of Poor on Roll, 55.
Average Rate, 3½d. per £. Average yearly Assessment, £485.
Inspector—John Thompson.

† Children in the parish from 5 to 15, attending school during the first week of April 1861, 324 ; of all ages, 350.

BAND OF HOPE LODGE OF ODD FELLOWS (estab. 1844).

James Greig, Secretary.   John Kitson Gledhill, Treasurer.
40 Members.

VILLAGE LIBRARY.

Open every Monday evening.
P. M'Vicar, Librarian.   No. of vols. 632.   Annual Subscription, 2s.

AYTON CURLING CLUB (estab. 1855.

President and Patron—Alex. M. Innes, Esq. of Ayton.
Patroness—Mrs Innes.
Vice-President—Walter Carter, Esq.
James Bowhill, Treasurer.   James T. S. Doughty, Secretary.
Entry-Money, 10s.   Annual Subscription varies.
Curling Pond at Littledean on the property of the Patron.

3RD BERWICKSHIRE RIFLE CORPS—(AYTON).

Capt.—David Poppelwell, Whiterig.   Lieut.—Jas. Martin, Millbank.
Ensign—Hilton Middleton, Cocklaw.
Chaplain—Rev. D. Cameron, sen.
Drill Instructor—James Dickson.
Secretary and Treasurer—
Effective Force, 70.   Honorary Members, .
Subscription of Honorary Members, 21s.
Competitions for medals and money prizes take place on New Years'
Day and Annual Holiday.

AYTON GAS COMPANY.

Balfour Balsille, farmer, Dykegatehead, Treas.   C. D. Colville, Secy.
John Swanston, Manager.
7s. 6d . per 1000 feet.   Amount of Stock, £600, pays 5 per cent

BANKS.

COMMERCIAL BANK OF SCOTLAND (established 1846)—James Bowhill,
Agent ; Andrew Whitlie, Accountant.
ROYAL BANK (established 1857)—Walter Carter, Agent ; George
Matthewson, Accountant.

INSURANCE AGENTS.

INSURANCE CO. OF SCOTLAND (Fire) ....James Bowhill.
SCOTTISH EQUITABLE LIFE ASSURANCE Co..James Bowhill.

SCOTTISH AMICABLE ....Wm. G. F. Tod.
PHŒNIX FIRE OFFICE....................John Jeffrey, M.D.
LIFE ASSOCIATION.....................Walter Carter.
SCOTTISH UNION......................Walter Carter.
UNITY FIRE........................Chas. D. Colville.
SCOTTISH TRADE PROTECTION SOCIETY......Chas. D. Colville.

SUNDRIES.

MEDICAL PRACTITIONERS——*John Jeffrey, M.D. ; James Cruick-
shank, surgeon.

SOLICITORS—James Bowhill ; *Charles David Colville, N.P.

MILLS, &c. : Ayton—Flour—John Nisbet.
Flemington—Corn—*James and *Peter Lawson.
Netherbyres—Corn—*Robert Bell.
Ayton—Paste and Milled Boards—Martin & Co., Millbank.
Bleachfield (Ayton)—Paste and Milled Board—William Martin,
Millbank.

CARRIERS—Hogan Fulton, to Coldingham every Saturday.   Robert
Guy, to Berwick every Saturday.

CONVEYANCE BY RAILWAY—North British main line to Edinburgh
and the north, Berwick and the south, and by the Dunse branch
line to Hawick and all parts of the west.
At the inns conveyances can be had to Eyemouth.

AYTON DISTRICT OF STATUTE LABOUR ROADS,

Including the parishes of Ayton, Eyemouth, Coldingham, and
Cockburnspath.
Two meetings annually, on the last Friday of April, and 26th Oct.
Charles D. Colville, writer, Ayton, District Clerk and Collector.
John Wilson, Chapelhill, Surveyor.

TRADES.

*Bathgate, Thomas, merchant
*Berry, James, mason
Bathgate Hotel, Mrs. Elizabeth Whitlaw
Black Bull Inn, Mrs. Whitelaw
Bowhill, James, writer
Bruce Brothers, tanners
*Cairns, William, baker
Chalmers, William, joiner
*Clark, Robert, grocer
Clay, Robert, blacksmith
Delgatty, Alexander, carter

Delgatty, Margaret, grocer
*Davidson, Adam, saddler
*Dunlop, James, tailor and clothier
*Edington, Archibald, shoemaker
Edington, Stuart, grocer
Gillie, Peter, saddler
*Henderson, John, joiner
Henderson, Alexander, tailor and clothier
Henderson, Alexander, clothier
Hume, R. M. painter
Kerr, John, mason
Knox, J. H., grocer
Mack, Peter, baker
Marshall, Robert, tailor
*Martin, William (of Ayton and Bleachfield Mills)
*M'Craw, James, slater
*Nisbet, John, joiner
*Orkney, James, merchant
*Patterson, James, shoemaker
Sanderson, A., baker
Scott, J. & W., drapers
Simpson, Alexander, baker
*Sinclair, David, grocer
*Sinclair, William, flesher
Storey, Thomas, draper
*Spratt, Andrew, hedger
Swanston, Robert, shoemaker
*Thomson, James, *sheriff officer*
*Thompson, Thomas, joiner
Watt, James, blacksmith
White, J. & J., clothiers
White, George, grocer
*Whitlie, J. & A., tailors and clothiers
White Swan Inn, Thomas Logan
*Wood, Joseph, mason

Railway Station

Ayton—Station-Master and N. B. R. Company's Coal Agent—
John Yule.

Village of Burnmouth

The hamlet, besides its fishing population, also contains the
following :—

Aitchison, Robert, fish-curer
Cairns, John, fishcurer
Dixon, Robert, baker and grocer

Falconar, Alexander, *schoolmaster*
Martin, Alexander, grocer and fish-curer
Martin, Robert, grocer
Martin, William, innkeeper
Wilson, Adam, innkeeper

Railway Station-Master—James Grey

RESIDENTS, FARMERS, &c., IN THE PARISH.

*Brodie, Thomas, farmer, Chesterbank
*Darling, David,   do. Ayton Mains
*Darling, John,   do.   do.
Flemington New Inn, Alice Holms
*Fulton, James, farmer, Whitefield
*Gibson, Thomas, do. Gunsgreenhill
*Inglis, William, do. Prenderguest
*Leitch, Alexander, do. Fairneyside
*Logan, Robert, do. Flemington
*Lugton, William, agricultural implement maker, Hillburn
*Middleton, Hilton, farmer, Cocklaw
*Middleton, William, jun., do.
*Middleton, William,   do.
*Moffat, James, gardener, Ayton Castle
*Nisbet, Archibald, farmer, Greystonlees
*Nisbet, David,   do.   do.
*Paterson, John,   do. Ayton House
Popplewell, David, do. Whiterig
*Tod, Peter,   do. Redhall
*Weatherhead, James, boat-builder, Brownsbank

SEATS OF COUNTY FAMILIES IN THE PARISH.

AYTON CASTLE.

The property and residence of *Alexander Mitchell Innes, Esq.,
of Ayton Castle, eldest son of the late William Mitchell Innes,
Esq., of Ayton Castle ; born 1811 ; succeeded, 1860 ; married
1st., 1840, Charlotte Gordon, daughter of the late Sir Thomas
Dick Lauder, Bart., of Fountainhall (she died in 1848) ; 2nd.,
1852, Fanny Augusta, youngest daughter of the late James
Vine, Esq., of Puckaster, Isle of Wight, and has issue—

*William Simpson, born 18—
*Norman Mitchell Innes, Esq., born 18—

Mr. Innes, who is a Magistrate for the counties of Berwick
and Mid-Lothian, and Lord of the Baronies of Ayton and

Whitehall (Berwickshire) was formerly Captain of the 47th Foot.

Town addresses—New Club, Edinburgh; Carlton Club, S.W. (*See* Earlston parish, p. 516).

GUNSGREEN HOUSE (*see* p. 595).

Situated near the mouth of the Eye on its north side and opposite the town of Eyemouth—the property of *Dr. Patrick Home of Gunsgreen; at present occupied by J. G. Wood, Esq., W.S., Edinburgh.

NETHERBYRES (*see* p. 596).

Situated also on the south side of the Eye, and about a mile from Eyemouth, the property and residence of *John Ramsay L'Amy, Esq., of Dunkenny, Forfarshire, eldest son of the late James L'Amy, Esq., of Dunkenny; born 1813; succeeded 1854; married, 1845, Mary Riche M'Leod, only daughter of the late William Mitchell Innes, E q , of Ayton Castle, Berwickshire, and has issue—

Christina, born 1846; died 1859.
James, born 1847; died 1865.
William, born 1850.
J. A. Ramsay, born 1852.
Norman, born 1854; died 1855.
Eustace George, born 1857.
Simpson Macleod, born 1860.
Mary Williamina.

Mr. L'Amy is a Justice of the Peace for the counties of Forfar and Berwick, and Deputy-Lieut. for the county of Forfar.

Other addresses—Dunkenny, near Forfar; New Club, Edinburgh; Junior United Service Club, S.W.

PEELWALLS.

Situated in the southern district of the parish, near the Dunse and Chirnside Road, and about 1 mile from Ayton—the property of Mrs. Cosens (Agnes Dickson, only child of the late John Dickson, Esq., of Peelwalls); married, 17th July 1863, George Weir Cosens, Esq., eldest son of the late Robt. Cosens, Esq., of Kames (Eccles parish); a magistrate for the county of Berwick, and Captain in H.M. 85th Light Infantry. Peelwalls is at present occupied by Col. Forbes, L.E.I.C.S.

REGISTERED VOTERS (Non-Resident).

Colville, Robert Kerr, surgeon, America
Edington, Stewart, baker, Berwick
Innes, Thomas Mitchell, Parsons Green, Edinburgh
Innes, Gilbert Mitchell, Lochbroom
Johnston, Rev. George, Edinburgh
Knight, Henry, merchant, Blandford
Laidler, Thomas, farmer, Chatton, Northumberland
Lyal, Smith, millwright, Manchester
M'Gregor, Thos. Dods (of Barnside, Abbey St. Bathans), The Brunt, Dunbar
Meikle, Henry, farmer, Banks, Linlithgow
Meikle, Robert, steward, Langton, Dorset
Meikle, Gilbert, Invarary
Meikle, Thomas, Mount Pleasant, Edinburgh.
Renton, David, Edinburgh

FOGO.

—•--

AN agricultural parish in the eastern district of the Merse, bounded on the north by Dunse and Edrom, on the east by Swinton, on the south by Eccles and Greenlaw and on the west by Polwarth. Its greatest length is 5 miles, and average breadth about 2 miles. Its area, according to the Ordnance Survey, is 4668 4-5th acres, of which 96 are in public or private roads, and 17 are under water. The remainder, with the exception of what is laid out in plantations, is under a high state of cultivation. "The surface of the parish may be described as consisting of two long parallel ridges of small elevations separated by the Blackadder—the south ridge sloping gradually into a level of considerable breadth. The higher ground, which is a deep black loam, is the most valuable and productive; the lower and flat ground being thinner, and having a tilly and stiff bottom." The Blackadder, which intersects the parish about half its length in a north-easterly direction and then bounds it from Edrom, is here a good trout fishing stream, free to the angler. Fogo is much exposed during the spring months to north and east winds, accompanied by cold chilling fogs or rain. The climate is, however, on the whole, good. The parish is intersected by good turnpike roads —that from Dunse to Coldstream crossing it in the east, and that from Dunse to Kelso passing through it from north to south. In the northern part of the parish, situated on the south bank of the Blackadder, is the small hamlet of Fogo, which is all the appearance of a village in the parish. It consists of the manse, church, school house, and a few cottages—the church is ancient and beautifully situated. Fogo is about 4 miles by the road from Dunse (in a direct line it is only 3 miles), and 8 by the road from Coldstream. The nearest railway station is that of Marchmont, in Polwarth parish, 2 miles distant from the hamlet.

Population of the parish in 1861, 559; who constituted 100 families, 2 of whom were returned as living in houses having no window, 16 in houses of one window, 30 in houses of two windows, and the remainder (52, the very high average of more than a half) in houses of three or more windows.

Assessed property in 1864-5, £7202 : 2 : 8.

The principal landed-proprietors in the parish are—Richard Trotter, Esq. of Charterhall; David Robertson, Esq. of Ladykirk; Sir H. H. Campbell, Bart., of Marchmont; David Milne Home, Esq. of Wedderburn.

Those marked thus (*) are Registered Voters.

RESIDENT JUSTICE OF THE PEACE—Hon. Colonel Cathcart of Caldra.

PUBLIC OFFICES — Heritors' Clerk, Session Clerk, Kirk Treasurer, Registrar of Births, Marriages, and Deaths, and Inspector of Poor—John Macfarlane.
Medical Officer and Public Vaccinator—Robert C. M'Watt, M D., Dunse.

POST OFFICE—Daily Post to and from Dunse. Andw. Elliot, runner. Arrival at Fogo, 8-30 a.m. ; despatch, 10 a.m.

CLERGY, &c.—Fogo is in the Presbytery of Dunse, and Synod of Merse and Teviotdale. Patron—the Crown.
Established Church—'Rev. R. F. Proudfoot (Inducted 1845). Sittings, 330. Average attendance at Sabbath School, 25.

FAST DAYS—In March, and on the last Thursday in July.

SCHOOLS†—Parochial—*John Macfarlane, master. Aver. attend , 70. Sewing (in connection with the Parochial)—Mrs. Macfarlane, mistress.

PAROCHIAL BOARD—Richard Trotter, Esq., chairman. Average No. of Poor on Roll, 9. Average Rate of Assessment, 1½d. per £ ; total Assessment in 1864-5, £106 : 16 : 10½.

CORN MILLS : Sisterpath—Alex. Hamilton, farmer. Cairnsmill — *Geo. Sanderson, farmer.

TILE WORK—Harcarse—John Tully.

TRADES, &c.

Allan, Andrew, grocer
Hamilton, George, cartwright
Lumsden, William, grocer .
Miller, Alexander, smith

RESIDENTS, FARMERS, &c., IN THE PARISH.

*Allan, Thomas, farmer, Fogorigg
*Hogg, John, farmer, Sisterpath Waulk Mill
*Hood, Thos., do., Bogend
*Rae, Henry, do., Fogo Eastend
*Robertson, John, do., Clerkenville

---

† Children in the parish from 5 to 15 attending school during the first week of April 1861, 84 ; of all ages. 91.

*Thomson, John, farmer, Easter Whinkerstones
*Thomson, Robert, do.,   do.
*Tully, John, tilemaker, Harcarse
*Torrance, George, farmer, Sisterpath
*White, Robert,   do., Ryselaw

SEATS, &c., OF COUNTY FAMILIES IN THE PARISH.

CALDRA HOUSE.

Situated on the Blackadder near to the hamlet—the property
and residence of the *Hon. Adolphus Frederick Cathcart; born
1803; married 1832, Margaret, second daughter of the late
William Foreman Home, Esq., of Wedderburn (she died 1861).
Is a Magistrate for the county of Berwick, a retired Lieut.-
Colonel, and a Lieut.-Colonel Commanding 1st Administrative
Battalion Berwickshire Rifle Volunteers.

CHARTERHALL HOUSE.

Situated in the southern part of the parish, an elegant modern
mansion—the property and occasional residence of Richard
Trotter, Esq. of Mortonhall and Charterhall; born 23d March
1797; succeeded his father, the late Lieut.-General Alexander
Trotter, 1825; married 1836, Mary, daughter of the late Gen.
Sir John Oswald, G.C.B., of Dunniker (she died 11th October
1851), and has issue—

Henry, Lieutenant Grenadier Guards, born 5th Jan. 1844.
John Oswald, born 17th January 1849.
Charlotte-Athole-Mary, married 27th July 1858, to Sir John
Marjoribanks of Lees, Bart. (see p. 500).
Margaret-Catherine.
Emily-Frances.

The estate of Charterhall has for generations been possessed
by the Trotter family, who have three-fourths of the parish,
and considerable property in neighbouring parishes.
Principal residence — Morton Hall, Liberton, Edinburgh.
Town address—

SWINTON.

——◆——

THIS parish, to which in 1761 was united that of Simprin, is
situated on the eastern part of the Merse. The boundaries
are—on the north Whitsome and Edrom, on the east Ladykirk, on the south Coldstream, and on the west Eccles. The
outline of the parish is slightly inclined to oblong; having a
length from east to west of about 4 miles, and a breadth of
about 3 miles. The area of the parish, according to the Ord-
nance Survey, is 5571$\frac{2}{3}$ acres; of which 96$\frac{1}{4}$ nearly are occupied
by roads, and 11 are under water. "The surface, neither
perfectly level nor yet at all hilly, consists of a succession of
low, parallel, wave-like ridges, ranging from east to west, with
interjacent level spaces of considerable extent, the soil being
in general deep and productive." The Leet, a small stream,
and a tributary of the Tweed, having its confluence at Coldstream (which see), intersects the parish (see Whitsome, p. 579,
foot-note). Situated in the centre of the parish, on the Leet
water, is the pleasant and important village of Swinton. It
is built round a large green, in which stands an ancient cross.
Its population in 1861 was 431. The old village of Simprin
has long been extinct. From 1699 until his translation to
Ettrick (see pp. 414-416) in 1707 the parish of Simprin was
under the charge of the Rev. Thomas Boston, and in its church
he first preached the substance of his "Fourfold State." Simprin lay along and within the eastern boundary of the present
parish. The post town is Coldstream, about 6 miles distant
from the village by the road. The most accessible railway
stations are at Norham, on the Berwick and Kelso line, 6 miles
distant; and at Dunse, which is the nearest market town, on
the Berwickshire line, about 5 miles distant. The main road
from Berwick to Kelso passes through the village.

Fairs—Quoted in the *Edinburgh Almanac* as taking place on
the 3rd Thursday of June and 4th Tuesday of October, have
been defunct for many years; but the custom of "crying"
them, as of old, is kept up.

The population of the entire parish, by the census of 1861,
was 964, who constituted 224 separate families, 119 of whom
were returned as living in houses having one window, 68 in
houses of two windows, and 37 as living in houses of three or
more windows.

Assessed property in 1864-5, £10,993 : 9 : 7.

The principal landed-proprietors in the parish are—Mrs.
Swinton of Swinton, Mrs. Clay Ker Seymer of Little Swinton,

(*see* p. 535, foot-note), Admiral Popham, of Greenrigs, etc., David Robertson, Esq. (of Ladykirk), of Simprin, Richard Trotter, Esq. (of Charterhall—*see* Fogo), of Swinton Mill.

Those marked thus (*) are Registered Voters in the parish.

DISTRICT POLICE OFFICER—Robert M'Kenzie, Swinton.

PUBLIC OFFICES—Heritors' Clerk, Inspector of Poor, Session Clerk, Kirk Treasurer, and Registrar of Births, Marriages, and Deaths —George Tweedie.

Medical Officer and Public Vaccinator—Aw. Morrison, surgeon.

Inspector of Nuisances—John Chalmers, joiner.

POST OFFICE—George Buchanan, postmaster. Daily post from Cold-stream.—Arrival, 2-10 p.m.; departure, 6 a.m. David Reid, runner.

CLERGY, &c.—Presbytery of Chirnside, Synod of Merse and Teviot-dale. Patron—The Crown.

Established Church—*Rev. James Logan (Inducted 1833). Sit tings, 366.

Free Church—*Rev. Thomas Wright (Inducted 1843). Sittings, 550. Average attendance at Sabbath School, 60.

FAST DAYS—First Thursday of March, and last Thursday of July.

SCHOOLS†—Parochial—*George Tweedie, master; aver. attend., 80. Free—Robert Clark, master; average attendance, 85.

PAROCHIAL BOARD—Alexander Barclay, Esq., Greenrigs, Chairman. Average number of Poor on Roll, 50. Rate of Assessment, 6d. per £; total Assessment 1864-5, £436.

FRIENDLY SOCIETY (established 1810)—For the purpose of allowing a weekly payment to members during sickness, or lameness, or old age Each member pays 6s. per annum, and during sickness gets 5s. per week for the first 13 weeks, 2s. 6d. for the next 13 weeks, and 1s. 6d. for the next 13 weeks, or till his sickness terminates; su-perannuated members are allowed 1s. 6d. per week for life. On the death of a member or his wife, £3 is allowed to defray funeral expenses. The business is conducted by ten of a committee, chosen annually, who meet on the third Friday of each quarter Number of members, 144. Jas. Spiers, Chairman; John Chalmers, Trea-surer; Thomas Hopper, jun., Clerk.

CURLING CLUB (estab. 1864)—D. Robertson, Esq., M.P., Patron; Mrs. Robertson, Patroness; Alexander Barclay, President; Jas. H. Calder, Vice-President; George Tweedie, Secretary; R. Clark, Treasurer. 28 Members. The Curling Pond is at Morningbank, on the Swinton estate, and close to the village of Swinton.

MEDICAL PRACTITIONER—Andrew Morrison, Swinton, surgeon.

---

† Children in the parish between 5 and 15, attending school during the first week of April 1861, 138; of all ages, 146.

QUARRY—Swinton Quarter—Heirs of Patrick Murray, Esq., proprie-tors; D. & W. Duns, builders, Dunse, lessees.

CARRIERS—Berwick, Alex. Mackay, Saturday; Leitholm, Thomas Brown, Thursday, and William Fair, Saturday; Kelso, Brown, Friday.

DISTRICT OF STATUTE LABOUR ROADS—Including the parishes of Cold-stream, Eccles, Fogo, Ladykirk, Swinton, and Whitsome. Meet-ings held at Swinton in April and October. Jonathan Melrose, Coldstream, Clerk. Mark Cossar, Greenknowe, Dunse, Surveyor.

TRADES, &c.

Aitchison, Robert, smith
*Anderson, John, farmer
*Anderson, William, do.
Beveridge, James, flesher
Bookless, James, & Son, drapers
Briggs, Thomas, smith
Buchanan, George, cabinet-maker
*Chalmers, John, joiner
Cossar, Robert, tailor
Craig, Alexander, slater
*Denholm, George, saddler
Duns, W. & D., quarry-masters
Henderson, Alexander, shoemaker
*Hopper, Thomas, cooper
Hope, Mrs., innkeeper
Hunter, John, joiner
Jeffrey, William, millwright
Lugton, Andrew, grocer
Lindsay, Miss, grocer
Miller, John, shoemaker
Penny, Alexander, baker
*Pitillo, John (late slater)
Purves, John, tailor
Reddin, William, shoemaker
Reddin, David, mason
Robertson, Alexander, joiner
Sharp, Robert, mason
Short, Leonard, grocer
*Spiers, James, labourer
Spence, Archibald, joiner
Watson, Thomas, baker
Wood, William, shoemaker
Young, John, tea merchant
Young, William, tailor

RESIDENTS, FARMERS, &c.

*Anderson, William, farmer, Morningbank
*Aiton, William,   do.   Crowfootbank
*Aiton, John,   do.   do.
*Barclay, Alexander,   do.   Greenrigs
*Calder, James H.,   do.   Swintonhill
*Davidson, George,   do.   Butterlaw
*Dawson, John,   do.   Swinton Bridge-End
*Edgar, William,   do.   Harcarsehill
*Gibson, John,   do.   Mountfair
*Gillespie, Alexander,   do.   Simprin
*Gillespie, John,   do.   do.
*Somervail, William,   do.   Little Swinton
  Somervail, Miss, Little Swinton
  Swine, Misses, Swinton
*Wilson, Joseph, farmer, Longbank

SEAT, &c., OF COUNTY FAMILY IN THE PARISH.

SWINTON HOUSE.

Situated about half-a-mile west from the village, an elegant modern edifice, occupying the site of one of great antiquity—the seat of Mrs. Swinton, of Swinton. The estate of Swinton has been in the possession of the same family, with one or two brief interruptions, since the Heptarchy, and has descended lineally from father to son without interruption for 800 years.

REGISTERED VOTERS (Non-Resident).

Lugton, Charles, blacksmith, Pinkie
Muckle, William,   , Ord
Popham, Rear-Admiral Brunswick L., Cardean House, Meigle, Forfarshire
Purves, James, farmer, Dunse
Robertson, David, of Ladykirk
Seymer, Henry Ernest Clay Ker, London (see **Legerwood** parish, p. 535, foot-note)

MERTOUN.

—◆—

THIS parish, which juts like a peninsula into Roxburghshire, is beautifully situated on the north bank of the Tweed, in the south-west part of Berwickshire. It is bounded on the north by Earlston, on the east by Smailholm and Makerstoun, on the south and west the Tweed bounds it from Maxton, St. Boswell's, and Melrose parishes in Roxburghshire. Its average length is 6 miles, and breadth from 2 to 3 miles; and its area, according to the Ordnance Survey, is 6536 acres—rather more than 81¼ of which are occupied by roads, and 162 are under water.

"The Tweed, wearing its richest dress of sumptuous beauty, flows along the whole western and southern boundary, and in its progress makes three large and unusually fine reduplications; one of which sweeps round Dryburgh Abbey, another round the church of Mertoun, and the third round the beautiful peninsula of Old Melrose, on the opposite bank. The ground rises in a great variety of gradient and outline, eastward and northward from the river, and is agreeably diversified with fine hedgerows and thriving plantations,—and exhibits, in its diversity of haugh and bold bank, cliffy steep, and gentle ascent, rolling surface, and level table-land—a scene of great picturesqueness within narrow limits. The view which meets the eye in passing from the village of Newtown, on the opposite bank, to visit Dryburgh Abbey is, for its smallness of scope, one of the most delightfully impressive in Scotland. But from the summit of Bemersyde hill, in the west where the ground in general is high, the parish, while picturesque in itself, commands a prospect of the vale of Melrose, and of a long eastward strip of the basin of the Tweed, a near view of the Eildon hills, and a distant one of the Cheviots, unitedly a landscape of exquisite loveliness, and many a romantic feature.* (See foot-note, p. 469.) The soil, towards the Tweed, especially in the haughs, is sharp, with a gravelly bottom; elsewhere it is, with few exceptions, a stiff clay, on a tilly bottom, of excellent quality for brick and tile making. Along the banks of the Tweed a fine red hard sandstone, capable of taking a fine polish, abounds." DRYBURGH ABBEY, finely embosomed in trees, is in the south-west part of the parish. Dryburgh Abbey, in one of the aisles of which is the tomb of Sir Walter Scott, is a great resort of tourists, and is much admired. In its imme-

---

* The only other portion of Berwickshire, of like beauty to Mertoun, is that part of Nenthorn parish containing the seat of Newton-Don, which also juts into Roxburghshire like a peninsula.

diate vicinity, erected by David Stuart, 11th Earl of Buchan, on a commanding height, is a rude colossal statue of the patriot Wallace, chiefly remarkable as being the workmanship of a common stone-mason who never learned sculpture. Near to Dryburgh is the old stronghold of BEMERSYDE, one of the fortalices so common on the Borders, built in conformity to an Act of Parliament in 1535, "for bigging of strengthis on the Borders;" to which has lately been made extensive additions, and now converted into a comfortable baronial residence, but still retaining in a great measure its ancient appearance. Next in interest among the seats in the parish is MERTOUN HOUSE,* the mansion of Lord Polwarth—a superb building occupying a situation upon the banks of the Tweed, in an extensive park studded with fine old trees. The library is of great extent and value, and contains many documents relating to the Marchmont family, barons of Polwarth (see p. 622 footnote). Upon the Mertoun estate, a little below the mansion house, on the opposite bank of the river, are the ruins of LITTLEDEAN TOWER, (see p. 218). The father of the present Lord Polwarth, best known as Hugh Scott of Harden, was one of the first to introduce the Border breed of Leicester sheep into the locality, and helped very materially to bring it to its present perfection and fame † For many years the rams from Mertoun have topped the great sales of Kelso (see p. 89).

---

* Erected in 1702. Its architect was Sir William Bruce.
† See account of the Kelso September Sale of Rams (1843), pp. 89 and 90. At the sale of last year (1864), only 2025 sheep were brought forward—a decrease of nearly 200 on 1863; but the prices realized were far above that of any previous year. Lord Polwarth again topped the market with a ram at £70, another he sold for £61, the next highest in the market; 3 he sold at £45 each, and one each £47 and £43. Other breeders sold at £57, £51, £33, £32, and £30. From £20 to £25 were common prices The average of Lord Polwarth's lot of 35—which always ranges from that number to 40, was £26 : 19 : 8½. At the first sale in which his Lordship exposed his sheep (1852) his average was only £4 : 8 : 7—Mr. Thomson, then of Haymount, and some others getting higher prices; but the prices then realized, by any one, were, compared with those now obtained, very small.
[We have delayed sending this sheet to press, to report on the Sale of 1865 (September 7 and 8). The number of sheep brought forward was 2186, being an increase of 161 over those of last year. 180 of these consisted of half-breds, which were sold on the first day; they created little interest, and realized comparatively small prices. The prices realized on the second day for the pure breds was beyond all precedent—Lord Polwarth again topping the market with rams at £95 and £83. Others he sold for £80, £75, £64, and £60 : 2 at £62 each, and 2 at £50 each—the average of his lot of 35 being £37 : 18 : 10½ ; total, £1328 · 0 · 7½ The next highest priced ram, which belonged to Mr. Stark, Mellendean, sold for £81. Mr. Stark likewise sold 2 at £55 each, and 2 at £40 each, besides 1 each at £52 10s. and £51—the average of his lot of 44 being

---

The parish contains four small hamlets :—CLINTMAINS DRYBURGH, BEMERSYDE, and WHITERIG—the first of which is the largest. The nearest market town is Melrose, about 4 miles distant from the centre of the parish. Nearest post town, St. Boswell's, about 2 miles distant. The nearest railway stations are— Maxton, on the Kelso line, and Newtown St. Boswells. The parish church is situated within the policy of Lord Polwarth, and stands a short distance from Mertoun House. The manse is near the village of Clintmains, and the parish school and school-house are in the same village.

Population of the parish in 1861, 730; who composed 136 separate families.†

Assessed property in 1864-5, £8768 : 5 : 8.

The principal landed-proprietors in the parish are—Lord Polwarth, Mertoun House, Hon. Mrs. B. Erskine of Dryburgh, Miss Haig of Bemersyde, John Meiklam, Esq., of Gladswood, and Capt. W. H. Riddell of Dryburgh House.

Those marked thus (*) are Registered Voters.

RESIDENT JUSTICES OF THE PEACE—Lord Polwarth, Mertoun ; John Meiklam, Esq., of Gladswood.

DISTRICT POLICE OFFICE—Earlston.

PUBLIC OFFICES—Heritors' Clerk, Inspector of Poor, Session Clerk,

---

£24, 3s. ; the seller next in order of price, was Mr. Purves, Burnfoot, whose top went for £48, and whose large lot of 100 averaged £12, 12s. ; the only other animal which brought a conspicuously high price was a ram of Mr. Calder's, Kelloe Mains, which sold at £42 ; below this to £20 were common prices. The aggregate amount for the half-breds sold the first day, was £738 : 2s ; for the whole-breds sold the second day, £18,322 : 2s ; grand total of the two days sale, £19,060 : 4s.
We may mention that the lowest average of any lot of thorough-breds sold on this occasion was greatly above Lord Polwarth's average of 1852.
On this occasion a lot of five prize gimmers belonging to Mr. Purves, Burnfoot, were sold at 100 guineas—20 guineas each—to go to Ireland.
The Scotsman, in its report on this sale, makes the following remarks :—" Breeders who expose their stock at this sale have certainly a rare chance of a market, and the prices obtained were certainly in many cases very handsome. The advantage of such a market for sellers and buyers is mutual, for if the prices obtained by breeders are high, the quality transferred to the possession of buyers is of the highest class. The sale of Lord Polwarth's rams is generally regarded with great interest, and when their turn came to-day, the ring was surrounded by an eager and interested assemblage. The biddings for the different rams, notwithstanding the figures to which many of them soon attained, were prompt, and the sale went on rapidly."]
† The local enumerator having made erroneous returns as to the housing accommodation of the parish, at the census of 1861, we have passed that piece of information, merely stating that its housing accommodation is up to the average of other agricultural parishes.

Kirk Treasurer, and Registrar of Births, Marriages, and Deaths—William Brunton.

Medical Officer and Public Vaccinator—Dr. W. Brown, Melrose.

POST OFFICE—Post Town, Newtown St. Boswell's. Postmistress at Clintmains—Mrs. Scott ; William Younger, Runner, arrives daily at 10.30 a.m., and departs at 2.30 p.m. Post town for Gladswood and the locality, Melrose ; Letters received and despatched twice a day by the Earlston messenger (*see* p. 133).

CLERGY, &c.—Presbytery of Lauder, and Synod of Merse and Teviotdale. Patron—Lord Polwarth.

Established Church—*Rev. Alexander M'Laren (Inducted 1864). Sittings, 380. Average attendance at Sabbath School,   .

FAST DAYS—Unfixed.

SCHOOL†—Parochial (Mertoun)—W. Brunton, master. Av. at., 72.

PAROCHIAL BOARD—Rev. Alexander M'Laren, Chairman. No. of Poor on Roll, 15.‡ Rate of Assessment, 4d. per £ ; total Assessment 1864-5, £156 : 13 : 2½.

SURGEON—Robert Purves, Dryburgh Mains.

CORN MILL—Mertoun—*James Hogarth, miller.

WHITERIG BRICK AND TILE WORKS—Lord Polwarth, proprietor ; Leonard Thomson, manager.

CARRIERS—Properly speaking, none. Goods are brought to the parish from the nearest stations—St. Boswell's and Maxton—by any cart that may pass.

RESIDENTS, FARMERS, &c., IN THE PARISH.

*Ainslie, John, farmer, Bemersyde West Mains
*Bell, John,   do.   Mertoun-Newstead
 Brown, John,   do.   Hallidon Mill
*Bruce, Robert,   do.   Whitehouse
*Crichton, William, Dryburgh Cottage
*Davidson, Robert, farmer, Bemersyde East-end
 Deans, George, land steward, Mertoun
*Dickenson, John, farmer, Maidenhall
*Marshall, Adam,   do.   Fens
 M'Gregor, Peter, land-steward, Gladswood
*Purdie, William, farmer, Butchercote
*Purves, Robert,   do.   Dryburgh Mains
 Rae, Robert,   do.   Whiterighill
*Robertson, Geo. D., do.   Dryburgh
 Robison, George,   do.   Brotherston

 Sanderson, T. D., farmer, Magdalen Hall
*Storey, Thomas,   do.   Dalcove Mains
*Turnbull, Thomas, do.   Spadeslee
 Walker, James, lessee of Dryburgh orchard †
*Whitehead, James, farmer, Third
*Whitehead, Wm.,   do.   do.
*Wood, James,   do.   Millfield

SEATS, &c., OF COUNTY FAMILIES IN THE PARISH.

BEMERSYDE.

Immediately above Dryburgh, commanding a fine view—the seat of the family of Haig, one of the oldest in the south of Scotland. Proprietress—Miss Haig (abroad);‡ present occupant—Lord Jerviswoode (appointed an Ordinary Lord of Session 1859, and a Lord Commissioner of Justiciary 1862), second son of the late George Baillie, Esq., of Jerviswoode and Mellerstain, and brother of the present Earl of Haddington ; born 3d November 1804 ; married 27th December 1831, Anne, 3d daughter of Hugh Lord Polwarth, and sister of the present Baron, and has issue.

Edinburgh address—10 Strathearn Road.

DRYBURGH ABBEY.

Near the abbey, beautifully situated on a height on the banks of the Tweed—the property of the Hon. Mrs. Biber Erskine ; ‖ presently occupied by Mrs. Baillie, of Jerviswoode, youngest daughter of the late Sir James Pringle, Bart. of Stichill, and widow of George Baillie, Esq. of Mellerstain and Jerviswoode), and her sons the Hon. Robert Baillie (late major in the army), born 25th June 1807, and the Hon. Thomas Baillie, Rear-Admiral of the Blue (1863), born 1811, and her youngest daughter the Hon. Lady Grizzel Baillie.

---

† Children in the parish from 5 to 15, attending school during the first week of April 1861, 126 ; of all ages, 130.

‡ A peculiarity of Mertoun parish is, that of its 15 poor on the roll 14 are women.

---

† Planted by David Stuart, 11th Earl of Buchan, and celebrated for its fruit.

‡ Messrs. Curle & Erskine, Melrose, take the general charge of the estate.

‖ John Berry, elder and only surviving daughter of the late Henry Lord Cardross (eldest son of Henry David, 12th Earl of Buchan), born 1833 ; married, 1856, the Rev. George Eden Biber, (only son of the Rev. Dr. Biber, Incumbent of Roehampton, Surrey), who assumed the name of Erskine of Dryburgh on the succession of Mrs. Erskine, and has issue—

    George Oswald Harry Erskine, born 1857.
    Henry Erskine, born 1858.
    Veronica Mary Stuart, born 1860.

Mrs. Erskine, who is Lady of the Barony of Dryburgh, is descended from a common ancestor with the Earl of Mar (*see* Wedderlie House, Westruther parish).

DRYBURGH HOUSE.

Also near the abbey—the property of Captain William Hutton Riddell (16th Lancers—*see* p. 353) ; presently occupied by Mrs. Monro Binning.

GLADSWOOD.

Situated in a beautiful vale, in close proximity to the Tweed—the seat of *John Meiklam, Esq, born 1809 ; married 1833 ; and has issue one daughter—Julia Adeliza.

Mr. Meiklam purchased the property in 1858 from the trustees of the late Lieut.-Col. Spottiswoode, of Gladswood.

MERTOUN HOUSE.

In a fine peninsula, formed by one of the picturesque windings of the river—the seat of Lord Polwarth, (Henry Francis Hepburne-Scott), eldest son of Hugh, 4th Lord, born 1800 ; succeeded 1842 ; married, 1835, Lady Georgiana, daughter of George Baillie, Esq., of Jerviswoode and Mellerstain, and sister of George 10th and present Earl of Haddington (she died 1859) and has issue—

Walter Hugh, *Master of Polwarth*, born 1838, married February 1863, his cousin Mary, eldest daughter of the Earl of Aberdeen, and has issue a son—Walter George. Residence—Humbie House, Haddingtonshire.

Henry Robert, born 6th January 1847.

Helen Georgiana, Katharine, and Harriet-Frances.

His Lordship is 12th Baron of Harden, a Representative Peer for Scotland, a Deputy-Lieutenant for the counties of Roxburgh, Berwick, and Haddington, and Lord-Lieutenant and Sheriff Principal of the county of Selkirk; late a Lord-in-Waiting on Her Majesty.

His Lordship assumes the additional name of Hepburne in consequence of the estates of the Hepburnes of Humbie having descended to the family through Helen Hepburne wife of Earl Tarras, the 8th Baron of Harden (*see* p. 358). The celebrated Wat Scott of Harden, who married the "Flower of Yarrow," was the 4th Baron ; he died in 1629.

London address— Carlton Club, S.W. ; 1 Regent Street, S.W.

REGISTERED VOTERS (Non-Resident).

Cockburn, Archibald, London (lessee of part of Bemersyde Water)
Erskine, Rev. Geo. E. B., Roehampton, London, S.W.
Riddell, Capt. George William Hutton
Thomson, William, farmer, Over Roxburgh

NENTHORN.

AN irregularly shaped parish, extending into Roxburghshire, which nearly cuts it in two, near the centre, into a shape somewhat resembling the figure 8. It is bounded on the north by Stichill and Hume, on the west by Earlston, on the east by Stichill and Ednam, and on the south by Kelso and Smailholm. Its greatest length is about 4½ miles, and breadth nearly 2 miles. Its area, according to the Ordnance Survey, is 3478½ acres, of which 58¾ are occupied by public and private roads, and 24¾ are under water. The soil of the northern part rests chiefly on a wet reddish clay ; the southern part being more in the valley of the Tweed, is richer, being for the most part a mixture of clay and gravelly loam. The climate is salubrious. The river Eden, here preserved, which divides and bounds the parish, abounds in trout, but salmon are stopped by Stichill Linn, at the eastern extremity of the parish (*see* Stichill parish p. 182). At the eastern extremity of the parish is situated NEWTON DON, the seat of Charles Balfour, Esq.,* a fine mansion with richly embellished grounds, and commanding a prospect embracing the entire vale of the Tweed to the Cheviots on the south, and to the east as far as the eye can reach. Visitors to the grounds of Newton-Don are admitted at all times. The flower garden behind the house is laid out with great taste, and the Eden, after its precipitation over the Linn, winds romantically betwixt forest-clad banks around and through the demesne. There is no village in the parish, a small hamlet bearing the same name, and where are the church and school house, is situated near the centre of the parish. Nearest market town, Kelso—distance from the church hamlet, 4 miles. Kelso is the nearest railway station for the hamlet, and Gordon for the northern districts of the parish.

Population of the parish in 1861, 461; which comprised 82 families, 27 of whom were returned as living in houses of one window, and 36 in houses of two windows.

Assessed property in 1864-5, £5641 : 3 : 10.

The principal landed-proprietors in the parish are—Frederick L. Roy, Esq. of Nenthorn, and Charles Balfour, Esq. of Newton-Don—both resident ; the Duke of Roxburghe (part of Courthill),and the Earl of Haddington (The Sneep) are also small proprietors.

---

* *See* foot-note, p. 612.

Those marked thus (*) are Registered Voters.

RESIDENT JUSTICES OF THE PEACE—Frederick L. Roy, Esq. of Nenthorn ; Charles Balfour, Esq. of Newton-Don.

DISTRICT POLICE OFFICE—Kelso.

PUBLIC OFFICES—Kirk Treasurer, Session Clerk, Inspector of Poor, and Registrar of Births, Marriages and Deaths—Alexander Virtue.

Medical Officer and Public Vaccinator—

POST OFFICE —Post town, Kelso—William Allan, messenger, passes the hamlet daily to and from Gordon ; arrives about noon at Nenthorn, and returns about 7 a.m. Letters for Newton-Don go by the Stichill messenger (see p. 184).

CLERGY, &c.—Nenthorn is in the Presbytery of Kelso, and Synod of Merse and Teviotdale. Patron—The Crown.

Established Church—*Rev. M. Hamilton Graham † (Inducted 1855). Sittings, 200.

Free Church—*Rev. Robert Lang (Inducted 1843). Sittings, 300.

SCHOOL ‡—Parochial—*Alexander Virtue, master. Average attendance, .

PAROCHIAL BOARD—Charles Balfour, Esq., Chairman. Number of Poor on Roll, 6. Assessment, d. per £ ; total Assessment in 1864-5, £76 : 19 : 2½. Poor House—Kelso Union.

CONVEYANCE—Gordon Carriers and Post Runner (see Kelso p. 77).

RESIDENTS, FARMERS, &c., IN THE PARISH.

*Black, John, farmer, Burnbrae
*Craig, John,　　do.　 Whitehill
*Hardie, Robert, do.　 Harrietfield
*Johnston, Ptk. do.　 Girrick
*Simson, George, do.　 Courthill
　Thom, William, head-gardener, Newton-Don
*Young, Thomas, farmer, Blinkbonny

SEATS, &c., OF COUNTY FAMILIES, IN THE PARISH.

NENTHORN HOUSE.

Situated on the Eden, near to the hamlet of Nenthorn—the seat and residence of *Frederick Lewis Roy, Esq., second son

-----

† Since the pages of Maxton parish (218-220) were printed off, the Rev. John Thomson is dead, and Mr Graham has been appointed to the living. A successor to Mr. Graham has not yet (July 1865) been appointed.
‡ Children in the parish from 5 to 15 attending school during the first week of April 1861, 88 ; of all ages 91.

-----

of the late William Roy, Esq. (who died 1825), born 1799, succeeded his brother James 1836 ; married 1827, his cousin Margaret Louisa, second daughter of the late Charles Maitland Makgill, Esq. of Rankeilour (who died 1848), and has issue—

*Frederick Lewis, yr. of Nenthorn, born 1836.
James, born 1837.
David Maitland Makgill Crichton, born 1843.
Mary Charlotte Maitland.
Emma Maitland.

Mr. Roy married second, 1853, Mary Catherine, daughter of the late Alexander Boswell, Esq., sheriff-substitute for Berwickshire (1836, etc.)

NEWTON-DON.*

The principal residence of Lady Eleanor Balfour, 3d daughter

-----

* Newton Don was formerly the seat of the Dons, baronets of Newton, now represented by Sir John Don Wauchope of Edmonstone (Mid-Lothian), who is lineally descended from Patrick 3d and youngest son of Alexander of Newton, 1st baronet (created 1667), who married, 1683, Anne Wauchope, eldest daughter of Sir John Wauchope of Edmonstone. The Wauchope male line becoming extinct, the estates devolved eventually on James the second son of this Patrick and Anne, who thereupon assumed the name of Wauchope. The present baronet, great-great-grandson of Patrick, succeeded as heir-male to the title on the death, at Hobart Town, Tasmania, 19th March 1862, of William Henry, 7th baronet, and comedian, who had been twice married, and left two daughters.—The extensive and valuable estates of the Dons, extending almost in a continuous line from the lower extremity of Ednam parish (Highridgehall) to beyond Rutherford* in Maxton parish, had all, previous to the succession of the last baronet, been sold piecemeal, except the family seat, grounds, and surrounding farms, which were purchased by Mr. Balfour in 1847 (see foot-note, p. 219).
On Sunday, June 7, 1795, two of the Misses Don, Elizabeth and Mary, (daughters of Sir Alexander Don, grandfather of the last baronet, and his wife Lady Harriet Cunningham, sister of Burns' Earl of Glencairn) ; and Miss Agnes Wilson (daughter of the late Dr. Wilson of Abbey Gardens, Kelso), were accidentally drowned in the Eden, near to the house. The incident is thus meagrely described in the British Chronicle (Kelso paper) of the Friday following :—
"On Sunday afternoon a most melancholy accident happened at Newton-Don, the particulars of which are very imperfectly known, and are likely to remain so, but the most authentic we have been able to obtain are as follows : The two Misses Don, accompanied by Miss Agnes Wilson, second daughter of Dr. Wilson, physician in this town, and a Miss Ramsay, from Edinburgh, went for a walk, by the bridge, to the island in the Eden. On their return home, they resolved to cross the water at the nearest, although considerably swelled by the

-----

* One of the Dons was Sir Alexander of Rutherford, contemporary with his brother James 2nd baronet of Newton. Sir Alexander died sans posterité, and the two estates were joined.

of James 8th Earl of Lauderdale; married 1815 James Balfour, Esq. of Whittinghame (who died 1845), and had issue—

James Maitland, of Whittinghame; married, 5th January 1840, Lady Blanche Gascoigne Cecil, second daughter of James 2nd Marquis of Salisbury; died February 1856, leaving, with other issue—Arthur-James (minor), now of Whittinghame (*see* Oldhamstocks).

*Charles Balfour, Esq. of Balgonie (in Fifeshire) and Newton-Don (residing at Newton-Don); born 1823; married 1st, 1860, the Hon. Adelaide Barrington, youngest daughter of William 6th Viscount Barrington (who died 1862), and has issue one son; married 2nd, 13th July 1865, Minnie Liddell, eldest daughter of Colonel the Hon. Augustus Liddell.

Mary, married to the Hon. Henry Arthur Herbert Esq. of Muckross, county Kerry, and has issue.

Anna, married to Lord Augustus Charles Lennox Fitzroy, 2nd son of Henry 5th Duke of Grafton, and died December 1857, leaving issue.

REGISTERED VOTER (Non-Resident).

Tait, James, farmer, Smailholm Mains

---

rains, rather than go round by the bridge. Miss Don got safely through, but Miss Ramsay, in following her, was carried down by the current, when Miss Don rushed in to her assistance, and unfortunately perished. This, it is said, is all that Miss Ramsay recollects, and she cannot even tell how she herself was saved. Miss Mary Don and Miss Agnes Wilson, there is no doubt, ran in to their assistance, and both shared the unfortunate fate of Miss Don. The distracted state of Miss Ramsay on getting out of the water, and missing her companions, prevented any discovery of the fatal accident till a woman, going to cross the Eden by the bridge, saw the body of Miss Mary Don floating down the rivulet, who immediately gave the alarm, but, alas! too late to save their lives, as every means used for their recovery proved ineffectual. The untimely fate of these three ladies, thus suddenly cut off in their bloom of youth, in the generous attempt to save their companions from perishing, has thrown an air of melancholy over almost every countenance in town and country—What then must their parents and relatives feel! the distress of the former is beyond the power of language to express, and such as even but few hearts are able to conceive."

After a lapse of 70 years this melancholy and almost mysterious accident has still its impression in the locality.

POLWARTH.

A SMALL agricultural parish in the centre of the county, forming part of the boundary between the upland district of the Lammermoors and the lower district of the Merse. The form of the parish is triangular, and is bounded on the north by Langton, on the south-east by Fogo, on the south-west by Greenlaw, and on the north-west by Longformacus. Its greatest length east and west is 4 miles, and its greatest breadth north and south, near its western extremity, is over 2 miles; it contains, according to the Ordnance Survey, 3013 acres; of which nearly 34 are occupied by roads, and 12¼ are under water. About one-third of the parish is of a hilly nature, and is covered with heath. Kyles hill, the highest point in the parish, is 1100 feet above the level of the sea. The southern part is undulating, and the soil is more fertile than in the northern part. The only streams are some of the small tributaries of the Blackadder. The climate is generally very healthy. Near the northern boundary is the ancient village of Polwarth; the only one in the parish. It has been built without any idea of regularity, being mostly clumps or rows of two or three houses, and is situated on very wet and swampy ground,* now considerably improved by draining. The parish church stands on a beautiful knoll, on the lands of Marchmont, nearly a mile south-east of the village. From an inscription on the wall it seems to have been originally built prior to the year 900, and repaired in 1378.† It was rebuilt on the old founda-

---

* Two old thorn trees formerly stood in the centre of the village green, and the bridal party at every marriage in the village, for upwards of three centuries, till about the beginning of the present century, danced round them. Hence the well known Border song, " Polwarth on the green."

† It was in the vaults of the old building that Sir Patrick Hume, the eminent protestant, lay concealed for six weeks, stealthily attended by his daughter Lady Grizzel (afterwards Baillie—*see* p. 516), whence he removed to Redbraes Castle (the former seat of the family, on the site of which the present mansion of Marchmont was built by Hugh, the late Earl), where, having a place of concealment beneath the floor in one of the rooms, he remained, till at length he was enabled to escape to Holland. After the Revolution, in which he had been very instrumental, he returned to Scotland, and was advanced to the dignities of Lord Polwarth and Earl of Marchmont; he was also constituted Sheriff-Principal of Berwickshire, one of the Extraordinary Lords of Session, and Lord High Chancellor of Scotland, &c., &c. Diana, the great-grand-daughter of Sir Patrick Hume, in 1754, married Walter Scott, 10th baron of Harden (she was the respected *Lady Di* of Woodside, Kelso), and it was through her that the late Hugh, Lord Polwarth, her son, succeeded to the title of Polwarth. The earldom of Marchmont

tions in 1703. The only mansion-house in the parish is MARCH-MONT,+ situated in a large, well-wooded, and tastefully disposed park, in the southern district of the parish, and about 2½ miles north-east from Greenlaw. In front of the house is an avenue over a mile long, 100 yards broad, and grandly lined with lofty trees. The Marchmont station on the Berwickshire branch of the North British Railway is near to the house, and, in a southerly direction, over a mile-and-a-half from the village, the line skirts the parish, and for over a mile bounds the Marchmont policy. The nearest market town is Dunse, about 4 miles north-east from the village. Greenlaw lies about the same distance south-west.

Population in 1861, 251; who comprised 51 separate families, 16 of whom were returned as living in houses of one window, 21 in house of two windows, and the remainder (14) in houses of three or more windows.

Assessed property in 1864-5, £2624 : 2s.

Sir Hugh H. Campbell, Bart., is proprietor of the entire parish, and is the only resident gentleman.

Those marked thus (*) are Registered Voters in the parish.

DISTRICT POLICE OFFICE—

PUBLIC OFFICES—Heritors' Clerk, Session Clerk, Kirk Treasurer, Inspector of Poor, and Registrar of Births, Marriages, and Deaths—Robert Smyth.

Medical Officer and Public Vaccinator—Dr. Tait, Dunse.

POST OFFICE—None in the parish. A Runner (James Sutherland) passes daily for Dunse at 7 a.m. on his way from Greenlaw, returning at 1 p.m.

CLERGY, &c.—Presbytery of Dunse, and Synod of Merse and Teviotdale. Patron—Sir H. H. Campbell.

Established Church—*Rev. Walter Home (Inducted 1823). Sittings, .

FAST DAYS—Thursday before the first Sabbath of August, and an unfixed day in February.

PAROCHIAL BOARD—Sir H. H. Campbell, Chairman. Average Rate of Assessment per £, 5d. ; total Assessment 1864-5, £106 : 16 :;10½. Average No. of Poor on Roll, 10.

SCHOOL‡ (Parochial)—*Robert Smyth, master. Aver. attend., 25.

Do. (supported by Lady Hume Campbell)—master. Av. attend., 25.

CONVEYANCE—By Rail to all parts.

CARRIERS—John Dick, Kelso, Greenlaw, and Dunse, passes once a fortnight on

CORN MILL—Polwarth—*Jasper Atchison.

QUARRY—Kyles Hill—Porphyry.

becoming dormant in 1793, on the death of Hugh, 3d Earl, the father of Lady Diana.

† Its style is semi-Paladian. The architect was the celebrated Robert Adam, F.R.S., etc.

‡ Children in the parish from 5 to 15 attending school during the first week of April 1861, 43 ; of all ages, 44.

TRADES, &c.

Brown, George, joiner,
Calder, George, baker
Halliday, Margaret, grocer
Johnston, John, smith
Virtue, Robert, mason
Watson, Isabella, grocer
Weatherston, William, tailor

RESIDENTS, FARMERS, &c.

*Aitchison, Andrew. farmer, Polwarth		
*Aitchison, John,	do.	do.
*Clinkscale, John,	do.	do.
*Cunningham, Wm.,	do.	Mount Robert
*Denholm, Robert,	do.	Polwarth
*Dodds, John,	do.	Cothill
*Runciman, Robert,	do.	Polwarth Rhodes

SEAT, &c., OF COUNTY FAMILY IN THE PARISH.

MARCHMONT.

The seat and residence of Sir Hugh Hume Campbell, Bart. ;† born 15th December 1812 ; succeeded his father 9th April 1823 ; married (first), Margaret, younger daughter of John Spottiswoode of Spottiswoode (see Westruther parish), and by her (who died 16th October 1839) had issue—

Helen married, 13th July 1854, to George Warrender, Esq. (eldest son of Sir John Warrender of Lochend, and late a Captain in the Coldstream Guards), and has issue—John, born 5th March 1859 ; George, born 18th August 1860 ; and three daughters—Juliana-Margaret Maitland, Alice-Helen, and Helen-Charlotte.

Sir Hugh married (second) 9th Oct. 1841, Juliana-Rebecca, only daughter of Lieut.-Gen. Sir Joseph Fuller, G.C.H.

London Address—10 Hill Street, Berkeley Square.

The heir-pres. to the title and entailed estates is Sir Hugh's cousin, Col. John Home Purves of Purves Hall, Eccles parish (which see).

† The father of the present baronet—Sir William Purves—assumed the surname of Hume Campbell, according to the will of Hugh, last Earl of Marchmont (his grand-uncle), on succeeding to the Marchmont estates.

CHIRNSIDE.

---·---

THIS parish is situated on the east side of the Merse. It is bounded by Coldingham on the north, Foulden and Ayton on the east, Edrom on the south, and Bunkle on the west. It is 3½ miles long, by about 3 miles broad ; its area, according to the Ordnance Survey, is 5594 acres, of which 73 are in roads (public and private), 15 are occupied by the railway, and 16½ are under water. The appearance of the parish is a rich plain, the only eminence being Chirnside Hill, from which one of the richest and most extensive views in the south of Scotland is obtained on all sides. This hill, which is one of the detached eminences belonging to the Lammermoor range, has rather a remarkable appearance. "It is distinguished by its elevation above the surrounding plain, and semi-circular aspect to the south, joined with the great expansion of its summit, and its gradual declination to the Whitadder." Its extreme height above the level of the sea is 466 feet, while that of the Whitadder at its base is about 100. The landscape from the hill is that of a plain, waved with long ridges, running chiefly in one direction, of more than 25 miles in extent—from the bay of Berwick to the Teviotdale Hills, on the west ; while directly south, and at almost the same distance, the hills and chains of Cheviot form a very striking boundary. The soil throughout the parish is rich, and for the most part is under a very high state of cultivation. The turnpike roads from Dunse to Ayton and from Dunse to Berwick intersect the parish ; they are both in good repair, as are also the various cross-roads with which Chirnside is well provided. The Whitadder, which, after being joined by the Blackadder at Chirnside Bridge, is here a considerable stream, and skirts the southern boundary the entire length of the parish, abounds in salmon and trout, and is much resorted to by anglers. "The temperature of the atmosphere is generally mild, the soil dry, and the climate healthy." In the southern part of the parish, situated on the road from Ayton to Dunse, is the small town or village of Chirnside, 9 miles from Berwick, 6 from Dunse, and 4 from Reston. It lies along the brow of the hill, on a fine healthy situation, and consists of two streets, the longer of which is about three-quarters of a mile in length. Since the opening of the railway the village has been much resorted to by summer visitors from Edinburgh. The parish also contains the small hamlet of ED-INGTON, which lies over 2 miles due east from the village, on the Berwick road. The Berwickshire branch of the North British line has a length of nearly 2 miles within and along the western boundary of the parish. Chirnside station, by the road, lies a little over a mile from the centre of the village, due west. Close to the village, and occupying a fine situation on the Whitadder, is NINEWELLS HOUSE, once the occasional residence of Hume the historian, whose father, and afterwards whose elder brother, possessed the estate, which is still held by their lineal descendant ; the present mansion, built in 1840-41, is in the Tudor style, and is embosomed in fine woods. The only other mansion in the parish is MAINES, built in 1834, situated on the side of Chirnside Hill, about 1 mile north-east from the centre of the village. The Rev. Henry Erskine, father of the founders of the Secession, was the first minister of the parish after the Revolution ; he died in 1696. Situated in the east side of Chirnside churchyard, is a monument to his memory, 25 feet high, erected by subscription in 1826.

Fair—Last Thursday of November—obsolete for all practical purposes.

The population of the village by the census of 1861, was 901 ; 405 of whom were males and 496 were females—the largest disproportion of the sexes of any town or village in the county, equal to 20 per cent.* (*see* Earlston, p. 506, and Melrose, p. 130). The population of the entire parish was 1502, who constituted 323 families, 140 of whom were returned as living in houses of one window, 72 in houses of two windows, and 111 (the full average) in houses of three or more windows.

Assessed property in 1864-5, £11,651 : 13 : 7.

The principal landed-proprietors in the parish are—Alex. Mitchell Innes, Esq. of Ayton Castle, who is the principal heritor ; William Hay, Esq. of Dunse Castle ; James Alexander Ross Hume (minor), of Ninewells ; Mrs. Hood (of Maines) 5 Salisbury Road, Edinburgh ; and Lady Frances Gordon, of Blackburn (5 Wilton Crescent, London—*see* Gordon parish, p. 537).

Those marked thus (*) are Registered Voters.

PUBLIC OFFICES—Heritors' Clerk, Session Clerk, Kirk Treasurer, and Registrar of Births, Marriages, and Deaths—Alexander Lightbody ; Assistant Registrar—Thomas Mack.
　　Inspector of Poor and Collector of Poor Rates—Thomas Mack.
　　Medical Officer and Public Vaccinator—Charles Stuart, M.D.
　　Excise Officer—George B. Allice.

---

* This great addition of females in the village is accounted for by the influx of mill-workers from Edinburgh and Glasgow, who are employed at Chirnside Bridge Paper Mill (*see* p. 574).

POST OFFICE—Margaret Darling, Chirnside, postmistress. Letters from North and South arrive at 10-45 a.m. and 9-18 p.m.; and are despatched at 8-30 a.m. and 5-21 p.m. Letters from Dunse arrive 9-30 a.m. and 5-21 p.m.; despatched 10 a.m. and 9-18 p.m. A town delivery takes place at 7-30 and 11 a.m.; Deliverer—Margaret Gibson; Country Deliverer—A. Turnbull. Messenger to Whitsome—Andrew Paterson; despatched at 11 a.m.

CLERGY, &c.—Chirnside is the seat of a Presbytery, in the Synod of Merse and Teviotdale. Patron—A. M. Innes, Esq. of Ayton Castle.

Established Church—*Rev. James Wilson (Inducted 1838). Sittings, 359. Average Sabbath School attendance, 60.

United Presbyterian Church—Rev. James Ker, A.M. (Inducted 1854). Sittings, 575. Average Sabbath School attendance, 65; at Minister's Bible Class, 65.

Reformed Presbyterian Church†—Rev. Robert Naismith (Inducted 1861). Sittings, 500. Aver. Sabbath School attend., 50; at Minister's Class, 25.

FAST DAYS—Last Thursdays in April and October.

SCHOOLS‡—Parochial (Chirnside)—*Alexander Lightbody, master. Average attendance, 80.

Ninewells School, established by the late Miss Hume—Thomas Muir, master. Aver. attend., 60.

Adventure School (Chirnside)—Henry Kerr, master. Av. at., 40.

Girls' School (Chirnside)—Miss Harriet, mistress. Av. at., 25.

PAROCHIAL BOARD—John Wilson, Esq., Edington Mains, chairman. No. of Poor on Roll, 55. Average Rate of Assessment, 6d. per £; total Assessment in 1864-5, £546:4:1.

LIBRARY—Parochial—Thomas Mack, librarian. No. of volumes, several hundreds. Annual Subscription, 2s.

HORTICULTURAL SOCIETY—President—Rev. James Wilson; Vice-President—John Wilson, Esq., Edington Mains; Secy. and Treas.—Mr. Thomas Muir.

CHIRNSIDE PLOUGHING SOCIETY—Confined to the farmers of the parish; held on alternate farms yearly, in February. Prizes, about £4, and the Highland Society's Medal. John Blackadder, Ninewells Mains, Secretary.

GAS COMPANY—Directors: George Wilson, chairman; Thomas Mack, Peter Scott, George Lugton, John Ormiston, Robert Rutherford, Thomas Muir, Thomas Doughty. Wm. Hunter, gasman. Rate, 13s. 4d. per 1000 feet. Amount of Stock, £400; no Dividend. John Edgley, Secretary and Treasurer.

---

† See p. 414—where we describe the Reformed Presbyterians (the *Covenanters*) as possessing only *one* congregation in the district, viz., Kelso; this other one at Chirnside shows we were in error. The Chirnside congregation is the oldest and has always been the strongest; but it, too, like the one at Kelso, has of late years greatly fallen off.

‡ Children in the parish from 5 to 15 attending school during the first week of April 1861, 252; of all ages, 269.

WATER COMPANY—Directors: Thomas Doughty, Chairman; George Wilson, Robert Rutherford, John Edgley, John Ormiston. Thos. Mack, Thomas Muir, George Lugton. Stock, £300; no Dividend.

MEDICAL PRACTITIONER—*Charles Stuart, M.D., Chirnside.

AUCTIONEER—Thomas Doughty, Chirnside.

AGRICULTURAL IMPLEMENT MANUFACTURER—Thos Brown, Edington.

MILLS—Chirnside Bridge Paper Mills (see 'Edrom parish, p. 574)—Young Trotter & Son.

Ninewells Waulk Mills—*William Martin.

Edington Saw Mills, on the property of William Hay, Esq., of Dunse Castle—J. Pringle, manager.

CORN AND FLOUR MILLS: Ninewells Mills—*William Gillies, miller; Edington Mills—*James Hay, miller.

QUARRIES: Edington Mill—William Hay, proprietor—unlet; Harelaw—A. Mitchell Innes, Esq., proprietor—unlet.

CONVEYANCE—By Railway to all parts. Station Master at Chirnside—Silvanus Tomlin.

CARRIER—William Common, to Berwick on Saturday.

TRADES, &c., IN THE VILLAGE.

*Allan, Adam, cattle-dealer
*Anderson, Henry, portioner
Bell, James, cabinetmaker
Blyth, David, brazier
Brown, Jane, grocer
Brough, R. B., innkeeper
Buglass, James, bootmaker
*Crichton, James, slater
Clark, Margaret, grocer
Cockburn, James, cooper
Cochrane, John
Common, William, grocer and carrier
Cowe, Isabella, nursery
Craig, Samuel, shoemaker
Darling, Margaret, draper, *postmistress*, etc.
Davidson, Alexander, flesher
*Denham, David, millwright
Dewar, Thomas, baker
Dippie, Anthony, blacksmith
*Doughty, Thomas, farmer, builder, and auctioneer
*Edgley, Alexander, joiner and grocer
*Edgley, Benjamin, joiner
*Edgley, John, grocer and ironmonger
Ferguson, John, tailor and draper
*Ferguson, John Swinton, tailor

*Fortune, George, baker
*Gibson, James, saddler
*Gray, William, flesher
*Hay, Peter, farmer
Heugh, John, shoemaker
*Hogg, David, tailor
*Hood, Robert, do.
Hume, John, & Co., bakers
Jeffrey, John, carpenter and joiner
*Johnston, George, slater
Knox, William, grocer
*Lugton, George, blacksmith
*Mack, Thomas, *inspector of poor*
Martin, John, Chirnside Nursery
Ormiston, John, shoemaker
Peacock, George, innkeeper
Renton, Thomas, brewer
Rutherford, Agnes, grocer
*Rutherford, Robert do.
*Reid, Robert, weaver
Scott, Elizabeth, grocer
Shiell, J. & D., drapers
Steel, William, grocer and draper
Steel, Andrew, millwright
Steel, George, millwright
Steel, Peter, millwright
Stevenson, William, baker
Turnbull, Adam, tailor
Waite, James, blacksmith
Weatherston, W., millwright
Wilson, George, grocer, draper, and spirit dealer
Wood, George, baker

RESIDENTS, FARMERS, &c., IN THE PARISH.

*Blackadder, John, farmer, Ninewells Mains
*Elliot, Robert,   do.,   Mains
Cowe, Robert,   do.,   Oldcastles
Doughty, Thomas,   do.,   Broadhaugh
*Flint, John,   do.,   Nethermains
Hay, Peter,   do.,   Ninewells Crofts
*Heatlie, Thomas,   do.,   Chirnside Mill
Scott, Mrs., Blackburn farm
*Scott, Peter, farmer, Chirnside Crofts
White, Alexander, farmer, Causewaybank
*Wilson, John,   do.,   Edington Mains
*Wilson, George,   do.,   Harelaw

SEATS OF COUNTY FAMILIES, &c., IN THE PARISH.

MAINES.

The property of Mrs. Hood of Maines; at present the residence of *James Grant Suttie, Esq., eldest son of Sir James Grant Suttie, Bart. of Balgone and Prestongrange; born 25th May 1830; married 6th August 1857, Lady Susan Harriet Innes Ker, elder daughter of James 6th Duke of Roxburghe (*see* p. 114), and has issue two daughters—Susan-Harriet and Harriet.

NINEWELLS.

The property of James Alexander Ross Hume (minor); born 1849; son of the eldest son of Adolphus M'Dowall Ross, M.D., by Catherine, youngest daughter of the late Baron Hume; presently residing with his mother on the Continent (*see* p. 281).

Ninewells House is temporarily occupied by Sir John and Lady Elizabeth Pringle, of Langton—*see* p. 570.

REGISTERED VOTERS (Non-Resident).

Craig, William, Portsmouth
Fife, Robert, farmer, Smailholm Mains
Hay, William, joiner, Edinburgh
Henry, John, Blackadder Mount
Martin, William, manufacturer, Greenlaw
Stark, Rev. James, Ayton

BUNKLE.*

——◆——

THIS parish, like many others in the south of Scotland, comprises what was formerly two distinct parishes—the parish of Preston having been united to that of Bunkle about the year 1720. The boundaries of Bunkle as now constituted are—on the north by part of Longformacus, Abbey St. Bathans, and Coldingham ; on the east by Coldingham and Chirnside ; on the south by Edrom and Dunse ; and on the west by Dunse. The outline of the parish is very irregular, but taken as a whole, resembles a triangle ; its greatest length from east to west is over 5 miles, and its greatest breadth north and south is over 4 miles. The area of the parish, according to the Ordnance Survey, is nearly 9256½ acres, of which 100¾ are in roads, 67⅛ are under water, and over 3¼ are occupied by the railway—the Dunse branch of the North British line crossing the extreme east corner of the parish. The lower part of the parish is nearly level, gradually sloping to the south-east. The northern part is hilly, a ridge of the Lammermoors, under the name of Bunkle Edge, traversing it. One of these hills, the most elevated spot in the parish, rises to the height of 879 feet above the sea. Copper has been wrought in the parish, but with only partial success ; it is the only instance of a mine in the district. The soil on the high lands was at one time poor, but has been much improved by lime and marl ; the rest of the parish is fertile and well cultivated. Dr. John Brown, the celebrated medical theorist, was born in the parish in 1735, and Dr. James Hutton in 1754 here introduced on his farm of Sligh-houses, the improved mode of husbandry.† " The atmosphere is generaly clear and salubrious, though sometimes, especially in spring and autumn, subject to a thick haze or mist." The church and manse are situated near the centre of the parish, about 5 miles north-east from Dunse (which is the nearest market town) by the road, and about the same distance north-west from Chirnside—the railway station of the latter being the nearest.‡ The school-house is at Lintlaw—1½ miles

* Ecclesiastically known as Bunkle (or Buncle) and Preston.
† He was the first to introduce the system of drill husbandry into the district, having seen it practised in Norfolk, from whence he introduced the improved plough. He was the first in the district to grow Swedish turnips.
‡ For the safety and convenience of the district, a handsome new stone bridge of three arches, having 120 feet water way, was built this summer (1865), at Blanerne ford, by the Rev. Francis Gordon Sandys-

nearer to Chirnside and about 1 mile nearer to Dunse. There is no village, inn, or toll-house in the parish of any kind. The Whitadder, which skirts the parish over the south and west, abounds with trout, and is much resorted to by anglers.

Population of the parish in 1861, 756 ; who composed 136 families, of whom 39 were returned as inhabiting houses of one window, 14 in houses of two windows, leaving the large proportion of 83 who inhabited houses of three or more windows.

Assessed property in 1864-5, £10,503 : 11 : 1.

The principal landed-proprietors in the parish are—Earl and Countess Home of Hirsel, who possess more than one-half of the parish ; Mrs. David Milne Home, of Billie—which lies at the eastern boundary of the parish, and on which are the remains of Billie Castle ; the Rev. Francis G. Sandys-Lumsdaine, of Blanerne ; Thomas Allan, Esq. of Sligh-houses ; J. R. Dunlop, Esq. of Mayfield (Berwick) ; Major W. H Smith of Cruiksfield ; Captain A. Monro of Prestonhaugh ; and John Elliot, Esq. of Easter Cruiksfield.

———————

Those marked thus (*) are Registered Voters.

DISTRICT POLICE OFFICE—Chirnside.

POST OFFICE—Post Town Dunse—Letters are received and despatched by runners from Dunse and from Edrom. Arriving at the Church about 1 p.m. and leaving about the same time.

PUBLIC OFFICES—Session Clerk, Heritors' Clerk, Registrar of Births, Marriages, and Deaths, and Inspector of Poor—Robt. Johnston.
     Kirk Treasurer—Rev. J. Dunlop.
     Medical Officer and Public Vaccinator—Dr. Tait, Dunse.

CLERGY, &c.—Bunkle is in the Presbytery of Dunse, and Synod of Merse and Teviotdale. Patron—Lord Home of Hirsel.
     Established Church—*Rev. John Dunlop (Inducted 1843). Sittings, 400.

FAST DAYS—Thursdays before first Sabbath of May and third Sabbath of November.

SCHOOL†—Parochial—*Robert Johnston, master. Aver attend., 50.

PAROCHIAL BOARD—Andrew Scott, Esq., Glendouglas, factor for the Earl of Home, Chairman. No. of Poor on Roll, 11. Average Rate of Assessment, about 1½d. per £ ; total Assessment in 1864-5, £116 : 6 : 9.

CONVEYANCE—Dunse, Edrom, Chirnside, Grant's House, and Reston railway stations, are all of convenient access from this parish.

———————

Lumsdaine ; he also did the cuttings of the roadway and embankments on the south side.

TRADES, &c.

Dippie, William, blacksmith, Preston
Henry, W., blacksmith, Hammerhall
Johnston, Thomas, tailor
Lawrie, John, gardener
Mack, Thomas, joiner, Preston
Mackay, Robert, gardener, Crossgatehall
Turnbull, R., shoemaker, Hammerhall

RESIDENTS, FARMERS, &c., IN THE PARISH.

*Aitchison, James, farmer, Hoardweel
*Allan, Thos. (sen., of Sligh-houses), farmer, Blackhouses
Allan, John (yr. of   do.   ) do., Billie Mains
Blackadder, John, farmer, East Blanerne
*Bowhill, Thomas,   do.,   Marygold
*Calder, Adam,   do.,   West Blanerne
*Dunlop, William,   do.,   Mayfield
*Elliot, John,   do.,   Primrosehill
Logan, Abraham,   do.,   Lintlaw (occasional—see Hassington, Eccles)
Wilson, Miss, Preston

SEATS OF COUNTY FAMILIES, &c., IN THE PARISH.

BLANERNE HOUSE.

Finely situated on the north bank of the Whitadder, and surrounded by extensive woods, in which are some very aged trees—the property of the Rev. Francis Gordon Sandys-Lumsdaine;† at present occupied by *George Mitchell Innes, Esq., 4th son of the late Wm. Mitchell Innes, Esq. of Ayton Castle.

---

† The Rev. Francis Gordon Sandys-Lumsdaine of Lumsdaine, (in Coldingham parish) and Blanerne, and of Innergellie in Fife, sole surviving son of the Rev. Edwin Sandys-Lumsdaine, Rector of Upper Hardres, Canterbury, and Mary Lillias, daughter of William Lumsdaine, Esq. (who on her brother's death in 1830 succeeded to the family estates) ; born 1828 ; married, 1857, Martha-Alice, daughter of the late John Cattley, Esq. of Shabden Park, Surrey, and has issue.
The Rev. F. G. Sandys-Lumsdaine succeeded to Lumsdaine, Blanerne, and Innergellie on the death of his mother in December last (1864). Blanerne is the principal residence of the family, and has been in their possession for many centuries.
Present address—Innergellie, Fifeshire.

CRUIKSFIELD HOUSE.

Situated on the southern boundary of the parish—the property and residence of *Major William Hope Smith of Cruiksfield.
This property belonged originally to the Abbey of St. Bathans, as its name indicates—Cruxfield,† corrupted into the present mode of spelling. There was here, a few years ago, a large thorn tree, round which, as a penance, the nuns were condemned to walk barefoot a distance of ten miles The thorn, from old age, was decayed down to the roots, and was dug up by the present proprietor in 1847. There is also a spring of very pure water, which for the last twenty-five years has only failed once—in 1842. Temp., 46° winter and summer.
Major Smith is a J.P. for the county ; is a Major in the Indian Army, and formerly served in the 15th Regiment, Madras Presidency.

EASTER CRUIKSFIELD.

The property and residence of John Elliot, Esq.

SLIGH-HOUSES (see introductory notice).

Situated near the centre of the parish—the property and residence of Thomas Allan, Esq., J.P.

REGISTERED VOTERS (Non-Resident).

Dunlop, John Renton, Esq. (of Mayfield), Berwick
Sandys-Lumsdaine, Rev. Francis G., Innergellie, Fife

---

† Crux, a cross—hence Cruxfield, or church land, the *supposed* derivation of the name.

FOULDEN.

—◆—

A SMALL agricultural parish in the eastern part of the Merse, bounded on the north by Ayton, on the east by Mordington, on the south by Hutton, and on the west by Chirnside. In form it is nearly a square, and measures about 2¼ miles each way. It contains, according to the Ordnance Survey, an area of 3298⅜ acres, of which nearly 36 are in roads, and 20 are under water. The appearance of the parish is that of an inclined plane, rising gently northwards from the banks of the Whitadder. Near its northern boundary are one or two hills having an elevation of from 500 to 600 feet. The soil is in the south a strong clay, near the middle of the parish it is of a sandy loam, and in the north it is light and moorish, which however is under cultivation. The climate is mild, being protected from north winds by the chain of hills in the northern part of the parish.* "Along the southern boundary runs the Whitadder water, being remarkably acclivitous banks, which rise from 120 to 150 feet above the level of the stream, and which on the Foulden side are repeatedly cloven by deep and wild ravines, bringing down rills and drainings from the central or northern districts. Near the upper end of two of these ravines or 'deans,' which deepen as they approach the Whitadder, stands the parish church of Foulden."† The village of Foulden which is close by, was formerly of considerable size, and was a burgh of barony, but it has now gone to decay, there being only about 70 inhabitants in it. Two fairs which used to be held here have long been defunct. Very handsome and attractive school-house accommodation has lately been erected here by Mr. Wilkie and the other heritors ; while the

village itself is the prettiest in the county, and the views from it are extensive and interesting, including Flodden Field, etc.
The nearest market town is Berwick, distant less than 5 miles from the village ; Chirnside is 3½ miles distant due west.
Population of the parish in 1861, 431 ; who constituted 85 families, 36 of whom were returned as living in houses of one window, 25 in houses of two windows, and the remainder (24), in houses of three or more windows.
Assessed property in 1864-5, £5563 : 2 : 10
The principal landed-proprietors in the parish are—John Wilkie, Esq. of Foulden, who possesses four-fifths of the rental ; and William Miller, Esq. of Nunlands—both resident ; and the Earl of Haddington (of Foulden Westmains).

Those marked thus (*) are Registered Voters.

RESIDENT JUSTICE OF THE PEACE—John Wilkie, Esq.

PUBLIC OFFICES—Heritors' Clerk, Session Clerk, Kirk Treasurer, Registrar of Births, Marriages, and Deaths, and Inspector of Poor—Alexander Dickson.
Medical Officer and Public Vaccinator—Charles Stuart, M.D. Chirnside.

POST OFFICE—Robert Scott, postmaster ; John Simpson, messenger, daily (Sundays excepted) from Berwick. Letters arrive at noon, and are despatched at 1 p.m.

CLERGY, &c.—Foulden is in the Presbytery of Chirnside, and Synod of Lothian and Tweeddale. Patron—John Wilkie, Esq. of Foulden.
Established Church—*Rev. Alex. Christison (Inducted 1821). Sittings, 166. Average attendance at Sabbath School, 15.

FAST DAY—Thursday before last Sunday of July.

SCHOOL†—Parochial—Alexander Dickson, master. Av. attend., 30.

PAROCHIAL BOARD—John Wilkie, Esq., Chairman. Average number of Poor on Roll, 8. Average Rate of Assessment 2d. per £ ; total Assessment in 1864-5, £85.

SOCIETY—A Cow Club is held in Foulden of much advantage to the villagers and others of the class.

CORN AND FLOUR MILL : Foulden—*Peter Inglis, miller.

CONVEYANCE—The railway station of most convenient access to the village is at Berwick. The Ayton station is most convenient for the northern districts of the parish, and Chirnside for the west.

CARRIERS—The Dunse and Chirnside carriers from Berwick pass on Saturday, and convey goods either way.

---

* The *Statistical Account of Berwickshire* (dated Oct. 1834) represents the parish of Foulden as insalubrious and having a high death rate ; but the last issued Reports of the Registrar-General (being for the years 1860 and 1861) show that the parish has now a death rate far below the average of our "*Register*," district," being, for the entire population, only two deaths a year ; or, by comparison with the health table, if Foulden had a population of 1000, its annual death rate would not be 5, whereas Berwickshire on the average has a death rate of 16 per 1000, Roxburghshire close on 20, and Selkirkshire 17. It is evident, from its very smallness, that this death rate of Foulden parish cannot be normal ; dealing with so small a population, a few extra deaths, more or less, would very materially alter the rate— *see* death rate table.
† Foulden Church is celebrated as having been the meeting place of the Commissioners sent by Queen Elizabeth to vindicate her execution of Mary Queen of Scots.

---

† Children in the parish from 5 to 15 attending school during the first week of April 1861, 64 ; of all ages, 67.

TRADES IN THE VILLAGE.

Jeffrey, George, blacksmith
Mason, Peter, shoemaker
Scott, Robert, tailor, general dealer, and *postmaster*
Smith, John, carpenter

RESIDENTS, FARMERS, &c., IN THE PARISH.

*Brown, George, manager, Foulden Newton
*Brown, David, farmer, Nunlands
*Brown, William, do.   do.
 Cockburn, Jas., do. Greenfield
*Craw, Henry Hewit, farmer, Foulden West Mains
 Donaldson, John, blacksmith, Nunlands
*Fender, Andrew, farmer, Foulden Deans
*Kerr, Alexander, do., Foulden Newmains
 Purves, Mrs., Foulden New Farm
 Renton, Robert, farmer, St. Johns
*Thompson, Richd., do., Fouldenhill
*White, Hector, do., Burnbank
 Whitlaw, James, do., Moorpark
*Wood, James, do., Foulden Bastille
 Wood, Robert, do., St. Johns

SEATS, &c., OF COUNTY FAMILIES IN THE PARISH.

FOULDEN HOUSE.

Situated to the east of the village—the property and residence of *John Wilkie, Esq. of Foulden.
Mr. Wilkie is a Justice of Peace and Deputy Lieutenant for the county of Berwick, and Lord of the Barony of Foulden.

NUNLANDS HOUSE.†

Situated about half a-mile north of the village—the residence and property of William Miller, Esq.

REGISTERED VOTER (Non-Resident).

Simpson, John, farmer, North Belton

† It may not be generally known that Nunlands is an ancient place, it being a charter by King James of the lands of Nunlands—part of the spiritual lands of the monastery of Dryburgh, in favour of Alexander Ramsay, Rector of Foulden, dated the 18th Oct. 1587. The only relic Mr. Miller, the present proprietor, possesses of the existence of the nunnery is a font.

WESTRUTHER.

—◆—

THIS parish which lies between the Lammermoor and Lauderdale districts, is bounded on the north by Cranshaws, on the east by Longformacus and Greenlaw, on the south by Legerwood and Gordon, and on the west by Lauder. The outline of the parish is irregular, slightly inclined however to circular; its length from north to south is above 6 miles, and its greatest breadth is about 5 miles. The area, according to the Ordnance Survey, is nearly 14,644 acres; of which 94 are occupied by roads, and about 14 are under water. The whole of the northern quarter presents the appearance of a continuous ridge of hills, whose bleak and barren summits are destitute of every attraction, save that of affording a wide prospect of the rich and beautiful scenery of Merse and Teviotdale. Of these hills, Twinlaw Cairns (the highest) has an elevation of 1466 feet—a black hill with two cairns or pyramidal piles of stone on the top of it, with which a legend is connected, and from which the name of the hill is derived; Raecleuch hill rises to 1255 feet; and The Flass to 1246 feet. The Blackadder rises in this parish, and its trout are good. Descending from this northern boundary the parish appears an extended valley, unbroken by hilly eminences, and intersected by spots of heath, pasture, and arable land; in the centre it rises throughout the whole extent, from west to east, to a considerable elevation, and again inclines to a gentle slope at the southern extremity at Bassendean. The general quality of the soil is light, with a rocky and gravelly subsoil. About 3 miles of the Edinburgh, Newcastle, and London mail-coach road skirts the southern border of this parish, and it is generally well supplied with roads. There are two small villages in the parish—the smaller, Westruther, containing about 100 inhabitants, is situated near its centre on the road between Dunse and Lauder, 10 miles from the former and 8 from the latter, and about 6 from Gordon, which is the nearest railway station; HOUNDSLOW, rather the larger, lies on the Lauder and Greenlaw road, about 2 miles to the south of Westruther. There are three mansions in the parish—WEDDERLIE HOUSE, situated about a mile north-east from the village of Westruther, a large ancient house peeping out from the midst of woods, formerly the property of the Edgars of Wedderlie, a noted family in the district 150 years ago; BASSENDEAN, a baronial looking house, at one time an old Border tower, situated at its southern extremity; and SPOTTISWOODE on the western boundary, a splendid new house in the Elizabethan style; it is surrounded by a very handsome terrace 300 feet in length, ornamented by handsome balustrades, pedestals, and vases. The corridor is lighted by a well proportioned tower in the centre of the building. The tower itself has a very striking effect, when viewed from a distance, overtopping the tall trees. The new house is connected with the old family mansion, which has undergone very important alterations, so that the whole has a unique appearance.

At Bassendean are the remains of a church, formerly used by the Cistercian nuns, now the burial place by the Homes of Bassendean. Evelaw Tower, which is still pretty entire, was one of those castellated houses that were common on the Borders before the union of the two kingdoms. Harit's Dyke (more properly a trench or ditch), which must have been a work of considerable labour, ran from N.W. to S.E. through this parish to the north of the village of Westruther, and said to have extended from Berwick westward along the whole county. The end to the north of Westruther may still be traced; elsewhere it is obliterated by agricultural operations. There seems to be no history, or even tradition, as to when, or for what purpose, it was made.

The nearest market towns are Lauder, distant 7 miles from the village of Westruther; and Dunse, distant 9 or 10 miles. The nearest and most convenient railway stations are Gordon, 5 miles; Greenlaw, 7 miles; and Stow, 11 miles distant.

Population in 1861, 786, who comprised 164 separate families, 53 of whom were returned as living in houses of one window, 69 in houses of two windows, and 42 in houses of three and more windows.

Assessed property in 1864-5, £7212 : 16 : 11.

The principal landed-proprietor in the parish is John Spottiswoode, Esq. of Spottiswoode, who possesses the larger part of the rental; the other proprietors are—Lord Blantyre (of Wedderlie and Cammerlaws), Major Home of Bassendean, Charles Simson, Esq. (of Under Bassendean), of Threepwood, the Earl of Lauderdale (of Harelaw), and James Curle, Esq. (of Evelaw), Melrose.

Those marked thus (*) are Registered Voters in the parish.

RESIDENT JUSTICE OF THE PEACE—John Spottiswoode, Esq. of Spottiswoode.

PUBLIC OFFICES—Heritors' Clerk, Registrar of Births, Marriages, and Deaths, Session Clerk, Kirk Treasurer, and Inspector of Poor—James Wilson.

Medical Officer and Public Vaccinator—Dr. Kynock, Greenlaw.

POST OFFICE—James Wilson, postmaster. Daily post to Lauder Arrival, 1 p.m.; Departure, 7 a.m. Peter Wright, messenger.

CLERGY, &c.—Presbytery of Lauder, and Synod of Merse and Teviotdale. Patron—the Crown.

Established Church—*Rev. Henry Taylor (Inducted 1844). Sittings, 280. Average attendance at Sabbath School, 20.

Free Church—*Rev. James Izzet (Inducted 1846). Sittings, 270. Average attendance at Sabbath School, 30.

FAST DAYS: Summer—Wednesday before the last Sabbath of June; Winter—unfixed; but same as Lauder—see p. 521.

SCHOOLS†—Parish (Westruther)—James Wilson, schoolmaster. Aver. attend., 55.

Free Church (Houndslow), partly supported by Major Home—Alexander Campbell, teacher. Av. attend., 50.

Auxiliary (Gateside), chiefly supported by Mrs. Spottiswoode and Lady John Scott—David Matthewson, teacher. Average attendance, 35.

PAROCHIAL BOARD—John Spottiswoode, Esq., Chairman. No. of Poor on Roll, 24. Rate of Assessment, 3d. per £; total Assessment, 1865-6, £190.

LIBRARY (Westruther Parochial)—Open every lawful day. 370 vols. Wm. Alcorn, librarian. Annual subscrip., 1s.; entry money, 2s.

TOTAL ABSTINENCE SOCIETY (Westruther)—President, Henry Cockburn. Members, about 60.

AGRICULTURAL SOCIETY—John Spottiswoode, Esq., President; Jas. Wilson, Secy. and Treas. Day of Competition, about New Year.

QUARRIES—There is a good quarry on Major Home's estate, and good whin is on both the Spottiswoode and Blantyre estates

TRADES, &c.

Village of Westruther

Aldcorn, William, shoemaker
Allan, Alexander, blacksmith
Gardiner, Janet, general dealer
Lowrie, Isabel, general dealer
Renton, David, clothier and meal dealer
Thistle Inn, Thomas Mossman
*Trotter, Thomas, cartwright

Village of Houndslow

Boyd, William, feuar
Brotherstone, Margaret, general dealer
Gourlay, James, grocer
Gray, John, general dealer

† Children in the parish from 5 to 15 attending school during the first week of April 1861, 124; of all ages, 127.

*Donaldson, Peter, feuar
Hardie, Adam, tailor
Hunter, Robert, mason
Hunter, William, farmer
Lothian, Thomas, general dealer
Mather, John, feuar
Mercer, Andrew, joiner

RESIDENTS, FARMERS, &c., IN THE PARISH.

*Allan, James, farmer, Whiteknowes		
*Brodie, Alex , senr., farmer, Harelaw		
*Brodie, Alex., jun.,	do.,	do.
Campbell, James,	do.,	Cowstrand
*Dickson, Richard,	do.,	Raeclengh
Elliott, William,	do.,	Evelaw
*Gibson, William,	do.,	Westruther Mains
*Hermiston, John,	do.,	Westertown of Westruther
*Hermiston, William,	do.,	do.	do.
*Luke, Robert,	do.,	Thornydyke Mains
*Logan, John,	do.,	Broomiebank
*Lyall, David,	do.,	Cammerlaws
*Mill, George,	do.,	Hindsidehill
*M'Dougal, David,	do.,	Bassendean Hill
Nisbet, Alexander,	do.,	Flass
*Outerson, Thomas,	do.,	Jordonlaw
*Purves, John,	do.,	Thornydykes
Simson, Mrs., Bassendean farm		

*Spark, Robt , farmer (of Whitehill), Heckspath, Gordon
Stewart, Alex. (farmer, Dodds), land-steward, Spottiswoode
Whiteburn Inn, *William Weatherhead*

SEATS, &c., OF COUNTY FAMILIES IN THE PARISH.

BASSENDEAN.†

The property and residence of John Hutcheson Fergusson Home, eldest son of the late James Fergusson, of Cross Hill, Ayrshire, Esq., advocate, one of the Principal Clerks of Session, Edinburgh, by Mary, daughter of Captain John Home of Bassendean ; Major late 33d Regiment, Bengal Infantry ; Captain-Commandant 4th Berwickshire Rifle Volunteers ; succeeded, 1860, his uncle, Lieut.-General John Home Home of Bassendean, formerly of the Grenadier Guards, Commander of

H.M. Forces in Canada, Colonel of the 56th Regiment, whose name and arms he assumed ; married (1st), 1851, Jane Anne, eldest daughter of the late James Walker, Esq, of Dalry (she died in 1852) ; (2d), in 1861, Dorothea, youngest daughter of the late Hugh Veitch, Esq., of Stewartfield ; has no issue. Is Lord of the Barony of Bassendean.

This estate is said, in *Douglas' Peerage*, under the title of " Earl of Home," to have belonged to the ancient family of Sir John Home of Cowdinknowes. The present Earl is said to be descended from the eldest son (of Sir John Home), and William, his brother, got the estate of Bassendean in 1577 by royal charter granted by King James VI.—" in recommpensatione of his service in the lang weirs against England and of the gryt heirshippes he sustainit." Major Fergusson Home is lineally descended from the said William, and Sir John Home of Kowdinknowes, by Margaret Kerr of Cessford, his wife.

Residences—E. I. U. S. Club, St. James' Square, London ; U. S. Club, Edinburgh.

SPOTTISWOODE.

The seat and residence of *John Spottiswoode, Esq. of Spottiswoode, eldest son of the late John Spottiswoode, Esq. ; born 1780 ; succeeded 1805 ; married, 1809, Helen, daughter of Andrew Wauchope, Esq. of Niddrie Marischall, Mid-Lothian, and has issue—

John, born 11th August 1811, Lieut.-Col. Grenadier Guards ; died, unmarried, 3rd November 1846.

Andrew, born 18th October 1812, Colonel in the Army, commanded the 1st Dragoon Guards in the Crimea and in India ; married Emily-Jane, second daughter of Lieut.-Col. Campbell, 9th Lancers ; and died, 12th August 1862, leaving a daughter.

Alicia-Ann (*see* Kirkbank, pp. 170, 171).

Margaret Penelope (*see* Marchmont House, p. 624).

Mr. Spottiswoode is a Justice of Peace and Deputy-Lieut. for Berwickshire, and Lord of the barony of Spottiswoode. London address—Carlton Club, S. W.

The family of Spottiswoode have had a local habitation and a name in this district before the commencement of authentic history, and several of its members have attained the highest honours in various departments both in church and state. The celebrated Archbishop Spottiswoode was a member of this family ; this memorable prelate, the author of the *History of the Church of Scotland*, was born in 1565. In 1633 he had the high honour of crowning King Charles I. at Holyrood, and was afterwards appointed Lord High Chancellor of the kingdom.†

---

† Post town for Bassendean and the locality—Gordon, Kelso.

† The Archbishop's Edinburgh residence in Carrubber's Close, lately

WEDDERLIE HOUSE.

The property and occasional residence of Charles Stuart, Baron Blantyre (in the peerage of Scotland), in the county of Lanark; born 21st December 1818; succeeded at the death of his father,* 22d September 1830; married 4th October 1843, Lady Evelyn Leveson Gower, 2d daughter of the Duke of Sutherland, and has issue—

Walter, *Master of Blantyre,* born 17th July 1851.
And four daughters—Mary, Ellen, Evelyn, and Gertrude.
Other seats—Erskine House, Renfrew; Lennox-Love, formerly Lethington, Haddington. Town House—8 Grosvenor Place.

REGISTERED VOTERS (Non-Resident).

Clay, John, farmer, Winfield, Chirnside
Curle, James, writer, Melrose
Elliot, Thomas, farmer, Blackhaugh
Fiddes, William, merchant, 4 Cowgate-head, Edinburgh
Mason, Wm. D., farmer, Wester Middleton, Gorebridge
Romanes, John, S.S.C., 7 Nelson Street, Edinburgh
Simson, Charles, Esq. of Threepwood
Thomson, James, tailor, Ceres

a wretched tenement, and inhabited by as wretched a population, has this year (1865), been rebuilt by Adam Black, Esq., publisher (late M.P. for Edinburgh), and designated "Spottiswoode Buildings"

* The late Lord Blantyre, who was a Lieut.-General and C.B , after undergoing all the dangers of the Peninsular campaigns, perished by an accidental shot in the commotions at Brussels in 1830. A monument, erected to his memory by the County of Renfrew, 80 feet high, and conspicuously seen from the Clyde, surmounts the swell of a ridge hill near to Erskine House (situated opposite Bowling), a splendid mansion in the Tudor style, built in 1828 after a design by Sir R. Smirke. Erskine was the original seat of the Lords Erkine, Earls of Mar, from whom the Erskines of Dryburgh are descended (*see* note, p. 616).

MORDINGTON.

—◆—

THIS parish is situated in the south-east corner of Berwickshire. It is bounded on the north by the parish of Ayton and the German Ocean, on the east by the liberties of Berwick and the German Ocean, on the south by Hutton, and on the west by Foulden. Its general outline is irregular, resembling a sand glass. Its extreme length is nearly 6 miles, and the extreme breadth is less than 2 miles. The total area, according to the Ordnance Survey, is 3069 4-5th acres, of which nearly 26 are occupied by railway, 114¼ are "foreshore," 34 are in roads, and 16 are under water. The north and north-western parts of the parish consist of high grounds, which slope gradually to the south. The shore presents an unbroken line of rugged sandstone rocks, in which are a great many caves formerly used for smuggling purposes (*see* Coldingham parish); its surface in the southern part is generally flat, with a slight declination to the Whitadder, which forms the southern boundary of the parish, and here abounds in salmon and trout; the trout fishing is very good and unrestricted. Excellent flounders come up with the tide and are freely caught with worm. The soil for some distance from the Whitadder, is a stiff clay, well adapted for wheat and beans; thence to the coast it is in general a light loam, excellent for raising turnips and for grazing; but on the loftiest parts of the high grounds it is thin and poor, and includes considerable tracks of heath, bog, and moss." The Northumberland coal field crops into this parish, and accessible seams exist of moderate thickness. On the Lamberton estate one o' these seams has a thickness of three feet and another of twenty inches, both of which have been wrought, but, we believe, not profitably. The parish also possesses fire clay and limestone. The climate is generally healthy; the winds most prevalent are south and west, which are frequently violent; cold east winds also prevail on the coast. The ruins of Edrington castle—a place of no small note in its day—are situated on the top of an almost perpendicular rock, overhanging the Whitadder.* The romantic and sequestered

* Queen Margaret is said by tradition to have been married here to James IV. of Scotland, but she was really married at Holyrood; and it was, however, stipulated that she should, without any expense to the bridegroom, be delivered to the Scottish king's commissioners at Lam-

fishing hamlet of Ross, at the north-western extremity of the parish, is too much an object of interest to the admirers of picturesque scenery not to be noticed ; it stands at the foot of an almost perpendicular ledge, divided by a rivulet, which in rainy seasons forms many beautiful cascades ; while the sea foam beneath, and the cottages standing almost close upon high water mark, give the scene a very striking appearance. The coast has been long famed for its white fish ; and at Ross the fishing is pursued with considerable energy (*see* Fishing Board Returns).* There is also a salmon fishing station on the coast, which rents at £60 per annum. Some of the heights in the parish command varied and beautiful prospects — extending to the Eildons on the south, the Lammermoors on the west, and to Bamborough on the east—the north is the wide ocean. " An abrupt hillock, near to Mordington House, called the Witches' Knowe (height 649 feet, and the highest point in the parish), was the scene of one of the last burnings for imputed witchcraft in Scotland."† In the north-east of the parish, just inside the boundary line from the liberties of Berwick, is the small hamlet of LAMBERTON ; near it is Lamberton Toll Bar, where marriages were formerly celebrated in the Gretna Green style, and, we may add, still are, although now rendered illegal and void by a late Act (*see* p. 482). In the northern part of the parish is the Lamberton race course ; no races have been run on it for some years, but they had a local celebrity at one time. Close to the eastern boundary of the parish is the small hamlet of Mordington, where are the church and school house ; further south, but also on the eastern boundary, is the Free church and manse. " Tibbie Fowler's Glen," often visited, and connected with which there is a song of much local celebrity, lies in the south part of the parish, not far from Edrington House. The nearest market town and railway station to Mordington and Lamberton is Berwick-on-Tweed, from each about 4 miles distant ; the nearest railway station to Ross is Burnmouth, about 1 mile distant by the road.

---

berton Kirk (the ruins of which are now the burial place of the Rentons of Lamberton). In the time of the present proprietor's grandfather, Edrington castle was four stories high, and close by there was a small village, the site of which is yet to be seen.

* Ross and Burnmouth (*see* p. 596), lie very near to each other and in the Fishery Board Returns are treated as one place. The fishermen of Ross and Burnmouth are very industrious, provident, and comparatively wealthy ; each head of a family is proprietor of his own house, built on a feu ; and, it is said, no young man of the village thinks of marrying till he is possessed of a house.

† This is repeated in all the works on the district, but dates or particulars we have been unable to trace :—" So late as the seventeenth century, *it is alleged*," is the most definite of the many indefinite assertions.

Population of the parish in 1861, 377 ; who constituted 77 separate families, 46 of whom were returned as living in houses of one window, 15 in houses of two windows, and the remainder (48) as living in houses of three or more windows.

Assessed property, salmon fishing on the coast included, in 1864-5, £3717 : 6s.

The principal landed proprietors in the parish are—Major A. Campbell Renton, of Lamberton ; George Chirnside, Esq., of Edrington House ; and James Jeffreys Oswald, Esq., of Edrington Castle.

Those marked thus (*) are Registered Voters.

RESIDENT JUSTICES OF THE PEACE—Maj. A. C. Renton, of Lamberton, and James J. Oswald, of Edrington Castle.

PUBLIC OFFICES—Heritors' Clerk, Session Clerk, Kirk Treasurer, Inspector of Poor, and Registrar of Births, Marriages, and Deaths—John Logan.

　　Medical Officer and Public Vaccinator—James Wilson, M.D., Tweedmouth.

POST OFFICE—Daily Post to Berwick-on-Tweed—John Simpson, Runner. Arrival at Mordington, 11 a.m. Despatch, 1-30 p.m.

CLERGY, &c.—Mordington is in the Presbytery of Chirnside, and Synod of Merse and Teviotdale. Patron—Major Renton of Lamberton.

　　Established Church—*Rev. Charles Blair (Inducted 1843). Sittings, 173.

　　Free Church—Rev. James Ketchan (Inducted 1844). Sittings, 172. Average attendance at Sabbath School, 40.

FAST DAY—Thursday before first Sabbath of July.

SCHOOLS†—Parochial—John Logan, master. Aver attend., 70.

PAROCHIAL BOARD—Mr. Thomas Darling, Mordington Mains, chairman. No. of Poor on Roll, 10. Average Rate of Assessment, 4d. per £ ; total Assessment in 1864-5, £110.

MILLS—Edrington—Corn.
　　Lamb's Mill—Corn—*Thomas Clazie, farmer.

TRADES, &c., IN MORDINGTON.

Allan, John, shoemaker
Blackhall, Alexander, sen., grocer and joiner
Blackhall, Alexander, jun., meal-dealer, &c.
Blackhall, Thomas, joiner

---

† Children in the parish from 5 to 15 attending school during the first week of April 1861, 74 ; of all ages, 80.

Bogue, John, joiner
Elliot, Robert & Andrew, tailors and clothiers
Hay, John, blacksmith
Jeffrey, Peter, do.
Martin, William, spirit dealer
Martin, Robert, grocer
Martin, Thomas, Howking, grocer

RESIDENTS, FARMERS, &c., IN THE PARISH.

*Darling, Thomas, farmer, Mordington Mains
Dixon, James, toll-keeper, Lamberton Toll, and grocer
*Elliot, James, farmer, Lamberton
*Thomson, John, toll-keeper, Mordington Toll

SEATS, &c., OF COUNTY FAMILIES IN THE PARISH.

EDRINGTON CASTLE.

In the south of the parish, in the immediate vicinity of the ruins of the former castle of Edrington, and surrounded on three sides by the Whitadder, in the midst of the most picturesque scenery—the seat and residence of *James Jeffreys Oswald, Esq., J.P.

EDRINGTON HOUSE.

Situated on the east bank of a small tributary of the Whitadder, in the southern part of the parish—the seat of George Chirnside, Esq., of Edrington (formerly of Hoprig), who purchased the property in 1864.

MORDINGTON HOUSE.

Situated on a rising ground near the centre of the parish—the seat of *Major Archibald Colin Campbell Renton, of Lamberton, J.P.

HUTTON.*

THIS parish lies between the Whitadder and the Tweed—the eastern boundary being about a mile west from the junction of these rivers. It is bounded on the north by the parishes of Chirnside, Foulden, and Mordington; on the east by Mordington and the liberties of Berwick; on the south-east by England (a detached part of the county of Durham); on the south-west by Ladykirk; on the west by Whitsome and Edrom. The Whitadder skirts it on the whole of the north and 1½ miles of the east; the Tweed skirts it on the south-east and separates it from England. The greatest length of the parish is 4½ miles, and greatest breadth 3½ miles. Its area, according to the Ordnance Survey, is 5648¼ acres; nearly 102¾ being occupied by public and private roads, and 132 being under water. The soil on the banks of the Tweed is a rich deep loam, but in the centre of the parish it is thin and moorish. The climate is very healthy. There are several valuable fishings at this part of the Tweed. "There are no antiquities of particular interest in the parish. The mansion-house of Hutton Hall, in ruins, is rather a curious specimen of an ancient Border keep. It is situated on the brink of an eminence not far from the Whitadder and overlooking that stream; the site is striking and uncommon." Mr. Philip Redpath, the editor of the *Border History* (written by his brother George, minister of Stichill), was minister of this parish. There are two villages—Hutton and PAXTON. The former having a population of 198, is situated a quarter of a mile south of the Whitadder. The parish church and schools are here. Paxton, having a population of 227, lies in the eastern part of the parish, also on the Whitadder. About 2½ miles south from this village is the Union Suspension Bridge across the Tweed, built in 1820, under the superintendence of the late Sir Samuel Brown, and which was

* "The parish of Fishwick was united to Hutton in 1614; and these two now form one parish. In this district the parishes must originally have been very small, as most of the present ones formed two [*e.g.*, Whitsome, Bunkle, and Swinton, etc.], and still are by no means large either in extent or population. Fishwick parish was situated on the north bank of the Tweed; the ruins of the church and churchyard yet remain. The site is very picturesque."—REV. JOHN EDGAR, in *Statistical Account of Berwickshire*, 1834. The ruins of Fishwick church are close upon the Tweed, a short way up from the chain bridge and opposite the village of Horncliff (in Northumberland)—*see* note, p. 503. There are occasionally burials in the churchyard.

the first of the kind erected in this country. The bridge is 361 feet in length, and weighs about 100 tons. It is much admired by visitors for its apparent lightness and great strength. Near the bridge and well seen from it is PAXTON HOUSE, an imposing edifice, built in the latter half of the last century. It contains a very fine gallery of paintings, and is surrounded by an extensive policy and gardens within a high park wall.

Berwick is the nearest market town, distant about 5 miles from Paxton and 7 from Hutton. The turnpike roads from Berwick to Dunse, and to Kelso by Swinton, cross the parish. These and the parish roads are all kept in excellent repair.

The population of the parish in 1861 was 1067, who constituted 245 separate families, 79 of whom were returned as living in houses of one window, 79 in houses of two windows, leaving 87 who lived in houses of three or more windows.

Assessed property in 1864-5, £10,626 : 19 : 6.

The principal landed-proprietors in the parish are—David Milne Home Esq. (of Milne Graden), of Paxton ; James Macbraire, Esq. of Broadmeadows and Fishwick ; John M'L. M'K. Grieve, Esq. of Hutton Hall (Paris) ; Rev. William Compton Lundie of Spital ; General James Stewart Fraser of Sunwick (Saumerez Manor, Jersey) ; Richard Trotter, Esq., of Morton Hall (of Fishwick Mains) ; and Lord Polwarth, Mertoun (of Crossrig).

Those marked thus (*) are Registered Voters.

RESIDENT JUSTICES OF THE PEACE—James Macbraire, Esq ; Rev. William Compton Lundie.

DISTRICT POLICE OFFICE—At Paxton.

PUBLIC OFFICES—Heritors' Clerk, Inspector of Poor, Session Clerk and Kirk Treasurer, Registrar of Births, Marriages, and Deaths —Robert Laurie.

Medical Officer and Public Vaccinator — Dr. Charles Stuart, Chirnside.

POST OFFICE (Hutton)—Mrs. Hosick, Postmistress. Letters arrive daily, from Berwick at 12 noon, and are despatched at 2-45 p.m. Archibald Pae, post-runner, who passes through Paxton, leaving and receiving letters. Mrs. Dickson, postmistress.

CLERGY, &c.—Presbytery of Chirnside, and Synod of Merse and Teviotdale. Patron—The Crown.

Established Church (Hutton)—*Rev. Robert Kirke (Inducted 1858). Sittings, 400. Average attend. at Sabbath School, 80.

FAST DAYS—Thursdays before the third Sabbath in June, and first Sabbath in December.

SCHOOLS†—Parochial (Hutton)—*Robert Laurie, teacher ; average attendance, 54.

Hutton Female—Agnes Gillespie, mistress ; average attend., 43.

Paxton Boys'—David Mason, master ; average attendance, 48.

 Do. Female—Ann Swan, mistress ; average attendance, 30.

PAROCHIAL BOARD—Rev. William C. Lundie, Chairman. Number of Poor on Roll, 53. Rate of Assessment, 5d. per £ ; total Assessment 1864-5, £461 : 15 : 1.

LIBRARIES—Hutton Village—Robert Flint, Librarian. 450 volumes. Paxton Village—David Mason, Librarian. 430 volumes.

FRIENDLY SOCIETY (Hutton—established 1812)—No. of members, 71. Secretary—Robert Laurie. Funds lent on bond above £800. Each member pays 1s. 6d. per quarter to the fund, and receives when sick or when disabled by age or otherwise, 5s. for first six weeks, 4s. for the next twenty-six weeks, and 2s. 6d. afterwards while disablement continues. The allowance for a member's funeral is £3, and for a member's wife, £2. On an average about £40 is spent yearly on sick and aged. The funds are increasing a few pounds every year. This is the oldest *friendly* society in the district. It commenced with a list of 28 members, and, after an existence of 55 years, one of the original members is still alive.

CORN AND FLOUR MILLS : Hutton—*James Hogg, miller and farmer. Clarabad—*David Porter, miller and farmer. Huttonhall Mill—*John Tait, miller and farmer.

QUARRY (a fine sandstone)—Clarabad—D. Milne Home, Esq., proprietor ; James Berry, builder, Ayton, lessee.

CONVEYANCE—Nearest Railway Station—Velvet Hall, on the Berwick and Kelso line ; by the Chain Bridge about 3 miles from Paxton, and 4½ from Hutton.

CARRIERS—To Berwick, Thomas Toucher, on Wednesday and Saturday ; puts up at Old Angel Inn, High Street. Mrs. White, on Saturday ; puts up at Mrs. Findlay's, Church Street. Both from Hutton.

TRADES, &c.

Village of Hutton

Allan, William, shoemaker
Allan, James, shoemaker
Allan, James, blacksmith
Dewar, Adam, baker
Flint, Robert, tailor
Ford, John, joiner
Johnston, William, general dealer
Lyle, William, spirit dealer

---

† Children in the parish from 5 to 15 attending school during the first week of April 1861, 197 ; of all ages, 210.

The Paxton Schools are kept up by David Milne Home, Esq., with aid from Government, and are under Government inspection.

Meldrum, Miss Ann
Middlemas, Joseph, general dealer
*Sanderson, Edward, joiner
Spark, Walter, tailor
Toucher, Thomas, general dealer and carrier
Whitlie, Benjamin, tailor
White, Isabel, carrier

Village of Paxton

Allan, Robert, shoemaker
Armstrong, James, tailor
Armstrong, James, shoemaker
Bain, Alexander, mason
*Ford, John, general dealer
Grieve, Robert, spirit dealer
Pringle, James, joiner
Redden, Henry, blacksmith
Reid, Henry, baker
Richardson, John, spirit dealer
*Schooler John, feuar
Scoular, Benjamin, joiner
Scoular, George,   do.
Weatherly, James, general dealer
*Weatherly, Thomas
*Wilson, George

RESIDENTS, FARMERS, &c., IN THE PARISH.

*Bird, James Brown, farmer, Fishwick
*Craig, Richard,   do.   West Fishwick
*Craig, Thomas,   do.   do.
*Davidson, George,   do.   Spital West Mains
*Davidson, Henry,   do.   do.
*Davidson, George,   do.   Crossrig
*Fish, William,   do.   Huttonhall Barns
*Gray, Ralph,   do.   Paxton North Mains
Hogg, *Thomas and *Robert, farmers, Broadmeadows
*Hood, William, farmer, Fishwick Mains
*Hosick, Daniel,   do.   Hutton Mains
*Lisle, Leonard,   do.   Caunybank
Middlemas, Joseph, do. Clarabad
*M'Leod, John,   do.   Nansfield
*Nisbet, John,   do.   Paxton South Mains
*Purves, Robert,   do.   Clairvale
*Scott, James,   do.   Sunwick
*Whitlie, John,   do.   Chesterfield
*Wilkinson, Robert, do.   Spital Mains

SEATS, &c., OF COUNTY FAMILIES IN THE PARISH.

MEADOW HOUSE.

Situated on the Whitadder—the property and residence of *James Macbraire, Esq. of Broadmeadows.

PAXTON HOUSE.

Situated on the north bank of the Tweed—the property of Mr. and Mrs. Milne Home ; at present occupied by the proprietor's family.

SPITAL HOUSE.

Near the centre of the parish—the property and residence of the Rev. William C. Lundie.

TWEEDHILL HOUSE.

Situated near to the Union Supension Bridge—the property of James Macbraire, Esq. ; at present unoccupied.

REGISTERED VOTERS (Non-Resident).

Cunningham, John S., of Caprington
Fraser, General James Stuart, Jersey
Grieve, John M'L. M'K , Esq. of Hutton Hall
Grieve, Robert, gardener, Kimmerghame
Linn, William, Widdrington tile-works
Macbraire, John, M.D.
Mushat, Robert, iron-founder, Dalkeith
Scott, Hon Walter H., *Master of Polwarth*
Stevenson, Robert, Newcastle.

ECCLES.

———•———

ECCLES is a rich agricultural parish in the southern part of the Merse, skirted for about 3 miles by the river Tweed, which forms the boundary from Northumberland on the south. Its other boundaries are—on the north Fogo, on the east Swinton and Coldstream, on the west Ednam and Stichill parishes (in Roxburghshire), and on the west Hume and Greenlaw. Its extreme length in a north-easterly direction is about 6¾ miles, and its extreme breadth about 5½ miles. According to the Ordnance Survey, it contains 12,488 acres; comprising 70¾ which are under water, and nearly 230¼ which are in public and private roads, with which perhaps Eccles is better provided than any other parish in the county. "The whole of the parish, with the exception of some slightly elevated parallel ridges called Cocket Ridge, Brae Dunstan, Bartlehill, Wormerlaw, and Eccles Hill, consists of a fine fertile plain, beautifully fenced, wooded, and cultivated." The only antiquity of interest in the parish is a curious monument of white sandstone, with antique sculpture, but without any inscription, standing at Crosshall, about a mile to the north of the village of Eccles. Of the origin or object of this monument there is no record. There are numerous springs in the parish, most of which are impregnated with sulphate of lime. The Leet water partly skirts the parish on the east, and there are various small burns intersecting the parish in all directions. Fishing restricted. The parish contains several fox covers, and it is otherwise finely situated for fox hunting—the Berwickshire hounds having their headquarters in the next parish (Coldstream), while the Duke of Buccleuch's hunt is generally accessible. Wild ducks largely frequent a partially drained bog near Birgham, both as a breeding and feeding place.

The parish contains three villages. ECCLES, in the southwest of the parish, consisting of one street, and resembling any other country village. It has no particular trade. The parish church is here. Of its ancient nunnery, the only remains are part of a wall and two vaulted cells contiguous to the churchyard. LEITHOLM, about 2 miles to the north-east of Eccles, is a much pleasanter village, the houses being superior, and having some very good shops; it is the largest village in the parish, and has a population of 305—142 males and 163 females. In the south of the parish, situated on a gentle rise overlooking the Tweed, is BIRGHAM, once a very noted place,

but now sadly decayed. It still has its grave-yard, situated in the south side of the village, the largest in the parish, and still in use by the farmers and villagers. Fifty years ago the remains of a church or chapel could be seen in the churchyard; no traces of it now remain above ground, but the spot is marked by a solitary elder tree. It was here that in 1291 Edward I. met the twelve competitors for the Scottish throne to decide their claims. In 1298 a meeting of the estates of Scotland was held here to consider a proposal of marriage between Prince Edward, son of Edward I., and Margaret of Scotland; and, according to Mackay Wilson (*vide* "Border Tales"), it was here that some ignominious act occurred on the part of the Scottish nobles, long, long ago, from which arose the saying, "Go to Birgham,"* which is a term of reproach in the district to this day. The parish also contains the hamlet of HASSINGTON, which lies over a mile due west from the village of Eccles.

The nearest market town is Kelso, about 6 miles distant from the village of Eccles. Coldstream, about the same distance, is the post town.

Total population of the parish in 1861, 1861, who composed 399 families; of whom 233 were returned as living in houses of one window, and 100 in houses of two windows, which leaves the small proportion of 66 as living in houses of 3 or more windows.

Assessed property in 1864-5, £22,846 : 4 : 2.

The principal landed-proprietors in the parish are—Sir H. Hume Campbell, of Marchmont, Marquis of Tweeddale, Earl of Home, Sir John Marjoribanks of Lees, M. D. Hunter, Esq. of Antonshill, John Gordon, Esq., of Belchester, Jas. Dickson, Esq., of Bughtrig, Geo. Greig, Esq., of Eccles, Thos. Nisbet, Esq. of Mersington, John Hood, Esq. of Stoneridge, Geo. Baird, Esq., of Stonefold (Stichill House), Major Home Purves of Purves Hall, W. F. Dobson, Esq., of Pittlesheugh, etc., David Robertson, Esq , of Ladykirk, M.P. for the county, James Thomson, Esq., of Earnslaw (Mungoswells, Dunse).

———————

RESIDENT JUSTICES OF THE PEACE—M. D. Hunter of Antonshill, Jas. Dickson, of Bughtrig, Arch. Dickson, yr. of Bughtrig, George Greig of Eccles, John Hood of Stoneridge.

DISTRICT POLICE OFFICE—Leitholm ; John Sligh, officer.

———————

"Go to Birgham," I suspect, has not the fine historical origin Mackay Wilson gives it. It is just equivalent to "Go to Banff," etc., and they are all of them, perhaps, mere softenings of "Go to ——" (some other place) The expression was founded on an alliteration, and, in full, is, "Go to Birgham and buy bickers."—*Correspondent.*

PUBLIC OFFICES—Heritors' Clerk, Session Clerk, Kirk Treasurer, and Inspector of Poor—John Stevenson, Eccles.

Medical Officers and Public Vaccinators — Dr. Turnbull, Dr. Brown, and Dr. Gillies, Coldstream.

POST OFFICE—*see* villages.

CLERGY, &c.—Presbytery of Dunse, and Synod of Merse and Teviotdale. Patron—the Crown.

Established Church (Eccles)—Rev. James Rutherford Watson (Inducted 1848). Sittings, 1000.

Free Church (Eccles) — Rev. Andrew Cunningham (Inducted 1845). Sittings, 280.

United Presbyterian Church (Leitholm)—Rev. Alexander Hay, M.A. (Inducted 1859). Sittings, 300 Average attendance at Sabbath School, 55.

FAST DAYS—Wednesdays before last Sabbaths of April and Otober.

SCHOOLS† : Parish (Eccles)—John Stevenson, master. Av. at., 115.

Adventure (Leitholm)—Adam Millar, teacher. Av. at., 95.

Subscription (Birgham)—Thomas Weatherston, teacher. In connection with this school there is a sewing school, supported by the Countess of Home. Mrs. Weatherston, mistress.

PAROCHIAL BOARD—John Hood, Esq., of Stoneridge, Chairman. No. of Poor on Roll, 56. Rate of Assessment, 6d. per £ ; total Assessment 1864-5, £540. Poor House—Kelso Combination.

LIBRARIES : Leitholm—Henry M'Dougal, librarian ; number of vols., about 250 ; annual subscription, 2s.

Birgham—Thomas Weatherston, librarian ; number of vols., 130 ; annual subscription, 1s.

ECCLES PLOUGHING SOCIETY—Thos. Graham, Esq., Bankhead, Secy.

AUCTIONEER (of Stock)—Thomas Penny, Bartlehill.

CORN MILLS: Leitholm—Alex. Wilson ; Mersington—Jas. Playfair.

CARRIERS : Leitholm—John Gibb, W. Fair, Thos. Brown, and John Riddell ; Eccles—John Grant ;—all to Kelso on Friday.

CONVEYANCE—Nearest railway stations to Eccles—Kelso and Greenlaw, each about 6 miles distant ; do. to Leitholm—Cornhill and Polwarth, each over 5 miles distant ; to Birgham—Cornhill for conveyances, 4 miles ; and Wark, by crossing the ferry, 2 miles.

QUARRIES : Eccles—George Greig, Esq., proprietor—unlet.

Bankhead—John Hood, Esq. of Stoneridge, proprietor ; Andrew Middlemas, mason, Eccles, lessee.

---

† Children in the parish from 5 to 15 attending school during first week of April 1861, 308 ; of all ages, 322.

TRADES.

Those marked thus (*) are Registered Voters.

Village of Eccles

Letters arrive by runner, James Scott, via Birgham, on his way to Hassington, &c., about 1·30 p m. ; and returns about 3 p.m.

Byres, William, tailor
*Cunningham, Rev. Andrew, *Free Church Manse*
Dodds, John, joiner
Grant, John, grocer
Middlemas, Andrew, mason ; lessee of Eccles quarry
M'Dougall, James, blacksmith
Pitt, David, shoemaker
Stenhouse, Mrs , innkeeper
Stevenson, John, *parochial schoolmaster*
*Watson, Rev. J. R., *The Manse*

Village of Leitholm

POST OFFICE—Elizabeth Smith, postmistress. Daily post from Coldstream at 12·40 a.m. ; Despatch at 4·15 p.m. Alexander Scott, messenger.

*Broomfield, James, joiner
*Chambers, James, innkeeper
*Fair, William, grocer
Glasgow, Robert, joiner
Hay, Rev. Alexander, *U. P. Manse*
*Marshall, Robert, tailor
*M'Dougall, Henry, shoemaker
Miller, Adam, schoolmaster
*Reid, John, cooper
Reid, Alexander, baker

Village of Birgham

POST OFFICE — W. Crichton, postmaster. Daily post from Coldstream, arrives at 12·40 p.m. ; James Scott, messenger, who goes on to Eccles and Hassington. Despatch to Coldstream at 4·25 p.m.

*Allan, George, blacksmith
Crichton, James, joiner
*Crichton, William, grocer and *postmaster*
Hall, James, innkeeper
*Hay, William, labourer
Lillico, Richard, flesher and grocer
*Lunham, Thomas, freeholder
Robson, George, blacksmith
Smith, James, tailor

Tait, Andrew, innkeeper
Weatherston, Thomas, teacher
White, Robert, joiner
*White, John, Birgham Cottage
*White, Thomas, do. do.

Hamlet of Hassington

Post—*see* Eccles.

White, John, joiner
Young, David, agricultural implement maker

RESIDENTS, FARMERS, &c.

*Aitchison, James, farmer, Kames West Mains
Aitken, James, farmer and cattle dealer, Wester Whitrig
Allan, James, gardener, Belchester
Allan,   do., Eccles House
*Bertram, William, farmer, Belmount
*Blackie, Robert, do. Stoneridge Mains
*Cowe, Peter,   do. Lochton
*Cumming, Andrew, do. Pittlesheugh
*Cumming, William, do. do.
*Dawson, James, do. Stonefold
*Dawson, William, do. do.
*Dove, John,   do. Eccles Newtown
Dunn, William, do. Birgham
*Fisher, Thomas, do. Sunnyside
*Graham, Thomas, do. Eccles Bankhead
Handyside, David, do. Crossball
Hogarth, George (of Marfield), Eccles Tofts
Hogarth, Mrs., Eccles Tofts
*Hume, Thomas, farmer, Wormerlaw
*Johnston, Patrick, do. Kennetsideheads
*Laidler, Joseph, do. Haigsfield
*Laidler, Joseph J., do. do.
*Lawrie, James, do. Leitholm Bridge-end
*Lawrie, John, do. Harlaw
*Lawrie, Michael, do. Hassington East Mains
*Logan, Abraham do. Hassington Mains
*Oliver, John, do. Hardacres
*Penny, Thomas, do. Bartlehill
*Playfair, James, miller, Mersington Mill
*Rathie, John, farmer, St. Foinhill
Robeson, Robert, farmer, Springwells
*Rutherford, George, do. Printonan
Simson, David, Kames East-end

*Simson, James, farmer, Loanknowe
*Simson, John, jun., do. do.
*Stenhouse, Adam, do. Wester Printonan
*Turnbull, Andrew, do. Blinkbonny
*Turnbull, John, do. Grizzelrig
*Waddell, Andrew, do. Birgham Haugh
*Whitehead, George, do. Earnslaw
*Wilson, James, miller, Leitholm
Young, Thomas, farmer, Todrig (*see* Coldstream, p. 499)

SEATS, &c., OF COUNTY FAMILIES IN THE PARISH.

ANTON'S HILL.

Situated near Leitholm, and surrounded by fine woods—the property and residence of *Matthew Dysart Hunter, Esq., J.P., eldest surviving son of the late General Sir Martin Hunter, G.C.M.G., G.C.H., of Medomsley, county Durham, by Jean, only daughter and heiress of James Dickson, Esq. of Anton's Hill; born 18 ; succeeded 18 ; married, 1852, Isabella Dorothea, eldest daughter of John Buckle, Esq. of Wharton House, Mid-Lothian, and has, with other issue—

Martin, born 1854.

BELCHESTER HOUSE.

Near the eastern boundary of the parish, where it is skirted by the Leet—the property and occasional residence of *John Gordon, Esq. of Cluny, eldest son of the late Col. John Gordon of Cluny (who was M.P. for Weymouth and Melcombe-Regis 1826-30); born 1822; succeeded 1858; married, 1862, Clara, daughter of the late Rev. James White of Bonchurch, Isle of Wight (she died 12th February 1864 without issue). Mr. Gordon is a Justice of Peace and Deputy Lieut. for the counties of Aberdeen, Banff, Nairn, and Inverness, and Lord of the Manor of Cluny.
Principal Seat—Cluny Castle, Aberdeenshire
London addresses—Carlton and Windham Clubs, S.W.

BUGHTRIG.

Situated about half-a-mile north-east of Leitholm—the property and principal residence of *James Dickson, Esq. of Chatto (Hounam parish, Roxburghshire), J.P.; succeeded his father, Archibald Dickson of Housebyres 1834, and his brother Major Dickson, of Chatto, in Chatto and his Berwickshire estates; born 18 ; married, 18 ,
and has issue—

*Archibald, younger of Chatto, J.P.

William (of Wellfield, Wilton—*see* p. 341)
And two daughters.

ECCLES HOUSE.

Situated near the village—the property and occasional residence of *George Greig, Esq., of Eccles, W.S.; born 1823; succeeded his father the late James Greig, Esq., in 1859. Mr. Greig is a Deputy-Lieut. and a J.P. for Berwickshire.

Edinburgh address—9 Abercromby Place.

KAMES.

Situated near to Leitholm—the property and residence of Mrs. Hood; succeeded, 1837, her brother, the late George Weir, Esq., of Kames, who was killed in the Rebellion in Canada, while Lieutenant in the 32nd Regiment; married (1st), Robert Cosens, Esq., R.N., who died in 1840, by whom she has issue—

George Weir Cosens (*see* p. 603).
Robert Cosens Weir, Lieut. 1st Royals, born 4th March 1840, assumed the name of Weir on succeeding to the property of his uncle, the late Thomas Weir Esq., of Bogangreen and Alemill (Coldingham parish), 4th March 1856; married, 19th June 1865, Caroline Antoinette, only daughter of the late Thomas Sommerville Irwin, Esq., H.E.I.C.S.

Mrs. Weir married (second), in 1844, John Hood, Esq., of Stoneridge (*see* p. 660).

Kames was at one time the residence and property of Henry Home, Lord Kames. Here he was born in 1696, and from it he assumed the title as Lord of Session. Here, too, he was visited in 1759 by Dr. Benjamin Franklin and son; and here, it is believed, some of his famous essays on agriculture were written.

After the death of Lord Kames, the property was purchased by a Capt. Riddel, who changed the name to *Besborough* (the name of the ship he commanded). When the property was purchased by the late Mr. Weir (in 1825), father of the present proprietress, the original name was resumed.

Kames is a delightful residence, built in the old Scottish gabled style, and is surrounded by very fine old trees.

MERSINGTON HOUSE.

Situated one mile west of Leitholm—the property of Major Thomas Nisbet (late of the 1st Dragoon Guards).

PURVES HALL.

Situated on the northern side of the parish—the property of

Col. John Home Purves, long the seat of the Purves family, last occupied by Sir Alexander Purves, grandfather of Sir Hugh Hume Campbell, Bart. of Marchmont (*see* p. 624) and of the present proprietor, Col. John Home Purves, who was born 1818; married, 1849, Caroline Maria, daughter of Admiral Hyde Parker, C.B., and has issue—

Charles Hyde, born 4th August 1850.
Augusta Louisa Helen.
Alexandra Mary Caroline.

Col. Home Purves was formerly of the Grenadier Guards; he is now Groom of the Privy Chamber to Her Majesty, and Equerry to H.R.H. the Duchess of Cambridge; and *heir.-pres.* to the Marchmont baronetcy (*see* p. 624).

SPRING HILL.

Situated to the west of the village of Birgham, on the banks of the Tweed—the property of the Earl of Home; at present occupied by Miss Hunter and Miss Elizabeth Bell.

STONERIDGE.

Situated about one mile west of Leitholm—the property of *John Hood, Esq.; at present occupied by Capt. John Allen Allen, of the Forfarshire Militia Artillery, and J.P. for Perthshire; married, 1860, Augusta, daughter of Major the Hon. Augustus George Frederick Jocelyn.

REGISTERED VOTERS (Non-Resident).

Alder, James, Tweedmouth
Crighton, James, merchant, 1 Kerr Street, Edinburgh
Cunningham, John, architect, Birkenhead
Darling, David, Alma Terrace, Londonderry
Baird, George, Esq., Stichill House
Dobson, W. Francis, Esq., Gravesend

---

* John Hood, Esq., only surviving son of the late Thomas Hood, Esq., of Hardacres, J.P.; succeeded his father's cousin John Hood, Esq., of Stoneridge, in 1810; married 1st, 1818, Janet Anne, second daughter of Alexander Low, Esq., of Annfield, county Fife, and has, with other issue—

Thomas Hood, born 1820; married, 1843, Charlotte, daughter of Col. Shapland, C.B.

Mr. Hood married 2nd, 1844, Mrs. Elizabeth Weir of Kames—*see* Kames.

Mr Hood is a J.P. and a Deputy Lieutenant for Berwickshire.

Dunglass, Right Hon. Lord, Hirsel
Elliot, Robert, grocer, Edinburgh
Greig, James, Australia
Greig, John B., solicitor, London
Humble, George, Esq. of Old Graden
Humble, John, Esq. of Waverley Cottage, Kelso
Home, Hon. James A., Hirsel
Home, David Milne, Esq. of Wedderburn
Home, Hon. William Sholto, Hirsel
Hume, Alexander, ironfounder, Manchester
Learmonth, George, Peebles
Marjoribanks, Stuart, London
Marshall, Alexander, labourer, Corbiehall, Fogo
Purves, Col. John Home, of Purves Hall
Robertson, T. Fair, Esq. of Sainfoin, Kelso
Smail, William A., Esq., of Overmains
Stewart, Basil, Lorchard Dell, Lanark
Thomson, James (of Earnslaw), Mungoswells
Wilson, Alexander, labourer, Langbank, Swinton

LONGFORMACUS.*

——◆——

AN irregularly shaped and hilly parish, situated entirely among the Lammermoors. It is bounded on the north by East-Lothian; on the east by the parishes of Dunse and Abbey St. Bathans; on the south by Langton, Polwarth, Greenlaw, and Westruther; and on the west by Cranshaws and Lauder. Its greatest length, from Willies Law, at the extreme north-west, to the boundary of Dunse or Abbey St. Bathans parishes, is over 10 miles; its greatest breadth, from where the Whitadder skirts it at the north to its point penetrating into Greenlaw and Polwarth parishes, is nearly 8 miles. Its total area, including a detached portion (of $1149\frac{1}{2}$ acres, which formed part of the old parish of Ellem) lying in Abbey St. Bathans (see paragraph, The Retreat, p. 665), is, according to the Ordnance Survey, $19,604\frac{1}{2}$ acres.†

The whole of the parish is hilly, and mostly pastoral. The greatest elevation is that of Willies Law 1626 feet, one of the highest of the Lammermoor range; Meikle Law, a little to the east, rises to 1518 feet; Byrecleuch Ridge, more easterly, 1335 feet, Wether Law, 1379 feet; while the highest point of Brown Law, at the extreme north, has a rise of 1032 feet. The two fine hills—the Great and Little Dirrington (the former 1309 feet in height) lie near the southern extremity of the parish, and form conspicuous landmarks. The detached part of the parish has no heights of note. The climate of the parish is cold but healthy. The small streams—the Dye and Watch, intersect the parish; the Whitadder skirts it for over 2 miles to the north; and the Fasney touches it at one of the northern points.‡ The district is an excellent trouting one, and gives its name to the celebrated Ellem Fishing Club, whose head-quarters are at Dunse (see p. 479). The parish of Longformacus contains excellent grouse shooting—that on Byrecleuch being esteemed as good as any, if not the best, in the Lammermoors. We may add that the grouse shooting on the Berwickshire hills far surpasses that of the Cheviots or Selkirkshire hills; the former being heathy affords better cover and abundance of food, while on the latter heath scarcely exists (compare with

---

* Properly the united parishes of Longformacus and Ellem, which were, on account of their contiguity, united by decree of annexation, 18th Feb. 1712.
† Next to Lauder and Coldingham, Longformacus is the largest parish in the county.
‡ See note, Cranshaws parish, p. 586.

p. 44) ; but the black-cock, which likes cover and feeds largely on the seeds of the coarse grass, and prefers the green hills, abounds in the Cheviots and Selkirkshire; while on the Lammermoors very few are met with, and those few principally about Spottiswoode, where, of late, they have been decreasing. The heath of the Lammermoors, too, affords shelter to the viper (locally known as the adder); it is met with frequently in this parish, and is more or less common along both sides of the range. We believe it is unknown on the Cheviots.* In the Whitadder otters abound, and are sometimes hunted. At The Retreat, in the detached part of the parish, as many as three have been observed in one pool.

On the side of Byrecleuch ridge, about a mile north-west from Byrecleuch, is a curious collection of stones. Although of immense extent, no tradition as to its origin exists, but it is supposed to mark the scene of some ancient conflict. It is known by the name of "Mutiny Stones."

Near the centre of the parish, situated on the Dye, about 2 miles west from where it joins the Whitadder, is situated the small village of Longformacus—a fine centre for anglers. The nearest market town is Dunse, 7½ miles distant from the village, where is also the nearest railway station. The road accommodation of the parish is bad ; in the upper grounds it is wretched.

Population of the parish in 1861, 448; who composed 86 families, 3 of whom were returned as living in houses having no window,† 26 in houses of one window, 33 in houses of two windows, and 24 in houses of three or more windows.

Assessed property in 1864-5, £6634 : 9s.

The principal landed-proprietor in the parish is—Mrs. Margaret T. Brown, of Longformacus (liferentrix and resident; Forbes Scott Brown, Esq. *fair*); the other extensive proprietors are—James Stewart Smyth, Esq. (63d Regt.), of Whitchester‡ and Ellem Cottage, the Duke of Roxburghe, who has a

---

* On *all* the high grounds of the district the golden plover and the curlew abound and breed in summer ; in winter they leave for the sea coast. For the dotterel, a rare species of plover, *see* Oldhamstocks. A few foxes frequent and breed about the hills (*see* note, p. 205).

† Some vagrants who had taken refuge for the night in barns.

‡ The estate of Whitchester, the property of James Stewart Smyth, Esq., Lieut. 63d Regiment, lies in the parishes of Longformacus and Dunse, on the southern slope of the Lammermoors, and consists mostly of fine rich old pasture and a considerable portion under wood. The rivers Dye and Whitadder skirt the estate on the north, and the Langton estates bound it on the west and south. Ellem Cottage is beautifully situated—embosomed amongst fine old trees on the banks of the Whitadder—about 6 miles distant from Dunse, on the road leading across the hills from Berwickshire to the Lothians. On the estate of Ellem a rich vein of copper is said to exist.

By the opening of the Berwickshire railway from Dunse to Melrose

---

shooting lodge at Byrecleuch, Lord Somerville, J. Turnbull, Esq. of Abbey St. Bathans, Sir George G. Suttie, Bart., the Earl of Wemyss, J. Spottiswoode, Esq. of Spottiswoode, and Lady Elizabeth Pringle.

Those marked thus (*) are Registered Voters in the parish.

DISTRICT POLICE OFFICER—

POST OFFICE—Alexander Anderson, postmaster. Letters arrive at Longformacus, six days a-week from Dunse, at 8-30 a.m. ; despatched at 11 a.m.

PUBLIC OFFICES—Session Clerk and Kirk Treasurer, Inspector of Poor, Registrar of Births, Marriages, and Deaths—William Wanless.

     Medical Officer and Public Vaccinator—Dr. Tait, Dunse.

CLERGY, &c.—Presbytery of Dunse, Synod of Merse and Teviotdale. Patron—Brown, of Longformacus.

     Parish Church—*Rev. Walter Weir (Inducted 1837). Sittings, . Precentor—John Brown. Average attendance at Sabbath School about 35.

     Free Church—Rev. James Rathie (inducted 1864). Sittings, Average attendance at Sabbath School.

FAST DAYS—In June, and in November when most light suits.

SCHOOL† (Parochial)—*Wm. Wanless, master; R. S. Gibb, assistant. average attendance, 40.

PAROCHIAL BOARD—   Chairman ; Members— Rev. Mr. Weir, and Mr. J. Rankine, Whitchester. Average number of Poor on Roll, 11. Rate of Assessment, 3d. per £ ; total Assessment 1864-5, £84 : 2 : 4½.

CORN MILL—*Andrew Luke, farmer.

TRADES, &c., IN THE VILLAGE.

Anderson, Alexr., grocer, general merchant, and *postmaster*
Anderson, Henry, joiner and church officer

---

there is a choice of routes to and from the Metropolis, either through the romantic scenery of Melrose and the Tweed, or by the fertile shores of the Firth of Forth. Tourists and anglers from all parts of the country avail themselves much of these facilities in reaching the banks of the Whitadder, where trouting is unsurpassed ; and excellent accommodation can at all times be had at the Ellem Fishing Hotel, which is situated on the Whitchester property. We may farther add that by the liberality of Mr. Smyth and the neighbouring proprietors, this district of the Whitadder with its tributaries is at all times open to anglers.

† Children in the parish from 5 to 15, attending school during the first week of April 1861, 65; of all ages, 69.

Blakebell, Isabella, grocer
*Fortune, James, feuar
Hislop, George, tailor
*Neil, John, blacksmith and innkeeper
Ovens, David, tailor and clothier
Wood, James, blacksmith

FARMERS, RESIDENTS, &c., IN THE PARISH.

*Allan, John, farmer, Billiemains
*Bertram, do. Blackerston (detached)
*Brodie, James, do. Leaston
*Brown, John, do. Townhead
 Craik, William, manager, Longformacus home farm
*Edgar, John, farmer, Caldra
 Ellemford Fishing Hotel† Buchan Kirk, innkeeper
*Elliot, Walter, farmer, Newhall
*Elliot, William, do. Ellemford
*Ford, John, do. Rigfoot
*Johnston, James, do. Cattleshiel
 Johnston, Thos., do. Fellcleugh
*Ranken, James, do. Whitchester
*Sheills, George, do. Horseupcleuch
*Thin, James, do. Smiddyhill

SEATS, &c. OF COUNTY FAMILIES IN THE PARISH.

LONGFORMACUS HOUSE.

Situated close to the village amidst extensive grounds and woods —the residence of Mrs. Margaret Turnbull Tait, widow of the late David Wardlaw Brown, Esq. (who died 1864), and eldest daughter of the late James Tait, Esq., of Edenside, Kelso.

ELLEM COTTAGE.

The residence of Mrs. Smyth, widow of the late James Smyth, Esq. (of Whitchester and Ellem), and eldest daughter of the late Captain Stewart, representative of the ancient family of Appin, in Argyleshire. Mr. Smyth died on 24th March 1847, and was succeeded by his son, James Stewart Smyth, Esq., born 9th January 1839; at present Lieutenant, 63d Regiment.

THE RETREAT.‡

In the detached portion of the parish, on the Whitadder—a

---

† On the Whitadder, over 3 miles north-west from the village.
‡ On the bank of the Whitadder, opposite The Retreat, but lying in

peculiar looking circle of a house, built as a shooting box for Lord Wemyss ;* at present occupied by Mr. Bertram, tenant of Blackerston.

REGISTERED VOTERS (Non-Resident).

the parish of Dunse, are the remains (the foundations only) of Edinshall, said to have been built by King Edwin, the founder of Edinburgh. From the peculiarity of these remains they possess great interest, and have afforded much speculation to the antiquary ; but no definite conclusion has been arrived at as to their origin or object.
 * Earl of Wemyss and March (Francis Wemyss-Charteris-Douglas); in the Peerage of Scotland—Baron Wemyss of Elcho, Earl of Wemyss, Baron Elcho and Methel, Earl of March, Viscount of Peebles, and Baron Douglas of Nidpath, Lyne, and Munard ; in the Peerage of the United Kingdom—Baron Wemyss of Wemyss ; a Baronet of Scotland and Nova Scotia; born 1795 ; succeeded, 28th June 1853, his father, Francis, as 8th Earl of Wemyss and 2d Earl of Wemyss and March ; married, 1817, Lady Louisa, born 1798, daughter of Richard, second Earl of Lucan, and has issue—

  Francis, Lord Elcho, born 1818 ; married, 1843, Lady Anne-Frederica Anson, second daughter of Thomas-George, 1st Earl of Lichfield, and has, with other issue—Francis, born 1844. Lord Elcho is M.P. for the county of Haddington, re-elected 1865 (formerly M.P. for East Gloucester), Lieut.-Col. of the London Scottish Volunteers, and late a Lord of the Treasury.
  Richard, born 25th July 1822, Lieut.-Col. Scots Fusilier Guards ; married, 2d August 1858, Lady Margaret Butler, eldest daughter of Richard, Earl of Glengall, and has issue.
  Walter, 92d Highlanders ; killed at Balaclava 1854.
  Frederick-William, Lieut., R.N. (Commanding Officer Coast Guard Station, Cockburnspath—see p. 591), born 1833 ; married, 1864, Lady Louisa Keppel, daughter of George Thomas, 5th Earl of Albemarle.
  Ann, married, 18th February 1852, to George Guy, 4th Earl of Warwick.
  Louisa, married, 7th December 1854, to William Wells, Esq., of Redleaf House, Kent.

  Lord Wemyss is Lord-Lieutenant of Peeblesshire (appointed 1853), and for long has been proprietor and Master of the fox-hounds whose head-quarters are at Coldstream (see p. 484).
  Seats—Gosford House, Seton, Amisfield, in Haddingtonshire ; Elcho Castle, Perthshire; and Stanway, Gloucestershire.
  Town residences—23 St. James' Place, London ; 68 Queen Street, Edinburgh.
  Winter residence—Lennel House, Coldstream (see p. 500).
  Lord Wemyss is sole proprietor of the detached part of Longformacus parish.

COLDINGHAM.*

———◆———

THIS parish, which *politically* and *parochially* (*see* foot-note), is next to Lauder, the largest in Berwickshire, lies on the north-eastern coast of the county. It is bounded on the north by the German Ocean, on the east by the German Ocean and parishes of Ayton and Eyemouth, on the south by Chirnside, and on the west by Cockburnspath. In figure it is very irregular; its extreme length, from a point about a mile west of Grant's House to another point near Ayton Mill, is 8 miles, its breadth averages 7 miles. The total area of the parish, as given in the Ordnance Survey, is 24,325¼ acres (including a detached portion, situated in Eyemouth parish, containing the mansion of Highlaws, which is 80⅝ acres) ; of this 71¾ acres are under water, 236¼ are in roads (public and private), 106½ are occupied by the railway, and 233 are "foreshore." At one time this parish was much larger than it is at present ; it then included all the parishes which now form its boundaries, and was termed Coldinghamshire. The surface of the parish is generally uneven, a part of the Lammermoor range of hills running in parallel lines from east to west throughout its entire length. Between these hills are many valleys of considerable extent, nearly all of them having its small stream flowing through it. None of the hills rise to a great height ; the principal of them are—Cross Law 743 feet, Laverlock Law 715 feet, Drone Hill 738 feet, Horsley Hill 860 feet, and several others varying from 500 to 600 feet. A great part of the parish consists of moorland unfit for cultivation, and is used for pasture. The lower grounds are fertile, and in a high state of cultivation. The climate from its being very much exposed to east and north-east winds is cold. Although abounding in small streams the only one worth mention is the Eye, which intersects the parish throughout its entire length. Most of the small streams are tributaries of the Eye.

The great object of interest in the parish is its bold and rocky coast—a length of fully 9 miles, allowing for headlands. Forming part of this coast is the celebrated promontory called St. Abb's Head, which presents a perpendicular face to the German Ocean, of nearly 200 feet high ;—its extreme height is 310 feet. The Head is separated from the mainland by a valley which fifty years ago was a quagmire, and at some unknown time was crossed by a bridge. The head consists of three hills. On the middle hill (Hare Law) a lighthouse 200 feet high was erected three years ago. About 150 yards to the north of the lighthouse the porphyry rocks have been ground down, smoothed, grooved, and serrated. A portion of these rocks was bared for the inspection of the Berwickshire Naturalists' Club on their June field day of this year, and have been left exposed ; the direction of the grooves were from W.N.W. to E.S.E. in one part, and from N.W. to S.E. in another. It was the opinion of the geologists present on the occasion, that ice moving from about N.W. over the surface had produced the effect. At Petticowick, the landing place for the lighthouse, may be seen a fine example of the junction of the greywacke rocks and the porphyry ; here the precipice is 300 feet high. The eastern hill (Kirkhill) has on its top the remains of a chapel and a burial ground. The chapel is known to have been erected by a prior of Coldingham, about the year 1380. The western hill (Fowlis) has on it nothing of interest. The old town of St. Abb's was situated between the Kirk Hill and what was the quagmire ; and on the neck of land called the Ramfolds, are the supposed, by some, remains of St. Ebba's Nunnery, from which the name of St. Abb's is derived. "Numerous caves and fissures, formerly the haunts of smugglers, exist in the neighbourhood of St. Abb's Head ; some of them of considerable dimensions, excavated out of the solid rock, are inaccessible by land, and can only be approached at low water and in the calmest weather. Their narrow entrances are completely blocked up by the rising tide, and a gentle breeze from the east speedily creates a dangerous surf." "The extraordinary contortions of the Silurian strata, which form part of these precipitous heights have long attracted the attention, and supplied materials for speculation to some of our most eminent geologists. They extend from Siccar Point (*see* p. 590) to Burnmouth,* on each side of the igneous rocks, which are intruded about St. Abb's Head.† The appearance of the promontory, when lashed with

---

* At Burnmouth the rocks of the Carboniferous era begin—the lower coal measures showing themselves slightly in Lamberton parish (*see* p. 644), and the secondary red sandstone being well represented. These extend eastward to Berwick-on-Tweed, and along the Northumberland coast, where, and as far south as Cheswick, the upper coal measures are distinctly visible.

† The following interesting notes on the geological formation and features of St. Abb's Head, are from the pen of George Tate, Esq., Aln-

billows and wrapt in spray, is sublime. From the lighthouse a noble view of the coast is obtained, extending from the Bell Rock and the Redhead of Angus on the north, to Bamborough

---

wick, Joint-Secretary and Treasurer of the Berwickshire Naturalists' Club (*see* Transactions, vol. iv. p. 127):—

"Coldingham stands on porphyry (a fire-formed rock), which ranges from the Eye water to the north side of Coldingham Sands. This rock is seen in the Eye, and it forms cliffs in the narrow glen in which flows the Cole Burn. The bold headland of St. Abb's is also porphyry, which extends from Coldingham Sands northward, about two miles, to Petticowick Cove, forming a promontory jutting into the sea; and more effectually resisting the wasting action of the German Ocean than the softer greywacke rocks, which it has pierced through and uplifted. The porphyry is usually of a reddish colour, having a clay stone base, through which are scattered a few crystals of felspar; at the north-east it is amygdeloidal, and not unfrequently contains green earth; in the more southern parts amygdeloidal tufa occurs. Some parts of the rock are softer than others, especially where there is tufa; and these portions have been hollowed out and caverned and worn into deep chasms; here, even in moderate weather, there is a heavy roll of the tide, and a hoarse gurgle is heard resounding among the caverns. The scenery is wonderfully varied, picturesque, and impressive. In front of the lofty cliffs are many detached masses of rocks. Some are single, surrounded by the sea, others are in groups; all, however, are fashioned by the elements into peculiar and not unfrequently grotesque forms; not a few resemble ruined buildings and towers. One rock in Petticowick bay, had for its old name "The Auld Wife'; its now modern name is "Lord Brougham," from an odd likeness to that distinguished orator; there are his wig, his marvellous nose, his projecting and heavy underlip, and a vivid imagination can even see the judge's robe.

"The stratified rocks in this district are greywacke and greywacke slate, being part of that formation which extends across Berwickshire in a west-south-west direction, and which has been ranked as lower Silurian by Murchison, and Cambrian by Sedgwick. These rocks are seen at the mouth of the Cole Burn and at Coldingham Sands, on the south side of the porphyry; they appear again at the north side in Petticowick Cove, where they form a series of remarkable foldings and curvatures, in one part dipping north by north-west 50 degrees, and at a short distance making a complete bend, and dipping 50 degrees to the south-east westward of St. Abb's Head. Greywacke forms the Raven's Brae. A deep swampy valley here separates the stratified from the igneous rocks. What probably this had been scooped out when the district was under water, for beneath the soil is a considerable accumulation of rounded water-worn stones. A natural cause was however not sufficient for the old chroniclers; one relates that, in the seventh century, the sea flowed miraculously into this valley, and that for seven days St. Abb's Head was converted into an Island, in order that the Virgin Queen Edelthyra and her two Holy Virgins, Sewenna and Sewara, might be protected from her husband King Egfrid. He had given her permission to become a nun in the sanctuary of Ebba, but changing his mind, he followed her to bring her back by force; but the miraculous flow of the water evidenced to him that the Deity was unfavourable to his purpose, and he therefore abandoned the attempt and returned to York. Viewed on a fine day with a clear blue sky above and a bright

Castle and the Fern Islands on the south.[*] Along the whole length of the coast, but about St. Abb's especially, which is a great breeding place for them, sea birds abound. Of these the principal are, the Guillemot or Scout, the Razor-bill, the Puffin or Tammy Norry, the Kittiwake, the Herring Gull, the Black-backed Gull, the Greater and Green Cormorants, the Raven, the Kestril, the Jackdaw, the Martin or White-rumped Swallow, the Shore Pipet, the Domestic Pigeon in a wild state, and in the winter season various kinds of Ducks. Owing to the visits of mischievous sportsmen and reckless fusilades from passing steam-boats, the number of birds is gradually diminishing. The rare red-legged Crow or Chough which once frequented the Head is now extinct. On Earnsheugh, one of the neighbouring peaks, the Common Gull and the Peregrine Falcon breed. Porpoises are numerous off the coast in the summer season, and the bottle-nosed whale and seal are occasional visitants—the porpoises and whales being attracted by the droves of herrings, on which they prey. Otters frequent the Eye and the rocky coves of St. Abb's Head.

Two miles west from St. Abb's Head are the promontory and ruin of Fast Castle. To the land side the only access is by a rocky path of only a few feet wide, bordered on either hand by a deep precipice. The castle—a donjon tower of moderate size, surrounded by flanking walls which rise without interval and abruptly from the very verge of the precipice—corresponds in some respects to the "Wolf's Craig" of Sir Walter Scott's "Bride of Lammermoor."

About one mile west from St. Abb's Head lies Coldingham

---

sun illuminating rock and sea, there is ever much beauty in the scene. Columns and broken masses of rock rise on the north side of the platform, whereupon the building stood; but through the opening between them, we look down a deep chasm, bounded on the north by lofty cliffs, adorned by lichens and mosses, here and there relieved with patches of the bright sea pink, and of the sea campion with its white flowers and glaucous green leaves. Isolated pillars and masses of rock stand in the midst of the sea, and, resembling a group of buildings, they have been named the Barn Yard. According to Scott, Melrose should be visited by moonlight, and I am told that when these rocks are viewed by moonlight the illusion is complete—the farm house with its chimney is seen, and beside it may be recognised the various buildings usually clustered around a farm house. Few spots would therefore be more fitted for recluses than this. Shut out from the world and placed amid impressive natural objects, they had around them abundant materials sugestive of thought, and calculated to excite the feelings; and if, in the calm and sunshine, there is much to minister to fancy, and gratify taste, how powerfully would such a scene impress the mind, when the wild wind blew, and the ocean was lashed into a storm."

[*] It is to be regretted that attempts have been made of late to prevent tourists and others going to St. Abb's Head. We observe legal measures are being taken by the public in the matter.

Loch, about 30 acres in extent; it is within 300 yards of the sea, and is 250 feet above its level. Its waters are pellucid, several fathoms deep, and it abounds in perch and water plants; but its exposed position prevents it being ornamented with trees or shrubs. Four hundred yards north of the loch, on the top of Earnsheugh, as it is commonly called, are two oblong British camps, each having three well marked ramparts on the S.W. or land side. There are other British camps on the adjoining hills."

Situated in a valley about a mile distant from the sea, is the small town of Coldingham, with a population of 836; it meets the eye of the stranger only on his near approach by the several descents, and with striking and picturesque effect. The houses present a scattered appearance, these on the northern side called Boggan being perched in the steep bank of a streamlet bearing the name of Rickleside Burn. On the other side flows another stream called Court Burn, both in deep channels, the main part of the town being situated on the rising ground between them. On a gentle eminence to the south of the town stands the remains of the ancient priory, recently repaired at great expense, and occupied as the parish church. It, with the surrounding ruins, from their beauty and antiquity, are much resorted to by visitors, especially during the summer and autumn months.*

Situated about one mile to the north on the sea coast, is the fishing village of Coldingham Shore. Its population (of 181) is included in that of Coldingham. The inhabitants are mostly engaged in fishing for cod, haddocks, turbot, lobster, and crabs; and, in their season, herrings, which are here extensively cured † (see Fishery Board Returns). Coldingham is becoming a place of repute for sea-bathing and summer visitors. Half-way between the town and the "shore" (half-a-mile from each) is a beautiful beach called Coldingham Sands, one of the finest bathing places in the kingdom.

Formerly the town of Coldingham used to be kept in a very filthy condition: the streets were unswept, dunghills accumulated before the doors, and pig-styes *containing pigs* were everywhere. This is now all changed for the better, and the town has not only its scavengers, but it has its inspector of nuisances. The parish of Coldingham is very healthy, as is shown by the great age of many of the paupers, as also by the average of deaths during the five years ending 1864, viz.—56 (nearly), which gives a death rate of rather less than 17 per 1000 per annum of its population, which is a low rate of mortality (*see* Death Rate Table, and compare).

The trade of Coldingham is principally dependent on agriculture and fishing.

The parish, *quoad civilia,* also contains the following villages:—RESTON (with a population of over 200), situated about 4 miles south of Coldingham and at the junction of the Berwickshire and the North British railways; here is an important railway station. AUCHENCRAW (having a population of over 150), near the southern boundary of the parish, and 2 miles south-west from Reston station. The hamlet of HOUNDWOOD, where are the *quoad sacra* church and manse and Free church, consists of a few detached houses, embracing about half-a-mile in length, pleasantly situated on the north side of the Eye, not far from the line of railway and about mid-way between the Grant's House and Reston stations. Within the parish there is also, at its western boundary, the hamlet and station of GRANT'S HOUSE.

A considerable portion of the lands in the parish of Coldingham were formerly *Runrigg,** but were divided by decreet of the Court of Session, at the instance of Patrick Home, Esq., of Wedderburn, and others. The process originated in the Sheriff-Court of Berwickshire, at the instance of Alexander Hay, Esq., of Huntingtower, and others, and was advocated to the Court of Session conform to four several letters of advocation. The decreet of division, which is of vast importance to the holders of property in and around Coldingham, is dated 28th July 1770 and 6th August 1772.†

---

* A very complete, interesting, and illustrated account of Coldingham Priory and its recent restoration, was published a few years ago by William K. Hunter of Wellfield. (Kelso: J. & J. H. Rutherfurd.)

† The Coldingham fishermen at one time resided in the hamlet of Northfield, situated about half-a-mile inland; but about forty years ago, houses were erected for them at the Shore by Henry Home Drummond, Esq., the proprietor; and in 1838, more houses were added. At present Coldingham Shore is leased with, and is part and parcel of the farm of Northfield. This peculiarity of position is much against its progress; under a different system it might be one of the most prosperous fishing villages on the coast, which at present *it is not,* but is rather a collection of hovels, where sanitary regulations are very little attended to.

---

* " *Runrigg-Lands* are lands where the alternate ridges of a field belonged to different proprietors. By the Act 1690, c. 23, a division of such lands was authorized to be made between the different proprietors according to their respective interests, with the exception of lands belonging to boroughs or incorporations. This decision may be insisted in before the Judge Ordinary or Justices of the Peace. Under the description of "Runrigg-lands" are comprehended lands where the portions consist not of ridges only, but of alternate portions of several acres each."—*Bell's Law Dictionary.*

† In it alone can be found the correct boundaries of many of the properties. In this document the public and servitude roads, agreed upon at the time by the parties to the Decreet of Division, as necessary for the accommodation of themselves and the public, are mentioned and described—the length and breadth of each being given. It is understood

The roads, with which the parish is well supplied, are in general kept in good repair. The nearest town to Coldingham is Eyemouth, 3 miles distant: Ayton is about 4 miles off. There is no weekly market either in Eyemouth, Ayton, or Coldingham. The railway station at Reston is about 3½ miles distant from the town. A survey, however, of a branch line from Reston to Eyemouth, *via* Coldingham, in connection with the N. B. R. has been made, and it is expected that when the harbour at Eyemouth is enlarged (*see* Eyemouth), this line will be proceeded with.

Fairs.— Second Tuesday of July (*o. s.*)* and second Tuesday of October (*o. s.*)*

In 1861 the population of the entire parish was 3237, who composed 675 families; 2 of whom were returned as living in houses having no window, 292 in houses of one window, and 218 in houses of two windows; leaving 163 (a small proportion) as living in houses of three or more windows.

Assessed property in 1864-5, £26,633 : 4 : 8.†

The principal landed-proprietors in the parish (*Coldingham district*) are—David Milne Home, Esq. of Wedderburn ; Henry Home Drummond, Esq. (of Blair Drummond) of Northfield ; Robert Weir Cosens,‡ Esq. of Bogangreen and Alemill (Lieut. 1st Royals); Sir James Hall, Bart. (of Dunglass), of Dowlaw ; F. G. Sandys Lumsdaine, Esq. (of Blanerne) of Lumsdaine ; George Richard Griffith,‖ Esq. (of Hendersyde Park, Kelso) of Burnhall and Silverwells—(*see* p. 181);‡ William Dickson,

---

that the present proprietor of Coldingham Law, A. T. Herriot, Esq., disputes the right of the public to visit the Law Hill without his permission, but it appears the public think differently, and act accordingly. No mention is made of the Law Hill in the Decreet of Division, but certain roads running through Coldingham Law are mentioned, and which cannot be shut up by any proprietor, as the Decreet of Division expressly prohibits and discharges all persons from encroaching thereupon in any way in time coming. The Decreet of Division is in the custody of the proprietor of Wedderburn for the time being, and may be seen by any party interested, in the office of Messrs. Sang & Adam, S.S.C., Edinburgh, the present agents of the proprietor of Wedderburn. The Common of Coldingham was also divided among the heritors and feuars towards the end of the last century, and the decreet may also be seen in the office of Messrs. Sang & Adam.

* That is, 1st Tuesdays on or between the 18th and 25th of July and October. These fairs were formerly of some importance, when the business done at them was chiefly in linen ; they are now fairs only in name.

† The highest assessment in the county. Eccles parish follows with £22,846 : 4 : 2 (*see* note, p. 130).

‡ *See* Eccles parish, p. 659.

‖ Since the sheet containing p. 181 was printed Mr. Griffith has succeeded to the estates of his uncle, Mr. Waldie, (who died 1865); he has now assumed the name of Waldie-Griffith, and has his principal residence at Hendersyde Park.

Esq. (solicitor, Alnwick), of Whitecross ; A. T. Herriot, Esq. of Coldingham Law ; Thos. Landale, Esq. of Templehall (S.S.C. Edinburgh); George Webster, Esq. of Hallydown (advocate, 56 Northumberland Street, Edinburgh); Geo. Denham, Esq. of Bee Edge; Wm. King Hunter, Esq. (of Wellfield, Dunse) of Pilmuir ; Dr. Robert Hood of Eastlaw (Edinburgh) ; Thos. Drybrough, Esq. of Press ; A. D. M'Tavish, Esq. of Abbey Park ; Rev. E. Home of Homefield and Paddockmyre ; A. Mitchell Innes, Esq. of Ayton Castle ; Heirs of Magnus Sandison, of Highlaws.

For the landed-proprietors in *Houndwood district*, see p. 676. Superior of Coldingham—Mrs. Milne Home of Wedderburn and Billie (Milne Graden). Superior of church lands in and around Coldingham (with the exception of Homefield and Paddockmyre,* which hold of the crown)—Earl of Home.

BARON BAILIE—James Watson, Esq., Dunse.

RESIDENT JUSTICES OF THE PEACE—*see* Residences, p. 683.

POLICE OFFICER—George Howlieston.

PUBLIC OFFICES—Registrar of Births, Marriages, and Deaths, and Session Clerk and Kirk Treasurer—Adam R. Tait.

   Inspector of Poor, Collector of Poor Rates, Inspector of Nuisances, and Heritor's Clerk—John Johnston.

   Sheriff-Officer and Constable—David Buglass.

   Medical Officer and Public Vaccinator—Jas. N. M'Dougall, M.D.

POST OFFICE—*see* Villages.

CLERGY, &c.—Presbytery of Chirnside, Synod of Merse and Teviotdale. Patron—The Crown.

   Established Church, Parochial (Coldingham)—Rev. David Munro (Inducted 1847). Sittings, 410. Average attendance at Sabbath School, 50. Precentor—N. Black ; Church Officer—David Buglass.

   U. P. Church—Rev. Andrew B. Robertson (Inducted 1856). Sittings, 528. Average attendance at Sabbath School, 50. Session Clerk—Peter Wilson ; Church Treasurer—David Cormack ; Clerk—George Darrie ; Mission Treasurer—Miss Renton ; Librarian and Treasurer to Congregational Library—Aw. Wilson ; Librarian to Sab. School Library—James Colvin ; Precentor—William Black ; Church Officer—David Gillies.

(*See* also p. 676.)

FAST DAYS—Thursday preceding the last Sunday of June, and about the third Sunday of December—varies according to moonlight.

---

* The Earl of Home disposed of the superiority of the lands of Homefield and Paddockmyre to the great-grandfather of the present proprietor in 1760.

SCHOOLS*—Coldingham, Parochial—Ad. R. Tait, master. Av. at. 80.
,,   Public Subscription School—Thos S. Happer, master. Av. at. 80. Founded 1811.
,,   Private School for Girls—Miss Jane Wilson, teacher. Av. attend. 58.
Coldingham Moor, Side—   Thomson, teacher. Av. at. .

PAROCHIAL BOARD (which also acts as a Sanitary Committee)—T. Landale, Esq., Chairman. Committee—A. T. Herriot, of Coldingham Law; W. Mack, of Berrybank; S. Craig, of Berryhaughs; Rev. E. Home. of Homefield; Rev. Mr. Munro; Messrs J. M'Gall, Hallydown; A. Wilson, and T. Renton, Coldingham ; and Robert Wood, Whitecross. Average Rate of Assessment, 5d. per £; total Assessment 1864-5, £952, 19s. 9d. Poor on Roll, 111. The poor in Houndwood are under the management of the Parochial Board, as before the erection *quoad sacra* of this district.

LIBRARIES—Public Subscription, Coldingham ; U. P. Congregational Library and Public Library at Reston ; Congregational Library at Houndwood.

LIGHT-HOUSE—(St. Abb's Head) opened 24th February 1861. Principal Light-Keeper—Robert Gillespie ; Assistant Light-Keeper—David M'Culloch.

MANUFACTURER—Thomas Renton, Coldingham—Cotton Stripes and Checks.†

FLOUR MILL (Coldingham)—James Brown, miller.

CONVEYANCE—By North British Railway to all parts from Reston and Grant's House stations.

CARRIERS: Berwick—Hogan Fulton, every Saturday ; Eyemouth—John Spence, daily ; Reston—Robert Blair, frequently.

SECOND BERWICKSHIRE ARTILLERY VOLUNTEERS (Coldingham)— Lieutenant Commanding—Andrew Oliver ; Sergeant-Major—Thomas Brown ; Drill Instructor—Corporal William Baker, R. A.; Trumpet-Major and Band-Master—Peter Buglass. Effective Force 53. Annual subscription, Honorary members' subscription,

(For lists in Houndwood district, *see* next columns.)

---

* Children in the entire parish between 5 and 15, attending school during the first week of April 1861, 506 ; of all ages, 522.
† For many years previous to 1862 about thirty weavers were employed in making the above, but owing to the very high price of cotton during the American Civil War, the trade was discontinued, but is now again resumed. It is many years since the manufacture of linens was given up.

Lists of that portion of Coldingham now forming the

Quoad Sacra Parish of Houndwood.

———•———

The part of the parish disjoined to form Houndwood is that lying most inland—the line dividing the old parish into two nearly equal portions.*
The principal landed-proprietors in this portion of the parish are — Mrs. Milne Home, of Wedderburn and Billie (Milne Graden) ; Mrs. Sarah Veitch or Coulson, of Houndwood ; Miss Mary E. Stirling, of Renton ; the Right Honourable the Countess of Home, of Brockholes ; William Home, Esq. of Fairlaw ; Rev. James Smellie, of Reston Mains ; Macdonald Hume (of Ninewells), of Fairney Castle ; Richard Trotter, Esq. (of Mortonhall) of Greenburn ; William Hood, Esq., of Sunnyside ; Thomas Anderson, Esq. of Shawbraes and Coveyheugh ; H. P. Hardie, Esq. of Stoneshiel ; William Mack, Esq. of Berrybank ; Nicol Milne, Esq., of Howpark ; George Home, Esq., of Newmains ; S. Craig, Esq, of Berryhaughs ; James Greenfield, Esq. of Coldlands ; James Turnbull, Esq. of Hillend ; Robert Denham, Esq. of Howburn.

———

RESIDENT JUSTICES OF THE PEACE—*See* Residences, pp. 683, 684.

PUBLIC OFFICES—All retained by the civil parish of Coldingham.

CLERGY, &c.—Presbytery of Chirnside, Synod of Merse and Teviotdale. Patron—Mrs. Milne Home, of Wedderburn and Billie.
    Established Church, *Quoad Sacra* (Houndwood) — Rev. David Drummond (Inducted 1851). Precentor—Alexander Gordon ; Librarian—George Hardie ; Officer—Peter Murray. Sittings, 500. Average attendance at Sabbath Schools, 90.
    Free Church (Houndwood)—Rev. Adam Spence (Inducted 1845). Sittings, 370. Average attendance at Sabbath School, . Superintendent of Sabbath School—Minister ; Session Clerk and Church Officer—Mark Aitken ; Treasurer—Peter Johnston ; Precentor—John Johnston.

---

* This division of Coldingham is shown on the map specially engraved to accompany the REGISTER, copies of which, mounted on cloth and done up in a case, can be had separately—price, 2s. 6d.
† This church was endowed by the late William Foreman Home, Esq. of Wedderburn, the Right Hon. the Earl of Home, the late Mrs. Norman M'Donald Hume of Ninewells, and the Endowment Committee of the Church of Scotland.

SCHOOLS—Reston, Parochial—Arch. M'Craith, teacher; aver. at., .
Houndwood, Side—Geo. Hardie, teacher. Av. attend., .
Auchincraw, Subscription—Alex. Bell, teacher. Av attend., .

WOOLLEN MILL: Coveyheugh—J. Dixon—Tweeds, Blankets, Plaidings, &c.

CORN AND FLOUR MILLS: East Reston—*Joseph Bartlie; Coveyheugh—James Hand; West Reston—James Wilson; Howburn—James Donaldson; Swinewood—Turnbull Gillies.

DIRECTORY.

PROFESSIONS, TRADES, &c.

Those marked thus (*) are Registered Voters in the parish.

Village of Coldingham

POST OFFICE—Thomas Renton, postmaster. Box closes for North and South by Ayton at 4.20 p.m.—Robert Spence, messenger. Box closes for the North by Eyemouth at 10 p.m.—John Preston, messenger. First Arrival from all parts. and town Delivery, at 9 a.m. Second ditto, and Delivery, at 12.30 p.m.

Anchor Inn, John Hood
Baker, William, corporal, Royal Artillery
Beattie, James, merchant tailor
Beattie, Mrs.; furnished lodgings
Blair, Robert, carter and carrier
Blair, William, tailor
Brown, James, blacksmith
*Brown, James Milldown, farmer; furnished lodgings
*Brown, Robert; furnished lodgings
Buglass, David, *sheriff officer*
Buglass, James, clock and watchmaker
Buglass, Peter, boot and shoemaker
Cairns, John Fuller, baker and corn dealer
Chisholm, Alexander, flesher
Cormack, Robt. & Daniel, fish-curers, Coldingham Shore
Cormack, Daniel, Coldingham Shore; furnished lodgings
Cormack, David, shoemaker
*Cormack, Robert, fish-curer (of R. & D. C.)
*Cossar, David, joiner
Cowe, Robert, Coldingham Shore; furnished lodgings
Cowe, William, smith
Craik, Isabel, gardener
Craik, Thomas, blacksmith
Curle, William, baker
Dickinson, Daniel, joiner and undertaker

Dickson, James, Coldingham Shore; furnished lodgings
Edgar, Alexander, wright
Edgar, Mrs.; furnished lodgings
*Ford, John, boot and shoemaker
Forsyth, Alexander, mason
Fulton, Hogan, grocer and carrier
Gillies, David, slater and plasterer
Gillies, Mrs. David; furnished lodgings
Gillies, Mrs. John; furnished lodgings
Gray, Misses. Bridge-end
Greenfield, Mrs. George, feuar
Greenfield, Mrs. James, Cross
Happer, Thomas S., teacher
Henderson, Alexander, saddler
Howlieston, George, *police officer*
Johnston, John, *inspector of poor, etc.*
*Lidgate, Robert, gardener
Laing, James, tailor
Logan, Misses, Hill House
Main, James, wright
Mason, Peter, boot and shoemaker
M'Dougal, James Nairne, M.D.
Morrison. John, cooper
*Munro, Rev. David, *Manse*
New Inn, Adam Pringle. (Horse and gig for hire.)
Oliver, Andrew, Bogangreen House; furnished lodgings
Paterson, Miss Mary; furnished lodgings
Paterson, Mrs. Thomas, feuar
Paterson, Mrs. W., Cross
Paxton, Thomas, grocer and spirit dealer
Purves, Francis, grocer
Renton, Thomas, general merchant and manufacturer
Robertson, Rev. A. B., *U. P. Manse* (Townhead House)
Simpson, David, parish roads' surfaceman
*Spence, Robert, feuar
Spence, John, carrier
Steele, James, cooper
Steele, Miss Alison, dressmaker
*Tait, A. R., parish school-house
Thomson, George, boot and shoemaker
Thorburn, Alexander, carter
Thorburn, John, carter
Thorburn, George, joiner
Thorburn, Robert, feuar
Thorburn, Peter, carter &c.
Thorburn, Robert, fisher, Coldingham Shore; furnished lodgings
Waldie, Miss Jane, dressmaker

White, John, blacksmith
Wilson, Andrew, merchant
Winram, James, grocer
Wilson, Miss Jane, teacher
Wood, Joseph, mason
Young, Mrs. Ann, grocer and spirit dealer ; furnished lodgings

Village of Auchincrow

POST OFFICE—John Fortune, Postmaster. Letters received daily by Ayton, the post town, at 1-10 p.m ; despatched at 3-50 p.m. Messenger—William Mason.

POLICE OFFICER—James Smith.

Allan, John, plate layer
Bell, Alexander, teacher
Cassells, David, grocer
Cockburn, James, grocer and tailor
Crombie, John, joiner
Dyat, Miss Margaret, grocer
Fortune, John, merchant and *postmaster*
*Fulton, John, smith
Hill, George, baker
*Hood, William, joiner
Laing, John, tailor
Lowrie, Michael, wright
Mason, James, shoemaker
Rintoul, David, innkeeper
Robson, George, mason

Hamlet and Railway Station of Grant's House*

POST OFFICE—Thomas Anderson, postmaster. A sub-office under Berwick. Letters received at 10 a.m. ; despatched at 9-15 a.m., and 3-20 p.m. Messenger to Houndwood, &c.—Agnes Gordon.

Campbell, George, mason
Fair, Edward, mason
*Grant, William, general merchant
*Mason, Alexander, shoemaker
*Renton, George, shoemaker
Shearlaw, James, innkeeper
*Turner, James, joiner
Wallace, John, wire fence maker

Station-master—David Elder

---

* The station at Grant's House lies within the boundary of the larger detached portion of Oldhamstocks lying in Berwickshire.

Hamlet of Houndwood

Post Town, Ayton—Letters arrive daily by Grant's House at 11-30, and are despatched at 11-45. Messenger—Agnes Gordon.

*Drummond, Rev. David, *Q. S. Manse*
Fortune, George, Woodland Cottage
Luke, David, blacksmith
Murray, Peter, plate layer
Purves, Thomas, innkeeper
*Spence, Rev. Adam, *Free Church Manse*

Village and Railway Station of Reston

POST OFFICE—Jas. Greenfield, postmaster. A sub-office under Ayton. Letters received daily at 12 noon ; despatched at 4-40 p.m. Messenger—

Broomfield, John, baker
Colvin, John, boot and shoe maker
Colvin, Robert, basket maker
Cowe, John, merchant, and coal depot
Denham, Robert, plate layer
Dunn, George, parish roads' surfaceman
*Darling, Alexander, Reston
Fowler, D. & G., wrights
*Fortune, John, portioner, West Reston
Gillies, Alexander, baker
*Greenfield, James (of Coldlands), merchant
Hogg, James, cattle dealer
Jeffrey, Peter, blacksmith
Liddle, John, veterinary surgeon
*M'Craith, Archibald, schoolmaster
M'Gregor, Hugh, seedsman
Matthison, John, tailor
Nelson, John, tailor
Public Library,   librarian
Red Lion Inn, *Robert Guy
Richardson, Robert, coal dealer
Smith, Mrs. Margaret, grocer
Swan Inn, Samuel Maclauchlan ; coal depot
Watson, George, wright
Wheat Sheaf Inn, Mrs. Redpath

Station-master—John Smith

Sundries in Coldingham District

Loraine, Adam, joiner, Broombank
Luke, David, smith, Scrogend
Luke, James, smith, Clay House
Patterson, Alexander, grocer, Coldingham Moor
Thomson, John, teacher, Coldingham Moor

Sundries in Houndwood District

*Blackhall, John, plate layer, Harelawside
Fleming, Robert, plate layer
Hardie, George, teacher, Renton
Henderson, Ralph, plate layer
Liddle, James, blacksmith, Houghhead
Loraine, Andrew, joiner, Renton Deanfoot

FARMERS, &c., IN THE PARISH.
COLDINGHAM DISTRICT.

Anderson, Thos., farmer, Fertilehall
*Bertram, James,   do.   Howpark
*Brown, John,   do.   Coldingham Moor
Brown, John,   do.   Sunnyside
*Brown, Walter,   do.   do.
*Calder, Thomas,   do.   Auchencraw Mains
Carr, Mrs. Thomas, Greenhead farm
Cormack, Robert, farmer, Godsmount
*Cowe, Robert,   do.   Dowlaw
*Cowe, William,   do.   Blackpotts
*Cowe, William,   do.   Warlawbank
*Cowe, Wm., jun.,   do.   Swansfield
*Craig, Samuel,   do.   Berryhaughs
Dalgetty, James,   do.   West Loch, &c.
Denham, James,   do.   Hopestead
*Edington, Peter,   do.   Lumsdaine
*Edington, Thomas, do.   Westerside
*Forsyth, Ebenezer, do.   Press
*Gibson, Anderson,   do.   Burnhall
*Gibson, William,   do.   do.
*Gillies, William,   do.   Coldingham Loan
*Glen, James,   do.   Fleurs
*Hastie, Thomas,   do.   Highlaws (detached)
*Herriot, James,   do.   Northfield
Hewit, James & Andrew, North Fallowknowe
Home, Mrs. Jessie, Paddockmyre
*Kerr, George, farmer, Coldinghamlaw
*Kerr, Peter,   do.   do.
*Kerr, John, H., do.   do.
*Lamb, Richard,   do.   Alemill
*Leitch, James,   do.   Abbey Park
Lothian, Thos.,   do.   Abbey Edge
*Milliken, Jas.,   do.   Pilmuir
Morrison, Wightman, do. Myrtlehall
*M'Gall, John,   do.   Hallydown
*M'Leod, John,   do.   Silverwells

*Oliver, Andrew, farmer, Bogangreen
*Robertson, James,   do.   Woodside
Romanes, Simon,   do. of Buskinburn
*Watt, John,   do.   Eastlaw
*White, Robert,   do.   Cairncross
*Wightman, Robert,   do.   Crosslaw
*Wilson, James,   do.   Reston Mains
*Wood, Robert,   do.   Whitecross
Wylie, James   do.   Huxton

HOUNDWOOD DISTRICT.

Aitchison, Peter, farmer, Fairlaw
*Allan, Robert A.,   do.   Greenburn
Anderson, James,   do.   Shawbraes
*Bartle, Joseph,   do.   East Reston
*Belaney, Charles,   do.   Hillend
*Bertram, John,   do. of Loneside, Reston
*Bell, Peter,   do.   Stoneshiel
Borthwick, John, Laverocklaw
*Borthwick, Maurice, farmer, Springhill
*Brown, George,   do.   Bogbank
*Brown, George,   do.   Howburn
*Fender, John,   do.   Mountalbane
*Fender, William,   do.   do.
*Fogo, James,   do.   Reston Hill
*Gillies, Turnbull,   do.   Swinwood
*Hand, James,   do.   Westwood
Hardie, William,   do.   Horsley
*Hope, Robert,   do.   Greenwood
*Logan, David,   do.   Fairney Castle
Moffat, George, manager, Renton estate
*Murray, James, farmer, Harelawside
*Murray, Thomas, do.   Brockholes
*Popplewell, David,   do. East Reston
Purves, John,   do.   Heughhead
*Purves, William,   do.   do.
Thorburn, William, do. Coldlands
*Webster, Alex. H.,   do. Lamington
Whitlaw,   , manager, Houndwood estate
*Wood, Thomas, farmer, Renton Barns

SEATS, &c., OF COUNTY FAMILIES AND SMALLER RESIDENCES IN THE PARISH.

Coldingham District.

COLDINGHAM LAW HOUSE.

Situated near to the village of Coldingham—the property and residence of Alexander T. Herriot, Esq., J. P.

HOMEFIELD.

Situated near the village—the property and residence of the Rev. Edward Home, of Paddockmyre and Homefield.

HIGHLAWS.

Situated near to Eyemouth, in the detached part of the parish —the residence of Mrs. Magnus Sandison.

PRESS HOUSE.

Near the centre of the parish—the residence of *Thomas Drybrough Esq., who purchased the property from Alexander Henderson, Esq.

TEMPLEHALL HOUSE.

Situated near Coldingham village—the property and summer residence of *Thomas Landale, Esq., S.S.C., J.P. Edinburgh address—18 Forth Street.

Houndwood District.

BERRYBANK.

Situated about 1 mile south-east from Reston station—the property and residence of *William Mack, Esq., J.P.

COVEYHEUGH HOUSE.

Situated near Reston—the property and residence of *Thomas Anderson, Esq., J. P.

FAIRLAW HOUSE.

About 1 mile south-west from Reston — the residence and joint property of *William Home, Esq., J. P. and *John Home, jun.

HOUNDWOOD HOUSE.

Situated about 2 miles west from Reston Station—the residence of Mrs. Coulson.

NEWMAINS.

Situated half-a-mile south from Reston—the property and residence of *George Home, Esq., J. P.

RENTON HOUSE.

Situated about 1 mile east of Grant's House—the residence of Lady Stirling (Mary Harriet Thornton, youngest daughter of Col. Thomas Begbie, late 44th Regiment), widow of the late Sir Samuel Home Stirling (he died 19th September 1861, and was succeeded by Sir Charles Elphinstone Stirling, 8th and present baronet, residing at Glorat, Stirlingshire); married 11th October 1854, and has issue two daughters—Mary and Eleanor.

STONESHIEL HOUSE.

About 2 miles south from Reston—the property and residence of *Henry Hardie, Esq.

SUNNYSIDE.

About 1½ miles south-west from Reston—the property and residence of *William Hood, Esq., J.P.

COUNTY VOTERS (Non-Resident).

REGISTERED IN COLDINGHAM PARISH.

Annandale, Alexander, sen., Polton Mills, Lasswade
Annandale, Alexander, jun.,   do.   do.
Annandale, James Hunter,   do.   do.
Bruce, Henry, Kenleith, Currie
Carr, Robert, farmer, Felkington
Cosens, Robert, Esq., of Bogangreen
Craig, George, Dunbar
Craig, Robert, Craigesk, Dalkeith
Cowe, John, gardener, Luffness
Darling, Adam, Governor's Yard, Berwick
Denholm, David, Woollands
Dale, John R., farmer, Auldhame, North Berwick
Davidson, James, Wilford, Nottingham
Dickson, James, Lamberton Toll
Dickson, William, Esq. (of Whitecross), Alnwick
Drummond, Henry Home, Esq. of Blair Drummond
Drummond, George H., Esq., Blair Drummond
Griffith, George R., Esq. of Hendersyde Park
Goodfellow, Walter, Blackburn
Henry, William, Broomhouse
Hood, Robt., Esq. (of Mains), 5 Salisbury Rd., Edinburgh
Houlieston, John, farmer, late of Coldlands
Hunter, William K., Esq. of Pilmuir, Dunse
Johnston, Thomas, Berwick
Mactavish, Alexander D. (of Abbey Park), Australia
Mason, Peter, shoemaker, Foulden

Meikle, John, Portobello
Milne, Nicol, Esq. of Faldonside, Melrose
M'Dougall, Thomas, Eskmills, Pennicuick
M'Intosh, Robert, Fountainside
Purves, Robert (Coldingham), Abroad
Sandys-Lumsdaine, Rev. E., Upper Hardres Rectory, Canterbury (*see* note, p. 633)
Smellie, Rev. James, Innerwick
Tullis, William, Auchmuty, Markinch
Turnbull, James, Edinburgh
Williamson, George, do.
White, James, farmer, Burnbank
Webster, George, Edinburgh

OLDHAMSTOCKS.

THE parish of Oldhamstocks belongs properly to Haddingtonshire, but two small portions of it belong to the county of Berwick. The larger part—in shape nearly a square, measuring 1⅓ mile on each side, and consisting of 1418¾ acres, of which 5¼ are occupied by the N. B. railway—lies quite detached from the rest of the parish, and is surrounded by the parishes of Cockburnspath, Coldingham, and Abbey St. Bathans; the smaller part, consisting of 928 acres, lies undetached from the rest of the parish, but is surrounded on three of its sides by Berwickshire, where the parishes of Abbey St. Bathans and Cockburnspath form its boundaries. In the larger portion is the farm of Butterdean and the railway station of Grant's House (*see* p. 679); in the smaller is the estate of Nether Monynut, and Luckie Sheil, belonging to the estate of Billie. In Haddingtonshire is the village of Oldhamstocks, the principal one in the parish (*see* p. 591—"Free Church") and the mansion-house of Dunglass, &c.

The total area of the two Berwickshire portions is 2347 acres; 7¾ of which (besides the 5¼ occupied by the railway) are in public and private roads, and a little over 2 are under water The larger portion is fertile and mostly under cultivation; the smaller portion partakes of the characteristics of the upper part of the parish generally which, inland, is barren and moorish. This portion is hilly--one point, Laughinglaw, rises to 1108 feet; and Coarselaw, lying partly in Cockburnspath, rises to 1042 feet.

The rare bird the Dotterel is a summer visitant (of about a fortnight in May) to the larger portion of this parish, and to the adjoining portion of Abbey St. Bathans. It loves to settle and feed upon the new ploughed moors. It is easily shot, and is most delicate eating (*see* note, p. 663).

According to the census of 1861 the Berwickshire portions of Oldhamstocks contained 125 inhabitants. The returns do not give their housing accommodation apart from that of the entire parish.

The assessed rental of the two portions (designated "Pendicles" at p. 472) is £1395, 10s. Their principal landed-proprietors are—Arthur James Balfour (of Whittingham, minor), of Butterdean (in the larger portion); James Weatherly, Esq., of Nether Monynut (*see* p. 516); and David Milne Home, Esq. (of Wedderburn), of Luckie Sheil (in the smaller portion).

The parish church, manse, school, &c. are at Oldhamstocks in Haddingtonshire. Minister—Rev. Thomas Mitchell. Patron

—James W. Hunter, Esq. of Thurston, Parochial School-master,* Registrar, etc.—vacant.

POST OFFICE for Butterdean, &c.—Grant's House; for Monynut—Dunse. The village of Oldhamstocks has a sub-office under Cockburnspath.

REGISTERED VOTERS FOR BERWICKSHIRE,

Residing in the larger part of the parish.

Bird, John, farmer, Butterdean
Wallace, John, portioner, Grant's House

In the smaller portion are no resident proprietors or farmers.

* Children of all ages in these two detached portions attending school during the first week of April 1861, 13.

EYEMOUTH.

——◆——

THIS is a small parish on the sea-coast, formerly a dependancy of Coldingham, of which a detached portion (Highlaws) is still in the centre of this parish. Eyemouth is bounded by Coldingham on the west, by the German Ocean on the north, and by Ayton on the south and east. Its general outline is square, and measures about 1½ miles on all sides. The area of the parish, according to the Ordnance Survey, is 1079½ acres, of which 21½ are public roads, 5 are under running water and 6½ under tidal, while 6½ consist of "foreshore"; the remainder beyond the limits of the town is mostly under cultivation. The coast line, allowing for headlands, which extends in length to about 1½ miles, is rocky and precipitous, averaging about eighty feet above the level of the sea. The Crimels, Killiedraught, and Eyemouth bay are the only accessible points. At the mouth of the Eye is the town of Eyemouth, an ancient seaport, and burgh of barony, with a small but excellent harbour opening into a safe, picturesque, semicircular bay, admitting vessels of small burthen at every stage of the tide. This is the only seaport town in the county of Berwick. The port is of great antiquity, having been known as early as the reign of Alexander II., when it was resorted to by the monks of that age, as a commodious harbour for importing supplies, and for shipping wool, hides, etc., in which they trafficked.* "The town, though not elegant, contains many good houses, possesses a neat spire towering up from its church, is well supplied with water, and the streets are well kept;" but it has no system, properly so called, of either water or drainage, while its streets are mostly narrow and twisted—not suited for free ventilation or the promotion of sanitary measures generally. Despite of these drawbacks, to which we may add, poor housing accommodation, the town stands out favourably in the Death Rate or Poor Roll Tables (Nos. 3 and 4). Although the parish may be said to con-

* In history the town is indirectly connected with the Gowrie Conspiracy; for centuries it was noted for the extent of its smuggling operations : "it has a dark and cunning look," almost every house having been erected with adaptations for the concealment of contraband goods.
    The first honour bestowed on John Churchill, who afterwards, in Queen Anne's time, became the great Duke of Marlborough, was the Lordship of Eyemouth, in the Scotch Peerage; this was through the influence of the Duke of York, afterwards James II. This honour seems to have been held only by the first Duke.

sist merely of the town (its qualifying country district is almost *nil*), its death rate is about the smallest per annum of all the town parishes in the district; its *legitimate* birth rate is the highest of *all* the parishes, and its *illegitimate* birth rate is *the* smallest. Its poor on the roll are a fair average, but not one of them is *insane.** Can any other town in the Empire of like population show the same results? Up till now the entire sanitary arrangements of the town have been under the management of the parochial board, and the expenses, met chiefly by a sanitary rate, were collected along with the poor rate. With the means at their disposal, the board have done their utmost to promote the amenity of the place; but as it cannot *enforce* either measures or rates, the population have adopted the Burgh Act of 1862, by which the Commissioners are bound to light, repair, cleanse, and drain every lane and street within the limits. When the commissioners have accomplished their work, it will be curious to compare the then death rates with those at present existing.†

The principal sources of employment in Eyemouth are the white and herring fisheries, which are here largely and energetically followed. As a haddock fishing station the town is said to be now the most important and noted in the kingdom.‡

---

* This was for the year 1864, as shown both by the Lunacy and Parochial Board Reports; since then *one* insane pauper has got on the roll.

† *See* Dr. Stark's remarks on sanitary measures, in the Notes to the Death Rate Table.

‡ "'Situated on the very key of the coast, the fishermen have access to the best haddock fishing grounds south and north, and at a moderate distance from land; and have also the means of conveyance by rail—from Burnmouth or Ayton stations—to the best markets in the kingdom. The fishermen are steady, industrious, and enterprising, and, we may add, wealthy, many of them being house proprietors and Registered Voters. Their boats are of the most approved class and build, and the fishing materials of the finest description.

With such natural and acquired advantages, the success of the fishing is almost a matter of certainty, and has rapidly increased in extent and importance. About 25 years ago there were only 10 boats employed, worth, with the lines, about £700; and the estimated value of fish landed during the year did not exceed £2000. From a reference to the Returns given at page 697, it will be seen that 34 boats are now employed, of 680 tons, valued at £7000, manned by 215 fishermen, and that the value of the fish landed is no less than £15,000. The fish are of superior quality, and are prepared with the greatest care by the curers, who, as a class, are noted for their skill, and command the highest price in all the markets (Glasgow principally) to which they are sent.

The trade having outgrown the original harbour accommodation, with a view to its improvement and enlargement by aid of a Government grant, a careful and minute survey of it was made in September of this year (1865) by the Messrs. Stevenson, C.E., Edinburgh ; and should funds be obtained sufficient to complete the projected improvements, Eyemouth Harbour will become one of the most accessible and commodious on the coast.

Eyemouth is 53 miles from Edinburgh, 8 from Berwick, and 3 from Ayton, where is the nearest railway station. The railway station at Burnmouth is about the same distance as that of Ayton. It has been proposed to form a railway from Reston station, *via* Coldingham, to Eyemouth, and we believe the line has been surveyed.

The population of the town of Eyemouth, by the census of 1861, was 1721; of the entire parish, 1804, who composed 378 families ; 177 of whom were returned as living in houses of one window, and 114 in houses of two windows, leaving the small proportion of less than one-fourth living in houses of three or more windows.

Assessed property in 1864-5, £5624 : 14 : 1.

The principal landed-proprietors in the parish are—David Milne Home, Esq., of Billie and Wedderburn ; Heirs of Magnus Sandison, of Highlaws ; George Webster, of Hallydown ; and Capt. Francis Ramsay (of Linthill). Cheltenham.

Superior—David Milne Home, Esq.

COMMISSIONERS—Appointed under the New Burgh Act, which was adopted on 4th December 1865—not yet elected.

BARONY OFFICER—James Smith.

POLICE OFFICERS—James Smith and James Benzies.

PUBLIC OFFICES, &c.

Session Clerk, Kirk Treasurer, Heritors' Clerk, and Registrar of Births, Marriages, and Deaths—James Cox.

Fishery Officer—Peter Wilson.

Poor, Inspector of—Archibald Todd.

Procurator-Fiscal, J. P.—James Bowhill—(Office, Ayton).

Stamps and Taxes—James Bowhill, Sub-distributor.

Medical Officer and Public Vaccinator—James Forsyth, M.D.

Collector of Poor Rates—Alexander John Dawson.

Collector of Statute Labour Conversion Money—Charles D. Colville, Ayton.

POST OFFICE.

John Johnston, Postmaster.

Mails arrive from Ayton at 11 a.m. and 9 p.m., and depart 7-15 a.m. and 4-50 p.m. Mails leave for Coldingham at 7-15 and 10-50 a.m.

The boats belonging to the coast are all built at Eyemouth by Mr. Weatherhead, and for material, workmanship, and build cannot be surpassed.

EYEMOUTH DISTRICT OF FISHERIES extends from Dunbar to Beadnell (in Northumberland) inclusive, but with the returns beyond the limits of Berwickshire we have no concern in the present publication.

2 x

CLERGY, &c.

Presbytery of Chirnside, and Synod of Merse and Teviotdale. Patron —The Crown.

ESTABLISHED CHURCH—Rev. Stephen Bell (Inducted 1845) Sittings, 450. Average attendance at Sabbath School, 40. Superintendent of Sabbath School—Minister ; Session-Clerk and Kirk Treasurer—James Cook ; Precentor—W. Windram ; Church Officer—James Scott.

FREE CHURCH—Rev. John Turnbull (Inducted 1822). Sittings, 300. Average attendance at Sabbath School, 60. Superintendent of Sabbath School, and Session-Clerk—William Macfarlane ; Treasurer—A. Bell ; Precentor—James Windrum ; Church Officer—William Miller.

U. P. CHURCH— Rev. James Harrower (Inducted 1857). Sittings, . Average attendance at Sab. School, 70. Superintendent of Sabbath School—John Dickson ; Session-Clerk—John Johnson ; Treasurer—Peter C. Renton ; Precentor—James Black ; Church Officer—Alexander Henderson.

EVANGELICAL UNION—Rev. Robert Finlay (Inducted 1864). Sittings, 250. Average attendance at Sabbath School, .

BAPTIST CHURCH—Various.

METHODIST CHURCH—

FAST DAYS—Established Church, Wednesday before full moon in January, and first Wednesday of July. United Presbyterian and Free Church, Wednesdays before second Sunday of January and July.

SCHOOLS.†

Parochial—James Cox, master ; average attendance, 65.

Do.   Infant—Christina Munro, teacher ; average attendance, 70.

Free Church—Walter M'Farlane, master ; average attendance, 70.

Do.   Infant—Christina Adam, teacher ; average attend., 170.

Private—D. Fraser, master ; average attendance, .

PAROCHIAL BOARD.

Peter Craig Renton, Chairman.

Average number of Poor on Roll, 44.
Rate of Assessment, 9d. per £. Total Assessment 1864-5, £410.

---

† Children in the parish between 5 and 15, attending school during the first week of April 1861, 340 ; of all ages, 356.

SANITARY COMMITTEE (Established 1856).

Robert Cormack.	John Johnston, fish-curer.
George Dickson.	D. Aitchison.
George Renton.	James Tait.
Thomas Alexander.	James Ford.

P. C. Renton, Chairman of Committee.
Archibald Todd, Inspector of Nuisances.

LODGE OF FREEMASONS (ST. EBB's—estab. 1757).

R. W. Master—Peter Todd, Redhall, Ayton.
Past Master—Charles D. Colville, Ayton.
Treasurer—Robert Dickson, Eyemouth.
Secretary—John Johnston, Eyemouth.
Number of Members, 40 to 50.

In 1787 the poet Burns was admitted into the mysteries of this Lodge, when, " on account of his remarkable poetical genius, he was admitted gratis—the members considering themselves honoured by having a man of such shining abilities for one of their companions."

LIBRARY (Public)—D. Fraser, Librarian. Subscription, 3s. per annum. 1900 Vols.

GAS COMPANY (estab. 1847).

Secy. and Treas.—Drysdale Aitchison.   Manager—James Whillis.
7s. 6d. per 1000 feet.
Capital, £800. Dividend, 5 per cent.

WATER COMPANY (estab. 1856).

A. Todd, Treasurer and Secretary.
No regular Rate.

HARBOUR TRUST.

ACTING TRUSTEES.

T. Allan, J. Bowhill, T. Calder, G. Dickson, E. Sturdy, John Innes R. A. Allan, and John Johnston.
Treasurer, J. Bowhill.   Clerk, Alex. J. Dawson.
Collector and Harbour Master, William Wright.

FISHERIES BOARD—Inspector for Eyemouth District—P. Wilson. Eyemouth.

SHIPPING LIST—The only vessel owned in Eyemouth is the coaster " Hawk," of 50 tons, James Patterson, owner.

CUSTOM HOUSE—Two Coast Guardsmen reside here : James Prout and James Rodger. Superintendent of Eyemouth and Burnmouth—Captain Jackson, R.N., Berwick. Burnmouth Officer—William Ralph.

GYMNASTIC GAMES AND BOAT RACES (estab. 1861).

Held at Eyemouth Fort in July—day unfixed.
Patron—David Milne Home, yr. of Wedderburn.
Secretary—John Johnston.
Amount of Prizes given in 1865, over £30.

1ST BERWICKSHIRE ARTILLERY CORPS—(EYEMOUTH.)

Peter Tod, Redhall, 1st Lieutenant Commanding.
James M. Patterson, 2nd Lieutenant.
James Forsyth, Hon. Surgeon.
Drill Instructor—Andrew Gallagher.   Bandmaster—J. Black.
Effective Force—50.   Honorary Members—6.
Subscription for Honorary Members, 21s.

BANK.

COMMERCIAL BANK OF SCOTLAND (opened 1832, sub-branch to Ayton)
—Jas. Bowhill, Agent ; Alex. John Dawson, Acting Sub-Agent.

INSURANCE AGENTS.

INSURANCE CO. OF SCOTLAND..James Bowhill, banker.
LIFE ASSOCIATION............P. C. Renton, merchant.
NORTH BRITISH ....P. C. Renton.
NORTHERN INSURANCE COY...John Johnston, grocer.
ROYAL INSURANCE COMPANY..J. & G. Forsyth, merchants.
SCOTTISH EQUITABLE.........James Bowhill banker.
SCOTTISH UNION COMPANY....P. C. Renton, grocer.

PROCURATOR, &c.—James Bowhill.
MEDICAL PRACTITIONER—*Dr James Forsyth.
CARRIERS—Berwick, G. Nisbet, Saturday ; Burnmouth, J. Dickson, daily, and thence by Railway to all parts.

TRADES, RESIDENTS, &c.

Those marked thus (*) are Registered Voters, and those thus (‖) are tenants of Acre-dale lands—*see* note, pp. 695 and 696.

*Aitchison, Drysdale, joiner
*Alexander, Thomas, fish-curer and cooper
  Allan, William, & Co., wood merchants
*Bell, Alexander (of B. & Glen)
  Bell, Rev. Stephen, *Manse*
*Bell & Glen, fish-curers
  Black Bull Inn, Stephen Landells
  Bogue, William, rope and sail maker
*Brack, Andrew, blacksmith
  Brack, A., grocer
*Brodie, William, sailor
  Cockburn, William, baker
*Collin, Alexander, fisherman
*Collin, James,   do.
  Commercial Bank, Alex. John Dawson, sub-agent
  Cormack, Robert, fish-curer
*Cormack, John,   do.
*Cox, James, *Parochial School*
  Cross Keys Inn, Robert Gibson
*Dickson, George, fish-curer
*Dickson, John (of R. & J. D.)
  Dickson, J., carrier
*Dickson, Robert (of R. & J. D.)
  Dickson, R. & J., fish-curers
  Dickson, W. & P., fish-curers
*Dougal, Robert, fisherman and merchant
*Douglas, Andrew, grocer
  Edington, Alexander, tailor
  Ewart, James, blacksmith
  Eyemouth Gas Company, James Whillis, manager
  Finlay, Rev. Robert, *Evangelical Union*
*Ford, James, shoemaker
  Forsyth, James, surgeon and druggist
  Forsythe, J. & G, merchants
*Forsythe, Robert, glazier
  Fraser, David, teacher
  Gibson, A., baker
*Gillie, James, cooper
*Gillie, John, fisherman
*Glen, Alexander (of Bell & G.), fish-curer
‖*Gray, David, farmer
  Gray, John,   do.
*Hair, John, farmer
  Harrower, Rev. James, *U. P. Manse*

*Harrington, Samuel, china merchant
*Hay, George, joiner
Hume, J., tailor and clothier
Innes & Craig, fish-curers
||Jordan, Robert, butcher
Johnston, A. & D., fish-curers
*Johnston, John,   do.
Johnston, James, North Burn Thrashing Mill
*Johnston, John, grocer, wine and spirit merchant
||*Landells, George, farmer
||*Landells, John,   do.
*Landells, William, joiner
*Lowrie, James, fisherman
M'Farlane, Walter, *Free Church School*
Nisbet, John, grocer
Paterson, James M., baker
*Paterson, Alexander, fisherman
*Patterson, James, ship-owner
*Patterson, Peter, fisherman
Post Office, John Johnston, postmaster
*Purves, Robert, tailor
||*Purves, Robert, farmer
*Renton, George, wood merchant
*Renton, Peter Craig, merchant
*Robertson, Adam
Royal Hotel, Alexander Crombie
*Scougal, Charles, nail-maker
Ship Inn, *William Patterson
Spears, William, fisherman
*Statham, Timothy, plumber
*Storey, Robert, shoemaker and butcher
Stott, Mrs., innkeeper
Stott, Robert, fish-curer
Tait, James, grocer
Tate, Mrs., innkeeper
Taylor, John, butcher
*Todd, Archibald, *Inspector of Poor*, and baker
*Turnbull, Rev. John, *Free Church Manse*
Weatherhead, James, boat-builder
||*Whitelaw, Peter, farmer
*Wilson, John, fish-curer
Wilson, Peter, *Fisheries' Inspector*

FARMERS AND RESIDENTS IN THE PARISH.

Brown, James & Peter, farmers, Acre-dale Lands‡

‡ " Acre-dale or Aiker-daill—a term sometimes met with in old deeds

Brown, James, farmer, Acre-dale Lands
Chrystal, William, do.   do.
*Craig, Alexander, do. Linthill
Hastie, Thomas,   do. Highlaws (part of Highlaws in Coldingham parish)
Paterson, Robert, Linthill House
Paterson, Wm., farmer, Eyemouth Mill
Purves, William, do.   Acre-dale Lands
Thorburn, Robert, do.   do.

FAMILY SEAT.

ST. ELLA'S LODGE.

Situated in the town of Eyemouth—the occasional residence of the Hon. Mrs. Charles St. Clair (Anne, 4th daughter of Sir John Pringle, Bart., of Newhall); married, 1854, Hon. Chas. St. Clair,† R.N., son of the late Lord Sinclair of Nesbit and Herdmanston; he died February 1863, leaving issue—

Susan Eva.
John Pringle, born April 1862.

REGISTERED VOTERS (Not Resident).

Allan, James, merchant, Berwick
Allan, Thomas,   do.,   do.
Cairns, John Fuller, baker, Coldingham
Craig, George, butler, Inveresk
Gillie, Home Purves, corn merchant, Berwick
Goodsman, James, Glasgow
Murray, George, accountant, Edinburgh
Purves, William, farmer, Marshall Meadows
Robertson, John A., M.D., Edinburgh
Ramsay, Francis, Paxton House
Renton, John, Manchester
Taylor, Leonard, London
Thomson, Samuel, do.
Turnbull, Richard, Redside, North Berwick

and writings, signifying lands in the neighbourhood of villages or towns, let in small portions of an acre or so."—*Bell's Law Dictionary.*
    The Acre-dale lands of Eyemouth consist of between 200 and 300 acres, and are divided into small farms of about 30 acres.
    † The Hon. Mr. St. Clair had previously married (in 1840) Isabella Jane, daughter of the late Wm. Foreman Home, Esq., of Paxton ;she died 1852, leaving with other issue—Wm. Home Chisholm, born 1841 ; Lieut. R.N. ; at present stationed at the Naval College, Portsmouth.

STATISTICS OF THE HERRING AND WHITE FISHERIES

FOR THE COAST OF BERWICKSHIRE FOR 1864.

Supplied by the Fishery Board for Scotland.[1]

No. 1.—WHITE FISHERY.

CONSISTING PRINCIPALLY OF HADDOCKS .[2]

	Eye-mouth.	Burn-mouth and Ross.	Colding-ham.	Dunglas or Cove.	TOTAL. for the Coast.
Fishing Department.					
No. of Boats employed	34	8	12	5	59
Supposed Tonnage . .	680	160	165	70	1075
No. of Fishermen and Boys employed[3] . .	215	54	53	27	349
Value of Boats and Lines	£7000	£1600	£1500	£630	£10,730
No. of Haddocks, Tur-bot, Cods, &c., caught, probably .	1,550,000	350,000	340,000	155,000	2,395,000
Supposed Value of do. at the boat side . .	£15,000	£3500	£3400	£1550	£23,450
Curing Department.[4]					
No. of Curing Estab-lishments	9	3	1	1	14
No. of Hands employ-ed in Baiting Lines, Splitting and Smok-ing the Fish, &c.§ .	300	35	65	55	455

[1] Head-Quarters—Royal Institution, Edinburgh. Secretary—Hon. B. F. Primrose. The courtesy of the Board in supplying, and of Mr. P. Wilson, District Inspector at Eyemouth, in compiling, these returns, we have gratefully to acknowledge.

[2] Cod, Ling, Turbot, and Halibut, are also caught by the Haddock lines, but they are few in number. Turbot and Halibut very seldom. In the Turbot Fishery, properly so called, nets are used ; these are sunk to the bottom where they stand up something like sheep pens.

[3] The number of fishermen and boys entered here as employed in the White Fishery, are included under Herring Fishery.

[4] The value of the fish sold cured can only be ascertained by direct

NOTES ON THE WHITE FISHERY TABLE.

THE boats used at Eyemouth and Burnmouth and Ross, in the white fishery, are all of large size, measuring from 48 to 55 feet in length, and from 17 to 19 in breadth. With one or two exceptions, they are full decked, and in value they average about £200, while the lines will cost £40 more. All the boats are manned by six or seven men each. Although Haddocks are good in August, the fishing for them does not begin till late in September, at the conclusion of the herring fishing, and is most energetically prosecuted from October to February (inclusive). In January they are in prime condition. In February, although the fishing is still energetically prosecuted, the fish spawns, falls off in flesh and quality, and, till April, is out of season. In May it again becomes good, and in June is once more at its best ;[1] but by this time it has got scarce, not from want of fish, but owing to the men being then engaged preparing for the herring harvest.

In England, especially away about Yarmouth, the haddocks are caught by trawling—a rough process which deteriorates their quality by bruising and breaking them. The Berwickshire coast will not admit of trawling, the ground being too rocky.[2] Next to Dublin Bay, where haddocks of enormous size are caught, we believe those of the Berwickshire coast are esteemed as of most value in the market.[3] The haddock does not take on salt so well as the cod, but is well adapted for smoking and curing in a half-dried state ; and thus we have the Finnan Haddock, the superiority of which, produced at Eyemouth, has brought it such wealth and repute.

The bait used along the coast is principally the mussel, and it has been calculated that 1400 tons of this shell-fish are annually imported, principally from Basten-deep and Lynn, into Eyemouth alone, to be thus used, at a cost of £2 per ton.[4]

Lobsters and Crabs do not constitue a part of the white fishery ; they form a distinct branch which is prosecuted only by a few old men.

application to the curer ; for us to go into this part of the matter would entail a delay in our publication : we are thus constrained to leave out what might have been further and interesting particulars.

§ The number of hands entered here as employed in the White Fishery, is additional to the number entered under Herring Fishery, all of whom are also employed in the White Fishery.

[1] At the sea-side, where its qualities are known, the goodness of a June haddock has become a proverb ; while inland, from its scarcity, it is then generally supposed to be out of season.

[2] Except for oysters, trawling is not practised in Scotland.

[3] The *blacker* the marks (St. Peter's finger and thumb) on each of the haddock's sides, the more rocky has been the feeding ground of the fish, and the better its quality ; thus the Eyemouth haddocks, caught from 10 to 20 miles off, on the rocky bottom, are more strongly marked and better in quality than those of Berwick-on-Tweed, which are caught on the soft grounds of the bay ; but the state of the weather very much affects the appearance of the haddock (as it does many other fish)—thus, both before and after a severe storm, the haddock has a blacker appearance all over.

[4] A ton per week is the average quantity required by each boat.

No. 2.—HERRING FISHERY.

Fishing Department.	Eye-mouth.	[1] Burn-mouth, and Ross	Colding-ham.	Dunglas or Cove.	TOTAL for the Coast.
No. of Boats employed	113	32	27	15	185
Supposed Tonnage .	1690	480	400	225	2795
No. of Fishermen and Boys employed during the season[2] . . .	565	160	135	75	935
Square yds. of Netting	2,657,760	752,640	635,040	352,800	4,393,240
Suppos'd Value of Boats and Nets	£18,025	£4800	£4310	£2250	£29385
Barrels caught	15,646	2071	666	349	18,732
Value of ditto at the boat side	£17,210	£2280	£730[4]	£455[4]	£20,675
Curing Department.					
No. of Curing Establishments	13	3	1	1	18
No. of Hands employed during the season Gutting, Curing, Driving, Coopering, &c.[3]	283	58	26	14	381
Capital supposed to be sunk in the trade .					
Barrels Cured, Gutted, & Ungutted (white)	7540	1301	367	51	9259
Do. do. (red)§ .					
Do. sent to Market, fresh or lightly salted	8106	770	299	298	9473
Val. of Herrings cured in addition to their value at the boat side, entered above .	£1100	£200	£55	£10	£1365
Do. do. lightly salted, in addition to their value at the boat side, entered above .	£1650	£155	£60	£60	£1925
Total Value of Boats, Nets, and Herrings .	£37,985	£7435	£5155	£2775	£53,350

[1] Ross (see Mordington Parish, p. 645) is included with Burnmouth (see Ayton Parish, p 566) in the returns. The two hamlets are situated very near to each other and may be said to constitute one village.

[2] *See* note No. 2, Wh. Fishery.   [3] See note (§) White Fishery.

[4] The Cove Boats land the greater part of their catch of Herrings at Dunbar. The Coldingham Boats land a great part of theirs at Eymouth, and elsewhere. This accounts for the comparatively small returns entered for these Stations.   § Included in number cured White.

NOTES ON THE HERRING FISHING TABLE.

THE Herring fishery is carried on with entirely different and distinct materials from the white fishery; the boats are smaller — mostly half-decked — and nets are used. The fishing on the coast generally begins in June, and is continued till the middle of September.

The nets used in June and July, when the herrings are still far off-shore are made of fine cotton cord or stout thread, the herring then being wild in habit and small in size, (in its richest state for eating fresh, but not suitable for curing). As the season advances, and the shoals get in-shore, a net of fine twine is used, worked into meshes of an inch square. Each net is about 50 yards long by 33 feet in depth. These nets which are now woven by machinery, were formerly made by the fishermen's families; but so many are now used that it would be impossible to make them by hand, each boat having a train of from 30 to 40 nets, which, when cast, stretch a mile or more in length; the nets, suspended about 18 feet from the surface by bladder or dog-skin floats are—one end attached to the boat—allowed to drift with the tide, and the herrings are caught by striking against the nets, in which they are entangled by the head.

It was at one time supposed that herrings were migratory, and only visited the coast in shoals at certain seasons of the year for the purpose of spawning; but it is now the generally received opinion that they exist around our coasts all the year over; they are often seen in the winter months, but at a great distance from land. In February and March they are sometimes caught, but generally of a poor quality.

The herring fishing partakes greatly of the nature of a lottery [for individual boats, but in the aggregate the returns are very large and certain]. One boat will sometimes get a large haul of herrings, and the one next may count its take by dozens, and this entirely independant of quality of nets or other material employed; and it sometimes happens that the herrings striking the nets with a downward course carry them to the bottom, when the nets are either lost or partially destroyed. At other times rough weather may set in and the nets of different boats become inextricably entangled and destroyed; but the certain, although irregular, chances of lucky hauls, and the bustle and excitement attending this branch of his calling give to it an overpowering charm to the fisherman. To the sea-side visitor the herring fishery possesses great novelty—few sights being more picturesque than the departing fleet of boats leaving the harbour at sunset, with their sombre-coloured sails set, spreading, some out to sea till lost in the distance—others along the coast, or under the precipitous headland; or of more interest than the same fleet returning, straggling in from sunrise till mid-day—some light, and sailing carelessly with the wind—others, heavy with fish and sunk to gunnels, and assisted by the heavy oars; then comes the unloading: the silvery fish shovelled into baskets * and emptied into carts for conveyance to the curing house, where women begin the process of gutting (by a quick insertion of a pointed knife under the head, a wrench, and out comes the gills and entrails, leaving the melt or roe), immediately followed by a wonderfully rapid arrangement in barrels—herrings and salt in alternate layers. A woman will thus pack a barrel containing 600 fish—each fish carefully arranged on its back, the layer forming a neat circle in the barrel—in 15 minutes. After packing, the barrels are on the following day, or as early

---

* Four of these baskets form the CRAN, the official measure.

as possible, headed up by the cooper. After lying ten days the barrels are re-opened and completely filled up and pickled; they are then ready to receive the Government inspection and brand, and forthwith may be shipped to Germany or the Mediterranean, where, as the best of Scotch Herrings, they command the *highest* price in the market. Instead of lying the 10 days necessary for thorough curing and Government inspection, vast quantities are sent off ungutted—mostly to large inland towns, to cure themselves by the way, or be consumed at once in a half-fresh state; or, by smoking, be converted into bloaters, as may best suit the fishmongers' requirements.

Mackerel are caught during the Herring season, but only to a trifling extent, and are not valued in the official returns.

COMPARATIVE TABLE No. 2,

Showing the Gross Value per Acre of each of the Parishes in Berwickshire (including house property and water), as per the Valuation returns (*see* p. 472); the Rise per Acre since 1856; and the Net Agricultural Value per Acre.

For Comparative Table of ROXBURGH *and* SELKIRK SHIRES *(of which this is a continuation) see p.* 463, *and Notes on ditto, pp.* 464-466.

No.		PARISH.	Average Real Rental per Acre, 1865.			Rise per Ac. since 1856.		Agricultural Value per Acre, 1865.		
			£	S.	D.	S.	D.	£	S.	D.
42	*I.—Town.*	Coldstream	2	4	4	3	8¾	1	7	3¾
43		Dunse	1	19	2¼	3	0¼	1	0	1¼
44		Lauder	0	11	3¾	0	11½	0	7	9¾
45	*II.—Village Agricultural.*	Ayton	2	3	11½	3	8¼	1	8	10
46		Chirnside	2	1	7¾	4	7¼	1	12	10¾
47		Coldingham	1	1	10¾	4	3¾	0	17	8¾
48		Earlston	1	2	2½	2	11¾	0	16	8
49		Eccles	1	16	7	3	5	1	12	6¼
50		Greenlaw	0	16	9½	1	10	0	12	2¼
51		Swinton	1	19	5½	6	7¾	1	15	0½
52		Cockburnspath	0	15	5½	0	0	0	13	3
53		Edrom	1	19	2¼	3	10¾	1	11	11¼
54		Gordon	0	17	1½	3	2	0	15	0¾
55		Hutton	1	17	7¾	2	2½	1	12	4
56	*III.—Agricultural.*	Bunkle	1	2	8¼	1	3¾	1	0	4¾
57		Fogo	1	10	10¼	3	0¾	1	7	3½
58		Foulden	1	13	8¾	2	5¼	1	10	9¾
59		Legerwood	0	15	8¼	1	10¼	0	14	1¾
60		LADYKIRK	1	19	9	0	10¾	1	14	3½
61		Langton	1	0	6¼	4	0¾	0	18	3¼
62		Mertoun	1	6	9¾	3	1¼	1	3	2¼
63		Mordington	1	4	2½	3	5¾	1	1	1
64		Nenthorn	1	12	5¼	4	1¾	1	7	8½
65		Polwarth	0	17	3¼	1	1½	0	14	9
66		Whitsome	1	16	8	5	0½	1	13	7¾
67		Oldhamstocks	0	11	10½	1	0	1	10	5½
68	*IV.—Graz.*	Abbey St. Bathans	0	7	8½	1	7	0	6	7¼
69		Channelkirk	0	10	0½	1	2	0	8	9
70		*Cranshaws*	0	3	11	0	6	0	3	7¼
71		Longformacus	0	6	9	0	7¼	0	6	0¾
72		Westruther	0	9	10	1	2¼	0	8	2¾
73		Eyemouth	5	4	2¾	19	1¼			
25		Hume (*see* Stichill & Hume, p. 463).		—		—			—	

NOTES

ON THE PRECEDING TABLE, HAVING REFERENCE MORE
ESPECIALLY TO THE COLUMN.
"AGRICULTURAL VALUE PER ACRE."

42. COLDSTREAM.—Trading, agricultural, and to a small extent horticultural and suburban. We arrive at the net agricultural value per acre by allowing £2 : 10s. for the house accommodation of each inhabitant—a small sum compared with Kelso (No. 5) or Melrose (No 6), p. 465; but the census returns show Coldstream parish to be poorly housed, and deducting the value of 150 acres for road accommodation* (see Galashiels, No. 1, p. 464). Water, pass. Coldstream (the country, not the town) must have largely benefited by its contiguity to the railway, for which no deduction is made.

43. DUNSE.—Trading, mostly agricultural and partly grazing, horticultural and suburban. £3 allowed for housing accommodation. The value of 120 acres deducted for road accommodation, and 50 for railway (see Galashiels, No. 1, p. 464) completed to Dunse. Water, pass.

44 LAUDER.—Trading, mostly moorish and partly agricultural. £2 : 10s all wed for housing accommodation, and the value of 164 acres deducted for roads. Water, pass.

45. AYTON.—Village, suburban, agricultural, and slightly horticultural. £2 : 10s. allowed for housing accommodation—the value of 96 acres for roads and 74 acres for railways deducted ; and as the water-power in the parish is most usefully employed—the 26 acres turning no less than five mills—we presume it has a proportional value, and calculate for it as 52 acres (see note. p. 464), but we add the value of 106 acres for "fore shore," as surface included in the acreage making no rent return (see note No. 2, p. 465).

46. CHIRNSIDE.—Village trading, and richly agricultural. £1 : 10s. allowed for housing accommodation, and the value of 73 acres deducted for roads and 15 for railways ; water being usefully employed, make an allowance for an extra half of its area, or for 30½ acres.

47. COLDINGHAM.—Slightly trading, half-grazing, and slightly horticultural. £1 : 10s. allowed for housing accommodation, and the value of 236 acres deducted for roads and 212 for railways. Water, pass ; but add for "fore shore" the value of 233 acres.

48. EARLSTON.—To a small extent manufacturing, mixed agricultural and grazing ; somewhat horticultural. The population is poorly housed. £2 allowed for each inhabitant's accommodation, and the value of 151 acres deducted for roads ; streams, pass.

49. ECCLES.—Village trading, richly agricultural ; poorly housed. £1 : 5s. allowed for each inhabitant, and the value of 230 acres deducted for roads ; water, pass.

50. GREENLAW.—Village trading, mostly agricultural ; well housed. £2 for housing accommodation allowed, and the value of 121 acres for roads ; railway newly constructed ; water, pass.

51-67. SWINTON to OLDHAMSTOCKS.—Agricultural—see note, p. 465—

* We find that roads are *not* included in the official valuation returns—*see* foot-note, p. 464.

Ancrum to Stichill—for our system of calculating the net value per acre, the exceptions being—

52. COCKBURNSPATH, which is well housed, and 25s. allowed for each of the population, while the value of 251 acres is added for "fore shore" (see Ayton, No. 45).

53. EDROM, having many gentlemen's residences—thus making it highly horticultural—and the valuable paper mill, £2 is allowed for housing accommodation.

55. HUTTON—56, BUNKLE—57, FOGO—well housed. 25s. allowed.

60. LADYKIRK—61, LANGTON—62, MERTOUN—64, NENTHORN—to some extent horticultural. £1 : 10s. allowed. *It will be observed that Ladykirk ranks highest in the net column.*

63. MORDINGTON.—The value of 114 acres added for "fore shore." and £68 deducted from the rental for the sea-coast salmon fishery, which is included in the returned rental of the parish ; the population being more than ordinarily well housed for an agricultural parish, 25s. allowed.

68-72. ABBEY ST. BATHANS to WESTRUTHER.—Grazing. See note, p. 464—Ashkirk to Southdean—for our system of calculating the net column. Exception—

70. CRANSHAWS.—This parish has no resident proprietors, and only one resident farmer ; while the window statistics show that the resident population live in houses of a very small order. Under the circumstances, we allow only 20s. for the housing accommodation of each of the population. *It will be observed that it figures the smallest of all the Berwickshire parishes, and of the district is only higher than Peebles.*

73. EYEMOUTH.—Fishing and trading. Its area is so small, and of so little agricultural importance, that we pass it in the net column.

NOTE.—In Berwickshire we find the parishes of a more mixed character, and not so clearly defined into town, trading, agricultural, etc., as those of Roxburgh and Selkirk shires : consequently the numerous exceptions in our classification.

COMPARATIVE TABLE No. 3,

Shewing the DEATH and BIRTH RATE of the District, compiled from the Sixth and Seventh detailed Annual Reports (being for the years 1860 and 1861) of the Registrar-General of Births, Deaths, and Marriages, in Scotland.

	Populat'n 1st April 1861.	Deaths yearly per 1000 population	Legitim. Births yearly per 1000.	Illegtim. Births yearly per 1000.
1. SCOTLAND	3,062,294	21.3	31.5	3.2
Counties.				
2. Roxburghshire	53,722	19.9	31.1	3.9
3. Selkirkshire	10,410	17.0	30.3	3.2
Selkirksh. & Ladhope	14,564	18.2	31.1	3.4
4. Berwickshire	36,488	16.0	28.0	3.3
Selkirkshire.				
5. Galashiels	3379	18.3	32.8	3.2
Galashiels & Ladhope	7333	19.9	33.0	3.5
6. Selkirk	4739	18.1	31.2	3.1
Roxburghshire.				
7. Hawick and Wilton	12,083	27.6	36.8	5.4
8. Jedburgh	5011	18.2	28.3	3.8
9. Kelso	5192	18.5	27.1	2.5
10. Melrose	3557	16.3	27.2	3.4
Berwickshire.				
11. Coldstream	2823	19.1	27.2	3.2
12. Dunse	3595	20.0	29.2	3.1
13. Lauder	2198	13.6	24.5	2.7
14. Eyemouth	1804	16.6	37.1	2.2
Large Village, Agricult.				
15. Roxburghshire	2238	17.4	25.4	4.9
16. Berwickshire	12,777	17.5	27.2	3.1
Small Vil., Agricult.				
17. Roxburghshire	11,102	15.9	26.8	3.3
18. Berwickshire	4784	14.0	26.1	4.3
Agricultural.				
19. Roxburghshire	2340	12.8	26.9	3.8
20. Berwickshire	6289	11.6	28.7	3.2
Grazing.				
21. Selkirkshire	2292	12.2	24.8	3.4
22. Roxburghshire	8045	19.1	27.3	4.3
23. Berwickshire	2218	14.4	27.5	4.9

EXPLANATORY NOTES ON PRECEDING TABLE.

IN compiling these returns from *two* Reports,* we have endeavoured to strike more reliable averages. It will be observed we give the parishes having small populations, in classified groups. This was necessary to prevent details needlessly minute; and we also found that the averages of such parishes were, individually, very unreliable, the accidental circumstance of a few additional deaths or illegitimate births being apt to convey very erroneous ideas of their sanitary condition or morality: these accidents are, however, modified in the aggregate. In calculating the illegitimate birth rates, we have departed from the general system of giving a comparison between them and the legitimate births. We prefer, as being more just, to give each rate in its proportion to the population. Take, for instance, Lauder (No. 13), whose legitimate birth rate, compared with population, is the smallest of all town parishes in the district, and whose illegitimate birth rate is much below the average. If births were here to be compared with births, it is evident that the proportion of illegitimates would be very materially raised, and give an erroneous and unjust impression of their number. By the same mode of comparison, to compare the illegitimate birth rate of an agricultural county with that of a manufacturing one would, as an evidence of moral laxity, be decidedly unjust to the former; and yet such is generally done. Thus Renfrew belongs to a group of counties only 7.9 per cent. of whose births are illegitimate; while Berwick belongs to a group giving the high per centage of 14, or nearly double; but if we calculate illegitimates by population, we find that for each 1000, Renfrew has 2.7, or, compared with Berwickshire, having considerably over three-quarters instead of over a half merely; while Ayr, which belongs to the same 7.9 per cent. group, has the high rate of 3.5, or close upon that of Roxburghshire. Lanark, which belongs to the same group, and, with Ayr and Renfrew, forms a subdivision, designated the South-Western Counties, stands at 3.2, and is equal to Selkirkshire *minus* Ladhope. But we think that illegitimacy is a very unfair test of the moral laxity of a town, parish, or district, unless it be taken in conjunction with the existence of the *social evil.* Now, as a rule, the social evil largely exists in the 7.9 per cent. group, while in many of the 14 per cent. group it is awanting, or exists only in a small degree—as, for example, our own district, and of the district the least so in Berwickshire. In

* These reports are the last issued by the Registrar-General, and in date their details correspond with the census and housing statistics given in the body of the *Register.*

further estimating the causes of illegitimacy, and comparing such births with legitimates, it should be further taken into account that "wherever the proportion of women in a married state is small [as it generally is in agricultural districts], legitimate births must be few; but where the proportion of married women is high, the proportion of legitimate births must be high;" and—moral laxity and the robustness (or child-bearing condition) of the women being equal—the illegitimates should be high or low in the inverse ratio; and here the comparatively greater robustness of the agricultural population also tells against it.*

---

* Of late it has been the frequent habit to write down the agricultural counties on the score of moral laxity: the writers judging by the per centage of illegitimate births in the returns, while the qualifying causes are overlooked. So far as our own district is concerned, it will be found by an inspection of Table No. 3, that the partly manufacturing one of Roxburgh is the most lax; Selkirk (which, *intact*, may be described as pastoral) the least lax; but with the manufacturing population of Ladhope included, the second; while Berwick, strictly agricultural—where the bondage system exists in greatest intensity (which is universally allowed to be a great cause of moral laxity)—may be reckoned as really the most virtuous. Or take the town parishes, and it will be observed that, as a rule, according to their manufacturing population so is their illegitimate proportion of births. It should be further stated, as bearing on the above (and telling all the more in favour of Berwick), that in the parishes of that county generally the proportion of *unmarried* women is large. Calculating from the returns of the Registrar-General on this head, we find that the proportion of unmarried women from 15 to 45 years of age (the child bearing age) in every 100 was, in—

Scotland.	Roxburgh.	Selkirk.	Berwick.
58.6	58.6	58.2	62.9

Judging from these figures, Berwickshire should have a small proportion of *legitimate* births (and the table shews this result) while of illegitimate births it is entitled to as high a proportion as that of its unmarried women, which it has not.

We think that a series of calculations gone into over the Scotch counties, shewing the proportions of illegitimacy compared with the unmarried female population, would bring out results tending greatly to qualify present received opinions on the subject, and prove the old saying, that figures can be made to read both ways. It should be further berne in mind, in estimating the comparative moral laxity of country compared with town—as shewn by the illegitimate births in the Registrar's returns—the well-known fact that the mothers expectant of illegitimate children *very* frequently migrate from their resident parish to some distance previous to the birth of the child;—for instance, in the case of servant girls, to their country homes, principally from necessity, and partly for concealment; and, wherever it is at all practicable, the child will be boarded thereafter in a rural parish. Wherever this system is carried out, it may readily be observed that the rural parishes thus

2. ROXBURGHSHIRE.—The county intact as returned in the Reports, viz.—including the Ladhope portion of Melrose parish, all Ashkirk parish but excluding the parts of Roberton, Selkirk, and Galashiels parishes situated in this county.

3. SELKIRKSHIRE.—Intact, as returned in the Reports, which include all Roberton and Selkirk parishes but exclude the Selkirkshire portions of Stow, Peebles, Innerleithen, and the Roxburghshire portions of Roberton and Galashiels.

Selkirkshire.—This line of calculation includes Ladhope in Roxburgh shire, which *parochially* forms part of Melrose parish. This district, containing part of the town of Galashiels, and belonging to it socially, should, in a matter of morals and death rate, be so calculated. It will be observed how this addition of a manufacturing population raises the averages of both the county and parish.

5. GALASHIELS.—Intact.

Galashiels and Ladhope—See note, *Selkirkshire.*

7. HAWICK (including WILTON).—Observe the high rate here given in all the averages—those of deaths and illegitimate births being the highest in the district and much above the average of Scotland, while the legitimate birth rate is the highest but one—Eyemouth, No. 14 (*see* pp 302 and 306, on the sanitary condition and housing accommodation of Hawick, and page 340, for the housing accommodation of Wilton).

8. JEDBURGH.—This town had the advantage of a system of drainage, but one not well executed (*see* p. 246) when the returns, from which we have calculated the averages, were compiled (1860-61). Since then Kelso, Hawick, etc., have introduced both thorough drainage and water, and we expect to shew the results arising therefrom, by a comparison with the present table, when our next issue is published: "the object of all these improvements being primarily to supply a purer atmosphere to the dwellings of the working-classes, and to afford their inmates the means of cleanliness; failing to do this, the end for which they were established has miscarried."*

---

become libelled with the immorality which, strictly speaking, had its source in the towns.

The reverse system of mothers expectant migrating to the lying-in hospitals of large towns does not obtain in this district, although, we believe, it does in some counties more conveniently situated for the purpose.

---

* We append, for the consideration of municipalities and proprietors of house property, the following suggestive remarks by Dr. Stark, Superintendent of the Statistical Department, Registrar-General's Office, on the operation of the Sanitary Acts:—

"These Acts require that a water-closet and sink be introduced into 'every house or part of a house occupied by a separate family,' (25 and 26 Vict., cap. 101, clause 210) and it seems desirable to ascertain what may have been the practical result of the enactment. The old houses in most of our towns are of a peculiar construction, with flats above one another, occupied by different families. Now, if under the directions of the clause above referred to, water-closets and more especially

NOTES ON THE DEATH AND BIRTH RATE TABLE.

9. KELSO.—It will be observed that the illegitimate birth rate of Kelso is, next to Eyemouth (No. 14), the smallest in the district, and fully a fourth below the average of Scotland. If judged by this standard, the town cannot *now* be blamed for laxity of morals—*see* p. 72, and Appendix, *Kelso* v. *Fullerton's Gazetteer.*

10. MELROSE (excluding Ladhope, *see Selkirkshire* and foot-note).— The small death rate of Melrose would seem to prove its reputation for salubrity to be well founded.

12. DUNSE.—*See* foot-note to No. 8.

13. LAUDER.—The smallest death and legitimate birth rates in the District (*see* remarks on the illegitimate averages, page 705). The high and airy position of the entire parish must tend greatly to reduce its death rate, which will be further affected by the smallness of its birth rate causing a comparatively small infantile mortality.

14. EYEMOUTH.—This town may be considered an anomaly ; its streets are narrow, twisted, and not over clean (like those of most small sea-ports); its population is poorly housed (*see* p. 690), and it had, at the date of the returns, no system of drainage, and yet its death rate is very small (next to Lauder, the smallest of all town parishes in the district ; and, be it remembered, that Eyemouth parish is nearly *all* town) ; its legitimate birth rate is the highest, and its illegitimate birth rate the smallest ; and of its poor on the roll, not one of them is insane (*see* p. 609).*

---

sinks, have to a considerable extent been introduced either into the apartments where the families live, or into their immediate vicinity, is it not possible that the increased vitiation of the air caused by their emanations may be one cause of the increased mortality manifested by the Returns? This statement is only conjectural, but it appears to merit consideration and inquiry. Even under the most favourable circumstances, it is notorious that unless sinks and water-closets have abundant ventilation, and are kept clean and in good working order, it is not easy to prevent the escape of noxious vapours. How much more may this be expected to occur in the close, confined dwellings occupied by large numbers of our town populations?

"It must be remembered that by the Census of 1861, upwards of 73 in every 100 families live in houses of one or of two rooms; and if, instead of removing all sources of vitiation of the air, we introduce a new source of vitiation to their limited dwellings, no other effect can follow than an increased mortality."

We may add to the above, that of all town parishes in the district, Kelso (p. 75), Melrose (excluding Ladhope, p. 130), and Dunse (p. 550), are the only ones in the district whose housing accommodation is up to the average of Scotland. While these facts seem to tell favourably on the death rate averages of Kelso and Melrose, they by some cause are modified in Dunse (No. 12) whose death rate is the highest in the district next to Hawick (No. 7).

* As these results seemed to us to be unique, we put the following queries to a valued Eyemouth correspondent :—

"KELSO, 26th Dec., 1865.

"Dear Sir—In the concluding notes on the Comparative Insane and Illegitimacy Tables for the District, some interesting observa-

15. ROXBURGHSHIRE.—Yetholm, with a population of 1207; Morebattle, 1031—total, 2238.

16. BERWICKSHIRE.—Ayton, 2014; Chirnside, 1502; Coldingham, 3241 ; Earlston, 1825; Eccles, 1861; Greenlaw, 1370; Swinton, 964—total, 12,77 7.

---

tions, at short length, might be made on the small death rate and the freedom of the population of Eyemouth from Insanity and Illegitimacy.

"We presume the population of Eyemouth is principally a fishing population.—If 565 men and boys are employed all the year round (*see* Herring Fishing Returns), the proportion of women and children added would make this class sum up to over 1200, while the entire population of the town is only 1721 ?

"Are the fisher class of Eyemouth given to *intermarrying* (like that of Newhaven for instance)? Are they physically robust, and, barring the dangers and hardships of the profession, long lived? Do you know if they are more or less than ordinarily subject to deafness, scrofula, and consumption (said to be the results of marriage consanguinity)? A reply to these queries might tell curiously on the interesting question at present agitating the philosophers as to whether the *supposed* ill effects of marriage consanguinity is not a delusion. Anyhow, it is a curious circumstance that Eyemouth, probably the worst built town in the district for sanitary measures, and one whose population is perhaps the worst housed, should have so high a life and birth rate and be so free from laxity and insanity— results which seem contrary to all rule in these matters.

"Do the queries here made apply also to the fishing villages of the coast.

"Does the one insane pauper *now* on the roll belong to the fisher class, and do the fisher class give their proportion to the poor roll?— We remain, &c., "J. & J. H. RUTHERFURD."

It will be observed that the reply, while interesting, accounts for the peculiarities in a very natural way :—

"A combination of favourable circumstances, in my opinion, accounts for the state of matters you mention. Eyemouth is built upon a foundation of beach and sand, and is thus naturally drained and dry. The occupation of the people is healthy and remunerative, enabling them to obtain and use a full amount of nourishing food. They are at an early period of life able to provide for themselves, and they marry young ; there is consequently little temptation to moral laxity. The offspring of young healthy people are stronger than the children of old people. The town is almost exclusively fisher. The people live to a good old age ; are robust and vigorous in health and constitution. They must have sprung from a good race, as there are no symptoms of nervous debility ; they are generally intellectual. There is a considerable mixture in the marriages, many fishers having for their wives the daughters of small farmers and tradesmen. Few paupers are from fishers—more generally from farm labourers and tradesmen. Old people are of much use to a fisherman, and can do many pieces of light labour when very feeble, and thus keep off the roll. The insane pauper on the roll is not a fisher (*see* note, p. 689). Burnmouth and Coldingham are not so healthy as Eyemouth. The people in the three towns are superior as fishers to most towns I have known— and I have had much experience over the East Coast."

17. ROXBURGHSHIRE.—Ancrum, 1511; Bowden, 866; Cavers, 1824; Lilliesleaf, 772; Roxburgh, 1178; St. Boswell's, 865; Smailholm, 554; Sprouston, 1305; Crailing, 673; Eckford, 957; Ednam, 599—total, 11,102.

18. BERWICKSHIRE.—Cockburnspath, 1194; Edrom, 1592; Gordon, 931; Hutton, 1067—total, 4784.

19. ROXBURGHSHIRE.—Linton, 608; Makerstoun, 380; Maxton, 497; Minto, 430; Stitchill, 425—total, 2340.

20. BERWICKSHIRE.—Hume, 420; Bunkle, 756: Fogo, 559; Foulden, 431; Ledgerwood, 599; Ladykirk, 564; Langton, 502; Mertoun, 729; Mordington, 377; Nenthorn, 461; Polwarth, 251: Whitsome, 640—total, 6289.

21. SELKIRKSHIRE.—Ettrick, 454; Kirkhope, 555; Yarrow, 643; Roberton, 640—total, 2292.

22. ROXBURGHSHIRE.—Ashkirk, 578; Bedrule, 222; Hobkirk, 771; Hounam, 289; Kirkton, 421; Oxnam, 592; Teviothead, 438; Southdean, 687; Castleton, 3688; Edgerston, 359—total, 8045.

23. BERWICKSHIRE.—Abbey St. Bathans, 179; Channelkirk, 671; Cranshaws, 134; Longformacus, 448; Westruther, 786—total, 2218.

From the Returns and some stray paragraphs picked up at random, we have been enabled to make up the following

COMPARATIVE NOTES ON TABLE No. 3.

THE average death rate for ENGLAND generally, for the years in question (1860-61), per 1000, was 26.1 [for Scotland generally, 21.3 *see* Table]; while the average of its four greatest cities—London, Liverpool, Manchester. and Birmingham—was 40.7. It was highest in Liverpool [there the infantile mortality is enormous], where the average rate for the two years was 48.5. In Manchester it was 42.5; in Birmingham, 39; and in London, 33; in the burghs of Edinburgh and Leith conjointly it was 24.6; for the burgh of Glasgow, 29.5; Greenock, 26.9. In Wiltshire the rate did not exceed 18; in Berkshire, Dorsetshire, and Westmoreland it was 18.5. In the whole of the English agricultural counties, taken collectively, the average for the two years was 21.1. Compare again with table, by which it will be seen that the death rate of Scotland generally is almost equally favourable with that of the agricultural counties of England, taken collectively; while Selkirkshire intact (*see* No. 3) is greatly below the most favourable of them (Wiltshire), and is only very slightly higher when taken in conjunction with the manufacturing population of Ladhope. If the comparison be extended to Berwickshire (No. 4), the result is still more in favour of the district

From these statements it would appear that the prospects of life in England are nearly twice as favourable to the dwellers in rural districts as to their brethren in the towns; while in Scotland, taking Selkirkshire and Greenock as fair averages, the difference in favour of country may be roughly fixed at a third.

Natural increase of population could not be appealed to as any test of comparative value of life in different places. It was greater in towns than in rural districts; marriages more numerous, young men earlier in a position to marry, and a far larger proportion of adults of a marriageable age were settled. The per centage of persons of the productive age (fifteen to forty-five) amounted in the four great towns to 49; but in the agricultural counties [England is here quoted—but a like disproportion, larger rather than less, obtains in Scotland], taken collectively, it did not exceed 42.5. Thus there are in the towns about 13 per cent. more persons of a marriageable age than are to be found among the rural districts. The marriage and birth rate for the two years in the four great cities, as compared with those in the agricultural counties, unmistakably shewed that the natural increase of population was materially influenced by different conditions of life. In Manchester the average number of marriages was 18.5 in every 1000; in the agricultural county of Hertford it was 5.8. In Scotland generally the marriage rate was 6.8; in Selkirkshire (*intact*-pastoral), 4.7; Roxburghshire, 5.7; Berwickshire, 5.8. The rate of Kelso (parish) was 5.3; that of Hawick and Wilton (parishes), 6.8; Edinburgh and Leith, 8.9; Glasgow, 8.9. Lauder, whose legitimate birth rate was so small, had the small marriage rate, for the same years, of 5. In Manchester the average number of births in every 1000 was 37.5; in Hertford, 30.5; the marriages in the English city being nearly fourfold more numerous than in the county; while the births there only exceeded the latter by about one-sixth. Comparing town with county in Scotland, we have the births shewing about the same proportion as the marriages—Glasgow having a birth rate of 41 per 1000; Greenock, 40.3; and by a reference to the table it will be seen that Hawick and Wilton, whose marriage rate is not above the average, have, excluding illegitimates, the high birth rate of 42.* As an instance of English inequality between town and county, in the matter of births, we may quote that in Manchester there were but two children to every married couple, while in Hertford there were five.

---

* Qualified by its excessive death rate of 27.6, thus reducing the proportion of births, compared with deaths, *below* the average; or, while Scotland generally has one-third more births than deaths per annum (the district generally has a proportion considerably higher), Hawick has only one-fourth.

We regret we have not the return of children to each married couple for Scotland, but the following foot-note bearing on the subject is interesting, and it seems to be corroborated by the statements above.* "The three causes adverse to health in towns were, vitiated air, constitutional syphilis, and the abuse of alcohol. The employment of married women also, especially when the mothers of young children, should in every way be discouraged. Cellar dwellings should be closed up, and alleys cleared out, and the sites which they occupied left open to serve the double purpose of air-shafts and play-grounds. Factories and workshops, instead of being piled up in the centre of our towns, should be scattered over the country in airy and healthy localities. If these suggestions were in any degree practicable, it would be admitted they could not be too often or too urgently pressed on those who had the power of enforcing them."

---

* "It appears that the married women of Scotland are more prolific than those of England, seeing that during the year 1861, every 314 wives at the child-bearing age gave birth to 100 children in Scotland; whereas it required 355 wives of the same age for every 100 births in England. As like results appear year after year, it may be assumed as proved that the Scottish married female is more prolific than the English married female."—Dr. STARK in *Report for* 1861.

COMPARATIVE TABLE No. 4.

ELEMENTARY EDUCATION—TESTED BY THE MARRIAGE REGISTERS FOR 1861.

Comparing Scotland in the aggregate with the District, we have the following results :—

	PER CENTAGE OF MEN		PER CENTAGE OF WOMEN	
	Sign. Names in full.	Signing with Marks.	Sign. Names in full.	Signing with Marks.
Scotland ...	89.4	6.1	78.7	21.3
Roxburgh*	94.8	5.2	91.9	8.1
Selkirk †...	98	2	91.8	8.2
Berwick	98.1	1	96.7	3.3

Here, again, we have results greatly in favour of the Berwickshire women.

Of *all* the counties in Scotland, Peebles, by this test, stood highest in the elementary education scale, where 100 per cent. of the men, and 96.9 per cent. of the women married in 1861 wrote their names in full. Berwickshire came next with 98.9 per cent. of the men, and 96.7 per cent. of the women (*see* table). If, however, we turn to the Register of 1860 we find that Berwickshire for that year stood the highest, having 98.9 per cent of the men and 96.3 of the women, Peebles being behind at 92.3 of the men and 94.2 of the women; but the lower position of the latter county that year may be accounted for by the influx of railway labourers (*see* p. 52) and be considered exceptional.‡

Comparing the education of England with Scotland, we give the following items compiled from different sources :—

During the year 1861, of the 20,896 men who married in Scotland, 18,679 signed their names in the marriage registers, and 2217 signed by mark. Of the 20,896 women who married, 16,439 signed their names in full, while 4457 signed by mark. These numbers shew that 89.4 per cent. of the men, and 78.7 per cent of the women who married during the year

---

* Including Ladhope.   † Excluding Ladhope.
‡ In both these years 100 per cent of the men in Kinross signed their names in full, but its average of women was only 89.

were able to sign their names in full; while 10.6 per cent of the men, and 21.3 per cent. of the women were obliged to sign by mark. This is a very much larger proportion of both men and women able to write their names than in England, where, in the marriage registers for 1863, 132,248 men and 116,094 women wrote their names at marriage; while 41,262 men and 57,461 women signed with marks. These numbers shew that in the aggregate 76 per cent. of the men, and 67 per cent. of the women wrote their names in full, while 24 per cent. of the men and 33 per cent. of the women made marks. It would appear therefore that more women can write in Scotland than men in England, and the same results are shewn year after year.

The proportions of the population who can and who cannot write vary greatly in different localities; thus, in London, 89 per cent. of the men and 82 per cent. of the women sign their names. In Monmouthshire and Wales the state of education estimated by this standard is very defective, where half the women who married signed with marks. Half the women also signed with marks in Lancashire. Glasgow furnishes upwards of 15 per cent. of males unable to write, while the proportion of men in Edinburgh unable to write is only 4 per cent.

In Scotland the counties of Ross, Cromarty, and Inverness seem to be in the most backward state as to elementary education, seeing that 31.9 per cent. of the men in Inverness, and 42.7 per cent. in Ross and Cromarty were obliged to sign their names by mark; while, to correspond with this, 52.8 per cent. of the women in Inverness, and 61.8 per cent. in Ross and Cromarty signed by mark [these counties showing an inferiority to even Wales or Lancashire]. In some counties and towns the large number of Irish in the population increases the proportion of persons who sign by mark. This is notably the case in the counties of Dumbarton, Renfrew, Lanark, and Wigton; and is the main cause why the male population of Glasgow, who cannot write, figures at 15 per cent.

We had also compiled a COMPARATIVE TABLE No. 5 on the Poor on the Roll and the Insane Poor of the District, but found, after considerable labour with figures and much correspondence and investigation, that it proved nothing, except perhaps that the town and *open* village parishes were subject to an influx of poor from the *close** village and purely country parishes, while in the case of the insane this circumstance did not even rule; *their* accumulation in different localities being the result of purely accidental causes.

We have also discovered that the published Returns of the Board of Supervision afford very erroneous data for Comparative Calculations, as some parishes very freely insert in their returns of poor on their roll what in other parishes would be returned as *casual poor;* while some, reversing this proceedure, return an entire family on the roll as *one* individual. On these accounts, and as the table occupied room to no reliable purpose, scarcely even to the gratification of curiosity, we have caused it, and its notes, to be expunged.

* By *close* villages, we mean those where a man or family likely to become a burden on the parish is turned out or refused admittance, to seek shelter in some town or village where the system is not enforced—a system thus described by Dr M'Culloch in his Statistical Account of Kelso:—

"To prevent the aged and infirm becoming burdens on the poor rate, it is the practice of some of the heritors of purely landward parishes, to demolish every cottar-house which is not absolutely necessary as accommodation for the needful complement of farm-labourers and country artisans. In this way, infirm labourers and widows are compelled, the moment they cease to be available workers, to leave their parishes in despite of all the ties of local attachment which may bind them to the spot, and to take their chance of an uncertain livelihood among strangers and in the unhealthy lanes and closes of a town."

A comparison of the different Parochial Rates (*see* the headings PAROCHIAL BOARD in each parish) will supply suggestive ideas as to how this system of *eviction* has been carried out, and the extent to which the town and some village parishes are thereby burdened.

ECCLESIASTICAL LISTS.

(For Patrons and other particulars, see Parochial Lists under CLERGY.)

Church of Scotland.

SYNOD OF MERSE AND TEVIOTDALE.
*Clerk—*Adam Gourlay, Minister of Lilliesleaf.
*Meets at Kelso on 2nd Tues. of Oct., and at Kelso,
Jedburgh, or Dunse, on 2nd Tues. of April.*

PRESBYTERY OF DUNSE.
*Clerk—*Robert S. Darling, Langton.
Meets at Dunse on 1st Tuesday of the month.

Place.	Minister.	Ordain.*
Abbey St. Bathans .	Thomas Davidson	1843
Bunkle and Preston	John Dunlop	1843
Cranshaws	W. M. Hutton, M.A.	1853
Dunse	John Macleod	1861
Boston Church		
Eccles	James R. Watson	1848
Fogo	Robert F. Proudfoot	1844
Greenlaw	Jn. Hunter Walker	1834
Langton	Robert S. Darling	1864
Longformacus	Walter Weir	1837
Polwarth	Walter Home	1823

PRESBYTERY OF CHIRNSIDE.
*Clerk—*Alex. Christison, Minister of Foulden.
*Meets at Chirnside on the 3rd Tuesday of March,
June, September, and December.*

Ayton	Daniel Cameron	1836
Chirnside	James Wilson	1838
Coldingham	David Munro	1845
Coldstream	Archibald Nisbett	1853
Edrom	James Wilson	1847
Eyemouth	Stephen Bell	1845
Foulden	Alexander Christison	1821
Houndwood	David Drummond	1845
Hutton	Robert Kirke	1845
Ladykirk	William Dobbie	1853
Mordington	Charles Blair	1843
Swinton	James Logan	1833
Whitsome		

PRESBYTERY OF KELSO.
*Clerk—*William Lamb, Minister of Ednam.
*Meets at Kelso on 1st Tuesday of February,
April, May, July, and December, and 2nd
Tuesday of October.*

Place.	Minister.	Ordain.
Ednam	William Lamb	1844
Kelso	James Smith	1829
North Church	Peter M'Kerron	1865
Linton	T. Leishman, M.A.	1852
Makerstoun	Andrew Mackie	1844
Morebattle	John Glen	1856
Nenthorn	John Barclay	1866
Roxburgh	William Lee	1843
Sprouston	R. Orange Bromfield	1833
Stitchill	Dugald Macalister	1846
Yetholm	A. Davidson, M.A.	1862

PRESBYTERY OF JEDBURGH.
*Clerk—*J. Fergusson, Minister of Edgerston.
Meets at Jedburgh—no fixed dates.

Ancrum	John Paton	1830
Bedrule	Archibald Craig, M.A.	1832
Cavers	Alex. Munn Maccoll	1854
Crailing	Adam Cunningham	1836
Eckford	Joseph Yair, M.A.	1829
Hawick	John Macrae, D.D.	1843
St. Mary's	John Thomson	1860
Hopekirk	John Ewen	1834
Hounam	George Watson	1865
Jedburgh	George Ritchie, M.A.	1834
Edgerston	John Fergusson	1855
Kirkton	George Hunter	1857
Minto	John P. Macmorland	1865
Oxnam	William Burnie	1859
Southdean	John Mair	1847
Teviothead	Robert Young	1854
Wilton	James Stewart	1849

PRESBYTERY OF LAUDER.
*Clerk—*Archibald Brown, Minister of Legerwood.
No fixed place or dates of Meeting.

Place.	Minister.	Ordain.
Channelkirk	James Walker	1862
Earlston	David Wm. Gordon	1807
Gordon	William Stobbs	1855
Lauder	Jas. Middleton, M.A.	1862
Legerwood	Archibald Brown	1858
Mertoun	Alexander M'Laren	1855
Smailholm	David Swan	1843
Stow	David Waddell	1841
Westruther	Henry Taylor, D.D.	1841

PRESBYTERY OF SELKIRK.
*Clerk –*Adam Gourlay, Minister of Lilliesleaf.
Meets at Selkirk—no stated times.

Ashkirk	William G. Smith	1840
Boswell's, St.	Thomas F. Johnston	1865
Bowden	J. Allardyce, M.A.	1844
Ettrick	John Falconer	1859
Galashiels	Kenneth M'Lea Phin	1841
Caddonfoot	Robert Small	
Kirkhope	John S. Gibson, M.A.	1851
Ladhope	Robert Blackstock	1858
Lilliesleaf	Adam Gourlay	1842
Maxton	Manners H. Graham	1855
Melrose	Chas. Herdman, M.A.	1846
Roberton	Chas. K. Greenhill	1844
Selkirk	J. Farquharson, M.A.	1857
Yarrow	James Russell, M.A.	1841
Newcastleton (in Langholm Presb.)	James Noble	1861

---

* The dates of *ordination*—a strictly ecclesiastical matter—are here given. Under the head CLERGY, in the individual parishes, the date of *induction* will be found. When these dates do not correspond, it will be understood that the minister to whom they apply was *ordained* to some charge previous to his present *inducted* one. Where the dates are the same, it implies both ordination and induction to his present charge.

Free Church.

SYNOD OF MERSE AND TEVIOTDALE.

Clerk—
Meets at Kelso on 2nd Tues. of October, and at Kelso, Jedburgh, Dunse, or Melrose, on 2nd Tues. of April.

PRESBYTERY OF DUNSE AND CHIRNSIDE.

Clerk - John Fairbairn, Minister of Greenlaw.

Meets at Dunse usually on the 1st Tuesday of each alternate month

Place.	Minister.	Ordain.
Allanton	John C. Fairbairn	1844
Coldstream	Alexander Rodger	1847
Dunse	John Fordyce	1854
Eyemouth	John Turnbull	1822
Greenlaw	John Fairbairn	1833
Houndwood	Adam Spence	1845
Langton	William Logan	1849
Longformacus	James Rathie	
Mordington	James Ketchan	1830
Swinton	Thomas Wright	1842

PRESBYTERY OF KELSO AND LAUDER.

Clerk—P. C. Purves, Minister of Morebattle.

Meets at Kelso 1st Tuesday of February, April, May, July, October, and December.

Eccles	Andrew Cunningham	1843
Gordon	John Fraser	1843
Kelso	Horatius Bonar, D.D.	1837
Sprouston		
Lauder	Thomas Waters	1843
Makerstoun	David Dobbie	1848
Morebattle	Peter C. Purves	1855
Nenthorn	Robert Lang	1843
Westruther	James Izzet	1846
Yetholm	John Coventry	1862

PRESBYTERY OF JEDBURGH.

Clerk—Thomas S. Anderson, Minister of Crailing.

Meets at Jedburgh on 1st Tues. of the months.

Ancrum	Hugh M. Rattray	1864
Newcastleton	Neil S. Ure	1861
Crailing	Thomas S. Anderson	1844
Denholm	J. M'Clymont	1837
Hawick	John A. Wallace	1827
	John M'Gregor	1859
Jedburgh	John Purves	1826
Wolflee	Robert Milligan	1863

PRESBYTERY OF SELKIRK.

Clerk—James Pirie, Minister of Bowden.

Meets at Selkirk—no stated dates.

Place.	Minister.	Ordain.
Ashkirk		
Bowden	James Pirie, M.A.	1855
Galashiels	James Selkirk	1861
Ladhope		
Melrose	William Cousin	1840
Selkirk	James Young	1860
St. Boswell's	John Duncan	1836
	Alex. Terras, M.A.	1861
Yarrow and Megget	Thos. M'Crindle, M.A.	1847

United Presbyterian Church.

The Synod meets at Edinburgh, in the Hall, 5 Queen St., on Mond. after 2nd Sab. of May.

PRESBYTERY OF BERWICK.

Clerk—Rev. Peter Mearns, Coldstream.

Meets at Berwick at irregular intervals.

Alnwick, Clayport St	William Limont	1851
...... Lisburn St.	David Donaldson	1843
Ayton, West	James Stark	1819
...... Summerhill	Thomas Montgomery	1846
Beaumont Union, (Coldstream)	David Taylor	1852
Belford (Northumb.)	John Hunter	1831
Berwick, Wallace Green	John Cairns, D.D.	1845
...... Chapel St.	James M'Leish	1859
...... Church St.	James Grierson Scott	1859
Chatton (Belford...)	David Young	1851
Chirnside	James Ker, M.A.	1854
Coldingham	Andrew B. Robertson	1856
Coldstream, West	Peter Mearns	1846
...... East	James Porteous	1815
Dunse, East Church	William Ritchie	1839
...... South	Daniel Kerr, M.A.	18 3
Embleton (Alnwick)	William Ross	1850
Eyemouth	James Harrower	1857
Horndean (Berwick)	John Stark	1849
Norham (Do.)	James T. Anderson	1847
Spittal (Do.)	William Porteous	1850
Stockbridge (Cockburnspath)	David M'Quater Inglis	1819
Sunderland, North	Hugh Glover	1842
Wooler, 1st cong.	Peter Whyte	1848
Cheviot Street	James L. Muirhead	1833

PRESBYTERY OF KELSO.

Clerk—Rev. James Jarvie, Kelso.

Meets at Kelso on 3d Monday of every month.

Place.	Minister.	Ordain.
Dunse, West	Charles Miller	1841
Greenlaw	John Milne, M.A.	1854
Jedburgh, Blackfriars	John Polson	1856
...... High St.	William Barr	1834
Kelso, 1st	Henry Renton, M.A.	1830
	Robert Whyte	1864
...... East	James Jarvie	1834
Leitholm	Alexander Hay, M.A.	1859
Morebattle	Robert Cranston	1815
	Mungo Giffen	1865
Stitchill	David Cairns	1854
Yetholm	Andrew Ritchie	1865

PRESBYTERY OF MELROSE.

Clerk—Rev. H. Stevenson, Melrose.

Meets at Melrose on 1st Tuesday of February, and of each alternate month thereafter.

Earlston, East	Alexander Henderson	1851
...... West	John Kechie	1851
Galashiels, East		
...... West	Robert Blair	1838
Hawick, West End	James Parlane, M.A.	1857
...... East Bank	James M'Ewen, M.A.	1856
...... Allars Ch.	Robert Muir, M.A.	1860
Innerleithen	John Law	1812
Lauder	George Robson	1834
Lilliesleaf	William Young, M.A.	1857
Melrose	Hugh Stevenson	1860
Newtown	David Lumgair	1844
Selkirk, 1st cong.	John Lawson	1850
...... West Church		
Stow	Alexander Mair, M.A.	1863
Newcastleton (in Annandale Pres.)	John Black	1829

Reformed Presbyterian Church.

(COVENANTERS.)

Both belong to the Presbytery of Edinburgh.

Clerk—Rev. John Guy, Kelso.

Chirnside	Robert Naismith	1861
Kelso	John Guy	1853

Episcopal Church of Scotland.

DIOCESE OF EDINBURGH.

Bishop—Right Rev. Charles Hughes Terrot, D.D.
Edinburgh; consecrated 1841.

Bishop Coadjutor—Right Rev. Thomas Baker
Morrell, D.D.; consecrated 1863.

Place.	Minister.	Ordain.
Dunse	Aug. E. Crowder, L.T.	1850

DIOCESE OF GLASGOW.

Bishop—Right Rev. William Scott Wilson, LL.D.,
Ayr; consecrated 1859.
Synod Clerk—Rev. J. G. Ryde, Melrose.
*Dates of Meeting unfixed, but generally in
Glasgow on the last Wednesday of August.*

Place.	Minister.	Ordain.
Galashiels	A. A. Jenkins	
Hawick	John Rose Dakers	1852
Jedburgh	John Moir, M.A.	1836
Kelso	J. Hill Scott	1860
Melrose	Jn. Gabriel Ryde, M.A.	1847
Selkirk	Robert Gibson	1857

SOCIETIES, &c., IN CONNECTION WITH THE LISTS OF REGISTRARS, INSPECTORS, &c. (*see* next page).

BOARD OF SUPERVISION FOR RELIEF OF THE POOR OF SCOTLAND.

Chambers, 125 George Street, Edinburgh.

The Right Hon. Sir John M'Neill, Chairman.
W. S. Walker, Esq. of Bowland (*see* note, p. 459), Secretary.
Alexander Campbell, Esq. of Auchindarroch, Visiting Officer for the Southern Districts.

ROXBURGHSHIRE AND BERWICKSHIRE ASSOCIATION OF INSPECTORS OF POOR (Instituted 1864).

For the purpose of affording free discussion on all matters of Parochial interest.

Head Quarters and General Place of Meeting, Kelso.
President—James Brown, Sprouston.
Vice-President—James Sloan, Jedburgh.
Secretary and Treasurer—Alexander T. Morrison, Kelso.
Meets Quarterly on the first Saturday of May, August, November, and February.

BORDER ASSOCIATION OF TEACHERS (Instituted 1864).

James Dickson, St. Boswell's, Chairman.
Francis Tocher, Melrose, Treasurer.
John Malcolm, Hobkirk, Secretary.

Meets three times a year—on the last Saturday of March, June, and October; places unfixed.
The Border Association comprises the Presbyteries of Dunse, Chirnside, Kelso, Lauder, Langholm, Selkirk, and Jedburgh. The Meetings are held in the principal towns in these Presbyteries, most suitable for the majority of members.

REGISTRY OFFICE (Register Office, Edinburgh).

William Pitt Dundas, advocate, Registrar-General.
George Seton, advocate, Secretary.
James Stark, M.D., Superintendent of Statistical Department.
George Bell, M.D., 16 Alva Street, Edinburgh, Inspector of Register.
Alfred C. C. List, Portland Street, Kilmarnock, Examiner for Roxburgh, Berwick, and Selkirk shires, &c.

Parochial Teachers; Registrars of Births, Marriages, and Deaths; and Inspectors of Poor.

(For Public Vaccinators, and further particulars, see Parochial Lists under "Education," "Public Offices," and "Parochial Board.")

COUNTY OF ROXBURGH.

No.	PARISHES.	PAROCHIAL TEACHERS.	REGISTRARS OF BIRTHS, &c.	INSPECTORS OF POOR.	DAY FIXED FOR ELECTION OF MEMBERS OF PAR. BOARD.	No.
1	Ancrum	A. G. Catto, F.E.I.S -	Alexander G. Catto -	Alexander G. Catto -	2d Saturday of March	1
2	Ashkirk	James Smellie, C.T. -	James Smellie - -	James Smellie - -	3rd Thursday of February	2
3	Bedrule..........	William M'Neil	William M'Neil -	Thomas Scott -	3rd Saturday of May	3
4	Bowden	John Dods, C.T.	John Dods - -	John Dods - -	3rd Thursday of January	4
5	Castleton........	John Brown, C.T.	John Brown -	John Brown -	1st Thursday of May	5
6	Cavers..........	John Greenfield, C.T.	George Moodie -	George Moodie -	Last Saturday of April	6
7	Crailing.........	Richard Amour -	Richard Amour -	Richard Amour -	2d Wednesday of January	7
8	Eckford..........	Henry R. Lawrie	Henry R. Lawrie -	Henry R. Lawrie -	4th Saturday of February	8
9	Ednam............	David Pringle - -	David Pringle -	David Pringle -	2d Saturday of April	9
10	Hawick	Anthony Dodds	Anthony Dodds -	Robert Seath -	4th Friday of October	10
11	Hobkirk	John Malcolm, C.T. -	William Sibbald -	William Sibbald -	4th Friday of October	11
12	Hounam.........	Alexander Davidson -	Alexander Davidson -	Alexander Davidson	Last Saturday of February	12
13	Jedburgh ......} Edgerston. ..}	A. Mounsey, C.T. - Thomas Oliver - -	Thos. Grieve - -} Thos. Oliver - -}	James Sloan -	3rd Tuesday of July	13
14	Kelso	G. D. Hunter F.E.I.S.	Colin A. Hutchinson -	Alex. T Morrison -	1st Monday of February	14
15	Kirkton	Thomas Little -	Thomas Little - -	Thomas Little -	3rd Friday of April	15
16	Lilliesleaf.......	James W. Mackay -	James W. Mackay -	James W. Mackay -	2d Saturday of June	16
17	Linton	Robert Henderson -	Robert Henderson -	Robert Henderson -	3rd Monday of February	17
18	Makerstoun.....	David Dods -	David Dods -	David Dods -	2d Thursday of January	18
19	Maxton	William Chisholm	William Chisholm -	William Chisholm -	2d Monday of April	19
20	Melrose (D.). ...} Ladhope (D.) }	Francis Tocher, C.T. -{	Thomas Murray - }Thos. Paterson - }	Thomas Murray -	1st Monday of April	20
21	Minto	John R. Hamilton -	John R. Hamilton -	John R. Hamilton -	2d Monday of June	21
22	Morebattle	John Swanston	John Swanston -	John Swanston -	Last Saturday of January	22
23	Oxnam	Matthew Little, C.T.-	Matthew Little -	Matthew Little -	2d Wednesday of February	23
24	Roberton	Thos. Anderson -	Thos. Anderson -	Thos. Anderson -	4th Saturday of January	24
25	Roxburgh	R C. Maxwell, C.T. -	William Laidlaw	Robert C. Maxwell -	4th Thursday of January	25
26	St Boswell's	J. Dickson. F.E.I.S. -	James Dickson -	James Dickson - -	3rd Thursday of May	26
27	Smailholm.......	Thomas Wood, C.T.	Thomas Wood -	Thomas Wood -	2d Wednesday of February	27
28	Southdean	Neil Taylor, F.E.I.S. -	Neil Taylor - -	Neil Taylor - -	4th Friday of February	28
29	Sprouston.......	James Brown -	James Brown -	James Brown -	1st Wednesday of February	29
30	Stitchel	Adam Douglas - -	Adam Douglas - -	Adam Douglas - -	4th Wednesday of January	30
31	Teviothead	Simon Little - -	Simon Little - -	(see foot-note, 31)		31
32	Wilton	J. A. Blane - -	James Shiel -	James Shiel -	1st Friday of July	32
33	Yetholm.........	R. M'Morran, C.T. -	Robert M'Morran -	Robert M'Morran -	4th Saturday of March	33

F.E.I.S.—Fellow of the Educational Institute of Scotland ; C.T.—Certificated Teacher ; M.A.—Master of Arts (*Magister Artium*).

31. See Hawick and Cavers—Teviothead not being a separate Parish for the purposes of the Poor Law (*see* pp. 262, 312):

COUNTY OF BERWICK.

No.	PARISHES.	PAROCHIAL TEACHERS.	REGISTRARS OF BIRTHS, &c.	INSPECTORS OF POOR.	DAY FIXED FOR ELECTION OF MEMBERS OF PAR. BOARD.	No.
1	Abbey St Bathans	George Watson, C.T. -	George Watson - -	George Watson - -	3rd Monday of January	1
2	Ayton	W. G. F. Tod - -	C. D. Colville - -	Thos. Thomson	1st Monday of March	2
3	Bunkle & Preston	Robert Johnston	Robert Johnston -	Robert Johnston -	2d Friday of May	3
4	Channelkirk	Alexander Davidson	Alexander Davidson -	Alexander Davidson	1st Friday of February	4
5	Chirnside	Alex. Lightbody -	Alex. Lightbody -	Thomas Mack - -	4th Monday of February	5
6	Cockburnspath ..	A. W. Henderson ·	A. W. Henderson -	A. W Henderson -	3rd Thursday of April	6
7	Coldingham...... ⎱ Houndwood* .. ⎰	A. R. Tait - - ⎱ Archibald M'Craith - ⎰	A. R. Tait - -	John Johnston -	2d Monday of November	7
8	Coldstream......	John Allison - -	John Allison - -	Adam Y. Henderson	4th Wednesday of January	8
9	Cranshaws.......	Robert Pringle, C.T. -	Robert Pringle - -	Robert Pringle - -		9
10	Dunse	John Mercer - -	Thomas Holywell -	John Waite - -	2d Wednesday of February	10
11	Earlston	Daniel Aitkenhead -	Robert Smith - -	Robert Smith - -	2d Wednesday of February	11
12	Eccles	John Stevenson - -	John Stevenson -	John Stevenson -	Last Saturday of January	12
13	Edrom	Charles Airth - -	Charles Airth - -	James B. Henderson	2d Monday of March	13
14	Eyemouth	James Cox -	James Cox - -	A. Todd - -	3rd Tuesday of May	14
15	Fogo............	John M'Farlane -	John M'Farlane -	John M'Farlane -	3rd Monday of April	15
16	Foulden.........	Alexander Dickson -	Alexander Dickson -	Alexander Dickson -	2d Wednesday of February	16
17	Gordon	Nicholas Dodds -	Nicholas Dodds -	Nicholas Dodds -	3rd Wednesday of February	17
18	Greenlaw	John Williamson	John Williamson -	John Williamson -	3rd Monday of January	18
19	Hume	James Cook, C.T.	James Cook -	James Cook -	3rd Saturday of November	19
20	Hutton	Robert Lawrie -	Robert Lawrie -	Robert Lawrie -	3rd Tuesday of February	20
21	Ladykirk........	J. H. Thomson -	J. H. Thomson -	J. H. Thomson -	3rd Friday of April	21
22	Langton	John Gow · -	John Gow -	John Gow . -	4th Monday of February	22
23	Lauder..........	John Lindsay, C.T. -	John Lindsay -	Thomas Broomfield	2d Friday of July	23
24	Legerwood......	John Smith - -	John Smith - -	John Smith - ~	Last Thursday of January	24
25	Longformacus. ..	William Wanless -	William Wanless -	William Wanless -	3rd Thursday of April	25
26	Mertoun........	Wm. Brunton, C.T. -	William Brunton -	William Brunton -	2d Thursday of February	26
27	Mordington.....	John Logan - -	John Logan -	John Logan - -	Last Friday of January	27
28	Nenthorn. ..,....	Alexander Virtue -	Alexander Virtue -	Alexander Virtue -	4th Saturday of January	28
	Oldhamstocks ...	Adam Grainger -	A. Grainger - -			
29	Polwarth	Robert Smyth - -	Robert Smyth -	Robert Smyth - -	3rd Thursday of April	29
30	Swinton	George Tweedie, C.T.	George Tweedie -	George Tweedie -	2d Monday of July	30
31	Westruther......	James Wilson - -	James Wilson - -	James Wilson - -	1st Tuesday of February	31
32	Whitsome........	John Turnbull - -	John Turnbull - -	John Turnbull -	3rd Friday of March	32

COUNTY OF SELKIRK.

No.	PARISHES.	PAROCHIAL TEACHERS.	REGISTRARS OF BIRTHS, &c.	INSPECTORS OF POOR.	DAY FIXED FOR ELECTION OF MEMBERS OF PAR. BOARD.	No.
1	Ettrick..........	George Hood - -	George Hood - -	George Hood - -	2d Friday of March	1
2	Galashiels	Alex. Williamson, M.A.	George Taket - -	John Thorburn -	1st Monday of May	2
3	Kirkhope	Hugh M'Morran -	Hugh M'Morran -	Hugh M'Morran -	3rd Friday of July	3
4	Selkirk, Parish..	Alex. Scott - - ⎱	John Dunn - - ⎱	James Hall - - ⎱	4th Friday of January	4
5	Do. Burgh..	James Millar, C.T. - ⎰		James Millar - - ⎰		5
6	Yarrow	William Bell, C.T. -	William Bell - -	William Dalgleish -	3rd Friday of May	6

REGISTRATION INFORMATION FOR SCOTLAND.

ABSTRACT OF THE ACT (17 & 18 VIC., CAP. 80). *

Arranged for the SOUTHERN COUNTIES REGISTER by the late Walter Hilson, Registrar of Kelso Parish, 1848 to 1865.

Inserted for its use in connection with the List of Registrars, and the universal individual responsibility which it entails—responsibility from which there is no appeal.

CHANGE OF SYSTEM.—From and after the 1st January 1855, Public attention is earnestly called to the following instructions relative to the Law as it is now in force.

Under the new system, all Births, Deaths, and Marriages, if intimated to the Registrar within the periods prescribed by the Act, as follows, will be Registered without any Fee being charged :—

BIRTHS.

On occasion of the birth of any Child, the Parents or Parent (or the Mother, in the case of an Illegitimate Child) must within Twenty-One Days thereafter, and under a Penalty of Twenty Shillings, in case of failure, attend Personally, and give information to the Registrar of the Parish or District, within which the Birth occurred.

---

* The Act for England is different ; it is briefly as follows :—

BIRTHS.— An infant should be registered within six weeks after its birth. In this case no fee is payable ; if after six weeks, a fee of 7s. 6d. is exacted.

MARRIAGES.—In the Established Church the registration virtually forms the last part of the ceremony ; the parties adjourning to the vestry and there making the requisite entries in the presence of witnesses. When the marriage takes place in a registered dissenting chapel, or at the registrar's office, the registrar must attend personally, and secure the requisite registration, else the marriage is invalid (see note, next page— " To those about to Marry " in England).

DEATHS.—Notice should be given of deaths to the district registrar. Let this be done early (no fixed time), that a certificate may be had to give the minister who performs the funeral service, else he (the minister) *may refuse to bury the body.*

NOTE.—With reference to the time within which a death must be registered, no time is fixed by the Act ; but any irregularity this might occasion is obviated by the provision in the Act—that every person who shall bury or perform any burial service for the burial of any dead body, for which no Certificate of Registration shall be delivered, and who shall not, within 7 days thereof, give notice to the Registrar, shall forfeit £10 for every such offence.

In case of the death or inability of the Parents, the Person in charge of any Child born, the Occupier of the House or Tenement in which the birth has taken place, and the Nurse present at the Birth, must attend and give information to the Registrar.

In the event of a failure to give the Notice above specified, the Parents, or other Persons above specified, and also any others having knowledge of the Particulars, shall, upon being required, Personally or in Writing, to do so, within three Months from the date of the birth, attend and give information to the Registrar, under a Penalty of Forty Shillings.

Any Person who shall find exposed any New Born Child, or the Dead Body of any New Born Child, shall forthwith give notice of the fact to the Registrar of the Parish or District, or to the Inspector of the Poor, or to the District Constable, under a Penalty of Forty Shillings.

In all cases where Three Months shall have expired after the Birth of a Child, it is not lawful to Register such Births, except under the Provisions of the 31st Section. The nature of these may be learned on application to the Registrar of the Parish or District.

DEATHS.

The nearest relatives present at the Death of any person, and the Occupier of the House or Tenement in which the Death took

---

"TO THOSE ABOUT TO MARRY " in England, the following is of importance:—In England the marriage ceremony must take place in a church, or licensed chapel (many dissenting chapels being licensed for this purpose), or in the registrar's office or registered building ; and *where a clergyman of the Established Church does not perform the ceremony*, the *Registrar must be present and two witnesses.* There must be open doors in all cases. It is felony to celebrate a marriage in a private house, unless by special license (from the Archbishop)—an expensive proceeding.

If the marriage takes place in a church or chapel of the Church of England, the service must be in conformity with the rubric prefixed to the office of matrimony in the Book of Common Prayer. But where the parties contract marriage in a registrar's office, no religious ceremony can be used, the exchange of consent required for the civil contract only being necessary. If, however, the marriage takes place in a registered dissenting chapel, there may be superadded to the civil contract whatever religious ceremony the minister of such church or persuasion is authorised by his church to use.

NOTE.—As to Marriages in the Register Office, religious service may, if the parties desire it, be added after the ceremony, but not *as a part of it.*

The marriage must be celebrated in canonical hours, *i.e.*—between 8 and 12 forenoon, unless it is by special licence, which dispenses with such hours.

If any persons knowingly and wilfully marry without conformity to the preceding regulations, the marriage is absolutely null and void.

place, must personally give notice of the Death to the Registrar of the Parish or District, within Eight Days thereafter, under a Penalty of Twenty Shillings.

Should the Parties above specified fail to give notice, such Persons, or any other having knowledge of the particulars, are bound, within Fourteen Days, from the date of the Death, upon being required to do so, Personally or in Writing, to attend and give the necessary information to the Registrar, under a Penalty of Forty Shillings.

In the event of any Person Dying not in a House or Tenement, the Occupier of the House or Tenement in which he was at the time lodging or residing, shall, upon receiving information of such Death, give, or cause to be given, notice to the Registrar of the Parish or District within which the Deceased lodged or resided, under a Penalty of Forty Shillings, in case of failure.

Where the Person deceased was himself the Occupier, then the inmates of such House or Tenement shall give the notice.

In cases where the residence or lodging of the Deceased is not known, then any Person present at the Death, or at the finding of the Body, and any Parish or Public Officer, or any Party to whom the Body shall be brought, must in like manner, and under the like Penalty, give the required notice.

Section XLI. provides for the transmission to the Registrar of Certificates of Death, in the form prescribed by the Act, by Medical Attendants, within Fourteen Days, under a Penalty of Forty Shillings, in case of failure.

The Undertaker or other Person having charge of the Interment of any person, shall, within Three Days after such Interment, and under a Penalty of Forty Shillings, transmit a Certificate of such Interment to the Registrar of the Parish within which the Death took place.

MARRIAGES.

In all cases of Regular Marriage, when the Certificates of the Proclamation of Banns are produced to the Registrar, the Parties will receive a certain Form to be filled up in the manner prescribed by the Act, which Form must be produced to the Minister solemnizing the Marriage, and Signed in his presence by the Contracting parties, by Witnesses, Male or Female, present thereat, not being less than Two in number, and by the Minister officiating. These Forms so authenticated, must be delivered to the Parties contracting the Marriage, who shall within Three Days thereafter, either deliver or send them by Post to the Registrar of the Parish within which the Marriage was solemnized. In the event of a failure so to deliver or send these Forms, the Husband, and failing the Husband the Wife, is liable to a Penalty of Ten Pounds.

The Registrar of a Parish or District is bound, on receiving Forty-eight Hours' notice, in writing, to attend Parties at the Solemnization of a Marriage with his Register-Book, and to make the proper entry therein, for which he is entitled to certain Fees.

Sections XLVIII. and XLIX. contain provisions relative to Marriages Irregularly Contracted, the nature of which may be learned on application to the Registrar of the Parish or District.

GENERAL INSTRUCTIONS.

Where parties fail to attend and give any notice required by the Act, after receiving Two Intimations to that effect from the Registrar, the Sheriff is directed, upon receiving Evidence of such failure, to issue his Warrant for Compelling Attendance—the Expense of which will fall on the Party in Default.

Printed Forms, setting forth the various particulars of the information required to be given under the Statute, are issued to the different Registrars by the Registrar-General, and will be furnished gratis to all Persons entitled to receive them; and the Registrars will also afford every necessary Instruction as to the proper mode of filling up the Forms prescribed by the Act.

Where several Parties are required by the Act to give any notice, it will be sufficient, to prevent liability for Penalties, if One of them shall give the notice required, and such notice may competently be sent by Post, if within the time prescribed by the Act.

COMPULSORY VACCINATION ACT FOR SCOTLAND.*

(26 and 27 Vict. cap. 8.)

EXPLANATORY STATEMENT.

(*A copy of which is given by the Registrar to the Informant of every child's birth at the time of its registration.*)

The duty of having Vaccination effected is imposed on the child's Father or Mother (in the case of an illegitimate child on the Mother), and in the event of the death, illness, absence, or

---

* For England, in brief, as follows :—

" VACCINATION ACT FOR ENGLAND.—It is imperative by law that parents should have every child vaccinated within *three* calendar months after birth, either by the appointed public vaccinator, or by a *legally qualified* practitioner.[1] If other than the parents are left in charge of the child, the vaccination must then be within *four* months of birth. If the child be not taken in eight days after vaccination to be examined by the medical practitioner in order to ascertain the result of the operation, parties not complying incur a penalty not exceeding 20s. The Registrars of each district are required to send
[1] *See* note *N.B.*, next page.

inability of both Father and Mother, on the person who has the care, nurture, or custody of the child. Such Father, Mother, or other person must cause the child [within *six* months] to be Vaccinated by a *registered* Medical Practitioner.* Immediately after the *Successful Vaccination* of the Child, the Operator is required to deliver a Certificate in the form of Schedule A [supplied by the Registrar along with, and annexed to, the Explanatory Statement], to the Father, Mother, or person in charge of the child, by whom it must be delivered or transmitted to the Registrar of the Parish (or District) in which the Birth of the child is registered, within *three days* after its date, for the purpose of being recorded in terms of the Vaccination Act.

Where the Medical Practitioner considers the child to be *in an unfit state for Vaccination,* he is required to deliver to the Father, Mother, or person in charge of the child, a Certificate in the form of Schedule B [also annexed to the Statement.] This Certificate remains in force for *two months* from the date of its delivery, *but no longer.* At the termination of that period, and of every succeeding period of two months, the Certificate must be *renewed* until the child shall have been successfully Vaccinated.

---

notices to the parents or guardians of children whose births they have registered, stating also the names and addresses of the public vaccinators, and the hours of attendance."

* N.B.—Certificates of Vaccination by Midwives and non-registered Medical Practitioners are quite invalid, and cannot be accepted by the Registrar as evidence of the operation having been performed.

If, after three successive Vaccinations, the Operator shall consider that the child is *Insusceptible of the Vaccine Disease,* he is required to deliver to the Father, Mother, or person in charge of the child, a Certificate in the form of Schedule C, [also annexed to the Statement.]

These Certificates [B and C] must be delivered or transmitted to the Registrar *within the same time,* [three days] and for the same purpose as the Certificate of Successful Vaccination [A].

Where one or other of the Certificates is not transmitted or delivered to the Registrar within six months after the Birth of any child taking place within his Parish (or District), the Registrar is required, within a period not exceeding one month, to intimate such failure, by a Notice through the Post Office, to the Father, Mother, or person in charge of the child ; and if the required Certificate is not furnished to the Registrar within *ten days* from the despatch of the Notice, the party at fault will be liable to a penalty not exceeding *Twenty Shillings,* and the further sum of *One Shilling* to be paid to the Registrar in respect of such Notice. Failing the payment of either of these sums, the said party will be liable to Imprisonment for a period not exceeding *ten days.*

[A certain latitude is allowed beyond these dates in wild and outlying highland districts, but the exceptions do not apply to any portion of the SOUTHERN COUNTIES.]

For the Appointed Parochial Vaccinators—*see* each Parish under the head " PUBLIC OFFICES."

APPENDIX.

THE "SOUTHERN COUNTIES' REGISTER" *V.* FULLERTON'S GAZETTEER.*

In reference to the aspersions on Kelso, in *Fullerton's Gazetteer*, noticed at pp. 72, 73, we have received the following letter:—

EDINBURGH, 13*th Oct.* 1865.

Messrs. J. & J. H. Rutherfurd, Kelso.

Gentlemen,—Let me request your attention to a passage respecting Messrs A. Fullerton & Co.'s "Gazetteer of Scotland" on pages 72 and 73 of your "Southern Counties' Register and Directory" of this year.

That passage speaks so of "Fullerton's Gazetteer" as to imply that it has always been strictly one work—that it first appeared in 1844—and that just what it was in that year, it continues to be in 1865. But Messrs. Fullerton & Co.'s "Gazetteer of Scotland" has really been two successive works, called respectively the "Topographical," and the "Imperial;" and the former was first issued in 1840, and ceased to be issued in 1854; while the latter was in main degree a new work of 1854-7, was first issued in these years, and underwent extensive revision in 1862. The facts of reconstruction and revision, done at great expense and with great care—facts so creditable to the publishers, and so essential to a correct account of the "Gazetteer"—these your "Register" entirely overlooks; and, at the same time, it does not know the "Gazetteer" as a book sold to subscribers or by order, but speaks of it as "circulated by means of hawkers."

Your "Register" also speaks, and "goes out of its way" to speak of the Gazetteer's account of Kelso as containing "some splenetic accusations against the moral character of the inhabitants"—remarks "written in an ill-natured spirit throughout"—remarks penned by a writer "both ignorant (wilfully or otherwise) and ill-natured"—"aspersions" —things which "gibbet Kelso as a little Paris and ignore its worth." Nothing of the sort. The articles on Kelso in both the old Gazetteer and the new are genial and almost complimentary; they speak cordially of the many good properties of Kelso; and they contain not a word arising from either heedlessness or unkindness. Your Register represents the Gazetteer's remarks as "especially objectionable when referring to the Kelso theatre." But the old Gazetteer states only such facts about the theatre as are recorded by Haig, and as seen, in substance, to be tacitly admitted by your Register itself; and the new

Gazetteer contains not a syllable about a theatre. Your Register further represents the Gazetteer as asserting that, when the French prisoners were in the town during the French War, the "Kelsonians" had, with "great facility, imbibed the spirit of French levity and dissipation." But the old Gazetteer says only that "many of them had with facility imbibed that spirit," and the new Gazetteer says not a word on the subject. The Gazetteer is further represented as saying that the Kelsonians had *then* "become inoculated with French laxity of morals and fashionable follies." But the old Gazetteer says only that the French prisoners, "to a very noticeable degree, inoculated the place with their fashionable follies, and, even in some instances, tainted it with their laxity of morals;" while the new Gazetteer retains only the portion of that statement which respects the follies, and cancels that portion which respects the morals. The Register's critique, too, implies the Gazetteer's alleged "aspersions" and "gibbetings" to refer to present time. But both Gazetteers speak only of the time from 1810 to 1814; and the old one expressly adds that, in years subsequent to these, the town had "assumed a more sedate character." Dr. M'Culloch himself, in 1838, in the very "panegyric" which your Register attempts to set off against the Gazetteer, makes mention of improvement in the town—improvement, too, in fully as grave matters as levity and dissipation; for he speaks of decrease in irregular marriages, decrease in the proportion of illegitimate births, and a return, in habits of economy among the common people, to a better course of feeling and conduct. The Gazetteer agrees throughout with Dr. M'Culloch; it does as ample justice to Kelso's excellences as he does; and it makes fair and full note of the various institutions which your Register itself regards as the best evidences of the town's good character. Even the old Gazetteer said on the very page on which the writer of your Register mainly had his eye, "Proportionately to the bulk of its population, Kelso is not a little wealthy in literary, social, patriotic, philanthropic, and religious institutions or societies."

I might have spared you the trouble of reading what I have now written. I might have simply sent to you a copy of the article on Kelso. Though I have chosen to speak of the old Gazetteer as well as of the new, I did not need to do so. The Gazetteer, as it exists now, or as it has existed since its issue of 1854-7, is devoid of all, or very nearly all, the matter on which your Register animadverts. I send you a copy of its article on Kelso; and I cannot doubt that, on reading it, you will see the propriety of inserting, in the second part of your Register a paragraph counteracting the passage on which I have commented. Let me state, in conclusion, that another revision of the Gazetteer is now in progress, and that, if you will favour me with facts or suggestions for improving the article on Kelso, I shall be most happy to receive them.—I am, etc.,

JOHN M. WILSON,

Editor of Imp. Gaz. of Scotland.

---

* We may mention, for the benefit of the general reader, that the following is of little interest except to those who belong to, or are connected with, KELSO, or have associations or dealings with it—a description which we find is wide enough to include, with very few exceptions, *all* our subscribers.

We gladly insert Mr. Wilson's letter in full, as we thereby have an opportunity of going into and exhausting the question. In justification of our remarks at pp. 72 73, we may state that our edition of Fullerton's Gazetteer is dated 1844. Of the "Topographical" edition, issued under the editorship of Mr. Wilson, we had no knowledge. The copy we have was got for the purpose of reference; and although the work is largely distributed over the country, it is the only copy but one we have had the opportunity of examining;* the other copy—a well fingered one—we chanced to come upon, some years ago, in an hotel at Kilmarnock, and, curiously turning up Kelso, we had, there and then, both our curiosity and horror gratified; for we read the article as if it wished to convey the impression that the town had been and *was* bad. Mr. Wilson quotes Haig's History of Kelso (published so long ago as 1825) for the facts concerning the Theatre contained in the *old* Gazetteer. From a close examination of Haig we find only the following paragraphs that have a reference to it:—

"Government having selected Kelso as a most eligible place for the reception of prisoners taken during the late war, who were admitted to their parole, a considerable number were sent thither in the month of November 1810, where they remained till June 1814; when, upon the conclusion of the general peace, they were sent home. During their stay, they conducted themselves with great propriety, and received the most civil and hospitable treatment from the inhabitants, which they repaid by contributing not a little to their amusement, by their theatrical and other exhibitions, to which the more respectable classes were invited. The greatest number of prisoners on parole stationed at Kelso never exceeded 230."—*Haig, p.* 97.

"Mr. Dubbs, of the Theatre-Royal, Edinburgh, as far as we have learned, was the first who introduced this polite amusement, by appearing with a respectable company of actors during the race-week in the year 1774; and, shortly after, a house in the Horse Market, built for the accommodation of the inhabitants when they could not obtain the Assembly-Room, at the Cross-Keys, for their balls or assemblies, was usually let to the manager, who fitted it up as a theatre on his occasional visits. But, to the French prisoners, who were here on parole during the late war, the inhabitants are indebted for having this place converted into a theatre, which they did at a very considerable expense, for our own amusement, performing in it occasionally, and distributing tickets of admission gratis; and at their departure, as a mark of their gratitude for the polite attention and kind treatment they had experienced, left the whole standing, with all their scenery and decorations."—*Haig, p.* 139.

But as a reverse picture to the *old* Gazetteer's statements, we may quote that Haig has also this to say of Kelso:—

"The manners of the inhabitants of Kelso in general are more polished than in most country towns, which in a great measure may be accounted for by its delightful situation, which constitutes it the resort of all the fashion in the vicinity, and of numerous visitors of the first rank in both kingdoms.

"The higher class are affable and courteous in their address, and benevolent and liberal in their dispositions.* The middle class are polite and obliging, hospitable and friendly. The lower class, in general, are sober, honest, and industrious; attentive to the interest of their employers, with a becoming deportment toward their superiors.

"The upper ranks dress in the first style of fashion, and the balls and assemblies present an elegance of female attire not to be exceeded out of the metropolis.

"The merchants, who form a most respectable class of the inhabitants, are just and honourable in their dealings, and are a credit to the station they occupy in the community. Indeed, it may be said of all ranks, that they perform the duties belonging to their different spheres with the strictest propriety and decorum.

"The community at large are also highly to be commended for a strict regard to their religious duties. Public worship is very generally attended, and the other exercises of the Sabbath performed in a most exemplary manner, so that the scenes which too often disgrace the streets of the metropolis on that holy day, are quite unknown there."—*p.* 104.

In Mr. Wilson's letter we have italicized the little word *then ;* and we may mention that this word, which so materially qualifies the sentence, neither appears in our account of Kelso in the "Register" (p. 72), nor—in the sense used by Mr. Wilson —in our edition of the *old* Gazetteer. In the latter, the paragraphs—the first, which occurs in vol. II. p. 84, is qualified with faint praise—are literally thus:—

"A small theatre was fitted up, at considerable expense, by the French prisoners during the last war, and, while they stayed, was conducted gratuitously by some of their own number; and, at their departure, it was left with all its appliances as an expression of delight with the Kelsonians on account of the facility with which many of them had imbibed the spirit of French levity and dissipation. But, in the aggregate, the town has of late assumed a more sedate character than belonged to it during years when it incurred some hazard of being distinguished chiefly by fashionable follies."

The second, occurring at p. 87, and at the conclusion of the article, Kelso is written down without any qualification:—

"From November 1810 till June 1814, Kelso was the abode of a body, never more than 230 in number, of French prisoners on parole, who, to a very noticeable degree, inoculated the place with their fashionable follies, and even, in some instances, tainted it with their laxity of morals."

We think that the words *inoculated and tainted,* here inserted, imply a state of matters scarcely temporary, and when read in the Gazetteer, in conjunction with the few sentences which follow, are such, we think, as would cause any ordinary reader to conclude that Kelso, not only had been, but still was a place of moral laxity and fashionable follies—seeing that the paragraph

---

* It belongs to a class of books that do not find their way much into the hands of either country or town booksellers in the regular trade.

* "Kelso weel beggit is worth fifteen shillings ony time," is an old vagrant saying, and to this day its charities (often very indiscriminate) are almost notorious over the empire.

quoted does not stand in the Gazetteer apart, but, as it were, an incidental sentence and mixed up with the names of worthy individuals still living when the paragraph was published.*

As specimens of the grudging way in which the writer in the old Gazetteer treats Kelso, we may quote the following:—

"Kelso was the birth-place of the famous Ballantyne Press, and the scene in which was printed the first edition of the 'Minstrelsy of the Scottish Border;' and at various periods it has displayed an energy and amount of literary enterprise, altogether beyond the proportion, either of its population or the advantages of its position."—*Old Gazetteer, and partly quoted in the new.*

Merit, of a presumptive kind, is here admitted, but it might have been added that Kelso was one of the first, if not the *very first*, provincial town in Scotland to adopt the printing press (*see* foot-note),† and we have shewn it was the second to publish a newspaper (*see* note, "Kelso Chronicle," p. 96).

---

* The French had left Kelso before our time, but the older inhabitants recollect them as possessed of many amiable qualities, of which "great mannerliness" (? good breeding) and buoyancy of spirits—in many instances under the depressing effects of great poverty—were most conspicuous. Of their peculiarities, the most singular, to the natives, was their habit of gathering for use different kinds of *wild weeds* by the road sides, and hedge roots, and killing small birds to eat—the latter a practice considered not much removed from cannibalism. That they were frivolous, we will admit, as many of them wore ear-rings, and one —a Pole—had a ring to his nose ; while all were boyishly fond of amusement, and were "merry good-natured creatures." But to assert that they were lax, is merely to state what any other body of men, similarly situated, would have been : English soldiers, for instance, are not immaculate, and they have a coarseness superadded from which the French were utterly free ; but when they left Kelso, we assert that their frivolity, such as it was, and their laxity, went with them.

† The first Scottish printers were Walter Chapman and Andrew Millar ; who, in consequence of a patent, established a press at Edinburgh in the year 1507. (CHALMERS, *Life of Ruddiman*, p. 80.) In 1508, they are known to have printed various pamphlets, a collection of which may be found in the Advocates' Library. The first volume of the *Breviarium Aberdonense* issued from their press in 1509 ; the second in 1510.—Of this very rare book a complete and well-preserved copy belongs to the library of the University of Edinburgh.
The establishment of printing-presses in the other principal towns of Scotland cannot so easily be traced. Knox's *Faythful Admonition unto the Professours of God's Truthe in England* was, if we may credit the title-page, printed at *Kalykow* or Kelso. [Is there any reason for not crediting the title page?—J. & J. H. R.] This work appeared in 1554. Aberdeen, the seat of a university, could not boast of a printing-press till a much later period. In the colophon of a poem on the death of Bishop Forbes, Edward Raban styles himself "Master printer, the first in Aberdeen." (*Funerals of Bishop Forbes*, p. 429, Aberd. 1635, 4to.)—DAVID IRVING'S *Lives of the Scottish Poets, &c.,* foot note, vol 1, p. 75.

When the general trade is mentioned it is with the following depreciatory fling :—

"Kelso is as poor in the aggregate productiveness of its manufactures, as it is showily rich in their variety. The dressing of skins, the tanning of hides, the currying of leather, the weaving of flannel, woollen cloth, and linen, the making of hats and of stockings, the working of iron, and the manufacture of candles, shoes, tobacco, and other articles, all have a place in the town ; but they do not jointly employ 200 workmen, and are all, with the exception of currying, stationary or declining, The number of looms in 1828 was 70 ; and in 1838, it had become reduced to 41. Yet the place has a very important trade in corn and cured pork.

Thus in the *old* Gazetteer, and transferred verbatim to the *new.*

At the date of the *old* Gazetteer— 25 years ago—the paragraph was possibly applicable to Kelso ; *then*, almost every town of the size in Scotland was "poor in the aggregate productiveness of its manufactures, and showily rich in their variety ;" it had been the normal state of things for centuries ; but we question if any other town described in the Gazetteer gets sneered at for this.* Most of the small towns, since characterised for energy, were then in, or had already passed through, a transition state, and taking advantage of their suitableness to progress in manufactures (in the modern sense of the word—for example Hawick and Galashiels) or traffic (*e.g.* Kelso—Jedburgh from its position, partly in both); and now (when the information of the *new* Gazetteer *ought* to apply) we have Kelso keeping a good front position in the locality, while its speciality is shop-keeping and the handicrafts or manufactures connected therewith. In its list of trades enumerated in the paragraph, may still be mentioned, dressing skins and making candles ; but hand-loom weaving (*see* note, p. 454), making stockings, hats, or tobacco, or *currying leather* (the trade quoted as the only one not declining) are all virtually defunct. A hat has not been made in Kelso for ten years, and, for a longer period, a skin has not been curried for the purposes of trade ; but while the town is thus credited with manufactures, to which it has little or no right, the really extensive manufactures of saddlery and coach building (both of very old date) are entirely omitted. Shoes,—although the manufacture is declining, — are now made both for home and wholesale trade and export ; saddlery is also extensively exported : this export trade in both has existed for over twenty years. The other handicrafts of Kelso may be described as adjuncts to its shops ; but, *as such*, we question if,

---

* Not only is Kelso the only town, so far as we have investigated the Gazetteer, which gets sneered at for its want of manufactures, but it is also the only one against which such charges as we have endeavoured to repel are made. This proves, if not ill-nature, at least partial justice.

in any town of its size in the kingdom, better or more varied work can be produced ;* while in its shops a class of goods will be found, suitable for a polished and wealthy community, which no other town of its size can surpass (*see* p. 302).

As an instance of changes in trade we may mention that forty years ago the shoe trade of Kelso was equal in importance to that of Selkirk, and from it many localities in Berwickshire and Northumberland drew their supplies. At that time it was the most important trade in the town, and employed most hands ; *now* we believe it has not a shoemaker apprentice; even the home manufacture of shoes seems to be dying out, and the same is the case in all the other Border towns.

"THE PLACE" does a very large pork curing trade (*see* note, p. 97), for which it deserves credit ; and it is the centre of an enormous corn (*see* p. 91, CORN EXCHANGE)† and cattle trade (*see* pp. 73, 75, 89, and note, 613) ; but the credit of these belong rather to its position and the energy and enterprise of the surrounding farmers.

Mr. Wilson draws a distinction between the "Kelsonians" and "the place ;" and we do seem to have transposed these words in our Register. But who constitute "the place" but the "Kelsonians?" In writing on the morals of a place, the streets are surely not meant, nor the walls of the houses, nor the cattle within the gates. As a rule, whenever the morality of a place is mentioned, the good or evil is understood to refer to its inhabitants—the "onians ;" and our impression is, that the effect of the statements published in the Gazetteer since 1840, has been to the prejudice of the *inhabitants* of Kelso.

---

* It is but due to the workmen of Kelso to state that as a class they are peculiarly provident Although neither numerous nor extravagantly paid, they have, as Odd Fellows, accumulated funds (Feby 1866) to the amount of £1850, and as Foresters £1013—a fact which speaks directly and indirectly for their general healthiness and regular habits of living ; while as members of the Benefit Societies they annually divide weekly savings amounting to over £500.

The Kelso societies of Odd Fellows and Foresters—like all the other early branches—were established on an erroneously small system of payments. When this was exposed by the Ratcliffe and other Tables, the members, instead of following the example of *all* the other local societies —dividing the funds, and breaking up—increased their payments to a safe rate—that of the Manchester statement—and held their position.

† At Kelso Corn Exchange, p. 91, we give a *reported* statement that more Corn is sold in it by the grower than in any other building in the Empire. Since that paragraph was printed we have had its accuracy questioned ; it is asserted that the Berwick-on-Tweed Exchange precedes Kelso as a grower's Market, but that Kelso comes second in the Empire, and is the first in Scotland.

Owing to the Corn Sales in each being by sample, the quantities really sold cannot be accurately ascertained.

Of Dr. M'Culloch's reference to irregular marriages (which he designates "the bane of the working classes"), we may state that when he wrote, these marriages were very frequent over the entire district, while in some agricultural parishes they were almost the rule In fact, the woman thought it a want of gallantry in the man if a "run-away" marriage was not proposed ;* but is it not a little curious, that but for the Doctor's notice of the fact in connection with a parish in no way notorious for it, this blot in our social system would have passed unnoticed in the statistical accounts of the three counties ! From which we conclude *he* had an honest pride in referring to a matter which all the other ministers thought best to ignore. And so with illegitimacy ; while he quotes improvement in that ugly feature, the others quote improvement in the smuggling or poaching habits of their parishioners, or state, that "as a body, they are sober-minded, honest, and contented ;" but the very few who allude to illegitimacy at all (only other 7 in Roxburghshire, 10 in Berwickshire,† none in Selkirkshire), do so merely to

---

* In 1838, when the doctor wrote, a run-away marriage was scarcely considered a social misdemeanour ; in reality it was merely an ecclesiastical offence, and as such the contracting parties were debarred from church privileges till they had been re-married by an ordained minister, or acknowledged their irregularity before the Kirk-session. These marriages, although still frequent in some localities of the district, are now, as a rule, considered disreputable by all classes ; and owing to a penalty being attached to them (thus practically holding out to the contracting parties a strong temptation to ignore their marriage), they are seldom registered, consequently are a greater evil than ever in some respects, as they leave the parties really married in the eye of the law, and as such liable to serious legal responsibilities, while, at the same time, the law practically acts as if they had no legal married position. Of all the Border Marriages in the district for the year 1861, only one pair paid the penalty (of 20s.), and got (by authority of the Sheriff) legally registered ; but it is to be presumed that many couples preferred the old way—the easier and cheaper—of being proclaimed in church and getting regularly married and registered. One of our correspondents (in Berwickshire) quoting "five or six" such marriages as having occurred in his parish since the passing of the Act (February 1856)—says, "all were subsequently married again, and registered in the regular way." At pp. 432-645 we have stated these Border Marriages to be now *illegal*—perhaps *actionable* would have been a more suitable word, as illegality may imply invalidity. At p. 645 we have inadvertently stated these marriages to be *void*—a mistake it will be observed.

Not only is Dr. M'Culloch the only writer in the statistical accounts of the district who takes notice of the Border marriages, but he also is the only one to notice the evictions of the poor from country parishes (*see* note, p. 716) which have been going on for the last fifty years, till now villages, once populous, have dwindled into mere hamlets.

† Out of 33 in Roxburghshire and 32 in Berwickshire. In Selkirkshire (4 parishes) the subject is ignored entirely.

mention the number of births which had occurred in so many years; and we are sorry to observe that, comparing these quotations, of thirty years since, with the Registrar's returns of the present day, illegitimacy seems largely on the increase.*

By our references to the *new* Gazetteer, it will be observed we have read Mr. Wilson's amended description of Kelso. The only difference between the accounts seems to have been made with the scissors—those portions that appear in the *new* Gazetteer being mostly reduced, but otherwise unaltered, from the old; even the following careless account of Kelso streets being reprinted verbatim, except with the insertion of a still more erroneous date. The *italics* are our own.

" The town consists of a central square or market-place, and divergent streets and alleys. The square is spacious and airy, very large for a provincial town, presided over on the east side by the elegant Townhouse, and edificed with neat modern houses of three stories, some of which have on the ground-floor good and even elegant shops. From the square issue *four* thoroughfares—Roxburgh-street, Bridge-street, Mill-wynd, and the Horse and Wood Markets. *Roxburgh-street goes off from the end of the Townhouse,* and runs sinuously parallel with the river, sending down its back-tenements on one side to the edge of the stream. Though irregular,

---

* Which is further proved by the following returns :—the proportion of illegitimates for Scotland during the year 1859, was per cent. 9.11.

      Do. 1860,   ,,   9.21.

      Do. 1861,   ,,   9.28.

" To whatever cause, then, it may be owing, it would appear that illegitimacy is on the increase."—*Report for* 1860.

In connection with the birth rates for Scotland, the report for 1861 announces the curious fact, proved by the observations and averages of seven years (1855 to 1861 inclusive), that of illegitimate boys born, there is 107.3 to each 100 girls; while of legitimate boys born, there is only 105.2 to each 100 girls.

---

and not anywhere elegant in its buildings, it has a pleasing appearance, *and bears the palm of both healthiness and general favour!* At present, it is upwards of ¼ a mile in length; but formerly it reached to what is now the middle of the Duke of Roxburghe's garden, having been curtailed at the further end to make improvements on the pleasure-grounds. Bridge-street goes off from the square opposite the exit of Roxburgh-street; and though inferior to it in length, is superior in general appearance, and contains many elegant houses. This street sends off *Oven-wynd, leading to Ednam-house,* and the Abbey-close, anciently the thoroughfare to the old bridge. Mill-wynd leaves the square, *and pursues a course parallel with Bridge-street, The street* called the Horse and Wood markets goes off in a direction at right angles with the other thoroughfares, and points the way to Coldstream and Berwick. At one time it was, over part of its extent, very narrow and inconvenient; but about 35 [the old Gazetteer says 20] years ago it was widened and otherwise improved."

The narrowness and inconvenience here mentioned, we suppose, alludes to an improvement which took place at Leadbetter Row, about the year 1803, then known as part of the Wood Market. In the quotation will be observed the mixture made of the Horse and Wood markets—streets leading in quite different directions. The paragraph seems to have been carelessly copied from Haig, in the first instance. In the *new* Gazetteer the important suburb of Forest Field, the "west-end" of Kelso, is not even mentioned.

Mr. Wilson's argument of the *new* edition of the Gazetteer having superseded the old one is to no purpose; the one has only superseded the other in present *sale*, but the different editions of the old still remain dispersed over the country to misrepresent the town; and therefore it is the more requisite, whatever the present or future intended editions be, that we put on record a protest against all inaccurate statements, in whichever edition they may appear.

ADDENDA.

THE BONDAGE SYSTEM.

Since the paragraphs on this subject, at pp. 49-51, were written (in 1864), the system has been greatly altered for the better. Last autumn the peasantry of the district began in earnest to agitate for its removal, and with a great amount of ability and prudence have not only carried their purpose, but have, as a rule, carried with them the sympathy of the public, and the goodwill of the farmers in the change.

The new system, which is variable and cannot be considered as yet definitely settled, beginning with the May term of this year (1866), is, that the hind having daughters engages them (the daughters) to do the ordinary field work, but at increased wages—thus, some farmers have engaged the whole family by paying the father 50s. or 60s. for each daughter he keeps at home, who are to be paid 10d. to 1s. a day as formerly; while others have hired with this difference—the daughters to be paid at the rate of fourteen or fifteen pence per day, but with no gratuity to the father, which brings their wages almost equivalent. In some instances strangers have been hired at the increased wage, but these cases are exceptional. Without doubt, the system now lies with the hinds themselves, to abolish or otherwise.

The agitation received considerable impetus by the Rev. John Thomson, of Rosalee, Hawick, offering a prize of £30 for the best essay by "farm-stewards, shepherds, ploughmen, and their sons and daughters, in the counties of Roxburgh, Selkirk, and Berwick, on the Evils of the system, and suggestions for their removal," which was still further advanced by the publication of two of the essays.*

If proof were wanted of the superior intelligence of our border peasantry, we could give no better examples than the essays quoted, the speeches delivered at Kelso and elsewhere by hinds and other workmen on the subject, and their many communications to the local newspapers. Of the speeches it may be said, that for good taste and moderation—and in some instances for point—they would have done credit to any ordained minister. The consequence is, that not only may they be said to have got rid of the system, but, along with the

---

* "The Evils of the Bondage System, with Suggestions for their Removal." A Prize Essay. By William Fairbairn, shepherd, Bartlehill, Berwickshire. Second edition, enlarged. Price 6d. Kelso: J. & J. H. Rutherfurd.

"Bondage and Bondagers: Remarks on the evils of the system, with suggestions for their mitigation or removal." By 'Free House.' Price 4d. Kelso: Mrs. Wilson, and J. Pattison.

riddance, they have bettered their circumstances, and forced the respect of the community.

In connection with the above, and for the grand truth which it asserts, we quote the following paragraph which appeared in the London *Field* of March 10, while reviewing Fairbairn's essay :—

"Thanks to the liberality of the Rev. John Thomson in giving a prize, we have a most interesting and ably written pamphlet on the nature, evils, and proposed remedy for the 'Bondage System,' as well as an example, in the author's person, *of the blessings of a sound system of national education*. We pause with wonder and admiration at the logical reasoning and clear well-expressed sentiments of a man who ocupies a position which in England is, alas ! too often filled by men destitute of even the rudiments of education."

THE EDINBURGH BORDER COUNTIES ASSOCIATION.
(ROXBURGH, BERWICK, AND SELKIRK.)
Instituted in 1865.

PATRONS.

His Grace the Duke of Buccleuch, K.G.	David Robertson, Esq. of Ladykirk, M.P., Lord-Lieutenant of Berwickshire.
His Grace the Duke of Roxburghe, K.T.	

President—The Hon. Lord Jerviswoode.

VICE-PRESIDENTS.

Sir Wm. Scott, Bart., of Ancrum, M.P.	George Dundas, Esq., advocate, Sheriff of Selkirkshire.
Sir David Brewster, K.H., LL D.	R. B. Maconochie, Esq., of Gattonside House.
Lieutenant-Colonel Macdonald of Powderhall.	James Reid, Esq., banker, Carlton Terrace, Edinburgh.
A. Campbell Swinton, Esq., yr. of Kimmerghame.	R. B. Blackburn, Esq., advocate, Edinburgh.
A. R. Clark, Esq., advocate, Sheriff of Berwickshire.	

Secretary—Thomas Usher, County Hall, Edinburgh.

Treasurer—George Scott, 13 Hanover Street, Edinburgh.

DISTRICT SECRETARIES.

Earlston—James Smail, Commercial Bank ; Galashiels—Alexander Rutherford, writer ; Jedburgh—Adam Turnbull, writer, banker ; Kelso, James H. Rutherfurd, bookseller ; Melrose—William M'-Bean, bookseller ; Selkirk—John Dunn, druggist.

The following are the objects of the Association :—1, The encouragement of friendly intercourse amongst the members. 2, The advancement of Education in the counties of Roxburgh, Berwick, and Selkirk, by the Distribution of Prizes, or otherwise. 3, To afford to young men from these counties, who may be recommended to its notice, assistance and advice in procuring situations, or otherwise. 4, The relief of natives of these counties in Edinburgh, in indigent or distressed circumstances.

Entry-money, 5s. Annual Subscription, payable 1st January, 5s. Honorary Life-Membership, £2, 2s. A single payment of One Guinea constitutes a Lady as an Honorary Contributor, and Donations are received from all who are interested in promoting the objects of the association.

The annual general meeting of the Association is held on the third Friday of January, for transacting the general business of the Association, and for electing the office-bearers for the following year. The annual dinner of the Association is held on the same day. In addition to the above, there are annually three stated meetings of Council—dates and place unfixed.

BERWICK, ROXBURGH, & SELKIRK COUNTIES' EDINBURGH ASSOCIATION.—(Estab. at Edinburgh, March 1866.)

Objects:—1st, To encourage and promote friendly intercourse amongst the Members. 2nd, To afford to young men from these counties who may be recommended to its notice, assistance and advice in procuring situations or otherwise. 3rd, The relief of deserving natives of these counties in Edinburgh in indigent or distressed circumstances.

Secretary—Thomas Wilson, 27 Charlotte Street, Leith.

EASTERN BORDER MISSION TO THE BLIND.
Supported by voluntary subscriptions and contributions.

The objects of this Association are to seek out and visit the Blind on both sides of the Eastern Border, to teach them to read in their own homes according to Moon's system of reading, to circulate books among them, and to instruct them in any other way that may seem expedient to the Committee. The Association was formally inaugurated at a public meeting held in the Town-hall of Kelso, on Friday, the 28th of October 1864, when the Right Hon. Lord Binning occupied the chair.

President—The Right Hon. the Earl of Haddington.

HONORARY VICE-PRESIDENTS.

The Most Noble the Marquis of Lothian.	Sir William Scott, Bart., M.P.
The Right Hon. the Earl of Minto.	David Robertson, Esq., M.P.
The Right Hon Lord Binning.	Principal Sir David Brewster.
	James Douglas, Esq., of Cavers.

ACTING OR SUB-COMMITTEE.

Major the Hon. R. Baillie.	Robert Oliver, Esq.
F. Russell, Esq.	Rev. Henry Renton, A.M.
John Ord, Esq.	Rev. Dr. Bonar.

With the Secretary and Treasurer.

Honorary Secretary—Jas. Tait, Esq., of the "Kelso Chronicle."

Honorary Treasurer—Jas. Douglas, Esq., Commercial Bank, Kelso.

Agent—Mr. Gilbert Maculloch.

The district contemplated in the operations of the Association extends from Hawick to Berwick, embracing the towns of Jedburgh, Kelso, Melrose, Galashiels, Selkirk, Lauder, Dunse, and Coldstream, with intermediate districts.

The number of Blind returned as existing in the district is above 100, many of them advanced in life, but a goodly proportion of them still susceptible of being taught to read.

The receipts of the Association, up to the annual meeting on 10th November 1865, were £78 : 19 : 1.

BORDER PIGEON MATCHES (Estab. 1861-62).

Major Dickins, Cornhill, Secretary and Manager.

James Steel, Kelso, Pigeon Purveyor.

Matches take place twice or thrice in each season, between 1st December and 15th February, by the kind permission of Sir George H. S. Douglas, of Springwood Park, in the Bridge-end Park, Kelso

Handicaps and Sweepstakes.   Hornsey-Wood Rules.

These Matches are now the most numerously attended in Scotland if not in the Empire. At the last match, 7th February 1866, the Handicap entries numbered 146, of whom 98 came to the cords. On the occasion over 800 pigeons were flown.

The freshness and first-rate quality of the pigeons flown at these matches has probably never been surpassed, and has helped in no small degree to establish their present popularity.

THE UNITED BORDER HUNT STEEPLE CHASES.
(Formerly the Berwickshire Steeple Chases.)
Revived 12th April 1861.

John B. Kellie, Dunse, Clerk of the Course, and Secretary.

Stewards elected annually.

The meeting is to be held annually in Berwickshire, Roxburghshire, and Northumberland. It was in Berwickshire this year, over the farm of Kimmerghame Mains, within three miles of Dunse. It is intended to be in Northumberland next year.

GLASGOW ROXBURGHSHIRE SOCIETY.
(Founded March 1857.)

This society was formed for the purpose of fostering friendship among those from the county, affording advice and assistance to young men coming to the city, and aiding persons residing in or near, or passing through Glasgow, who are either natives or the widows or children of natives of the county, who may have fallen into unfortunate circumstances.

The admission of ordinary members is an entry-money of £4, 4s., payable either at once or by yearly instalments of 10s. 6d., or an annual subscription of 5s. during membership ; and of honorary members by a donation of £1, 1s.

Secretary—Walter Hilson, 6 John Street.

KELSO BREAD SOCIETY.

Instituted 1855, for the purpose of supplying indigent women with bread, gratis, during the winter months.

Average Income, £45.

Secretary and Treasurer—Mrs. Logan, Goshen.

KELSO PHILHARMONIC SOCIETY.

Established 1864 for the study of high class sacred music.

President—W. Fred. Vernon.   Secretary—S. Lawrie.
Conductor—Mr. Cook.

Ordinary members, about 60 ; subscription, 2s.
Honorary do.   over 30 ;   do.   5s.

KELSO MECHANICS' INSTITUTE AND CLUB.
(Founded 1866.)

Combining Working Men's Club and Reading Room with the Institute proper. It has a circulating Library of upwards of 500 volumes, and is patronised by all classes of the community.

Patron—His Grace the Duke of Roxburghe.

President—Dr. Francis Douglas, late E.I.C.S.

COMMITTEE.

Mr. Oliver, Mr. Mackenzie, Mr. Balmer, Mr. J. Henderson (tobacconist), Mr. Adams (bookbinder).

Librarian—Mr. J. Henderson (teacher).   Treasurer—Mr. G. F. Dodds.
Secretary—Mr. W. Fred. Vernon.

Annual Subscription—Honorary Member, 5s. ; Ordinary do., 2s. 6d.

KELSO RACES.

The Caledonian Hunt Meeting, it seems, is now held at Kelso once in *four* years (we state once in *five* years at page 92), consequently it will be held here this year instead of next year, as stated. This is owing to the Meeting at Stirling having been discontinued.

The following places now constitute the rotation :—Kelso, 1866 (and again in 1870 if no alteration takes place); Perth, 1867 ; Ayr, 1868 ; Edinburgh (over Musselburgh Course), 1869.

The last Meeting held at Stirling was in 1854.

BUILDINGS IN KELSO.

At length Kelso has ceased to be barren in buildings possessed of architectural merit, (*see* notes pp. 78, 302), in the Free Church, Roxburgh Street, erected at a cost of nearly £5000 for Dr Bonar, and the façade of Stuart & Mein's new seed stores, Wood Market.

The Church, completed to the steeple, is in the Lombardo-

Gothic style, freely and ornately treated, of Mr. Pilkington, Edinburgh, its architect ; the style of the seed stores is an Italian, enriched with emblematical figures and carvings— architect, Mr. James W. Smith.

These, as specimens of public and private buildings, merit general praise, and, as an innovation in the right direction, the special gratitude of the community.

EDNAM PARISH.

Mr. Douglas Moffat, of Harpertoun, etc., intends to build a residence on his estate near to the present farm-house of High-ridgehall — a fine situation overhanging the Tweed.

HOUNAM AND OXNAM PARISHES.

Archibald Stewart, Esq., 18 Royal Terrace, Edinburgh, has succeeded to the estates of the late Mrs. Stavert, of Philogar and Cunzierton (pp. 226, 229).

JEDBURGH YOUNG MEN'S CHRISTIAN ASSOCIATION.
(Estab. 1866.)

For the mental and spiritual improvement of its members. Holds weekly meetings on the Sabbath mornings.

President—Mr. A. C. Mounsey, Rector.
Vice-Presidents—Jas. Manson and Thomas Oliver.
Treas.—John D. Peacock. Secy.—Sam. H. Crosbie.
Committee—Messrs. John Turnbull, T. C. Halliburton, H. D. Telfer, Andrew Brown, Francis Dickison.

JEDBURGH BORDER GAMES (Instituted 1853).

These Games are the principal in the district, and are held on the Dunion Moor, about 2 miles from the town, annually, on the second Friday of August, or as near the 12th of August as possible, that being the birth-day of the Marquis of Lothian, in honour of whom the Games are held. The average annual amount given in prizes is £60, collected by subscription in Jedburgh and district ; prizes are also generally given by Jedburgh lads resident in Edinburgh, Manchester, and other places.

President—Mr. William Veitch.

1st ROXBURGHSHIRE (JEDBURGH) RIFLE VOLUNTEER BAND.
(Estab. 1866.)

Patron—W. M. Scott, Esq., yr. of Ancrum, (Capt. 1st Rox. R. V.)
President—John S. Turnbull, Esq., Port House.
Secretary and Treasurer—James Brown, Clerk.
Interim Band-master—John Bennet, jun.

HARESTANES (near Jedburgh).

Situated near to the eastern corner of Ancrum parish and within the grounds of Mounteviot—which occupy a considerable portion of both Crailing (*see* p. 224) and Ancrum parishes. Harestanes is supposed to have been the site of Druidical stones, some trace of which were visible within living memory. The etymology of the name strengthens this belief, it signifying temple or holy stone. The place has been the haunt of the early races. A fine specimen of a stone hammer or hatchet was found near it some years ago. The possessor left the Marquis of Lothian's employment for the south of England, carrying the ancient implement with him, thus separating it from the district whose early history it illustrated.

HAWICK HAND-BALL MATCH.

This game is played on a Monday in the end of February, ruled by the moon's changes. The opposing players are the residents east and west of the Slitrig, locally known as the Eastla' and Westla' Water Men. The rivers are frequently the area of the sports, and the players engage in these games with an ardour which the often flooded wintry streams cannot chill.

Fish Table for the District,

Supplied by Mr. James Steel, Fishmonger. Bridge Street, Kelso.

S. denotes that the Fish is in Season; F. in Finest Season; O. Out of Season.

Name of Fish.	Jan.	Feb.	Mar.	April	May	June	July	Aug.	Sept.	Oct.	Nov.	Dec.
Brill	S	S	S	S	S	O	O	O	O	S	S	S
Carp	S	S	S	S	S	S	S	S	S	S	S	S
Cockles	S	S	S	O	O	O	O	O	S	S	S	S
Cod	F	S	S	O	O	O	O	O	S	S	S	F
Crabs	O	O	O	S	F	F	F	F	F	O	O	O
Dabs	S	S	S	S	S	S	S	S	O	O	O	O
Dace	F	F	O	O	O	S	S	S	F	F	F	S
Eels	S	S	S	O	O	O	O	O	S	F	F	S
Flounders	S	S	S	O	O	O	O	O	O	S	S	S
Gurnets	O	O	O	O	S	S	S	S	S	O	O	O
Haddocks	F	S	O	O	S	S	S	S	S	F	F	F
Halibut	S	F	F	S	S	F	F	S	S	S	S	S
Herrings	S	O	O	O	S	S	F	F	S	S	S	S
Ling	S	S	S	O	O	O	O	O	S	S	S	S
Lobsters	O	O	O	S	F	F	F	S	S	O	O	O
Mackerel	O	O	O	S	S	S	S	O	O	O	O	O
Mullet	O	O	O	S	S	S	O	O	O	O	O	O
Mussels	S	S	S	S	O	O	O	O	S	S	S	S
Oysters	S	S	F	F	O	O	O	O	S	S	S	S
Plaice	S	O	O	O	S	S	S	S	S	S	S	S
Prawns	O	O	S	F	F	F	F	S	O	O	O	O
Salmon	O	S	S	F	F	F	F	S	O*	O	O	O
Shrimps	S	S	S	S	S	O	O	O	S	S	S	S
Skate	F	F	F	F	F	F	S	S	O	O	S	S
Smelts	S	S	S	S	S	O	O	O	O	U	S	S
Soles	S	O	O	O	S	S	S	S	O	S	S	S
Sprats	S	O	O	O	O	O	S	S	S	O	S	O
Thornback	O	O	O	O	O	O	S	S	S	S	S	O
Trout	O	S	S	F	F	F	F	F	S	S	O	O
Turbot	S	O	O	O	S	S	S	S	S	S	S	S
Whitings	F	F	O	O	O	S	S	S	S	F	F	F

* Tweed Salmon may be had up to the middle of this month.

Note.—Sea Fish may generally be had all the year, whether in or out of season, as they are protected by no "close time," (oysters excepted); but as a rule, fish out of season are inferior in quality and are often unwholesome.

THE END.

SOUTHERN COUNTIES' REGISTER ADVERTISEMENTS.

INDEX TO ADVERTISEMENTS.

Every Advertisement equal to one column or more is here specified ; shorter announcements are classed as Miscellaneous.

NOTE.

IT may interest Advertisers to know that the list of subscribers to the Register numbers 958, disposed as follows:—

Kelso, Town and Parish	. . .	121	Galashiels and Ladhope . . .	70	Coldstream, Town and Parish . .	26
Hawick Do.	. . .	101	Selkirk	52	Dunse, ...	34
Jedburgh Do.	. . .	31			Earlston and Lauder	32
Melrose Do.	. . .	50	Ettrick, Yarrow, and parts of Parishes	21	Country Parishes	120
Country Parishes	. . .	154				
Total for Roxburghshire	. .	457	Total for Selkirkshire . . .	143	Total for Berwickshire . . .	212

Kelso Corn Exchange, 16; Edinburgh and Glasgow, 56; Miscellaneous, (Scotland generally, Northumberland, London, &c.,) 53; Australia, 14; New York, &c., 7.

In addition to these, the sheets of about 100 incomplete copies have been got from us during the process of printing (we had at last to put a stop to this); these we will recal and replace with the complete book, (advertisement sheets included). A circulation of 1050 copies is thus actually secured; and judging from the pressure we have had during the last six months, for the complete work, the likelihood is that it will soon be sold out.

FARM BUSINESS BOOKS

PREPARED BY

J. & J. H. RUTHERFURD.

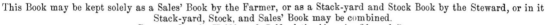

THE BOOK OF

CORN ACCOUNTS, AND THE STACK-YARD & BARN STOCK.

This Book may be kept solely as a Sales' Book by the Farmer, or as a Stack-yard and Stock Book by the Steward, or in it Stack-yard, Stock, and Sales' Book may be combined.

PRICES—Stoutly Half bound Calf, cloth sides, 4s. 6d. and 7s

The object of this book is to help farmers to keep an accurate account of the grain grown, thrashed, and sold, the whole being so arranged as to shew the size of each field, the number of stacks obtained, the time when thrashed, the amount of good and of light grain produced, the date and manner of disposal, the price and net receipts, also the yield per acre of each field.

At the end are attached some supplementary leaves to shew the consumpt of grain on the farm for feeding and other purposes. The whole simplified by special rulings and printed headings, and accompanying each book is a wrought-out example or KEY.

"*According to this arrangement any farmer may keep an accurate account, with almost no trouble, of the whole produce of grain from his farm, the money he obtains for it, and the way in which the whole crop is disposed of; and such accounts kept from year to year would be of very great value.*"—KELSO CHRONICLE, Nov. 11, 1864.

"*Every farmer ought to keep an account with each field that he cultivates* [which this book does], almost with every beast that he rears. As it is, a man may farm several hundred acres without being able to tell whether he loses or gains by any particular crop. As long as he pays his way on the whole he is satisfied, and he never inquires where his profits come from."—*The Times.*

WORKERS' TIME AND WAGE BOOKS,

Drawn up for Weekly Accounts—the most useful for Small Farms. 1s. each, and upwards.

Drawn up for Monthly Accounts—the most useful for Large Farms. 1s. 6d. each, and upwards.

Either style is done up in a variety of thicknesses and bindings.

"Can you recommend me to a good system of Farm Book-keeping?"

"*We would recommend you to procure 'Worker's Day Book,' and 'Barn Book,' prepared and published by J. & J. H. Rutherfurd, Kelso.*"— Answer to a Correspondent in the NORTH BRITISH AGRICULTURIST of 9th November 1864.

THE REAPERS' TIME AND WAGE TABLE,

On a Sheet, for Harvest Labour. Price, post free, 9d.

"*A very useful document for such farmers as cut their crops by time.*"—SCOTTISH FARMER.

MILLERS' CORN-GRINDING BOOKS,

Ruled and Headed throughout.

(OVER.

Worker's Day Book, Barn Book, and Reaper's Time and Wage Table.

"To keep farm accounts properly is not often an easy matter; there are so many different things to be taken into account, and one item here has so often to be set-off against another item there, that to make out any really good system has been felt as a want. There are no doubt some very excellent farm account books, but the objection to these has been the price. Now, in these books issued by the Messrs. Rutherfurd, the charge has been so reduced as to bring it within reach of all. The 'Barn Book' may be had for 4s. 6d., or 7s. for a large size. The 'Worker's Day Book' is only 1s., and the 'Time and Wage Table,' a sheet, for which the charge is 9d. post free. But though thus cheap, we may add that the manner of keeping the accounts is both simple and clear. In each of the books a specimen is given of the plan to be adopted; and certainly nothing apparently could be devised more simple.....They may be safely recommended as affording a really simple and effectual way of keeping farm accounts"—*The Field* London, March 25, 1865.

These Books and forms, so far as we understand farm labour, seem to us to give certain and easy methods of keeping correct accounts, while they do not omit anything requisite, to a complete index of the returns of every field on a farm."—*The Border Advertiser*, Nov. 18, 1864.

TO LANDED PROPRIETORS, FACTORS, AGENTS, &c.

Game Books, Cellar Books, Poultry Books, Estate Time and Pay Bills, &c., &c., drawn up, Ruled and Printed.

Miscellaneous Works and Compilations on Farm Book Keeping,

Issued by Stephens (Author of the "Book of the Farm"), a set of Seven Small Folio Volumes, price 22s. Those recommended by the Royal Agricultural Society of England, issued by Halifax & Co., London, a set of Five Volumes, price to non-subscribers, £2, 10s. Cowell's Improved Farmer's Account Book, one folio volume, price 8s.

After a very long experience in the compilation of books for farmers, we question if a complete set of farm books suitable for general use can be compiled—those that we publish have no pretensions to being a complete set: they are only useful auxiliaries, capable of being used with any system. In all this district there is perhaps no two farmers who keep their books alike, or who would find it convenient to do so. If some practical farmer—one who has not been brought up in a bank, a lawyer's office or with an accountant, would compile a treatise on the subject, by which each man might be enabled to work out a tangible set of books,—not a mere system of *Memorandums* as bookeeping too often is with farmers especially, but something simple, yet scientific, and which he could modify to suit his own requirements—it would be a boon to the farming community.—J. & J. H. R.

Stephens' Practical Treatise on Farm Bookkeeping, price 2s. 6d. Inglis, do., do., just published, 2s.

All the Standard Publications on

AGRICULTURE, GRAZING, AND GARDENING.—Including

Richardson's Handbooks; Land Measuring, Draining, and Cattle Weighing Tables.

Mayhew, Stonehenge, &c., on the Horse; Books or Dairy Stock, on Botany, on Agriculture, Chemistry, &c., &c. Loudon's Cyclopedias, "Our Farm Crops," "Our Domesticted Animals," "The Henwife," Stonehenge on the Dog, do. on the Grayhound, Lockhart Morton on the Resources of Estates. Low on Landed Property and the Economy of Estates, &c., &c.

KELSO : J. & J. H. RUTHERFURD, 17 SQUARE, KELSO.

NOTES ON STATIONERY BOOKS, &c.

(*See Stationery Books*, p. 16.)

ON THE BINDING OF STATIONERY BOOKS.

Extracted from the " PAPER TRADE REVIEW. "

. . . " It is of course proper that stationery books shall have the plainness which ought to characterise business books. But, on the other hand, we think there should be an absence of clumsiness, and the evidence of *neatness* and *good taste* about them. But the first great excellence to which the attention of the stationery binder should be directed, is the SUBSTANTIALITY and FIRMNESS of stitching and glueing of the book before boarding. This is of the *first* importance in the binding of stationery books. In letterpress books it is not so essential as in a stationery book. Business books receive greatly more wear and fatigue than letterpress books, and there is a greater size of leaf, which weakens a stitch easier than a small one. But, perhaps, the cause [of the frequent inferiority of this class of bookbinding] is mainly owing to the fact that the stitching of these books is performed by girls, and, consequently, there is in their work a feebleness and weakness to which no amount of good boarding and finishing can give strength. How completely does the reputation of good binding rest upon good stitching. The little sins of this department tell on every book. Many a handsome Russia-banded ledger has disappointed its owner by the faulty and careless manner of its stitching. *The entire success of the work depends on the manner and faithfulness in which this stitching is performed.* Too much pains cannot be bestowed to make this work secure and trustworthy. It should be the duty of every binder to winnow out every careless and insufficient worker in this department, and raise the status of the stitchers work by sufficient encouragement. *But it is to be feared that even good stitching [often] suffers from bad thread.*"

[To secure the effects of good stitching, we use a *nine-ply lint thread*, manufactured expressly for ourselves.—J. & J. H. R.]

TO THE CUSTOMER.

Extracted from the " PAPER TRADE REVIEW. "

" The Binder has very often but scant justice in doing a book, on account of the inconsiderate haste in which it is sometimes wanted. Nothing is more common than for business people to forget the ordering of their books until they are wanted, and of course they must be *got up* in American quickness. In such circumstances, the Binder has no chance of giving the book that time and attention which good work requires. When such a book is in use, it gives way, of course, but the fact of its being *got up* in such speed is forgot, and the fact of inferiority and insufficiency only remembered.

. . . *It is unfair to the Ruler, the Binder, and the Stationer to have their work hurried through their hands in the time that would barely suffice to page it well.*"

ON THE QUALITY OF STATIONERY BOOK PAPER.

Note by J. & J. H. Rutherfurd.

If it be important that the *binding* of stationery books be thoroughly executed, it is still more important that the *Paper* of which they are made, be of good quality—that it be tough enough to stand tear and wear, and have compactness and fibre to stand erasures without becoming spongy —merits which are not insured by mere thickness—indeed, excess of thickness is a suspicious quality, implying an abundance of material not always derived from linen rags. Paper of whatever thickness, if it shows the least appearance of crack or fraying out at the back of a fold, is totally unfit for the making up of heavy stationery books, intended to be in use for some years. This especially applies to Ledgers, etc., whose leaves get frequent turning over. With

a

day-books, which have more tossing about than turning over, and are generally a shorter time in hand, the *binding* becomes of equal or primary importance ; but an inferior, especially if a thick paper, let its binding be ever so good, will not stand much knocking about, as the thread cuts it at the stitching.

Real *hand-made* paper of good quality—such as Whatman's or Ansell's (and of such only should heavy important stationery books be made)—feels between the fingers, according as it is thick or thin, like vellum or parchment, and itswear will be somewhat similar. Second qualities of hand-made paper, and even the best occasionally, are apt to have a partially loose fibre on the surface, which, by catching the pen, and causing a blot, may make the writer think he has got inferior stuff to work upon ; but it really proves that the paper has the grand quality of fibre, and is not composed of merely machine-made pulp.

Low qualities of machine-made paper, generally made up with a portion of *pipeclay* or *Derbyshire spar* (sometimes equal to 50 per cent.) can now be sent out with a fineness of finish and an appearance of quality very deceiving to the uninitiated. This paper, which always feels hard and stiff, and often of a *glassy* smoothness, breaks or cracks if folded, runs the ink like blotting paper after any attempt at erasure ; and although often made up into massive serviceable looking books, is quite unfit for the purpose, as the purchaser, sooner or later, generally finds out.

The smaller class of business books—such as quarto Cash books—require neither the expensive binding nor paper of the class of books already treated of ; but the purchaser will find it to his comfort, and a real economy in the end,

to have a good quality of both, however small the size of the book may be.

A really good business book, like everything else good, can only be purchased at a fair price. We make this remark, as purchasers—especially those who renew their business books but seldom—(for, as a rule, the heavier the customer's account is for business books, the more he values quality, and, that given, the less he grudges price) often seem taken aback by the price of a well-bound book made of Whatman's or Ansell's paper, and purchase one of an inferior class, which proves no satisfaction in the using, and no credit to the producer.

For really good second-class papers, suitable for the smaller and less important sizes of business books, we find none so satisfactory as those of ANNANDALE, who keeps his papers of this quality remarkably free from adulteration (see Nos. 6 to 8 of our List) ; and it is from these that all our medium Paper Books are made. Papers No. 1 to 5 are more suitable for correspondence than for making up.

A HINT ABOUT FASTENING ENVELOPES.

Wet slightly *both sides* of the flap, and press down. If the Envelope be very thick and stiff, wet the *upper* side again after pressing down.

The most expeditious, cleanest, and safest process is to use the *lips*. Treated thus, a thousand Envelopes may be closed in a few minutes, and not a grain of gum transferred from its proper use.

There is philosophy in wetting *both* sides of the flap.

The same rule applies to fastening Postage Stamps or Adhesive Labels of any kind.

MISCELLANEOUS FANCY ARTICLES.

Paper Maché Writing Cases and Ink Stands.
Christmas Cards and Envelopes.
Bookmarkers, all lengths, with Ivory and Gilt Pendants.
Do., Coventry manufacture.
Match Boxes, in Fancy Wood and Leather.
Perry's new class of Patent Ivory Pencil Cases, with knife, penholder, &c.
Penmaking Machines.

Ladies' and Gentlemen's Travelling Desks and Despatch Boxes, in Roan, Morocco, and Russia.
Paper Knives and Reading Hooks, in Bone, Ivory, and Pearl.
Gold Presentation Pen and Pencil Cases.
Ivory, Pearl, and Shell Steel Penholders.
Ivory, Paper Maché, and Ass-skin Tablets, 'Where is its,' &c.

Rosewood Date Cases, Ring Stands, and Card Racks, in Gilt Mountings.
Lock-up Envelope Boxes in Oak and Leather.
Blotting Books in Roan and Morocco, with and without Locks.
Fancy Metallic Books, and Pocket Wallets.
Perforated and Embossed Cards.
Do., Mounted and Unmounted, for Bookmarkers.

J. & J. H. Rutherfurd guarantee all Goods stamped with, or sent out under cover of, their

Trade  *Mark,*

to be of the Best possible Quality of its kind.

REVISED PRICE LIST
OF
WRITING PAPERS, ENVELOPES, &C.,
SOLD BY
J. & J. H. RUTHERFURD.

◆

THIS Establishment has been for many years celebrated for GENERAL STATIONERY, especially for Superior Qualities of Writing Papers, and Business and Farmers' Books. Many of the Papers in this List are direct from the Manufacturer, and are offered Retail at the Lowest Prices.

This List has been systematically arranged, so that any particular Paper may be easily selected, or orders repeated, with the certainty of receiving invariably the kind wanted. Every opportunity is taken to improve qualities.

ORDINARY 8vo NOTE.

	⅌ Qr. 24 shts	⅌ Pkt. 20 doz.	
For Special Correspondence.		s.	d.
1. Treble Thick, Best Cream Laid. *Hollingsworth's Rolled,* or *Joynson's Glazed* .	6d	4	6
2. Double Thick, Best Crm. Laid, *Hollingsworth's Rolled,* or *Pirie's high Glazed* .	...	4	3
3. Thick, Best Cream Laid, *High Glazed* .	5d	3	6

ORDINARY 8vo NOTE—*continued.*

	⅌ Qr.	⅌ Pkt.	
4. Treble Thick, Best Blue Laid, *Glazed* .	...	5s	0
5. Thick, Best Blue Laid, *Glazed* .	5d	3	6
For Ordinary Correspondence.			
6. Thick, Blue Laid, *Annandale's, Rolled* .	4d	2	8
7.*Ex. Thick, Fine Cm. Laid, *do. do.* .	4d	2	6
8.*Sup. Cream Laid, *do. Glazed* .	4d	2	6
For Household Purposes.			
9.*Fine Cream Laid. *Annandale's Rolled,* a good useful Paper .	...	2	0
10. Thin Mid-Cream Laid, *Rolled* .	...	1	8
The Patent Straw Paper.			
11. This Paper being made of Straw, is more brittle than ordinary Paper, but it is pleasant to write on, and is preferred by many for common purposes, *best English make—the Scotch is very inferior* .	2d	10 doz. Packet 0	8

* (Nos. 7 and 8) Special attention is called to these Papers, as the repeated orders and increasing demand for them indicate their general usefulness; *they are fit for any ordinary purpose.* No. 9 is of the same *quality,* but thinner.

CARD SIZES.

	⅌ Qr.	10 doz.	
12. Albert, Treble Thick Crm. Laid, *Glazed*	...	2	3
13. Do., Thick Cream Laid, *High Glazed*	4d	1	6
14. Do., Mid-Quality .	3d	1	0
15. Queen's, Thick Cream Laid, *High Glazed*	3d	1	2
16. Princess's, *High Glazed* . . .	3d	1	0

COMMERCIAL (Extra Size) NOTE.

	⅌ Qr.	20 doz.	
17. Thin Cream Laid or Blue Wove . .	...	1	10
18. Thick Cream Laid	4d	2	9
19. Sup. Thick Cream Laid, *Glazed* .	5d	3	6
20. Sup. Ex. Thick Cream Laid, *Glazed* .	6d	4	4

FOREIGN NOTE.

	℔ Qr. 24 shts	℔ Box 10 doz.	
			s. d.
21. All Colours, Waterlined (*Best French make*),* 2 sheets and Envelope, under ¼ oz.	5d	2 0	

* Much of the Foreign Waterlined Paper sold is Belgian make, which is inferior to the French.

A great variety of all sizes of Tinted Waterlined Note Paper, ordinary thickness.

MOURNING NOTE.

Broad.	Middle	Narrow	Italian

Any ordinary width of Border best Lond. finish	℔ Qr.	20 doz.
22. Extra Thick Cream Laid, *Hollingsworth's Rolled, one page* . . .	6d	4 9
23. Do. Do. *two pages* . . .	...	5 6
24. **Albert Size**, Best Cm. Laid, *two pages* .	6d	4 9
25. **Queen's Size**, Do., Do. .	5d	4 0
Also with *Double and Treble Broad Borders*, and *bordered on four pages*, in *ordinary*, *Italian*, and *mixed styles* .	6d	℔ Box 10 doz.
26. **Foreign**, Extra Size, (*French make**) .	8d	3 0
27. Old 4to Size, Cream Laid, all Borders .	10d to 1s 2d	

* See note at No. 21.

Funeral Letters. Intimations, &c., Printed at an Hour's Notice, and, when requisite, addressed and despatched.

BLANK FUNERAL LETTERS TO FILL UP, 6d. PER DOZEN.

For Specimens of Memorial Card, &c., see Printing Office Notice.

HAND-MADE LETTER PAPERS.

	℔ Qr.	20 doz.
28. Cream Laid, *Whatman's second quality* .	10d	8 6
29. Thin Blue Laid, *Whatman's* . .	9d	7 0
30. Extra Thick Crm. and Blue Laid, *Glazed*	1s 4d	12 0
31. **Large** Blue Laid, *Glazed** . .	1s 6d	12 6

* See notes under No. 37.

HAND-MADE NOTE PAPERS.*

	℔ Qr.	20 doz.
32. Cream Laid, *Whatman's second quality* .	...	4s 6
33. Thick Blue Laid, *Glazed*, *Whatman's* .	7d	5 6
34. Extra Thick Do., *Rolled*, *Ansell's* .	...	6 0
35. Do., *Rough*, *Whatman's*, (very scarce)	...	6 6
36. Super-Thick Cream Laid, *Glazed* .	8d	6 6
37. Treble Thick Cream Laid, *Whatman's* (scarce)	...	7 6

Whatman's and other Kent hand-made Papers have continued to go up steadily in price ever since the Abolition of the Duty in October 1861.

* The outside quires in each packet of hand-made Papers are generally Broken, Torn, and Short in the Number of Sheets; this is also the case, to some extent, with the best machine-made papers.

LETTER PAPER (4to Size).

	℔ Qr.	20 doz.
38. **Small Post** Fine Cream Laid, *Rolled* .	...	3 6
39. Do., Superfine Thick Cream Laid . *Rolled*	7d	5 4
40. Do., Superfine Thick Cream Laid *Glazed*	9d	7 0
41. **Large Post** Fine Cream Laid, *Glazed* .	9d	7 0
42. Do., Fine Thick Crm. Laid, *do.* .	10d	8 0

FOREIGN EXTRA SIZE (4to.)

	℔ Qr.	20 doz.
43. Waterlined *French Make* . .	10d	...
44. Blue Wove, plain, *English Make*, J.W. .	...	

OFFICIAL PAPERS.

	℔ Qr.	20 Qrs.
45. **Pott**, Best Scroll, *Annandale's* .	8d	12 0
46. Foolscap, Common Scroll .	6d	8 6
47. **Foolscap**, Good Thick Yellow Wove	8d	12 0
48. Do., Fine Thick, *all shades* .	10d	...
49. Do., Ex. Sup. Thick, *Glazed* .	1s 0d	16 0
50. Do., Hand-made Blue Laid .	1 4	...
51. **Folio Post**, Do., Do. *Whatman's*	2 2	...
52. **Large Do.**, Do., Do. Do.	2 6	...
53. **Medium** and **Royal** Sizes, Do.	...	...

RULED PAPERS.

	Per Quire.
54. Pott, Faint, *for Copies—all kinds* . .	8d
55. Do., Faint and Red, *for Accounts, all kinds*	10d and 1s
56. F'cap, Blue Laid, *for Do., all kinds*	1s to 1s 6d
57. Foolscap, Best, *for Process and Specifica- tions—Whatman's make* . . .	1s 6d
58. Folio Post, Best Blue Laid, for Petitions and Statements, *Whatman's* . .	2s 2d to 2s 6d
59. Extra sizes do., do. . .	2s 9d to 4s 6d

Papers Ruled to any Pattern.   *Sermon and MS. Papers.*

KITCHEN AND HOUSE PAPERS.

	℔ Qr.	Per Rm.
60. Good Gray, 9 lbs.	...	3 6
61. Do., Do. 13 lbs. . . .	4d	4 0
62. Best English Small Hand, 20 lbs. . .	1s	18 0
63. Demy Tea	4d	...
64. Scotch Gray, Finest Double Crown as Closet Paper, in pkts. of 200 each .	... 6d	7 6

Ordinary Brown Paper, all sizes and qualities, 4d to 3s6d per Qr. Cartridge Paper, all sizes and qualities ; Gummed Preserve Paper ; Preserve Labels ; Tissue ; Baking Gray ; and Filtering.

	Per dozen.
65. Round Desserts, Thin *French*, or Thick *English*	9d to 1s 6d
66. Oval do., *French or English* .	1s 3d - 2s 6d
67. Plate Papers—Round . . .	5d to 1s 3d
68. Do., do., Oval . . .	1s 3d to 2s
69. Ham Frills, White or Tinted .	1s 0d
70. Cutlet Do., . .	1s 0d
71. Soufflé or Fondu Papers, *Paris Make* .	1s 6d
72. Silver Bouquet Papers, *Real* . .	6d each

Fruit Cups, 6d. per Dozen.
Ornamental Bill of Fare Cards, 1d. to 4d. each.

Special Bills of Fare printed in Gold and Colours, and general Forms of them Designed and Engraved.—Specimens of both can be seen at the Shop.

BLOTTING PAPERS.

	Per Quire.
73. Ordinary Red	10d
74. Best Thick Pink and White (18 lbs.) .	1s 6d
75. Do. Ex. Thick, White or Coloured, *Hard*	2s 6d

Small BLADS, 4d. ; 4to, do., 6d. ; Do., Extra Thickness, and Solids, 1s. & 1s. 6d.

Blotting Books Re-filled and Cases Repaired.
BLOTTING AND WRITING CASES, ALL QUALITIES AND SIZES.

ADHESIVE ENVELOPES.

HIGH SHAPES		℔ Pkt.	℔ 250.
Vellum—*double thick.*			
76. For Ordinary 8vo. Note, Folded in 4 .		2⅜d	1 10
77. „ do. Folded in 3 .		3d	2 3
78. „ Large 8vo. do. Folded in 3 .		3½d	2 8
Best Cream and Blue Laid, treble thick.			
79. For Ordinary 8vo. Note, Folded in 4 .		3½d	2 9
80. „ do. Folded in 3 .		4d	3 6
81. „ Large 8vo. do. Folded in 3 .		5d	4 0
Foreign.		℔ doz.	
82. For Large 8vo. Note . . .		2½d	...
Oblong and Small Shapes, with Fancy Dies, and impressed with " Marseilles," and " Southampton " . . .		3d & 4d	...
(See Note at No. 23.)			
Black Bordered.			℔ Gross
83. Mid-Cream Laid, Cameo . . .		3d	2 9
84. Best *London Make*, Relief . . .		4d	3 9
85. Foreign, Waterlined		4½d	...

Tinted, and other Extra Qualities, French Shapes—Albert, Queen's, and Miniature Sizes, &c.

Business Envelopes, all qualities, sizes, and prices.

Official and Cloth-lined Envelopes of all sizes ; Banker's Safety ; &c., &c.

	℔ Yard.
86. Brown Web Paper, 4½ feet wide, for underlaying Carpets and Rough Papering Walls	2d
87. Fine Web Cartridge for Hanging Wardrobes, 4½ feet wide	1s
88. Rough do , for Large Drawings . .	1s 6d
89. Tracing Cloth, yard wide, best quality .	2s 3d

TRACING PAPER, Plain and Glazed, Double-Double Crown Size, 6d. to 8d. per sheet.

Ordinary Qualities of BROWNS, GRAYS, and PURPLES, for Grocers, &c.

Card Plate Engraved, any Style, 2s. to 3s.

			℔ 50.	℔ 100
Ivory Cards, and Printing,	*Ladies'*	*Size.*	2s 6d	4s 6d
Do.,	do.,	*Gentlemen's Size.*	2s 3d	4s 0d

MISCELLANEOUS STATIONERY.

Quills and Quill Pens, 6d. to 6s. per quarter ; and in Boxes, 6d., 1s., 1s. 6d., 2s., 2s. 6d., and 3s. each.
Quill Nibs, in Boxes, 6d., 1s., 2s., and 4s.
Best Sealing Wax, 1d., 2d., 4d., and 8d. per Stick.
Best Parcel Wax, 2s. 6d. per lb.
Plain, Address, and Calling Cards.
Botanical Paper, 1s. 9d. per Quire.
Mounting and other Boards.
Reeves & Son's Colours.
Drawing and Common Pencils.
Crayon Papers, all tints.
Drawing Papers, rough & smooth

Elastic Bands.
Pocket Books, Purses, Wax Vestas
Slates and Slate Pencils.
Red Tape, 1d., 2d., and 3d. per piece.
Liquid Gum, 1d., 6d., and 1s. per Bottle.
Chinese Cement, 6d. per Bottle.
Black, White, & Coloured Chalks —French and Italian.
Marking Ink, 6d. and 1s. per Bot.
Gold Shells (*Real*), 1s. each.
Silver do. (*Real*), 8d. each.
Camel, Fitch, and Sable Hair Pencils.
Carbonic Paper.

Goodall's and *De La Rue's Playing Cards* (Duty reduced), 10*d.* to 3*s.* 6*d.* a Pack.

CASES for holding PLAYING CARDS, Single, 6d., Double, 1s. and 1s. 6d.

TOURIST CASES AND PAPETRIES,
ALL SIZES.

CARD CASES, IN LEATHER, SHELL, & PEARL.
(For Souvenirs of the District, see pp. 17 and 18.)

J. & J. H. RUTHERFURD'S
SELECTED STEEL PENS
Manufactured expressly after their own instructions, and combining many improvements.

NIBS, FINE AND MEDIUM POINTS,
For "Correspondence," and "Book-keeping,"

In QUARTER, HALF, and GROSS BOXES, at 9d., 1s. 4d., and 2s. 6d. each.

BARREL PENS FOR ROUGH WORK, IN BOXES OF ONE DOZ. AT 1s. EACH

"IMPROVED STEEL PENS.—Our attention has been directed to a superior sort of 'Fine Writing and Correspondence Steel Pen' (nibs), manufactured and carefully selected expressly for our townsmen, Messrs. Rutherfurd. They are finely pointed, elegantly shaped, nicely polished, and very flexible, and have the initials J. H. R. engraven on the back. Nibs for Book-keeping and Ordinary Writing, and Barrel Pens for Rough Work and Addressing are, we understand, in course of preparation."—*Kelso Chronicle*, 6th Nov. 1863.

Steel Pens by all the Best Makers.
(See Gillot's and Heath's Adverts.)

Ledgers, Journals, Day Books and Paper Books,
ALL SIZES.

FARMERS' CORN, BARN, & WORKERS' DAY BOOKS.
(*See* pp. 3 and 4).

Note, Cash, & other Agricultural Business Books.

Orders for Paper Books, to pattern rulings, carefully attended to.

Private Ledgers, Cash Books, &c.,
WITH OR WITHOUT LOCKS.

School Copy and Cyphering Books—Plain, Set, and Ruled,
1d., 2d., 3d., 4d., 6d., 1s., 1s. 6d , and 2s. each.

(See Remarks on "Business Books" at pages 5 to 8.)

MISCELLANEOUS GOODS

FOR

CHRISTMAS TREES,

JUVENILE GIFTS,

BIRTH-DAY PRESENTS,

&c. &c. &c.

WOOD WORK

FROM

MELROSE ABBEY,

ABBOTSFORD GARDEN,

AND

KELSO ABBEY.

AT J. & J. H. RUTHERFURD'S, 17 SQUARE, KELSO.

Snuff Boxes.	Watch Stands.	Knitting Wire Cases.	Brooches.
Cigar Cases.	Ink Stands.	Ladies' Companions—	Bracelets.
Lancet Cases.	Writing Folios.	Fitted.	Lip Salve Boxes.
Crochet Cases.	Match Boxes.	Ladies' Reticules—Fitted.	Lozenge Boxes.
Needle Cases.	Note Books.	Scissor Cases and Sheaths.	Napkin Rings.
Erasers.	Pen Wipers.	Thimble Cases.	Portemonnaies.
Thermometer Boxes.	Pocket Books.	Rulers.	Reel Cases and Boxes.
Spectacle Cases.	Pincushions.	Wafer Boxes.	Quaighs.
Knife Cases.	Pincushion Tubs	Writing Cases.	Pails.
Trinket Boxes	Pin Cases and Boxes.	Taper Stands.	Ring Trays.
Card and Counter Boxes.	Ointment Boxes.	Measure Cases.	Silk Winders.
Calling Card Cases (pull-	Envelope Openers.	Stamp Boxes (hinged,	Vinegarettes.
off and hinged)	Pen Trays and Racks.	round, and pull-off).	Work Boxes.
Bookmarkers.	Pencil Cases.	Stamp Books.	Pin Boxes.
Paper Cutters.	Penholders.	Cotton Ball Boxes.	Waxers.
Card Trays.	Emery Cushions.	Glove Boxes.	Pounce Cups.
Envelope Boxes.			

The following Books are kept in Wood and Clan Tartan Boards:—

Scott's "Lay of the Last Minstrel."	Scott s "Poetry," complete	Burns' Poems. Shakespeare.
,, "Lady of the Lake."	Aytoun's "Lays," *Illustrated.*	"Golden Maxims."
,, "Lord of the Isles."	Younger's "River Angling."	"Hymns of Faith and Hope."
,, "Marmion."	Leyden's "Poems."	Dr. Bonar's "Blood of the Cross." &c.

J. & J. H. Rutherfurd guarantee all the Wood Work supplied by them to be really of the wood it professes to be; it having been all manufactured for them at Mauchlin, from wood sent by them specially, and is only to be had at their own Establishment and at Miss Elliot's, High Street, Melrose.

"MELROSE ABBEY RELICS.—Several years ago, when the town drain was being taken through the 'Dowcot' Park, belonging to the Duke of Buccleuch, and situated between the Abbey and the Tweed, a fine beam of black oak was discovered about six feet below the surface of the ground. It is now being taken up, it is understood, by Mr. Rutherfurd, stationer, Kelso, for the purpose of being turned into souvenirs. It is evidently in a good state of preservation. It measures about seven inches broad by ten deep, but not being as yet taken up its length is not known. On the upper side there is a groove two inches broad by one deep, from which it is thought that the beam may have been used as a tramway for taking stones to the Abbey."— *Correspondent of Scotsman.*

CARTE DE VISITE ALBUMS,

STEREOSCOPES, STEREOSCOPIC SLIDES,

CARTES, VIEWS, &c.

AT J. & J. H. RUTHERFURD'S, KELSO.

CARTE DE VISITE ALBUMS IN ENDLESS VARIETY.

SMITH'S (of London) NEW STYLES,

At Prices varying from 2s. 6d. (holding 12 Portraits, 1 on a page) to £3, 3s. (holding 200 Portraits, 4 on a page), splendidly done up in Russia and Morocco, with clasps, gilt mountings, and durable cloth inside linings.

FRENCH MAKE,

Very Cheap and Handsome, but with no durable qualities.

INTERMEDIATE QUALITIES BY BARRETT AND OTHERS.

CARTE DE VISITE PORTRAITS.

MYALL'S NEW SERIES OF THE ROYAL FAMILY, 1s. 6d. EACH.

LOCAL PORTRAITS, 1s. TO 3s. EACH.

WONDERS OF THE STEREOSCOPE

REVISED PRICE LIST

OF

DIES AND DIE STAMPING,

AT

J. & J. H. RUTHERFURD'S, KELSO.

◆

No.		Price
1.	CYPHER, one or two letters	6/
2. 3. }	MONOGRAM, two or three letters	7/ to 8/
4.	CREST AND MOTTO	8/ to 9/
5.	Do. Do. with INITIAL	9/ to 10/6
6.	ADDRESS AND CREST	14/6 to 16/
7.	ARMS, CREST, AND MOTTO . . . about	25/
8.	ADDRESS DIE	6/ to 6/6
9.	BUSINESS DIE	6/6 to 7/6
10.	Do. Do. . . . . . . about	5/6

RELIEF DIE STAMPING.

PER REAM (480 sheets), any size of Paper.

One Die and One Colour	3/4
One Die and Two Colours (see No. 6)	3/9
One Die in Gold (see No. 4)	7/6
Plain *	1/6

ENVELOPES, PER 1000, any size.

One Die, One Colour	6/8
One Die, Two Colours (No. 6)	7/6
One Die, in Gold (No. 4)	14/
Plain *	1/3

Smaller quantities than the above charged somewhat proportionately higher, and larger quantities proportionately lower.

---

* No charge for Plain Stamping when 4 Reams of Paper or 2000 Envelopes are taken.

The Ptarmigan
Ben Lomond

Pinnaclehill.
Kelso.

J. & J. H. RUTHERFURD'S

SPECIMENS OF DIES AND DIE STAMPING,

See previous page.

J. & J. H. R. guarantee their DE CUTTING and STAMPING to be of the best quality; and a comparison of their Prices with those advertised by Edinburgh and London houses will show them to be moderate.　With them, too, a Ream of Paper, whatever be its size, means but 480 sheets.*

* Many Scotch establishments are apt, for instance, to send the enormous quantity of 1920 sheets of note paper, 3840 of card paper, and 960 of 4to post, when a Ream is ordered, and to charge it in proportion— much to the customer's surprise.　Some of them have also a habit of counting and charging Quires on the same liberal scale.

DRAWING REQUISITES.

COLOURS.

In Single Cakes, 1s. to 5s. each, by Winsor & Newton, Reeves, Barnard & Sons, and others. Assortments of Do. of the best quality, in Boxes. Do. of second quality, 6d. to 2s. 6d. Penny Colours.

Moist Colours procured to order at two or three days' notice.

CHALKS.

Black square French—Nos. 1, 2, and 3, 1d. each. Do., best Italian, 1s. per oz. White square—Nos. 1, 2, and 3, 1d. each. Coloured, in Wood, in assorted dozen boxes, at 1s. and 2s. Green's Indelible, 1s. per box. Prepared Charcoal. Porte Crayons and Stumps, 6d. each. White Chalk, square, for School use.

SUNDRIES.

China Ink—real and imitation; Gold and Silver Shells, real, 6d. and 1s. each; Gold Leaf; Chinese White, in bottles; Prepared Ox Gall.

BLACK LEAD PENCILS AND RUBBER.

Drawing Pencils—Morell's, 6d. each; Cohen's, and others, 3d. each ; a few old *real* Cumberlands, 8d. each. Drawing Pencils, in flat leather cases, assorted letters. Common Pencils, ½d. to 3d. each ; J. & J. H. R.'s own—1d. and 2d. each.* Pocket Book and Case Pencils—1d and 2d. each ;

---

* Excellent pencils, of all letters, made in Germany, where nearly *all* the Black Lead Pencils are now manufactured—Cumberland producing very few indeed, if any, except from *German* lead.

Metallic Book do., best quality, 3d each. India Rubber—common, Vulcanic, and Patent, in pieces of any size ; Green's Ink Eraser, in cakes, 4d. and 6d.

HAIR PENCILS.

Best Sable, 3d. to 1s ; best Fitch, 3½d. and 5d. ; common Camel, in ordinary quills, 1d.; in Swan quills, 4d. each ; Flat Camel, in tin, for varnishing and damping copying books, all sizes and prices ; Long Camel, for lettering, 2d. each.

PAPERS AND BOARDS.

Whatman's Drawing, with smooth surface, all sizes from Demy at 2d. to Double Elephant at 1s. per sheet ; Whatman's Do. Imperial size (only), with rough surface, Nos. 1, 2, and 3, 6d. and 8d. per sheet ; Do., extra rough, 1s. Drawing Cartridge, 1d. to 2½d. per sheet ; Continuous Do., in webs, 4½ feet wide, 1s. per yard. Crayon Papers, all kinds and tints. London Superfine Boards, all sizes and thicknesses ; Mounting Do. Graduated Tints, all sizes—oval, round, and square. Tracing Paper, 3d. and 6d per sheet ; Do. Cloth, 2s. per yard.

Metallic Paper, in sheets, for Pencil Sketching.

Drawing Solids of any size or quality made to order.

MATHEMATICAL INSTRUMENTS

Sets, on Cards, at 1s. and 1s. 6d. each ; Do., in Boxes, 2s. 6d. to 20s. Scales, in Wood and Ivory. Rulers, round and flat, in Ebony and in Wood of the District. Parallel Rules. T Squares.

Perry's and other Patent Pencil Cases, in Silver, Wood, and Ivory, with and without knives, &c., 2d. to 13s. 6d. each.

Permanent Leads—red, black, and blue, for Perry's and others' Pencil Cases.

J. & J. H. RUTHERFURD'S PERMANENT BLACK INKS.

No. 1.

New Registration

No. 2.

School Ink.

Rutherfurd's New Registration Ink.

A mixture possessing the *flowing* qualities of Duncan & Flockhart's Ink with the *immediate Blackness* of that of Morell. 4*d*, 6*d*, 1*s*, and 2*s*. *per Bottle.*—See Specimen No. 1.

An excellent INK for Office and Household use, admitting of immediate drying by the blotting paper, with little detriment to the colour.

NOTE.—Ink of this quality may not show its *immediate* blackness when first drawn, but it does after exposure to the atmosphere for a few days in the ink glass. After being written with, whether or not newly drawn, it soon becomes of an intense black. To preserve the quality of *any* INK, the bottle containing it should be carefully corked. In summer, if it show a tendency to get mouldy (and however intrinsically good an Ink may be, exposure in *summer* will soon affect its quality), a little hot spirits should be added to the bottle or ink glass; in winter this will also keep the ink glass from freezing. The tendency of some ink not to pass from the pen to the paper, as if greasy, will be often remedied by placing a piece of blotting or other paper under the hand when writing, the cause being perspiration. We have long observed that greasy Ink and Bad Ink are greatly summer complaints.

Rutherfurd's School Ink.

One Shilling per Quart Bottle.—See Specimen No. 2.

Also an **excellent** INK, with a colour of great intensity when dried by evaporation (as slowly written copies at school generally are); but when hastily dried by the blotting paper, its colour is apt to be considerably reduced, and its permanency is inferior.

Black Ink of various qualities.

Perth, Liverpool, Duncan & Flockhart's, Reid's (of Montrose), Morell's "Registration," &c., At 1*d*, 2*d*, 4*d*, 6*d*, 2*s*, and 2*s* 6*d per Bottle, or in Jars at* 3*s* 6*d.*

Copying Ink.

DUNCAN & FLOCKHART'S, 9*d*, 1*s* 6*d, and* 3*s per Bottle,* will take three or four copies. HOPE'S COMMERCIAL BLUE BLACK, 1*s* and 2*s*, useful for ordinary writing, and where *one* good copy is required.

Duncan & Flockhart's, and Reid's Ordinary Inks also, with care, take one good copy.

Coloured Inks.

Cochrane's Scarlet, Stephens' Red, Wilson's Perfumed Violet, Cochrane's Magenta for Steel Pens. Leaf Green, Permanent Blue, Blue Black, &c., &c., *from* 1*d* to 1*s* 6*d.*

Marking Ink.

By Lessey, 1*s* and 6*d*; by Bond, with Stretcher 1*s* and 6*d.*

Ink Glasses in Crystal, Black Wood, Papier Mache, and Wood of the District.

J. & J. H. RUTHERFURD'S

SELECT

READING CLUB.

ESTABLISHED 1859.

TERMS PER ANNUM.

Ordinary Subscription . . . £0 16 0
> This Subscription entitles a Member to the use of One Complete Book (of one or *more* volumes) at a time, and the use of the Periodicals over and above.

Full Subscription 1 5 0
> Entitling a Member to Two Complete Books at a time (consisting of *two* or *three* volumes each), or to *Three* Books, if in single volumes only, and the use of Periodicals over and above.

Full Subscription, entitling a Member to Double the quantity of Books . 2 2 0

Full Subscription, entitling a Member to Thrice the quantity of Books . 3 3 0

And so on, £1 : 1s. for every additional 2 or 3 Books (which may consist of from 3 to 6, or more volumes), with the corresponding **extra** Periodicals.

The operations of the Club begin in November, but temporary Subscribers may enter at any time, at the following rates, for a full supply of books, and at a proportionately lower rate for a limited supply :—

One Week . .	1s.	Three Months .	8s.
One Month . .	3s.	Six Months . .	15s.

Every New Book of interest is added to the Club immediately on Publication. Members have also the right of recommending books.

The Club is Open Daily, and Books are exchangeable at pleasure.

TO COUNTRY SUBSCRIBERS.

J. & J. H. R. beg respectfully to inform their Country Subscribers that owing to the accumulation of work at the Club, on Market Days especially, they find it a great inconvenience and encroachment on time to send off the quantities of books they do at present, in parcels, papered and addressed; they have therefore provided a supply of different sized strong, buttoning-up, sail-cloth BAGS with shoulder straps, capable of being permanently addressed, which will be supplied to Subscribers at cost price (2s. 6d. and 3s.). As these will save Subscribers themselves the inconvenience of parcelling and addressing, the benefit will be mutual.

In despatching books to the country by carrier or private conveyance, J. & J. H. R. guarantee every attention.

A List of the New Books added to the Club is published Quarterly and sent to Subscribers.

Lord; and of the Patriarchs—by Dr. Cumming—2 vols. Expository Outlines of Sermons, 2 vols.; etc.

"Sunday Magazine," "Good Words," "Christian Treasury," "Family Treasury," "Sunday at Home," "Leisure Hour," "Child's Companion," etc.—Volumes for the year.

All Taylor's Large Type Religious Publications.

A Large Stock of the Tract Society's Publications; the Kelso Tracts, etc., etc.

DR. BONAR'S Books always in Stock.—See lists of Dr. Bonar's Works among Publication advertisements.

Sabbath School Prize Books, Cards, Tickets, Hymn Books, etc.

MISCELLANEOUS RELIGIOUS LITERATURE

JAMES'S "Young Man's Guide," "Young Woman's Guide," etc.

HANNA'S "Last Day of Our Lord's Passion"; "Forty Days After;" and "Earlier Years."

The Life and Letters of the Rev. F. W. Robertson (of Brighton), 2 vols., *just published.*

BIOGRAPHIES—M'Cheyne, Rev. E. M. Philips, Rev. Joseph Sortain, Mrs. Schimmelpenninck, Rev. James Sherman, "True Yoke-fellows in the Mission Field," "Burning and Shining Lights," "Work of Earnest Men," by Tweedie; "Lives made Sublime;" "Scottish Covenanters," by Dodds; Mary Lundie Duncan; Mrs. Oliphant's Life of Edward Irving—*cheap edition.*

MACDUFF, Memories of Genneserat, Prophet of Fire, Footsteps of St. Paul, Hart and the Waterbrook, Sunsets on the Hebrew Mountains, Grapes of Eschol; *just published,* The Shepherd and his Flock.

KILLIN'S "Our Friends in Heaven," and "Our Companions in Glory."

"Heaven our Home," "Meet for Heaven," etc.

DR. TWEEDIE, "Home," "The Early Choice," "Springtime and Harvest," etc.

DOMESTIC AND GENERAL UTILITY, REFERENCE, &C.

COOKERY BOOKS—Miss Acton's, 7s. 6d.; Meg Dods', 5s.; Francatelli's, 5s.; Cre-Fydd's Family Fare, 7s. 6d.; The British, 3s. 6d.; "by a French Lady," 5s.; Mrs. Williamson's, 4s.; English and Australian, 4s.; Beeton's Dictionary, 3s. 6d.; Everybody's Pudding Book, 2s. 6d. The Breakfast Book, 2s. 6d.; Reid's "Rational," 1s.; Chambers's, 1s.; Soyer's, 7s. and 1s.; "What to do with the Cold Mutton," 2s. 6d.; How to Cook Apples, 6d.

Webster and Parke's Encyclopædia of Domestic Economy (*reduced to* 15s. 6d.); Beeton's Household Economy; Macaulay's Medical Dictionary, *new and enlarged edition,* 10s. 6d.; and other popular Medical Works.

CHAMBERS' Cyclopædias, Encyclopædia, and Book of Days; MAUNDERS' Treasuries, 5 vols. at 10s. each; "Enquire Within" series. 2s. 6d. each; etc.

GENERAL LITERATURE.

Works suitable for Libraries and Family Reading. A Large Stock of H. G. Bohn's Libraries, Chambers's Miscellaneous Publications, Hugh Miller's Books, Strahan's Popular Series, Railway Volumes, etc. All the Works of Local interest—William Chambers's History of Peeblesshire, in a handsome royal 8vo volume, profusely illustrated 31s. 6d.; Jeffrey's Roxburghshire, 4 vols.; Black's and Nelson's Guides; etc.

JUVENILE WORKS—a large selection of those published by T. Nelson and Sons (Edinburgh), James Hogg and Sons, (London), W. & R. Chambers (Edinburgh), Routledge & Co. (London), and others—including all the books by R. M. BALLANTYNE and A. L. O. E.

Days and Nights in the East, by Rev. Dr. Bonar. Palestine, for the Young, by the Rev. A. A. Bonar.

CHILDREN'S PICTURE BOOKS, on Paper and Linen.

BOOKS FOR THE COUNTRY.

Louden's Encyclopædias of Agriculture and Gardening, *new editions,* 31s. 6d. each. Stephens' Book of the Farm, 2 vols., £3, 3s. Low's Domestic Animals, *reduced,* 5s. 6d. The Complete Grazier, by Youatt, *new edition,* edited by Burn, 21s. Our Farm Crops, 2 vols., 15s. 6d. Johnson's Gardener's Dictionary, *new edition,* 5s. 6d. *Lately published,* Wilson (of Edington Mains) on British Farming, 12s. And all the other standard publications on Agriculture, Grazing, and Gardening.

Land Measuring, Draining, and Cattle Weighing Tables.

Finlay Dun and Professor Dick on Veterinary Science. Mayhew, Stonehenge, etc., on the the Horse.

Books on Poultry, Dairy Stock, Botany, and Agricultural Chemistry.

The Agriculture of Roxburghshire and Berwickshire, *a prize essay*, 1s. 6d.

Low on Landed Property, *reduced in price*, 9s. 6d.

Lockhart Morton on the Resources of Estates, 32s.

Howitt's Rural Life of England, complete in one vol., 12s. 6d.

Kirkby and Spence's Etymology, *cheap edition*, 6s.

Noel Humphrey's Butterfly Vivarium, 6s. 6d.

Richardson's Rural Handbooks, 1s. each.

Routledge's   Do.   Do.   by the Rev. J. G. Wood, and others, 1s. plain, 3s. 6d. coloured.

Samuelson on the Earth Worm, 3s. 6d. ; and on the Honey Bee, 6s. &c. &c.

SPORT.

All the standard books on ANGLING, including Stodart, *reduced*, 3s. 6d. ; Stewart, 3s. 6d. ; Younger, *new edition*, 3s. (*see* advert.) &c. &c.

Stonehenge on the Dog, 15s. ; Do. on the Greyhound, 21s.

The Dead Shot, 5s. ; The Hunting Field, 5s. ; etc.

POETRY.

All the Best Editions in Morocco Antique, and Cloth Bindings. Messrs. Rutherfurd would particularly call attention to their New Edition of

LEYDEN'S SCENES OF INFANCY,

Illustrated with Views of Kelso, Leyden's Birth-place, etc. (See advert.)

DEVOTIONAL POETRY.

Lyra Consolationis, edited by Dr. Bonar—*just published,* 5s. ; Fosberry's Hymns for the Sick and Sorrowing, 7s. 6d. ; Lyra Germanica, 1st and 2d series, 5s each, *illustrated edition*, 21s. ; Lyra Anglicana, 3s. 6d. ; Lyra Americana, 3s. 6d. Lyra Sacra, 5s. ; Ryle's Hymns for the Church on Earth, 4s. ; Keble's Christian Year, *various editions ;* Keble's Lyra Innocentium ; Barbauld's Prose Hymns, *illustrated edition*, 7s. 6d ; Watt's Hymns, *illustrated edition*, 7s. 6d.; Hymn Books for School use—Gall's, Bateman's, etc.

New Selection of Hymns for Sabbath Schools, published by J. & J. H. R., *one halfpenny* *

* This Selection contains 35 of the newest and most popular Hymns at present in use.

EDUCATION.

Arithmetics, Grammars, Dictionaries, &c., &c., and all the French, Latin, and Greek Books in use in the District.

MUSIC (at Half-price).

A Large Stock always on Hand of Quadrilles, Waltzes, Polkas, Overtures, and nearly every Scotch Song published.

D'ALBERT'S CELEBRATED DANCE MUSIC.

Books of Psalmody ; for the Concertina, the Christy's Minstrels, &c. Piano and other Tutors. Wood's Songs of Scotland, 3 vols.. Half-bound Calf, 31s. 6d. ; Do. Airs of Scotland, 1 vol., Cloth, 7s. 6d. Scottish Songs—a Souvenir, in Clan-Tartan Binding, 12s. 6d. The Chorale Book for England, 10s. 6d.

Vocal Melodies of Scotland, arranged with Symphonies and Accompaniments for the Pianoforte (as Songs, Duets, and Trios), by the late Finlay Dun and the late John Thomson, complete in 1 vol. 4to., elegantly Half-bound in Morocco, price 21s.

Music not in Stock procured at two days' notice.*

* When specially ordered a trifle has to be added for postage. Copyright Music remaining in the hands of the composer (a rare occurrence) is only reduced one-fourth.

PERIODICALS.

All the principal Weekly, Monthly, and Quarterly Periodicals regularly supplied (see pp. 39 and 40). London and Edinburgh Newspapers supplied by post direct.

*** Newspapers and all the smaller class of Railway Directories and Periodicals are charged a trifle extra for credit.

ALMANACS, CALENDARS, AND POCKET BOOKS.

ILLUMINATED

ILLUSTRATED AND

HANDSOMELY BOUND BOOKS FOR

CHRISTMAS GIFTS AND

Marriage Presents.

A very Large Selection.

MAPS AND ATLASES.

Keith Johnston's Royal Atlas, *lately published*, Half-bound, Morocco, or Russia, £5 : 15 : 6.

A. & C. Black's General Atlas, *new edition*, Half Morocco, £3.

A large selection of School Atlases, 2s. 6d. to 10s. 6d.

Johnston's Wall Maps, 5s. each; Nelson's, 13s. 6d. each; Chambers' Parlour Maps, 5s. each.

Black's Large Map of Scotland, in parts, for the Pocket, 2s. 6d. each; complete in 12 Sheets in a Case, £2 2s.; complete in one Sheet on Rollers, varnished, £2 : 12 : 6.

Johnston's County Maps of Berwick, Selkirk, Roxburgh, and Dumfries, in Cases for the Pocket, or on Rollers, 7s. 6d., 15s., and 30s. each.

Black's and Blackwood's small Pocket Maps, 1s. each.

Pocket County Maps of Northumberland, Cumberland, and Durham, 2s. 6d. each.

Just Published,

RUTHERFURD'S

MAP OF THE SOUTHERN COUNTIES

(Roxburgh, Berwick, Selkirk, and part of Northumberland.)

Carefully compiled by J. Bartholomew, Edinburgh, F.R.G.S. from the Ordnance Survey Plans, on the scale of one-third of an inch to the mile. For beauty of engraving and geographical accuracy, this Map surpasses any County Maps of the District ever yet published—it forms an excellent Hunting Map. Price, Mounted on Cloth in a handy Case for the Pocket, or elegantly Mounted to hang up, and Varnished, 2s. 6d.; Extra Copies, 3s. 6d.

"The map is produced in a style of remarkable excellence; it seems thoroughly accurate and trustworthy, handy in size, minute and complete in its information, easy of reference, and beautifully produced."—*Kelso Chronicle*, Sept. 1865.

"This Map, we understand, is intended to form part of the forthcoming 'Border Counties' Register,' published by Messrs. Rutherfurd of Kelso. As far as regards the counties of Roxburgh, Selkirk, and Berwick, it is the most useful ever published. Not only can you see the county boundaries at a glance but you can also accurately delineate the parishes in each, trace to the eighth part of a mile the line of every railway, and run your finger with certainty along any public road you want to explore—let it be the Statute Labour, Turnpike, Parochial, or Hill. After a close examination of the part representing this immediate locality, we have been unable to detect an error in it. It recommends itself to every Borderer."—*Border Advertiser*, Dec. 1865.

"It has been executed with Mr. Bartholomew's usual accuracy and beauty of engraving."—*Edinburgh Daily Review*, Oct. 1865.

Agents, by Special Appointment,

FOR THE SALE OF

ORDNANCE SURVEY PLANS & MAPS.

Parishes, Estates, and Farms Extracted, Arranged, and Mounted in any Style.

NEW PRINTING OFFICE AND BINDERY.

J. & J. H. RUTHERFURD

RESPECTFULLY intimate to their Friends and the Public that, having erected, at the FOOT OF HORSE MARKET, KELSO,

NEW PRINTING AND BOOKBINDING PREMISES,

fitted up with every new improvement and convenience in both branches, they are prepared to execute any orders for Printing or Bookbinding, in any style, and at the Shortest Notice.

PRINTING DEPARTMENT

(Under the management of Mr. D. Cottam).

Books, Law Papers, Pamphlets, Catalogues, Circulars, Invoices and Bill-heads, Cards, Cheques, Presentation Labels (in Gold and on Satin), Adhesive and Parchment Addresses, Labels, Game Labels on Parchment and Card, and all kinds of General Printing, including

Funeral Letters and Intimations,

which can be had in any quantity at one or two hours' notice. (See next page.)

For the production of Book and Jobbing Work, J. &. J. H. R. possess nearly 300 varieties of Type, Ornaments, and Casts.

Every attention is paid to printing Nursery and Flower Catalogues in a superior style, for the illustration of which they have a special selection of superior Woodcuts.

LITHOGRAPHING AND ENGRAVING

at City Prices, expeditiously executed by one of the first Edinburgh Establishments.

BOOKBINDING DEPARTMENT

(Under the management of Mr. W. Adams).

RUSSIA and MOROCCO—Plain and Antique.

CALF—Plain, for Library Books; Coloured, Extra, and Tree pattern—whole and half.

SHEEP AND IMITATION CALF—all Styles.

CLOTH CASING—Stamped and Plain.

Great attention is paid to the important matter of STATIONERY BINDING (*see* Note on Stationery Books, pp. 5 and 6).

Specimens of any style, including a peculiarity of the Establishment, the

Oak Root,

and a great variety of Books bound in WOODEN BOARDS, from places of interest in the district, can be seen at the Shop.

Drawings, Prints, Maps, and Plans mounted; and Portfolios of any size made for holding them.

Libraries Classified, Repaired, and Catalogued.

Sacred to the Memory of

GEORGE AUGUSTUS GREVILLE, SEN.

WHO DIED AT KIRKLANDS HOUSE,

DECEMBER 26, 1865.

PRINTED SPECIMEN

OF A

MEMORIAL CARD.

THESE Cards, beautifully and emblematically *embossed*, are convenient for collecting in Vases or Albums as Memorials of Deceased Friends. In England, they have superseded the ordinary Intimation Notes, and are getting into use in this District. Their cost does not greatly exceed the ordinary Intimation. Black-Bordered Envelopes of size, etc., to suit, can also be had at

J. & J. H. RUTHERFURD'S, 17 SQUARE, KELSO.

SPECIMEN

OF A

FUNERAL CARD.

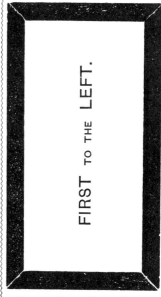

FIRST TO THE LEFT.

SOLD AT 6D. PER SET OF EIGHT

AT

J. & J. H. RUTHERFURD'S.

LIST OF THE PRINCIPAL PERIODICALS

REGULARLY SUPPLIED BY

J. & J. H. RUTHERFURD, 17 SQUARE, KELSO.

MISCELLANEOUS.

(MONTHLY)

All the Year Round (*Dickens*) 9d and 11d
Once a Week, 1s to 1s 6d
Chambers' Encyclopædia, 7d
   ,,   Journal, 7d and 8½d
Cassell's Family Paper, 5d and 6d
The Quiver, 6d
Family Herald, 6d
Art Journal, 2s 6d
Christian Treasury, 6d
Family Treasury ,,
Good Words ,,
Christian Work ,,
Leisure Hour ,,

Sunday at Home, 6d
Sunday Magazine, 7d

British Herald   1d
British Messenger ,,
British Workman ,,
Band of Hope, ½d
Children's Paper, etc., etc., ½d and 1d.
Missionary Record (*Established Church*), 1½d
Do. (*Free Church*), 1d
Juvenile Records (*Established and Free*), ½d each

MAGAZINES (MONTHLY).

The Cornhill, 1s
Macmillan's ,,
St James's ,,
Temple Bar ,,
London Society, 1s
Blackwood's, 2s 6d

Fraser's, 2s 6d
Dublin University, 2s 6d
The Sixpenny, 6d
Fashions, 1s and 1s 6d
Englishwoman's, 1s
The Argosy, 6d

REVIEWS (QUARTERLY)

The Edinburgh, 6s
Quarterly   ,,

North British, 6s
Journal of Prophecy, 2s. 6d

WEEKLY.

Chambers' Journal, 1½d
Punch, 3d   Fun, 1d

All the Year Round, 2d
Once a Week, 3d

RAILWAY DIRECTORIES.

Bradshaw, 6d
Murray's, 3d

North British, 1d
Brydone's & Cameron's, 2d each

J. &. J. H. RUTHERFURD

Take the opportunity, on the completion of those Volumes of Periodicals for the past year, quoted on the opposite page, to inform their Customers that they shall be happy to receive copies of them, or of any other Periodicals, for Binding.

Miscellaneous Binding, Maps and Plans Mounted, and all work connected with the Trade, executed on their own premises with Despatch and Economy.

Plans of Farms and Estates extracted from the Ordnance Survey, and Mounted in any Style.

London Illustrated News; Gardener's Chronicle; Athenæum; The Times; Scotsman; Scottish Farmer; North British Agriculturist; and other London and Provincial Newspapers regularly supplied by POST DIRECT.
Advertisements and Notices inserted in the London and Provincial Papers.

BOOKBINDING   BOOKBINDING

By J. & J. H. RUTHERFURD, 17 SQUARE, KELSO,

AT THE FOLLOWING MODERATE TERMS:—

SUNDAY MAGAZINE	FAMILY TREASURY	ALL THE YEAR ROUND
GOOD WORDS	CHAMBERS's ENCYCLOPÆDIA	LEISURE HOUR
CHRISTIAN TREASURY	CHAMBERS'S JOURNAL	SUNDAY AT HOME

And other Periodicals of the size,

Half Calf, neat and stout, 3s 6d per Volume; Do., Plain, 3s; Do., Extra, 4s 6d; Half Sheep, 2s 6d.

| BLACKWOOD'S MAGAZINE | MACMILLAN'S MAGAZINE | ST. JAMES'S MAGAZINE |
| CORNHILL MAGAZINE | THE REVIEWS | And others of the size |

Half Calf, neat and stout, 2s 6d; Extra, 3s; Plain, 2s; Half Sheep, 1s 6d.

ILLUSTRATED NEWS, THE FIELD, etc.   ART JOURNAL

Stoutly Half-Bound, from 6s to 9s per Vol.   **Half-Calf, extra, 5s 6d to 6s.**

SCOTT'S COMMENTARY | COLLINS' BIBLE | CASSELL'S BIBLE

And volumes of the size sent out by Canvassers,

Full Calf, Marbled Edges, very stout, 7s 6d to 10s 6d; Do. Extra, with Gilt Edges, 12s 6d to 15s.

In Morocco, Antique Style, Gilt or Coloured Edges, 20s to 25s.

Strong loose Black Leather Covers on Pocket and Family Bibles, fitted to order, 1s to 7s 6d.
Music carefully repaired and stoutly half-bound, 3s 6d to 5s 6d per vol; Piano Tutors, full music size, stoutly half-bound,
1s 6d to 2s 6d each.

MRS. WILSON,

BOOKSELLER, STATIONER, BOOKBINDER, AND NEWS-AGENT.

No. 43 SQUARE, KELSO,

Begs to return her sincere thanks to her Friends and Patrons, and to assure them that it will be her aim to have always in hand a large and select class of goods in the various departments of her business.

NOTE PAPERS.

Hollingsworth's Treble thick, best cream laid, 4s 9d per packet of 20 dozen.

Pirie's double thick, best cream laid, high glazed, 6d. per quire, or 4s 3d per packet.

Treble thick, best blue laid, glazed, 5s per packet.

Annandale's thick, fine blue wove. 4d per quire, 2s 9d per packet.

    Do.   Fine cream laid, a good useful Paper, 2s per do.

All the other sizes and qualities of writing papers in general use.

BOOKS.

Mrs. W. has always on hand a large assortment of Books of every description, including many in Elegant Bindings, suitable for Presents. Also, cheap editions of Shakespeare, Burns, Scott, Byron, Milton, and other standard authors.

BOOKBINDING.

Mrs. W. can, with the greatest confidence, solicit orders in this department, feeling assured that her customers will have their work done to their entire satisfaction. All the Periodicals, including

GOOD WORDS	CHAMBERS' JOURNAL
CHRISTIAN TREASURY	ALL THE YEAR ROUND
FAMILY TREASURY	SUNDAY MAGAZINE. &c., &c.

AND

Collins' Bible, Cassell's Bible, and Vols. of the size, Bound in all the different styles, and at very reasonable terms.

All the Newspapers and Periodicals supplied punctually.

STUART & MEIN,

NURSERYMEN, SEEDSMEN, AND FLORISTS,

KELSO,

Beg to inform their numerous Friends and Customers that the following CATALOGUES may be had free, on application, viz.—

1. FRUIT TREES.
2. FOREST & ORNAMENTAL TREES AND SHRUBS.
3. ROSES AND PANSIES.
4. HOLLYHOCKS.
5. BEDDING AND OTHER PLANTS.
6. VEGETABLE & FLOWER SEEDS.
7. AGRICULTURAL SEEDS.
8. DUTCH BULBS.
9. GLADIOLI.
10. CONIFERÆ.

Nurseries—Rosebank, Inch Field, and Croft House.

SEED SHOP,   22 WOODMARKET

HENRY TAIT,

NURSERYMAN AND SEEDSMAN,

SYDENHAM, KELSO,

Has for sale a fine Stock of Apple and Pear Trees, Gooseberry and Currant Bushes, Evergreen and Flowering Shrubs, Thorns, and Forest Trees, and all kinds of Garden and Field Seeds.

JAMES HENDERSON,

GENERAL DRAPER,

SILK MERCER AND CLOTHIER,

23 & 24 SQUARE, KELSO,

HOLDS a Large and varied Stock of New and Seasonable Goods. Each department is replete with everything New and really useful. A magnificent choice of the leading Fabrics in Dress Materials for Ladies' wear—French Merinos, Winceys; Linen, Cotton, and Woollen Goods of every description, well worth special attention. The Fancy Stock comprises every Novelty of the Season.

TAILORING
IN ALL ITS BRANCHES.

An extensive Stock of West of England and Yorkshire Cloths, and Scotch and English Tweeds. The Qualities are such as can be confidently recommended. The Prices are strictly Moderate; and in the Cutting Department a Superior Fit is guaranteed.

Inspection and comparison respectfully solicited.

DRAPERY WAREROOM,
6 UNION STREET, KELSO.

DAVID ADAMS begs to tender his most grateful acknowledgment of the kind patronage of the Inhabitants of Kelso since commencing business here, and to assure them that it will be always his ambition to merit a continuance and increase of the same, by keeping a well-assorted Stock of the most Useful as well as Fashionable Goods, and selling them at the Lowest remunerative Prices. The following list comprises the leading articles of his Stock, viz.:—

Men's Clothes, Under-Clothing, Cottons, Ticks, Prints, Union Stuffs, Muslins, Linens, Winceys, Plaids, Shawls, and Handkerchiefs; Cotton, Linen, and Woollen Shirts and Drawers; Hosiery; Knitting Yarns and Knitting Cotton; Cloth and Tweed Caps; Gloves, Carpet Shoes, Umbrellas, Braces, Threads, and Small Wares. MILLINERY.

EXCELLENT CONGOU TEA at 3s. 2d. per lb. (in $\frac{1}{4}$ lb. packets 3s. when 1 lb. or more is taken at a time and paid for, cash.

A LARGE DISPLAY OF
NEW DRAPERY GOODS
Suitable for the Season, at
JOHN KENNEDY'S
GENERAL DRAPERY ESTABLISHMENT
8 & 10 HORSE MARKET, KELSO.

MITCHELL & BALMER,
GENERAL DRAPERS, SILK MERCERS, & CLOTHIERS,
16 SQUARE, KELSO.

WILLIAM SADLER,
TAILOR AND CLOTHIER,
21 ROXBURGH STREET, KELSO.

2 ROXBURGH STREET, KELSO.

ESTABLISHED 1790.

HENDERSON & Co.,

(Successors to Mr. John Henderson)

SILK MERCERS, GENERAL DRAPERS, HABERDASHERS, CLOTHIERS,

HATTERS, AND HABIT MAKERS.

TAILORING AND CLOTHING ESTABLISHMENT,
COMMERCIAL HOUSE,
BRIDGE STREET, KELSO.

LUGTON & PORTEOUS,

FROM their constantly increasing returns, are glad to see that the principles on which they conduct their Business, are appreciated by the Gentlemen of the District. Their motto is to supply the very best Material and Work, at the lowest possible prices; and having secured such workmen as cannot be surpassed, they are in a position to supply Gentlemen with as elegant a style, and as good a fit, as any Metropolitan house can do, while their charges are at least a *fourth less.*

BLACK DRESS SUITS, MORNING SUITS,
OFFICE SUITS, SHOOTING SUITS,
SERVANTS' LIVERIES, LADIES' RIDING HABITS,
PULPIT AND BAR GOWNS, HATS, CAPS, SHIRTS,
UNDERCLOTHING, &c.
Home-Knitted Hosiery of all kinds.

COMMERCIAL HOUSE,

BRIDGE STREET, KELSO.

LUGTON & PORTEOUS

RESPECTFULLY call attention to the Large and Rich Stock of all classes of Drapery Goods they always have on hand.

They themselves, as well as their Milliner, visit London frequently, and can always give Ladies the choice of the First·Fashions in

MANTLES, JACKETS,

SHAWLS, BONNETS, HATS, DRESSES,

SILKS, &c., &c.

Every kind of Millinery and Dressmaking done on the Premises, by Experienced Hands.

ANDREW HOGARTH
Painter and Paper Hanger,
13 & 15 WOODMARKET,
(New Premises)
KELSO.

WILLIAM M'GREGOR,

HOUSE PAINTER AND PAPER-HANGER,

AND DEALER IN

Paper-Hangings, Oil Paints, Varnishes, Turpentine, Brushes, &c.

SQUARE, KELSO.

GEO. BALLANTINE,

GROCER, WINE AND SPIRIT MERCHANT,

28 SQUARE, KELSO.

WILLIAM BROOMFIELD,

GROCER AND PROVISION MERCHANT,

29 SQUARE, KELSO.

Teas, Hams, Bacon, Lard, and Cheese.

SUPERIOR OLD PORT AND SHERRY WINES.
CLARET, CHAMPAGNE, &c.
BRANDY, HOLLANDS, JAMAICA RUM.
GLENLIVET, ISLAY, AND PLAIN MALT WHISKY.
REID'S LONDON IMPERIAL STOUT.
BASS AND ALLSOPP'S PALE INDIA ALE.
YOUNGER'S EDINBURGH ALE AND BEER.
FINEST TEAS, COFFFES, AND SPICES.
W. & G. LAW'S (EDINBURGH) COFFEES.

D. HASTIE & Co.,

TEA, WINE, AND SPIRIT, MERCHANTS,
5 WOOD MARKET, KELSO.

JAMES PLUMMER,

GROCER, PORK CURER, AND

DEALER IN RABBITS,

101 & 111 ROXBURGH STRET,

KELSO.

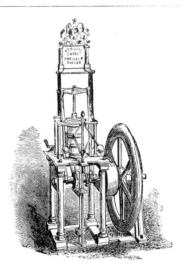

COFFEE GROUND BY STEAM POWER.

IMPORTANT IMPROVEMENTS.

JAS. SHIELS devotes particular attention to the Roasting of the Beans, which is always done on the premises, and upon which the excellence of the beverage so much depends; and as he has just received delivery of a large Stock, which he has purchased on very advantageous terms, and as his extensive business in this article enables him to have it at all times fresh ground, his Customers may always rely upon being supplied with Coffee of the Best Quality at the Lowest possible Prices.

JAMES SHIELS,

TEA AND COFFEE DEALER,
21 & 22 SQUARE, KELSO.

LIST OF WINES, BRANDIES, &c.

	℔ Dozen.
Superior Port from the Wood . . .	28s. to 36s.
Old Crusted Ditto	40s. to 54s.
Very Old Vintage Wine 12 to 15 years in bottle	60s. to 84s.
Fine Dinner Sherry . . .	24s. to 30s.
Superior Pale, Golden, and Brown . .	32s. to 48s.

Clarets, Champagne, Burgundy.

Sparkling Hock and Moselle, Madeira, &c., at Moderate Prices.

Liqueurs and Cordials.

	℔ Gallon.
Martell's and Hennessy's Fine Old Cognac Brandy	27s. to 33s.
Very choice old and rare quality . .	36s. to 39s.
Jamaica Rum	15s. to 18s.
Loopuyt's Hollands . . .	15s. to 16s. 6d.
London Old Tom	15s.

Glenlivet, Islay, and other Highland Whiskies, 15s. to 18s.

Bass and Co.'s and Allsopp's Pale India Ale, Younger's Edinburgh Ale.

Reid's Imperial London Stout in first-rate condition.

JOHN HOGG,
TEA, WINE, AND SPIRIT MERCHANT,
13 SQUARE, KELSO.

THE Subscriber begs to intimate that he has just received to hand a direct importation of very superior

Amontillado and Vino de Pasto Sherry,

much admired for their dryness and delicacy of flavour.

PRICE.
(In quantities of 6 dozen and upwards)

Vino de Pasto	... ...	48s. ℔ Doz.
Amontillado	... ...	52s. ,,

The above are usually sold at much higher prices.

JAMES SHIELS,
IMPORTER OF FOREIGN WINES AND SPIRITS,
21 & 22 Market Square, & 1 Mill Wynd,
KELSO.

SMITH & SON,
PORK-CURERS AND HERRING MERCHANTS,
KELSO.

D. MAXWELL & SON,
COACH BUILDERS,
CRAWFORD STREET, KELSO.

CARRIAGES of every description made to order of the Best Material, under their own practical superintendence, from the most approved London Designs, and finished in First Style.

Repairs carefully executed on the most reasonable terms.

BLACK SWAN INN,
5 HORSE MARKET,
KELSO,
THOS. IRVINE, Proprietor.

SLIGHT'S
COMMERCIAL TEMPERANCE HOTEL,
14 WOOD MARKET, KELSO.

Busses pass and re-pass to and from every Train.

THOMAS DAVIDSON.
BOOT AND SHOE MAKER,
28 WOOD MARKET, KELSO,

BEGS most respectfully to intimate that he has a Large Quantity of READY-MADE BOOTS and SHOES, suitable for Ladies, Gents, Youths, and Children's Wear, which he will offer at very Low Prices.

GEORGE SCOTT,
BOOT AND SHOE MAKER,
19 BRIDGE STREET, KELSO.

Boots and Shoes of every description at
G. WOOD'S,
BOOT AND SHOE MAKER,
No. 7 ROXBURGH ST., KELSO.

STRATHEARN & Co.,
STAFFORDSHIRE WAREHOUSE,
24 BRIDGE STREET, KELSO.

CHINA TEA AND BREAKFAST SETS.
BOHEMIAN VASES.
A Large Stock of BROWN WARE always on hand.
DINNER AND DESSERT SERVICES.

Banquets or Private Parties Supplied on Moderate Terms.

FAMILY ORDERS PROMPTLY AND CAREFULLY ATTENDED TO.

24 BRIDGE STREET, KELSO.

JAMES ALLAN,
SADDLER AND HARNESS MAKER,
48 SQUARE, KELSO.

J. & J. JOHNSTON,
WHOLESALE AND EXPORT SADDLERS,
IRON MERCHANTS,

ROPE,   SHEEP-NET

TWINE, AND   MANUFACTURERS

Agents for Fleming's Tobacco Juice (Duty free).

ARCHITECTURAL DESIGNS, SPECIFICATIONS,
ESTIMATES, AND INSPECTIONS,
BY
JOHN MICHIE,
No. 9 COAL MARKET, KELSO.

ROBERT BRUNLEES,
SHEEP-NET, ROPE, & TWINE MANUFACTURER,
153 ROXBURGH STREET, KELSO.

TWINE  ROPES

C. SMITH,
SHEEP NET MANUFACTURER,
11 BOWMONT STREET, KELSO.

Sheep Nets repaired.

BENJAMIN DICKISON & SON,
BUILDERS AND CONTRACTORS,
SHEDDEN PARK ROAD, KELSO.

ANDREW ROBERTSON,
BUILDER AND CONTRACTOR,
77 ROXBURGH STREET, KELSO.

JOHN MICHIE,
SLATER, GLAZIER, AND ROOF PLUMBER,
Also Dealer in all Sorts of
SLATES, GLASS, CHIMNEY CANS,
PUTTY, MASTIC, PORTLAND AND ROMAN CEMENTS,
9 COAL MARKET, KELSO.

GEORGE GILRAY'S

Furnishing Ironmongery & Iron Bedstead Warehouse

SQUARE, KELSO.

Register and Kinnaird Grates, Hot-Air Stoves, American Cooking Stoves, Kitchen Ranges, Dish Covers, and Baths.

BEST SHEFFIELD TABLE AND POCKET CUTLERY.

IRON BEDSTEADS, &c.

Careful and experienced workmen sent out.

FORREST & SON,

GUN AND FISHING ROD MAKERS,

35 SQUARE, KELSO.

REDPATH & SONS,

Jewellers, Hardware Merchants,

GENERAL WAREHOUSEMEN,

AND SHOE FACTORS,

26 ROXBURGH STREET, KELSO.

JOHN GRAY,

GENERAL FURNISHING IRONMONGER,

SQUARE, KELSO,

RESPECTFULLY invites inspection to his Large and Select Stock of KINNAIRD and REGISTER GRATES, KITCHEN RANGES, FENDERS, FIRE-IRONS, &c., comprising all the Newest Designs. ELECTRO-PLATED, NICKEL SILVER, and BRITANNIA METAL GOODS. WARRANTED TABLE CUTLERY, TRAYS, WAITERS, BASKETS, DISH COVERS, BATHS, IRON BEDSTEADS. CHILDREN'S COTS, &c., &c., and all the minutiæ of Furnishing Ironmongery

Grate, Fender, Iron Bedstead, Bath, and Furnishing Ironmongery Warehouse,

SQUARE, KELSO.

J. MILLAR & CO., WATCHMAKERS,

JEWELLERS AND PHOTOGRAPHERS, 18 ROXBURGH STREET, KELSO.

JAMES AITKEN,

JEWELLER,
WATCH MAKER,
AND
HARDWARE
MERCHANT.

SILVER &
ELECTRO-PLATED
GOODS.

IRONMONGERY
*Furnished or made to
order.*

FISHING TACKLE AND FANCY GOODS.

14 SQUARE, KELSO.

JAMES RICKETS

(Sucessor to Messrs. G. & J. Humble),
CABINET MAKER, UPHOLSTERER, UNDERTAKER,
AND APPRAISER,
CRAWFORD STREET, KELSO.

ROBERT RATHIE,

LICENSED POSTMASTER,

12 BOWMONT STREET, KELSO,

Can always supply JOB
and POST HORSES for
Hire. A Private Omnibus is kept for the use of
Private Families. Horses
Broke to Double or Single
Harness.

*Gentlemen can be accommodated with Good Hunters during
the Season.*

E. HARDIE,

CABINET MAKER,
𝔘𝔭𝔥𝔬𝔩𝔰𝔱𝔢𝔯𝔢𝔯, 𝔞𝔫𝔡 𝔘𝔫𝔡𝔢𝔯𝔱𝔞𝔨𝔢𝔯,
18 SQUARE, KELSO.

WILLIAM NICHOL,

CABINET MAKER & UPHOLSTERER,
10 HORSE MARKET, KELSO.

GEORGE SMITH

CABINET MAKER, UPHOLSTERER, AND
PAPER HANGER,
21 SHEDDEN PARK ROAD, KELSO.

MOLLISON & M'VITIE,

ENGINEERS AND MILLWRIGHTS,
EARLSTON, AND BOWMONT STREET, KELSO.

ROBERT SCOON.

BUTCHER,
1 ROXBURGH STREET,
KELSO.

JOHN TURNBULL,

FLESHER,
3 BRIDGE STREET, KELSO.

Veal, Corned Beef, Salt Rounds, Pork, Pickled Tongues, &c.

WILLIAM CAMERON,

PHARMACEUTICAL CHEMIST,

44 BRIDGE STREET, KELSO.

Physician's, Surgeon's, and Family Prescriptions accurately prepared under personal superintendence of the Principal, with Drugs and Chemicals of the purest quality only. Copies preserved.

A select stock (always on hand) of Genuine Patent, and Proprietary Medicines, Eau de Cologne, Perfumery, Pomades, &c ; also a large assortment of Brushes—Hair, Tooth, Nail, and Flesh ; and every other ar ticlerequisite for the Toilet, from first-class manufacturers in London and Paris.

HORSE AND CATTLE MEDICINES.

Leeches, Photographic Chemicals.

AGENT FOR

J. SCHWEPPE & Co., and BAILDON'S CELEBRATED
ÆRATED MINERAL WATERS.

SMITH'S SPARKLING GINGER BEER,

For family use, that will keep, neither becoming too flat nor too brisk.

LIEBEG'S EXTRACT OF BEEF.

In Pots, 1 oz. equal to 2 lbs. of Beef without bone or tendon.

Orders from the Country punctually attended to.

GEORGE F. DODDS,

𝔠𝔥𝔢𝔪𝔦𝔰𝔱 𝔞𝔫𝔡   𝔇𝔯𝔲𝔤𝔤𝔦𝔰𝔱,

MEDICAL HALL, KELSO.

Agent for Kelso and the District for

J. SCHWEPPE & Co.'s CELEBRATED SODA WATER.
STRUVE & Co.'s CELEBRATED SELTZER WATER.
DUNCAN, FLOCKHART, & Co.'s LEMONADE, SODA &
POTASH WATERS.

MR. W. FRED. VERNON,

RESIDENT DENTAL SURGEON,

114 ROXBURGH STREET, KELSO.

(For Engagements, see Advert. in front.)

KELSO MARKET ANNOUNCEMENTS.

GRAIN COMMISSION AGENCY.

MR. GEORGE THOMSON,

At the commencement of a New Season, begs to remind his Friends and the Public that he has Resumed the Commission Agency, and that they may rest assured that all Business intrusted to him will receive his undivided attention.

22 London St., Edinr., 1865.

In attendance weekly at Kelso & Berwick Corn Exchanges.

STUART & MEIN,

(Seedsmen to the Union Agricultural Society,)

KELSO,

Are supplying the following *Genuine New Seeds,* which have been proved to germinate well :—

NEW CLOVER SEEDS, Free from Weeds.
RYE GRASSES, of sorts, pure, and well cleaned.
NATURAL GRASSES FOR PERMANENT PASTURE.
TURNIP SEEDS, saved from *Improved Bulbs* carefully picked and selected.

S. & M. are at present booking orders for the following TURNIP SEEDS :—

SKIRVING'S PURPLE TOP SWEDE,
Saved by Mr. HOPE, Fenton Barns, East Lothian. 8d. pr. lb.

EAST LOTHIAN PURPLE TOP SWEDE,
Saved by an Eminent East Lothian Farmer. 8d. per lb.

STALLS.

No. a4 CORN EXCHANGE, KELSO.
No. 20 CORN EXCHANGE, BERWICK.
No. 6 CORN EXCHANGE, ALNWICK.

[*See Advert., p.* 44.

WILLIAM DEANS,

NURSERYMAN, SEEDSMAN, AND FLORIST,

JEDBURGH,

Attends the Kelso Market and Corn Exchange, weekly.

See Jedburgh Advertisements.

ANDREW DUNN,

CORN MERCHANT,

5 EDENSIDE ROAD, KELSO.

Always on Hand.

FINEST LINSEED CAKE, BRAN, &c.,

SUPER-PHOSPHATE OF LIME,

DISSOLVED BONES,

AND

NITRATE OF SODA.

Stall No 41 Kelso Corn Exchange.

GRAIN STORES AT KELSO STATION.

THOMAS OVENS,

GALASHIELS,

IMPORTER OF

GUANOES, OILCAKES, & AGRICULTURAL SEEDS.

GOODS DESPATCHED FROM LEITH, LIVERPOOL, AND BERWICK.

In attendance on Market Days at
No. 8 CORN EXCHANGE, EDINBURGH.
No. 5 CORN EXCHANGE, DALKEITH.
No. a3 CORN EXCHANGE, KELSO.
Melrose, Hawick, Jedburgh, Earlston, &c.

NOTICE.

GEORGE INGRAM & Co.,

WESTBANK BRICKWORKS,

PORTOBELLO,

Beg to intimate to their numerous Friends and Customers in the Counties of Berwick, Roxburgh, and Selkirk that Mr. Andrew Thomson, of Mainhill, St. Boswell's, who regularly attends the Markets, will be glad to receive Orders and Payment of Accounts on behalf of the Firm.

N.B.—Geo. Ingram & Co. have always on hand a Large Stock of Drain and Sewerage Pipes, Common and Fire Bricks, Vent Linings, Chimney Cans, Flooring Pavement, Garden Pots, &c., &c.

JEDBURGH ANNOUNCEMENTS.

WILLIAM DEANS,

NURSERYMAN, SEEDSMAN AND FLORIST,

2 CANONGATE, JEDBURGH,

In returning thanks to his numerous friends and customers for the kind patronage which he has received for the past Forty Years, begs to intimate that Catalogues of the following may be had on application, post free, viz. :—

1. GARDEN, FLOWER, AND AGRICULTURAL SEEDS
2. FRUIT AND FOREST TREES.
3. GRAPE VINES.
4. SHRUBS, BEDDING PLANTS.
5. FLORIST FLOWERS, ROSES.
6. GLADIOLI, GREENHOUSE PLANTS, &c., &c.

Nurseries—Hillside, Oak Vale, and Anna House.

W. D.'s HOT AIR STOVE,

By which a large number of Churches and Public Buildings have been Heated. The Cheapest, Safest, Simplest, and Most Powerful Heating Apparatus, as well as a great saving of fuel. *Prices on application.*

W. D. attends the Kelso Market and Corn Exchange, weekly.

HORSES MEASURED & NEATLY FITTED. HORSE CLOTHING, RUGS, WHIPS, BRUSHES, &c.

ALEX. RUTHERFURD,

Harness-Maker and Saddler,

HIGH STREET,

JEDBURGH.

THE DISPENSARY,

4 HIGH STREET,

JEDBURGH.

JAMES BOYD,
SILK DYER, SCOURER, &c.

KENMORE DYE WORKS,
JEDBURGH.

*Foreign and British Shawls, Moreen and Damask Cleaned,
Dyed, and Finished. Chintz Cleaned and Glazed.*

**Satins, Brocades, Velvets, French Merinoes, Winceys,
Carpets, Hearth-rugs, and Crumbcloths Cleaned.**

JAMES ROBERTSON,
GENERAL AND FURNISHING IRONMONGER,
MARKET PLACE, JEDBURGH.

MELROSE ANNOUNCEMENTS.

WALTER SLATER,
FAMILY GROCER,
TEA, WINE, AND SPIRIT MERCHANT,
HIGH STREET, MELROSE.

GEORGE DOUGLAS,
IRON, SEED, GUANO, AND CAKE MERCHANT,
HIGH STREET, MELROSE.

Warehouses—Wilderness, and Railway Station.

JAMES WALKER,
CHEMIST AND DRUGGIST,
HIGH STREET, MELROSE.

ALEXANDER DAVIDSON,
AUCTIONEER AND APPRAISER,
ALSO
SHEEP AND CATTLE SALESMAN,
MELROSE.

Fortnightly Sales of all kinds of Farm Stock.

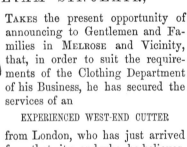

Fancy Articles, and Souvenirs of the District.

In this Department Miss E. has a very extensive and varied Stock of Articles made from Abbotsford Garden, Melrose Abbey, and Kelso Abbey Wood, specially for her own sale.

AGENT FOR PULLER & SON, DYERS TO THE QUEEN, PERTH.

Branch of Messrs. Rutherfurd's (Kelso) Book Club.

Orders for Printing and Bookbinding punctually attended to.

An Assortment of
J. & J. H. Rutherfurd's Series of Farm Books
Always on hand, consisting of
CORN BOOKS, FARM-YARD BOOKS, WORKERS' TIME BOOKS, AND REAPERS' TIME TABLES.

Berlin Wools of all shades, Stamped Work and Small Wares, and an assortment of Knitted Work.

POST OFFICE, MELROSE,
March 1866.

H. ROGERS,
RAILWAY HOTEL,
ST. BOSWELL'S STATION.

The Nearest Hotel to Dryburgh Abbey and the River Tweed.

HORSES, CARRIAGES, AND DOG CARTS FOR HIRE.

HAWICK ANNOUNCEMENTS.

IMPORTANT TO STOCK FARMERS.

HOPPER'S
BATH FOR DIPPING SHEEP.

THOS. H. HOPPER

BEGS to remind Stock Farmers, &c., that he is the Original and only Preparer of this justly Celebrated Sheep Dipping Composition, now so extensively used with olive oil instead of soft soap.

Beware of imitations. The genuine kind is sealed with black wax, with name and address of the proprietor in red letters.

Address all Orders
T. H. Hopper, Chemist, Medicine Warehouse, Hawick.

JOHN DAVIDSON,
DESIGNER, MODELLER,
PLASTERER, AND DEALER IN CEMENTS
6 ALLARS CRESCENT, HAWICK.

VICTORIA HOTEL.

GEORGE BURNS.

GOOD ACCOMMODATION FOR TRAVELLERS.

52 HIGH STREET, HAWICK.

JAMES TURNBULL,
GROCER, WHOLESALE & RETAIL SPIRIT DEALER,
51 HIGH STREET, HAWICK.

HENRY PATTERSON,
LICENSED AUCTIONEER, APPRAISER, &
WOOL MERCHANT,
61 HIGH STREET, HAWICK.

Sales of Stock held periodically at Langholm.

WILLIAM WOODCOCK,
RAG AND CHINA MERCHANT,
54 HIGH STREET, HAWICK.

SHALLOW BATH

WALTER GRIEVE & Co.,
PLUMBERS,
GAS-FITTERS, SLATERS AND GLAZIERS,
16 BUCCLEUCH STREET, HAWICK.

THOMAS CHARTERS,
BAKER AND CONFECTIONER,
68 HIGH STREET, HAWICK.

JELLIES, CREAMS, AND ICES.
CHRISTENING, WEDDING, & SUPPER CAKES TO ORDER.
ORNAMENTED DISHES. TEA BREAD AND BISCUITS.
TARTS, PIES, AND SANDWICHES DAILY.

ANDREW WAUGH,
TAILOR, CLOTHIER, HATTER & SHIRT MERCHANT
38 HIGH STREET, HAWICK.

WALTER FORSYTH,
FLESHER,
40 HIGH STREET,
HAWICK.

J. GUTHRIE & SONS,
PLUMBERS, GAS-FITTERS, SLATERS & GLAZIERS
61 HIGH STREET, HAWICK.

SELKIRK ANNOUNCEMENTS.

JAMES HARDIE,
PAINTER, PAPER-HANGER, AND DECORATOR,
MARKET PLACE, SELKIRK.

JAMES MILLAR,
WATCH MAKER,
MARKET PLACE,
SELKIRK.

JOHN BROWN,
WATCH MAKER AND JEWELLER,
HIGH STREET, SELKIRK.

JOHN SCOTT.
Painter and Paper-Hanger,
HIGH STREET,
SELKIRK.

Pattern Books from the Best Houses
FREE ON APPLICATION.

MRS. WOOD,
HIGH STREET, SELKIRK,
AGENT FOR
Littlejohn's Celebrated Edinburgh Confectionary.

EVERY ARTICLE IN
CONFECTIONARY AND FRUIT,
SUITABLE FOR
DINNERS, DESSERTS, WEDDINGS,
Christenings, Birth Days, and Evening Parties,
Procured to order at the shortest notice.

Cakes, Shortbread, Party Sweetmeats, &c.

ALSO A SELECT STOCK OF
STATIONERY,
CHRISTMAS CARDS AND LEAFLETS,
WOOD WORK OF THE DISTRICT,
BERLIN WOOLS, PATTERNS,
AND
SMALL WARES.

AGENT FOR PULLER & SON, DYERS, PERTH.

6

DUNSE ANNOUNCEMENTS.

PHILIP WILSON,
CORN FACTOR & COMMISSION AGENT,
Agent for
SUN FIRE, AND SCOTTISH WIDOWS' LIFE ASSURANCE COMPANIES,
RIDDOCK'S, WAKELIN, & Co.'s MUSSELBURGH LINSEED CAKE.

House—West Cottage, Dunse.

JOHN WADDELL,
TEA, WINE, AND SPIRIT MERCHANT,
MARKET PLACE, DUNSE.

BLACK BULL HOTEL,
JAS. LAUDER, PROPRIETOR,
BLACK BULL STREET, DUNSE.

Posting in all its departments.

RICHARD STEPHENSON,
GENERAL & FURNISHING IRONMONGER,
DEALER IN BAR IRON AND STEEL,
CONTRACTOR FOR THE ERECTION OF WIRE FENCING,
SADDLER AND HARNESS MAKER,
MANUFACTURER OF ROPES, SHEEP-NETS, & TWINE,
Agent for the sale of all kinds of Agricultural Implements,
MARKET PLACE, DUNSE.

BATHING AND RUNNING SHEEP.

FARMERS Supplied, to any extent, and on the most reasonable terms, with all the requisites for DIPPING and RUNNING SHEEP, including TOBACCO JUICE, made in Bond, from *Duty free Tobacco*, and warranted to contain the active properties of *one and a half pounds of Tobacco in each Gallon.*

TOBACCO.	TOBACCO PAPER.
SPIRITS OF TAR.	SOFT SOAP.
SPIRITS OF TURPENTINE.	SUBLIMATE.
GALLIPOLI OIL.	SWEET OIL.
TRAIN OIL.	LARD, OIL, &c.
HELLEBORE.	SULPHUR.
SALTPETRE.	ARSENIC.
POTASHES.	SODA ASH.

Sole Agent for the District for
HOPPER'S IMPROVED SHEEP DIP, and
RAWDIN'S (*Duty Free*) TOBACCO JUICE, as above.

WILLIAM GUNN,
PHARMACEUTICAL CHEMIST,
(*By Examination*)
MARKET PLACE, DUNSE.

WELLFIELD ACADEMY,
NEAR DUNSE.

BOARD AND EDUCATION FOR YOUNG GENTLEMEN.

THE Course of Study in this School includes all the subjects of a Liberal Education in ENGLISH, MODERN LANGUAGES, CLASSICS, and MATHEMATICS. The Fees are moderate.
The Prospectus, with a Syllabus of the Curriculum, may be obtained from MR. WOOD, the Head-Master.

ROBERT G. SWAN,
AUCTIONEER,
ALBERT COTTAGES, DUNSE.

JAMES DEWAR,
CABINET-MAKER, UPHOLSTER, & UNDERTAKER,
MURRAY STREET, DUNSE.

COLDSTREAM ANNOUNCEMENTS.

FLODDEN FIELD WOOD WORK,
SUITABLE FOR

CHRISTMAS AND NEW YEAR GIFTS, BIRTH-DAY PRESENTS,
GIFTS FROM COLDSTREAM, ETC.

Comprising upwards of 60 different articles, useful and ornamental. Each article is embellished with a view of some object of interest in the district, local and historical. The above goods are much admired for their chaste design and exquisite finish, and are guaranteed to be made of wood which grew on

> "Flodden's fatal field,
> Where shiver'd was fair Scotland's spear,
> And broken was her shield!"

and are only to be had at the Establishment of

A. & R. ROBB,
FAMILY GROCERS,
BOOKSELLERS AND STATIONERS,
HIGH STREET, COLDSTREAM.

A detailed List on application.

JAS. COMMON & SON, Watch & Clockmakers, JEWELLERS, &c., HIGH STREET, COLDSTREAM.

SHALLOW BATH

GEORGE SMITH,
FURNISHING & GENERAL IRONMONGER,
COLDSTREAM,

Iron Bedsteads, Grates, Ranges, Fenders & Fire Irons.
CUTLERY, ELECTRO-PLATED GOODS.
LAMPS, OILS, CHIMNEYS, &c.   CHINA, CRYSTAL & EARTHENWARE.

Illustrated Catalogue and Price List Post Free.

PETER HOGARTH,

Painter and Paper-Hanger,

HIGH STREET,

COLDSTREAM.

ROBERT TURNBULL,
WATCH AND CLOCK MAKER,
AND JEWELLER,
HIGH STREET, COLDSTREAM.

PERFECT SAFETY IN SHEEP-DIPPING.

M'DOUGALL'S PATENT
NON-POISONOUS
SHEEP-DIPPING COMPOSITION,

Warranted Free from Arsenic, Mercury, or other Mineral Poisons.

This Composition possesses the following advantages :—

1. It may be used for Dipping, Pouring, or Smearing, without the slightest danger to Sheep or Lambs of any age, and with perfect safety to persons applying it.

2. It effectually and speedily destroys Ticks, Lice, and other Vermin ; after its application the Sheep are enabled to feed with comfort, and will consequently improve more rapidly in condition.

3. It is the best cure for the ravages of the Maggot Fly.

4. It is an effectual remedy for the Scab or Shab, possesses remarkable healing and antiseptic properties, and prevents contagion from skin diseases.

5. It improves the appearance, and increases the growth of the Wool, imparting to it a fine soft greasy feeling, and in this respect differs from other baths, for while generally they tend to deprive the Wool of its natural oil or "yolk," it tends to preserve and add to it.

6. It is easy of application, and a very cheap and inexpensive application ; the cost for Dipping is less than $1\frac{1}{4}$d, for Smearing about 2d, and for Pouring about $\frac{1}{2}$d each Sheep.

SOLD IN TINS AND CASKS AS FOLLOWS:—

5 ℔ Tins for Dipping 25 Sheep			....	£0	2	6
10 ℔ ,,	,,	50 ,,	....	0	5	0
15 ℔ Casks	,,	75 ,,	....	0	7	6
20 ℔ ,,	,,	100 ,,	....	0	10	0
50 ℔ ,,	,,	250 ,,	(measure included)	1	5	0
100 ℔ ,,	,,	500 ,,	,,	2	10	0
200 ℔ ,,	,,	1000 ,,	,,	5	0	0

AGENTS.

Edinburgh—Raimes & Co., Leith Walk, and C. Newton, 12 Gayfield Square ; *Peebles*—A. G. Blackie ; *Penicuick*—W. Wilson ; *Galashiels* —A. Yellowlees, and John Dun ; *Selkirk*—Yellowlees Brothers ; *Kelso*—W. Robertson, V.S. ; *Berwick*—J. Davidson, chemist ; *Haddington*—J. |Hardie ; *Dunse*—R. Stephenson ; *Hawick*—J. Wield, druggist ; *Melrose*—Wield & Corson, druggists ; *Glasgow*—F. H. M'Leod, wool-broker.

Retail Agents appointed in most Towns in Scotland.

WHOLESALE AGENTS FOR SOOTLAND—
CARRUTHERS & ALLAN, Dumfries.

LADIES'

RIDING

HABITS.

FROM

3 TO 8

GUINEAS.

HOLTUM AND WELSH,

HABIT MAKERS,

6 GEORGE STREET, EDINBURGH.

As H. & W. devote particular attention to this department of their Business, they with confidence solicit Ladies to favour them with their Orders, every Habit being cut and finished in the best style, and a perfect fit guaranteed.

PATTERN HABITS IN STOCK, TO SHEW THE DIFFERENT DESIGNS.

VELVET

HUNTING CAPS,

BEST QUALITY.

FELT

HUNTING HATS,

NEW SHAPE.

HOLTUM AND WELSH,

BREECHES MAKERS,

6 GEORGE STREET, EDINBURGH.

SCARLET WATERPROOF CLOTH, PATENT BEAVERS, AND TREBLE-MILLED MELTONS, FOR HUNTING COATS.

NEWEST MATERIALS FOR HUNTING VESTS.

CORDS—every SIZE, MAKE, and COLOUR—for HUNTING BREECHES.

Every Garment Guaranteed a Perfect Fit.

BEST QUALITIES.   CASH PRICES.

AGRICULTURAL, VEGETABLE, & FLOWER SEEDS.

DRUMMOND BROTHERS

(Sons of Mr. Peter Drummond, of Stirling)

Commenced Business in September 1864 at the under-noted address, where by studied attention to the wishes of Customers, and anxious endeavours to supply only the best Seeds, &c., they respectfully hope to gain an annually increasing share of the confidence and trade of the Country.

CATALOGUES.

The following Priced Lists may be had:—

HYACINTHS, TULIPS and other DUTCH ROOTS *(Descriptive)*, in September.
GLADIOLI *(Descriptive)*, in November.
VEGETABLE and FLOWER SEEDS *(Descriptive)*, in January.
AGRICULTURAL SEEDS, in Spring.

The "Percentage" Question.

As announced in their GARDEN SEED LIST for this year (1866), DRUMMOND BROTHERS are convinced that it would be *better for all parties* were the custom relinquished, which is so general in the Retail Seed and Nursery Business, of giving to Gardeners and other heads of departments a percentage on their Employers' Accounts, either on paying them themselves, or after their Employers have done so; and, consequently, after much consideration, *they have resolved not to give percentages to Employés.*

From the effect this Announcement already seems to have had in some quarters, Drummond Brothers feel warranted in respectfully soliciting the support of those who make a point of the principle involved.

TERMS—Five per cent. allowed for Cash within a Month.
Regarding FREE DELIVERY, see Catalogues.

DRUMMOND BROTHERS,
SEEDSMEN, NURSERYMEN, AND FLORISTS,
52 GEORGE STREET, EDINBURGH.

Nurseries—Larkfield, Ferry Road ; Rosebank, Wardie.

PLANTING SEASON.

DEAN PARK NURSERY,

QUEENSFERRY ROAD, EDINBURGH.

Landed Proprietors and others are respectfully invited to inspect the Stock of FOREST TREES, HARDY SHRUBS, &c., on the New Nursery at Dean Park. Having been raised and grown on a fresh fertile soil, the Plants are finely developed, free from all disease, and particularly well adapted for Transplanting to high exposed localities. On application, samples, with prices, sent to any part of the United Kingdom.

The Stock of ORNAMENTAL TREES and EVERGREEN SHRUBS, from 3 to 20 feet in height, for planting and giving immediate effect in Villa Gardens, Lawns, &c., are also worthy of inspection. Having been all Transplanted to their present situation within the past eighteen months, they will lift with excellent roots.

ROBERT T. MACKINTOSH,

NURSERY AND SEEDSMAN,

DEAN PARK NURSERY,

AND

12 MELBOURNE PLACE, EDINBURGH.

May be had free on application, R. T. Mackintosh's Treatise on the best assorted Grass Seeds for sowing down Land.

7

JAMES YOUNG & Co.,

MANUFACTURERS,

27 AND 29 CROSSCAUSEWAY, EDINBURGH.

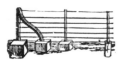

4d. to 1s. 6d. per Yard.

PLAIN and ORNAMENTAL IRON and WIRE FENCING, with Self-winding Pillars, Rope Wire and Wire, Plain and Galvanized, for Horses, Cattle, and Sheep, Fruit, Espaliers, &c.

CONTINUOUS BAR and HURDLE FENCING.

2d. to 1s. 9d. per. Yard.

PRIZE GALVANIZED WIRE NETTING for Poultry, Horses, Sheep, Rabbits, Hares, &c.

STRONG WIRE NETTING, specially prepared for fixing on Iron Railing for protecting Flowers.

Gate, 35s. 6d. with Pillars, &c., complete.
Without Pillar for stone or wood, 19s.

All kinds Plain and Ornamental Gates, Railing, &c. Stable Fittings, with Enamelled Mangers, Guttering, &c.

Best Prepared Black Varnish for Wood and Iron. For Outside-Work, 1s. 8d. per gal.

SELF-FIXING AND SELF-WINDING RATCHET PILLARS FOR WIRE FENCING, Arranged for Wire Rope and Solid Wire.

Strained Iron and Wire Fencing, with Iron Foundations instead of Stone—specially prepared. Fencing Materials, including Standards, Pillars, Stays, Wedges, Wire, &c., arranged for Parties erecting their own Fences, and supplied accordingly.

IRON AND WOOD GREEN HOUSES. GALVANIZED CORRUGATED IRON SHEETS FOR ROOFING. HOT WATER ENGINEERS. IRON HOUSE BUILDERS

SOFA GARDEN CHAIR, 38s. 6d.

FERN LEAF CHAIR, 30s. to 45s.

All beautifully Painted, Green Oak, &c.

ROYAL GARDEN CHAIR, 3 to 8 feet long, 30s. to 50s.

JAMES YOUNG & Co.—*Continued.*

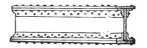 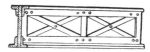

CAST AND WROUGHT IRON BEAMS AND GIRDERS, for Buildings, Bridges, &c.

CAST AND WROUGHT IRON SADDLE-BOILERS, ENGINE BOILERS, &c.

All Kinds Iron Bridges for Carriage and Passenger Traffic.

All Kinds of Iron and Wire Work, Flower Stands, Arbours, Arches, and Garden Chairs.

DRAWINGS, ESTIMATES, and every Information furnished by

JAMES YOUNG, & Co., 27 & 29 Crosscauseway, EDINBURGH.

MORISON AND CO.

MANUFACTURERS OF BILLIARD TABLES,

78 *GEORGE STREET, EDINBURGH.*

BAGATELLE

and

CURLING TABLES.

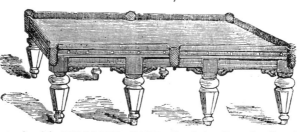

NEW TOPS,

CLOTHS, & CUSHIONS

Supplied.

—

INSPECTION INVITED.

M. & Co. are now able to furnish **BILLIARD TABLES** of the Best Quality, in every respect equal to the best London-made Tables,

AND AT VERY MODERATE PRICES.

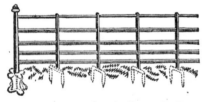
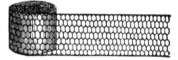

BY ROYAL APPOINTMENT.

RICHARD WHYTOCK & CO.,

Carpet Manufacturers to Her Majesty,

CABINET-MAKERS & UPHOLSTERERS,

DECORATORS, CARVERS, AND GILDERS,

IMPORTERS OF FOREIGN CARPETING, FANCY CABINET WORK, AND FURNITURE STUFFS,

HOUSE AND PROPERTY AGENTS,

AND

FUNERAL CONDUCTORS,

Nos, 9 & 11 George Street, and Rose Court,

EDINBURGH.

JURORS' AWARDS.

INTERNATIONAL EXHIBITION, LONDON, 1862,
Prize Medal "FOR CABINET FURNITURE."
INTERNATIONAL EXHIBITION, LONDON, 1862,
Honourable Mention "FOR VARIOUS CARPETING."
INTERNATIONAL EXHIBITION, DUBLIN, 1865,
Prize Medal "FOR ENGRAVED BEDROOM FURNITURE."

Special Designs accurately executed to suit every style of Architecture and Interior Decoration.

THE "ANCHOR" LINE

OF

TRANSATLANTIC STEAM PACKET SHIPS.

HIBERNIA, ... 1616 Tons, J. Craig, *Commander.*
CALEDONIA, ... 1393 ,, Robert Ferrier, ,,
BRITANNIA, ... 1393 ,, James Laird ,,
UNITED KINGDOM, 1255 ,, R. D. Munro ,,
COLUMBIA, ... 1800 ,, (Now Building)

(unless prevented by unforeseen circumstances)
are intended to sail regularly between

GLASGOW AND NEW YORK,

as under:

FOR NEW YORK.	FROM NEW YORK.
CALEDONIA, Saturday, 7th April.	CALEDONIA, Saturday, 28th April
HIBERNIA, Saturday, 21st ,,	HIBERNIA, Saturday, 12th May.
BRITANNIA, Saturday, 5th May.	BRITANNIA, Saturday, 26th ,,
CALEDONIA, Saturday, 12th ,,	CALEDONIA, Saturday, 9th June.
HIBERNIA, Saturday, 2d June.	HIBERNIA, Saturday, 23d ,,
BRITANNIA, Saturday, 16th ,,	BRITANNIA, Saturday, 7th July.
CALEDONIA, Saturday, 30th ,,	CALEDONIA, Saturday, 21st ,,
HIBERNIA, Saturday, 14th July.	HIBERNIA, Saturday, 4th Aug.

and thereafter every alternate Saturday.

FARES.

SALOON CABIN, 13 & 15 Guineas; FORWARD CABIN, 10 Guineas;
INTERMEDIATE, 8 Guineas; STEERAGE, 7 Guineas.

Baggage.—Passengers are requested to look after their own baggage, the Ship not being responsible for its safety unless booked and paid for. SALOON Passengers are allowed 20 cubic feet; FORWARD CABIN. 15 cubic feet; INTERMEDIATE and STEERAGE. 10 cubic feet FREE, any excess being charged for at the rate of One Shilling per Cubic Foot.

For Freight or Passage apply to
FRANCIS MACDONALD & CO.,
6 Bowling Green, New York.
HANDYSIDE & HENDERSON,
45 & 51 Union Street, Glasgow.

TO HER MAJESTY, AND THE LATE PRINCE CONSORT.
THEIR ROYAL HIGHNESSES THE PRINCE AND PRINCESS OF WALES.

VENTILATORS
FOR STABLES AND COW HOUSES.

PREVENTS AND CURES THE CATTLE DISEASE AND PLEURO-PNEUMONIA.

As supplied to Windsor Castle, and the Royal Stables at Windsor;
and for Public and Private Buildings.

WATSON'S SELF-ACTING SYPHON VENTILATORS,

For Churches, Chapels, Schools, Gentlemen's Houses, Shed Factories, Drying Rooms for Cloth and Wool, Workshops, Warehouses, Banks, Counting-Houses; and to remove Heat and Steam and the smell of Cooking.

VENTILATION WITHOUT VIOLENT DRAUGHT.

Nearly the whole of Windsor Castle is ventilated by these Ventilators; as were the Chapels Royal, St. James's and St. George's, for the Marriage of the Princess Royal and the Prince of Wales.

THE Self-Acting SYPHON VENTILATORS are to be had only of **CHARLES WATSON**, F.R.S.A., &c., &c., the Inventor and Patentee, at his Works, Nos. 1, 2, and 3 BOND STREET, **HALIFAX**; London Office—26 *Bartholomew Villas, Bartholomew Road, Kentish Town, N.W.*

About 13,000 of these Ventilators have been successfully applied to Churches, Schools, Factories, Dwelling Houses, Steamboats, Stables, Drying Stoves, Workshops, Warehouses, Farm Buildings, &c.

TESTIMONIAL FOR A 9-STALL STABLE.

From ALLEN MILL, Esq., *Spottiswoode, Lauder, Berwickshire.*

Dear Sir,—I have enclosed cheque for Ventilator. The Ventilator acts well, and keeps the Stable free from all bad smells. It will soon pay on the harness alone.

TESTIMONIAL FOR A 26-STALL STABLE.

From C. GAPP, Esq., *Great Western Royal Riding School, Gloucester Crescent, Hyde Park, London, June 23, 1862.*

Dear Sir,—I have had your Ventilators in my Stables for 26 horses, for more than four years; the Ventilators have saved me two and three horses yearly. My horses used to suffer much from throat affections, and inflammation, before I used your Ventilators, but since you ventilated my stable and corn lofts, my horses have been quite free from these diseases, and have ever since been ready and able for their work at all times.

My Riding School, ventilated by you, is always free from stable smell, and smell of tan, and is as pleasant at all times as out of doors. Having proved your Ventilators for more than four years, I can strongly recommend them for stables; the expense of the Ventilators was repaid to me within a year.

TESTIMONIAL FOR A PUBLIC HALL, FOR MEETINGS.

Port of Hull Society, and Sailors' Orphan Institution, Sailors' Institute, Waterhouse Lane, Hull, 19th of April 1864.

Dear Sir,—Our Institute has been thoroughly tested, over and over again, having been crowded to the doors on many occasions since I last wrote to you, so that I am now enabled to speak with the most perfect confidence, and am happy to say that the Ventilation is so complete, and the temperature so entirely under control, that it leaves nothing to be desired. You will remember that some members of our committee, when you had an interview with them, were somewhat sceptical as to your success; they are now so thoroughly satisfied, that they would be glad to extend your system as far as they may have the means of doing so.

I shall be glad to answer any enquiries upon the subject if you would make any reference to me.—I am, &c., JOHN WRIGHT, Hon. Secy.

Earl Russell has graciously favoured J. T. Davenport with the following:—"Extract of a despatch from Mr. Webb, H.B.M.'s Consul at Manilla, dated Sept. 17, 1864:—'The remedy most efficacious in its effects (in Epidemic Cholera) has been found to be CHLORODYNE, and with a small quantity given to me by Dr. Burke I have saved several lives.'"

CONSUMPTION, ASTHMA, BRONCHITIS, WHOOPING COUGH, NEURALGIA, DIARRHŒA, RHEUMATISM, SPASMS, &c.

CAUTION!!

CHLORODYNE.

IN CHANCERY.

VICE-CHANCELLOR SIR W. PAGE WOOD stated that Dr. J. COLLIS BROWNE was undoubtedly the Inventor of Chlorodyne; that the story of the Defendant, FREEMAN, was deliberately untrue, which, he regretted to say, had been sworn to—See *Times*, July 13, 1864.

Eminent Hospital Physicians of London state that Dr. J. COLLIS BROWNE was the discoverer of Chlorodyne; and they prescribe it largely, and mean no other.

The Public, therefore, are cautioned against using any other than Dr. J. COLLIS BROWNE's Chlorodyne, which is extensively used in Hospitals at home and abroad, and is affirmed by medical testimony, which accompanies each Bottle, to be the most efficacious Medicine ever discovered for Consumption, Coughs, Colds, Asthma, Bronchitis, Spasms, Rheumatism, &c. No home should be without it.

Earl Russell communicated to the College of Physicians that he had received information from the Governor-General of Manilla, that of all medicines tried in Cholera, &c., " Chlorodyne was the most effective." See The Lancet, *Dec. 31, 1864.*

From M'GREGOR CROFT, M.D., M.R.C., Physician, London, late Staff-Surgeon, to H.M.F.

"After prescribing Dr. J. Collis Browne's Chlorodyne, for the last three years, in severe cases of Neuralgia and Tic-Douloureux, I feel that I am in a postion to testify to its valuable effects. Really, in some cases it acted as a charm, when all other means had failed. Without being asked for this report, I must come forward and state my candid opinion that it is a most valuable medicine."

From GRIFFITH GOULSTONE, M.D., Surgeon to the Steam Ship Great Eastern.

"I can confidently state that Chlorodyne is an admirable Sedative and Anti-Spasmodic, having used it in Neuralgia, Hysteria, Asthma, and Consumption, with remarkably favourable results. It relieved a fit of asthma in four minutes, where the patient had suffered eleven years in a most distressing manner, no previous remedy having had so immediate and beneficial effect."

This INVALUABLE REMEDY produces quiet refreshing sleep—relieves pains, calms the system, restores the deranged functions, and stimulates healthy action of the secretions of the body—without creating any of those unpleasant results attending the use of opium. Old and young may take it at all hours and times when requisite.

Beware of spurious—The only genuine has the words "DR. J. COLLIS BROWNE'S CHLORODYNE," on the Government Stamp. Sold in Bottles at 2s. 9d. and 4s. 6d.; sent free on receipt of stamps.

Sole Manufacturer—J. T. DAVENPORT,
33 GREAT RUSSELL STREET, BLOOMSBURY SQUARE, LONDON.

8

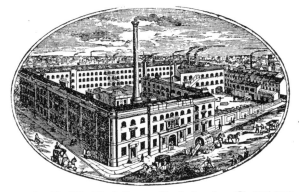

BY ROYAL COMMAND.

METALLIC PEN MAKER TO THE QUEEN.

JOSEPH GILLOTT

Respectfully invites the attention of the Public to the following Numbers of his

PATENT METALLIC PENS,

Which for Quality of Material, Easy Action, and Great Durability, will ensure universal preference.

FOR LADIES' USE—For fine neat writing, especially on thick and highly-finished paper, Nos. 1, 173, 303, 604. In extra fine points.

FOR GENERAL USE—Nos. 2, 164, 166, 168, 604. In fine points.

FOR BOLD FREE WRITING—Nos. 3, 164, 166, 138, 604. In medium points.

FOR GENTLEMEN'S USE—For large, free, bold writing. The Black Swan Quill, Large Barrel Pen, No. 808. The patent Magnum Bonum, No. 263. In Medium and and Broad Points.

FOR GENERAL WRITING—No. 263. In extra-fine and fine points. No. 810. New Bank Pen. No. 262. In fine points. Small Barrel. No. 840. The Autograph Pen.

FOR COMMERCIAL PURPOSES—The celebrated three-hole Correspondence Pen, No. 382. Ditto four hole ditto, No. 202. The Public Pen, No. 292. Ditto with Bead, No. 404. Small Barrel Pens, fine and free, Nos. 392, 405, 603.

TO BE HAD OF EVERY RESPECTABLE STATIONER IN THE WORLD.

WHOLESALE AND FOR EXPORTATION AT THE

Manufactory, Victoria Works, Graham Street, and at 96 New Street, Birmingham; 91 John Street, New York; and at the London Depot, 37 Gracechurch Street, E.C.

LITERARY ANNOUNCEMENTS.

J. & J. H. RUTHERFURD'S PUBLICATIONS.

Ordinary Editions, price in Cloth, 8d each.
In Paper, for distribution, 6d. each.

CHRISTIAN'S POCKET LIBRARY.

AMONGST the many religious works of the present day there appears to be room for a small series of Treatises, devoted specially to the elucidation of the Gospel. It is believed that such a series, neatly got up, and of a convenient size, might be both seasonable and acceptable. There are many such Treatises, both ancient and modern, already before the public, yet still it is not on that account inexpedient or undesirable that additions should be made to this department of sacred literature.

The series consists of small volumes, neatly bound in cloth.

Eighteenth Thousand.

1. *Blood of the Cross.* By the Rev. Dr. BONAR.

Fifth Thousand.

2. *Looking to the Cross.* By the Rev. W. Cudworth.
"A small volume of great practical value."—*Christian News.*
"Greatly enhanced by the notes and preface by Dr. Bonar."—*Witness.*

Third Thousand.

3. *No Condemnation; or, the True Ground of* Christian Triumph. By the Rev. JOHN PURVES, Jedburgh.
"This is an eminently spiritual and practical treatise, deserving a prayerful perusal."—*Aberdeen Banner.*

4. *The Bleeding Heart; or, I am Anxious.* By the Rev. DAVID THOMPSON.
"Full of Gospel truth and comfort."—*Aberdeen Banner.*

5. *The Obedience of Christ.* By the Rev. A. J. CAMPBELL, late of Melrose.
"An excellent little volume in which a deeply interesting subject is stated and applied with great clearness and faithfulness."—*Northern Warder.*

Seventh Thousand.

6. *Brief Thoughts Concerning the Gospel.* With preface, introduction and notes, by the Rev. H. BONAR, D.D. A New and Enlarged Edition.

7. *Baptism : What says the Bible as to its Mode* and Subjects ? By the Rev. T. P. HUNT.
"The subject of Baptism is here discussed with great clearness, on the broad principles of Bible common sense."—*Witness.*

Twelfth Thousand.

8. *The Gospel Pointing to the Person of Christ.* By the Rev. A. BONAR, Collace.

Seventh Thousand.

9. *Christ is All.* By the Rev. T. WILCOX. With great additions by the Rev. H. BONAR, D.D.
"The best edition we have seen of this precious little book. And it is all the more precious because of its additions."—*Missionary Record.*

LARGE TYPE EDITIONS.

Price in cloth 1s. each.

1. *Blood of the Cross.* By the Rev. HORATIUS BONAR, D.D. *(published.)*
"There is a charm about Dr Bonar's writings that has procured for them a deservedly high place in the religious literature of the present day. The deep piety and thorough earnestness which make his public ministrations and pastoral visits so impressive, pervade all his publications. Dr Bonar has cultivated the intellect as well as the heart. There is food for both the devotional and the intellectual. His last which is now before us, is fully equal to any of his previous publications. It merits an extensive circulation, and we feel confident that it will obtain it."—*Witness.*
"Like some other works which Dr Bonar has given to the world, this book is eminently practical, and founds its practical instruction upon the grandest and most stirring themes of the gospel. What can incite to holiness and activity in the service of God, like a searching view of thy 'love of Christ' and the 'Blood of the Cross.' So this book teaches : may it be widely read."—*Christian Instructor.*

6. *Brief Thoughts on the Gospel.* With Dr. BONAR's additions. *(preparing for publication).*
"If you wish to see my views stated clearly and distinctly, read the First Part of Brief Thoughts."—*Dr Chalmers. See Life.* Vol. I. p. 307.
".... I think I must at least see the kind of mercy of God in sending such a messenger. ..... It is called 'Brief Thoughts.'"—*Vide Life of Rev. J. Macdonald of Calcutta.* Pp. 98 and 494.

8. *The Gospel Pointing to the Person of Christ.* By the Rev. A. A. BONAR. *(published).*
"An admirable little book, fraught with consolation to doubting and sorrowful Christians."—*Scottish Guardian.*

THE GIFT BOOK OF THE LOCALITY.

LATELY PUBLISHED,

A HANDSOME ILLUSTRATED EDITION OF

Leyden's Scenes of Infancy, and Border Poems, &c.

With Life from the materials of Sir Walter Scott, and Rev. James Morton, Holbeach.   Edited by ROBERT WHITE, Esq., Newcastle, Author of " History of the Battle of Otterbourne," etc.

PRICES.

Cloth, 6s. 6d.; Calf, red edges, 10s. 6d. and 11s. 6d. ; Morocco antique, or extra, 12s. 6d. and 13s. 6d. ; in Clan Tartan and in Wood of the District, with Painted Vignette, 20s. and 21s.

Illustrations.

The Illustrations consist of Leyden's Birth-place, Kelso, Jedburgh, Hermitage Castle, Melrose, Kelso Abbey, and Abbotsford.

The best copies have, in addition, a PHOTOGRAPH OF THE MONUMENT TO LEYDEN lately erected at Denholm.

" As a contribution to the literature of the country, and as reflecting peculiar lustre on this district, this work should stand in very high estimation. The poems of Dr. Leyden are among those literary works which time cannot destroy, and age only improves. They have been read with pleasure and profit by many who now shine as lights in the world, and some of whom have traced their first inspirations to the draughts of pure poesy with which the work abounds. The ' Scenes of Infancy' is a poem of itself sufficient to make the reputation of any author; and it is difficult which to admire most—the polished language in which the ' thoughts that breathe and words that burn' are conveyed to the reader, or the fine manly and noble sentiments that breathe through almost every line of the poem. We cannot conclude this notice without bestowing our meed of praise on the manner in which the work before us is printed. The general ' getting-up' is unexceptionable, and does high credit to a town which was honoured in having printed at one of its presses the first edition of the ' Minstrelsy of the Scottish Border.' The type is clear and well brought up, the illustrations are gems in their way, and the binding and general appearance of the work is equal to very many which we have seen issued from the Edinburgh and Metropolitan press."—*Kelso Mail.*

LEYDEN'S SCENES OF INFANCY—*Continued.*

The following Correspondence is extracted from "Notes and Queries," 1859.

"STANDARD OFFICE, MONTROSE, *May* 1859.

"Permit me to remind those who purpose paying a tribute to the memory of Leyden that his Poems, exquisitely beautiful as they are, are little known at the present day : the only collected edition (by the Rev. J. Morton) having long been out of print, and being now never met with. What the public know of Leyden and his works is chiefly through the loving references to him in the writings of Sir Walter Scott, 'Christopher North,' and others, who were his personal friends. A re-publication, therefore, of his *Poetical Remains*, would not only further the object of those who take an interest in his memory, but would confer a boon on those of the present generation endowed with a taste for poetry   Colton, surely a competent judge, in tran-

scribing into his *Lacon* a piece of Leyden's (' Ode to an Indian Gold Coin') says—' There is so much of true genius and poetic feeling of the highest order in the following stanzas, that I cannot withstand the temptation of enriching my barren pages with so beautiful a gem. This ode of Dr. Leyden's, in my humble opinion, comes as near perfection as the sublunary muse can arrive at, when assisted by a subject that is interesting, and an execution that is masterly.'—C.B."

"Your correspondent, C. B., will be glad to learn that an edition of the poetical works of Leyden, with the Memoir by Sir Walter Scott, and supplementary notes by Mr. Robert White of Newcastle, the historian of the Battle of Otterbourne, was published by Messrs. Rutherfurd of Kelso last year."—E. H. A.

Reduced in price to 5s. 6d. (by post, 6s.), In 4to, handsomely bound in cloth, and containing many plates,

HISTORY OF THE PRIORY OF COLDINGHAM,

FROM THE EARLIEST DATE TO THE PRESENT TIME,

COMPILED FROM THE MOST AUTHENTIC AUTHORS, ANCIENT AND MODERN,

BY W. K. HUNTER, Esq. OF WELLFIELD.

"Here is a work fit at the first glance to set the teeth of an antiquary on edge, in expectation of a feast according to his taste. It may be supposed, however, from the character borne by antiquaries, of having a relish for a fare which is reckoned dry and unpalatable by popular readers, that it may be suited for their appetite alone; but we are happy to assure our readers that such is not the case, and that, on the contrary, it will be found to be brimful with interesting historical facts, from which much useful information may be derived, and many profitable

lessons deduced. . . Altogether we congratulate the author on the ability with which he has accomplished his labour. The volume externally is exceedingly handsome, and the printing and illustrations executed in first class style."—*Kelso Chronicle.*

"Dear Sir— . . The history of the parish is full of interest, and I rejoice that the record of it has fallen into hands capable of doing it ample justice.—Yours sincerely, *Francis Scott* (late M.P. for Berwickshire)."

KELSO : J. & J. H. RUTHERFURD.

Just Published, price 3s., Handsomely Bound in cloth, and a proper size for the Pocket,

A NEW EDITION OF

RIVER ANGLING FOR SALMON AND TROUT.

By the late JOHN YOUNGER, St. Boswell's.

With additional and re-written Chapters on Creeper, Stone-Fly, and Worm Fishing, by the Editor; and a Portrait and Memoir of the Author.

"This is a new and improved edition of one of the most pleasant and useful little books on this pleasant subject—it is needless to say what we have said before, that John Younger's instruction and advices as to angling are most valuable, as the fruits of long experience and great shrewdness."—*Scotsman.*

"To the young Trout-Fisherman, we say, get Younger's little book and study it, and you have the whole art of Trout Fishing. To old fishermen we can say that it is the best and most practical book upon this class of fishing ever published."—*The Field.*

"'The Shoemaker of St Boswell's,' as he was designated in all parts of Scotland, was an excellent prose writer, a respectable poet, a marvellously gifted man in conversation; and in all that related to the 'gentle art' of fishing, the very highest authority of his day. * * * His is the Angling Book for Scotland. * * * It is a genial pleasant book to read independent of the information contained in it. There is one part of the book that will be read with interest; that is the biography of the author, the simple heart-stirring narrative of the life-struggle of a highly-gifted, humble, and honest mechanic—a life of care, but also a life of virtue."—*London Review.*

"Taken altogether, the book must assume a high position as an original piscatorial authority—the result of many years' keen observation."—*Border Advertiser.*

"On all subjects of interest in the art it will be found full of information of the soundest and most ingenious description. The adept and the inexperienced will alike esteem it. On the subjects of when, where, and how to fish, as well as what to fish for, and what to fish with, will be found sage advice, grounded on long experience."—*Kelso Chronicle.*

"The publishers of this little volume deserve the highest credit for its handsome and elegant appearance. It contains an excellent portrait of Younger in his cobbler's apron. It is printed in a clear type, on good paper, and is very tastefully bound. We are glad to see such a production emanating from a publishing office in Roxburghshire."—*Hawick Advertiser.*

A few copies of the 1861 *edition, containing Younger's "Fresh Hints on the Nature of the Salmon," etc., price 3s. 6d., are still to be had.*

"To us who leave the gentle art, to more patient and painstaking spirits than our own, the best part of the book is that which contains 'some Fresh Hints on the Nature of the Salmon,' and for conducting the Salmon Fisheries of the Tweed."—*Sunderland Times.*

KELSO : J. & J. H. RUTHERFURD, 17 SQUARE.

LONDON AND EDINBURGH: W. BLACKWOOD & SONS.

GLASGOW: JAMES MACLEHOSE.

MISCELLANEOUS
PUBLICATIONS OF J. & J. H. RUTHERFURD.

In Small 8vo (under the Author's sanction), complete edition,
cloth, price 2s.

THE BIBLE IN THE FAMILY.

BY THE REV. H. BOARDMAN.

With Preface by the Rev. A. J. CAMBBELL, late of Melrose.

In Fcap. 8vo, price 5s., cloth stout.

THE COMING AND THE KINGDOM OF THE LORD JESUS

BEING AN EXAMINATION OF THE WORK OF THE REV. DR.
JOHN BROWN, ON THE SECOND COMING OF THE LORD.

BY THE REV. H. BONAR, D.D.

In Royal 8vo, stoutly bound in cloth, reduced to 10s. 6d.

THE HISTORY OF REVIVALS OF RELIGION;

OR, THE HISTORICAL COLLECTIONS OF J. GILLIES, D.D.,
AS TO THE SUCCESS OF THE GOSPEL.

With Preface, Additions, and Copious Index, by the Rev. Dr.
BONAR.

Only 6 copies left, reduced to 12s. 6d.

The Abridged Statistical History of Scotland.

Illustrative of its Physical, Industrial, Moral, and Social Aspects,
etc., etc. Arranged Parochially; with Biographical,
Historical, and Descriptive Notices.

BY THE LATE JAMES H. DAWSON, ESQ., KELSO.

Price 2s. 6d., cloth; extra, gilt edges, 3s. 6d.,

RUTHERFURD'S BORDER HANDBOOK;

BEING A GUIDE TO THE REMARKABLE PLACES, PICTURESQUE,
SCENERY, AND ANTIQUITIES OF THE BORDER.

Illustrated with many Engravings on Steel, a Map of the
District, and Chart of the Railway.

Large Type Small Book, price 2d.

CHRIST IS ALL.

BY THE REV. HORATIUS BONAR, D.D.

MESSRS. CHAMBERS'S ANNOUNCEMENTS.

Chambers's Narrative Series of Standard Reading Books.
The latest Editions now ready.

Chambers's Graduated Writing Books,
(Embodying a carefully considered and strictly progressive system of Penmanship) are being prepared.

Chambers's Readings in English Poetry.
Just ready.   Price Two Shillings.

Chambers's Miscellany of Useful and Entertaining Tracts,
In Weekly Numbers at a Penny each, are preparing for Re-publication.   New and Improved Issue.

Chambers's Historical Questions and Answers.
Third Edition.   Now Ready.   Price Half-a crown.

Chambers's Questions and Answers in British History
Are now ready.   Price One Shilling.

Chambers's Historical and Miscellaneous Questions and Answers
In one vol., are ready.   Price 4s. 6d.

Chambers's Readings in English Literature.
(Prose and Poetry).   Price 3s. 6d.   Ready.

Chambers's Useful Hand-Books,
Sixpence each, are in the Press.

Etymology.
By Dr. GRAHAM of Edinburgh.   New and entirely recast Edition.   Price Two Shillings.

Script Wall Sheets.
A Set in Preparation.

Farm Book-keeping.
By W. INGLIS.   Just ready.   Price Two Shillings.

Ready Reckoner.
Price Sixpence.   Just Ready.

Electricity.
By Dr. FERGUSON of Edinburgh.   Brought down to the present time.   Amply Illustrated.   In the Press.

For Specimens of Messrs. Chambers's Publications, Teachers are requested to apply to 339 High St. Edinburgh.

9

WORKS ON AGRICULTURE, &c.

Just Published, price 5s., a Fourth Edition of
A PRACTICAL TREATISE ON THE CULTIVATION OF

THE GRAPE VINE.

By WILLIAM THOMSON,
Gardener to His Grace the Duke of Buccleuch, Dalkeith Park.

This day is published, in 8vo, price 5s.,
A PRACTICAL TREATISE ON THE CULTURE OF

THE PINE-APPLE.

By DAVID THOMSON,
ARCHERFIELD GARDENS, HADDINGTONSHIRE.

The Book of the Farm. By HENRY STEPHENS, F.R.S.E. 2 vols. royal 8vo, with Engravings, price £3 half-bound.
"The best practical book I have ever met with."—*Prof. Johnston.*

In the Press.
Physiology at the Farm, in Rearing and Feeding the Live Stock. By WILLIAM SELLER, M.D., F.R.S.E., and HENRY STEPHENS, F.R.S.E. In 1 vol.

The Book of Farm Buildings: their Arrangement and Construction. By HENRY STEPHENS, F.R.S.E., Author of "The Book of the Farm," &c.; and R. S. BURN, Engineer. Royal 8vo, pp. 562, illustrated with 1045 Engravings; half-bound, £1, 11s. 6d.

The Book of Farm Implements and Machines. By JAMES SLIGHT and R. S. BURN. Edited by HENRY STEPHENS, F.R.S.E. Royal 8vo, with 875 Engravings, Price £2, 2s. half-bound.

The Book of the Garden. By CHARLES M'INTOSH. 2 vols. Royal 8vo, with 1055 Engravings, Price £4, 7s. 6d. half-bound.

The Forester. By JAMES BROWN, Wood Manager to the Earl of Seafield. Third Edition, greatly enlarged, royal 8vo, with numerous Engravings on Wood, Price £1, 10s. half-bound

Farm Accounts: A Practical System of Farm Book-Keeping; being that recommended in "The Book of the Farm" by HENRY STEPHENS, F.R.S.E. Royal 8vo, price 2s. 6d. Also, SEVEN FOLIO ACCOUNT-BOOKS, constructed in accordance with the System. Price 22s.

PROFESSOR JOHNSTON'S WORKS.

Experimental Agriculture. Being the Results of Past, and Suggestions for Future, Experiments in Scientific and Practical Agriculture. 8s.

Elements of Agricultural Chemistry and Geology. Eighth Edition, 6s. 6d.

A Catechism of Agricultural Chemistry and Geology. Fifty-seventh Edition, 1s.

On the Use of Lime in Agriculture. 6s.

Instructions for the Analysis of Soils. Fourth Edition, 2s.

Dairy Management and Feeding of Milch Cows. Being the recorded Exprience of Mrs. AGNES SCOTT, Winkston, Peebles. Second Edition. Foolscap, 1s.

The Yester Deep Land-Culture. Being a Detailed Account of the Method of Cultivation which has been successfully practised for several years by the Marquis of Tweeddale at Yester. By HENRY STEPHENS, Esq., F.R.S.E. Author of the "Book of the Farm." In Small 8vo, with Engravings on Wood, 4s. 6d.

A Manual of Practical Draining. By HENRY STEPHENS, F.R.S.E., Author of the "Book of the Farm." Third Edition, 8vo, 5s.

A Catechism of Practical Agriculture. By HENRY STEPHENS, F.R.S.E., Author of the "Book of the Farm," &c. In Crown 8vo, with Illustrations, 1s.

The Relative Value of Round and Sawn Timber, shown by means of Tables and Diagrams. By JAS. RAIT, Land-Steward at Castle-Forbes. Royal 8vo, 8s. hf.-bd.

W. BLACKWOOD & SONS, EDINBURGH AND LONDON.   Sold by Messrs. RUTHERFURD, Kelso.

PUBLICATIONS OF THE RELIGIOUS TRACT SOCIETY.

Just published, Crown 8vo, 5s. 6d., cloth boards,

THE AWAKENING OF ITALY AND THE CRISIS OF ROME. By Rev. J. A. WYLIE, LL.D., Author of " The Papacy," &c.

SCIENCE and CHRISTIAN THOUGHT. By JOHN DUNS, D.D., F.R.S.E., Professor of Natural Science, New College, Edinburgh, Author of "Biblical Natural Science." Crown 8vo, 4s. 6d., cloth boards.

THE TWO NEW YEAR'S DAYS, and other Narratives and Sketches. By G. E. SARGENT. Foolscap 8vo, 2s. 6d., cloth boards.

A HANDBOOK OF ENGLISH LITERATURE. By JOSEPH ANGUS, D.D., F.R.A.S., Examiner of English Literature at the London University ; Author of " The Bible Handbook," &c. 12mo, 5s., cloth boards ; 6s. 6d. extra.

ALYPIUS OF TAGASTE. A Tale of the Early Church. By Mrs. WEBB. Engravings. Crown 8vo, 3s. 6d., cloth boards. [*New.*

GOLDEN HILLS : a Tale of the Irish Famine. By the Author of " Cedar Creek." With Engravings. Crown 8vo. 3s. 6d., extra cloth boards.

FROM DAWN TO DARK IN ITALY : a Tale of the Reformation in the Sixteenth Century. Numerous fine Engravings. Imperial 16mo. 4s. cloth boards.

LYRA AMERICANA ; Hymns of Praise and Faith. From the American Poets. Crown 8vo. 3s. 6d., cloth boards.

BRITISH NORTH AMERICA ; comprising Canada, British Columbia, Nova Scotia, New Brunswick, Prince Edward's Island, Newfoundland, &c. With Maps. Fcap. 8vo. 3s. 6d., cloth boards.

ARCTIC DISCOVERY AND ADVENTURE. Royal 18mo. With a Map. Cloth boards, 3s. 6d.

HOME IN HUMBLE LIFE. Fcap. 8vo. 2s., cloth boards.

HOURS WITH WORKING WOMEN. A Book for Mothers' Meetings and District Visitors. 1s., cloth boards.

BIBLE SKETCHES AND THEIR TEACHINGS. For Young People. By SAMUEL G. GREEN, B.A. First Series. From the Creation to the Israelites' Entrance into Canaan. Fcap. 8vo. 2s. 6d.. cloth boards.

THE PILGRIM'S PROGRESS. By JOHN BUNYAN. *Cheap Edition.* 32mo. 6d. in limp cloth ; 8d. cloth boards. Illustrated.

BUNYAN'S PILGRIM'S PROGRESS. In Bold Type. 8vo. With Portrait. 3s. 6d., bevelled boards.

THE LEISURE HOUR LIBRARY. Each Volume complete in itself, containing 288 pages with Illustrations, price 2s., handsomely bound in cloth, or 1s. paper covers.

Remarkable Adventures from Real Life.
Sea Sketches about Ships and Sailors.
Sunday in Many Lands.
A Race for Life, and other Tales.
Cedar Creek : a Tale of Canadian Emigration.
Birds and Bird Life.
Barthel Winkler, and other Tales, from the German.
Commercial Tales and Sketches.
Shades and Echoes of Old London. By John Stoughton.
Fables and Stories. By Mrs. Prosser.
The Ferrol Family, and other Tales of Domestic Life.
Frank Layton : a Tale of Australian Life.
Fairly-cum-Forelands, and other Village Tales.

LONDON : 56 PATERNOSTER ROW, 65 ST. PAUL'S CHURCHYARD, and 164 PICCADILLY. Sold by the Booksellers.

See the Society's " General Catalogue " for a large variety of Works suited for Families, Presents, and Rewards, post free on application.

BLACK'S
New Map of Scotland

SCALE 4 MILES TO THE INCH.   IN 12 SHEETS.

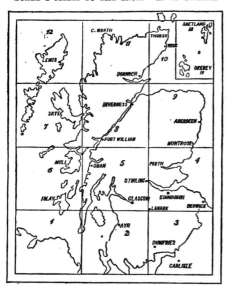

Any of the sheets may be had separately in cases for the pocket, 2s. 6d. each.

OR,

1. Complete in Box Case	...	...	...	...	£1 1 0
2. Each sheet mounted on Cloth, in Box Case	...	1 8 0
3. On Rollers Varnished	...	...	...	...	2 2 0

EDINBURGH: A. & C. BLACK.

KELSO: J. & J. H. RUTHERFURD.

WILLIAM RITCHIE'S PUBLICATIONS.

RITCHIE'S CHURCH REGISTERS

BAPTISMAL REGISTERS, 6s. & 10s.	BURIAL REGISTER, 6s. and 10s.
PROCLAMATION DO. 6s. & 10s.	COMMUNION ROLL BOOK, 7s. & 11s.

RITCHIE'S SCHOOL REGISTERS

GENERAL REGISTER, 2s. 6d. & 4s.	SABBATH SCHOOL REGISTER, 1d.,
DAILY CLASS REGISTER, 6d., 1s., 2s., and 3s.	2d., 4d., 6d., and 1s.
FOOLSCAP FOLIO DAILY CLASS RE-	SCHOOL ACCOUNT BOOK, 4s. 6d.
GISTER, 6d., 1s., 3s., and 4s.	SCHOOL LOG BOOK, 6s.
REGISTER OF FEES, 2s. 6d. and 4s.	PORTFOLIO to accompany LOG
SEWING REGISTER, 2s. 6d.	BOOK, 1s. 9d. ; with FLAPS,
	2s. 6d.

TUNE NAMES, 2 mounted on a board, at 4d. per Board. Lists on application.

FIGURES FOR DISPLAYING NUMBERS OF TUNES, 8d. per set of 10 ; 10 sets, 6s.

EASY QUESTIONS ON SCRIPTURE HISTORY, from the Creation of Adam to the close of Old Testament History, in 3 parts, price 2d. each.

LARGE TYPE TEXTS FOR EVERY DAY IN THE YEAR, on 12 Cards, in Tin Case, price 3s.

BIBLE TEACHINGS: BEING THREE CATECHISMS—On the Constitution of the Presbyterian Church ; On Baptism ; On the Lord's Supper. By Rev. C. F. Buchan, D.D., Fordoun. Price 4d.   Fifth edition.

CATECHISM ON BAPTISM. By same Author. Price 1½d.

TEXT BOOK FOR YOUNG COMMUNICANTS. By Rev. Norman Macleod, D.D., Glasgow. Price 1d.   27th Thousand.

COMPANION TO THE LORD'S SUPPER. By Rev. James Cochrane, Cupar-Fife. Square 24mo, cloth, price 1s. 6d. Third edition.

CATECHISM ON THE LORD'S SUPPER. By C. F. Buchan, D.D., Fordoun. Price 1d.   Tenth Thousand.

Edinburgh: WILLIAM RITCHIE, 16 Elder Street.

BY ORDER OF ALL BOOKSELLERS.

10

NEW SCHOOL AND COPY BOOKS

ISSUED BY THE

SCOTTISH SCHOOL-BOOK ASSOCIATION.

		s.	d.
MY FIRST BOOK, 12 pp. 18mo, sewed	0s.		1d
MY SECOND BOOK, 24 pp., 18mo, sewed	0		1½
MY THIRD BOOK, 48 pp., 18mo, sewed	0		3
*MY FOURTH BOOK, 128 pp., 18mo, cloth	0		6
*MY FIFTH BOOK, 128 pp., 18mo, cloth	0		9
*MY SIXTH BOOK, 160 pp., foolscap, cloth	1		0
PROGRESSIVE LESSONS IN READING, 240 pp., 12mo, cloth	1		6
THE ADVANCED READING BOOK, 432 pp., 12mo, cloth	2		6
MY FIRST BOOK, in large type for Sheet Lessons,	1		6
*PRINCIPLES OF ENGLISH GRAMMAR, including ANALYSIS OF SENTENCES, 144 pp., 18mo, cloth	0		9
COMPLETE SYSTEM OF ARITHMETIC, enlarged, 192 pp., 12mo, cloth	1		6

		s.	d.
SELF INTERPRETING ARITHMETIC, 100 pp., 18mo, cloth		0	6
OUTLINES OF MODERN GEOGRAPHY, 4 Maps, 128 pp., 12mo, cloth		1	0
MANUAL OF ENGLISH PRONOUNCIATION, 18mo		0	4
THE YOUNG CHILD'S GRAMMAR, 18mo, sewed		0	3
THE YOUNG CHILD'S GEOGRAPHY, 18mo, sewed		0	3
FIRST LESSONS IN ARITHMETIC, 18mo, sewed		0	3
LATIN RUDIMENTS, with Copious Exercises		2	0
,, DELECTUS, with Explanatory Notes		2	0
OUTLINES OF ANCIENT GEOGRAPHY		2	0
SHORTER CATECHISM, with Queries and explanations		0	1½

Specimen Copies of any of the Books marked (*) will be sent free to any Teacher on receipt of Two Postage Stamps, by application to Mr. Collins.

THE PROGRESSIVE COPY BOOKS,

WITH ENGRAVED AND TRACED HEADLINES, PRICE 2D. EACH.

Printed on fine Thick Cream Wove Paper, with stout covers, foolscap.

1. Initiatory Lessons, Traced	7. Text with Capitals, Short Words	13. Small Hand with Capitals
2. Initiatory Lessons, Traced	8. Text with Capitals, Full-line Words	14. Text, Half-Text, and Small
3. Combination of Letters, Traced	9. Text and Half-Text Alternately	15. Commercial Hand
4. Combination of Letters, Traced	10. Half-Text with Capitals	16. Ladies' Hand, Initiatory
5. Combination of Letters	11. Half-Text and Small Alternately	17. Ladies' Hand, Finishing
6. Text, Short Words	12. Small Hand, Short Words	18. Figures and Ornamental Letters

The attention of Teachers is respectfully called to the above Series of Copy Books, which will be found superior in arrangement and value to any others in the market.

A very liberal discount is allowed to Teachers and Retailers on all the Publications of the Scottish School-Book Association.

WILLIAM COLLINS, 139 Stirling's Road, GLASGOW; and 37 Cockburn Street, EDINBURGH.

KELSO: J. & J. H. RUTHERFURD. And all Booksellers.

[J. & J. H. Rutherfurd always keep on hand a large Stock of the above Books, which they supply to Teachers on the same terms as the Publisher.]

SCOTTISH
Trade Protection Society.

ESTABLISHED 1852.

Chief Offices, 8 & 11 BANK STREET, EDINBURGH.
GLASGOW, 54 WEST NILE STREET.

Chairman.
ADAM MOSSMAN, Esq., 30 Princes Street, Edinburgh.

Vice-Chairman.
DAVID DICKSON, Esq., Wholesale Stationer, Edinburgh.

Directors.

JOHN WILSON, Merchant.	C. STEIN, Corn Factor, Leith.
J. S. CUNNINGHAM, Seedsman.	J. RUSSELL, Wood Merchant.
RICHARD RAIMES, Merchant.	R. MARSHALL, Merchant.
T. ROBERTSON, Publisher.	ALEX. GOWANS, Merchant.
Councillor DRYBROUGH.	Councillor MACKIE.
JOHN MILLAR, Merchant.	JAMES GULLAND, Merchant.
D. NICHOL (Cowan & Co.)	GEO. HARRISON, Merchant.
C. W. ANDERSON, Leith.	P. SAMUEL, Merchant.
J. D. MARSHALL, Jeweller.	CHAS. LAWSON, Jun.
J. SINCLAIR, Corn Merchant.	JAMES RICHARDSON (Richardson
A. WHYTOCK (Whytock & Co.)	Brothers).
D. RITCHIE (J. Lees & Co.)	JAMES TOD (Mould & Tod).

D. R. M'GREGOR, Leith.

Extraordinary Directors.

THE LORD PROVOST of Edinr.	THE CHAIRMAN of the Chamber
THE MASTER of the Merchant	of Commerce.
Company.	ADAM BLACK, Esq.
Sir JOHN DON WAUCHOPE, Bart.	CHARLES COWAN, Esq.

Treasurer—ROBERT WALKER, Esq., Publisher.

Consulting Counsel.	*Accountant.*
A. GIFFORD, Esq., Advocate.	J. M. MACANDREW. Esq., C.A.

Law Agents—WHITE-MILLAR & ROBSON, S.L. and S.S.C.

Manager.	*Secretary.*
GEORGE T. BATHGATE.	P. MORISON.

Bankers—THE BANK OF SCOTLAND.

Annual Subscription, One Guinea.

HERITABLE SECURITIES.
INVESTMENT ASSOCIATION (LIMITED).
CAPITAL, £500,000.

DIRECTORS.

JOHN DRYBROUGH, Esq., 15 Coates Crescent.
JAMES FORMAN, Esq., Advocate, 6 Drummond Place.
GEORGE H. MARSHALL, Esq., 3 Heriot Row.
J. DICK PEDDIE, Esq., Architect, 3 South Charlotte Street.
ROBERT REID, Esq., 19 Heriot Row.
ALEX. WOOD, Esq., M.D., 10 St Colme Street.
GEORGE CADELL BRUCE, Esq., C.E., 21 Castle Street.
KENNETH MACKENZIE, Esq., C.A., Northumberland Street.
Law Agents—MURRAY & BEITH, W.S., 43 Castle Street.

THE Company receives Deposits on liberal terms, the money being withdrawable at pleasure or on short notice. Deposits are also received for *fixed periods*, for which a higher rate of interest is given.

The Company also receives money on Debenture for 3, 5 or 7 years, at 4 to $4\frac{1}{2}$ per cent.

The Association Lends only on Heritable Property, and Depositors and Debenture Holders have thus all the safety of Heritable Security, with the additional Guarantee of the Company's Large Subscribed Capital.

LOANS are granted on the Security of Land, Houses, and every description of Heritable Property.

For further particulars apply at the

COMPANY'S OFFICE, 55 FREDERICK ST., EDINBURGH.

AND. PATERSON, *Manager.*

THE OTAGO & SOUTHLAND INVESTMENT COMPANY (Limited) NEW ZEALAND.

(*Incorporated under "The Companies Act* 1862.")

Capital, £500,000, in 50,000 Shares of £10 each.

FIRST ISSUE, 25,000 SHARES.

DIRECTORS.

W. W. Cargill, Esq.	A. L. Elder, Esq.	A. Morrison, Esq.
G. H. Donaldson, Esq.	J. Harbottle, Esq.	J. R. Morrison, Esq.
S. B. Edenborough, Esq.		J. D. Thomson, Esq.

Auditors—J. Sawyer, Esq. ; C. H. Robinson, Esq.

Bankers :—The Imperial Bank (Limited), Lothbury, London.
.. The Bank of Scotland, } for Scotland.
.. The British Linen Company Bank, }

COMMITTEE IN OTAGO.

John Bathgate, Esq. | E. B. Cargill, Esq. | Thomas Dick, Esq.
A. W. Morris, Esq. (*Manager*). W. H. Reynolds, Esq.

Bankers—The Bank of Otago (Limited).

THIS Company is prepared to receive Loans on Debenture in sums of £100 and upwards, for 3, 4, 5, 6, or 7 years, bearing interest at the rate of Six per cent. per annum, payable by Coupons at the Bankers of the Company in London, on 1st January and 1st July. These Loans are amply secured by the uncalled Capital of the Company, as well as by the First Mortgages on Land and House Property in New Zealand, which are carefully selected by the Local Committee at Dunedin.

Also, as Agents to make Investments, and to effect Loans upon Mortages approved by the Local Committee in New Zealand on the most favourable terms, Interest being paid half-yearly in London.

Money received on Deposit for shorter periods at rates to be agreed on.

Application to be made at the Offices, 5 Adams' Court, Old Broad Street, London, E.C.

ALEX. GRACE, *Secretary.*

THE BANK OF OTAGO

(LIMITED)

NEW ZEALAND.

Incorporated under "The Companies Act 1862."

Capital, £500,000, in 25,000 Shares of £20 each.

(WITH POWER TO INCREASE.)

Head Office—5 ADAMS' COURT, OLD BROAD ST., LONDON, E.C.

DIRECTORS.

W. W. Cargill, Esq.	A. L. Elder, Esq.	A. Morrison, Esq.
G. H. Donaldson, Esq.	J. Harbottle, Esq.	J. R. Morrison, Esq.
S. B. Edenborough, Esq.		J. D. Thomson, Esq.

Auditors—J. Sawyer, Esq. ; C. H. Robinson, Esq.

Bankers :—The Imperial Bank (Limited), Lothbury, London.
.. The Bank of Scotland, and } for Scotland.
.. British Linen Company Bank, }

COLONIAL ESTABLISHMENTS.

DUNEDIN. PORT CHALMERS. INVERCARGILL. CLUTHA FERRY.
QUEENSTOWN. RIVERTON.

Branches, or Agencies, in all the New Zealand Provinces. Agencies in South Australia, Victoria, New South Wales, and Queensland.

The Directors grant Letters of Credit payable on presentation, and Drafts at thirty days' sight, upon the Branches, negotiate Bills, or forward them for collection ; and transact every description of Banking and Exchange Business between this Country and New Zealand on the most favourable terms.

Letters of Credit may also be obtained of the Bank of Scotland, and British Linen Company Bank.

By order of the Court, ALEX. GRACE, *Secretary.*

THE SCOTTISH PROVINCIAL ASSURANCE COMPANY,

ESTABLISHED 1825.

INCORPORATED BY ACT OF PARLIAMENT.

HEAD OFFICE, ABERDEEN.

Office in Edinburgh—65 PRINCES STREET. | Office in London—20 CANNON STREET, CITY.
Office in Glasgow—111 ST. VINCENT STREET. | Office in Dublin—34-B COLLEGE GREEN.

Office in Montreal—PLACE D'ARMES.

EDINBURGH BOARD OF DIRECTORS.

Professor Sir JAMES Y. SIMPSON, of Edinburgh University, F.R.C.P., *Chairman.*

J. S. Johnston, Esq., S.S.C.	David Rhind, Esq., Architect.
William Leckie, Esq., Banker.	John Richardson, Esq., W.S.

Consulting Physician—James Dunsmure, Esq., M.D., 53 Queen Street.   *Resident Secretary*—Andrew Robertson.

Bankers—THE ROYAL BANK OF SCOTLAND.

LIFE DEPARTMENT.

The Policies, now in course of being issued by this Company, are free from all unnecessary restrictions, and secure every advantage derivable from the system of Life Assurance. The Premiums are strictly moderate.

The Participation Scheme was begun in 1840, and the oldest Policies for £1000 in connexion with it, which may become Claims after payment of the Premiums falling due in the current financial year, are increased to £1372, 12s.; those for larger or smaller sums being proportionately augmented. Bonus Additions may be surrendered for their value in cash, or an equivalent reduction of future Premiums, the Assured having their choice in all cases.

It is provided by the Company's Act of Incorporation, that Investigations shall take place at intervals not exceeding Five Years, and intermediate Bonuses are allowed when Participating Policies, in force at one Division of Profits, become Claims before another division—an arrangement which secures for such cases advantages similar to those claimed for Annual Investigations.

The business in this department has been greatly extended within the last few years.

Prospectuses, with every information, may be had on application.

FIRE DEPARTMENT.

All Losses, so soon as satisfactorily ascertained, are liberally and promptly settled.

Losses arising from explosion of gas are paid by this Company.

Common, Hazardous, and Doubly Hazardous Risks, are undertaken at the usual rates of 1s 6d, 2s 6d, and 4s 6d per cent. respectively. Special Insurances at increased rates.

CHARLES F. GRIFFITH, *Manager.*
ALEX. STABLES, Jun., *Secretary.*

INSURANCE COMPANY OF SCOTLAND,

95 GEORGE STREET, EDINBURGH.

INSTITUTED 1821.

United in 1847 with the Alliance Office, having a Capital of Five Millions Sterling.

GOVERNOR—HIS GRACE THE DUKE OF HAMILTON AND BRANDON.

DEPUTY-GOVERNORS.

THE RIGHT HONOURABLE THE EARL OF ROSEBERRY, K.T. | HIS GRACE THE DUKE OF ATHOLE, K.T.

THE RIGHT HONOURABLE VISCOUNT STRATHALLAN.

ORDINARY DIRECTORS.

GEORGE CUNNINGHAM, Esq. of Newton, C.E.
JAMES R. DYMOCK, Esq., 30 Buccleuch Place.
JOHN NAIRNE FORMAN, Esq., W.S., 8 Heriot Row.
WILLIAM KENNEDY, Esq., W.S., 59 Northumberland Street.

CHARLES MACGIBBON, Esq., Architect, 7 East Claremont St.
ROBERT PAUL, Esq., Banker, 2 Bruntsfield Place.
JOHN RIDDLE STODART, Esq., W.S., 2 Drummond Place.
CHARLES TROTTER, Esq. of Woodhill, Perthshire.

MANAGER—ALEXANDER CALDER.

BANKERS—THE COMMERCIAL BANK OF SCOTLAND.

FIRE INSURANCE.

The Directors invite attention to the following important advantages enjoyed by persons who are insured with this Company :—

Perfect Security.—The Capital of Five Millions Sterling, and the Personal Responsibility of upwards of a thousand Proprietors, rendering this undoubted.

An immediate and liberal Settlement of Losses, on the Claim being satisfactorily adjusted.

Persons desirous of making Assurances for Seven Years by one Payment, will be charged for six years only, both on the Premium and Duty.

Losses occasioned by Lightning will be made good.

Losses caused by Explosion of Gas in Buildings on which this Company has Insurances will be paid.

Buildings on which Assurances are proposed, will be surveyed free of any expense to the Party, if required.

No Charge made for endorsing Policies.

No Charge made for a Policy in any case, however small the amount insured.

The Government Duty on Fire Insurances being now reduced, parties presently insured will be enabled to increase existing Insurances very considerably without increasing their payments under the old rate of Duty ; and those who have hitherto been unprotected can now be Insured on very favourable terms.

Full information afforded at the Head Office and Agencies of the Company.

AGENTS.

KELSO.........James Tait, W.S.	SELKIRK.......Lang & Steedman, writers.	DUNSE.........J. B. Kellie, Sheriff Clerk Dep.
JEDBURGH.. { James Stedman, writer. { William Elliot, writer.	GALASHIELS...Robert Stewart, banker.	EARLSTON... { William Mercer, merchant. { Thos. Clendinnen, manufacturer
HAWICK.......Wilson & Anderson, writers.	BERWICK......W. H. Logan, banker.	Lauder.......Andrew Torrie, merchant.
MELROSE.......Thomas Mitchell, engineer.	AYTON.........James Bowhill, banker.	
	COLDSTREAM...William Cunningham, writer.	

EDINBURGH LIFE ASSURANCE COMPANY,

ESTABLISHED 1823.

EDINBURGH (Head Office), 22 GEORGE STREET.

Moderate Rates of Premium Yearly, Half-Yearly, or Quarterly. Nine-tenths of the Profits septennially divided among the Assured.

The following are a few examples of Bonus Additions under Five Declarations of Profits to 31st August 1863, according to endurance of Policy, &c.:—

Age Assuring.	Sum Originally Assured.	Total Bonuses Declared to 31st August 1863.	Amount with Bonus Additions.
50	£999	£2208 7 0	£3207 7 0
48	1500	2832 13 0	4332 13 0
51	500	882 16 0	1382 16 0
46	300	405 6 0	705 6 0
42	700	868 10 0	1568 10 0

A full Table of Bonus Additions, *all exceeding one hundred per cent.*, is given in the Company's Prospectus.

No charge in effecting a Policy beyond payment of the requisite Premium.

Prospectus and Forms of Proposals for Assurance may be had gratis at the above address, or of the Company's Agents throughout the Kingdom

GILBt. L. FINLAY, *Manager.*

WM. DICKSON, *Secretary*

AGENTS.

BERWICK-ON-TWEED
- Mr. J. C. WEDDELL, Solicitor.
- Mr. A. PURVES, Auctioneer.
- Mr. ROBERT HENDERSON, Merchant.

COLDSTREAM .... Mr. WM. W. BARCLAY, Merchant.
GALASHIELS .... Messrs. A. HERBERTSON & SON, Builders.
GREENLAW .... Mr. HENRY MILLER, Merchant.
HAWICK .... Mr. JAMES HARKNESS, Builder.
JEDBURGH .... Mr. WILLIAM ELLIOT, Writer.
KELSO .... Mr. ROBERT SWAN, Writer.
LILLIESLEAF .... Mr. THOMAS TURNBULL, Postmaster.
MELROSE .... Messrs. CURLE & ERSKINE, Writers.
MINTO .... Mr. JNO. R. HAMILTON, Teacher.
SELKIRK .... Mr. PETER RODGER, Writer.

THE SCOTTISH FIRE INSURANCE COMPANY

(LIMITED).

CAPITAL—*ONE MILLION STERLING.*

HEAD OFFICE:
31 GEORGE STREET, EDINBURGH.

DIRECTORS.

Chairman—ALLAN A. MACONOCHIE WELWOOD, Esq. of Meadowbank and Garvock.

Dep.-Chairman—ALEX. HAMILTON, Esq., LL.B., W.S., Edinburgh.

HENRY MOFFAT, Esq. of Eldin, S.S.C., Edinburgh.
JOHN MILLER, Esq., C.E., Edinburgh.
JAMES FORMAN, Esq., Advocate, Edinburgh.
DAVID DICKSON, Esq., Wholesale Stationer, Edinburgh.
JOHN HALIBURTON KING, Esq. of Balerno.
CHARLES MACKINLAY, Esq., Merchant, Leith.
THOMAS SPROT, Esq., W.S., Edinburgh.
GEORGE CADELL BRUCE, Esq., C.E., Edinburgh.

Manager—J. RHIND CARPHIN, C.A.   *Secretary*—JOHN HURRY.

Glasgow Office: 123 ST. VINCENT STREET.

GLASGOW DIRECTORS.

Chairman—MARK SPROT, Esq. of Garnkirk.

WILLIAM MORISON, Esq., Merchant, Glasgow.
J. P. KIDSTON, Esq., Merchant, Glasgow.
JAMES STEVENSON, Jr., Esq., Merchant, Glasgow.
JAMES RODGER, Esq., Merchant, Glasgow.
M. E. ROBINOW, Esq., Merchant, Glasgow.

Secretary—ARCHIBALD LAWSON.

INSURANCES against Loss by Fire are effected by this Company on almost every description of Property, at the Lowest Rates of Premium commensurate to the Risk, giving full effect to the Reduction of Duty.

FARMING STOCK INSURANCES with or without the Average Clause.

Policies transferred from other Offices free of expense. No charge for Stamps in any case.

CLAIMS are settled immediately on the amount of the loss being ascertained.

Applications for Agencies to be made to the Manager.

J. R. CARPHIN, *Manager.*

JOHN HURRY, *Secretary.*

THE NORTHERN FIRE AND LIFE
ASSURANCE COMPANY.

Head Offices—EDINBURGH AND LONDON.
Edinburgh—20 ST. ANDREW SQUARE.

REALISED ASSETS, over … … … … … …	£800,000.
ANNUAL REVENUE, over … … … … … …	£270,000.

LIFE DEPARTMENT.

The Company, by its *moderate Premiums*, its extensive resources, and *liberal conditions*, offers inducements in the transactions of every form of Life Assurance such as no other sound and well conducted Office can surpass.

Participation Branch.—The *Whole Profits* (less Expenses for Management and Guarantee) *are divided among the assured.*

The *Bonus Additions* have in many instances exceeded *70 per cent. of the Premiums paid.*

Non-Participating Policies are issued at the Lowest Scale of Rates consistent with safety.

EXAMPLES OF RATES
FOR £100 AT DIFFERENT AGES, VIZ.:—

Age	25	30	35	40	45	50	60
	£ s. d.	£ s. d.	£ s. d.	£ s. d.	£ s. d.	£ s. d.	£ s. d.
With Profits	2 1 11	2 8 0	2 14 11	3 3 11	3 14 3	4 7 4	6 16 8
Without Profits	1 17 1	2 2 7	2 8 8	2 16 8	3 5 9	3 19 0	6 6 3

The ordinary rates cover residence in all parts of the world distant more than 33° from the Equator.

FIRE DEPARTMENT.

Fire Insurances effected at the current rates of Premium. No charge is now made for Policy Stamp, and Losses are settled in a prompt and liberal manner.

Losses by Lightning and Explosion from Gas made good.

Farming Stock.

AGRICULTURAL PRODUCE (Live and Dead), and IMPLEMENTS of HUSBANDRY insured, for a year, or any period short of a year, *without average clause* (no Duty) … … … … … **5s. per cent.**

Transfers from other Offices accepted free of expense.

Prospectuses and Forms of Proposal can be obtained at the various Offices and Agencies of the Company.

ROBERT CHRISTIE, JUN., *Secretary.*

20 ST. ANDREW SQUARE, EDINBURGH.

ANCRUM,—Mr A. G. CATTO, Schoolmaster. LAUDER,—Mr GEO. WATSON, Merchant.

LIFE ASSOCIATION OF SCOTLAND—Continued.

In Class B (Unconditional Assurance),

The Policies are almost without Conditions or Restrictions of any kind. The Class, however, is not intended for persons residing in, or likely to proceed to, unhealthy climates, nor for Naval or Military Men.

No Restictions whatever are Imposed, as regards Occupation, or Place of Residence, or Travelling, and

No Extra Premiums beyond the premium stipulated in the Policy, can be payable. Further,

The Policy cannot be Forfeited by omission to pay a Premium at the proper time through accident or oversight; and, after five years, a Whole of Life Policy will not be forfeited by Non-payment of a Premium from whatever cause, provided payment be made within a year, with a fine.

Bonus Additions to the Sums Assured in participating Policies are made in this Class at the Allocations of Profit, every five years.

The Lists are closed annually at 5th December.

IN EITHER CLASS

A SMALL PRESENT OUTLAY on the part of the Policy-holder, may be combined with a large ultimate benefit,—*a considerable portion of the Premiums being left unpaid as long as the Assured pleases.*

INCREASING POLICES are issued by which the Sums Assured increase by the mere lapse of time to double the original amount, without increase of Premiums.

SURRENDER OF POLICY, OR LOAN ON ITS SECURITY. If a Whole-Life Policy be after a time surrendered a liberal value will be allowed. Or, without cancelling the policy, a sum, nearly equal to its Office value at the time, may be obtained in loan.

LIFE ANNUITIES.

PERSONS DESIROUS TO INCREASE THEIR INCOME WILL FIND THE ASSOCIATION'S RATES OF ANNUITY MOST FAVOURABLE.

(See large Prospectus for further Details and Tables.)

Agencies in almost every Town in Great Britain and Ireland.

EDINBURGH, 82 PRINCES STREET,
December 1865.

JOHN FRASER, *Manager.*
ROBERT RAINIE, *Secretary.*

Mottat : JAMES J. BURKE, Union Bank.
Thornhill : Mr. FINGLAND, Chemist.

New Business in 1865.

New Assurances exceed . . . £1,043,000
New Premiums (*two single Premiums £411*) exceed 35,000

This immense New Business does not include any "Re-assurances with other Offices" (as is usual in Life Assurance accounts), nor a single Policy having been issued above the Society's limit of risk.

Progress since last Bonus.

	1860.	1865.
New Assurances . . .	£389,305	£1,043,000
Invested Funds . . .	3,518,230	4,280,000
Annual Revenue . . .	412,767	587,000
Interest on Investments . . .	£4 p.c.	£4:7s. p.c.

The Progress made in every Branch of the Society's Operations, as disclosed by the above Figures, affords the most conclusive evidence of the high position held by the Scottish Widows' Fund in public estimation.

Public Usefulness.

Claims paid since 1815 . . . £5,020,000
Claims paid in 1865 alone . . . 331,563

Claims are paid in full on the simple receipt of the parties entitled thereto in virtue of the Policy itself, or of Assignments, or under English, Irish, or Scotch Administration granted in their favour.

ANNUAL PREMIUM FOR THE ASSURANCE OF £100,
WITH PARTICIPATION IN THE WHOLE PROFITS REALISED.

Age.	Premium.	Age.	Premium.	Age.	Premium.	Age.	Premium.	Age.	Premium.
20	£2 2 1	27	£2 8 6	34	£2 16 9	41	£3 8 2	48	£4 3 7
21	2 3 1	28	2 9 7	35	2 18 2	42	3 10 0	49	4 6 11
22	2 3 11	29	2 10 8	36	2 19 9	43	3 12 0	50	4 10 7
23	2 4 9	30	2 11 9	37	3 1 3	44	3 14 1	51	4 14 8
24	2 5 7	31	2 12 11	38	3 3 0	45	3 16 4	52	4 18 11
25	2 6 6	32	2 14 2	39	3 4 6	46	3 18 7	53	5 3 6
26	2 7 6	33	2 15 5	40	3 6 3	47	4 1 1	54	5 8 5

GENERAL SUMMARY.

The magnitude of the Society's Business, Funds, Revenues, and Profits ; the scale on which all these are increasing ; and the purely Mutual principle under which the Society's affairs are conducted for the sole benefit of the Assured, justify the expectation, that in the SCOTTISH WIDOWS' FUND every benefit of which the system of Life Assurance is capable will be realised.

Forms of Proposal and Prospectuses sent free of charge on application.

SAMUEL RALEIGH, *Manager.*
J. J. P. ANDERSON, *Secretary.*

HEAD OFFICE,
9 ST. ANDREW SQUARE, EDINBURGH.
April 1866.

Dumfries { ALEXANDER SIMPSON, *Writer.*
{ W. MARTIN, Dardarroch, Dunscore Kirk.

FURNISHINGS.

CARPETS, &c.

The Newest Patterns in Brussels, Tapestries, Scotch, Kidderminster, and 3-ply Carpets, with Rugs to match ; Hemp Carpeting ; Cocoa Matting, in various widths ; Floor Cloths in all the different widths.

CURTAINS, &c.

Newest Patterns in All Wool Damasks, Union do., Turkey Cloths, Pekin Cloths, French Chintzes, Cretonne Chintzes, English Chintzes, White and Printed Dimities, Muslin Curtains, Patent Velvet Pile Fringe for Draperies, Curtain Bands, Bell Ropes, Silk Borderings, Utrecht Velvets, &c., &c.

FURNITURE.

Dining Room Furniture, Drawing Room Furniture, Library Furniture, Bed Room Furniture, Hall Furniture—*made on the Premises.*

BEDS, &c.

Brass and Iron Bedsteads, Spring Mattresses, Hair Mattresses, Flock do. and Straw Palliasses, Feather Beds, Bolsters, and Pillows.

At E. HARDIE'S,

No. 18 SQUARE, KELSO.

Patterns forwarded on application.

GENTLEMEN'S DRESS.

Superfine Cloths, warranted Permanent Dye.

Coatings, Doeskins, Tweeds, Vestings—by the yard, or made to measure.

The New Patent Summer Vest.

Satin Hats, newest styles.

Felt, Merino, and Straw Hats, in all the Fashionable Shapes.

Coloured, Wool, and White Dress Shirts.

Collars, Wristbands, Ties, Scarfs.

Braces, Belts.

Silk and Cambric Pocket Handkerchiefs.

Gloves.

Cotton, Merino, and Lambs' Wool Hosiery and Underclothing.

AT

MILNE BROTHERS,

General Drapers,

Nos. 8 and 10 WOODMARKET, and

No. 3 HORSEMARKET,

KELSO.

SCOTTISH DRAINAGE AND IMPROVEMENT COMPANY.

INCORPORATED BY ACT OF PARLIAMENT, 19 and 20 Victoria, cap. 70 (7th July 1856).

DIRECTORS.

Sir ARCHD. HOPE of Craighall, Bart., *Chairman.*
GEORGE PATERSON, Esq. of Castle Huntly.
WM. SKINNER, Esq. of Corra, W.S.

HEW CRICHTON, Esq., S.S.C.
R. MARSHALL, Esq., Gateside, Kirkliston.
JOHN RONALD, Esq., S.S.C., *Managing Director.*

CHARLES RITCHIE, S.S.C., Secretary.

THIS COMPANY has had its powers *amended* and *enlarged*, under the Act 23 and 24 Vict. (23d July 1860), and is now ready to negotiate LOANS, to any amount, Repayable by Yearly or Half-Yearly Instalments, during any period not exceeding Twenty-five years—to be applied for any of the following purposes:—

1. The Drainage of Land.
2. The Irrigation and Warping of Land.
3. The Embanking of Land.
4. The Enclosing *and Dividing of Land*, AND THE MAKING AND STRAIGHTENING OF MARCHES, BY WALLS, HEDGES, AND DYKES, AND BY IRON OR WIRE FENCES, OR OTHERWISE.
5. The Improving of Drains, Streams, or Watercourses of Land.
6. The Reclamation of Land.
7. The Making of Permanent Farm Roads, *and Permanent Tramways and Railways.*
8. The Clearing of Land.
9. The Erection of Farm Houses, and other Buildings required for Farm purposes, and the Improvement of, and Additions to, Farm Houses and other Buildings for Farm purposes, already Erected, so as such Improvement or Additions be of a permanent nature, TO THE WHOLE EXTENT OF THE EXPENDITURE.
10. The Planting for Shelter, or for any Beneficial Purpose.
11. The Construction or Erection of any Engine-houses, Water-Wheels, Saw and other Mills, Kilns, Shafts, Wells, Tanks, Reservoirs, Dams, Leads, Pipes, Conduits, Watercourses, Bridges, Weirs, Sluices, &c., for Agricultural purposes.
12. The Erection of any Engines or Machinery in connection with Improvements in Drainage or Irrigation.
13. The Construction or Improvement of Jetties or Landing Places on the Sea Coast, or on the Banks of Navigable Rivers or Lakes, for the Transport of Cattle, Sheep, or other Agricultural Stock and Produce, and of Lime and Manure, and other Articles and Things for Agricultural and Farming purposes.

Information will be afforded, and Forms supplied, on application to the Managing Director; or to the Secretary at the Office of the Company, 20 Hill Street, Edinburgh.

TO

TRUSTEES, INSURANCE OFFICES, CHARITABLE INSTITUTIONS, SOLICITORS, BROKERS, AND THE GENERAL PUBLIC.

Mortgage Debentures, registered at the Government Office of Land Registry, 34 *Lincoln's Inn Fields, London, W.C., under the powers of the Mortgage Debenture Act,* 1865, bearing $4\frac{1}{2}$ per cent. interest, issued for the sum of £50 and upwards, for terms of from one to ten years and transferable by indorsement.

The Mortgage Debentures are secured :

1st. By the deposit with the Registrar in terms of the Act, of an equal aggregate at least of Mortgages and rentcharges upon real property, and of securities upon rates and assessments upon the owners and occupiers of real property, within the powers of the Act of Parliament.

2nd. By the guarantee of the uncalled capital of £900,000, of the Land Securities Company Limited (The Lord Naas, M.P., President), of which £500,000 by the Act is absolutely appropriated as additional security to the holders of the Mortgage Debentures.

In every case a Statutory Declaration under the Act must be made and filed at the Office of Land Registry by a Surveyor or Valuer approved by the Government Inclosure Commissioners for England and Wales, that the Estates charged are at least one-half more in value than the advances made upon them, including all previous charges, if any.

Registers of the Mortgages and other Securities, and of the Mortgage Debentures, are kept in the Office of Land Registry.

The Registered Mortgage Debentures, of which no over issue is possible, are endorsed by the Registrar as conclusive evidence that the requirements of the Act of Parliament have been complied with.

Trustees having a general power to invest upon the security of Shares, Stocks, Mortgages, Bonds or Debentures of Companies, incorporated by or acting under the authority of an Act of Parliament, are authorised by the 40th *section of the Act to invest in the Registered Mortgage Debentures.*

Apply to the Hon. WILLIAM NAPIER, Managing Director, Land Securities Company Limited, 3 Parliament Street, London, S.W., and Messrs HUNTER, BLAIR, & COWAN, W.S., 7 York Place, Edinburgh.

List of Subscribers to the 1990 Edition

Aberdeen and North East of Scotland Family History Society
I. Abernethy, Heiton
Dr A. Y. Adam, Galashiels
R. Adams, Hawick
George Ainslie, Melrose
Miss Kathleen A. Allan, St. Boswells
John A. Allison, Dunbar
A. Gordon Anderson, Galashiels
Miss E. Anderson, Newcastleton
Ian Andrew Anderson, Edinburgh
Mrs J. K. Anderson, Hawick
Mrs M. Anderson, Galashiels
Miss M. G. Anderson, Greenlaw
Mary B. Anderson, South Queensferry
Anglo-Scottish Family History Society
Ian T. Archibald, Greenlaw
A. Armstrong, Newcastleton
Clan Armstrong Trust Ltd.
Thomas Armstrong, Kelso
W. A. Armstrong, Newcastleton
J. W. Bainbridge, Berwick-upon-Tweed
Mr R. Barbour, Hawick
Mr A. L. Barcroft, Longniddry
Mr J. B. Barr, Pressen, Cornhill-on-Tweed
Elizabeth R. Barrie, Eldinhope
Mrs A. Bateman, Selkirk
Colin Beattie, Edinburgh
John A. Beedle, Hawick
Mary W. Bell, Hawick
E. Roma Benicki, Lavezzola, Italy
Mr & Mrs H. G. Bennet, Stockstruther
Mr Archibald I. Berry, Stonehaven
Robert Grant Berry, Galashiels
Berwickshire District Council Museum Service
Dr G. A. C. Binnie, Ladykirk
C. Black, Duns
Miss Joanna Blake, Kelso
Mrs M. J. Blake, Kelso
Mr Walter Blake, Kelso

Borders College, Galashiels
Borders Family History Society
Dr E. R. Brewster, Duns
Mrs J. C. Brodie, Galashiels
Andrew Brown, Dalkeith
Mr F. Brown, Selkirk
Helen Brown, Leitholm
Mr & Mrs I. Brown, Peebles
John Brown, Galashiels
Rosamund Brown, Selkirk
Rutherford Bruce, Calaburn Farm
David Brunton, Selkirk
Mrs I. C. Bryant, Kelso
Jennifer J. Bryce, Linton
Mr A. Buckham, Galashiels
G. Burney, Hawick
M. J. Campbell, Galashiels
Mrs Rena Campbell, Penicuik
Mrs N. Carlyle, Hawick
Mrs Helen D. Carss, Selkirk
Alan Carter, Galashiels
Miss F. P. Chalmers, Hawick
Mrs Helen Charters, Hawick
W. Charters, Hawick
Bill Chisholm, Jedburgh
Mr A. W. Clark, Hawick
Miss M. R. M. Clark, Gattonside
A. S. Clarke, Yarrow
L. H. Cleat, Gavinton
Isobel Cleghorn, Selkirk
Mrs M. Cleghorn, Melrose
F. M. Clow, Kelso
Mr & Mrs James Clyde, Peebles
Mrs Evelyn W. Cockburn, Galashiels
R. Collin, Little Sutton
Terry Connor, Earlston
Mrs C. M. Cooper, Denholm
Mrs J. M. Cormack, Kelso
David T. Cowban, Hawick

G. Cowban, Hawick
Miss A. S. Cowper, Edinburgh
Mrs A. W. Crawford, Hawick
Alastair Cumming, Hawick
Alex G. Cumming, Hawick
Mrs B. Cumming, Hawick
Mrs R. C. B. Currie, Dunfermline
Mrs I. Cuthbertson, Hawick
Alex Cuthill, Selkirk
Andrew Dalgleish, Hawick
George Dalgleish, Edinburgh
Peter Daniel, Foulden
Helen O. Darling, Gordon
Mrs J. B. Darling, Penicuik
Mr & Mrs D. and I. Davey, Hawick
Mr J. Davidson, Hawick
Mrs Audrey A. Dawson, Derby
Charles Denoon, Maxton
John S. Dent, Lilliesleaf
Mrs N. M. Diamond, Leitholm
J. H. Dick, Hawick
W. Dickson, Hawick
Miss J. Dodds, Galashiels
Mrs A. Douglas, Kelso
Alex K. Douglas, Newcastleton
Catherine B. Douglas, Hawick
Mrs E. J. Douglas, Hawick
J. H. Douglas, Craigsford, Earlston
Nicola Douglas, Selkirk
Mrs V. Douglas, Galashiels
Paul Draper, Edinburgh
Mr R. H. Dun, Galashiels
Mrs S. Duncan, Newstead
James Dunlop, Hawick
James Eaton, Cranshaws
Anne Elliot, Flörsheim/Main, W. Germany
Mr Peter S. Elliot, Hawick
Ettrick and Lauderdale Museum Service
B. W. Evans, St. Boswells
Elspeth A. Ewan, Yetholm
Dr Lorna A. Ewan, Edinburgh
R. N. Fairbairn, Lauder

Brian Edward Falconer, Hawick
Edward Falconer, Hawick
Eric Falconer, Galashiels
Miss Mary Farries, Hawick
Mrs M. V. Fender, Portsmouth
Miss J. P. S. Ferguson, Edinburgh
Mrs M. Fish, Kelso
Miss E. M. V. Fleming, Troon
Janet B. Fleming, Crookhouse Farm
Jean Fleming, Linton
John Y. Fleming, Linton
Matthew Fleming, Jedburgh
Matthew J. Fleming, Kelso
Thomas G. Fleming, Jedburgh
Mrs F. Fletcher, Hawick
Mrs Jennifer Fox, Hawick
Colin W. Frater, Galashiels
Tom Frizzell, Morebattle
Mrs Sanna Gaffney, Boone, N. Carolina, USA
Catherine M. Gardner, Teviothead
Charles W. J. Gibb, Melrose
Philip Gibb, Galashiels
Pringle Gibb, Selkirk
Lady Gibson, Edinburgh
W. Gillies, Jedburgh
Mr H. C. Gilroy, Darnick
Miss M. B. Gilroy, Darnick
W. R. Girvan, Buckholm Farm
Mrs E. M. Gladstone, Hawick
Mrs M. Gooch, Bath
J. R. Goodfellow, Kelso
Mr P. H. Goodfellow, Whitchesters Farm
Mrs A. Goodson, Marlefield, Morebattle
Gerald M. Graham, Hawick
Mrs Maureen Graham, Hawick
A. W. Gray, Penicuik
Mrs J. Gray, Hawick
Mr K. A. Gray, Hawick
Michael M. Gray, Galashiels
Mrs V. M. Gray, Boleside
J. W. Greenhill, Glasgow
Mr J. H. Grieve, Darnick

John S. Grieve, Hawick
Philip N. Grindell, Whiteburn Farm
Mrs Muriel Grzybowski, Selkirk
Douglas Hall, Spottiswood
Mr James Hall, Galashiels
Mrs Alison Halley, Dalkeith
John M. Hamilton, Hawick
Grace C. Hardie, Selkirk
William Hardie, Lauder
H. Harkness, Makerstoun
D. W. Harvey, Stow
David W. Harvey, Lauder
The Rev Bruce J. L. Hay, Smailholm
Tom Henderson, Selkirk
Heritable Securities
Mr D. A. Hill, Hawick
Jean Hirst, Kirk Yetholm
Frank Hislop, Selkirk
Mrs I. Hogarth, Selkirk
D. Hogg, Hawick
James C. Hogg, Hawick
Mrs A. Holford, Selkirk
Douglas Hope, Lauder
I. T. Hope, Selkirk
Iain G. Hope, Sunwick Farm Cottages, Paxton
Noreen Hoy, Crewe
G. T. Huggan, Duns
William C. Huggins, Glasgow
George M. Hume, Hawick
Ivor Renwick Hume, Earlston
Mrs Sylvia Hume, Earlston
Anne Hunter, Craigend, Stow
Mrs Elspeth Innes, Melrose
John Irvine, Hawick
Jedforest Historical Society
George R. Johnston, Galashiels
Mr & Mrs James Johnston, Roxburgh
Douglas W. Johnstone, Dunning
Mrs E. A. Johnstone, Galashiels
James Johnstone, Galashiels
Sarah Johnstone, Wester Wooden, Eckford
Miss Catherine Kerr, Galashiels

R. H. Kinghorn, Camptown
Mrs Christine Kyle, Hawick
Ian R. J. Landells, Lauder
Ian W. Landles, Hawick
Alex Lauder, Hawick
Mrs R. Lawrie, Selkirk
Mrs J. H. Leach, Wetherby
Mr & Mrs George Lees, Morebattle
Mrs Helen S. Leishman, Galashiels
Miss Caroline R. Letton, Galashiels
Rev S. G. Letton, Brechin
Mrs Joyce Lewis, Earlston
Alfred Leyland, Lanton
The Library, Dept. of Adult & Continuing Education,
    University of Glasgow
Liddesdale Heritage Association
Mr Andrew Linton, Hawick
Literary and Philosophical Society of Newcastle upon Tyne
Mrs A. R. Little, Dinlabyre
T. Little, Melrose
Mrs Christine Loggie, Whitburn
Eleanor M. Lovell, Whitehope Cottage, Yarrow
Mrs M. Lunn, Hawick
Peter William Lyal, Galashiels
Mrs A. McArthur, Duns
Mrs Irene McAulay, St Boswells
Mrs J. D. McDevitt, Galashiels
A. J. MacDonald, Neidpath Castle
Mrs Agnes J. Macdonald, Kelso
John Gordon MacDonald, Hawick
W. R. D. Macdonald, Hawick
J. L. McDougal, Blythe
I. R. McEwan, Blue Houses, Hassington
Margaret McIntyre, Hawick
Mrs Fay Mackay, Clovenfords
Hugh K. Mackay, Hawick
D. McKendrick, Selkirk
Mrs F. M. Mackie, Birgham
Mrs A. H. McLean, Galashiels
Mrs Margaret McLean, Galashiels
R. S. MacLean, Brig O'Turk, Callander
Innes MacLeod, Biggar

Dr W. McLeod, Edinburgh
Mr R. L. McMorran, Aberdeen
Mr & Mrs A. K. McRae, Galashiels
Teresa Maley, Selkirk
Mrs J. Mann, Galashiels
Philip Marsden, Hawick
Mrs Barbara R. Marshall, Reston
D. H. Martin, Hawick
James Martin, Birgham
Robert R. Mason, Jedburgh
Catherine Maxwell, Bonjedward
David K. Maybury, Whitchester
Mrs F. O. Mayes, Chester, S. Carolina, USA
Sandra Mein, Galashiels
Andrew Mercer, Whitslaid
John Millar, Nether Whitlaw
J. R. Milner, Mellerstain
Mrs D. M. Mitchell, Henderland
Mrs. J. B. Mitchell, Ettrickbridge
Jean Moffat, Peebles
Mr Rae Montgomery, Lanark
Mrs E. Rosalind Moon, Galashiels
Mrs Margaret Moore, Hawick
Vivienne S. Moore, Hawick
Mrs E. Morris, Pilmuir
R. J. Morris, Dept. of Economic History, University of
    Edinburgh
Ann & Robert Naismith, Galashiels,
National Library of Scotland
Hugh H. Neilson, Galashiels
Newcastle Upon Tyne Central Library
J. M. Nicholson, Galashiels
Mrs T. Noon, Manderston
Miss Zilla Oddy, Denholm Dean
Neil O'Hara, Galashiels
Old Gala Club: Galashiels Local History Association
Anne Oliver, Hawick
Mrs E. Oliver, St. Boswells
Mr John Oliver, Hawick
Miss Ruth Ovens, Galashiels
J. N. Paterson, Morebattle
Janet Patterson, Hawick

Mr R. E. Payne, Hawick
Mrs M. Pearson, Galashiels
R. F. Penfold, Reading
Mr. & Mrs H. R. Penton, Jedburgh
Margaret Perris, Galashiels
Planning and Development Dept., Borders Regional
    Council
Dr & Mrs A. Pollok, Galashiels
Mrs S. Porteous, Hawick
F. H. Potts, Hownam
Mrs D. Pratt, Hawick
Mrs J. S. Pringle, Galashiels
Mr Robert Purdie, Jedburgh
Mr J. W. Rae, Roberton
James Rae, Galashiels
Moira M. Ramsay, Selkirk
Euphemia B. Rankin, Galashiels
Elizabeth W. Redpath, Dundee
Alison B. Reed, St. Boswells
Mr George M. Richardson, Melrose
W. M. Robb, Kelso
C. C. Robertson, Eckford
Mrs Grace A. Robertson, Hawick
Miss S. E. Robertson, Edinburgh
Mr J. H. Robeson, Kelso
Mrs M. J. Robson, Newcastleton
Mrs D. A. Rolls, Jedburgh
Mr A. J. Romanis, Hawick
Mrs E. M. Ross, Poynton
Roxburgh District Museums
Mrs M. Runcie, Melrose
J. D. Rutherford, Galashiels
Miss J. Sanderson, Kelso
A. I. S. J. Scott, Currie
C. A. Scott, Earlston
E. Anne Scott, Heddon-on-the-Wall
Frank T. Scott, Hawick
Mr. James Scott, Hawick
Mr. & Mrs. John M. Scott, Bridge of Weir
L. J. Scott, Bath
Mrs M. L. Scott, Hawick
Scottish Genealogy Society

The Selkirk Weekender

Mrs. Isabelle C. S. Shaw, Drummore, By Stranraer
Ann Short, Hawick
Mrs E. Sinclair, Newcastleton
Mrs Janet Slade, Galashiels
Mrs Beatrice Smellie, Posso Farm
Mr David W. Smith, Kelso
Jo-Anne Smith, Ferniehirst Castle
Mrs Margaret Smith, Selkirk
Michael B. Smith, Edinburgh
Mr Michael J. Smith, Galashiels
Mrs Louise Sneddon, Hawick
Mr Kenneth J. Spowart, Scottish Widows' Fund
Major John Sprot, Clerklands
Kathleen Stalker, Galashiels
Susan M. Stalker, Galashiels
Mrs M. Stanford, Dundee
James W. Stenhouse, Kelso
David Stewart, Hawick
Mr & Mrs K. Stewart, Bartlehill, Coldstream
Mrs K. W. Stewart, Inverurie
Mrs Mabel Stewart, Tushielaw
Mr & Mrs W. J. Stewart, Galashiels
Nigel Sumerling, Bowden
Sir W. B. Swan, Eyemouth
Mrs K. L. Swinton, Kelso
Ernest E. Tait, Haysike
Mrs J. Tait, Kelso
Mrs Kathleen Tansley, Hutton
Mr & Mrs A. C. Taylor, Galashiels
Mrs Elizabeth Telfer, Philiphaugh
Mr A. Thomson, Hawick
Mr D. S. Thomson, Lauder
Helen C. Thomson, Hawick
William Thomson, Hawick
W. L. Thorburn, Duns
Charles Thurnam & Sons Ltd, Hawick
Mr. A. J. T. Timberlake, Reston
Dr C. C. Tinline, Birmingham
G. A. Todd, Selkirk
Sandra Todd, Galashiels
D. R. Torrance, Edinburgh

Mrs Carol Trotter, Greenlaw
John Tullie, Teviothead
Mrs M. M. Turnbull, Kimmerghame Mains, Duns
Norman J. Turnbull, Hawick
Mr & Mrs R. Turnbull, Earlston
Mrs Rita C. Turnbull, Hawick
Tweeddale Museum
Mrs H. Vardy, Galashiels
Ronald Veitch, Newcastle Upon Tyne
Thomas Waddell, Galashiels
Mrs W. M. Waldie, Gordon
Mr & Mrs Vaughan Walker, St. Helens, Selkirk
W. Y. Walker, Lauder
Mrs Margaret Wallis, Haysike
R. S. Walthew, Whitsome Crofts, Duns
Mr. J. Wanless, Darnick
Ronald A. Webb, Galashiels
Ian Hamilton Weir, Jedburgh
Mrs P. Weir, Torsonce Mains, Stow
Mr J. D. Wheelans, Lilliesleaf
Mrs A. W. Whillans, Hawick
Mr A. C. White, Hawick
Mrs Sandra White, Kelso
Sandra Whittaker, Stichill
Mrs J. Wichary, Kelso
Eileen Wilson, Philhope
Mrs Wilson-Croome, Alswear
William J. Windram, Darnick
George O. Wood, Hawick
Miss M. J. Wood, Epsom
Mr P. C. Wood, Newstead
David M. Young, Yetholm
Mrs E. M. T. Young, Morebattle
Mr O. I. Young, Kelso
William N. Young, Melrose

JAMES STEEL,

LICENSED DEALER IN GAME,

FISHMONGER AND POULTERER,

11 BRIDGE STREET,

KELSO,

Is open to Contract for RABBITS and all
kinds of GAME in any part of Scotland.

Commissions for Tweed Salmon carefully executed.